ARBITRATION, CONCILIATION AND MEDIATION

LAW AND PRACTICE

General Editor
Abhinandan Malik
BA, LLB (HONS.) (NALSAR), LLM (UNIV. OF TORONTO)

ARBITRATION, CONCILIATION AND MEDIATION

LAW AND PRACTICE

covering
Arbitration and Conciliation Act, 1996
Mediation Act, 2023
and
related Acts and Rules

JUSTICE M.L. SINGHAL
Former Judge, Allahabad High Court
and
Gauhati High Court
Revising Author of *Bholeshwar Nath's Cases and Materials on Code of Civil Procedure*

EBC
Lucknow | Delhi | Prayagraj | Guwahati
Bengaluru | Ahmedabad | Nagpur | Kolkata

EBC

Website: www.ebc.co.in, E-mail: sales@ebc-india.com, Webstore: www.ebcwebstore.com

Lucknow (H.O.): 34, Lalbagh, Lucknow-226 001
Phones: +91–522–4033600 (30 lines), Fax: +91–522–4033633

Delhi: 1267, Kashmere Gate, Old Hindu College Building, Delhi-110 006
Phones: +91–11–23917616, +91–9313080904, Fax: +91–11–23921656

Bengaluru: 25/1, Anand Nivas, 3rd Cross, 6th Main, Gandhinagar, Bengaluru-560 009, Phone: +91–80–41225368

Prayagraj: Manav Law House, Law Publishers & Booksellers, Near Prithvi Garden, Opp. Dr Chandra's Eye Clinic, Elgin Road, Civil Lines, Prayagraj-211 001
Phones: +91–532–2400877, 2422023, Fax: +91–532–2623584

Ahmedabad: Satyamev Complex-1, Ground Floor, Shop No. 7
Opp. High Court Gate No. 2 (Golden Jubilee Gate)
Sarkhej—Gandhinagar Highway Road, Sola, Ahmedabad-380 060
Phones: +91–9228012539, +91–7567903245

Nagpur: F-9, Girish Heights, Near LIC Square, Kamptee Road, Nagpur-440 001
Phones: +91–712–6607650, +91–7028924969

Guwahati: Advika, Unit No. 205, 2nd Floor, M.G. Road, Pan Bazar, Guwahati-781 001
Phone: +91–8736091956

Kolkata: Ground Floor, Malik House, 7, Hare Street, Kolkata-700001
Phone: +91–033–48089874, +91– 9170413377

www.scconline.com/blog
Facebook: Eastern Book Company | SCC Online
Twitter: @ebcindia | @scconline_
Instagram: @scconline_ | @ebcwebstore
Linkedin: Eastern Book Company | SCC Online
YouTube: @easternbookcompany | @thescconline

First Edition, 2025

9788119868490

Published by Eastern Book Company, 34, Lalbagh, Lucknow–226 001 under licence from EBC Publishing (P) Ltd., Lucknow
Printed and Produced by Thomson Press (India) Ltd., Noida

Preface

Prior to the enactment of the Arbitration and Conciliation Act, 1996, the law of arbitration was contained in three enactments, *viz.* the Arbitration Act, 1940, the Arbitration (Protocol and Convention) Act, 1937 and the Foreign Awards (Recognition and Enforcement) Act, 1961. The Arbitration Act, 1940 remained in force for more than five decades; during the course of time, it was felt that the Arbitration Act, 1940 had become outdated, and a new Act was necessary to make it more responsive to contemporary requirements. It was also recognised that our economic reforms may not become fully effective if the law dealing with the settlement of both domestic and international commercial disputes remains out of tune with such reforms. Like arbitration, conciliation was also getting increasing worldwide recognition as an instrument for settlement of disputes. There was, however, no general law on the subject in India.

The United Nations Commission on International Trade Law (UNCITRAL) adopted in 1985 the Model Law on International Commercial Arbitration. The General Assembly of the United Nations had recommended that all countries give due consideration to the said Model Law in view of the desirability of uniformity of the law of arbitral procedures and the specific needs of international commercial arbitration practice. The UNCITRAL also adopted in 1980 a set of Conciliation Rules. The General Assembly of the United Nations had recommended the use of these Rules in cases where disputes arise in the context of international commercial relations and the parties seek amicable settlement of their disputes by recourse to conciliation. An important feature of the UNCITRAL Model Law and Rules is that they have harmonised concepts on arbitration and conciliation of different legal systems of the world and thus contain provisions which are designed for universal application.

Though the UNCITRAL Model Law and Rules are intended to deal with international commercial arbitration and conciliation, they could, with appropriate modifications, serve as a model for legislation on domestic arbitration and conciliation. The present Act seeks to consolidate and amend the law relating to domestic arbitration, international commercial arbitration, enforcement of foreign arbitral awards, and to define the law relating to conciliation, taking into account the UNCITRAL Law and Rules.

In the present Act, the policy adopted is of the least judicial intervention. The 2015 Amendment has ensured the independence, neutrality and impartiality of the arbitrator. The award of the arbitrator shall be made within a period of six months from the date the Arbitral Tribunal enters upon the reference. To reduce the intervention of courts, the government introduced amendments to the Act in the year 2019. The 2019 Amendment brings a lot of reliance on arbitral institutions. It also focuses on the establishment of the Arbitration Council of India, which has been vested with powers and duties under the Act. Thereafter came the 2021 Amendment to the Act, which focused on the deletion of Schedule 8 [*inserted by* the 2019 Amendment Act] and the provisioning of grounds for seeking a stay under Section 36 of the Act.

With the introduction of the Mediation Act, 2023, Part III of the 1996 Act is rendered otiose, and consequently, the Mediation Act seeks to remove the provisions on conciliation from the 1996 Act.

The present commentary deals with all the intricate questions of law and facts arising from the date the arbitrator is appointed and the award passed is finally executed.

The statutory law and case law are up-to-date.

The present commentary is on par with other quality publications of the publisher.

I hope the present commentary will be appreciated by the Members of the Bench and the Bar both.

—JUSTICE M.L. SINGHAL
Former Judge
Allahabad and Gauhati High Courts

Date: October 31, 2024
Place: Lucknow

About the Author

Justice M.L. Singhal had a long judicial career. He joined the U.P. Judicial Services in 1964, later promoted to U.P. Higher Judicial Service and elevated to the Bench of the High Court of Allahabad. Prior to his elevation to the Bench, he worked as District Judge at Pithoragarh, Sultanpur, Azamgarh, and Lucknow. He also worked as a Law Advisor at the U.P. Public Service Commission, Allahabad, as Special Secretary (Law) in the Law Department of the U.P. Government, and as Director of Judicial Training & Research Institute, U.P. at Lucknow. He also worked as Judge at Gauhati High Court, Agartala Branch.

As an author, he has been writing, revising and editing law books for the last 50 years. He has updated two editions of Shri Bholeshwar Nath and Suranjan Chakraverti's CPC—a unique compilation/reference on the Civil Procedure Code, 1908; Sohoni's Commentary on Criminal Procedure Code, 1973; Sir John Woodroffe and Amir Ali's Law of Evidence and Sarkar's Commentary on the Code of Civil Procedure, 1908. By his writing, he has touched almost every topic in civil law and criminal law.

Brief Contents

Part II
ENFORCEMENT OF CERTAIN FOREIGN AWARDS

Part III
CONCILIATION

Part IV
SUPPLEMENTARY PROVISIONS

MEDIATION ACT, 2023

APPENDICES

Detailed Contents

ARBITRATION AND CONCILIATION ACT, 1996

PRELIMINARY

Preliminary (*Contd.*)

Part I

ARBITRATION

General Provisions (*Contd.*)

General Provisions *(Contd.)*

General Provisions (*Contd.*)

Arbitration Agreement (*Contd.*)

Arbitration Agreement (*Contd.*)

Arbitration Agreement (*Contd.*)

Arbitration Agreement (*Contd.*)

Arbitration Agreement (*Contd.*)

Arbitration Agreement (*Contd.*)

Arbitration Agreement (*Contd.*)

Arbitration Agreement (*Contd.*)

Arbitration Agreement (*Contd.*)

Composition of Arbitral Tribunal (*Contd.*)

Composition of Arbitral Tribunal (*Contd.*)

Composition of Arbitral Tribunal (*Contd.*)

Composition of Arbitral Tribunal (*Contd.*)

Composition of Arbitral Tribunal (*Contd.*)

Composition of Arbitral Tribunal (*Contd.*)

Composition of Arbitral Tribunal (*Contd.*)

Composition of Arbitral Tribunal (*Contd.*)

Composition of Arbitral Tribunal (*Contd.*)

Composition of Arbitral Tribunal (*Contd.*)

Composition of Arbitral Tribunal (*Contd.*)

Composition of Arbitral Tribunal (*Contd.*)

Jurisdiction of Arbitral Tribunals (*Contd.*)

Jurisdiction of Arbitral Tribunals (*Contd.*)

Conduct of Arbitral Proceedings (*Contd.*)

Conduct of Arbitral Proceedings (*Contd.*)

Conduct of Arbitral Proceedings (*Contd.*)

Making of Arbitral Award and Termination of Proceedings (*Contd.*)

Making of Arbitral Award and Termination of Proceedings (*Contd.*)

Making of Arbitral Award and Termination of Proceedings (*Contd.*)

Recourse Against Arbitral Award (*Contd.*)

Recourse Against Arbitral Award (*Contd.*)

Recourse Against Arbitral Award (*Contd.*)

Recourse Against Arbitral Award (*Contd.*)

Recourse Against Arbitral Award (*Contd.*)

Recourse Against Arbitral Award (*Contd.*)

Recourse Against Arbitral Award (*Contd.*)

Finality and Enforcement of Arbitral Awards (*Contd.*)

Finality and Enforcement of Arbitral Awards (*Contd.*)

Appeals (*Contd.*)

Miscellaneous (*Contd.*)

PART I-A

ARBITRATION COUNCIL OF INDIA

PART II

ENFORCEMENT OF CERTAIN FOREIGN AWARDS

New York Convention Awards (*Contd.*)

New York Convention Awards (*Contd.*)

Geneva Convention Awards (*Contd.*)

Part III

CONCILIATION

Part IV

SUPPLEMENTARY PROVISIONS

Supplementary Provisions (*Contd.*)

MEDIATION ACT, 2023

CHAPTER I

PRELIMINARY

Preliminary (*Contd.*)

CHAPTER II

APPLICATION

CHAPTER III

MEDIATION

Mediation (*Contd.*)

Chapter IV

MEDIATORS

Mediators (*Contd.*)

CHAPTER V

MEDIATION PROCEEDINGS

CHAPTER VI

ENFORCEMENT OF MEDIATED SETTLEMENT AGREEMENT

CHAPTER VII

CHAPTER VIII

CHAPTER IX

CHAPTER X

COMMUNITY MEDIATION

Community Mediation (*Contd.*)

CHAPTER XI

MISCELLANEOUS

APPENDICES

Sectionwise Contents

Arbitration and Conciliation Act, 1996

Arbitration and Conciliation Act, 1996 (*Contd.*)

Arbitration and Conciliation Act, 1996 (*Contd.*)

Mediation Act, 2023

Mediation Act, 2023 (*Contd.*)

Mediation Act, 2023 (*Contd.*)

Mediation Act, 2023 (*Contd.*)

Table of Cases

B

C

D

E

F

G

H

I

J

L

M

N

O

P

Q

R

S

T

U

V

W

Y

Z

ARBITRATION AND CONCILIATION ACT, 1996

Arbitration and Conciliation Act, 1996[1]

[Act 26 of 1996]

[16th August, 1996]

An Act to consolidate and amend the law relating to domestic arbitration, international commercial arbitration and enforcement of foreign arbitral awards as also to define the law relating to conciliation and for matters connected therewith or incidental thereto

Whereas the United Nations Commission on International Trade Law (UNCITRAL) has adopted the UNCITRAL Model Law on International Commercial Arbitration in 1985;

And whereas the General Assembly of the United Nations has recommended that all countries give due consideration to the said Model Law, in view of the desirability of uniformity of the law of arbitral procedures and the specific needs of international commercial arbitration practice;

And whereas the UNCITRAL has adopted the UNCITRAL Conciliation Rules in 1980;

And whereas the General Assembly of the United Nations has recommended the use of the said Rules in cases where a dispute arises in the context of international commercial relations and the parties seek an amicable settlement of that dispute by recourse to conciliation;

And whereas the said Model Law and Rules make significant contribution to the establishment of a unified legal framework for the fair and efficient settlement of disputes arising in international commercial relations;

And whereas it is expedient to make law respecting arbitration and conciliation, taking into account the aforesaid Model Law and Rules;

Be it enacted by Parliament in the Forty-seventh Year of the Republic as follows:—

Statement of Objects and Reasons.—The Statement of Objects and Reasons for this Bill are as follows:—

The law on arbitration in India is at present substantially contained in three enactments, namely, the Arbitration Act, 1940, the Arbitration (Protocol and Convention) Act, 1937 and the Foreign Awards (Recognition and Enforcement) Act, 1961. It is widely

1. Received the assent of the President on 16-8-1996 and published in the Gazette of India, Extra., Pt. II, S. 1, dt. 19-8-1996, No. 55, pp. 1–36. As amended by Act 3 of 2016, Act 33 of 2019, Act 3 of 2021 and Act 32 of 2023.

felt that the 1940 Act, which contains the general law of arbitration, has become outdated. The Law Commission of India, several representative bodies of trade and industry and experts in the field of arbitration have proposed amendments to this Act to make it more responsive to contemporary requirements. It is also recognised that our economic reforms may not become fully effective if the law dealing with settlement of both domestic and international commercial disputes remains out of tune with such reforms. Like arbitration, conciliation is also getting increasing worldwide recognition as an instrument for settlement of disputes. There is, however, no general law on the subject in India.

2. The United Nations Commission on International Trade Law (UNCITRAL) adopted in 1985 the Model Law on International Commercial Arbitration. The General Assembly of the United Nations has recommended that all countries give due consideration to the said Model Law, in view of the desirability of uniformity of the law of arbitral procedures and the specific needs of international commercial arbitration practice. The UNCITRAL also adopted in 1980 a set of Conciliation Rules. The General Assembly of the United Nations has recommended the use of these Rules in cases where the disputes arise in the context of international commercial relations and the parties seek amicable settlement of their disputes by recourse to conciliation. An important feature of the said UNCITRAL Model Law and Rules is that they have harmonised concepts on arbitration and conciliation of different legal systems of the world and thus contain provisions which are designed for universal application.

3. Though the said UNCITRAL Model Law and Rules are intended to deal with international commercial arbitration and conciliation, they could, with appropriate modifications, serve as a model for legislation on domestic arbitration and conciliation. The present Bill seeks to consolidate and amend the law relating to domestic arbitration, international commercial arbitration, enforcement of foreign arbitral awards and to define the law relating to conciliation, taking into account the said UNCITRAL Model Law and Rules.

4. The main objectives of the Bill are as under:—

(*i*) to comprehensively cover international commercial arbitration and conciliation as also domestic arbitration and conciliation;

(*ii*) to make provision for an arbitral procedure which is fair, efficient and capable of meeting the needs of the specific arbitration;

(*iii*) to provide that the arbitral tribunal gives reasons for its arbitral award;

(*iv*) to ensure that the arbitral tribunal remains within the limits of its jurisdiction;

(*v*) to minimise the supervisory role of courts in the arbitral process;

(*vi*) to permit an arbitral tribunal to use mediation, conciliation or other procedures during the arbitral proceedings to encourage settlement of disputes;

(*vii*) to provide that every final arbitral award is enforced in the same manner as if it were a decree of the court;

(*viii*) to provide that a settlement agreement reached by the parties as a result of conciliation proceedings will have the same status and effect as an arbitral award on agreed terms on the substance of the dispute rendered by an arbitral tribunal; and

(*ix*) to provide that, for purposes of enforcement of foreign awards, every arbitral award made in a country to which one of the two International Conventions relating to foreign arbitral awards to which India is a party applies, will be treated as a foreign award.

5. The Bill seeks to achieve the above objects.

Statement of Objects and Reasons Amending Act 3 of 2016.—The general law relating to arbitration is contained in the Arbitration and Conciliation Act, 1996 (hereinafter referred to as the Act). The Act, which is based on the UNCITRAL Model Law on International Commercial Arbitration, as adopted in 1985 by the United Nations Commission on International Trade Law (UNCITRAL), applies to both international as well to domestic arbitration.

2. The Act was enacted to provide for speedy disposal of cases relating to arbitration with least court intervention. With the passage of time, some difficulties in the applicability of the Act have been noticed. Interpretation of the provisions of the Act by courts in some cases have resulted in delay of disposal of arbitration proceedings and increase in interference of courts in arbitration matters, which tend to defeat the object of the Act. With a view to overcome the difficulties, the matter was referred to the Law Commission of India, which examined the issue in detail and submitted its 176th Report. On the basis of the said report, the Arbitration and Conciliation (Amendment) Bill, 2003, was introduced in the Rajya Sabha on 22nd December, 2003. The said Bill was referred to the Department related Parliamentary Standing Committee on Personnel, Public Grievances, Law and Justice for examination and report. The said Committee, submitted its report to the Parliament on 4th August, 2005, wherein the Committee recommended that since many provisions of the said Bill were contentious, the Bill may be withdrawn and a fresh legislation may be brought after considering its recommendations. Accordingly, the said Bill was withdrawn from the Rajya Sabha.

3. On a reference made again in pursuance of the above, the Law Commission examined and submitted its 246th Report on "Amendments to the Arbitration and Conciliation Act, 1996" in August, 2014 and recommended various amendments in the Act. The proposed amendments to the Act would facilitate and encourage Alternative Dispute Mechanism, especially arbitration, for settlement of disputes in a more user friendly, cost effective and expeditious disposal of cases since India is committed to improve its legal framework to obviate in disposal of cases.

4. As India has been ranked at 178 out of 189 nations in the world in contract enforcement, it is high time that urgent steps are taken to facilitate quick enforcement of contracts, easy recovery of monetary claims and award of just compensation for damages suffered and reduce the pendency of cases in courts and hasten the process of dispute resolution through arbitration, so as to encourage investment and economic activity.

5. As Parliament was not in session and immediate steps were required to be taken to make necessary amendments to the Arbitration and Conciliation Act, 1996, to attract foreign investment by projecting India as an investor friendly country having a sound legal framework, the President was pleased to promulgate the Arbitration and Conciliation (Amendment) Ordinance, 2015.

6. It is proposed to introduce the Arbitration and Conciliation (Amendment) Bill, 2015, to replace the Arbitration and Conciliation (Amendment) Ordinance, 2015, which inter alia, provides for the following, namely—

(*i*) to amend the definition of "Court" to provide that in the case of international commercial arbitrations, the Court should be the High Court;

(*ii*) to ensure that an Indian Court can exercise jurisdiction to grant interim measures, etc., even where the seat of the arbitration is outside India;

(*iii*) an application for appointment of an arbitrator shall be disposed of by the High Court or Supreme Court, as the case may be, as expeditiously as possible and an endeavour should be made to dispose of the matter within a period of sixty days;

(*iv*) to provide that while considering any application for appointment of arbitrator, the High Court or the Supreme Court shall examine the existence of a prima facie arbitration agreement and not other issues;

(*v*) to provide that the arbitral tribunal shall make its award within a period of twelve months from the date it enters upon the reference and that the parties may, however, extend such period up to six months, beyond which period any extension can only be granted by the Court, on sufficient cause;

(*vi*) to provide that a model fee Schedule on the basis of which High Courts may frame rules for the purpose of determination of fees of arbitral tribunal, where a High Court appoints arbitrator in terms of Section 11 of the Act;

(*vii*) to provide that the parties to dispute may at any stage agree in writing that their dispute be resolved through fast track procedure and the award in such cases shall be made within a period of six months;

(*viii*) to provide for neutrality of arbitrators, when a person is approached in connection with possible appointment as an arbitrator;

(*ix*) to provide that application to challenge the award is to be disposed of by the Court within one year.

7. The amendments proposed in the Bill will ensure that arbitration process becomes more user friendly, cost effective and lead to expeditious disposal of cases.

8. The Bill seeks to replace the aforesaid Ordinance.

Statement of Objects and Reasons Amending Act 33 of 2019.—The Arbitration and Conciliation Act, 1996 (the said Act) was enacted to consolidate and amend the law relating to domestic arbitration, international commercial arbitration and enforcement of foreign arbitral awards and also to define the law relating to conciliation and for matters connected therewith or incidental thereto. The said Act was amended by the Arbitration and Conciliation (Amendment) Act, 2015 to make arbitration process cost effective, speedy, with minimum court intervention.

2. The promotion of the institutional arbitration in India by strengthening Indian arbitral institutions has been identified critical to the dispute resolution through arbitration. Though arbitral institutions have been working in India, they have not been preferred by parties, who have leaned in favour of ad hoc arbitration or arbitral institutions located abroad. Therefore, in order to identify the roadblocks to the development of institutional arbitration, examine specific issues affecting the Indian arbitration landscape and also to prepare a road map for making India a robust centre for institutional arbitration both domestic and international, the Central Government constituted a High Level Committee under the Chairmanship of Justice B. N. Srikrishna, Former Judge of the Supreme Court of India.

3. The terms of reference of the Committee, inter alia, include,—

(*a*) to examine the effectiveness of existing arbitration mechanism by studying the functioning and performance of arbitral institutions in India;

(*b*) to devise a road map to promote institutional arbitration mechanisms in India; and

(*c*) to evolve an effective and efficient arbitration eco-system for commercial dispute resolution and suggest reforms in the Arbitration and Conciliation Act, 1996.

4. The High Level Committee submitted its Report on 30th July, 2017. With a view to strengthen institutional arbitration in the country, the said Committee, inter alia, recommended for the establishment of an independent body for grading of arbitral institutions and accreditation of arbitrators, etc. The Committee has also recommended certain amendments to the said Act to minimise the need to approach the Courts for appointment of arbitrators. After examination of the said recommendations with a view to make India a hub of institutional arbitration for both domestic and international arbitration, it was decided to amend the Arbitration and Conciliation Act, 1996.

5. Accordingly, a Bill, namely, the Arbitration and Conciliation (Amendment) Bill, 2018 was introduced in Lok Sabha on the18th July, 2018 and was passed by that House on the 10th August, 2018 and was pending in Rajya Sabha. However, the Sixteenth Lok Sabha was dissolved and the Bill got lapsed. Hence, the present Bill, namely, the Arbitration and Conciliation (Amendment) Bill, 2019.

6. The salient features of the Arbitration and Conciliation (Amendment) Bill, 2019, inter alia, are as follows—

(*i*) to amend Section 11 of the Act relating to "Appointment of Arbitrators" so as to change the present system of appointment of arbitrators by the Supreme Court or High Court, to a system where the arbitrators shall be appointed by the "arbitral institutions" designated by the Supreme Court or High Court;

(*ii*) in case where no graded arbitral institutions are available, the Chief Justice of the concerned High Court may maintain a panel of arbitrators for discharging the functions and duties of arbitral institutions;

(*iii*) to insert a new Part 1-A to the Act for the establishment and incorporation of an independent body, namely, the Arbitration Council of India for the purpose of grading of arbitral institutions and accreditation of arbitrators, etc.;

(*iv*) to amend Section 23 of the Act relating to "Statement of claim and defence" so as to provide that the statement of claim and defence shall be completed within a period of six months from the date the arbitrator receives the notice of appointment;

(*v*) to provide that the arbitrator, the arbitral institutions and the parties shall maintain confidentiality of information relating to arbitral proceedings and also protect the arbitrator or arbitrators from any suit or other legal proceedings for any action or omission done in good faith in the course of arbitration proceedings; and

(*vi*) to clarify that Section 26 of the Arbitration and Conciliation (Amendment) Act, 2015, is applicable only to the arbitral proceedings which commenced on or after 23rd October, 2015 and to such court proceedings which emanate from such arbitral proceedings.

7. The Bill seeks to achieve the above objectives.

PRELIMINARY

SHORT TITLE, EXTENT AND COMMENCEMENT [S. 1]

1. *Short title, extent and commencement.*—(1) This Act may be called the Arbitration and Conciliation Act, 1996.

(2) It extends to the whole of India:

[2][* * *]

Explanation.—In this sub-section, the expression "international commercial conciliation" shall have the same meaning as the expression "international commercial arbitration" in clause (*f*) of sub-section (1) of Section 2, subject to the modification that for the word "arbitration" occurring therein, the word "conciliation" shall be substituted.

(3) It shall come into force on such date[3] as the Central Government may, by notification in the Official Gazette, appoint.

STATE AMENDMENTS

Union Territory of Jammu and Kashmir.—In its application to the Union Territory of Jammu and Kashmir, in sub-section (1), *omit* the proviso and Explanation. [*Vide* S.O. 1123(E), dated 18-3-2020 (w.e.f. 18-3-2020)].

Union Territory of Ladakh.—In its application to the Union Territory of Ladakh, in sub-section (1), *omit* the proviso and Explanation. [*Vide* S.O. 3774(E), dated 23-10-2020].

COMMENTS

Corresponding old law

Section 1 corresponds to Section 1, Arbitration Act, 1940.

Legislative changes

Arbitration and Conciliation (Amendment) Act, 2019 (33 of 2019)

Proviso to sub-section (2) has been omitted by Amendment Act 34 of 2019. Prior to omission it read as under:

---

2. *Omitted* by Act 34 of 2019, Ss. 95, 96 and Sch. V (w.e.f. 31-10-2019). Prior to omission it read as:

   "Provided that Parts I, III and IV shall extend to the State of Jammu and Kashmir only in so far as they relate to international commercial arbitration or, as the case may be, international commercial conciliation."

3. 22-8-1996 [*Vide* Noti. No. G.S.R. 375(E), dt. 22-8-1996].

Provided that Parts I, III and IV shall extend to the State of Jammu and Kashmir only in so far as they relate to international commercial arbitration or, as the case may be, international commercial conciliation.

Section 1(3): Date of commencement of the Act

The Arbitration and Conciliation Ordinance was originally promulgated by the President on 16 January 1996. The second Ordinance came in its place on 26 February 1996 which was again replaced by the third Ordinance on 26 June 1996. These ordinances were issued, necessitated by the circumstances for continuing the operation of the new Act. The new Act 26 of 1996 received the President's assent on 16 August 1996 and was published in the Gazette of India (Extra.), Part II, Section 1, dated 19 August 1996.

Gazette Notification No. GSR 375(E), dated 22 August 1996 reads:

> In exercise of the powers conferred by Sub-section (3) of Section 1 of the Arbitration and Conciliation Act, 1996 (26 of 1996), the Central Government hereby appoints the 22nd day of August 1996, as the date on which the said Act came into force.

By Gazette Notification, the Act was brought into force with effect from 22 August 1996. But as the Act is being a continuation of the Arbitration and Conciliation Ordinance, the Act is deemed to have been effective from 25 January 1996 when the first Ordinance came into force.[4]

When the demand for referring the dispute for arbitration was made and the suit was filed before 26 January 1996, held, the Old Act, 1940 would apply for adjudicating the dispute.[5]

History of arbitration in India

Resolution of disputes through arbitration was not unknown in India even in ancient times. Settlement of disputes through arbitration is the alternate system of resolution of disputes whereby the parties to a dispute get the same settled through the intervention of a third party. The role of the court was limited to the extent of regulating the process. During the ancient era of Hindu law in India, there were several machineries for settlement of disputes between the parties. These were known as *Kulani* (village council), *Sreni* (corporation) and *Puga* (assembly).[6] Likewise, commercial matters were decided by Mahajans and Chambers. The resolution of disputes through the panchayat was a different system of arbitration subordinate to the courts

4. *Fuerst Day Lawson Ltd.* v. *Jindal Exports Ltd.*, (2001) 6 SCC 356.
5. *Shetty's Constructions Co. (P) Ltd.* v. *Konkan Railway Construction*, (1998) 5 SCC 599.
6. *See*, P.V. Kane, *History of Dharmasastra*, Vol. 3 (Bhandarkar Oriental Research Institute, Poona 1946) 242.

of law. The Arbitration Tribunal, in ancient times, would have the status of panchayat in modern India.[7] The ancient system of a panchayat has been given due statutory recognition through various Panchayat Acts subsequently followed by the Panchayat Raj Act, 1994. It has not been constitutionally recognised in Article 243 of the Constitution of India.

The first Indian Act on arbitration law came to be passed in 1899 known as the Arbitration Act, 1899. It was based on the English Arbitration Code contained in the provisions relating to the law of arbitration which were extended to the other parts of British India. Thereafter, the Arbitration Act, 1940 (Act of 1940) was enacted to consolidate and amend the law relating to arbitration. This Act came into force on 1 July 1940. It is an exhaustive Code insofar as law relating to the domestic arbitration is concerned. Under this Act, arbitration may be without a suit pending or in a pending suit. This Act empowered the courts to modify the award [S. 15], remit the award to the arbitrators for reconsideration [S. 16] and to set aside the award on specific grounds [S. 30]. The 1940 Act was based on the English Arbitration Act, 1934. The 1934 Act was replaced by the English Arbitration Act, 1950 which was subsequently replaced by the Arbitration Act, 1975. Thereafter, the 1975 Act was also replaced by the Arbitration Act, 1979. There were, however, no corresponding changes in the 1940 Act. The law of arbitration in India remained static.

The disastrous result, which ensued from the abuse of the 1940 Act, were noticed by the Supreme Court, in *Guru Nanak Foundation* v. *Rattan Singh and Sons*[8]. D.A. Desai J, speaking for the court, expressed the concern and anguish of the court about the way in which the proceedings under the 1940 Act were conducted and without an exception challenged in courts. His Lordship observed:[9]

> Interminable, time consuming, complex and expensive court procedures impelled jurists to search for an alternative forum, less formal, more effective and speedy for resolution of disputes avoiding procedural claptrap and this led them to the Arbitration Act, 1940 ('Act' for short). However, the way in which the proceedings under the Act are conducted and without an exception challenged in courts, has made lawyers laugh and legal philosophers weep. Experience shows and law reports bear ample testimony that the proceedings under the Act have become highly technical accompanied by unending prolixity, at every stage providing a legal trap to the unwary. Informal forum chosen by the parties for expeditious disposal of their disputes has by the decisions of the courts

7. *See*, Justice S. Varadachariar, *Hindu Judicial System*, 98.
8. (1981) 4 SCC 634.
9. *Ibid*, 636, para 1.

been clothed with 'legalese' of unforeseeable complexity. This case amply demonstrates the same.

This was the arena of domestic arbitration and domestic awards.

International scenario

Difficulties were also being faced in the international sphere of trade and commerce. With the growth of international trade and commerce, there was an increase in disputes arising out of such transactions being adjudicated through arbitration. One of the problems faced in such arbitration, related to recognition and enforcement of an arbitral award made in one country by the courts of other countries. This difficulty was sought to be removed through various international conventions. The first such international convention was the Geneva Protocol on Arbitration Clauses, 1923, popularly referred to as "the 1923 Protocol". It was implemented with effect from 28 July 1924. This protocol was the product of the initiative taken by the International Chamber of Commerce (ICC) under the auspices of the League of Nations. The 1923 Protocol sought to make arbitration agreements and arbitration clauses, in particular, enforceable internationally. It was also sought to ensure that awards made pursuant to such arbitration agreements would be enforced in the territory other than the State in which they were made.

The 1923 Protocol proved to be inadequate. It was followed by the Geneva Convention on the Execution of Foreign Arbitral Awards, 1927 and is popularly known as "Geneva Convention of 1927". This convention was made effective on 25 July 1929. India became a signatory to both the 1923 Protocol and the 1927 Convention on 29 October 1937. It was to give effect to both the 1923 Protocol and the 1927 Convention that the Arbitration (Protocol and Convention) Act, 1937 was enacted in India. Again a number of problems were encountered in the operation of the 1923 Protocol and the 1927 Geneva Convention. It was felt that there were limitations in relation to their fields of application. Under the 1927 Geneva Convention, a party in order to enforce the award in the country of an origin was obliged to seek a declaration in the country where the arbitration took place to the effect that the award was enforceable. Only then could the successful party go ahead and enforce the award in the country of origin. This led to the problem of "double exequatur", making the enforcement of arbitral awards much more complicated.

In 1953, the ICC promoted a new treaty to govern international commercial arbitration. The proposals of ICC were taken up by the UN Economic and Social Council. This, in turn, led to the adoption of the

Convention on the Recognition and Enforcement of Foreign Arbitral Awards at New York in 1958 (New York Convention). The New York Convention is an improvement on the Geneva Convention of 1927. It provides for a much more simple and effective method of *recognition and enforcement* of foreign arbitral awards. It gives a much wider effect to the validity of arbitration agreements. This convention came into force on 7 June 1959. India became a State signatory to this convention on 13 July 1960. The Foreign Awards (Recognition and Enforcement) Act, 1961 was enacted to give effect to the New York Convention.

Thus, prior to the enactment of the Arbitration Act, 1996 the law of arbitration in India was contained in the Arbitration (Protocol and Convention) Act, 1937; the Arbitration Act, 1940 and the Foreign Awards (Recognition and Enforcement) Act, 1961. There were no further amendments in the aforesaid three Acts. Therefore, it was generally felt that the arbitration laws in India had failed to keep pace with the developments at the international level.[10]

Preamble

The preamble of the Act makes it amply clear that Parliament has enacted the Act almost on the same lines as the Model Law which was drafted by the UN Commission on the International Trade Law. The provisions of the Act should be interpreted keeping in mind the Model Law as the concept under the present Act has undergone a complete change. It will, therefore, be useful to take note of the corresponding provisions of the UNCITRAL Model Law. The whole object and scheme of the Act is to secure an expeditious resolution of disputes. Therefore, where a party raises a plea that the Arbitral Tribunal has not been properly constituted or has no jurisdiction, it must do so at the threshold before the Arbitral Tribunal so that remedial measures may be immediately taken and time and expense involved in hearing of the matter before the Arbitral Tribunal which may ultimately be found to be either not properly constituted or lacking in jurisdiction, in proceedings for setting the award may be avoided. Such a plea must be raised before the Arbitral Tribunal right at the beginning and normally not later than in the statement of defence.[11]

The legislative intent underlying the 1996 Act is to minimise the supervisory role of the courts in the arbitral process and quick nomination/appointment of arbitrators, leaving all contentions issues to be decided by the arbitrators.[12]

---

10. *Bharat Aluminium Co.* v. *Kaiser Aluminium Technical Services Inc.*, (2012) 9 SCC 552.
11. *GAIL* v. *Keti Construction (I) Ltd.*, (2007) 5 SCC 38.
12. *Food Corporation of India* v. *Indian Council of Arbitration*, (2003) 6 SCC 564.

Nature and scope of arbitration as a mode of dispute resolution

Arbitration is a mechanism or a method of resolution of disputes that, unlike court, takes place in private, pursuant to agreement between the parties. The parties agree to be bound by the decision rendered by a chosen arbitrator after giving a hearing. The endeavour of the court should be to honour and support the award as far as possible.[13]

The process of settlement of disputes through arbitration is a process of settlement *extra cursum curiae* and the parties are at liberty to choose their judge.[14]

Arbitration is considered to be an important alternative dispute redress process which is to be encouraged because of the high pendency of cases in courts and cost of litigation. Arbitration has to be looked up to with all earnestness so that the litigants public has faith in the speedy process of resolving their disputes by this process.[15]

Arbitration—Not adjudication by a statutory body

An arbitrator or an Arbitral Tribunal is not statutory. It is a forum chosen by the consent of the parties as an alternative to resolution of disputes by the ordinary forum of law. The essence of arbitration without assistance or intervention of the court is the settlement of disputes by a tribunal of the own choosing of the parties. The law of arbitration does not make the arbitration, an adjudication by a statutory body but it only aids in the implementation of the arbitration contract between the parties which remains a private adjudication by a forum consensually chosen by the parties and made on a consensual reference.[16]

Courts and arbitrators/Arbitral Tribunals—Distinction

Courts, unlike arbitrators or Arbitral Tribunals, are the third great organ under the Constitution—legislative, executive and judicial. Courts are institutions invested with the judicial power of the State to finally adjudicate upon disputes between litigants and to make formal and binding orders and decrees. Litigation is very different from arbitration. The former is a legal action in a court of law where judges are appointed by the State, and the latter is a resolution of a dispute between two contracting parties by persons chosen by them to be arbitrators. These persons need not be even necessarily

13. *Markfed Vanaspati & Allied Industries* v. *Union of India*, (2007) 7 SCC 679; *Hindustan Life Care* v. *N. Ramesh*, 2008 SCC OnLine Mad 737: (2009) 2 LW 68.
14. *Delta Mechcons (India) Ltd.* v. *Marubeni Corpn.*, (2008) 15 SCC 772.
15. *State of J&K* v. *Dev Dutt Pandit*, (1999) 7 SCC 339.
16. *Dharma Prathishthanam* v. *Madhok Construction (P) Ltd.*, (2005) 9 SCC 686.

qualified trained judges or lawyers. Arbitrators are not courts. Civil courts pass decrees and orders for payment of money and the terms "decree and order" are defined in CPC. Arbitrators are persons chosen by parties to adjudicate their disputes. They are not courts and they do not pass orders or decrees for the payment of money; they make awards.[17]

Object and scheme of the Arbitration Act, 1996—Speedy remedy

The object of the Arbitration Act, 1996 is to provide a speedy and alternative solution to the dispute and avoid protraction of ligation. Under the old Act of 1940, after making the award and prior to execution, there was a procedure for filing and making an award a rule of court, *i.e.* a decree. Since the object of the new Act is to provide speedy and alternative solution to the dispute, the same procedure is not available as such cannot be insisted upon under the new 1996 Act, when it has been advisedly eliminated. If separate proceedings are to be taken, one for deciding the enforceability of a foreign award and the other thereafter for execution, it would contribute to protracting the litigation and adding to the sufferings of a litigant in terms of money, time and energy.[18]

The whole object and scheme of the 1996 Act is to secure expeditious resolution of disputes.[19]

1996 Act is intra vires and constitutional

The Arbitration and Conciliation Act, 1996 is intra vires and constitutional.[20]

1996 Act, a self-contained and exhaustive Code

Before the coming into force of the Arbitration and Conciliation Act, 1996 with effect from 16 August 1996 the law relating to domestic arbitration was contained in the Arbitration Act, 1940, which in turn was brought in place of the Arbitration Act, 1899. Apart from the Arbitration Act, 1940 there were two other enactments of the same genre. One called the Arbitration (Protocol and Convention) Act, 1937 (for execution of the Geneva Convention Awards) and the other called the Foreign Awards (Recognition and Enforcement) Act 1961 (FARE Act, 1961) for the enforcement of the New York Convention Awards. The aforesaid three Acts were replaced by the Arbitration and Conciliation Act, 1996 which is based on the UNCITRAL Model Law and is broadly compatible with the Rules of Arbitration of ICC. The Arbitration

17. *Paramjeet Singh Patheja* v. *ICDS Ltd.*, (2006) 13 SCC 322.
18. *Fuerst Day Lawson Ltd.* v. *Jindal Exports Ltd.*, (2001) 6 SCC 356; *P. Manohar Reddy & Bros.* v. *Maharashtra Krishna Valley Development Corpn.*, (2009) 2 SCC 494.
19. *GAIL* v. *Keti Construction (I) Ltd.*, (2007) 5 SCC 38.
20. *Babar Ali* v. *Union of India*, (2000) 2 SCC 178.

and Conciliation Act, 1996 that has repealed the Arbitration Act, 1940 and also the Acts of 1937 and 1961, consolidates and amends the law relating to domestic arbitration, international commercial arbitration, enforcement of foreign arbitral awards and defines the law relating to conciliation and provides for matters connected therewith and incidental thereto taking into account the UNCITRAL Model Law and Rules.

Provisions in Section 9, Arbitration and Conciliation Act indicate an intention on the part of the legislature to make the Arbitration and Conciliation Act, 1996 a self-contained self-operative Code with regard to the subject-matter of arbitration and conciliation. The Arbitration and Conciliation Act, 1996 is enacted to make the law a self-contained Code and the provisions of the CPC are not applicable, unless specifically made applicable.

Under Section 6 of the Foreign Awards (Recognition and Enforcement) Act, 1961, the court, on being satisfied that the foreign award was enforceable under the Act, would first order the award to be filed and then *proceed to pronounce judgment according to the award*. The judgment would lead to a decree against which no appeal would lie except insofar as the decree was in excess of or not in accordance with the award. Section 49 of the present Act makes a radical change in that where the court is satisfied that the foreign award is enforceable, the award itself would be deemed to be a decree of the court. It, thus, not only omits the procedural formality for the court to pronounce judgment and decree to follow on that basis but also completely removes the possibility of the decree being in excess of, or not in accordance with the award. Thus, even the limited basis on which an appeal would lie under sub-section (2) of Section 6 of the 1961 Act *is taken away*. There is, thus, no scope left for an appeal against an order of the court for the enforcement of a foreign award. It is for this reason, Section 50(1)(*b*) provides for an appeal only an order refusing to enforce a foreign award under Section 48.[21]

Changes brought in by 1996 Act

The 1996 Act has introduced several changes, notable are:

1. Fair resolution of a dispute by an impartial tribunal without any unnecessary delay or expenses.
2. Party autonomy is paramount subject only to such safeguards as are necessary in public interest.

---

21. *Fuerst Day Lawson Ltd.* v. *Jindal Exports Ltd.*, (2011) 8 SCC 333.

3. The Arbitral Tribunal is enjoined with a duty to act fairly and impartially.[22]

Source of jurisdiction of arbitrator—Arbitration clause

The source of jurisdiction of the arbitrator is the arbitration clause.[23]

The arbitrator or umpire, as the case may be, has no authority or jurisdiction to abdicate the terms of the contract or what the parties desired under the contract.[24]

The general law of arbitration, either English or Indian, does not prevent the arbitrators or an umpire from deciding questions of their own jurisdiction provisionally or tentatively and to proceed to make their award on that basis, though their provisional or tentative decision would be subject to the final decision by the court. If the court takes a contrary view, their award will not be given effect to.[25]

1996 Act should be interpreted keeping in view the UNCITRAL Model Rules

There exists a sharp distinction between the provisions of the Arbitration Act, 1940 and the 1996 Act. The philosophy of the 1996 Act is different. The 1996 Act is required to be read keeping in view the UNCITRAL Model Rules.[26]

The 1996 Act is very different from the Arbitration Act 1940. The provisions of the 1996 Act have, therefore, to be interpreted and construed independently and in fact reference to the 1940 Act may actually lead to misconstruction. The provisions of 1996 Act have to be interpreted being uninfluenced by the principles underlying the 1940 Act. In order to get help in construing these provisions, it is more relevant to refer to the UNCITRAL Model rather than the 1940 Act.[27] For interpretation of the Act of 1996, objects as set out in the Act, are to be followed and not the provisions of the Arbitration Act, 1940.[28]

---

22. *Centrotrade Minerals & Metals Inc.* v. *Hindustan Copper Ltd.*, (2006) 11 SCC 245.
23. *Wellington Associates Ltd.* v. *Kirit Mehta*, (2000) 4 SCC 272.
24. *Ispat Engg. & Foundry Works* v. *SAIL*, (2001) 6 SCC 347.
25. *Renusagar Power Co. Ltd.* v. *General Electric Co.*, (1984) 4 SCC 679.
26. *India Household and Healthcare Ltd.* v. *LG Household and Healthcare Ltd.*, (2007) 5 SCC 510; *GAIL* v. *Keti Construction (I) Ltd.*, (2007) 5 SCC 38; *Konkan Railway Corpn. Ltd.* v. *Rani Construction (P) Ltd.*, (2002) 2 SCC 388.
27. *Sundaram Finance Ltd.* v. *NEPC India Ltd.*, (1999) 2 SCC 479.
28. *Delta Construction Systems Ltd.* v. *Narmada Cement Co. Ltd.*, 2001 SCC OnLine Bom 630: (2002) 1 Mah LJ 684.

Two-tier arbitration procedure

Where the clause in the arbitration agreement provides for domestic arbitration and thereafter prefers an international forum, it is not contrary to public policy. Settlement of disputes through a two-tier arbitration procedure is permissible under the laws of India, does not violate the fundamental or public policy of India.[29]

1996 Act—Applicability of

In a contract with a foreign company in the agreement clause relating to applicability of laws, the parties agreed that all questions or disputes arising between them shall be settled in accordance with the laws of India (procedural and substantive), it was held that the provisions of the Arbitration and Conciliation Act, 1996 would be applicable to settlement of disputes between the parties.[30]

Agreement between the parties was entered into before the Arbitration and Conciliation Act, 1996 came into force but the proceedings were started after the Act came into force. It was held that the proceedings would be governed by the Arbitration and Conciliation Act, 1996.[31]

The parties, at the time of entering into the partnership deed, wanted to incorporate the arbitration clause for getting their disputes resolved through the means of arbitration and that was incorporated in the deed. At the same time, instead of incorporating the name of the statute, *i.e.* the Arbitration Act of 1996, the Act of 1940 was mentioned. At that time, the Act of 1940 stood repealed. It can only be viewed as a mere misquoting of the name of the statute. By merely naming the statute applicable as the Arbitration Act, 1940, it cannot be said that the arbitration clause itself is inoperative. The law that has to be applied is one under the 1996 Act.[32]

Provisions of Evidence Act, 1872

The provisions of Evidence Act, 1872 do not apply to arbitral proceedings.[33]

Where the arbitrator has given reasons for awarding interest, which are reasonable and not perverse, the High Court will not scrutinise the same.[34]

The arbitration is a procedure to determine legal rights and obligations of the parties judicially with binding effect, which is enforceable in law. The

---

29. *Centrotrade Minerals & Metal Inc.* v. *Hindustan Copper Ltd.*, (2017) 2 SCC 228.
30. *ONGC Petro Additions Ltd.* v. *Daelim Industrial Co. Ltd.*, (2015) 13 SCC 176.
31. *Steel Fabs* v. *State of Uttarakhand*, 2015 SCC OnLine Utt 2736.
32. *Ibid.*
33. *D.V. Anand* v. *Hindustan Petroleum Corpn. Ltd.*, 2018 SCC OnLine Del 9594.
34. *Subhash Verma* v. *Darshan Singh*, 2019 SCC OnLine Del 7169.

arbitrators are appointed by the parties to do justice in the sense of arriving at a "fair decision" and not in the sense of "judicial justice". The arbitrator is not bound by a strict law of evidence as contained in the Evidence Act, 1872.[35]

Interpretation of statutes

(*a*) *Heading/marginal note*

Section heading or marginal note can be relied upon to clear any doubt or ambiguity in the interpretation of any provisions and to discern the legislative intent. The section heading constitutes an important part of the Act itself, and may be read not only as explaining the provisions of the said section but it also affords a better key to the constructions of the provisions of the section which follows than might be afforded by mere preamble. The said principle of interpretation can be applied to understand and construct the various clauses of an arbitration agreement also, which is in the realm of commercial contract. While interpreting so the court may not depend on the text but context as well in order to fully comprehend the context and meaning of the clause.[36]

(*b*) *External aids*

The external aids to construction are parliamentary debates, history leading to the legislation, other statutes which have a bearing, dictionaries, thesaurus.[37]

When the language of any statutory provision is clear and unambiguous, it is not necessary to look for any extrinsic aid to find out the meaning of statute in as much as language used by legislature is indicative of legislative intent.[38]

(*c*) *UNCITRAL Model Law and judgments thereon*

The Statement of Objects shows that the UNCITRAL Model Law was only taken into account in drafting of the Arbitration and Conciliation Act, 1996. The Act and the Model Law are not identically drafted. Under Section 11, the appointment of an arbitrator in the event of a party to the arbitration agreement failing to carry out his obligation to appoint an arbitrator is to be made by the Chief Justice or any person or institution designated by him (now

---

35. *Shri Gouri Ganesh Shri Balaji Constructions* v. *PWD*, 2018 SCC OnLine MP 978: (2018) 3 MP LJ 163.
36. *Eastern Coalfields Ltd.* v. *Sanjay Transport Agency*, (2009) 7 SCC 345.
37. *Commr. of Customs* v. *Dilip Kumar & Co.*, (2018) 9 SCC 1.
38. *All Kerala Parents' Assn. of Hearing Impaired* v. *State of Kerala*, (2018) 2 SCC 410.

by the arbitral institution designed by Supreme Court, in the case of international commercial arbitration by the High Court, in the case of arbitrators other than international commercial arbitration), under Section 11 of the Model Law is to be made by a court. Section 34 is altogether different from Section 34 of the Model Law. The Model Law, the judgments and literature are therefore not a guide to the interpretation of the Act, and especially, of Section 11 thereof.[39]

(*d*) *Internal aids*

The long title, the preamble, the heading, the marginal note, punctuation, illustrations, definitions or a definition clause, a proviso to a section, explanation, examples, a schedule to the Act, etc. are internal aids to construction.[40]

(*e*) *General principles of interpretation of statutes*

Interpretation is a process by which the court determines the meaning of the statutory provision for the purpose of applying it to the situation before it.[41]

It is well accepted that a statute must be construed according to the intention of the legislature and the courts should act upon the true intention of the legislation while applying law and while interpreting law. If the statutory provision is open to more than one meaning, the court has to choose the interpretation which represents the intention of the legislature.[42]

The well settled principle is that when the words in a statute are clear, plain and unambiguous and only one meaning can be inferred, the courts are bound to give effect to the meaning irrespective of consequences. If the words in a statute are plain and unambiguous, it becomes necessary to expound these words in their natural and ordinary sense. The words used declare the intention of the legislature. Nevertheless, if the plain language results in absurdity, the court is entitled to determine the meaning of the word in the context in which it is used keeping in view the legislative purpose.[43]

While interpreting a statutory law, if any doubt arises as to the meaning to be assigned to a word or a phrase or a clause used in an enactment and such word, phrase or clause is not specifically defined; it is legitimate and indeed mandatory to fall back on the General Clauses Act. However, when there is repugnancy or conflict as to the subject or context between the

39. *Konkan Railway Corpn. Ltd.* v. *Rani Construction (P) Ltd.*, (2002) 2 SCC 388.
40. *Commr. of Customs* v. *Dilip Kumar & Co.*, (2018) 9 SCC 1.
41. *Anurag Mittal* v. *Shaily Mishra Mittal*, (2018) 9 SCC 691.
42. *Commr. of Customs* v. *Dilip Kumar & Co.*, (2018) 9 SCC 1.
43. *Ibid.*

General Clauses Act and a statutory provision which falls for interpretation, the court must necessarily refer to the provisions of the statute.[44]

A statute which provides for an arbitration between the parties and a taxing statute must be interpreted differently. The provisions of Arbitration and Conciliation Act, 1996 are not in pari materia with the provisions of the Income Tax Act.[45]

That interpretation is best which makes the textual interpretation match the contextual.[46]

(f) "May" and "shall"

Where the parties have used both the words "may" and "shall" at different places in the same clause, the parties must be deemed to have used the words "may" and "shall" with due deliberation.[47]

(g) Interpretation of contract

The terms of the contract will have to be interpreted/understood in the way the parties wanted and intended them to be, particularly in the agreements of arbitration, where party autonomy is supreme.[48]

(h) Arbitration agreement/clause—Interpretation of

The rules of interpretation require the arbitration clause to be read in the ordinary and natural sense, except when that would lead to an absurdity. No part of a term or clause should be considered as a meaningless surplusage when it is in consonance with the other parts of the clause and expresses the specific intention of parties.[49]

Decisions under Arbitration Act, 1940 and Foreign Awards (Recognition and Enforcement) Act, 1961

Decisions rendered under the Arbitration Act, 1940 or under Foreign Awards (Recognition and Enforcement) Act, 1961 should be considered with caution as the Act of 1996 purports to bring a new approach to arbitration.[50]

---

44. *Ibid.*
45. *TDM Infrastructure (P) Ltd.* v. *UE Development India (P) Ltd.*, (2008) 14 SCC 271.
46. *CIT* v. *Canara Bank*, (2018) 9 SCC 322.
47. *Wellington Associates Ltd.* v. *Kirit Mehta*, (2000) 4 SCC 272.
48. *Bharat Aluminium Co.* v. *Kaiser Aluminium Technical Services Inc.*, (2016) 4 SCC 126.
49. *National Agricultural Coop. Mktg. Federation India Ltd.* v. *Gains Trading Ltd.*, (2007) 5 SCC 692.
50. *Shin-Etsu Chemical Co. Ltd.* v. *Aksh Optifibre Ltd.*, (2005) 7 SCC 234.

Decided cases under the preceding Act of 1940 have to be applied with caution for determining the issues arising for decision under the new Act.[51]

Arbitrable matters

All disputes relating to rights in personam are arbitrable, therefore, the choice is given to the parties to choose this alternative forum. A claim of money by a bank or a financial institution cannot be treated as right in rem which is not arbitrable.[52]

Non-arbitrable disputes

The well recognised examples of non-arbitrable disputes are:

1. Disputes relating to rights and liabilities which give rise to or arise out of criminal offences.
2. Matrimonial disputes relating to divorce, judicial separation, restitution of conjugal rights, child custody.
3. Guardianship matters.
4. Insolvency and winding up matters.
5. Testamentary matters (grant of probate, letters of administration and succession certificate).
6. Eviction or tenancy matters governed by special statutes. Where the tenant enjoys statutory protection against eviction and only Special Courts are conferred jurisdiction to grant eviction or decide the disputes.

Generally and traditionally all disputes relating to rights *in personam* are considered to be amenable to arbitration; and all disputes relating to rights *in rem* are required to be adjudicated by courts and public tribunals, being unsuited for private arbitration. This is not, however, a rigid or flexible rule. Disputes relating to subordinate rights *in personam* arising from rights *in rem* have always been considered to be arbitrable.

The 1996 Act does not specifically exclude any category of disputes as being not arbitrable. Sections 34(2)(*b*) and 48(2) of the Act, however, make it clear that an arbitral award will be set aside if the court finds that "the subject-matter of the dispute is not capable of settlement by arbitration under the law for the time being in force".[53]

---

51. *Firm Ashok Traders* v. *Gurumukh Das Saluja*, (2004) 3 SCC 155.
52. *M.D. Frozen Foods Exports (P) Ltd.* v. *Hero Fincorp Ltd.*, (2017) 16 SCC 741.
53. *Booz Allen & Hamilton Inc.* v. *SBI Home Finance Ltd.*, (2011) 5 SCC 532.

There is a difference between a non-arbitrable claim and a non-arbitrable subject-matter. Former may arise on account of scope of an arbitration agreement and also when the claim is not capable of being resolved through arbitration. General non-arbitrability of the subject-matter relates to non-arbitrability in law. Exclusion or non-arbitrability when clearly expressed would have no difficulty. However, exclusion or non-arbitrability of subjects or disputes from the purview of a private forum like arbitration by necessary implication requires setting out of the principles that should be applied.[54]

Serious cases of fraud—Non-arbitrable disputes

Those cases, where there are serious allegations of fraud, are to be treated as non-arbitrable.[55]

Civil disputes

The Arbitration and Conciliation Act, 1996 is applicable even to civil disputes and not only to commercial disputes. The Act applies to domestic arbitrations, international commercial arbitrations and conciliations. The applicability of the Act does not depend upon the dispute being a commercial dispute. Reference to arbitration and arbitrability depends upon the existence of an arbitration agreement, and not upon the question whether it is a non-commercial civil dispute also.[56]

Non-commercial civil disputes

The Act of 1996 applies to domestic arbitrations, commercial arbitrations and conciliations. The applicability of the Act does not depend upon the dispute being a commercial dispute. Reference to arbitration and arbitrability depends upon the existence of the arbitration agreement whether it is a civil dispute or commercial disputes. There can be arbitration agreements in non-commercial civil disputes also.[57]

Dispute relating to terms of private contract

Where in a private contract between the government and private corporation, a dispute relating to terms of contract arises, proper course would be reference to arbitration or institution of suit and not writ petition.[58]

---

54. *DSIIDC* v. *HR Builders*, (2022) 4 HCC (Del) 123.
55. *A. Ayyasamy* v. *A. Paramasivam*, (2016) 10 SCC 386; *Ameet Lalchand Shah* v. *Rishabh Enterprises*, (2018) 15 SCC 678.
56. *H. Srinivas Pai* v. *H.V. Pai*, (2010) 12 SCC 521.
57. *Ibid.*
58. *State of U.P.* v. *Bridge & Roof Co. (India) Ltd.*, (1996) 6 SCC 22.

No provision in 1996 Act for reference to arbitration by the intervention of the court

There is no provision in the Arbitration and Conciliation Act, 1996 for referring the matter to an arbitrator by the intervention of the court. However, if during the pendency of the proceedings in the court, the parties have entered into an agreement then they have to proceed in accordance with the provisions of the new Act and when award is made, it is a decree and it cannot be filed in the High Court and it has to be filed in the court as defined in clause (*e*) of Section 2 of the new Act for its enforcement as a decree under Section 36 of the new Act. If there is challenge to the award, recourse has to be under Section 34 of the new Act.[59]

Trusts Act, 1882 (2 of 1882)

Disputes arising inter se trustees in relation to their appointments, powers, duties, obligation removal, etc. are disputes arising under the Trusts Act, to be decided by the civil court, remedy under Arbitration Act is impliedly barred by Section 9 CPC.[60]

Possibility of arbitration cannot thwart criminal proceedings

The provision incorporated in the agreement for referring the disputes to arbitration is not an effective substitute for a criminal prosecution when the disputed act is an offence. Arbitration is a remedy for affording reliefs to the party affected by the breach of the agreement; but the arbitrator cannot conduct a trial of any act which amounted to an offence, *albeit*, the same act may be connected with the discharge of any function under the agreement.[61]

Period of limitation

The Arbitration and Conciliation Act, 1996 is a special law in terms of Section 29(2), Limitation Act, 1963, the 1996 Act provides a limitation period different from that prescribed under the Limitation Act, 1963.[62]

Electricity Act, 1910 and Arbitration Act, 1940

The Indian Arbitration Act being a general provision relating to settlement of disputes by arbitration and Electricity Act having carved out certain matters only as available for determination by arbitration, on the principle of

---

59. *T.N. Electricity Board* v. *Sumathi*, (2000) 4 SCC 543.
60. *Vimal Kishor Shah* v. *Jayesh Dinesh Shah*, (2016) 8 SCC 788.
61. *Trisuns Chemical Industry* v. *Rajesh Agarwal*, (1999) 8 SCC 686.
62. *Union of India* v. *Popular Construction Co.*, (2001) 8 SCC 470.

generalia specialibus non derogant what has been provided in the Electricity Act would override the general provision contained in the Indian Arbitration Act, 1899, which subsequently came to be repealed by the Arbitration Act of 1940. So the matters relating to which there is no direction in the Electricity Act requiring the same to be determined by arbitration cannot be subject-matter of arbitration. This is for the reason that the Electricity Act being not only a special Act on the subject of which disputes covered by the Act could be decided by arbitration but also because it is a later Act than the Indian Arbitration Act of 1899.[63]

SARFAESI Act, 2002

The provisions of arbitration are not inconsistent with the provisions of Securitisation and Reconstruction of Financial Assets and Enforcement of Security Interest Act, 2002, but are complementary to each other. SARFAESI proceedings are in the nature of enforcement proceedings while arbitration is an adjudicatory process. SARFAESI proceedings and arbitration proceedings can go hand in hand.[64]

National Highways Act, 1956

The provisions of Arbitration Act, 1996 apply to every arbitration under the National Highways Act, 1956 subject to the provisions of 1956 Act.[65]

Bihar Public Works Contracts Disputes Arbitration Tribunal Act, 2008 (21 of 2008)

The arbitration agreement stipulated the applicability of the Central Act, State Act would not apply.[66]

63. *Punjab SEB* v. *Bassi Cold Storage*, 1994 Supp (2) SCC 124.
64. *M.D. Frozen Foods Exports (P) Ltd.* v. *Hero Fincorp Ltd.*, (2017) 16 SCC 741.
65. *PRA Computers (P) Ltd.* v. *Union of India*, 2020 SCC OnLine Utt 319.
66. *State of Bihar* v. *Brahmaputra Infrastructure Ltd.*, (2018) 17 SCC 444.

Part I

ARBITRATION

CHAPTER I
General Provisions

DEFINITIONS [S. 2]

2. *Definitions.*—(1) In this Part, unless the context otherwise requires,—

(*a*) "arbitration" means any arbitration whether or not administered by permanent arbitral institution;

(*b*) "arbitration agreement" means an agreement referred to in Section 7;

(*c*) "arbitral award" includes an interim award;

[1][(*ca*) "arbitral institution" means an arbitral institution designated by the Supreme Court or a High Court under this Act;]

(*d*) "arbitral tribunal" means a sole arbitrator or a panel of arbitrators;

[2][(*e*) "Court" means—

(*i*) in the case of an arbitration other than international commercial arbitration, the principal civil court of original jurisdiction in a district, and includes the High Court in exercise of its ordinary original civil jurisdiction, having jurisdiction to decide the questions forming the subject-matter of the arbitration if the same had been the subject-matter of a suit, but does not include any civil court of a grade inferior to such principal civil court, or any Court of Small Causes;

(*ii*) in the case of international commercial arbitration, the High Court in exercise of its ordinary original civil jurisdiction, having jurisdiction to decide the questions forming the subject-matter of the arbitration if the same had been the subject-matter of a suit, and in other cases, a High Court having jurisdiction to hear appeals from decrees of courts subordinate to that High Court;]

(*f*) "international commercial arbitration" means an arbitration relating to disputes arising out of legal relationships, whether contractual or not,

---

1. *Ins.* by Act 33 of 2019, S. 2(*i*)(A) (w.e.f. the date to be notified).
2. *Subs.* by Act 3 of 2016, S. 2(I)(A) (w.r.e.f. 23-10-2015). Prior to substitution it read as:

   '(*e*) "Court" means the Principal Civil Court of Original Jurisdiction in a district, and includes the High Court in exercise of its ordinary original civil jurisdiction, having jurisdiction to decide the questions forming the subject-matter of the arbitration if the same had been the subject-matter of a suit, but does not include any civil court of a grade inferior to such Principal Civil Court, or any Court of Small Causes;'

considered as commercial under the law in force in India and where at least one of the parties is—

(*i*) an individual who is a national of, or habitually resident in, any country other than India; or

(*ii*) a body corporate which is incorporated in any country other than India; or

(*iii*) [3][* * *] an association or a body of individuals whose central management and control is exercised in any country other than India; or

(*iv*) the Government of a foreign country;

(*g*) "legal representative" means a person who in law represents the estate of a deceased person, and includes any person who intermeddles with the estate of the deceased, and, where a party acts in a representative character, the person on whom the estate devolves on the death of the party so acting;

(*h*) "party" means a party to an arbitration agreement.

[4][(*i*) "prescribed" means prescribed by rules made under this Act;

(*j*) "regulations" means the regulations made by the Council under this Act;]

(2) **Scope.**—This Part shall apply where the place of arbitration is in India.

[5][Provided that subject to an agreement to the contrary, the provisions of Sections 9, 27 and [6][clause (*b*)] of sub-section (1) and sub-section (3) of Section 37 shall also apply to international commercial arbitration, even if the place of arbitration is outside India, and an arbitral award made or to be made in such place is enforceable and recognised under the provisions of Part II of this Act.]

(3) This Part shall not affect any other law for the time being in force by virtue of which certain disputes may not be submitted to arbitration.

(4) This Part except sub-section (1) of Section 40, Sections 41 and 43 shall apply to every arbitration under any other enactment for the time being in force, as if the arbitration were pursuant to an arbitration agreement and as if that other enactment were an arbitration agreement, except in so far as the provisions of this Part are inconsistent with that other enactment or with any rules made thereunder.

(5) Subject to the provisions of sub-section (4), and save in so far as is otherwise provided by any law for the time being in force or in any agreement in force between India and any other country or countries, this Part shall apply to all arbitrations and to all proceedings relating thereto.

---

3. The words "a company or" *omitted* by Act 3 of 2016, S. 2(I)(B) (w.r.e.f. 23-10-2015).
4. *Ins.* by Act 33 of 2019, S. 2(*i*)(B) (w.e.f. the date to be notified).
5. *Ins.* by Act 3 of 2016, S. 2(II) (w.r.e.f. 23-10-2015).
6. *Subs.* for "clause (*a*)" by Act 33 of 2019, S. 2(*ii*) (w.e.f. the date to be notified).

(6) **Construction of references.**—Where this Part, except Section 28, leaves the parties free to determine a certain issue, that freedom shall include the right of the parties to authorise any person including an institution, to determine that issue.

(7) An arbitral award made under this Part shall be considered as a domestic award.

(8) Where this Part—

(*a*) refers to the fact that the parties have agreed or that they may agree, or

(*b*) in any other way refers to an agreement of the parties, that agreement shall include any arbitration rules referred to in that agreement.

(9) Where this Part, other than clause (*a*) of Section 25 or clause (*a*) of sub-section (2) of Section 32, refers to a claim, it shall also apply to a counter-claim, and where it refers to a defence, it shall also apply to a defence to that counter-claim.

STATE AMENDMENTS

Uttar Pradesh.—In its application to the State of Uttar Pradesh, in sub-section (1), for clause (*e*), the following clause shall be *substituted*, namely—

"(*e*) 'Court' means the principal Civil Court of original jurisdiction in a district, which shall include the court of the Additional District Judge where so assigned by the District Judge and includes the High Court in exercise of its ordinary original civil jurisdiction, having jurisdiction to the decide the questions forming the subject-matter of the arbitration if the same had been the subject-matter of suit, or any Court of small causes.". [*Vide* U.P. Act No. 16 of 2019, S. 4, dated 29-11-2019].

COMMENTS

Corresponding old law

Section 2 corresponds to Section 2, Arbitration Act, 1940.

UNCITRAL Model Law

Article 2. *Definitions and rules of interpretation*

For the purposes of this Law:

(*a*) "arbitration" means any arbitration whether or not administered by a permanent arbitral institution;

(*b*) "arbitral tribunal" means a sole arbitrator or a panel of arbitrators;

(*c*) "court" means a body or organ of the judicial system of a State;

(*d*) where a provision of this Law, except article 28, leaves the parties free to determine a certain issue, such freedom includes the right of the parties to authorize a third party, including an institution, to make that determination;

(*e*) where a provision of this Law refers to the fact that the parties have agreed or that they may agree or in any other way refers to an agreement of the parties, such agreement includes any arbitration rules referred to in that agreement;

(*f*) where a provision of this Law, other than in Articles 25(*a*) and 32(2)(*a*), refers to a claim, it also applies to a counter-claim, and where it refers to a defence, it also applies to a defence to such counter-claim.

Legislative changes

Arbitration and Conciliation (Amendment) Act, 2015 (3 of 2016)

In the Arbitration and Conciliation Act, 1996 (26 of 1996), in Section 2:

(I) in sub-section (1),—

(A) for clause (*e*), the following clause shall be *substituted*, namely—

'(*e*) "Court" means—

(*i*) in the case of an arbitration other than international commercial arbitration, the principal Civil Court of original jurisdiction in a district, and includes the High Court in exercise of its ordinary original civil jurisdiction, having jurisdiction to decide the questions forming the subject-matter of the arbitration if the same had been the subject-matter of a suit, but does not include any Civil Court of a grade inferior to such principal Civil Court, or any Court of Small Causes;

(*ii*) in the case of international commercial arbitration, the High Court in exercise of its ordinary original civil jurisdiction, having jurisdiction to decide the questions forming the subject-matter of the arbitration if the same had been the subject-matter of a suit, and in other cases, a High Court having jurisdiction to hear appeals from decrees of courts subordinate to that High Court;';

(B) in clause (*f*), in sub-clause (*iii*), the words "a company or" shall be *omitted*;

(II) in sub-section (2), the following proviso shall be *inserted*, namely—

"Provided that subject to an agreement to the contrary, the provisions of Sections 9, 27 and clause (*a*) of sub-section (1) and sub-section (3) of Section 37 shall also apply to international commercial arbitration, even if the place of arbitration is outside India, and an arbitral award made or to be made in such place is enforceable and recognised under the provisions of Part II of this Act.".

NOTES ON CLAUSES

"Clause 2 of the Bill seeks to amend Section 2 of the Arbitration and Conciliation Act, 1996 to re-define some of the expressions used in the Act. A proviso below sub-section (2) is inserted to provide that some of the provisions of Part I of the Act shall also apply to International Commercial Arbitration, even if the place of arbitration is outside India."

Arbitration and Conciliation (Amendment) Act, 2019 (33 of 2019)

In the Arbitration and Conciliation Act, 1996 (26 of 1996), in Section 2:

(*i*) in sub-section (1),—

(A) after clause (*c*), the following clause shall be inserted, namely:—

'(ca) "arbitral institution" means an arbitral institution designated by the Supreme Court or a High Court under this Act;

(B) after clause (*h*), the following clauses shall be inserted, namely:—

'(*i*) "prescribed" means prescribed by rules made under this Act;

(*j*) "regulations" means the regulations made by the Council under this Act.';

(*ii*) in sub-section (2), in the proviso, for the word, brackets and letter "clause (*a*)", the word, brackets and letter "clause (*b*)" shall be substituted.

Scope and application

Section 2 is a definition section, defining the various terms used throughout the Act. The various terms defined in this section are:

Arbitration, clause (*a*)
Arbitration agreement, clause (*b*)
Arbitral award, clause (*c*)
Arbitral institution, clause (*ca*)
Arbitral Tribunal, clause (*d*)
Court, clause (*e*)
International commercial arbitration, clause (*f*)
Legal representative, clause (*g*)
Party, clause (*h*)
Prescribed, clause (*i*)
Regulations, clause (*j*)

Sub-section (2) lays down that Part I of the Act shall apply where the place of arbitration is in India, an arbitral award made under Part I shall be considered as a domestic award.

"Arbitration" [S. 2(1)(*a*)]

Arbitration is a binding voluntary alternative dispute resolution process by a private forum chosen by the parties. If a party, with open eyes and full knowledge and comprehension of the relevant provision enters into a contract with a government/statutory corporation/public sector containing an arbitration agreement providing that one of its Secretaries/Directors shall be the arbitrator, he cannot subsequently turn round and contend that he is agreeable for settlement of disputes by arbitration but not by named arbitrator who is an employee of the other party.[7]

Arbitration is an efficacious and alternative way of dispute resolution between the parties. The method of arbitration has evolved over the period of time to help the parties to speedily resolve their disputes through this process and, in fact, the Act recognises this aspect and has elaborate provisions to cater to the needs of speedy disposal of disputes.[8]

In *Balmukund Pandey* v. *V.K. Singh*[9], it was held that the law existing on the date of making of request by the petitioner would apply to govern the arbitral proceedings. Petitioner made a representation for the appointment of an arbitrator on 21 October 1998 pursuant to which the sole arbitrator was appointed. On the said date, the Arbitration Act, 1940 had ceased to operate and the 1996 Act was in operation. The Arbitral Tribunal, therefore, acted rightly in taking up the claim of petitioner under the provisions of the 1996 Act.

(*a*) *Arbitrator is not a court*

An arbitrator is not a court. Arbitrators are persons chosen by the parties to adjudicate their disputes.[10] Arbitrator is not a court, but is the outcome of agreement.[11]

An arbitrator is not a court for the purpose of Section 195 CrPC.[12]

(*b*) *Arbitration clause separable*

Under the scheme, the arbitration clause is separable from the other clauses of the partnership deed. The arbitration clause constitutes an agreement by itself.[13]

7. *Indian Oil Corpn. Ltd.* v. *Raja Transport (P) Ltd.*, (2009) 8 SCC 520.
8. *NBCC Ltd.* v. *J.G. Engg. (P) Ltd.*, (2010) 2 SCC 385.
9. 2009 SCC OnLine MP 30: (2010) 1 MP LJ 372.
10. *Paramjeet Singh Patheja* v. *ICDS Ltd.*, (2006) 13 SCC 322.
11. *Union of India* v. *Ambica Construction*, (2016) 6 SCC 36.
12. *Manohar Lal* v. *Vinesh Anand*, (2001) 5 SCC 407.
13. *Firm Ashok Traders* v. *Gurumukh Das Saluja*, (2004) 3 SCC 155.

"Arbitration agreement" [S. 2(1)(*b*)]

As stated by clause (*b*) "arbitration agreement" means an agreement referred to in Section 7. *See*, commentary under Section 7 *infra*. An arbitration agreement must be interpreted having regard to the language used in it.[14]

The bracket portion in an arbitration agreement is only for the purposes of further explanation. It cannot be allowed to control the main clause.[15]

Where the contract has several annexures/attachments, prepared at different points of time, unless a contrary intention is apparent, the latter in point of time would normally prevail over the one earlier in point of time.[16]

In *Kotak Mahindra Bank Ltd.* v. *Deepak Jawaharlal Gupta*[17], parties agreed to settle their dispute in the court, exclusively, at Chennai. Though agreement took place/signed in Mumbai, it was decided that the court in Chennai shall have exclusive jurisdiction that needs to be respected from every angle and the court of Mumbai will have no jurisdiction.

(*a*) *Arbitration clause—Nature of*

An arbitration though an independent part of the contract, is an agreement within an agreement. It is a collateral term of the contract, independent of and distinct from its substantive terms.[18]

(*b*) *Arbitration agreement—Form and essential elements*

The definition of "arbitration agreement" in Section 2(*b*) of the Act shows that an arbitration agreement is not required to be in any particular form. What is required to be ascertained is whether the parties had agreed that if any dispute arose between them in respect of the subject-matter of the contract, such dispute should be referred to arbitration. In that case, such an agreement would certainly spell out an arbitration agreement. It is also clear that the agreement must be in writing and to interpret the agreement as an "arbitration agreement" one has to ascertain the intention of the parties and also treat the decision as final. If the parties had desired that a dispute must be referred to arbitration for decision and that they would abide by that decision, it must be held that the intention of the parties was to have an arbitration agreement.[19]

14. *P. Manohar Reddy & Bros.* v. *Maharashtra Krishna Valley Development Corpn.*, (2009) 2 SCC 494.
15. *Dozco India (P) Ltd.* v. *Doosan Infracore Co. Ltd.*, (2011) 6 SCC 179.
16. *M.K. Abraham & Co.* v. *State of Kerala*, (2009) 7 SCC 636.
17. 2009 SCC OnLine Bom 1738: (2010) 4 Mah LJ 358.
18. *M.R. Engineers & Contractors (P) Ltd.* v. *Som Datt Builders Ltd.*, (2009) 7 SCC 696; *I.T.E.C. Ltd.* v. *India Exhibition Management (P) Ltd.*, 2008 SCC OnLine All 533.
19. *Punjab State* v. *Dina Nath*, (2007) 5 SCC 28.

Arbitration being a matter of contract, the parties are entitled to fix the boundaries so as to confer and limit the jurisdiction and legal authority of the arbitrator. An arbitration agreement can be comprehensive and broad to include any dispute or can be confined to specific disputes. The scope of arbitrator's jurisdiction invariably arises when the disputes that are arbitrable are enumerated or the arbitration agreement provides for exclusions as in case of excepted matters, *i.e.* the matters which the parties expressly exclude certain disputes to be referred to arbitration in respect of which the Arbitral Tribunal may not have jurisdiction to adjudicate such disputes. The will of the parties as to the scope of arbitration is a subjective act personal to the parties.[20]

Merely because the words "arbitration" and "arbitrator" were not used in the clause of the word order, it was no ground to hold that the said clause was not an arbitration agreement within the meaning of Section 2(*b*) of the Act. As the parties intended to make a reference to arbitration and to treat the decision of the arbitrator as final, the clause in the work order was construed as an arbitration agreement.[21]

In construing the intention of the parties in arbitration agreement, due importance should be given to parties' autonomy.[22]

The essential elements of an arbitration agreement are:

1. There must be a present or future difference in conviction with some contemplated matter.
2. There must be the intention of the parties to settle such differences by a private tribunal.
3. The parties must agree in writing to be bound by the decision of such tribunal.[23]

A mere letter cannot be deemed to be an arbitration agreement between the parties.[24]

Reference in a contract to a document containing an arbitration clause constitutes an arbitration agreement if the contract is in writing and the

---

20. *Delhi State Industrial & Infrastructure Development Corpn. Ltd.* v. *HR Builders*, (2022) 4 HCC (Del) 123.
21. *Punjab State* v. *Dina Nath*, (2007) 5 SCC 28; *Consolidated Construction Consortium Ltd.* v. *SDMC*, (2022) 6 HCC (Del) 439.
22. *Sime Darby Engg. SDN. BHD.* v. *Engineers India Ltd.*, (2009) 7 SCC 545.
23. *Bihar State Mineral Development Corpn.* v. *Encon Builders (I) (P) Ltd.*, (2003) 7 SCC 418.
24. *GAIL* v. *Sarvodaya Glass Industries*, 2004 SCC OnLine All 294: (2004) 55 ALR 165.

reference is such as to make that arbitration clause part of the contract, in terms of sub-section (5) of Section 7, Arbitration and Conciliation Act.[25]

An arbitration agreement must contain the broad consensus between the parties that the dispute and the differences should be referred to an Arbitral Tribunal.[26] Arbitration agreement cannot be uncertain or unmeaningful. Parties are to be ad-idem to the arbitration and such an intent must be clear from the contract relied upon between the parties.[27]

In order to constitute a valid, binding and enforceable arbitration agreement, the requirements contained in Section 7 have to be satisfied strictly. These requirements apart from others are: 1) there has to be an agreement; 2) it has to be in writing; 3) parties must sign such agreement, in other words, the agreement must bear the signatures of the parties concerned; and 4) such agreement must contain an arbitration clause. Failure to satisfy any of the four conditions would render the arbitration agreement invalid and unenforceable, and in consequence would result in dismissal of the application filed under Section 11, Arbitration and Conciliation Act, 1996 at its threshold.[28]

Prima facie opinion expressed in a report is no ground to refer the issue to arbitration in the absence of any agreement requiring such reference.[29]

In *State of Orissa* v. *Bhagyadhar Dash*[30], a clause in a government contract provided that the decision of the Superintending Engineer as regards the rates of non-technical work shall be final. The clause operated in a limited sphere, did not provide for reference of dispute between the parties to arbitration. The clause also did not provide that the decision of the Superintending Engineer would be binding on the parties or that the Superintending Engineer had to act judicially. It was held that the clause was not an arbitration agreement. Reference of dispute between the parties to the arbitrator was not proper.

In a dispute arising between the government and the contractor, Government Order provided for referring dispute between contractor and department to departmental arbitrator if the value was less than ₹2 lakhs and to court if the value was more than ₹2 lakhs. It was held that the expression "claims for more than ₹2 lakhs should be referred to Court"

25. *Premlaxmi and Co.* v. *Trafalgar House Construction India Ltd.*, 1998 SCC OnLine Bom 398: (1998) 3 Mah LJ 695.
26. *Bihar State Mineral Development Corpn.* v. *Encon Builders (I) (P) Ltd.*, (2003) 7 SCC 418.
27. *Nilesh C. Sanghani* v. *Rakesh V. Zangda*, 2007 SCC OnLine Bom 530: (2007) 6 Mah LJ 242.
28. *Vimal Kishor Shah* v. *Jayesh Dinesh Shah*, (2016) 8 SCC 788.
29. *Karan Singh* v. *State of J&K*, (2004) 5 SCC 698.
30. (2011) 7 SCC 406.

does not mean referred to court for referring it to arbitration. The parties are free to approach the court having competent jurisdiction for adjudicating all their claims above ₹2 lakhs.[31]

Contract clause made provision for settlement of disputes relating to specification, design, quality and workmanship and the technical aspects by an officer of one of the parties. It was held that it was not an arbitration clause.[32]

(c) *Arbitration clause—Determination of—Where contract consists of a printed form with cyclostyled amendments, typed additions/corrections, handwritten corrections*

If a contract consists of a printed form with cyclostyled amendments, typed additions and deletions and handwritten corrections, an endeavour should be made to give effect to all the provisions. However, in the event of apparent or irreconcilable inconsistency, the following rules of construction will normally apply:

1. the cyclostyled amendments will prevail over the printed terms;
2. the typewritten additions will prevail over the printed terms and cyclostyled amendments; and
3. handwritten corrections will prevail over the printed terms, cyclostyled amendments and typewritten additions. These rules have evolved from the maxim of construction that "written, stamped or typed additions, when inconsistent with the printed terms, would normally prevail over the printed terms" and proceeds on the assumption that the printed form contained the original terms, and changes thereto were incorporated by the cyclostyled amendments, followed by changes by typewritten additions and lastly the handwritten additions.[33]

(d) *Bill of Lading*

In *Pyrites, Phosphates and Chemicals Ltd.* v. *Sebilan Compania*[34], the opening part of the Bill of Lading specifically provided that "all terms and conditions of the relevant charter party are deemed to have been incorporated herein". Further, one of the conditions of carriage as provided in the Bill of Lading stipulated that all terms and conditions in the charter party stand incorporated. One clause in the charter party contained an arbitration

31. *Rajam Engg. Contractors* v. *State of T.N.*, 2006 SCC OnLine Mad 103: (2006) 1 CTC 769.
32. *State of Rajasthan* v. *Nav Bharat Construction Co.*, (2005) 11 SCC 197; see also, *Bharat Bhushan Bansal* v. *U.P. Small Industries Corpn. Ltd.*, (1999) 2 SCC 166.
33. *M.K. Abraham & Co.* v. *State of Kerala*, (2009) 7 SCC 636.
34. (2002) 9 SCC 353.

clause and provided that each party may appoint an arbitrator out of the panel of arbitrators maintained by Indian Council of Arbitration and that disputes between the parties will be settled according to the provisions of the arbitration agreement. It was held that such incorporation in the Bill of Lading amounted to a binding arbitration agreement between the parties.

"Arbitral award" [S. 2(1)(*c*)]

Clause (*c*) defines an "arbitral award". However, clause (*c*) does not define "arbitral award", it merely says that "arbitral award" includes an interim award. Where the arbitrator/Arbitral Tribunal after hearing the parties pronounces its verdict on the dispute(s) referred to, it is an arbitral award.

Whereas under the 1940 Act only an interim award or final award could be made, four types of awards are contemplated under the 1996 Act, *viz.* interim award, additional award, settlement or agreed award and final award.[35]

An award possesses all the elements of validity even though it has not been formally enforced and it may be relied upon in a litigation between the parties relating to the same subject-matter.[36]

Family arrangement is not an award.[37]

Not every order, decision or adjudication passed to the interim stage of arbitration proceedings would assume the character of an arbitral award. The predominant tests to treat an "interim award" or "partial final award" as an "arbitral award" under Section 2(1)(*c*) of the said Act would be three fold:

1. that it satisfies the tests of the form and contents of an award under sub-section (1), (2) and (3) of Section 31 of the said Act;
2. it is in relation to "any matter" with respect to which a final arbitral award can be made; as specified under sub-section (6) of Section 31 of the said Act; and
3. the nature, extent and intendment of such order, decision or adjudication.

If all these tests are satisfied, then, interim award or partial award shall become an "arbitral award" as per Section 2(1)(*c*) of the said Act and consequently, the bar of limitation under sub-section (3) of Section 34

35. *Centrotrade Minerals & Metals Inc.* v. *Hindustan Copper Ltd.*, (2006) 11 SCC 245.
36. *Cheran Properties Ltd.* v. *Kasturi & Sons Ltd.*, (2018) 16 SCC 413.
37. *Narendra Prasad Singh* v. *Ram Ashish Singh*, 2018 SCC OnLine Pat 1145: (2019) 2 PLJR 961.

of the said Act shall be attracted in each case, even in respect of such an award.[38]

In view of the definition given in Section 2(1)(*c*), an interim award is also an arbitral award which can be challenged by making an application in accordance with Section 34 of the Act.[39]

The courts of Delhi where award was passed as well courts in Jhansi where the workshop of North Central Railway was to be modernised, would have jurisdiction to entertain application filed under Section 34, Arbitration and Conciliation Act, 1996.[40]

"Arbitral institution" [S. 2(1)(*ca*)]

Clause (*ca*) is newly inserted by the Arbitration Amendment Act, 33 of 2019. It simply states that "arbitral institution" means an arbitral institution designated by the Supreme Court or a High Court under this Act.

Sub-section (3) of Section 11 (amended by Act 33 of 2019) provides that the Supreme Court shall have the power to designate arbitral institutions from time to time, which have been graded by the Arbitration Council of India under Section 43-I for the purpose of this Act. In respect of those High Court jurisdictions where no graded arbitral institutions are available, the Chief Justice of the High Court concerned may maintain a panel of arbitrators for discharging the functions and duties of the arbitral institution, any reference to the arbitrator shall be deemed to an arbitral institution for the purpose of Section 11.

"Arbitral Tribunal" [S. 2(1)(*d*)]

The definition of "arbitral tribunal" in Section 2(1)(*d*) of the 1996 Act is in *verbatim* as in Article 2(*b*) of the UNCITRAL Rules.[41] As defined by clause (*d*), "arbitral tribunal" means a sole arbitrator or a panel of arbitrators. The parties are free to determine the number of arbitrators, provided that the number of arbitrators shall not be an even number. Where the parties fail to agree on the number of arbitrators to be appointed in the case, the Arbitral Tribunal shall consist of a sole arbitrator. *See*, comments under Section 10 *infra*.

Jurisdiction of an arbitrator to hear and decide a dispute is derived from an arbitration agreement. What confers jurisdiction on the arbitrators to

---

38. *Aero Club* v. *Solar Creations (P) Ltd.*, 2020 SCC OnLine Bom 472: (2021) 2 Mah LJ 186.
39. *Union of India* v. *High Court of Allahabad*, 2001 SCC OnLine All 371: 2001 All LJ 1896.
40. *Union of India* v. *Larsen & Tubro Ltd.*, 2023 SCC OnLine All 1117: (2023) 4 All LJ 490.
41. *Sime Darby Engg. SDN. BHD.* v. *Engineers India Ltd.*, (2009) 7 SCC 545.

hear and decide a dispute is an arbitration agreement and where there is no such agreement, there is initial want of jurisdiction which cannot be cured even by acquiescence. The arbitrators shall derive their jurisdiction from the agreement and consent.[42]

"Court" [S. 2(1)(*e*)]

Section 2(1)(*e*) expressly recognises that not only the District Courts but also the High Courts exercising original civil jurisdiction would have jurisdiction under the 1996 Act. Hence, there is no question of "uniformity rule" being required to be applied. There cannot be a rule of uniformity applied between the unlikes, *i.e.* subordinate courts governed by CPC and High Courts governed by Letters Patent.[43] Principal civil court of original jurisdiction insofar as Chennai is concerned is the High Court.[44] Competent court referred to in Section 2(1)(*e*) is a court which can entertain a suit between the parties.[45] District Court is the principal civil court of the original jurisdiction in a district and is the "court" for the purpose of executing the award passed under the Arbitration Act.[46]

The word "court" defined in Section 2(1)(*e*) not only includes the principal civil court of original jurisdiction, *i.e.* Court of Principal District Judge or District Judge(s), but also includes the Court of Additional District Judge(s), therefore, any application filed under any provision of the 1996 Act before the court after passing of the award, including applications under Section 34 or 36 of the 1996 Act, can be heard and decided not only by the District Judge(s), but also by the Court of Additional District Judge(s), upon being made over by the District Judge by a general or special order.[47]

Section 2(1)(*e*) of the Act defines "court" to mean the principal civil court of original jurisdiction in the district. The definition is both inclusive and exclusive. It specifically includes the High Court in exercise of its ordinary original civil jurisdiction within the ambit of the definition of "court" and excludes "civil courts of a grade inferior to such Principal Civil Court" and court of small causes. This definition includes the High Court wherever the High Court exercises original jurisdiction. The definition of "court" has

42. *Dharma Prathishthanam* v. *Madhok Construction (P) Ltd.*, (2005) 9 SCC 686.
43. *Jindal Vijayanagar Steel (JSW Steel Ltd.)* v. *Jindal Praxair Oxygen Co. Ltd.*, (2006) 11 SCC 521.
44. *Dynasty Developers (P) Ltd.* v. *Jumbo World Holdings Ltd.*, 2006 SCC OnLine Mad 1078: (2006) 5 CTC 740.
45. *Annamar & Co.* v. *T.N. Housing Board*, 2009 SCC OnLine Mad 2670: (2010) 2 CTC 31.
46. *Rajashree Shrinivas Joshi* v. *Omega Information Systems*, 2009 SCC OnLine Bom 198: (2009) 3 Mah LJ 303.
47. *A Suo Moto Taken* v. *State of Chhattisgarh*, 2018 SCC OnLine Chh 617.

thus been narrowed down to mean and include the District Court and the High Court in exercise of its ordinary original civil jurisdiction.[48]

The High Court of Orissa does not exercise the original civil jurisdiction. Sub-section (2) of Section 2, Orissa Civil Courts Act, 1984 provides that the Court of the District Judge shall be the principal court of original civil jurisdiction in the district and the explanation provides that for the purpose of this sub-section, the expression "District Judge" shall not include an Additional District Judge. Thus, for the State of Odisha, the District Judge is the "court" within the definition of the aforesaid section and not the High Court.[49]

Legislature in its wisdom thought it necessary to confer jurisdiction to decide the questions forming the subject-matter of a suit under the Act with the "principal civil court" of a "district" and by excluding any other civil court of a grade inferior to such principal civil court or any Court of Small Causes. Principal civil court of original jurisdiction in a district would mean and include only the Principal District Judge of the district.[50]

Expression "principal civil court of original jurisdiction" occurring in Section 2(1)(*e*) insofar as the city of Chennai is concerned is High Court and not city civil court.[51]

The court where an application under Section 9 can be filed, is the court which would have jurisdiction to entertain a suit on the basis of the facts given in the application under Section 9. The place where arbitration may take place is not relevant for deciding the jurisdiction of the court. In *Mikuni Corpn.* v. *UCAL Fuel Systems Ltd. Carburettors Ltd. Siemens VDO Automotive*[52], neither the petitioner nor the respondent had their office or place of business in Delhi. No cause of action or part of cause of action arose in Delhi. Held, court has no jurisdiction to entertain the application under Section 9.

In *Shivhare Road Lines* v. *HPCL and Mittal Energy Ltd.*[53], a tender was accepted at Gwalior. Part of the cause of action had arisen within the territory of the principal civil court at Gwalior. The Chief Justice or his designate would be those within whose local limits the principal civil court is constituted. Since the principal civil court would have jurisdiction

48. *Dynasty Developers (P) Ltd.* v. *Jumbo World Holdings Ltd.*, 2008 SCC OnLine Mad 16: (2008) 1 CTC 580.
49. *Bedabyas Barik* v. *Sukanti Barik*, 2019 SCC OnLine Ori 380.
50. *Betamax Ltd.* v. *State Trading Corpn.*, 2019 SCC OnLine Kar 2092: ILR 2019 Kar 4877.
51. *Sundaram Finance Ltd.* v. *M.K. Kurian*, 2006 SCC OnLine Mad 56: (2006) 1 CTC 433.
52. 2008 SCC OnLine Del 127: ILR (2008) 2 Del 367.
53. 2012 SCC OnLine MP 5779: (2012) 4 MP LJ 446.

at Gwalior, had it been within its domain, the Chief Justice or his designate would have decided the application for appointment of arbitrator.

District Judge is a court within the meaning of Section 2(1)(*e*), is competent to try applications filed under Section 14 of the Act.[54]

The "court" includes the Court of Additional District Judge.[55]

Supreme Court is not "court" for the purpose of Section 2(1)(*e*)

Definition of "court" in Section 2(1)(*e*) is materially different from its predecessor or contained in Section 2(*c*) of the 1940 Act. The Supreme Court cannot possibly be considered to be "court" within the meaning of Section 2(1)(*e*) of the 1996 Act even if it retains seisin over the arbitral proceedings.[56] Section 2(1)(*e*) contains an exhaustive definition marking out only the principal civil court of original jurisdiction in a district or a High Court having original civil jurisdiction in the State and no other court is "court" for the purpose of Part I of Arbitration and Conciliation Act, 1996. In no circumstances, the Supreme Court is a "court" for the purpose of Section 2(1)(*e*).[57]

Jurisdiction of High Court to hear application under Section 9

The parties themselves in *Jindal Vijayanagar Steel (JSW Steel Ltd.)* v. *Jindal Praxair Oxygen Co. Ltd.*[58], had chosen Mumbai to be the situs of arbitration proceedings. Dispute resolution meeting, a pre-condition for invoking an arbitration clause was also held in Mumbai. When the respondent filed an application under Section 9, the appellant-company was having its office at Mumbai, and was carrying on business at Mumbai, its Directors were also sitting at Mumbai. During the pendency of the petition under Section 9, the appellant had shifted its registered office at Mumbai. It was held that the Bombay High Court had territorial jurisdiction to entertain an application under Section 9 filed by the respondents. If a court has no territorial jurisdiction (but is otherwise competent to hear a matter), should the matter be heard and decided by such a court without demur, the judgment will be valid and not void or non-est. The relevant time to determine the existence of the territorial jurisdiction would be when the matter is heard.

---

54. *SAIL* v. *Pratima Kanungo*, 2019 SCC OnLine Ori 460: (2019) 128 CLT 223.
55. *W.B. Housing Infrastructure Development Corpn.* v. *Impression*, 2016 SCC OnLine Cal 1556: (2016) 3 CHN 153; *I.T.I. Ltd.* v. *District Judge, Allahabad*, 1998 SCC OnLine All 359: 1998 All LJ 2115.
56. *State of Jharkhand* v. *Hindustan Construction Co. Ltd.*, (2018) 2 SCC 602; *State of W.B.* v. *Associated Contractors*, (2015) 1 SCC 32.
57. *State of W.B.* v. *Associated Contractors*, (2015) 1 SCC 32.
58. (2006) 11 SCC 521.

(*a*) *Allahabad High Court*

The Allahabad High Court does not exercise original civil jurisdiction, it is not a court as defined in Section 2(1)(*e*).[59]

(*b*) *Additional District Judge*

The court of Additional District Judge is not a principal civil court for the purpose of Section 2(1)(*e*) of the Act; therefore it has no jurisdiction to dispose of objections filed under Section 34 of the Act.[60]

Section 4(2) of the Kerala Civil Courts Act, 1957 empowers Additional District Judge with powers to discharge functions of District Judge. There is no jurisdictional error in Additional District Judge hearing petitions under the Act of 1996.[61]

Commercial disputes—Jurisdiction of court

In case of commercial disputes involving arbitration, only a commercial court of the status of District Judge or Additional Judge is a competent court to entertain matters under Sections 9, 14, 34 and 36 of 1996 Act.[62] Suits involving commercial disputes filed in ordinary civil jurisdiction are not maintainable in such jurisdiction.[63]

Designated commercial court/Judge subordinate to the rank of Principal Civil Judge/Principal Civil Court in District has jurisdiction to hear all applications or appeals under the Arbitration and Conciliation Act, 1996, other than those arising out of international commercial arbitrations.[64]

"International commercial arbitration" [S. 2(1)(*f*)]

"International commercial arbitration" means an arbitration relating to disputes arising out of legal relationships, whether commercial or not, considered as commercial under the law in force in India and where at least one of the parties is:

(*i*) an individual who is a national of, or habitually resident in, in any country other than India; or

---

59. *Ashish Kumar Sadh* v. *Putul Chaubey*, 2015 SCC OnLine All 9371: (2016) 115 ALR 587.
60. *Northern Coalfields Ltd.* v. *Aluminium Industries Ltd.*, 2013 SCC OnLine All 13492: (2013) 99 ALR 89.
61. *Kasim V.K.* v. *M. Ashraf*, (2021) 1 HCC (Ker) 379.
62. *Tahsildar, Mangalagiri Mandal* v. *Mangalagiri Pattana Padmasali Bahuthama Sangham*, 2020 SCC OnLine AP 1701: (2021) 1 ALT 120.
63. *Laxmi Polyfab (P) Ltd.* v. *Eden Realty Ventures (P) Ltd.*, 2021 SCC OnLine Cal 1457: (2021) 2 Cal LT 214.
64. *Jaycee Housing (P) Ltd.* v. *High Court of Orissa*, (2023) 1 SCC 549.

(*ii*) a body corporate which is incorporated in any country other than India;

(*iii*) an association or a body of individuals whose central management or control is exercised in any country, other than India; or

(*iv*) the government of a foreign country.

Section 2(1)(*f*) of Arbitration and Conciliation Act, Act 1996 defines the expression "international commercial arbitration" only for a limited purpose, *namely*, for the purpose of Part I of the Arbitration and Conciliation Act, 1996.[65]

In *Amway (India) Enterprises (P) Ltd.* v. *Ravindranath Rao Sindhia*[66], where both the petitioner, husband and wife, applied to become distributors of company as sole proprietorship concern with Code of Ethics with Central Management and control of association or body of individuals only exercised in India, both the petitioners nationals and habitually resident in the US, it was held that arbitration becomes an international commercial arbitration notwithstanding the fact that individual, body corporate or government of a foreign country referred to in Section 2(1)(*f*) carry on business in India. The Delhi High Court had no jurisdiction to appoint an arbitrator.

As per Section 2(1)(*f*), to be an "international commercial arbitration", three factors ought to be fulfilled—1) arbitration; 2) considered as commercial under the laws in force in India; and 3) at least one of the parties is national or habitual resident in any country other than India. In *Mankastu Impex (P) Ltd.* v. *Airvisual Ltd.*[67], since the respondent is a company incorporated under the laws of Hong Kong, international commercial arbitration would apply.

Where one of the parties to both the arbitration agreements is an American company along with two Indian companies both of them become an "international commercial agreement".[68]

International commercial arbitration [S. 2(1)(*f*)], English Arbitration Act compared

Whereas Indian Arbitration and Conciliation Act, 1996 lays emphasis on one of the parties being outside India, the English Act for the purpose of domestic arbitration agreement excludes a body corporate which is incorporated and whose central control or management is exercised in a State

65. *PASL Wind Solutions (P) Ltd.* v. *GE Power Conversion (India) (P) Ltd.*, (2021) 7 SCC 1.
66. (2021) 8 SCC 465.
67. (2020) 5 SCC 399.
68. *Sasan Power Ltd.* v. *North American Coal Corpn. (India) (P) Ltd.*, (2016) 10 SCC 813.

other than the UK. Thus, under the English Act what is being considered is a domestic arbitration agreement when a body corporate is incorporated in a State other than the UK; whereas under the Indian Act only a body corporate which is only incorporated in a State outside India is included within the meaning of international commercial arbitration.[69]

International commercial arbitration [S. 2(1)(*f*)], domestic arbitration excluded

"International commercial arbitration" and domestic arbitration connote two different things. The 1996 Act excludes domestic arbitration from the purview of international commercial arbitration. A company which is incorporated in a country other than India is excluded from the said definition.[70]

An analysis of Section 2(1)(*f*) would show that whatever be the transaction between the parties, if it happens to be entered into between persons, at least one of whom is either a foreign national, or habitually resident in, any country other than India; or by a body corporate which is incorporated in any country other than India; or by the government of a foreign country, the arbitration becomes an international commercial arbitration notwithstanding the fact that the individual, body corporate or government of a foreign country referred to in Section 2(1)(*f*) carry on business in India through a business office in India. In such a case, the Supreme Court has jurisdiction to appoint an arbitrator. The Delhi High Court had no jurisdiction to appoint an arbitrator.[71]

Where an international commercial arbitration is *held in India*, the provisions of Part I would compulsorily apply and parties are free to deviate only to the extent permitted by derogable provisions of Part I.

In cases of international commercial arbitrations held *outside India*, provisions of Part I would apply unless the parties by agreement express or implied, exclude all or any of its provisions. In that case the laws or rules chosen by the parties would prevail. Any provision in Part I which is contrary to or excluded by that law or rules will not apply in the later case.[72]

In *Bhatia International* v. *Bulk Trading S.A.*[73], it has been laid down that the parties can exclude the application of all or any provision(s) of Part I by agreement express or implied. In *Dozco India (P) Ltd.* v. *Doosan*

69. *TDM Infrastructure (P) Ltd.* v. *UE Development India (P) Ltd.*, (2008) 14 SCC 271.
70. *Ibid.*
71. *Amway (India) Enterprises (P) Ltd.* v. *Ravindranath Rao Sindhia*, (2021) 8 SCC 465.
72. *National Agricultural Coop. Mktg. Federation India Ltd.* v. *Gains Trading Ltd.*, (2007) 5 SCC 692; *Bhatia International* v. *Bulk Trading S.A.*, (2002) 4 SCC 105.
73. (2002) 4 SCC 105.

Infracore Co. Ltd.[74], in agreement between the Indian company and the foreign company, the arbitration clause stipulated that the law governing the agreement would be Korean law and the seat of arbitration would be Seoul in Korea. The court observed that it amounted to express exclusion of Part I, and there was clear agreement between the parties excluding Part I of the Act. Application for appointment of arbitrator under Section 11(6) before the Supreme Court did not lie, hence was rejected.

In *Comed Chemicals Ltd.* v. *C.N. Ramchand*[75], respondent, a British national and a professional expert, entered into an MOU with the appellant-company for providing technical "know-how" and expert advice to the appellant for which the appellant was required to pay fees. The respondent was also made a Director Technical and also Chief Executive Officer of the subsidiary company of the appellant, 40 per cent equity shares in the subsidiary company were also allotted to him. It was held that a Director is not a *mere* employee or servant of the company. The respondent was working in dual or double capacity, *i.e.* 1) as an employee; and 2) as a Director. The functions to be performed by him were supervisory and related to policy making decisions in the affairs of the company. Any dispute between the applicant company and respondent, would, therefore, be covered by the clause in the question of the arbitration agreement which provided for arbitration. Application filed before the Supreme Court for appointment of arbitrator was found maintainable. Sole arbitrator was appointed in the case to decide the dispute which had arisen between the parties.

Contract providing that arbitration would be governed by foreign law—Part I be excluded

The parties had agreed that notwithstanding Article 33, the arbitration agreement contained in Article 34 shall be governed by the laws of England. This necessarily implied that parties had agreed to exclude the provisions of Part I of the Article. It was held that the Delhi High Court did not have the jurisdiction to entertain the petition filed by the respondents under Section 9 of the Act, the mere fact the appellants had earlier filed similar petitions was not sufficient to clothe the Delhi High Court to entertain the petition filed by the respondents under Section 9 was rejected.[76]

74. (2011) 6 SCC 179.
75. (2009) 1 SCC 91.
76. *Videocon Industries Ltd.* v. *Union of India*, (2011) 6 SCC 161.

Venue Hong Kong

In the present case the arbitration clause provided that the matter in dispute shall be referred to and finally resolved by arbitration in accordance with the provisions of the Arbitration and Conciliation Act, 1996 (or any statutory modification, enactment or amendment thereof) and the venue shall be Hong Kong. Held, merely because the parties had agreed that the venue of arbitration shall be Hong Kong, it did not follow that the laws in force in Hong Kong will apply. Therefore, the Arbitration and Conciliation Act, 1996 will apply. Therefore, the 1996 Act will govern the appointment of arbitrator, the reference of disputes and the entire process and procedure till the award is made and executed/given effect to.[77]

International commercial arbitration held within India or outside India

In *National Agricultural Coop. Mktg. Federation India Ltd.* v. *Gains Trading Ltd.*[78], the Supreme Court applied and reiterated the law laid down in *Bhatia International* v. *Bulk Trading S.A.*[79]. Where an international commercial arbitration is held in India, the provisions of Part I would compulsorily apply and the parties are free to deviate only to the extent permitted by the derogable provisions of Part I. In cases of international commercial arbitrations held outside India provisions of Part I would apply unless the parties by agreement, express or implied, exclude all or any of its provisions. In that case the laws or rules chosen by the parties would prevail. Any provision in Part I which is contrary to or excluded by that law or rules will not apply in the latter case.

In *Bharat Aluminium Co.* v. *Kaiser Aluminium Technical Services Inc.*[80], the question raised before a five-judge Bench of the Supreme Court was whether the law laid down in *Bhatia International*, followed in *Venture Global Engg.*[81], is correct, in view of Section 2(2) and (7), Arbitration and Conciliation Act, 1996, according to which Part I of the 1996 Act applies to arbitrations held in India. In view of the conflict between two members of the Bench as to the applicability of Part I, the matter had been placed before a three-judge Bench, which had directed that the matter be placed before this five-judge Bench.

---

77. *National Agricultural Coop. Mktg. Federation India Ltd.* v. *Gains Trading Ltd.*, (2007) 5 SCC 692.
78. *Ibid*; see also, *Videocon Industries Ltd.* v. *Union of India*, (2011) 6 SCC 161.
79. (2002) 4 SCC 105.
80. (2012) 9 SCC 552.
81. *Bhatia International* v. *Bulk Trading S.A.*, (2002) 4 SCC 105 and *Venture Global Engg.* v. *Satyam Computer Services Ltd.*, (2008) 4 SCC 190, were overruled prospectively.

The five-judge Bench held that Part I applies only to arbitrations (domestic as well as international) that have their juridical or legal seat within the territory of India. If upon a construction thereof, the arbitration agreement is held to provide for the seat of arbitration outside India, Part I would be inapplicable to the extent inconsistent with the arbitration law of the seat of arbitration, even if the arbitration agreement purports to provide that the 1996 Act shall govern arbitration proceedings. Awards made in foreign-seated international commercial arbitration are subject to the jurisdiction of Indian courts only when the same are sought to be enforced in India in accordance with, and only to the extent provided for by, provisions of Part II. Further, no application for interim relief and no suit for interim injunction simpliciter is maintainable in India in respect of foreign-seated international commercial arbitration.

An arbitration will be an international commercial arbitration where at least one of the parties to it is an individual who is a national of, or habitually resident in, any country other than India. Even if one of the parties is habitually resident in a country other than India but a national of India, this provision would still be applicable, and it would be an international commercial arbitration.[82]

Foreign seated international commercial arbitration

Balco[83] has prospective application. Case is applicable to agreements entered prior to 6 September 2012, *i.e.* the date of the decision.[84]

International commercial agreement governed by laws of foreign country—Place of arbitration in India—Part I applies

If the place of arbitration is in India, even in respect of international commercial agreements governed by laws of another country, parties are entitled to invoke provisions of Part I. Part I equally applies to such arbitrations held outside India, unless excluded by express agreement or by implication.[85]

"Legal representative" [S. 2(1)(*g*)]

Section 2(11) CPC contains similar definition of the term "legal representative" and provides as under:

---

82. *Aslam Ismail Khan Deshmukh* v. *ASAP Fluids (P) Ltd.*, 2019 SCC OnLine Bom 304.
83. *Bharat Aluminium Co.* v. *Kaiser Aluminium Technical Services Inc.*, (2012) 9 SCC 552.
84. *Harmony Innovation Shipping Ltd.* v. *Gupta Coal India Ltd.*, (2015) 9 SCC 172.
85. *Cauvery Coffee Traders* v. *Hornor Resources (International) Co. Ltd.*, (2011) 10 SCC 420.

> "'Legal representative' means a person who in law represents the estate of a deceased person and includes any person who inter-meddles with the estate of the deceased and where a party sues or is sued in representative character, the person on whom the estate deserves on the death of the party, so suing or sued;"

The difference between the two is that, the last words in Section 2(11) CPC are "*suing or sued*", in the Arbitration Act, these words have been replaced by the words "*so acting*".

The definition of "legal representative" in Section 2(1)(*g*), Arbitration and Conciliation Act, 1996 became necessary because such representatives are bound by and also entitled to enforce an arbitration agreement. Section 30, Arbitration and Conciliation Act, 1996 clearly says that an arbitration agreement is not discharged by the death of a party. The agreement remains enforceable by or against the legal representatives of the deceased. A person who has the right to represent the estate of the deceased person occupies the status of a legal representative. In view of Section 35, persons claiming under the rights of a deceased person are the personal representatives of the deceased party and they have the right to enforce the award and are also bound by it. The arbitration agreement is enforceable by or against the legal representatives of a deceased party provided that the right to sue in respect of the cause of action survives.[86]

Assignee of decree holder in terms of Order 21 Rule 16 CPC filed application under Section 47 CPC by taking recourse to Section 146 CPC read with Section 2(1)(*g*), Arbitration and Conciliation Act. It was held, the transferee of right in property can apply for execution of decree without separate assignment of decree.[87]

Legal representation—Power of attorney holder

Party to arbitral proceeding gave power of attorney. The holder of power of attorney is a natural intermeddler who can continue arbitral proceedings after the death of a party.[88]

"Party" [S. 2(1)(*h*)]

"Party" means a party to an arbitration agreement. The expression "party" as defined in Section 2(1)(*h*) of the 1996 Act indicates a person who is a party to an arbitration agreement, does not include the agent of the party to such agreement, does not include advocate for the party. It is one thing for

---

86. *Ravi Prakash Goel* v. *Chandra Prakash Goel*, (2008) 13 SCC 667.
87. *Vaishno Devi Construction* v. *Union of India*, (2022) 2 SCC 290.
88. *Steel Fabs* v. *State of Uttarakhand*, 2015 SCC OnLine Utt 2736: (2015) 5 Arb LR 586.

an advocate to act and plead on behalf of a party in a proceeding and it is another for an advocate to act as the party himself. Any reference, therefore, made in Sections 31(5) and 34(2) of the 1996 Act can only mean the party himself and not his or her agent or advocate empowered to act on the basis of a vakalatnama.[89] "Party" includes the legal representative of the deceased.[90]

The word "party" has to be construed to the person directly connected with and involved in the proceedings and who is in control of the proceedings before the arbitrator.[91]

Financier

Proceedings under Section 9 of the Act are maintainable only between parties to arbitration agreement. A financier cannot be said to be a party to arbitration agreement between opposite parties, cannot seek impleadment for protection of his right under Section 9 of the Act.[92]

"Prescribed" [S. 2(1)(*i*)]

"Prescribed" means prescribed by the rules made under the Arbitration and Conciliation Act, 1996.

"Regulations" [S. 2(1)(*j*)]

"Regulations" means the regulations made by the Arbitration Council of India under the Arbitration and Conciliation Act, 1996. *See*, new Part I-A added by Amendment Act 33 of 2019.

Interest on Delayed Payments to Small Scale and Ancillary Industrial Undertakings Act, 1993 and Arbitration and Conciliation Act, 1996

Section 6(2)(*g*) of the Interest on Delayed Payments Act, 1993 expressly incorporates the provisions of the Arbitration and Conciliation Act, 1996. Apart from such express incorporation, Section 6(2) of the Act goes further and creates a legal fiction whereby disputes referred to it are deemed to have been made pursuant to an arbitration agreement as defined in Section 7(1) of the 1996 Act. Incorporation of the provisions of the 1996 Act into Section 6 of the Act has also been effected by Section 2(4) and (5) of the 1996 Act.

Proceedings pending before Uttar Pradesh Industry Facilitation Council set up under Industrial Undertakings Act, 1993 are proceedings under the

89. *Benarsi Krishna Committee* v. *Karmyogi Shelters (P) Ltd.*, (2012) 9 SCC 496.
90. *Salman Anwar* v. *Ram Jharokhi*, 2016 SCC OnLine MP 9815: (2016) 4 MP LJ 428.
91. *Union of India* v. *Tecco Trichy Engineers & Contractors*, (2005) 4 SCC 239.
92. *SREI Infrastructure Finance Ltd.* v. *Bhageeratha Engg. Ltd.*, 2009 SCC OnLine Gau 30: (2009) 6 Gau LR 828.

Arbitration Act, 1996. Questions about the validity of the proceedings or whether giving of notice under Section 21 of the Act is to be construed as a precondition to the exercise of jurisdiction by Council are questions to be decided by the Council. Court(s) has no jurisdiction to stay proceedings pending before the Council.[93]

M.P. Madhyastham Adhikaran Adhiniyam, 1983

The provisions of M.P. Madhyastham Adhikaran Adhiniyam, 1983 being inconsistent with the provisions of the Arbitration and Conciliation Act, 1996 are saved under Section 2(4) of the 1996 Act. Further, the M.P. Adhiniyam is neither repugnant to nor has been rejected by the Arbitration and Conciliation Act, 1996.[94]

Part I shall apply where the place of arbitration is in India [Sub-s. (2) of S. 2]

Part I applies compulsorily to all arbitrations held in India and all proceedings relating thereto. The parties can deviate only to the extent permissible by derogable provisions of Part I.[95]

In *Bhatia International*[96], the Supreme Court held:

> Sub-section (2) of Section 2 provides that Part I would apply where the place of arbitration is in India. It does not provide that Part I shall not apply where the place of arbitration is not in India. It also does not provide that Part I will 'only' apply where the place of arbitration is in India. Thus, the legislature has not provided that Part I is not to apply to arbitrations which take place outside India. The use of the language is significant and important. The legislature is emphasising that the provisions of Part I would apply only to arbitrations which take place in India, but not providing that the provisions of Part I will not apply to arbitrations which take place out of India. The wording of sub-section (2) of Section 2 suggests that the intention of the legislature was to make provisions of Part I compulsorily applicable to an arbitration, including an international commercial arbitration, which takes place in India. Parties cannot by agreement override or exclude the non-derogable provisions of Part I in such arbitration. By omitting to provide that Part I will not apply to international commercial arbitrations which take place out of India, the effect would be that Part I would also apply to international commercial arbitrations held out of India. But by not specifically providing that the provisions of Part I apply to international commercial arbitrations held out of India, the intention of the legislature appears to be to allow parties to provide by

93. *Secur Industries Ltd.* v. *Godrej & Boyce Mfg. Co. Ltd.*, (2004) 3 SCC 447.
94. *M.P. Rural Road Development Authority* v. *L.G. Chaudhary Engineers & Contractors*, (2012) 3 SCC 495.
95. *Bhatia International* v. *Bulk Trading S.A.*, (2002) 4 SCC 105.
96. *Ibid.*

> agreement that Part I or any provision therein will not apply. Thus, in respect of arbitrations which take place outside India, even the non-derogable provisions of Part I can be excluded.

The Supreme Court concluded thus:

> The provisions of Part I would apply to all arbitrations and to all proceedings relating thereto. Where such arbitration is held in India the provisions of Part I would compulsorily apply and the parties are free to deviate only to the extent permitted by the derogable provisions of Part I.

In cases of international commercial arbitrations held out of India, provisions of Part I would apply unless the parties by agreement, express or implied, exclude all or any of its provisions.[97]

In terms of *Bhatia International*[98], provisions of Part I of 1996 Act apply to international commercial arbitration conducted outside India unless the parties by agreement expressly or impliedly had excluded all or any provisions of 1996 Act. In the instant case, the terms and conditions of the arbitration agreement provided that the disputes and arbitration shall be subject to the rules of Refined Sugar Association London and governing laws of contract is English law. It was held that the courts in India are excluded from interfering with the instant arbitral award. Petition filed under Section 34 of the Act for setting aside the award was dismissed.[99] In the instant case also under clause of charter agreement, the parties chose to exclude the application of Part I of Arbitration and Conciliation Act, 1996 to the arbitration proceedings between them by choosing London as the venue for arbitration and by making English law applicable to arbitration. It is now well settled that where the parties choose a judicial seat of arbitration outside India and provide that the law which governs the arbitration will be a law other than Indian law, Part I of the Act would not have any application and, therefore, the award-debtor would not be entitled to challenge the award by raising objections under Section 34 before a court in India. A court in India could not have jurisdiction to entertain such an objection under Section 34 of the Act.[100] In *Harmony Innovation Shipping Ltd.* v. *Gupta Coal India Ltd.*[101], the agreement stipulated that the contract is to be governed and construed according to English law. Intended effect was to have a seat of arbitration at London. It was held that the court in India would not have jurisdiction as there was implied exclusion.

---

97. *Ibid.*
98. *Ibid.*
99. *Sakuma Exports Ltd.* v. *Louis Dreyfus Commodities Suisse Sa*, (2015) 5 SCC 656; *Eitzen Bulk A/S* v. *Ashapura Minechem Ltd.*, (2016) 11 SCC 508.
100. *Eitzen Bulk A/S* v. *Ashapura Minechem Ltd.*, (2016) 11 SCC 508.
101. (2015) 9 SCC 172.

Part I deals with arbitrations where the seat is in India and has no application to a foreign seated arbitration. Part I applies only if the place of arbitration is in India. Part II is not concerned with arbitral proceedings at all. It concerns only with the enforcement of a foreign award. Part II does not apply to arbitration proceedings once commenced in a country outside India.[102]

Arbitration if governed by Part I or both Parts I and II—Determination of

From the scheme of the Arbitration and Conciliation Act, 1996 and the language of Section 2(2), it is clear that Part I of the Act applies to all arbitrations which take place in India. It is irrelevant whether any of the parties to such arbitration agreement is an Indian entity (either a citizen or body incorporated in India, etc.) or not. If two non-Indian entities agree to have their disputes resolved through the process of arbitration with the seat of arbitration in India, such an arbitration would obviously be governed by the provisions of Part I of the Act. By virtue of the law declared by the Supreme Court in *Bhatia International* v. *Bulk Trading S.A.*[103], even if the seat of arbitration is not in India, if one of the parties to such an arbitration is an Indian entity, Part I would apply unless parties by agreement in such a case choose to exclude the application of all or some of the provisions of Part I by an agreement, express or implied, exclude all or any of its provisions. In that case, the laws or rules chosen by the parties would prevail. Any provision in Part I, which is contrary to or excluded by that law or rules will not apply.[104]

In *Bharat Aluminium Co.* v. *Kaiser Aluminium Technical Services Inc.*[105], the respondent had invoked the provisions of English law for the settlement of unsettled disputes between the parties. The intention of the parties to apply English law to the arbitration agreement and not to limit it to the conduct of arbitration was fairly clear from Article 22 of the arbitration agreement. Application under Section 34, Arbitration and Conciliation Act, 1996 for setting aside the foreign award was not maintainable.

Part I of the Arbitration Act, 1996 is applicable only to all the arbitrations which take place within the territory of India. The provision contained in Section 2(2) is not in conflict with any of the provisions either in Part I or Part II of the Arbitration Act, 1996. In a foreign seated international commercial arbitration, no application for interim relief would be

102. *PASL Wind Solutions (P) Ltd.* v. *GE Power Conversion (India) (P) Ltd.*, (2021) 7 SCC 1.
103. (2002) 4 SCC 105.
104. *Sasan Power Ltd.* v. *North American Coal Corpn. (India) (P) Ltd.*, (2016) 10 SCC 813.
105. (2016) 4 SCC 126.

maintainable under Section 9 or any other provision as the applicability of Part I of the Arbitration Act, 1996 is limited to all arbitrations which take place in India. Similarly, no suit for interim injunction simpliciter would be maintainable in India, on the basis of an international commercial arbitration with a seat outside India.[106]

The law laid down in *Balco*[107], shall apply to all the arbitration agreements executed hereafter.[108]

Where the judicial seat of arbitration at London and the arbitration agreement is governed by English law, Part I of the Arbitration Act would not be applicable. A Section 14 application made under Part I would consequently be not applicable.[109] The last paragraph of *Balco*, has to be read with two caveats that where the court comes to a determination that the judicial seat in outside India or where law other than the Indian law governs the arbitration agreement, Part I of the Arbitration and Conciliation Act, 1996 would be excluded by necessary implication.[110]

The place of arbitration determines the law that will apply to the arbitration and related matters like challenges to the award, etc. The significant determinant in each case is the agreement of the parties as to the place of arbitration where, in fact, the arbitration took place. If in pursuance of the arbitration agreement the arbitration took place outside India, there is clear exclusion of Part I of the Arbitration Act. In *IMAX Corpn.* v. *E-City Entertainment (India) (P) Ltd.*[111], arbitration was held in London without any demur from any of the parties. All the three awards, *i.e.* two partial final awards and the third final award were made in London and communicated to the parties. The court noted that it was a clear case of exclusion of Part I.

The choice of another country as the seat of arbitration inevitably imports an acceptance that the law of that country relating to the conduct and supervision of arbitration will apply to the proceedings. Clause in the arbitration agreement stipulated that the arbitral proceedings shall be in accordance with International Chamber of Commerce (ICC) Rules. It was held that courts in England and not in India have jurisdiction, Part I of the Act would not be applicable.[112]

---

106. *Bharat Aluminium Co.* v. *Kaiser Aluminium Technical Services Inc.*, (2012) 9 SCC 552; [*Bhatia International* v. *Bulk Trading S.A.*, (2002) 4 SCC 105 & *Venture Global Engg.* v. *Satyam Computer Services Ltd.*, (2008) 4 SCC 190.]
107. *Bharat Aluminium Co.* v. *Kaiser Aluminium Technical Services Inc.*, (2012) 9 SCC 552.
108. *Ibid*; *Bhatia International* v. *Bulk Trading S.A.*, (2002) 4 SCC 105 & *Venture Global Engg.* v. *Satyam Computer Services Ltd.*, (2008) 4 SCC 190.
109. *Union of India* v. *Reliance Industries Ltd.*, (2015) 10 SCC 213.
110. *Ibid.*
111. (2017) 5 SCC 331.
112. *Roger Shashoua* v. *Mukesh Sharma*, (2017) 14 SCC 722.

International commercial arbitrations—Express exclusion of Part I—Appointment under Section 11(6), declined

In *Dozco India (P) Ltd.* v. *Doosan Infracore Co. Ltd.*[113], certain disputes had arisen between the petitioner-company registered in India and a respondent-company incorporated in Seoul, South Korea with its principal place of business at Seoul. The petitioner issued a notice to the respondent-company for appointment of arbitrator to resolve the disputes between the parties, as the respondent did not take any action, the petitioner filed an application under Section 11(6) before the Supreme Court for the appointment of arbitrator. The respondent opposed the application and contended that only Rules of Arbitration of ICC would apply, the Supreme Court in India did not have jurisdiction to appoint arbitrator in the case, the petitioner cannot invoke the provisions of 1996 Act as there was express exclusion of the Indian Arbitration Act, 1996. The court held that articles of distributorship agreement between the parties in the case spelled out a clear agreement between the parties excluding Part I of the Act. Since the interpretation of articles of distributorship agreement suggested that the law governing the arbitration will be Korean law and the seat of arbitration will be Seoul in Korea, there was no question of appointment of arbitration by the Supreme Court under Section 11(6), Arbitration and Conciliation Act, 1996. Petition under Section 11(6) for appointment of arbitrator was rejected.

Foreign award may be enforced in India

A foreign award passed in international commercial arbitration may be enforced in India.[114]

Sub-section (3) of Section 2, Scope

This part (Part I) shall not affect any other law for the time being in force by virtue of which certain disputes may not be submitted to arbitration.

Sub-section (4) of Section 2, Scope

Part I of the Arbitration and Conciliation Act, 1996 except sub-section (1) of Section 40, Sections 41 and 43 shall apply to every arbitration under any other enactment for the time being in force, as if the arbitration were pursuant to an arbitration agreement, except insofar as the provisions of Part I are inconsistent with that other enactment or with the rules made thereunder.

---

113. (2011) 6 SCC 179.
114. *Venture Global Engg.* v. *Satyam Computer Services Ltd.*, (2008) 4 SCC 190.

In view of Section 2(*d*), the State Act will cover a dispute even after the termination of the works contract.[115]

Arbitration and Conciliation Act, 1996, Section 2(4)—M.P. Madhyastham Adhikaran Adhiniyam, 1983 (29 of 1983)

In a dispute relating to works contract, State law prevails over the Arbitration and Conciliation Act,1996. If the dispute is not arbitrable under the State Act, the parties need to seek remedy from civil court. The Arbitration and Conciliation Act, 1996 would not apply.[116]

Sub-section (5) of Section 2, Scope

Subject to the provisions of sub-section (4) of Section 2 and save insofar as is otherwise provided by any other law for the time being in force or in any agreement in force between India and any other country or countries, Part I of Arbitration and Conciliation Act, 1996 shall apply to all arbitrations and to all proceedings relating thereto.

Sub-section (6) of Section 2, Construction of references

Where Part I of the Act, except Section 28 leave the parties free to determine a certain issue, that freedom shall include the right of the parties to authorise any person including an institution, to determine that issue.

Sub-section (7) of Section 2, Domestic award

Section 2(7) states that an award made under this Part (Part I) shall be construed as a domestic award.

Awards in arbitration proceedings which take place in a non-convention country are not considered to be "foreign awards" under the said Act. They would thus not be covered by Part II. An award passed in an arbitration which takes place in India is a domestic award. There would thus be no need to define an award as a "domestic award" unless the intention was to cover awards which would otherwise not be covered by the definition. Strictly speaking, an award passed in an arbitration which takes place in a non-convention country would not be a domestic award. Thus, the necessity to defend a domestic award as including all awards made under Part I. The definition indicates that an award made in an international commercial

---

115. *M.P. Rural Road Development Authority* v. *L.G. Chaudhary Engineers and Contractors*, (2018) 10 SCC 826.
116. *Shri Gouri Ganesh Shri Balaji Constructions* v. *PWD*, 2018 SCC OnLine MP 978: (2018) 3 MP LJ 163.

arbitration held in a non-conventional country is also considered to be a "domestic award".[117]

Sub-section (8) of Section 2, Scope

Where Part I of the Act:

(*a*) refers to the fact that the parties have agreed or that the parties may agree; or

(*b*) in any other way refers to an agreement of the parties;

(*c*) that agreement shall include any arbitration rules referred to in that agreement.

Sub-section (9) of Section 2, Counterclaims

Where Part I of the Act other than clause (*a*) of Section 25 or clause (*a*) of sub-section (2) of Section 22, refers to a claim, it shall also apply to an counterclaim and where it refers to a defence, it shall also apply to a defence to that counterclaim.

RECEIPT OF WRITTEN COMMUNICATIONS [S. 3]

3. *Receipt of written communications.*—(1) Unless otherwise agreed by the parties,—

(*a*) any written communication is deemed to have been received if it is delivered to the addressee personally or at his place of business, habitual residence or mailing address, and

(*b*) if none of the places referred to in clause (*a*) can be found after making a reasonable inquiry, a written communication is deemed to have been received if it is sent to the addressee's last known place of business, habitual residence or mailing address by registered letter or by any other means which provides a record of the attempt to deliver it.

(2) The communication is deemed to have been received on the day it is so delivered.

(3) This section does not apply to written communications in respect of proceedings of any judicial authority.

---

117. *Bhatia International* v. *Bulk Trading S.A.*, (2002) 4 SCC 105.

COMMENTS

Corresponding old law

Section 3 in material particulars corresponds to Section 42, Arbitration Act, 1940. The said Section 42 read as under:

42. *Service of notice by party or arbitrator.*—Any notice required by this Act to be served otherwise than through the Court by a party to an arbitration agreement or by an arbitrator or umpire shall be served in the manner provided in the arbitration agreement, or if there is no such provision, either—

(*a*) by delivering it to the person on whom it is to be served, or

(*b*) by sending it by post in a letter addressed to that person at his usual or last known place of abode or business in India and registered under Chapter VI of the Indian Post Office Act, 1898 (6 of 1898).

UNCITRAL Model Law

Article 3. *Receipt of written communications*

(1) Unless otherwise agreed by the parties:

(*a*) any written communication is deemed to have been received if it is delivered to the addressee personally or if it is delivered at his place of business, habitual residence or mailing address; if none of these can be found after making a reasonable inquiry, a written communication is deemed to have been received if it is sent to the addressee's last-known place of business, habitual residence or mailing address by registered letter or any other means which provides a record of the attempt to deliver it;

(*b*) the communication is deemed to have been received on the day it is so delivered.

(2) The provisions of this article do not apply to communications in court proceedings.

Scope and application

Section 3 lays down the principles about the receipt of written communications sent by the parties. Unless otherwise agreed by the parties—

(*a*) any written communication is deemed to have been received if it is delivered to the addressee

(*i*) personally, or

(*ii*) at his place of business, or

(*iii*) habitual residence, or

(*iv*) mailing address, and

(*b*) if none of the places referred to above can be found after making a reasonable inquiry, a written communication is deemed to have been received if it is sent to
  (*i*) the addressee's last known place of business,
  (*ii*) habitual residence, or
  (*iii*) mailing address

(*c*) by registered letter or by any other means which provides a record of the attempt to deliver it. [S. 3(1)]

The communication is deemed to have been delivered on the day it is delivered. [S. 3(2)]

Section 3 does not apply to written communications in respect of proceedings of any judicial authority. [S. 3(3)]

There is presumption of service of letters sent by UPC.[118]

Receipt of written communication

If a written communication is delivered to the addressee personally at the place of his business, it shall be deemed to have been received by him on the day it was delivered. In *Kailash Rani Dang* v. *Rakesh Bala Aneja*[119], the copy of the award was sent to the party at the place which was, in fact, the subject-matter of dispute between the parties. The postman stated that the said party was not present at that place, on the next day he refused to receive the communication even when it was tendered to him. The postman endorsed the said fact on the envelope and returned it to the sender. The court held, in fact by virtue of Section 3(1)(*a*) read with Section 3(3), it could be presumed that the document/award had indeed been delivered to the said party. Application under Section 34 for setting aside the award filed beyond limitation was rejected.

Letter appointing arbitrator—When comes into effect

The order made by a statutory authority or an officer exercising the powers of that authority comes into force so far as the authority/officer is concerned from the date it is made by the authority/officer concerned. But so for the affected party is concerned, the order made by the party would be the date on which it is communicated. Section 3(2), Arbitration and Conciliation Act, 1996 is a mere recitation of the aforesaid general principle of law. In *Bipromasz Bipron Trading Sa* v. *Bharat Electronics Ltd.*[120], an application

118. *Budhiraja Mining & Constructions Ltd.* v. *Ircon International Ltd.*, 2012 SCC OnLine Del 2568: (2012) 130 DRJ 116.
119. (2009) 1 SCC 732.
120. (2012) 6 SCC 384.

for appointment of arbitrator was objected by the respondent on the ground that the arbitrator had been appointed by the respondent on 19 July 2007 and the said application was filed after that date, *i.e.* on 21 July 2011. Order dated 19 July 2007 was received by the counsel for the petitioner through email on 26 July 2011. It was held that the order appointing arbitrator though made on 19 July 2011 would be deemed to be received by the affected party (petitioner) and effective against it only on and from the day it was delivered to it on 26 July 2011. The appellant's application for appointment of arbitrator was maintainable and could not be rejected on the opposition that the respondent had already appointed arbitrator when the present application was pending.

Communication of award

In *Francisco A. D'souza* v. *L and T Finance Ltd.*[121], the arbitrator had sent various notices and copy of the award at last known addresses of the petitioners mentioned in the petition. Notices sent by the arbitrator in the past at the same addresses were received by the petitioners. Petitioners admitted that they were residing at the same two addresses. It was held that the petitioners were served with the copy of the award.

No prescribed procedure for service of notice through the court under the Arbitration Act

There is no prescribed procedure for service of notice through the court under the Arbitration Act. Provisions of this section are procedural in nature and apply to all notices that are required to be serviced otherwise than through the court. If a notice is duly sent to the person's address and there is evidence to that effect, it must be treated as good and proper notice.[122]

WAIVER OF RIGHT TO OBJECT [S. 4]

4. *Waiver of right to object.*—A party who knows that—

(*a*) any provision of this Part from which the parties may derogate, or

(*b*) any requirement under the arbitration agreement,

has not been complied with and yet proceeds with the arbitration without stating his objection to such non-compliance without undue delay or, if a time-limit is provided for stating that objection, within that period of time, shall be deemed to have waived his right to so object.

---

121. 2015 SCC OnLine Bom 6864: (2015) 5 Mah LJ 390.

122. *Kuljit Singh & Co.* v. *Engg. Projects (India) Ltd.*, 2007 SCC OnLine Del 1474: ILR (2008) 1 Del 816.

COMMENTS

Corresponding old law

Section 4 is new, and did not appear in the Arbitration Act, 1940.

UNCITRAL Model Law

Article 4. *Waiver of right to object*

A party who knows that any provision of this Law from which the parties may derogate or any requirement under the arbitration agreement has not been complied with and yet proceeds with the arbitration without stating his objection to such non-compliance without undue delay or, if a time-limit is provided therefor, within such period of time, shall be deemed to have waived his right to object.

Scope and application

Section 4 postulates that where a party to the arbitration proceedings knows that any provision of Part I from which the parties may derogate or any requirement under the arbitration agreement has not been complied with and yet proceeds with the arbitration without stating his objection to such non-compliance without undue delay or, if a time-limit is provided therefor, within such period of time, shall be deemed to have waived his right to object.

Question of waiver can only be raised by the party during the arbitration proceedings.[123]

In *PWD* v. *Chandragiri Construction Co.*[124], a retired Superintendent Engineer was appointed as sole arbitrator by the government department at the request of the contractor. Department participated in the proceedings without raising any objection. Department had waived their rights to object arbitration afterwards. In *Jayesh H. Pandya* v. *Subhtex India Ltd.*[125], arbitration proceedings had continued beyond the prescribed period of four months. The petitioners stood by and allowed the arbitrator to fix a time schedule for the filing of the pleadings. The arbitrator was justified in coming to the conclusion that the petitioners by their conduct waived their objection to observe punctilious observance of the time schedule for four months. Where the plea regarding the bar of limitation was never raised before the arbitrator, such plea cannot be raised in proceedings under Section 34 or in

123. *Jain Automobiles H.P.C. Dealer* v. *Hindustan Petroleum Corpn. Ltd.*, 2020 SCC OnLine All 2242.
124. 2011 SCC OnLine Mad 343: (2011) 2 CTC 669.
125. 2008 SCC OnLine Bom 299: (2008) 5 Mah LJ 749.

appeal arising therefrom.[126] In *PWD* v. *Chandragiri Construction Co.*[127], appellant-department by their conduct waived their rights to object to the jurisdiction of the arbitrator. In *Vijayakumar Raju* v. *Indus Ind Bank Ltd.*[128], when by an agreement the petitioner has consented to the appointment of the arbitrator by the first respondent-company, he should have challenged the appointment of the arbitrator if he had grievance if any in accordance with Section 13(2) of the Act.

Presumption against ouster of a court's jurisdiction cannot be made to operate as an estoppel against law in the absence of any bar either explicit or by necessary implication. Application of the bar of Section 4 against challenge to the mandate of the arbitrator would be mulilative of the basic features of the Act.[129]

Objections regarding jurisdiction and applicability of the new Act should be raised at the earliest point of time. In *Kirloskar Computer Services Ltd.* v. *Lakshmi General Finance Ltd.*[130], the party appeared before an arbitrator and participated in proceedings without raising objections and with definite intention that the new Act would apply. Parties had also contested application under Section 9. Party shall be deemed to have waived the plea regarding jurisdiction in not having raised the same at earliest point of time.

As provided by Section 4, a party which knows the requirement under the arbitration agreement has not been complied with and still proceeds with the arbitration without raising an objection as far as possible, waives its right to object. In *BSNL* v. *Motorola India (P) Ltd.*[131], the High Court had appointed an arbitrator on a petition filed by the respondent. At this stage the matter was closed unless further objections were to be raised. If further objections were to be made after this order, they should have been made prior to its first arbitration hearing. But the appellants had not raised any such objections. It was held that the appellants had clearly failed to meet the stated requirement to object to the arbitration without delay, as such their right to object was deemed to have been waived.

---

126. *Vimal G. Jain* v. *Vertex Financial Services (P) Ltd.*, 2007 SCC OnLine Bom 116: (2007) 3 Mah LJ 866.
127. 2011 SCC OnLine Mad 343: (2011) 2 CTC 669.
128. 2009 SCC OnLine Mad 885: (2009) 4 LW 86.
129. *State of Arunachal Pradesh* v. *Subhash Projects and Mktg. Ltd.*, 2006 SCC OnLine Gau 57: (2006) 3 Gau LR 939.
130. 2006 SCC OnLine Mad 496: (2006) 4 CTC 509; *Quippo Construction Equipment Ltd.* v. *Janardan Nirman (P) Ltd.*, (2020) 18 SCC 277.
131. (2009) 2 SCC 337; *D. Ranganayakulu* v. *Supdt. Engineer, NSRC O&M*, (2010) 13 SCC 113.

Petitioner already raised objection to appointment as not being unanimous, conduct of petitioner did not amount to waiver under Section 4.[132]

Waiver of right to object to the composition of Arbitral Tribunal

Unless an objection as to the composition of the Arbitral Tribunal is made before the Arbitral Tribunal within time prescribed under Section 16(2), there would be deemed waiver of objection under Section 4. Sections 10 and 16 read together clearly indicate that the parties may derogate from the provisions of Section 10. Where the parties have appointed two arbitrators to resolve their differences, had participated in the arbitral proceedings and award was then passed, objections raised by the respondents that arbitration by two arbitrators was not permitted under Section 10, therefore, the award was unenforceable and not binding would be deemed to have been waived. Section 34 does not permit challenge to an arbitral award merely on the ground that the composition of the Arbitral Tribunal was in conflict with the provisions of Part I of the Act. The respondents had not raised objection as to the composition of the tribunal as provided under Section 16, they were held to have waived their right to object. Order of the High Court setting the award was reversed.[133]

Waiver of objection as to jurisdiction of the arbitrator

Section 4 of the Act of 1996 speaks about waiver of the right to object and requires that the party who knows that any requirement under the arbitration agreement has not been complied with and yet proceeds with the arbitration without stating his objection to such non-compliance without undue delay or, if the time limit is provided for stating that objection, within the period of time, shall be deemed to have waived his right to so object. The appellant participated before the Arbitral Tribunal on different dates and filed its pleading; it would be deemed that the appellant has waived his right to object to the jurisdiction of the Arbitral Tribunal on the principles of waiver.[134]

In *Quippo Construction Equipment Ltd.* v. *Janardan Nirman (P) Ltd.*[135], it was held that considering the facts that the respondent failed to participate in the proceedings before the arbitrator and did not raise any submission that the arbitrator did not have jurisdiction or that he was exceeding the scope of his authority, the respondent must be deemed to have waived all such objections.

---

132. *Arun Kumar Bhunia* v. *Badal Midya*, 2019 SCC OnLine Cal 9410: (2019) 4 Cal LT 545.
133. *Narayan Prasad Lohia* v. *Nikunj Kumar Lohia*, (2002) 3 SCC 572.
134. *SAV Steels (P) Ltd.* v. *Ekta Ispat and Power Ltd.*, 2015 SCC OnLine Chh 204.
135. (2020) 18 SCC 277.

Waiver of objection to territorial jurisdiction

Company raised objections as to the question of territorial jurisdiction. State raised preliminary objection regarding maintainability of objections under Section 34. Court proceeded to decide objections on merit and upheld the award without dealing with issues regarding territorial jurisdiction. It cannot be said that the State had waived their rights to object on the question of territorial jurisdiction.[136]

Contract was concluded at Mohali. Tender was accepted at Chennai. Venue of arbitration was fixed at Chennai. Exclusive jurisdiction clause signed by parties conferred jurisdiction upon courts at Chennai. Courts at Chennai have exclusive jurisdiction to entertain objections filed under Section 34.[137]

Writ petition—Maintainability of

Existence of an arbitration clause does not debar the court from entertaining writ petition. It is well settled that availability of an alternative remedy does not prohibit the High Court from entertaining a writ petition in an appropriate case. The High Court may entertain a writ petition, notwithstanding the availability of an alternative remedy, particularly (*i*) where the writ petition seeks enforcement of a fundamental right; or (*ii*) where there is failure of principles of natural justice; or (*iii*) where the impugned orders or proceedings are wholly without jurisdiction; or (*iv*) the vires of an Act is under challenge.[138]

Waiver of right to object—Delay in pronouncement of award [S. 4(*b*)]

There was a delay of nine months in the pronouncement of the award by the arbitrator. The petitioner participated in the arbitral proceedings without any objection, award was passed, clearly attracted waiver of right to object.[139]

---

136. *Shivalik Fastners (P) Ltd.* v. *Union of India*, 2019 SCC OnLine P&H 7255: PLR (2019) 196 P&H 800.
137. *Ibid.*
138. *U.P. Power Transmission Corpn. Ltd.* v. *CG Power & Industrial Solutions Ltd.*, (2021) 6 SCC 15.
139. *Sidhi Industries* v. *Religare Finvest Ltd.*, 2017 SCC OnLine Del 6939: (2017) 238 DLT 97.

EXTENT OF JUDICIAL INTERVENTION [S. 5]

5. *Extent of judicial intervention.*—Notwithstanding anything contained in any other law for the time being in force, in matters governed by this Part, no judicial authority shall intervene except where so provided in this Part.

COMMENTS

Corresponding old law

Section 5 is new, did not find place in the Arbitration Act, 1940.

UNCITRAL Model Law

Article 5. *Extent of court intervention*

In matters governed by this Law, no court shall intervene except where so provided in this Law.

Scope and application

The Arbitration and Conciliation Bill of 1995 which preceded the 1996 Act stated as one of its main objectives the need to "minimise the supervisory role of the Courts in the arbitration process". This objective has found expression in Section 5 of the Act which prescribes the extent of judicial intervention in no uncertain terms.[140]

Under Section 5 of the 1996 Act, courts are restrained from interfering with the arbitration except in the manner provided in the 1996 Act.[141] The inference of judicial authority has to be kept at the minimum.[142]

Civil court is specifically barred under Section 5 of the Act of 1996 to adjudicate subject-matter of arbitration.[143]

Minimisation of judicial invention in terms of Section 5, Arbitration and Conciliation Act, 1996 does not mean that the court should interpret the provisions of Arbitration and Conciliation Act, 1996 even more narrowly than warranted by language of the provisions of the Arbitration and Conciliation Act, 1996 themselves.[144]

---

140. *Union of India* v. *Popular Construction Co.*, (2001) 8 SCC 470.
141. *CDC Financial Services (Mauritius) Ltd.* v. *BPL Communications Ltd.*, (2003) 12 SCC 140.
142. *Damodar Valley Corpn.* v. *Central Concrete & Allied Products Ltd.*, 2006 SCC OnLine Cal 660: (2007) 2 CHN 441.
143. *Limras Lottery Trading & Co.* v. *State of Mizoram*, 2017 SCC OnLine Gau 1482.
144. *Chintels (India) Ltd.* v. *Bhayana Builders (P) Ltd.*, (2021) 4 SCC 602.

Once the parties have agreed to resolve their disputes by arbitration, the jurisdiction of the civil court is clearly ousted by reason of Section 5, Arbitration and Conciliation Act, 1996.[145]

Part I of the 1996 Act deals with domestic arbitration. Section 5 which is contained in Part I defines the extent of judicial intervention in arbitration proceedings. It says that notwithstanding anything contained in any other law for the time being in force, in matters governed by Part I, no judicial authority shall intervene except where so provided in that part. Section 5 brings out clearly the object of the new Act, *namely*, that expeditiously and less expensively and when there is an arbitration agreement, the court's intervention should be minimal.[146]

The opening non-obstante clause of Section 5 clearly indicates that it overrides the provisions of any other statute. As a result judicial intervention is permissible only where it is specifically provided in Part I of the Act. The principal object of Section 5 is to promote and encourage resolution of disputes expeditiously and less expensively. Especially when there is an arbitration agreement, the court's intervention should be minimal.[147]

It is not open to the civil court to go into the question of non-existence of an arbitration agreement in a suit for declaration, both in view of the stringent provisions of Section 5, Arbitration and Conciliation Act and the power bestowed upon the Arbitral Tribunal to rule on its own jurisdiction by Section 16 of the Act, more so, as the decision of the Arbitral Tribunal would be amenable to be assailed within the ambit of Section 34 of the Act. Arbitral Tribunal is endowed with ample power and jurisdiction to rule on its own jurisdiction and it would not, therefore, be open to the civil court to pass an injunction against an arbitral proceeding in the teeth of the provisions of Section 5, Arbitration and Conciliation Act, 1996 and Section 16 thereof.[148]

Section 5, Arbitration and Conciliation Act, 1996 restricts unnecessary intervention in the arbitration proceedings by judicial authorities. Writ petition challenging the order of recalling documents is not maintainable.[149]

---

145. *Sudarshan Vyapar (P) Ltd.* v. *Madhusudan Guha*, 2012 SCC OnLine Cal 13125: (2013) 5 CHN 394.
146. *P. Anand Gajapathi Raju* v. *P.V.G. Raju*, (2000) 4 SCC 539.
147. *Sandip Industries* v. *Bajaj Steel Industries Ltd.*, 2008 SCC OnLine Bom 659: (2008) 6 Mah LJ 313.
148. *Handicrafts & Handlooms Exports Corpn. of India Ltd.* v. *Ashok Metal Corpn.*, 2010 SCC OnLine Del 2099: (2010) 117 DRJ 370.
149. *Pennar Aluminium Co. Ltd.* v. *National Aluminium Co. Ltd.*, 2019 SCC OnLine Ori 370.

Section 5 does not regulate the operation of Section 34.[150]

Limited extent of judicial intervention under 1996 Act vis-a-vis 1940 Act

The extent of control and operation of a court under the 1940 Act was far more extensive and elaborate than the 1996 Act. The 1940 Act does not merely stop with the initiation and enforcement of an arbitration and its award but effectively provides for intervention at every stage of the arbitration proceedings up to its final consideration and enforcement as if it were a regular suit, whereas under the 1996 Act the scope of intervention is not that of a civil court as it could do in the matter of a suit.[151]

Judicial authority

The 1996 Act does not define the term "judicial authority", what is defined in Section 2(1)(*e*) thereof is "court". In its ordinary parlance "judicial authority" would comprehend a court defined under the 1996 Act but also courts which would either be a civil court or other authorities which perform "judicial functions" or "quasi-judicial functions". The expression "judicial authority" must be interpreted having regard to the purport and object for which the 1996 Act was enacted.[152]

"Judicial authority" has to be understood as taking in courts as defined in Section 2(1)(*e*) or any other judicial *fora* including a special tribunal like the consumer forum.[153]

(*a*) *Board for Industrial and Financial Reconstruction (BIFR)—Judicial authority*

BIFR exercises statutory functions. It is a quasi-judicial authority. It exercises powers under the CPC. In *Morgan Securities & Credit (P) Ltd.* v. *Modi Rubber Ltd.*[154], it was held that BIFR is a judicial authority within the meaning of Section 5, Arbitration and Conciliation Act, 1996.

---

150. *Damodar Valley Corpn.* v. *Central Concrete & Allied Products Ltd.*, 2006 SCC OnLine Cal 660: (2007) 2 CHN 441.
151. *Umesh Goel* v. *H.P. Coop. Group Housing Society Ltd.*, (2016) 11 SCC 313.
152. *Morgan Securities & Credit (P) Ltd.* v. *Modi Rubber Ltd.*, (2006) 12 SCC 642.
153. *SBP & Co.* v. *Patel Engg. Ltd.*, (2005) 8 SCC 618.
154. (2006) 12 SCC 642.

Exclusion of jurisdiction of court in arbitration agreement

In *Mullaperiyar Environmental Protection Forum* v. *Union of India*[155], the lease deed under which the law in question was raised provided that whether dispute/question arose between the lessor and the lessee touching upon the rights, duties or liabilities of either party would be referred to two arbitrators and then to an umpire if they differed. The dispute in the case was not about the rights, duties and obligations or interpretation of any part of the agreement. The controversy raised was whether the water in the reservoir can presently be increased to 142 feet having regard to the safety of the dam. The full water level was 152 feet. It was reduced to 136 feet in 1979. The aspect of increase of water level was dependent upon the safety of the dam after strengthening steps have been taken. The court held that the dispute was not liable to be referred to arbitration. Relief sought was granted under Article 32 of the Constitution.

Arbitration proceedings vis-a-vis proceedings in civil court

In *Ardy International (P) Ltd.* v. *Inspiration Clothes & U*[156], in a pending civil suit, the respondent filed an application under Order 39 Rules 1 and 2 CPC for restraining the arbitration proceedings sought to be commenced by the appellant. The appellant filed an objection to the said application and resisted the same. The court held that once objection to the said application under Order 39 Rules 1 and 2 CPC was raised by the appellant bringing the existence of an arbitration agreement to the notice of the court, thereafter proceedings could only have been continued within parameters of Section 89 of the 1996 Act. There was no question of the court under Section 8 restraining arbitration proceedings. Proceeding under Section 8 could never result in an order restraining the arbitration proceedings.

Common questions involved in suit and arbitration proceedings

Where common questions were involved in civil suit and the arbitration proceeding, proceedings in the suit were stayed till the decision in arbitration proceedings to avoid conflicting decisions.[157]

Inherent powers of court in respect of arbitration proceedings

There is no provision in the Act for the court to fix a time-limit for the conclusion of an arbitration proceeding but the court can opt to do so in exercise of its inherent power on the application of either party. However,

155. (2006) 3 SCC 643.
156. (2006) 1 SCC 417.
157. *Lafarge India (P) Ltd.* v. *Emami Realty Ltd.*, 2016 SCC OnLine Cal 4964.

where the arbitration agreement itself provides the procedure for the enlargement of the time by the arbitrator, the court cannot exercise its inherent powers in extending the time fixed by the parties in the absence of the consent of either of them.[158]

Anti-arbitration injunction

Anti-arbitration injunction can be issued only in exceptional circumstances.[159]

Interim orders by High Court in writ petitions interfering with arbitration

Under Section 5 of the 1996 Act, the courts are restrained from interfering with the arbitration proceedings except in the manner provided in the 1996 Act. Whatever may be the merits of the writ application, the High Court should have regard to Section 5 of the Act before granting interim relief. The interim orders passed by the High Court would amount to a violation of the mandate of Section 5. The respondents were restrained from moving any applications in the pending writ petition which would have the effect of interfering with the continuance and conclusion of the arbitration proceedings.[160]

Jurisdiction of High Court to entertain writ petition under Articles 226 and 227

Once the matter reaches the Arbitral Tribunal or the sole arbitrator, the High Court would not interfere with the orders passed by the arbitrator or the Arbitral Tribunal during the course of arbitral proceedings and the parties can approach the court only in terms of Section 37 or Section 34 of the Act. The party aggrieved by any order of the Arbitral Tribunal unless has a right of appeal under Section 37 of the Act, has to wait until the award is passed by the tribunal.[161]

If the award of the arbitrator goes against the petitioner, it can challenge the award on the grounds available to it under Section 34 of the Act. Mere fact that this may cause it the inconvenience of having to await the conclusions of the arbitral proceedings is no ground to entertain a writ at intermediate stage. An attempt to expand the scope for interference would defeat the object and purposes of the Act.[162]

---

158. *NBCC Ltd.* v. *J.G. Engg. (P) Ltd.*, (2010) 2 SCC 385.
159. *Lafarge India (P) Ltd.* v. *Emami Realty Ltd.*, 2016 SCC OnLine Cal 4964.
160. *CDC Financial Services (Mauritius) Ltd.* v. *BPL Communications Ltd.*, (2003) 12 SCC 140.
161. *SBP & Co.* v. *Patel Engg. Ltd.*, (2005) 8 SCC 618.
162. *Cadre Estate (P) Ltd.* v. *Salochna Goyal*, 2010 SCC OnLine Del 3520: (2010) 119 DRJ 457.

Judicial review (Writ petitions)

The power of judicial view vested in superior courts undoubtedly has wide amplitude but when there exists an arbitration agreement, the writ court would not ordinarily exercise its discretionary jurisdiction to enter into dispute. As questions of fact and law are involved, the High Court instead should leave the parties to avail remedy under the arbitration clause existing in the contract.[163]

Writ petition filed in respect of dispute covered by arbitration clause—Plea of availability of alternative remedy

In *Krishan Lal* v. *Food Corporation of India*[164], the dispute was related to the forfeiture/return of security amount of ₹5 lakhs deposited by the appellant. It is true that the dispute in terms of an arbitration agreement ought to be referred to the arbitration. However, the High Court had entertained writ petition as early as in the year 2002, the present appeals before the Supreme Court were pending for the last more than 10 years. The Supreme Court held that relegating the parties to arbitration was not feasible at this stage, especially when the proceedings before the arbitrator may also drag on for another decade. Availability of an alternative remedy for adjudication of the disputes was, therefore, not a ground that could be pressed into service at the belated stage and was, therefore, rejected.

Existence of arbitration clause—Writ remedy when not barred

Arbitration clause is not a bar to invocation of writ jurisdiction when injustice and rule of law violated. Constitutional powers vested in the High Court or Supreme Court cannot be fettered by an alternative remedy available to the authorities.[165]

Interest on Delayed Payments to Small Scale and Ancillary Industrial Undertakings Act, 1993—Proceedings before the Facilitation Council—Jurisdiction of court

Proceedings pending before the Uttar Pradesh Industry Facilitation Council set up under the Industrial Undertakings Act are proceedings under the Arbitration and Conciliation Act, 1996. Validity of the proceedings or whether giving notice under Section 21 is a condition precedent for the exercise of jurisdiction by the Council, such questions are to be decided by

163. *Empire Jute Co. Ltd.* v. *Jute Corpn. of India Ltd.*, (2007) 14 SCC 680.
164. (2012) 4 SCC 786.
165. *Union of India* v. *Tantia Construction (P) Ltd.*, (2011) 5 SCC 697.

the Council. The court has no jurisdiction to stay proceedings before the Council.[166]

ADMINISTRATIVE ASSISTANCE [S. 6]

6. *Administrative assistance.*—In order to facilitate the conduct of the arbitral proceedings, the parties, or the arbitral tribunal with the consent of the parties, may arrange for administrative assistance by a suitable institution or person.

COMMENTS

Corresponding old law

Section 6 is new and did not appear in the Arbitration Act, 1940.

UNCITRAL Model Law

Article 6. *Court or other authority for certain functions of arbitration assistance and supervision*

The functions referred to in Articles 11(3), 11(4), 13(3), 14, 16(3) and 34(2) shall be performed by... [Each State enacting this model law specifies the court, courts or, where referred to therein, other authority competent to perform these functions.]

Scope and application

As provided in this section in order to facilitate the conduct of the arbitral proceedings, the parties or the Arbitral Tribunal with the consent of the parties, may arrange for the administrative assistance by a suitable institution or person.

166. *Secur Industries Ltd.* v. *Godrej & Boyce Mfg. Co. Ltd.*, (2004) 3 SCC 447.

Chapter II
Arbitration Agreement

ARBITRATION AGREEMENT [S. 7]

7. *Arbitration agreement.*—(1) In this Part, "arbitration agreement" means an agreement by the parties to submit to arbitration all or certain disputes which have arisen or which may arise between them in respect of a defined legal relationship, whether contractual or not.

(2) An arbitration agreement may be in the form of an arbitration clause in a contract or in the form of a separate agreement.

(3) An arbitration agreement shall be in writing.

(4) An arbitration agreement is in writing if it is contained in—

(*a*) a document signed by the parties;

(*b*) an exchange of letters, telex, telegrams or other means of telecommunication [1][including communication through electronic means] which provide a record of the agreement; or

(*c*) an exchange of statements of claim and defence in which the existence of the agreement is alleged by one party and not denied by the other.

(5) The reference in a contract to a document containing an arbitration clause constitutes an arbitration agreement if the contract is in writing and the reference is such as to make that arbitration clause part of the contract.

COMMENTS

Corresponding old law

Section 7 corresponds to Section 2(*a*), Arbitration Act, 1940. The definition of "arbitration agreement" in the new Act is a comprehensive and enlarged one, the definition given in the 1940 Act was a brief one. Section 2(*a*) of 1940 Act read as under:

(*a*) "arbitration agreement" means a written agreement to submit present or future differences to arbitration, whether an arbitrator is named therein or not;

---

1. *Ins.* by Act 3 of 2016, S. 3 (w.r.e.f. 23-10-2015).

UNCITRAL Model Law

Article 7. *Definition and form of arbitration agreement.*—

(As adopted by the Commission at its thirty-ninth session, in 2006)

(1) "Arbitration agreement" is an agreement by the parties to submit to arbitration all or certain disputes which have arisen or which may arise between them in respect of a defined legal relationship, whether contractual or not. An arbitration agreement may be in the form of an arbitration clause in a contract or in the form of a separate agreement.

(2) The arbitration agreement shall be in writing.

(3) An arbitration agreement is in writing if its content is recorded in any form, whether or not the arbitration agreement or contract has been concluded orally, by conduct, or by other means.

(4) The requirement that an arbitration agreement be in writing is met by an electronic communication if the information contained therein is accessible so as to be useable for subsequent reference; "electronic communication" means any communication that the parties make by means of data messages; "data message" means information generated, sent, received or stored by electronic, magnetic, optical or similar means, including, but not limited to, electronic data interchange (EDI), electronic mail, telegram, telex or telecopy.

(5) Furthermore, an arbitration agreement is in writing if it is contained in an exchange of statements of claim and defence in which the existence of an agreement is alleged by one party and not denied by the other.

(6) The reference in a contract to any document containing an arbitration clause constitutes an arbitration agreement in writing, provided that the reference is such as to make that clause part of the contract.

Legislative changes

Arbitration and Conciliation (Amendment) Act, 2015 (3 of 2016)

In Section 7 of the principal Act, in sub-Section (4), in clause (*b*), after the words "or other means of telecommunication", the words "including communication through electronic means" shall be *inserted*.

NOTES ON CLAUSES

Clause 3 of the Bill seeks to amend clause (*b*) of sub-section 7 of the principal Act to expressly provide that an arbitration agreement contained in the form of communication through electronic means shall also be treated as an arbitration agreement in writing.

Scope and application

"Arbitration agreement" means an agreement by the parties to submit to arbitration, all or certain disputes, which have arisen or which may arise between them in respect of certain legal relationships, whether contractual or not.

An arbitration agreement may be in the form of an arbitrator clause in a contract or in the form of a separate agreement.

An arbitration agreement shall be in writing. An arbitration agreement is in writing if it is contained in—

(*a*) a document signed by the parties;
(*b*) an exchange of letters, telex, telegrams or other means of telecommunication including communication through electronic means which provide a record of the agreement; or
(*c*) an exchange of statements of claim and defence in which the existence of the agreement is alleged by one party and not defined by the other.

The reference in a contract to a document containing an arbitration clause constitutes an arbitration agreement if the contract is in writing and the reference is such as to make that arbitration clause part of the contract.

The existence of an arbitration agreement as defined in Section 7 is a condition precedent for the exercise of power to appoint an arbitration/ Arbitral Tribunal under Section 11. It is not possible to appoint an arbitrator to adjudicate the disputes between the parties in the absence of an arbitration agreement or mutual consent.[2] The existence of a valid arbitration clause in agreement is necessary for attracting the provisions of Arbitration and Conciliation Act, 1996.[3]

An arbitration clause, though an integral part of the contract, is an agreement within an agreement. It is a collateral term of a contract, independent of and distinct from its substantive terms.[4]

The terms of an arbitration agreement have to be interpreted in a broad common sense manner.[5]

The rules of interpretation require the arbitration clause to be read in the ordinary and natural sense, except when that would lead to an absurdity. No part of a term or clause should be considered as a meaningless surplusage

2. *Jagdish Chander* v. *Ramesh Chander*, (2007) 5 SCC 719.
3. *M.P. Paschim Kshetra Vidyut Vitran Co. Ltd.* v. *SERCO BPO (P) Ltd.*, 2017 SCC OnLine MP 2025: (2018) 3 MP LJ 295.
4. *M.R. Engineers & Contractors (P) Ltd.* v. *Som Datt Builders Ltd.*, (2009) 7 SCC 696.
5. *GAIL* v. *Keti Construction (I) Ltd.*, (2007) 5 SCC 38.

when it is in consonance with the other parts of the clause and expresses the specific intention of the parties.[6]

Section 7 of the Act states that an "arbitration agreement" is an agreement by the parties to submit to arbitration all or certain disputes which have arisen or which may arise between them in respect of a defined legal relationship, whether contractual or not. The arbitration agreement may be in the form of an arbitration clause in a contract or in the form of a separate agreement and shall be an agreement in writing. An arbitration agreement is in writing if it is contained in any of the clauses, *i.e.* Section 7(4)(*a*) to (*c*) of the Act. Once these ingredients are satisfied there would be a binding agreement between the parties and the aggrieved party can invoke the jurisdiction of the court under Section 11(6) of the Act.[7] It is not open to the civil court to go into the question of non-existence of an arbitration agreement in a suit for declaration, both in view of the stringent provisions of Section 5, Arbitration and Conciliation Act and the power bestowed upon the Arbitral Tribunal to rule on its own jurisdiction by Section 16 of the Act, more so, as the decision of the Arbitral Tribunal would be amenable to be assailed within the ambit of Section 34 of the Act. Arbitral Tribunal is endowed with ample power and jurisdiction to rule on its own jurisdiction and it would not, therefore, be open to the civil court to pass an injunction against an arbitral proceeding in the teeth of the provisions of Section 5, Arbitration and Conciliation Act, 1996 and Section 16 thereof.[8]

Sub-section (1) to Section 7, Arbitration and Conciliation Act ordains that the arbitration agreement should be in respect of disputes arising from a defined legal relationship, whether contractual or not. The expression "legal relationship", again not defined in the Arbitration and Conciliation Act, means a relationship which gives rise to legal obligations and duties and, therefore, confers a right. These rights may be contractual or even non-contractual. Non-contractual disputes would require a separate or submission arbitration agreement based on the cause of action arising in tort, restitution, breach of statutory duty or some other non-contractual cause of action.[9]

Definition of arbitration agreement as found in Section 7 is applicable to Part I. Section 45 comes under Chapter 1 of Part II and arbitration agreement referred thereto cannot be understood in terms of Section 7 of the Act.[10]

6. *National Agricultural Coop. Mktg. Federation India Ltd.* v. *Gains Trading Ltd.*, (2007) 5 SCC 692.
7. *Powertech World Wide Ltd.* v. *Delvin International General Trading LLC*, (2012) 1 SCC 361.
8. *Handicrafts & Handlooms Exports Corpn. of India Ltd.* v. *Ashok Metal Corpn.*, 2010 SCC OnLine Del 2099: (2010) 117 DRJ 370.
9. *Vidya Drolia* v. *Durga Trading Corpn.*, (2021) 2 SCC 1.
10. *Andritz Oy.* v. *Enmas Engg. (P) Ltd.*, 2007 SCC OnLine Mad 461: (2007) 4 CTC 186.

Section 45 of the Act makes it mandatory for a judicial authority seized of an action in a matter when the parties have made an agreement to refer them to arbitration, except in these circumstances specified therein. Section 7 has no application to a case covered by Section 45 of the Act, the definition of "arbitration agreement" as contained in Section 7 cannot be expanded and read into Section 45 of the Act.[11] Mere allegation of fraud against the respondent would not result in the case being unfit for adjudication before the agreed mode of Arbitration Tribunal.[12]

Contracts arising out of and which are incidental to the main contract would necessarily have to be referred to and be decided in the same arbitration proceedings. The exclusion, if any, would have to be specifically pleaded and proved by the party so contending.[13]

Existence of valid arbitration agreement—Mode of determination

The existence of a valid arbitration agreement should be determined from the facts and circumstances of the case including the intention of the parties gathered from the correspondence exchanged between them, surrounding circumstances and conduct of parties. The agreement need not be in any particular form and the use or absence of the words "arbitration", "arbitrator" or "arbitrators" or "reference" therein is immaterial. The terms of any other contract are not relevant for determining the said question, especially when the other contract is not between the same parties.[14] Under the arbitration clause, in *Visa International Ltd.* v. *Continental Resources (USA) Ltd.*[15], the parties intended to settle disputes finally in accordance with the provisions of the Act in case of failure to arrive at an amicable settlement. The court held, the Act would govern the appointment of arbitrator, the reference of the disputes and the entire process and procedure of arbitration from the stage of appointment of arbitrator, till the award is made and executed or given effect to. Once the parties agree for resolution of dispute in accordance with the Arbitration and Conciliation Act, the Act takes care of the entire processes and procedure.[16] When the specific intention of the parties is clearly evident from the arbitration clause, the same cannot be treated as vague on the ground that it does not satisfy the suggested checklist of all the matters to be considered while drafting an arbitration agreement.

11. *Virender Yadav* v. *Aerosvit Airlines*, 2008 SCC OnLine Del 968: (2008) 153 DLT 250.
12. *MMTC Ltd.* v. *Shiv Sahai*, 2014 SCC OnLine Mad 9487: (2014) 5 LW 722.
13. *Ispat Industries Ltd.* v. *Baby Samuel and Co.*, 2008 SCC OnLine Bom 1037: (2009) 1 Mah LJ 1000.
14. *Visa International Ltd.* v. *Continental Resources (USA) Ltd.*, (2009) 2 SCC 55.
15. *Ibid.*
16. *Ibid.*

The clause provided that all disputes would be subject to Mumbai jurisdiction "under arbitration". From this clause, it cannot be said that parties have agreed to refer the disputes between them to the decision of a private tribunal for adjudication; that the private tribunal is empowered to adjudicate upon the disputes and that the decision of the tribunal would be binding upon them. The clause in question cannot be construed as an agreement to refer disputes to arbitration.[17]

In *Global Cements Ltd.* v. *Associated Cement Companies Ltd.*[18], parties to the agreement contemplated that in case of question or difference or dispute between them in relation to the contract would be referred to one of the two named arbitrators. Parties did not record a mere possibility of agreeing to an arbitration in future. Intent of parties to have their disputes settled by a private adjudication before an Arbitral Tribunal was clear. It was held that the agreement constituted an agreement to refer disputes to arbitration.

In *Satya Prakash & Bros. (P) Ltd.* v. *State of U.P.*[19], a clause contained in the contract bond signed between the parties provided that the dispute between the employer and domestic contractor would be settled in accordance with the provisions of Arbitration and Conciliation Act, 1996 and an arbitrator by way of agreement between the parties would be appointed. It was held that such a clause is an arbitration clause within the meaning of Section 7.

In *Goyolene Fibres (India) (P) Ltd.* v. *M.P. SEB*[20], there was no specific arbitration clause indicating intention of the parties for resolving the dispute through the constitution of Arbitration Tribunal as could be gathered by the agreement in question. The relevant clauses only indicated that the mechanism for resolution of dispute was to be in accordance with "laws of India". This term was a vague and wide term and could not be construed to mean as a reference for resolution of dispute by arbitration. There was no arbitration clause in the agreement and in the absence of an arbitration clause being available under Section 7 of the 1996 Act, the application under Section 11 of the 1996 Act was not maintainable. A clause in an agreement relating to a decision by the expert or the authority cannot be termed as an arbitration clause in view of the missing elements of the judicious decision making process.[21] In *Divya Shivlaks Impex* v. *Shantilal Jamnadas Textiles*

---

17. *Reshamsingh and Co. (P) Ltd.* v. *Dharti Dredging and Infrastructure Ltd.*, 2010 SCC OnLine Bom 959: (2010) 5 Mah LJ 438.
18. 2012 SCC OnLine Bom 712: (2012) 4 Mah LJ 867.
19. 2010 SCC OnLine All 267: (2010) 79 ALR 275.
20. 2011 SCC OnLine MP 362: (2011) 4 MP LJ 683.
21. *M.P. Paschim Kshetra Vidyut Vitran Co. Ltd.* v. *SERCO BPO (P) Ltd.*, 2017 SCC OnLine MP 2025: (2018) 3 MP LJ 295.

(P) Ltd.[22], there was no clause in the written contract executed between the parties. Clause printed on the invoice, "this sale is subject to the sale disputes and Arbitration Rules of Mumbai Piece goods Merchants Mahajan", was not an arbitration agreement between the parties. The Merchant's Mahajan had no jurisdiction to adjudicate upon the dispute. In *Scholar Publishing House (P) Ltd.* v. *Khanna Traders*[23], the appellant-company was engaged in the business of printing and publishing and supply paper to the appellant and the invoice raised by the claimant at the time of the delivery of goods, contained a stipulation that in case of any dispute including dispute of non-payment in respect of the invoice, the same would be referred to "Paper Merchants Association" for arbitration. In the undermentioned case, a contrary view was taken. Appellant filed objections to the award and contended that he had never consented for arbitration and that the mere issuance of an invoice containing stipulation for referring disputes to arbitration, after conclusion of an oral agreement of sale and delivery of goods, was unilateral and did not evidence consensus ad-idem and further did not satisfy the conditions with regard to the existence of an arbitration agreement as per Section 7 of the Act. It was held that there is no straitjacket formula to say whether an invoice can or cannot amount to a binding arbitration clause. Section 7 of the Act does not compel the parties to adhere to any particular form of agreement or document and an arbitration agreement can be inferred through a series of correspondence or from the conduct of the parties. In this case, identically phrased invoices containing the arbitration stipulation were accepted and acted upon for more than a decade, and therefore, there was no merit in the contention of the appellant, and hence, appeal was dismissed.

Arbitration agreement means an agreement by the parties to submit disputes between them in respect of a defined legal relationship, to arbitration. An arbitration agreement may either be in the form of an arbitration clause in a contract or take the form of a separate agreement. An arbitration agreement has to be in writing but it may be contained in a document signed by the parties, exchange of communication and exchange of a statement of claim and defence in which an allegation that there exists an arbitration agreement is not denied by the other party.[24]

In the present case, apart from the fact that clause 18 of the development agreement uses the terms "arbitration" and "arbitrator(s)", it has clearly enunciated the mandatory nature of reference to arbitration by using the term "shall be referred to arbitration of a sole arbitrator mutually appointed, failing which, two arbitrators, one to be appointed by each party to dispute

22. 1999 SCC OnLine Bom 122: (1999) 2 Mah LJ 223.
23. 2013 SCC OnLine Del 2708: ILR (2013) 5 Del 3343.
24. *ONGC Ltd.* v. *Discovery Enterprises (P) Ltd.*, (2022) 8 SCC 42.

or difference". Method of appointing the third arbitrator has also been clearly mentioned wherein the two selected arbitrators are to appoint a third arbitrator. Even the governing law was chosen by the parties to be "the Arbitration and Conciliation Act, 1996 or any re-enactment thereof". These three recitals strongly point towards an unambiguous intention of the parties at the time of formation of the contract to refer their dispute(s) to arbitration.[25]

An arbitration agreement can be entered into only with the consent of the parties. Once, an arbitration agreement is entered into it may be invoked by any of the parties unilaterally. If one of the parties refused to abide by the arbitration agreement, the other party is entitled to invoke or enforce it under the said Act. Where an award is set aside, the commencement of the arbitration again is pursuant to and under the existing arbitration clause.[26]

In the absence of express denial of acceptance of communication/ agreement, it was presumed that there was a concluded contract. Existence of an arbitration agreement was also presumed.[27]

Signature is not a formal requirement of an arbitration agreement either under Section 7(4)(*b*) or Section 7(4)(*c*) or under Section 7(5) of the Act. Even if every page of the contract agreement is not signed, both the parties are bound by the arbitration clause.[28] Merely because an agreement speaks of reference of dispute, it does not automatically become an arbitration agreement and the same must be determined according to the circumstances and intention of the parties in each particular instance. There was no binding or enforceable agreement between the parties. It was held that the same was inoperative.[29]

Which approach as to interpretation of an arbitration agreement should be adopted in a particular case would depend upon various factors including the language, the parties, nature of relationship, the factual background in which the arbitration agreement was entered, etc. In case of pure commercial disputes, a more appropriate principle of interpretation would be the one of liberal construction as there is a presumption in favour of one-stop adjudication.[30]

25. *Babanrao Rajaram Pund* v. *Samarth Builders & Developers*, (2022) 9 SCC 691.
26. *Associated Constructions* v. *Mormugoa Port Trust*, 2010 SCC OnLine Bom 1071: (2010) 5 Mah LJ 739.
27. *Siddhi Vinayak Industries (P) Ltd.* v. *Virgoz Oils & Fats PTE Ltd.*, 2010 SCC OnLine Cal 1982: (2011) 1 Cal LT 110.
28. *Sai Engg. Contractors* v. *Railways*, 2009 SCC OnLine AP 473: (2009) 3 AP LJ 391.
29. *Sara International Ltd.* v. *Golden Agri International (P) Ltd.*, 2010 SCC OnLine Del 2238: (2010) 118 DRJ 471.
30. *Vidya Drolia* v. *Durga Trading Corpn.*, (2021) 2 SCC 1.

Arbitration agreement not required in any particular form

An arbitration agreement is not required to be in any particular form. What is required is to gather the intention of the parties as to whether they had agreed for resolution of disputes through arbitration. Section 7 does not prescribe any particular form and it is immaterial whether or not the expression "arbitration", or "arbitrator" or "arbitrators" have been used in the agreement.[31]

Arbitration agreement/clause what constitutes—Principles summarised

The principles as to what constitutes an arbitration agreement are the following:

1. The intention of the parties to enter into an arbitration agreement shall have to be gathered from the terms of the agreement. If the terms of the agreement clearly indicate an intention on the part of the parties to the agreement to refer their disputes to a private tribunal for adjudication and a willingness to be bound by the decision of such tribunal on such disputes, it is an arbitration agreement. While there is no specific form of an arbitration agreement, the words used should disclose a determination and an obligation to go to arbitration and not merely contemplate the possibility of going for arbitration. Where there is merely a possibility of the parties agreeing to arbitration in future, as contrasted from an obligation to refer disputes to arbitration, there is no valid and binding arbitration agreement.
2. Even if the words "arbitration" and "Arbitral Tribunal (or arbitrator)" are not used with reference to the process of settlement or with reference to the private tribunal which has to adjudicate upon the disputes, in a clause relating to settlement of disputes, it does not detract from the clause being an arbitration agreement if it has the attributes or elements of an arbitration agreement. They are: (*a*) the agreement should be in writing; (*b*) the parties should have agreed to refer any disputes (present or future) between them to the decision of a private tribunal; (*c*) the private tribunal should be empowered to adjudicate upon the disputes in an impartial manner, giving due opportunity to the parties to put forth their case before it; and (*d*) the parties should

31. *Visa International Ltd.* v. *Continental Resources (USA) Ltd.*, (2009) 2 SCC 55; *M. Dayanand Reddy* v. *A.P. Industrial Infrastructure Corpn. Ltd.*, (1993) 3 SCC 137; *Bihar State Mineral Development Corpn.* v. *Encon Builders (I) (P) Ltd.*, (2003) 7 SCC 418; *A.B. Mallikarjuna* v. *Jubliant Biosys Ltd.*, 2009 SCC OnLine Kar 475: (2010) 5 KCCR 3906.

have agreed that the decision of the private tribunal in respect of the disputes will be binding on them.

3. Where the clause provides that in the event of disputes arising between the parties, the disputes shall be referred to arbitration, it is an arbitration agreement. Where there is a specific and direct expression of intent to have the disputes settled by arbitration, it is not necessary to set out the attributes of an arbitration agreement to make it an arbitration agreement. But where the clause relating to settlement of disputes, contains words which specifically exclude any of the attributes of an arbitration agreement or contains anything that detracts from an arbitration agreement, it will not be an arbitration agreement. For example, where an agreement requires or permits an authority to decide a claim or dispute without hearing, or requires the authority to act in the interests of only one of the parties, or provides that the decision of the authority will not be final and binding on the parties, or that if either party is not satisfied with the decision of the authority, he may file a civil suit seeking relief, it cannot be termed as an arbitration agreement.
4. But mere use of the word "arbitration" or "arbitrator" in a clause will not make it an arbitration agreement, if it requires or contemplates a further or fresh consent of the parties for reference to arbitration. For example, use of words such as "parties can, if they *so desire*, refer their disputes to arbitration" or "in the event of any dispute, the parties *may also* agree to refer the same to arbitration" or "if any disputes arise between the parties, they should consider settlement by arbitration" in a clause relating to settlement of disputes, indicate that the clause is not intended to be an arbitration agreement. Similarly, a clause which states that "if the parties so decide, the disputes shall be referred to arbitration" or "any disputes between parties, if they so agree, shall be referred to arbitration" is not an arbitration agreement. Such clauses merely indicate a desire or hope to have the disputes settled by arbitration, or a tentative arrangement to explore arbitration as a mode of settlement if and when a dispute arises. Such clauses require the parties to arrive at a further agreement to go to arbitration, as and when the disputes arise. Any agreement or clause in an agreement requiring or contemplating a further consent or consensus before a reference to arbitration, is not an arbitration agreement, but an agreement to enter into an arbitration agreement in future.[32]

32. *Jagdish Chander* v. *Ramesh Chander*, (2007) 5 SCC 719.

Essential elements of arbitration agreement

The essential elements of an arbitration agreement are:

There must be a present or future difference in connection with some contemplated matter.

There must be the intention of the parties to settle such differences by a private tribunal.

The parties must agree in writing to be bound by the decision of such tribunal.[33]

In order to constitute a valid binding and enforceable arbitration agreement, the requirements contained in Section 7 have to be satisfied strictly. These requirements apart from others are: 1) there has to be an agreement; 2) it has to be in writing; 3) parties must sign such agreement, in other words, the agreement must bear the signatures of the parties concerned; and 4) such agreement must contain an arbitration clause. Failure to satisfy any of the four conditions would render the arbitration agreement invalid and unenforceable, and in consequence would result in dismissal of the application filed under Section 11, Arbitration and Conciliation Act, 1996 at its threshold.[34]

The agreement would be an agreement in writing if it is contained in a document signed by the parties. Arbitration clause contained in the letter signed by the petitioner alone was not a valid arbitration agreement.[35]

An arbitration agreement must contain the broad consensus between the parties that the dispute and the differences should be referred to an Arbitral Tribunal.[36]

Where the arbitration agreement does not specify the disputes between the parties to be referred to arbitration or exclude certain claims/disputes from the purview thereof, it must be presumed that the parties had agreed to submit all disputes to arbitration, which have arisen or which may arise between them.[37]

It is not necessary that the words "reference" or "arbitration" or similar expression should actually be used in the agreement. It would be sufficient

33. *Bihar State Mineral Development Corpn.* v. *Encon Builders (I) (P) Ltd.*, (2003) 7 SCC 418.
34. *Vimal Kishor Shah* v. *Jayesh Dinesh Shah*, (2016) 8 SCC 788.
35. *Pramod Chimanbai Patel* v. *Lalit Constructions*, 2002 SCC OnLine Bom 546: (2002) 3 Mah LJ 846.
36. *Bihar State Mineral Development Corpn.* v. *Encon Builders (I) (P) Ltd.*, (2003) 7 SCC 418.
37. *Sai Trading Co.* v. *Sangli Miraj and Kupwad City Municipal Corpn.*, 2010 SCC OnLine Bom 1093: (2010) 5 Mah LJ 765.

if agreement in substance amounts to arbitration agreement. To determine the real nature of agreement, it is necessary to ascertain what was the intention of parties while entering into agreement. In *Mohan Singh* v. *H.P. State Forest Corpn.*[38], the contractor had bound himself that in case of any difference/dispute the decision of the Managing Director shall be final and binding. Though words "reference" or "arbitration" were not used in clause, the sole effect of words used in clause amounted to reference of dispute to arbitration of the Managing Director whose decision had been agreed to be final and binding. The trial court acted legally in interpreting the clause to be an arbitration clause.

Allegation of fraud

The petitioner firm had entered into agreement with the contractor for development and construction of property. The contractor did not deny signing of contract and the steps taken by him to develop property in terms thereof. His allegation of fraud in the execution of the agreement that he was not allowed to read the contract before signing was not believed. Arbitration clause was not null and void.[39]

Agreement by parties to submit to arbitration, all or certain disputes [Sub-s. (1)]

The words in sub-section (1) of Section 7 "means an agreement by the parties to submit to arbitration" postulate an agreement which necessarily or rather mandatorily requires the appointment of an arbitrator/or arbitrators. Section 7 does not cover a case where the parties agree that they "may" go to suit or that they may also go to arbitration. Thus, unless the document filed by the party before the Chief Justice of India or his designate is an "arbitration agreement" as defined in Section 7, requiring a reference in a mandatory sense, no reference can be made to the "Arbitral Tribunal".[40] In this case, arbitration clause 5 of the agreement used the words "may be referred"; in clause 4 of the agreement, the parties desired that in the case of disputes, the civil courts at Bombay are to be approached by way of a suit. This was followed by clause 5 with the words "it is *also* agreed" that the dispute may be referred to arbitration which implied that parties need not necessarily go to civil court by way of suit, but can also go before an arbitrator. This was merely an enabling provision. When both the clauses are read together, it was clear that it was not the intention of the parties that

38. 1998 SCC OnLine HP 22.
39. *Bihar Home Developers and Builders* v. *Narendra Prasad Gupta*, 2021 SCC OnLine Pat 1355: (2021) 3 PLJR 385.
40. *Wellington Associates Ltd.* v. *Kirit Mehta*, (2000) 4 SCC 272.

arbitration was to be the sole remedy. Clause 5 of the agreement was not a firm or mandatory arbitration clause and it postulated a fresh agreement between the parties that they will go to arbitration.[41]

Where none of the documents indicated that parties ever agreed for settlement of dispute through any independent body, no arbitration agreement authorising court to make reference was executed, court refrained itself from appointing arbitrator for settlement of disputes between the parties. Application was rejected.[42]

The essence of arbitration is adjudication of disputes by independent/neutral person/body. There was a licence agreement between the allottee of land and India Trade Promotion Organisation (ITPO). Clause in the agreement provided that disputes arising between the parties shall be referred to sole arbitration of the Chairman of the ITPO or his nominee whose decision shall be binding on the parties. It was held, it was not an arbitration clause, appointment of the arbitrator by the nominee of the Chief Justice was set aside.[43]

The use of the word "may" in the arbitration clause indicates that fresh consent of both the parties for arbitration is necessary.[44]

"Disputes which have arisen or which may arise" between the parties [Sub-s. (1)]

A dispute can be said to arise only when one party to the arbitration agreement makes or asserts a claim/demand against the other party to the arbitration agreement and the other party refuses/denies such claim or demand.[45] Third parties not signatory to the partnership deed were not covered by the arbitration clause.[46]

In construing the intention of the parties in arbitration agreement, due importance should be given to the parties' autonomy.[47]

Consensus ad-idem

Consensus ad-idem between the parties is a necessary ingredient to constitute an arbitration agreement. The clause in the partnership deed between the

41. *Ibid.*
42. *Acurite Contractors & Engineers* v. *Allahabad Agricultural Institute Deemed University*, 2011 SCC OnLine All 1764: (2012) 90 ALR 564.
43. *International Amusement Ltd.* v. *India Trade Promotion Organisation*, (2015) 12 SCC 677.
44. *Companies Act, 1956, re* v. *Kota Straw Board (P) Ltd.*, 1970 SCC OnLine Raj 36: 1971 RLW 151.
45. *Deutsche Post Bank Home Finance Ltd.* v. *Taduri Sridhar*, (2011) 11 SCC 375.
46. *H.G. Oomor Sait* v. *O. Aslam Sait*, 2001 SCC OnLine Mad 465: (2001) 3 CTC 269.
47. *Sime Darby Engg. SDN. BHD.* v. *Engineers India Ltd.*, (2009) 7 SCC 545.

parties provided that in the event of disputes arising between the parties, the same shall be mutually decided by the parties or shall be referred to arbitration if the parties so decide. If the clause had merely said that in the event of dispute arising between the parties, they shall be referred to arbitration, it would have been an arbitration agreement. The court held that the main attribute of an arbitration agreement, *namely*, consensus ad-idem to refer the disputes to arbitration was missing in the case, there was not an arbitration agreement as defined in Section 7.[48]

The arbitration clause has to be gathered from the documents executed between the parties in the form of a contract or otherwise, but the intent to refer to arbitration has to be expressed or implied. It cannot be uncertain or unmeaningful. The parties are to be ad-idem to make a reference of their dispute to the arbitration and such an intent must be clear from the material on record, particularly the contract relied upon between the parties. The law was, in fact, liberalised to the extent that where the party might have taken a stand on a mistaken or wrong understanding of the law, it is not precluded; from changing its stand, even in accordance with such a clause. Thus, existence of an arbitration clause is *sine qua non* for reference of a dispute to the arbitration. In *Nilesh C. Sanghani* v. *Rakesh V. Zangda*[49], an arbitration clause was uncertain and, in fact, was not even a concluded contract between the parties. It was an offer to give resignation by the petitioner in a letter addressed to the Board of Directors of the respondent-company. This would clearly show that there was no written contract or agreement between the parties and the endorsement by one of the respondents would not bind the company as such. In any case the arbitration clause was vague, uncertain and incapable of being construed to conclude that parties were ad-idem for referring their dispute to the arbitration.

The legislative purpose appears to be that the parties consciously and by mutuality agree to refer the disputes between them for adjudication to an Arbitration Tribunal in terms of the contract or constituted as per the arbitration agreement and under the provisions of the Act. Unilateral expression of reference to arbitration would not satisfy the ingredients of this provision. There has to be a clear unambiguous intent on the part of the parties recorded in writing in a contract or by various modes as indicated in Section 7, before a reference can be made. The intent could be gathered from the documents but it has to be a definite expression. In *Ashoka Buildcon Ltd.* v. *Maharashtra State Road Development Corpn. Ltd.*[50], there was no proper and valid arbitration agreement between the parties as contemplated under

48. *Jagdish Chander* v. *Ramesh Chander*, (2007) 5 SCC 719.
49. 2007 SCC OnLine Bom 530: (2007) 6 Mah LJ 242.
50. 2008 SCC OnLine Bom 464: (2008) 5 Mah LJ 67.

the provisions of the Act. Filing of a suit by the petitioner itself indicated the conduct and intent of the petitioner that the claim in relation to that contract never understood to be covered by the arbitration clause between the parties.

Disputes shall be referred to parties if the parties so determine—No arbitration agreement

In *Jagdish Chander* v. *Ramesh Chander*[51], para 16 in the partnership deed provided that if there is any dispute touching the partnership between the parties, the same shall be mutually decided by the parties or shall be referred to arbitration if the parties so determine. The expression "determine" indicates that the parties are required to reach a decision by the application of mind. There was no arbitration agreement between the parties. The provision enabled arbitration only if the parties mutually decide after the consideration as to whether the dispute should be referred to arbitration. The court held that the main attribute of an arbitration agreement, *namely*, consensus ad-idem to refer the disputes to arbitration was missing in the case, there was no arbitration agreement, as defined under Section 7.

Difference of opinion—Means dispute [Sub-s. (1)]

Difference of opinion means dispute. Difference of opinion leads to "disputes, it is very difficult" to imagine that difference of opinion and disputes are altogether different things.[52]

"Arbitration agreement may be in form of arbitration clause or in form of a separate agreement" [Sub-s. (2)]

An arbitration agreement may be in the form of an arbitration clause or in the form of a separate agreement. The 1996 Act does not prescribe any form for an arbitration agreement. The existence of an arbitration clause has to be ascertained from the intention of the parties as gathered from correspondence exchanged between them, the agreement in question and surrounding circumstances.[53]

Arbitration agreement is not required to be in any particular form. What is required to be ascertained is whether the parties have agreed that if disputes arise between them in respect of subject-matter of the contract, such disputes shall be referred to arbitration, then such an agreement would spell out an arbitration agreement.[54]

---

51. (2007) 5 SCC 719.
52. *N. Radhakrishnan* v. *Maestro Engineers*, (2010) 1 SCC 72.
53. *Nandan Biomatrix Ltd.* v. *D 1 Oils Ltd.*, (2009) 4 SCC 495.
54. *Rukmanibai Gupta* v. *Collector*, (1980) 4 SCC 556.

An agreement appointing an arbitrator need not be in any particular form. Requirement is submission to arbitration, which should be in writing. Such submission need not be signed by parties. No formal agreement or compromise is required for appointment of arbitrator or submission of disputes to arbitration.[55]

Arbitration clause in main/implementation agreement—Applicability to MOU

Implementation agreement entered into between the parties provided for arbitration in clause 20 and it was contended that MOU did not merge with the implementation agreement. MOU, however, was described by the parties as Appendix A to the implementation agreement. It was held that the second recital read with clause 2.2 of the implementation agreement suggested that the MOU had merged with the implementation agreement and, therefore, the disputes that were referable to arbitration under the implementation agreement in terms of clause 20, were to include disputes arising under the MOU, even though the latter document did contain a separate arbitration clause.[56]

"An arbitration agreement shall be in writing" [Sub-s. (3)]

The mandate of the Arbitration and Conciliation Act, 1996 is that the arbitration agreement shall be in writing.

An agreement to submit present or future disputes to arbitration should be in writing, need not be signed by the parties. It is sufficient if terms are reduced to writing and agreement is established. When an arbitration agreement is disputed and it is alleged that blank papers were signed, one who pleads free consent and pleads existence of agreement must prove it.[57]

On reading Section 7, Arbitration and Conciliation Act, 1996 it is clear that under sub-section (3) of Section 7 of the said Act, it is imperative that an arbitration agreement must be in writing. Sub-sections (4) and (5) of Section 7 explain as and when arbitration agreement is considered to be in writing. Written agreement means an agreement in which the terms agreed by the parties are reduced into writing. It is, therefore, not necessary that the agreement must be signed by both the parties. In *Babaji Automotive* v. *Indian Oil Corpn. Ltd.*[58], the existence of a valid arbitration agreement

---

55. *S.S.M. Soundappan* v. *K.G. Balakrishnan*, 1997 SCC OnLine Mad 503: (1997) 2 CTC 385.
56. *UHL Power Co. Ltd.* v. *State of H.P.*, (2022) 4 SCC 116.
57. *S.S.M. Soundappan* v. *K.G. Balakrishnan*, 1997 SCC OnLine Mad 503: (1997) 2 CTC 385.
58. 2005 SCC OnLine Cal 291: (2005) 4 CHN 74.

can be spelt out from the conduct of the parties. The petitioner admittedly signed the lubricants distributorship agreement accepting all its terms and conditions. The petitioner in furtherance of the said agreement took delivery of lubricants from the said corporation. When he committed defaults, under clause 39 of the agreement, the disputes and differences between the parties were referred to arbitration, it was not open to the petitioner to deny the existence of a valid arbitration agreement.

For invocation of an arbitration clause there has to be a written agreement. Where no written agreement has been executed, the question of invocation of an arbitration clause would not arise.[59] In *Travancore Devaswom Board* v. *Panchamy Pack (P) Ltd.*[60], the High Court refused to entertain the writ petition on the ground that the same involved questions of facts. However, while doing so, it referred the dispute to arbitration and appointed a sole arbitrator. The order of the High Court appointing arbitrator was challenged. Section 7(3), Arbitration and Conciliation Act, 1996 clearly provides that an arbitration agreement shall be in writing. In this case, there was no agreement at all, quite apart from the fact that there was no writing to this effect. The High Court had not in the impugned order recorded any consent as was contended by the respondent. In the absence of an agreement in writing, the High Court's order referring the dispute to arbitration was not sustained.

Section 7(4) prescribes a mandatory requirement of written statement to be produced. Allowing a party to prove a written agreement by and evidence of its contents by secondary evidence in terms of Section 63(5), Evidence Act, 1872 would be to legislate another sub-section which the court cannot do. Consequently, an arbitrator cannot be appointed.[61]

Where the arbitrator had rendered an award, though there was no arbitration agreement between the parties, the arbitrator had exceeded his jurisdiction, hence, the award was set aside.[62]

In *NSK India Sales Co. (P) Ltd.* v. *Proactive Universal Trading Co. (P) Ltd.*[63], the arbitration clause was contained as part of an unsigned document which provided for declaration in the General Terms of Business (GTB) at the back of the document. On the document which contained this clause, there was no signature of respondent, there cannot be an arbitration clause by implication. An arbitration agreement has to be in writing.

59. *Dasmesh Communication* v. *BSNL*, 2009 SCC OnLine All 1453: (2010) 78 ALR 107.
60. (2004) 13 SCC 510.
61. *Yashwant Chunilal Mody* v. *Yuysuf Karmali Kerwala*, 2013 SCC OnLine Bom 1246: (2014) 3 Mah LJ 111.
62. *Gill and Co. (P) Ltd.* v. *Patodia Ginning Factory*, 2016 SCC OnLine Bom 2184: (2016) 3 Mah LJ 890.
63. 2015 SCC OnLine Mad 10355: (2015) 4 LW 417.

Oral arbitration agreement not recognised

Sub-section (3) of Section 7, Arbitration and Conciliation Act, 1996 provides that an arbitration agreement shall be in writing.[64]

It is mandatory that there must be an arbitration agreement which must be in writing. The said writing need not mention about the word "arbitration" but there must be exchange of communication in writing in order to infer that the parties were ad-idem with regard to the dispute resolution forum within the ambit and scope of Section 7 of the 1996 Act and the nature of dispute to be resolved by it. Such record of exchange of communication/ letters is/are sufficient to hold the consensual acceptance of the intent of one party to refer the dispute for arbitration by the other party through such communication.[65]

In the absence of an arbitration agreement, the court can refer to arbitration only with the written consent of the parties either by way of joint memo or joint application.[66]

A contract can be entered into even orally. A contract can be spelt out from correspondence or conduct. But an arbitration agreement is different from a contract. An arbitration agreement can come into existence only in the manner contemplated under Section 7. If Section 7 says that an arbitration agreement should be in writing, it will not be sufficient for the petitioner in an application under Section 11 to show that there existed an oral contract between the parties.[67]

Where the commercial offer of the petitioner containing arbitration clause for resolution of disputes was accepted by the respondent through email and correspondence exchanged between the parties, finally charter party agreement was entered into by them, arbitration clause it did not suffer from vice of being unclear and absence of formal signed agreement was not significant.[68]

It is not necessary that a contract has to be inferred from a formal document with signature and authentication. Even oral agreement pending documentation, or even a draft agreement is treated to be binding upon the parties. Contract can be enforced.[69]

---

64. *Kailash Baruah* v. *Hinduja Leyland Finance Co.*, 2017 SCC OnLine Gau 1083: (2017) 5 Gau LR 571.
65. *Subhash Projects and Mktg. Ltd.* v. *Assam Urban Water Supply and Sewerage Board*, 2019 SCC OnLine Gau 3510: (2019) 5 Gau LR 625.
66. *Kerala SEB* v. *Kurien E. Kalathil*, (2018) 4 SCC 793.
67. *Indowind Energy Ltd.* v. *Wescare (I) Ltd.*, (2010) 5 SCC 306.
68. *Trimex International FZE Ltd.* v. *Vedanta Aluminium Ltd.*, (2010) 3 SCC 1.
69. *Siddhi Vinayak Industries (P) Ltd.* v. *Virgoz Oils & Fats PTE Ltd.*, 2010 SCC OnLine Cal 1982: (2011) 1 Cal LT 110.

An arbitration agreement in writing when contained in document signed by parties, exchange of letters, telegrams, telex, etc. [Sub-s. (4)]

Sub-section (3) of Section 7 mandates that an arbitration agreement shall be in writing and sub-section (4) of Section 7 provides that an arbitration agreement is in writing if it is contained in—

(*a*) a document signed by the parties;

(*b*) exchange of letters, telex, telegrams or other means of telecommunication, including communication through electronic means which provide a record of the agreement; or

(*c*) an exchange of statements of claim and defence in which the existence of the agreement is alleged by one party and not denied by the other.

Even in absence of duly signed agreement by parties, agreement can be inferred from other written communication exchanged between them. Arbitration agreement can be inferred from other documents approved and signed by parties, informal exchange of email, letters, telex, telegrams, etc.[70]

Arbitration agreement can come into existence by exchange of letters, correspondence or a demand which is not denied and acted upon by the other party.[71]

With regard to arbitration, a written contract is very much essential and the same should be signed by both parties and further minimum words are necessary so as to constitute a clause of arbitration.[72]

Any documents/letter in support of the original agreement gives indication of reference for arbitration, and can be treated as part and parcel of the arbitration agreement.[73]

Arbitration clause in contract concluded through email

In the absence of signed agreement between the parties, it would be possible to infer from various documents duly approved and signed by the parties in the form of emails, letter, telex, telegrams and other means of telecommunication.[74] In Section 7(4), clause (*b*) added by Amendment Act 3 of 2016 also provides that an arbitration is in writing if it is contained inter alia in

70. *M.P. Paschim Kshetra Vidyut Vitran Co. Ltd.* v. *SERCO BPO (P) Ltd.*, 2017 SCC OnLine MP 2025: (2018) 3 MP LJ 295.
71. *A Contractors (I) Ltd.* v. *National Buildings Construction Corpn. Ltd.*, 2021 SCC OnLine TS 3648.
72. *International Nut Alliance LLC* v. *Beena Cashew Co.*, 2014 SCC OnLine Mad 425: (2014) 3 LW 156.
73. *Kohli Bros.* v. *Atlantis Multiplex (P) Ltd.*, 2007 SCC OnLine All 156: (2008) 1 All LJ 611.
74. *Trimex International Fze Ltd.* v. *Vedanta Aluminium Ltd.*, (2010) 1 SCC 1: 2010 CLC 312: 2010 (1) Scale 574.

other means of communication including through electronic means which provide a record of agreement. Letters, telegrams, telex, etc. containing an arbitration agreement requires proof that such letters, telex, telegrams, etc. were exchanged by the parties, mutually delivered and actually received by each other. There was no proof that the appellant, in fact, delivered invoices containing the arbitration agreement to the respondents. Therefore there cannot be said to have been an exchange of letters, etc. as required by Section 7(4)(*b*), Arbitration and Conciliation Act.[75]

Faxed agreements [S. 7(4)(*b*)]

Faxed agreements are acceptable under Section 7 of the Act. Section 7(4)(*b*) covers agreements that are sent via facsimile (fax) as they are "other means of telecommunication".[76] Faxed copy of the charter party agreement which contained an arbitration clause, signed by both the parties, was found sufficient to prove the existence of the arbitration agreement.[77]

For determining the existence of arbitration agreement faxed copy can be relied on. It cannot be rejected on ground, *viz.*:

1. it is a copy and not original;
2. signed by one and not by both the parties;
3. one of the parties did not sign every page.[78]

Arbitration clause—Determination of—Where contract consists of a printed form with cyclostyled amendments, typed additions/corrections, handwritten corrections

If a contract consists of a printed form with cyclostyled amendments, typed additions and deletions and handwritten corrections, an endeavour should be made to give effect to all the provisions. However, in the event of apparent or irreconcilable inconsistency, the following rules of construction will normally apply: 1) the cyclostyled amendments will prevail over the printed terms; 2) the typewritten additions will prevail over the printed terms and cyclostyled amendments; and 3) handwritten corrections will prevail over the printed terms, cyclostyled amendments and typewritten additions. These rules have evolved from the maxim of construction that "written, stamped or typed additions, when inconsistent with the printed terms, would normally prevail over the printed terms" and proceeds on the assumption that the printed form contained the original terms, and changes thereto were incorporated by

75. *Mikesh Corpn.* v. *Picotee Exports*, 2009 SCC OnLine Bom 456: (2009) 4 Mah LJ 514.
76. *Great Offshore Ltd.* v. *Iranian Offshore Engg. & Construction Co.*, (2008) 14 SCC 240.
77. *Ibid.*
78. *Ibid.*

the cyclostyled amendments, followed by changes by typewritten additions and lastly the handwritten additions.[79]

"Statements of claim and defence" [S. 7(4)(*c*)]

The words, "statements of claim and defence" occurring in Section 7(4)(*c*) of the Act, are not restricted to the statements of claim and defence filed before the arbitrator. If there is an assertion of an arbitration agreement in any suit, petition or application filed before any court, and if there is no denial thereof in the defence/counter/written statement thereto filed by the other party to such suit, petition or application, it can be said that there is an "exchange of statements of claim and defence" for the purposes of Section 7(4)(*c*) of the Act. If in the application filed under Section 11 of the Act, the applicant asserts the existence of an arbitration agreement with each of the respondents and if the respondents do not deny the said assertion in their statement of defence, the court can proceed on the basis that there is an arbitration agreement in writing between the parties.[80]

When the appellant gave the guarantee letter he could not be imputed with the knowledge that the loan agreements which were to be executed in future would contain an arbitration clause. Further, the appellant did not state in his letter that he would be bound by the terms of the loan agreements that may be executed by the borrower. Therefore, the question of the appellant agreeing to the arbitration clause does not arise. The appellant, who had not signed the loan agreements containing the arbitration clause, cannot be deemed to be a party to the arbitration and bound by the awards.[81]

Statement made by the appellant by which the Chief Engineer was appointed as an arbitrator can be said to be one made under clause (*c*) of sub-section (4) of Section 7 of the Act.[82]

Original agreement containing arbitration clause superseded/novated by another agreement—Survival of arbitral clause

Arbitration clause being a component of contract perishes with the contract if the said contract is superseded/substituted by another. In *Young Achievers* v. *IMS Learning Resources (P) Ltd.*[83], the parties entered into a fresh contract by novation/substitution of original agreement by mutual consent. New agreement did not contain any provision in respect of any disputes

79. *M.K. Abraham & Co.* v. *State of Kerala*, (2009) 7 SCC 636.
80. *S.N. Prasad* v. *Monnet Finance Ltd.*, (2011) 1 SCC 320.
81. *Ibid.*
82. *Krishna Bhagya Jala Nigam Ltd.* v. *G. Harischandra Reddy*, 2005 SCC OnLine Kar 58: (2005) 2 Kant LJ 409.
83. (2013) 10 SCC 535.

arising under the original agreement or any settlement between the parties nor did it contain an arbitration clause to resolve disputes by arbitration. New agreement was a pure and simple novation of the original contract by mutual consent. Rejection of reference of disputes to arbitration by the High Court was held proper. Similarly, in *Larsen & Toubro Ltd.* v. *Mohan Lal Harbans Lal Bhayana*[84], clause 25 in the original agreement which contained an arbitration clause was materially modified by subsequent agreements. Modalities of raising arbitration were completely novated. As per modified agreement only after award was rendered and nothing remained that might qualify as dispute between appellant and respondent referable to arbitration. It was held that no arbitration clause existed between the appellant and the respondent, the High Court was in error in holding that clause 25 of original agreement in unamended form survived.

Original agreement contained an arbitration clause and subsequently when supplemental agreement was entered, clause 11 clearly stated that original agreement would remain in force. Supplemental agreement was entered in terms of original agreement, hence arbitration clause mentioned in original agreement stood incorporated in subsequent supplemental agreement.[85]

Arbitration clause in the tender document does not survive with the execution of the construction agreement.[86]

In *Ashoka Tubewell & Engg. Corpn.* v. *Union of India*[87], arbitration clause in the agreement provided that no person other than the Gazetted Railway Officer should act as arbitrator and if that is not possible, matter should not be referred to arbitration at all. However, in application under Section 11 before the Chief Justice of the High Court, both the claimant-contractor as well as the respondent agreed to the appointment of a former judge of the High Court. It was held, once parties had given consent for the appointment of a former judge as arbitrator, there was a new contract by way of *novation*, whereby parties had agreed to appoint someone else than the named arbitrator. Parties having given consent cannot challenge the validity of the award on the ground that the arbitrator was not validly appointed.

84. (2015) 2 SCC 461.
85. *Chaitanya Builders & Leasing (P) Ltd.* v. *Tulsi Ram*, 2013 SCC OnLine Mad 2511: (2014) 1 MWN (Civil) 7 (DB).
86. *Space Infra Build (India) (P) Ltd.* v. *Dell International Services India (P) Ltd.*, 2012 SCC OnLine Kar 6347: ILR 2012 Kar 4446.
87. (2015) 5 SCC 702.

Accord and satisfaction—Survival/Extinguishment of arbitration agreement

Bald plea of fraud, coercion, duress or undue influence is not enough, a party who sets up such plea must prima facie establish the said allegation by placing material before the Chief Justice/his designate. In *New India Assurance Co. Ltd.* v. *Genus Power Infrastructure Ltd.*[88], the respondent-claimant after receiving payment under the insurance policy and signing letter of subrogation in favour of insurance company in full and final settlement of its claim under the policy, sought appointment of arbitrator on the ground that it signed said letter due to extreme financial difficulties and under duress, coercion and undue influence exercised by appellant. On the facts of the case, it was held that the plea raised by the respondent was bereft of any details and particulars and was a bald assertion. The respondent never made any protest or demur when a letter of subrogation was signed but issued only after three weeks. The financial condition of the respondent was not so precarious as to suggest that discharge and signing of a letter of subrogation was because of exercise of undue influence. The discharge and execution of letter of subrogation was voluntary and free from any coercion or undue influence, upon execution of letter of subrogation there was full and final settlement of the claim and dispute existed for exercising power under Section 11 of the Act, the Chief Justice of the High Court was not justified in appointing arbitrator.

In *ONGC Mangalore Petrochemicals Ltd.* v. *ANS Constructions Ltd.*[89], where the claimant contends that a discharge voucher or no-claim certificate has been obtained by fraud, coercion, duress or undue influence and the other side contests the correctness thereof the Chief Justice/his designate must look into this aspect to find out, at least prima facie, whether or not the dispute is bona fide and genuine. Where the dispute raised by the claimant with regard to validity of the discharge voucher or no-claim certificate or settlement agreement prima facie, appears to be lacking in credibility, there may not be a necessity to refer the dispute to arbitration at all. A bald plea of fraud, coercion, duress or undue influence is not enough and the party who sets up such a plea, must prima facie establish the same by placing material before the Chief Justice/his designate. In this case, the contractor alleged that he had issued "No Dues Certificate" under coercion/undue influence and raised a claim of ₹98.88 crores as losses sustained by him. Facts of the case showed that the contractee-company issued a certificate after receiving the final bill, mutually signed by both the parties. Certificate was issued

88. (2015) 2 SCC 424.
89. (2018) 3 SCC 373.

voluntarily by the contractor. No rights/obligations remained between the parties. Power under Section 11 was not exercised.

Arbitration agreement—Determination—Legal pleas, relevancy of

Whether there is an arbitration agreement or not, has to be decided with reference to the contract documents and not with reference to any contention raised before a court of law after the dispute has arisen. Reference to pleadings raised by the petitioners before the Jordanian courts would have been relevant if the plea was that the arbitration agreement between the parties is contained in the exchange of statement of claim and defence in which the existence of arbitration agreement is alleged by one party and not denied by the another, as contemplated under Section 7(4)(*c*) of the Act.[90]

Arbitration agreement—Need to be signed by both the parties

An arbitration agreement need not be signed by both the parties. An inference as to the existence of an arbitration agreement can be drawn from the acts of the parties to the agreement by way of their exchange of letters and information through fax, email, etc.[91]

In order to constitute an arbitration agreement, it need not be signed by all the parties. Section 7(3) of 1996 Act provides that the arbitration agreement shall be in writing, if it is a document signed by all the parties. Section 7(4)(*b*), however, shows that a written document which may not be signed by the parties, even then it can be an arbitration agreement. Section 7(4)(*b*) provides that an arbitration agreement can be culled from an exchange of letters, telex, telegrams or other means of communication which provide a record of the agreement. Thus, an arbitration agreement even though in writing need not be signed by the parties, if the record of arbitration is provided by the exchange of letters, telegrams or other means of telecommunication. An arbitration agreement even if not signed by the parties can be spelled out from the correspondence exchanged between the parties. In *Govind Rubber Ltd.* v. *Louids Dreyfus Commodities Asia (P) Ltd.*[92], the intention of the parties as appeared from the correspondence exchanged between the parties could be inferred that there had been meeting of minds between the parties as they were ad-idem to the terms of the sales contract which contained the forum of dispute resolution in Singapore Commodity Exchange.

---

90. *Groupe Chimique Tunisien SA* v. *Southern Petrochemicals Industries Corpn. Ltd.*, (2006) 5 SCC 275.
91. *Shakti Bhog Foods Ltd.* v. *Kola Shipping Ltd.*, (2009) 2 SCC 134.
92. (2015) 13 SCC 477.

A contract note executed in accordance with Regulation No. 3.5 of the Regulation of the National Stock Exchange of India signed only the registered broker and containing a stipulation that the contract would be subject to rules, bye-laws and regulations, which, in turn, provided for arbitration can constitute a valid arbitration agreement even though it was signed by the trade-member.[93]

"Articles of agreement" in the Letter of Intent (LoI) does not create any contractual obligation between the parties as it remains unexecuted and unsigned by the parties, and therefore, there is no arbitration agreement between the parties.[94]

Signature is not a formal requirement of an arbitration agreement either under Section 7(4)(*b*) or Section 7(4)(*c*) or under Section 7(5) of the Act. Even if every page of the contract agreement is not signed, both the parties are bound by an arbitration clause.[95]

Commercial offer made by the petitioner containing an arbitration clause was accepted by the respondent through a letter. Absence of formally signed agreement between the parties did not affect the acceptance of the offer. Application by the petitioner for appointment of arbitrator was allowed.[96]

Arbitration clause need not be stamped

The law does not require that an arbitration clause incorporated in a contract should be stamped.[97] Section 7 does not require that the parties should stamp the agreement.[98]

Doubting the ruling in *Vidya Drolia* v. *Durga Trading Corpn.*[99] of a coordinate three-judge Bench, which affirmed the judgment in *Garware Wall Ropes Ltd.* v. *Coastal Marine Constructions & Engg. Ltd.*[100], the issue "whether the statutory bar contained in Section 35 of the Stamp Act, 1899 applicable to instruments chargeable to stamp duty under Section 3 read with the Schedule to the Act, would also render the arbitration agreement contained in such an instrument, which is not chargeable to payment of stamp duty, as being non-existent, unenforceable, or invalid, pending

93. *Viraj Holdings* v. *Motilal Oswal Securities (P) Ltd.*, 2002 SCC OnLine Bom 558: (2002) 4 Mah LJ 65.
94. *Scon Contracts* v. *Neena Dhingra*, 2007 SCC OnLine Del 1375: (2008) 146 DLT 343.
95. *Sai Engg. Contractors* v. *Railways*, 2009 SCC OnLine AP 473: (2009) 3 AP LJ 391.
96. *Durga Krishna Store (P) Ltd.* v. *Union of India*, 2017 SCC OnLine Gau 1090: (2018) 1 Gau LR 100.
97. *Geo-Group Communications Inc.* v. *IOL Broadband Ltd.*, (2010) 1 SCC 562.
98. *Sai Engg. Contractors* v. *Railways*, 2009 SCC OnLine AP 473: (2009) 3 AP LJ 391; *A.B. Mallikarjuna* v. *Jubliant Biosys Ltd.*, 2009 SCC OnLine Kar 475: (2010) 5 KCCR 3906.
99. (2021) 2 SCC 1.
100. (2019) 9 SCC 209.

payment of stamp duty on the substantive contract/instrument?" referred to be authoritatively settled by a five-judge Bench.[101]

A five-judge Bench of the Supreme Court has held that non-payment or deficient payment of stamp duty on substantive contract comprising/containing clause or substantive arbitration agreement in cases where payment of stamp duty is mandatory renders such arbitration agreement as non-existence pending payment of (the balance) stamp duty. In such cases, appointment of arbitrator by court or reference to arbitration is impermissible until the deficiency in stamp duty is made good in accordance with law.[102]

Having regard to larger ramifications of *N.N. Global*[103], the Supreme Court viewed that proceedings should be placed before a seven-judge Bench to reconsider the correctness of the view by the five-judge Bench. In *Interplay between Arbitration Agreements under the Arbitration and Conciliation Act, 1996 and the Indian Stamp Act, 1899, In re*[104], the seven-judge Bench observed that the Arbitration Act is a legislation enacted to inter alia consolidate the law relating to arbitration in India and it will have primacy over the Stamp Act and the Contract Act, 1872 in relation to arbitration agreements. The court held the following:

a. Agreements which are not stamped or are inadequately stamped are inadmissible in evidence under Section 35 of the Stamp Act. Such agreements are not rendered *void* or *void ab initio* or unenforceable;
b. Non-stamping or inadequate stamping is a curable defect;
c. An objection as to stamping does not fall for determination under Section 8 or 11 of the Arbitration Act, 1996. The concerned court must examine whether the arbitration agreement *prima facie* exists;
d. Any objections in relation to the stamping of the agreement fall within the ambit of the arbitral tribunal; and
e. The decisions in *N.N. Global* (five-judge Bench) and *SMS Tea Estates (P) Ltd.* v. *Chandmari Tea Co. (P) Ltd.*[105] are overruled.

Arbitration agreements contained in letters or correspondence can fall within the umbrage of the stamp duty.[106]

Arbitration agreement—Registration not compulsory

An arbitration agreement embodied in a main agreement is a separate agreement. Invalidation of the main agreement does not necessarily invalidate

101. *N.N. Global Mercantile (P) Ltd.* v. *Indo Unique Flame Ltd.*, (2021) 4 SCC 379.
102. *N.N. Global Mercantile (P) Ltd.* v. *Indo Unique Flame Ltd.*, (2023) 7 SCC 1.
103. *Ibid.*
104. 2023 SCC OnLine SC 1666.
105. (2011) 14 SCC 66.
106. *N.N. Global Mercantile (P) Ltd.* v. *Indo Unique Flame Ltd.*, (2023) 7 SCC 1.

the arbitration agreement. An arbitration agreement is not required to be compulsorily registered. Going by the doctrine of severability, denying the benefit of an arbitration agreement to a party on the ground of any deficiency in the main agreement, may not be apposite.[107]

Arbitration agreement by Will or unilateral declaration

Neither a Will nor any subsequent declaration by the testator can be construed as an agreement for arbitration. Even if by a Will or any unilateral declaration the testator expressed desire that his children should settle their disputes by arbitration, the parties cannot be subjected to arbitration without there being any express or implied contract between the parties for the same. In *Vijay Kumar Sharma* v. *Raghunandan Sharma*[108], Respondent 1 and the appellant were brothers. Appellant filed suit for partition and separate possession of ancestral properties. The testator-father had made a declaration subsequent to the execution of Will expressing his desire for settlement of disputes by an arbitrator designated in the declaration. Respondents 2 and 3 (executors of Will) filed an application under Section 8, Arbitration and Conciliation Act, 1996 for arbitration. Respondent 1 field application under Section 9(6) of the Act for the appointment of arbitrator, which was allowed by the High Court. In appeal, the Supreme Court held that there was no arbitration agreement as defined in Section 7 between the parties. Nor was there any communication (through letters, telegrams, etc.) referring to or recording an arbitration agreement between the parties. The Will also did not contain any provision for arbitration. Order for appointment of arbitrator, passed by the High Court was set aside.

Joint arbitration where common relief is sought against persons jointly and severally liable—Permissible

If *A* has a claim against *B* and *C* and *A* has arbitration agreement with *B* and *A* has also separate agreement with *C*, there is no reason why *A* cannot have joint arbitration with *B* and *C*. Obviously having an arbitration between *A* and *B* and another arbitration between *A* and *C* in regard to the same claim would lead to conflicting decisions. In such a case, to deny the benefit of a single transaction against *B* and *C* on the ground that the arbitration agreements against *B* and *C* are different would lead to multiplicity of proceedings, conflicting decisions and cause injustice. It would be proper and just to say that when *A* has a claim jointly against *B* and *C*, and when there are provisions for arbitration in respect of both *B* and *C*,

107. *Parsvnath Developers Ltd.* v. *Future Retail Ltd.*, (2022) 2 HCC (Del) 516.
108. (2010) 2 SCC 486.

there can be a single transaction.[109] As the first respondent had a single claim against the second respondent and as there was provision for arbitration in regard to both of them and as the Bombay Stock Exchange had permitted a common arbitration, the appellant's contention that there could not be common arbitration against the appellant and the second respondent was not accepted.[110]

General conditions of contract providing for arbitration clause

To constitute an arbitration agreement for the purposes of Sections 7 and 11, two requirements should be satisfied, *first*, there should be an arbitration agreement between the parties to the dispute, and *secondly*, it should relate to or be applicable to the dispute in regard to which appointment of an arbitrator is sought. General conditions providing for arbitration would apply in regard to any contract by placing purchase order and not to any dispute in regard to tender or bid or not placing purchase order. In *BSNL* v. *Telephone Cables Ltd.*[111], respondent raised a dispute as to damages sustained on account of non-placing of purchase order. It was held, respondent was not entitled to invoke an arbitration clause as there was no arbitration agreement in the absence of purchase order.

Once it is seen that in none of the pre-contract or post-contract documents there is any reference to the general conditions, an auction purchaser cannot be bound by the arbitration clause contained in the general conditions. The general conditions which contain arbitration clause, was neither made part of it, nor even referred to either in the tender catalog or in the bid sheet or sale advice. It was held, there was no arbitration agreement in existence between the parties, there cannot be a reference of the dispute to the arbitration.[112]

In *Shiv Om Polynets (P) Ltd.* v. *Marine Fabrics*[113], an arbitration clause was also included in terms and conditions. It was held, where there is reference in a contract to a document containing an arbitration clause, such reference constitutes an arbitration agreement, if the contract is in writing and the reference is such as to make that arbitration clause of part of the contract.

---

109. *P.R. Shah, Shares & Stock Brokers (P) Ltd.* v. *B.H.H. Securities (P) Ltd.*, (2012) 1 SCC 594.
110. *Ibid.*
111. (2010) 5 SCC 213; see also, *M.P. Paschim Kshetra Vidyut Vitran Co. Ltd.* v. *SERCO BPO (P) Ltd.*, 2017 SCC OnLine MP 2025: (2018) 3 MP LJ 295.
112. *AMK & Co.* v. *Deputy Chief Materials Manager*, 2011 SCC OnLine Mad 2345: (2012) 4 CTC 271.
113. 2013 SCC OnLine Cal 1070: (2013) 1 Cal LT 592.

Arbitration agreement, matter of contract

An arbitration agreement is a matter of contract between the parties. So long as the contract does not militate against the provisions of the Arbitration Act 1940, nothing in law prevents the arbitration agreement between the parties being given effect to in full.[114]

Incorporation of ICA Rules (Rules of Council of Arbitration) in arbitration agreement—Parties can retain power to appoint arbitrator

In *C.M.C. Ltd.* v. *Unit Trust of India*[115], arbitration clause provided thus:

> Each party shall appoint an arbitrator and the arbitrators so appointed shall appoint an umpire to whom the matter on which the arbitrators disagree will be refereed.... The arbitration proceedings shall be conducted in accordance with the Rules prescribed by the Indian Council of Arbitration.

It was held that the provision that the proceedings shall be conducted in accordance with the rules prescribed by the Indian Council of Arbitration does not, in any manner, militate against the retention of the power by the parties of appointing an arbitrator or constituting an Arbitral Tribunal. The parties are free to adopt a procedure for appointment of an arbitrator.[116]

Institutional arbitration—Non-mentioning of specific institution, inconsequential

What is required is to gather the intention of the parties as to whether they have agreed for resolution of disputes through arbitration. What is required to be decided in an application under Section 11 is whether there is an arbitration agreement as defined in the said Act. In *Nandan Biomatrix Ltd.* v. *D 1 Oils Ltd.*[117], the name of a specific institution was not indicated in the relevant clause of the supply agreement. However, the parties unequivocally agreed for resolution of disputes through an ad hoc arbitration. Therefore, there existed a valid arbitration agreement between the parties.

Survival of arbitration agreement clause after termination/discharge of main contract

It is well settled that even if an agreement ceases to exist, the arbitration clause remains in force and any dispute pertaining to the agreement ought

114. *C.M.C. Ltd.* v. *Unit Trust of India*, (2007) 10 SCC 751.
115. *Ibid.*
116. *Ibid.*
117. *Ibid.*

to be resolved according to the conditions mentioned in the arbitration clause.[118] Though the performance of charter party agreement had come to end but it was still in existence for some purposes, *viz.* the effect of vessel's non-delivery as per the prescribed mechanism and its continued use beyond the stipulated time and thus the arbitration clause in the said charter party agreement operated in respect of these and other allied purposes. The court held, notwithstanding the expiry of the period fixed in the time charter party, the said charter party did not get extinguished, inter alia, for the purpose of determination of disputes arising thereunder and the arbitration clause contained therein could be invoked.[119]

In *Everest Holding Ltd.* v. *Shyam Kumar Shrivastava*[120], joint venture agreement (JVA) though was cancelled and terminated as alleged, but it was a valid JVA containing a valid arbitration agreement for settlement of disputes arising out of or in relation to the subject-matter of JVA. Respondents' plea that the disputes could not be referred to the arbitration as the agreement was not in existence as of today was held devoid of merit and rejected.

Doctrine of separability of the arbitration clause/agreement

It is well settled in arbitration jurisprudence that an arbitration agreement is a distinct and separate agreement, which is independent from the substantive commercial contract in which it is embedded. This is based on the premise that when parties enter into a commercial contract containing an arbitration clause, they are entering into two separate agreements, *viz.*: (*i*) the substantive contract which contains the rights and obligations of the parties arising from the commercial transaction; and (*ii*) the arbitration agreement which contains the binding obligation of the parties to resolve their disputes through the mode of arbitration. The autonomy of the arbitration agreement is based on the twin concepts of separability and kompetenz-kompetenz. The doctrines of separability and kompetenz-kompetenz though inter-related, are distinct, and play an important role in promoting the autonomy of the arbitral process. The doctrine of separability of the arbitration agreement connotes that the invalidity, ineffectiveness or termination of the substantive commercial contract, would not affect the validity of the arbitration agreement, except if the arbitration agreement itself is directly impeached on the ground that the arbitration agreement is void ab initio.[121]

118. *N. Srinivasa* v. *Kuttukaran Machine Tools Ltd.*, (2009) 5 SCC 182; *Bharat Petroleum Corpn. Ltd.* v. *Great Eastern Shipping Co. Ltd.*, (2008) 1 SCC 503.
119. *Bharat Petroleum Corpn. Ltd.* v. *Great Eastern Shipping Co. Ltd.*, (2008) 1 SCC 503.
120. (2008) 16 SCC 774.
121. *N.N. Global Mercantile (P) Ltd.* v. *Indo Unique Flame Ltd.*, (2021) 4 SCC 379.

The concept of separability or severability of an arbitration agreement from the underlying contract is a legal fiction which acknowledges the separate nature of the arbitration agreement. The separate nature of the arbitration agreement from the underlying contract is one of the corner-stones of arbitration law.[122]

Arbitration agreement in purchase order—Invoices for supplies—Relevancy

In *Groupe Chimique Tunisien SA* v. *Southern Petrochemicals Industries Corpn. Ltd.*[123], the purchase orders placed by the respondents with the petitioner were the contract between the parties and they were subject to Fertilizer Association of India Terms and Conditions For Sale and Purchase of Phosphonic Acid (FAI terms), which contained an arbitration clause. Section 7(5), Arbitration and Conciliation Act, 1996 specifically provides that where there is a reference in a contract (in this case, the purchase order) to a document containing an arbitration clause (in this case, FAI terms) such reference constitutes an arbitration agreement, if the contract is in writing and the reference is such as to make that arbitration clause a part of the contract. This case fell under Section 7(5) of the Act and there was an arbitration clause between the parties as per clause 15 of FAI terms. The respondent contended that in the invoices for the supplies there was no reference to FAI terms or arbitration agreement, and therefore, the disputes were not arbitrable. The court held, the purchase orders were the contracts. Invoice is a document which is prepared with reference to the supplies made under the contract. Where the contract (purchase order) incorporates an arbitration agreement by reference, the invoice need not contain a provision for arbitration. There was an arbitration clause as per FAI terms.

Purchase order though contained an arbitration clause would not constitute an arbitration agreement as it was not signed by both the parties. Application for referring the parties to arbitration by virtue of purchase order was dismissed.[124] In *N.E.P.C. India Ltd.* v. *S. Gopakumar, Proprietor, Cape Electric Corpn.*[125], there was no contract in writing and consequently there cannot be any reference with regard to the clause contained in the purchase order in the contract. It cannot be presumed that the respondent accepted the said clause of the contract in writing, signed by the parties.

122. *Interplay between Arbitration Agreements under the Arbitration and Conciliation Act, 1996 and the Indian Stamp Act, 1899, re*, 2023 SCC OnLine SC 1666.
123. (2006) 5 SCC 275.
124. *Saagrr Infra Ltd.* v. *Pioneer Tools & Hardware*, 2012 SCC OnLine Mad 3997: (2012) 6 CTC 282.
125. 2009 SCC OnLine Mad 361: (2009) 1 LW 896.

Order of the court below rejecting the request of the respondent to refer the matter to arbitration was just.

Work order

In *Telecommunications Consultants India Ltd.* v. *K.S. Nair*[126], in the subsequent work order between the parties, there was a specific clause that the standard documents referred to in the earlier work order between the parties would be deemed to form and be read and construed as part of the latest work order/contract. The specific clause in the earlier agreement entered into between the parties would reveal that the standard documents referred to are the form of proposal, the specification, the drawings and the letter of acceptance. It was held, by virtue of an arbitration agreement contained in form of proposal, dispute between the parties out of the subsequent work order shall be resolved only through arbitration. Application for appointment of arbitrator was allowed.

Unless a special reference to the arbitration clause is mentioned in the bank guarantee, the same cannot be read into the bank guarantee and when there was no arbitration clause in the bank guarantee, the application under Section 9, Arbitration and Conciliation Act, 1996 was not maintainable.[127]

In *Sahyadri Earthmovers* v. *L and T Finance Ltd.*[128], the borrowers had nowhere denied the existence of such arbitration agreement to settle their dispute arising out of the same, therefore, also the guarantor just cannot take shelter of non-mentioning of specific arbitration clause in the deed of guarantee to say that there exists no specific arbitration agreement between the parties. There existed an arbitration clause in the agreement between the parties which covered to settle the dispute between the financier and the borrowers and the guarantors, as all these documents were interlinked and interconnected.

Standard form contracts—Arbitration agreement/clause

In *State of Orissa* v. *Bhagyadhar Dash*[129], clause 10 of the general conditions of contract empowered the Engineer-in-Charge to execute non-tendered additional items of work and if the contractor was not satisfied with the determination of rate of such work, the rate to be finally determined by the Superintending Engineer. It was held, it was not an arbitration clause. It did not provide for reference of disputes between the parties to arbitration. The

126. 2012 SCC OnLine Mad 978: (2012) 6 CTC 633.
127. *BEFESA AGUA* v. *IVRCL Infrastructure and Projects Ltd.*, 2013 SCC OnLine Mad 1167: (2013) 3 CTC 414.
128. 2012 SCC OnLine Bom 1861: (2013) 2 Mah LJ 302
129. (2011) 7 SCC 406.

said clause was intended to except such matters from the scope of arbitration prior to deletion of clause 23 (which hitherto was dealing with settlement of disputes by arbitration till 24 December 1981) from conditions of contract. Hence, after deletion of clause 23, clause 10 of the conditions was not an agreement.

Mere issuance of Letter of Intent (LoI)—Whether arbitration agreement comes into existence

A LoI merely indicates a party's intention to enter into a contract with the other party in future. A LoI is not intended to bind the either party ultimately to enter into a contract. It is a prelude to a contract. Clause C in the LoI provided that the purchase order shall be subject to the general conditions of purchase. The LoI provided that it would be followed by a detailed purchase order which had an arbitration clause. It was held, the general conditions of the contract which contained the arbitration clause were not made part of the LoI. The LoI was an order for supply. A mere LoI did not bring into existence an arbitration agreement. Tender document by itself is neither an agreement nor a contract.[130]

Incorporation of arbitration clause from another document, main contract [Sub-s. (5)]

Sub-section (5) of Section 7 provides that reference in a contract to a document containing an arbitration clause constitutes an arbitration agreement, if the contract is in writing and the reference is such as to make that arbitration clause part of the contract.

The wording of Section 7(5) of the Act makes it clear that a mere reference to a document would not have the effect of making an arbitration clause from that document, a part of the contract. There should be a special reference indicating a mutual intention to incorporate the arbitration clause from another document into the contract. The exception to the requirement of special reference is where the referred document is not another contract, but a standard form of terms and conditions of trade transactions or regulatory institutions which publish or circulate such standard terms and conditions for the benefit of the members or others who want to adopt the same. Section 7(5) requires a conscious acceptance of the arbitration clause from another document, by the parties, as a part of their contract, before such arbitration clause could be read as a part of the contract between the parties. But the Act does not contain any indication or guidelines as to the conditions to be fulfilled before a reference to a document in a contract can

130. *Dresser Rand S.A.* v. *Bindal Agro Chem Ltd.*, (2006) 1 SCC 751.

be construed as a reference incorporating an arbitration clause contained in such document into the contract. In the absence of such statutory guidelines, the normal rules of construction of contracts will have to be followed.[131] Section 7(5) requires conscious acceptance of an arbitration clause from another document by parties as part of their contract before such arbitration clause could be read as part of their contract.[132]

In *M.R. Engineers & Contractors (P) Ltd.* v. *Som Datt Builders Ltd.*[133], wordings in the sub-contract "it shall be carried out on terms and conditions as applicable to the main contract" disclosed only intention to adopt only terms and conditions in main contract relating to execution of work and not other parts thereof. The arbitration clause in the main contract could not be said to have formed part of the sub-contract between the parties. It was held, the arbitration clause in the main contract did not apply to the disputes arising with reference to the sub-contract.

Reference in contract to document containing arbitration clause constitutes an arbitration agreement if the arbitration clause is part of contract.[134]

In *Premlaxmi and Co.* v. *Trafalgar House Construction India Ltd.*[135], the language of the letter dated 19 September 1995 provided that all the terms and conditions of contract (except those specifically excluded) of Tata Electric Company's tender documents were made applicable on a back to back basis. The tender document was sent as Annexure "A" along with the letter. The annexure made a mention in condition 23 as follows:

> In case any dispute or difference shall arise between the OWNER or the Engineer on his behalf and the contractor touching or concerning this contract or the construction, meaning, operation or effect thereof or of any clause herein contained or as to the rights, duties or liabilities of the parties hereto respectively or of the ENGINEER under or by virtue of these presents or otherwise or touching the subject-matter of these presents or arising out of or in relation thereto (except as to matter left to the sole discretion of the ENGINEER) the same shall be referred to the arbitration of a single arbitrator in case the parties can agree upon one, otherwise, to two arbitrators, one to be appointed by each party and an umpire to be appointed by the two arbitrators before entering upon the references and in either case in accordance with the subject to the provisions of the Indian Arbitration Act, 1940, or any statutory modification or re-enactment thereof for the time being in force.

---

131. *M.R. Engineers & Contractors (P) Ltd.* v. *Som Datt Builders Ltd.*, (2009) 7 SCC 696.
132. *Ibid.*
133. (2009) 7 SCC 696.
134. *Premlaxmi and Co.* v. *Trafalgar House Construction India Ltd.*, 1998 SCC OnLine Bom 398: (1998) 3 Mah LJ 695.
135. 1998 SCC OnLine Bom 398: (1998) 3 Mah LJ 695.

The court held that the intention of the parties was clear that arbitration clause would also be applicable.

Where general conditions of sale contain an arbitration clause, in terms of Section 7(5), it forms a valid arbitration agreement.[136]

Arbitration clause in standard form of contract—Incorporation by reference [Sub-s. (5)]

Section 7(5) provides that the reference in a contract to a document containing an arbitration clause constitutes an arbitration agreement if:

(*i*) the contract is in writing; and

(*ii*) the reference is such as to make that arbitration clause part of the contract.

A conscious acceptance of the arbitration clause found in another document is necessary for the purpose of incorporating into the contract.[137]

Section 7(5) of the Act stipulates that the reference in a contract to a document containing an arbitration clause constitutes an arbitration agreement if the contract is in writing and the reference is such as to make that arbitration clause part of the contract.[138]

An arbitration clause in an earlier contract cannot be incorporated by a general reference. The exception to the rule is a reference to a standard form of contract by trade association or a professional institution in which case a general reference would be sufficient for incorporation of an arbitration clause.[139]

A general reference to a consensual standard form is sufficient for incorporation of an arbitration clause. In *Inox Wind Ltd.* v. *Thermocables Ltd.*[140], purchase order was issued by the appellant in which it was clearly mentioned that supply would be as per terms mentioned therein and in the attached standard terms and conditions. The respondent by his letter confirmed its acceptance of the terms and conditions mentioned in the purchase order except delivery period. Dispute between the parties arose after the delivery of the goods. There was nothing on the record to show that the standard form attached was of a trade association or a professional body. However, the respondent was aware of the standard terms and conditions which were

---

136. *Shiv Om Polynets (P) Ltd.* v. *Marine Fabrics*, 2013 SCC OnLine Cal 1070: (2013) 1 Cal LT 592.
137. *MMTC Ltd.* v. *Sterlite Industries (India) Ltd.*, (1996) 6 SCC 716; *Inox Wind Ltd.* v. *Thermocables Ltd.*, (2018) 2 SCC 519.
138. *Shinhan Bank* v. *Carol Info Services Ltd.*, 2023 SCC OnLine SC 303.
139. *Inox Wind Ltd.* v. *Thermocables Ltd.*, (2018) 2 SCC 519.
140. *Ibid.*

attached to the purchase order. The purchase order was a single contract and the general reference to the standard form even if it was not by a trade association or a professional body was sufficient for the incorporation of the arbitration clause.

A general reference to another contract will not be sufficient to incorporate the arbitration clause from the referred contract into the contract under consideration. There should be a special reference indicating a mutual intention to incorporate the arbitration clause from another document into a contract. The exception to the requirement of special reference is where the referred document is not another contract but a standard form of terms and conditions of trade associations or regulatory institutions which publish or circulate such standard terms and conditions for the benefit of others who want to adopt the same.[141]

In *Duro Felguera, S.A.* v. *Gangavaram Port Ltd.*[142], in the MOU, original Package No. 4 of tender document was referred only to have more clarity on technical and execution related matters. It was held, such general reference to original Package No. 4 of tender document was not sufficient to hold that arbitration clause in the original Package No. 4 of tender document was incorporated in the MOU.

The wordings of Section 7(5) make it clear that a mere reference to a document would not have the effect of making an arbitration clause from that document a part of the contract. The reference to the document in the contract should be such that it shows the intention to incorporate the arbitration clause contained in the document into the contract. If the intention of the legislature was to import an arbitration clause from another document, merely on reference to such document in the contract, sub-section (5) would not contain the latter part which reads "and the reference is such as to make that arbitration clause part of the contract". In *Elite Engg. & Construction (Hyd.) (P) Ltd.* v. *Techtrans Construction India (P) Ltd.*[143], agreement between the appellant and the respondent did not contain an arbitration clause, however, clause 2 of the agreement provided that conditions relating to works and quality specified in the agreement between the construction-contractor and employer would be binding on the sub-contractor/appellant and clause 9.10 provided that terms and conditions of agreement between contractor and employer will be applicable for items not mentioned in agreement clauses. It was held, arbitration clause was not intended to be made as part of the contract between the appellant and

141. *Duro Felguera, S.A.* v. *Gangavaram Port Ltd.*, (2017) 9 SCC 729.
142. *Ibid.*
143. (2018) 4 SCC 281.

the respondent. Appellant's petition under Section 11 for appointment of arbitrator was dismissed.

Even number of arbitrators mentioned in arbitration agreement

There is nothing in Section 7 to indicate the requirement of the number of arbitrators as part of the arbitration agreement. Thus, the validity of the arbitration agreement does not depend on the number of arbitrators specified therein. The number of arbitrators is dealt with separately in Section 10 which is a part of machinery provision for working of the arbitration agreement. Therefore, an arbitration agreement specifying an even number of arbitrators cannot render an arbitration agreement invalid.[144] In *MMTC Ltd.* v. *Sterlite Industries (India) Ltd.*[145], arbitration clause provided that each party shall nominate one arbitrator and the two arbitrators shall then appoint an umpire before proceeding with the reference. It was held, the arbitration agreement was valid as it satisfied the requirement of Section 7 of the Act.

Nomination of arbitrator amounts to appointment

Nomination virtually amounts to selection/appointment of arbitrator.[146]

Arbitration agreement, when not disputed

A party which has not disputed the arbitration clause is normally bound by it and is obliged to comply with the procedure laid down under it. Such a procedure must be given due importance by the court as being part of the terms of the contract of arbitration.[147]

Government contract with supplier—Compliance of Article 299 of the Constitution

In *State of U.P.* v. *Combined Chemicals Co. (P) Ltd.*[148], the Director of Industries had invited tender for supply of certain goods. In pursuance thereof he on behalf of the Governor, accepted respondent's bid subject to terms and conditions in acceptance letter itself, tender form and agreement. The terms and conditions postulated execution of formal agreement only if required. The respondent had completed all the formalities, had deposited the securities and dispatched a duly signed agreement to the Director of

144. *MMTC Ltd.* v. *Sterlite Industries (India) Ltd.*, (1996) 6 SCC 716.
145. *Ibid.*
146. *Datar Switchgears Ltd.* v. *Tata Finance Ltd.*, (2000) 8 SCC 151.
147. *Ibid.*
148. (2011) 2 SCC 151.

Agriculture. The Director of Agriculture did not sign the formal agreement sent by the respondent. There was substantial compliance with Article 299 of the Constitution and contract stood executed between the government and the supplier and absence of formal agreement could not negate the same. Terms and conditions in the tender form were treated as part of the contract, the supplier was held entitled to invoke the arbitration clause contained therein for the breach of the contract by the department concerned.

Amalgamation of company—Successor company held bound by arbitration clause

In *Geo-Group Communications Inc.* v. *IOL Broadband Ltd.*[149], the respondent-company was the successor-in-interest of company *E*. After the amalgamation of company *E* with the respondent-company, all the rights and obligations of company *E* including those mentioned in share subscription and Shareholder Agreement (SHA) stood transferred in law to the respondent-company. Scheme of amalgamation inter alia specifically provided that the respondent-company will be bound by all the obligations and liabilities of any nature of company *E*. It was held that the successor company was bound by the arbitration clause.

Absence of arbitration agreement—Arbitration not possible

Reference to arbitration under Section 7, Arbitration and Conciliation Act, 1996 is not possible in the absence of arbitration agreement.[150]

Arbitration agreement—Existence of—Burden of proof

Burden of proof lies on the party alleging the existence of an arbitration agreement.[151]

The burden to prove that a valid contract containing an arbitration clause existed, first rested on the applicant who moved the Supreme Court for the appointment of the arbitrator. By producing the faxed charter party agreement (which contained an arbitration clause) which on its face appeared genuine and legitimate, the applicant had discharged its initial burden. The onus, thereafter, had shifted on the respondent to prove that the said agreement was forged.[152]

---

149. (2010) 1 SCC 562.
150. *M.P. Rural Road Development Authority* v. *L.G. Chaudhary Engineers & Contractors*, (2012) 3 SCC 495; *Kvaerner Cementation India Ltd.* v. *Bajranglal Agarwal*, (2012) 5 SCC 214.
151. *Subhash Projects and Mktg. Ltd.* v. *Assam Urban Water Supply and Sewerage Board*, 2019 SCC OnLine Gau 3510: (2019) 5 Gau LR 625.
152. *Great Offshore Ltd.* v. *Iranian Offshore Engg. & Construction Co.*, (2008) 14 SCC 240.

Termination of contract—Subsistence of arbitration clause

An arbitration clause is a collateral term in the contract, which relates to resolution of disputes, and not performance. Even if the performance of the contract comes to an end on account of repudiation, frustration or breach of contract, the arbitration clause would survive for the purpose of resolution of disputes arising under or in connection with the contract. The position has been statutorily recognised in Section 16(1) which inter alia provides that an arbitration clause which forms part of the contract, has to be treated as an agreement independent of the other parts of the contract and a decision that a contract is null and void shall not *ipso jure* the invalidity of the arbitration clause.[153]

Agreement completing its tenure

Where the agreement has completed its full tenure, it automatically ceases to be operative, an arbitrator cannot be appointed.[154]

Arbitration agreement by unregistered/non-existing company—Invalid

Section 7 defines an arbitration agreement as an agreement by parties to submit to arbitration. The word "party" is defined in Section 2(1)(*h*) of the Act as a party to an arbitration agreement. An agreement enforceable by law is a contract. An agreement has to be between two or more persons. Therefore, if one of the parties was not in existence when the contract was made, then there was no contract and if there was no contract, there is no question of a clause in such a contract being an arbitration agreement between the parties.[155] When one of the parties to the lease agreement and management agreement was a non-existent imaginary party, there was no contract. This clearly showed that there was no valid arbitration agreement between the parties which could be enforced.[156] Two agreements containing arbitration clauses, in *A.P. Tourism Development Corpn. Ltd.* v. *Pampa Hotels Ltd.*[157], were signed on 30 March 2000 by the Chairman of the appellant and Managing Director of the respondent. The certificate of registration issued by the Registrar of Companies showed that the date of incorporation of the respondent was 9 April 2003. A certificate under Section

153. *National Agricultural Coop. Mktg. Federation India Ltd.* v. *Gains Trading Ltd.*, (2007) 5 SCC 692.
154. *Rajib Basu Ray* v. *Carlsberg India (P) Ltd.*, 2016 SCC OnLine Cal 5725: (2017) 1 Cal LJ 65.
155. *A.P. Tourism Development Corpn. Ltd.* v. *Pampa Hotels Ltd.*, (2010) 5 SCC 425.
156. *Ibid.*
157. (2010) 5 SCC 425.

149(3), Companies Act, 1956 was issued by the Registrar of Companies only on 6 June 2003 certifying that the respondent was entitled to commence business. It was thus clear that the respondent in the application under Section 11 was non-existent on 30 February 2002 when the arbitration agreement was entered into. The arbitration agreement was held not enforceable. Application filed under Section 11 for appointment of arbitrator was rejected.

Unregistered arbitration agreement—Arbitrator not appointed

Main agreement between parties contained an arbitration clause, though being a compulsory registrable document, was not registered. Arbitration agreement being unregistered cannot be acted upon. No arbitrator can be appointed on the basis of such arbitration agreement. The applicant was directed to file a fresh application for appointment of arbitrator after payment of requisite stamp duty.[158]

Arbitration agreement—Group of Companies—Non-signatory company, if can be bound

A non-signatory can be bound by an arbitration agreement based on the doctrine of a group of companies where the conduct of the parties evidences a clear intention of the parties to bind both the signatory as well as the non-signatory parties. Courts and Tribunals have invoked the doctrine of "group of companies" to join a non-signatory member of the group, if they are satisfied that the non-signatory company was by reference to the common intention of the parties, a necessary party to the contract. Where an arbitration agreement is entered into by one of the companies in the group, the non-signatory affiliate or sister or parent concern is held to be bound by the arbitration agreement, provided that the facts and circumstances of the case demonstrate that it was the mutual intention of all parties to bind both the signatories and the non-signatory affiliates in the group. The doctrine provides that a non-signatory may be bound by an arbitration agreement where the parent or holding company, or a member of the group of companies is a signatory to the arbitration agreement and the non-signatory entity on the group has been engaged in the negotiation or performance of the commercial contract, or made statements indicating its intention to be bound by the contract, the non-signatory will also be bound and benefitted by the relevant contracts.[159]

---

158. *Ansal Properties & Infrastructure Ltd.* v. *Jhamru Chandaram*, 2016 SCC OnLine Raj 10748: (2017) 2 WLC 485; *Bvm Projects (P) Ltd.* v. *Ghanshyam Singhal*, 2016 SCC OnLine Raj 10674: (2017) 1 WLC 343.

159. *Esha Kedia* v. *Milan R. Parekh*, (2022) 6 HCC (Del) 184.

A party, which is not a signatory to a contract containing an arbitration clause, may be bound by the agreement to arbitrate if it is an alter ego of a party which executed the agreement. This constitutes a departure from the ordinary principle of contract law that every company in a group of companies is a distinct legal entity. A non-signatory may be bound by the arbitration agreement where 1) there exists a group of companies, and 2) parties have engaged in conduct or made statements indicating an intention to bind a non-signatory.[160]

To apply the group of companies doctrine, the courts or tribunals, as the case may be, have to consider all the cumulative factors laid down in *ONGC Ltd.* v. *Discovery Enterprises (P) Ltd.*[161] Resultantly, the principle of single economic unit cannot be the sole basis for invoking the group of companies doctrine.[162]

Two-tier arbitration procedure

Where the clause in the arbitration agreement provides for domestic arbitration and thereafter prefers an international forum, it is not contrary to public policy. Settlement of disputes through a two tier arbitration procedure is permissible under the laws of India, does not violate the fundamental or public policy of India.[163]

A contract providing for a two-tiered reference clearly mentioned that parties would be bound by Uniform Almond Export Contract Terms and Conditions, which in turn contained an arbitration agreement. Held, the two-tiered reference does not qualify as an "arbitration agreement".[164]

Arbitrable matters

All disputes relating to rights *in personam* are arbitrable, therefore, the choice is given to the parties to choose this alternative forum. A claim of money by a bank or a financial institution cannot be treated as right *in rem* which is not arbitrable.[165]

---

160. *ONGC Ltd.* v. *Discovery Enterprises (P) Ltd.*, (2022) 8 SCC 42. See also, *Cox & Kings Ltd.* v. *SAP India (P) Ltd.*, (2024) 4 SCC 1.
161. (2022) 8 SCC 42.
162. *Cox & Kings Ltd.* v. *SAP India (P) Ltd.*, (2024) 4 SCC 1.
163. *Centrotrade Minerals & Metal Inc.* v. *Hindustan Copper Ltd.*, (2017) 2 SCC 228.
164. *Campos Bros. Farms* v. *Matru Bhumi Supply Chain (P) Ltd.*, 2019 SCC OnLine Del 8350: (2019) 261 DLT 201.
165. *M.D. Frozen Foods Exports (P) Ltd.* v. *Hero Fincorp Ltd.*, (2017) 16 SCC 741.

Excepted matters

Parties can provide in an arbitration clause for "excepted matters", *i.e.* a specific matter to be excluded from the purview of the arbitration clause. In respect of such "excepted matters", the Arbitral Tribunal would have no jurisdiction to decide. The issue of non-arbitrability of the dispute can be considered by the court at the stage of deciding a Section 11 application, if the facts are very clear and glaring, and in view of the specific clauses of the agreement. Upon conducting preliminary inquiry, if it is found that the dispute is in respect of the "excepted matters", the matter cannot be referred to arbitration. The court has to examine and record a prima facie finding as to whether there is an arbitration clause or not and whether the disputes which are sought to be referred to arbitration are covered by an arbitration agreement or not.[166]

Parties to the contract may agree to the exclusion of certain matters from the purview of the arbitration.[167]

Additional work

Original contract provided for certain work and additional work was entrusted to such a contractor. It was held, additional work is only contingent work in the original contract and the arbitration clause contained in the original contract would be applicable for additional work also. Award passed by the arbitrator in favour of the contractor in respect of the additional work done was upheld.[168]

Requirement of security in arbitration clause

In *S.K. Jain* v. *State of Haryana*[169], a government contract arbitration clause postulated that the contractor could not invoke arbitration without furnishing security at the rates specified in the contract, though no such restriction was imposed on the government. It was held that the restriction was valid.

Condition in arbitration clause mandating pre-deposit of 10 per cent of the amount claimed, arbitrary

A condition in arbitration clause mandating pre-deposit of 10 per cent of amount claimed in order to avoid frivolous claims by party invoking

---

166. *Sorin Group Italia S.R.L.* v. *Neeraj Garg*, (2022) 6 HCC (Del) 395.
167. *Indian Oil Corpn. Ltd.* v. *NCC Ltd.*, (2023) 2 SCC 539.
168. *PWD* v. *Chandragiri Construction* Co., 2011 SCC OnLine Mad 343: (2011) 2 CTC 669.
169. (2009) 4 SCC 357.

arbitration is arbitrary, being not only excessive or disproportionate but leading to wholly unjust result. Said condition struck down.[170]

Arbitration clause in arbitration agreement—Criminal proceedings are not barred

In case of breach of agreement in relation to commercial transaction, the presence of an arbitration clause in the agreement is no bar to criminal prosecution against the party concerned if any such breach constitutes a criminal offence, even prima facie.[171]

Trust deed

Settler had executed a trust deed in favour of the beneficiaries, the deed was signed by the settler alone. Beneficiaries cannot be regarded as party to the deed. The court held, trust deed including the arbitration clause does not satisfy the requirements of Section 2(1)(*b*) and 2(1)(*h*) read with Section 7, Arbitration and Conciliation Act, 1996, hence, trust deed cannot be construed as an "arbitration agreement" within the meaning of Section 7, Arbitration and Conciliation Act, 1996. Application of the respondent filed under Section 11 for appointment of the arbitrator was dismissed.[172]

M.P. Madhyastham Adhikaran Adhiniyam, 1983

A clause dealing with claims relating to questions arising during the execution of a contract is not a clause for arbitration. When a clause in a contract between the appellant-State and respondent-contractor provided for decision by the Superintending Engineer and reference to Chief Engineer on questions relating to specifications designs, etc. and respondent invoked the jurisdiction of the two authorities under the said clause and later being aggrieved by their decision sought arbitration under Section 7, M.P. Madhyastham Adhikaran Adhiniyam, 1983, precluded from seeking arbitration under that Act. Dismissal of the appellant's revision by the High Court was held proper.[173]

Industrial Disputes Act, 1947 [S. 2(*p*)]

Settlement entered into by the parties in respect of dispute between them under Section 2(*p*), Industrial Disputes Act is not an arbitration agreement

---

170. *ICOMM Tele Ltd.* v. *Punjab State Water Supply & Sewerage Board*, (2019) 4 SCC 401; *Lombardi Engg. Ltd.* v. *Uttarakhand Jal Vidyut Nigam Ltd.*, (2024) 4 SCC 341.
171. *S.W. Palanitkar* v. *State of Bihar*, (2002) 1 SCC 241.
172. *Vimal Kishor Shah* v. *Jayesh Dinesh Shah*, (2016) 8 SCC 788.
173. *State of M.P.* v. *K.K. Shukla and Co.*, (2001) 10 SCC 194.

under Section 7, Arbitration and Conciliation Act as there was no legal relationship, either contractual or otherwise, between the parties prior to arising of dispute.[174]

Indian Motion Picture Producers' Association (IMPPA)

Articles of association of IMPPA providing for resolution of the disputes between its members by way of arbitration, constitutes the arbitration clause.[175]

Assignability of arbitration clause

An arbitration clause in its very nature is assignable. If a contract is otherwise assignable, arbitration clause will not make it non-assignable.[176] In the absence of a specific bar in an agreement, assignee can invoke an arbitration clause in an agreement between the assignor and borrower.[177]

Review

In the absence of any arbitration agreement between the parties, the whole proceedings of arbitration, the award passed by the arbitrator and the order upholding the award are liable to be set aside. Review petition was allowed.[178]

Real Estate (Regulation and Development) Act, 2016 (16 of 2016)

The petitioner firm had entered into agreement with the contractor for development and construction of property. There was an arbitration clause. The Arbitration and Conciliation Act, 1996, however, cannot be said to be inconsistent with provisions of RERA Act, more so when the contractor himself disputes its applicability for want of jurisdictional issue. It cannot be said that the firm's right to seek arbitration is foreclosed in light of the RERA Act.[179]

---

174. *Sant Nilobarai Transport (P) Ltd.* v. *Ganesh Container Movers Syndicate*, 1999 SCC OnLine Bom 388: (1999) 3 Mah LJ 216.
175. *Gaurang* v. *Vinay A. Choksi*, 2014 SCC OnLine Bom 1139: (2014) 6 Mah LJ 570.
176. *Wescare (I) Ltd.* v. *Subuthi Finance Ltd.*, 2008 SCC OnLine Mad 539: (2008) 4 CTC 561.
177. *Kogta Financial India Ltd.* v. *Jayesh Kishorlal Dawda*, 2011 SCC OnLine Mad 777: (2011) 6 CTC 182.
178. *State of M.P.* v. *Dewas Udyog*, 2011 SCC OnLine MP 1182: (2012) 1 MP LJ 269.
179. *Bihar Home Developers and Builders* v. *Narendra Prasad Gupta*, 2021 SCC OnLine Pat 1355: (2021) 3 PLJR 385.

POWER TO REFER PARTIES TO ARBITRATION WHERE THERE IS AN ARBITRATION AGREEMENT [S. 8]

8. *Power to refer parties to arbitration where there is an arbitration agreement.*—[180][(1) A judicial authority, before which an action is brought in a matter which is the subject of an arbitration agreement shall, if a party to the arbitration agreement or any person claiming through or under him, so applies not later than the date of submitting his first statement on the substance of the dispute, then, notwithstanding any judgment, decree or order of the Supreme Court or any court, refer the parties to arbitration unless it finds that prima facie no valid arbitration agreement exists.]

(2) The application referred to in sub-section (1) shall not be entertained unless it is accompanied by the original arbitration agreement or a duly certified copy thereof.

[181][Provided that where the original arbitration agreement or a certified copy thereof is not available with the party applying for reference to arbitration under sub-section (1), and the said agreement or certified copy is retained by the other party to that agreement, then, the party so applying shall file such application along with a copy of the arbitration agreement and a petition praying the court to call upon the other party to produce the original arbitration agreement or its duly certified copy before that court.]

(3) Notwithstanding that an application has been made under sub-section (1) and that the issue is pending before the judicial authority, an arbitration may be commenced or continued and an arbitral award made.

STATE AMENDMENTS

Union Territory of Jammu and Kashmir.—In its application to the Union Territory of Jammu and Kashmir, after Section 8, *insert* the following sections, namely:—

Sections 8-A and 8-B

"**8-A.** *Power of the court, seized of petitions under Sections 9 or 11 of the Act, to refer the dispute to Mediation or Conciliation.*—(1) If during the pendency of petitions under Sections 9 or 11 of the Act, it appears to the court, that there exists elements of a settlement which may be acceptable to the parties, the court may, with the consent of parties, refer the parties, for resolution of their disputes, to,—

(*a*) mediation; or

(*b*) conciliation.

---

180. *Subs.* by Act 3 of 2016, S. 4(*i*) (w.r.e.f. 23-10-2015). Prior to substitution it read as:

"(1) A judicial authority before which an action is brought in a matter which is the subject of an arbitration agreement shall, if a party so applies not later than when submitting his first statement on the substance of the dispute, refer the parties to arbitration."

181. *Ins.* by Act 3 of 2016, S. 4(*ii*) (w.r.e.f. 23-10-2015).

(2) The procedure for reference of a dispute to mediation is as under—

(*a*) where a dispute has been referred for resolution by recourse to mediation, the procedure framed under that Act shall apply;

(*b*) in case of a successful resolution of the dispute, the Mediator shall immediately forward the mediated settlement to the referral court;

(*c*) on receipt of the mediated settlement, the referral court shall independently apply its judicial mind and record a satisfaction that the mediated settlement is genuine, lawful, voluntary, entered into without coercion, undue influence, fraud or misrepresentation and that there is no other legal impediment in accepting the same;

(*d*) the court shall record a statement on oath of the parties, or their authorised representatives, affirming the mediated settlement as well as a clear undertaking of the parties to abide by the terms of the settlement;

(*e*) if satisfied, the court shall pass an order in terms of the settlement;

(*f*) if the main petition, in which the reference was made is pending, it shall be disposed of by the referral court in terms thereof;

(*g*) if the main petition, in which the reference was made stands disposed of, the mediated settlement and the matter shall be listed before the referral court, which shall pass orders in accordance with clauses (*iii*), (*iv*) and (*v*);

(*h*) such a mediated settlement, shall have the same status and effect as an arbitral award and may be enforced in the manner specified under Section 36 of the Act.

(3) With respect to reference of a dispute to conciliation, the provisions of Part II of this Act shall apply as if the conciliation proceedings were initiated by the parties under the relevant provision of this Act.

8-B. *Power of the court, seized of matters under Sections 34 or 37 of the Act, to refer the dispute to Mediation or Conciliation.*—(1) If during the pendency of a petition under Section 34 or an appeal under Section 37 of the Act, it appears to the court, that there exists elements of a settlement which may be acceptable to the parties, the court may, with the consent of parties, refer the parties, for resolution of their disputes, to:—

(*a*) mediation; or

(*b*) conciliation.

(2) The procedure for reference of a dispute to mediation is as under:—

(*a*) where a dispute has been referred for resolution by recourse to mediation, the procedure framed under the Act shall apply;

(*b*) in case of a successful resolution of the dispute, the Mediator shall immediately forward the mediated settlement to the referral court;

(*c*) on receipt of the mediated settlement, the referral court shall independently apply its judicial mind and record a satisfaction that the mediated settlement is genuine, lawful, voluntary, entered into without coercion, undue influence, fraud or misrepresentation and that there is no other legal impediment in accepting the same;

(*d*) the court shall record a statement on oath of the parties, or their authorized representatives, affirming the mediated settlement, a clear undertaking of the parties to abide by the terms of the settlement as well as statement to the above effect;

(*e*) if satisfied, the court shall pass an order in terms of the settlement;

(*f*) if the main petition, in which the reference was made is pending, it shall be disposed of by the referral court in terms thereof;

(*g*) if the main petition, in which the reference was made stands disposed of, the mediated settlement and the matter shall be listed before the referral court, which shall pass orders in accordance with clauses (*iii*), (*iv*) and (*v*);

(*h*) such a mediated settlement, shall have the status of a modified arbitral award and may be enforced in the manner specified under Section 36 of the Act.

(3) With respect to reference of a dispute to conciliation, the provisions of Part III of the Act, shall apply as if the conciliation proceedings were initiated by the parties under the relevant provision of this Act." [*Vide* S.O. 1123(E), dated 18-3-2020 (w.e.f. 18-3-2020)].

Union Territory of Ladakh.—In its application to the Union Territory of Ladakh, after Section 8, *insert*,—

"**8-A.** *Power of Court, seized of petition under Section 9 or Section 11 to refer dispute to mediation or conciliation.*—(1) If during the pendency of petition under Section 9 or 11, it appears to the Court, that there exists elements of a settlement which may be acceptable to the parties, the Court may, with the consent of parties, refer the parties, for resolution of their disputes, to,—

(*a*) mediation; or

(*b*) conciliation.

(2) The procedure for reference of a dispute to mediation shall be as under:—

(*a*) where a dispute has been referred for resolution by recourse to mediation, the procedure framed under this Act shall apply;

(*b*) in case of a successful resolution of the dispute, the Mediator shall immediately forward the mediated settlement to the referral court;

(*c*) on receipt of the mediated settlement, the referral court shall independently apply its judicial mind and record a satisfaction that the mediated settlement is genuine, lawful, voluntary, entered into without coercion, undue influence, fraud or misrepresentation and that there is no other legal impediment in accepting the same;

(*d*) the Court shall record a statement on oath of the parties, or their authorised representatives, affirming the mediated settlement as well as a clear undertaking of the parties to abide by the terms of the settlement;

(*e*) if satisfied, the Court shall pass an order in terms of the settlement;

(*f*) if the main petition, in which the reference was made is pending, it shall be disposed of by the referral Court in terms thereof;

(*g*) if the main petition, in which the reference was made stands disposed of, the mediated settlement and the matter shall be listed before the referral Court, which shall pass orders in accordance with clauses (*c*), (*d*) and (*e*); and

(*h*) such a mediated settlement, shall have the same status and effect as an arbitral award and may be enforced in the manner specified under Section 36.

(3) With respect to reference of a dispute to conciliation, the provisions of Part II of this Act shall apply as if the conciliation proceedings were initiated by the parties under the relevant provision of this Act.

8-B. *Power of Court, seized of matters under Section 34 or Section 37, to refer dispute to mediation or conciliation.*—(1) If during the pendency of a petition under Section 34 or an appeal under section 37, it appears to the Court, that there exist elements of a settlement which may be acceptable to the parties, the court may, with the consent of parties, refer the parties, for resolution of their disputes, to—

(*a*) mediation; or

(*b*) conciliation. (2) The procedure for reference of a dispute to mediation shall be as under:—

(*a*) where a dispute has been referred for resolution by recourse to mediation, the procedure framed under this Act shall apply;

(*b*) in case of a successful resolution of the dispute, the Mediator shall immediately forward the mediated settlement to the referral Court;

(*c*) on receipt of the mediated settlement, the referral Court shall independently apply its judicial mind and record a satisfaction that the mediated settlement is genuine, lawful, voluntary, entered into without coercion, undue influence, fraud or misrepresentation and that there is no other legal impediment in accepting the same;

(*d*) the Court shall record a statement on oath of the parties, or their authorised representatives, affirming the mediated settlement as well as a clear undertaking of the parties to abide by the terms of the settlement;

(*e*) if satisfied, the Court shall pass an order in terms of the settlement;

(*f*) if the main petition, in which the reference was made is pending, it shall be disposed of by the referral Court in terms thereof;

(*g*) if the main petition, in which the reference was made stands disposed of, the mediated settlement and the matter shall be listed before the referral Court, which shall pass orders in accordance with clauses (*c*), (*d*) and (*e*);

(*h*) such a mediated settlement, shall have the status of a modified arbitral award and may be enforced in the manner specified under Section 36.

(3) With respect to reference of a dispute to conciliation, the provisions of Part III of this Act, shall apply as if the conciliation proceedings were initiated by the parties under the relevant provision of this Act." [*Vide* S.O. 3774(E), dated 23-10-2020].

COMMENTS

Corresponding old law

Section 8(1) corresponds to Section 34, Arbitration Act, 1940. Section 34 of the 1940 Act read as under:

34. *Power to stay legal proceedings where there is an arbitration agreement.*—Where any party to an arbitration agreement or any person claiming under him commences any legal proceedings against any other party to the agreement or any person claiming under him in respect of any matter agreed to be referred, any party to such legal proceedings may at any time before filing a written statement or taking any other steps in the proceedings, apply to the judicial authority before which the proceedings are pending to stay the proceedings; and if satisfied that there is no sufficient reason why the matter should not be referred in accordance with the arbitration agreement and that the applicant was, at the time when the proceedings were commenced, and still remains, ready and willing to do all things necessary to the proper conduct of the arbitration, such authority may make an order staying the proceedings.

UNCITRAL Model Law

Article 8. *Arbitration agreement and substantive claim before court*

(1) A court before which an action is brought in a matter which is the subject of an arbitration agreement shall, if a party so requests not later than when submitting his first statement on the substance of the dispute, refer the parties to arbitration unless it finds that the agreement is null and void, inoperative or incapable of being performed.

(2) Where an action referred to in paragraph (1) of this article has been brought, arbitral proceedings may nevertheless be commenced or continued, and an award may be made, while the issue is pending before the court.

Legislative changes

Arbitration and Conciliation (Amendment) Act, 2015 (3 of 2016)

In Section 8 of the principal Act,—

(*i*) for sub-section (1), the following sub-section shall be *substituted*, namely—

"(1) A judicial authority, before which an action is brought in a matter which is the subject of an arbitration agreement shall, if a party to the arbitration agreement or any person claiming through or under him, so applies not later than the date of submitting his first statement on the substance of the dispute, then, notwithstanding any judgment, decree or order of the Supreme Court or any court, refer the parties to arbitration unless it finds that prima facie no valid arbitration agreement exists.";

(*ii*) in sub-section (2), the following proviso shall be *inserted*, namely—

"Provided that where the original arbitration agreement or a certified copy thereof is not available with the party applying for reference to arbitration under sub-section (1), and the said agreement or certified copy is retained by the other party to that agreement, then, the party so applying shall file such application along with a copy of the arbitration agreement and a petition praying the Court to call upon the other party to produce the original arbitration agreement or its duly certified copy before that Court.".

NOTES ON CLAUSES

Clause 4 of the Bill seeks to amend Section 8 of the principal Act to specify that the judicial authority shall refer the parties to arbitration unless it finds that prima facie no valid arbitration agreement exists. A proviso below sub-section (2) is inserted to provide that where the original arbitration agreement or certified copy is not available with the party applying under sub-section (1), and is retained by the other party, such a party shall file a copy of the arbitration agreement along with the application under sub-section (1) praying the court to call upon the other party to produce the original agreement or its duly certified copy before the court.

2015 Amendment

Four amendments have been made in Section 8 by the 2015 Amendment:

1. The relevant "party" that is entitled to apply seeking reference to arbitration has been clarified/amplified to include persons claiming "through or under" such a party to the arbitration agreement.
2. Scope of examination by the judicial authority is restricted to a finding whether "no valid arbitration exists" basis.
3. The cut off date by which an application under Section 8 is to be presented has been defined to mean "the date of" submitting the first statement on the substance of dispute.
4. The amendments are expressed to apply notwithstanding any prior judicial precedent.

New proviso to Section 8(2) has been added to allow a party that does not possess the original or certified copy of the arbitration agreement on account of it being retained by the other party, to nevertheless apply under Section 8 seeking reference, and call upon the other party to produce the same.[182]

Scope and applicability

Proceedings under Section 8 correspond to Section 34 of the 1940 Act.[183] Having regard to the provisions of Section 85 of the 1996 Act and the provisions of the General Clauses Act, the application filed under Section 8 in respect of a proceeding which had commenced before the 1996 Act came

182. *Ameet Lalchand Shah* v. *Rishabh Enterprises*, (2018) 15 SCC 678.
183. *Malaysian Airlines Systems-II* v. *Stic Travels (P) Ltd.*, (2001) 1 SCC 509.

into force, is maintainable.[184] Section 34 of 1940 Act enabled the court to grant stay of proceeding pending in civil court. Section 8 empowers civil court/other judicial authority to refer matters to arbitration. Object of the 1996 Act is to advance contractual consensus.[185]

Except Section 8, there is no other provision in the Act that in a pending suit, dispute is required to be referred to the arbitrator.[186]

The power of the court to refer the parties to arbitration is contained in Section 8 alone. Once Section 8(1) is held to be the source of power to pass such an order, it must follow that the application in which such an order is passed is under Section 8 in general and under sub-section (1) thereof in particular. It is immaterial under which an enactment suit is filed.[187]

After amendment of Section 8 by the 2016 Amendment, the court's enquiry is limited to see whether a valid arbitration agreement exists in a matter which is arbitrable.[188]

Rights of parties with regard to contract need not be considered now within the ambit of Section 8 of the 1996 Act.[189]

Section 8(1) says that the court shall refer parties to arbitration and has no discretion in that matter.[190]

Even if there is an arbitration agreement between the parties, and even if the dispute is covered by the arbitration agreement, the court where the civil suit is pending, will refuse an application under Section 8 of the Act, to refer the parties to arbitration, if the subject-matter of the suit is capable of adjudication only by a public forum or the relief claimed can only be granted by a special court or tribunal.[191]

For the interpretation of Section 8, Section 5 has no bearing.[192]

The 1996 Act is a comprehensive law enacted by the legislature which includes the entire field of arbitration including the foreign arbitration. Section 5 of the Act debars judicial intervention where the parties agreed to resolve the disputes through arbitration save and except, the scope and limitation as provided in the said Act itself. Section 8 has given a mandate

184. *TISCO Ltd.* v. *N.B. Exports*, 2003 SCC OnLine Kar 334: (2003) 4 Kant LJ 284.
185. *Wankanner Jain S.W.S.* v. *Jugal Kishore*, 2001 SCC OnLine Mad 528: (2001) 3 CTC 656.
186. *Sukanya Holdings (P) Ltd.* v. *Jayesh H. Pandya*, (2003) 5 SCC 531.
187. *Conros Steels (P) Ltd.* v. *Lu Qin (Hong Kong) Co. Ltd.*, 2014 SCC OnLine Bom 2305: (2015) 1 Mah LJ 434.
188. *Lindsay International (P) Ltd.* v. *Laxmi Niwas Mittal*, 2022 SCC OnLine Cal 171.
189. *Romola Bhattacharjee* v. *Twilight Properties (P) Ltd.*, 2012 SCC OnLine Cal 11925: (2013) 1 ICC 98.
190. *Sugaland Damani Finlease Ltd.* v. *P. Subramania Reddy*, (2000) 3 CTC 74.
191. *Mukesh Singh Tomar* v. *Rakesh*, 2012 SCC OnLine MP 9605: (2013) 1 MP LJ 233.
192. *Sukanya Holdings (P) Ltd.* v. *Jayesh H. Pandya*, (2003) 5 SCC 531.

to the judicial forum to refer the disputes pending before it to arbitration in case there had been an agreement to the said effect. Section 16 empowers the Arbitral Tribunal to decide its own jurisdiction if it is questioned by any party.[193]

Section 8 can be used only in furtherance of the arbitration agreement and not to resist the arbitral proceedings.[194]

The court must be competent to entertain the dispute in order to exercise jurisdiction under Section 8 of the Act. It must arrive at a finding that the subject-matter of the dispute is also covered by the arbitration agreement. Certified copy of the agreement must be placed before the court.[195]

Arbitration clause cannot be rejected merely on the ground that the parties mentioned the Arbitration Act of 1940.[196]

The language of Section 8 is peremptory in nature. Therefore, in cases where there is an arbitration clause in the agreement, it is obligatory for the court to refer the parties to arbitration in terms of their arbitration agreement and nothing remains to be decided in the original action after an application under Section 8 is made except to refer the dispute to an arbitrator. Clause of arbitration is applicable to oral agreement as well.[197]

The mere filing of an application under Section 8, Arbitration and Conciliation Act, 1996 would not confer jurisdiction on the court in which the application is filed over the arbitral proceedings and all applications arising out of the agreement. Section 8 applies to a judicial authority, which expression is of a wider connotation than a court. An application under Section 9 for an interim measure has to be moved before a court. Single Judge of the High Court was in error in holding that once an application under Section 8 is filed, it is only that court where the application was pending would have jurisdiction over the arbitral proceedings and till that application under Section 8 was pending before the court of Vadodara, the Bombay High Court would not have jurisdiction to pass any order in relation to arbitral proceedings, including under Section 9.[198]

---

193. *Korp. Gems (India) (P) Ltd.* v. *Precious Diamond Ltd.*, 2006 SCC OnLine Cal 317: (2007) 2 CHN 544.
194. *Saha & Gupta Enterprise* v. *Indian Oil Corpn. Ltd.*, 2007 SCC OnLine Cal 339: (2007) 3 CHN 781.
195. *Union of India* v. *Surya Alloy Industries Ltd.*, 2010 SCC OnLine Cal 2329: (2011) 1 CHN 290.
196. *NTPC* v. *A.P. Singh*, 2008 SCC OnLine Del 1343: (2009) 107 DRJ 276.
197. *Ashapura Mine-Chem Ltd.* v. *Gujarat Mineral Development Corpn.*, (2015) 8 SCC 193; *Sundaram Finance Ltd.* v. *T. Thankam*, (2015) 14 SCC 444; *Mahesh Agarwal* v. *Indian Oil Corpn. Ltd.*, 2008 SCC OnLine Cal 5: (2008) 2 CHN 696.
198. *Sharda Raje Uday Singh Rao Gaekwar* v. *Veer Corpn.*, 2011 SCC OnLine Bom 1631: (2012) 2 Mah LJ 242.

Section 8 creates an embargo on the judicial authority to entertain any action brought before it which is a subject-matter of an arbitration agreement but to refer the parties to arbitration.[199] Where the petitioner himself requested the trial court to refer the dispute for arbitration instead of appointing arbitrator by exercising power under clause of the agreement, the trial court had no option but to direct the parties to get the arbitrator appointed through the court.[200]

On application under Section 8, the judicial authority is bound to refer the parties to arbitration if it is found that the matter is covered by the arbitration clause in the agreement provided that the application is made before submitting his first statement on the substance of the dispute.[201] What can be referred to the arbitrator is only the dispute or matter between the parties which the arbitrator is competent or empowered to decide.[202] Question as to whether the arbitration agreement is attracted or not is not to be decided by the civil court. The Arbitral Tribunal has the jurisdiction under Section 16, Arbitration and Conciliation Act, 1996 to decide as to whether the arbitration agreement is applicable to the dispute raised between the parties to the agreement or not.[203]

Section 16, Arbitration and Conciliation Act, 1996 operates in different situations and Section 8 of the Act operates in a different situation.[204]

Where subject-matter in suit and arbitration is different, no reference can be made under Section 8 of the Act.[205]

Where respondents had invoked the specific provisions of the Arbitration and Conciliation Act, 1996 and the parties were litigating on the same basis, order of reference to arbitration under Section 151 CrPC was held not justified.[206]

Once the parties have consented and allowed the civil proceedings to continue, they cannot subsequently invoke the arbitration clause and make the deed clause alive after the same has been ignored and not invoked.[207]

---

199. *Shiv Om Polynets (P) Ltd.* v. *Marine Fabrics*, 2013 SCC OnLine Cal 1070: (2013) 1 Cal LT 592.
200. *Tata Finance Ltd.* v. *Sumit Khamsera*, 2005 SCC OnLine Raj 68: (2005) 4 RLW 2676.
201. *Fishermen Coop. Socy. Ltd.* v. *Fishermen Coop. Socy., Ltd.*, 2007 SCC OnLine AP 884: (2008) 1 AP LJ 28.
202. *Satish* v. *Gujarat Tele Links (P) Ltd.*, 2013 SCC OnLine Bom 904: (2013) 6 Mah LJ 420.
203. *Nicholas Piramal India Ltd.* v. *Zenith Drugs and Allied Agencies (P) Ltd.*, 2007 SCC OnLine Gau 52: (2008) 2 Gau LR 418.
204. *Eureka Builders* v. *Gulabchand*, 2013 SCC OnLine Kar 678: (2013) 1 Kant LJ 675.
205. *Eagle Agro-Farm (P) Ltd.* v. *Eagle Soraj Townships (P) Ltd.*, 2013 SCC OnLine Bom 1614: (2014) 5 Mah LJ 330.
206. *Ibid.*
207. *Ministry of Sound International Ltd.* v. *Indus Renaissance Partners Entertainment (P) Ltd.*, 2009 SCC OnLine Del 11: (2009) 156 DLT 406.

In case of presenting a matter before the judicial authority and the matter is such as is subject to the arbitration agreement, the authority may refer the parties to arbitration provided the parties so apply.[208]

Section 8(1) provides that if a party applies for referring the matter to arbitration then and only then the court can refer the matter to the arbitration. To take the benefit of arbitration clause, party to the contract is required to apply for that relief, mere existence of arbitration clause cannot oust the jurisdiction of civil court.[209]

If a suit is brought by a party to the arbitration agreement to challenge the agreement or award or a suit to affirm agreement or award in spite of arbitration agreement, such suits are clearly barred by the provisions of Section 8 of the Act. Relief has to be granted by way of the provisions of the Arbitration Act itself.[210] Action of the defendant in filing its own suit amounted to invoke or enforce the arbitration clause.[211]

The matter which is before the judicial authority must be the subject-matter of an arbitration agreement. Application should be made before the party making the same submits his first statement on the substance of the dispute. Application should be accompanied by original arbitration agreement or a duly certified copy thereof.[212]

As per Section 8 of the said Act, in case where there is an arbitration clause in the agreement, it is obligatory on the part of the court to refer the parties to arbitration in terms of their arbitration agreement. There is a scope under Section 9 of the Act for a party to such agreement to pray and obtain an interim protection from the principal civil court as designated, even prior to or during arbitration proceedings.[213]

The arbitration is an alternative dispute resolution (ADR) mechanism which is resorted to by the parties with their consent. The parties have to be ad-idem for it. The respondents, in the earlier instance, themselves indicated the intent not to be bound by the arbitration agreement on the petitioner's claim for the trade mark. The petitioner has now accepted that opposition and has invoked the civil court's jurisdiction on trade mark. Where both

208. *Aksh Optifibre Ltd.* v. *Shin Etsu Chemical Co., Ltd.*, 2005 SCC OnLine Raj 153: (2005) 2 RLW 1000.
209. *Mahesh Kumar* v. *SRTC*, 2005 SCC OnLine Raj 71: (2005) 4 RLW 2667.
210. *Ford Credit Kotak Mahindra Ltd.* v. *M. Swaminathan*, 2005 SCC OnLine Mad 102: (2006) 1 LW 758.
211. *Kush Dairy Ltd.* v. *H.P. Printers (P) Ltd.*, 2013 SCC OnLine Del 1349: (2013) 135 DRJ 724.
212. *Global Trade Finance Ltd.* v. *Sudarshan Overseas Ltd.*, 2009 SCC OnLine Bom 1264: (2010) 4 Mah LJ 367.
213. *Maa Sarada & Co.* v. *Sahidul Hoque*, 2015 SCC OnLine Gau 392: (2016) 6 Gau LR 525.

the parties were ad-idem that the dispute raised by the petitioner was not arbitrable, the parties could not have been referred to arbitration. The application filed by the respondents under Section 8, Arbitration and Conciliation Act, 1996 was dismissed.[214]

Section 8 of 1996 Act and Section 34, Arbitration Act, 1940

It was the consistent approach of the court of law including the Supreme Court to stay the suit as and when the court was approached under Section 8. In the old law specially under Section 34 of the 1940 Act there was some discretion left to the court. However, such discretion is no longer left to court because of the stringent provision under Section 8 of the 1996 Act.[215]

Notwithstanding any judgment, decree or order of the Supreme Court or any court

The language of amendment to Section 8 of the Act is clear that the amendment to Section 8(1) of the Act would apply notwithstanding any prayer, judgment, decree or order of the Supreme Court or any other court.[216]

Twin conditions precedent

The two conditions precedent for an arbitration agreement to enable a defendant to invoke Section 8 are:

1. it should be between the parties to the dispute; and
2. it should relate to or be applicable to the dispute.[217]

The two essential duties that the judicial authority receiving an application under Section 8 of the 1996 Act has to perform are to assess whether there is in existence a valid arbitration agreement and to ascertain whether the dispute that is sought to be raised before it is covered by the arbitration agreement. If either is answered in the negative, the application for a reference has to fail.[218]

Respondent-plaintiff had filed a suit against the defendants, a company and its two Directors for the recovery of certain sum with interest allegedly due in regard to 1) price of two consignments supplied by the plaintiff to the nominees of the first defendant-company; and 2) the value of nine samples

214. *Sagar Ratna Restaurants (P) Ltd.* v. *DS Foods*, (2021) 2 HCC (Del) 752.
215. *Basundhara Towers (P) Ltd.* v. *Binapani Daw*, 2005 SCC OnLine Cal 639: (2006) 3 CHN 240; *Kishan Mimani* v. *Indu Kocher*, 2011 SCC OnLine Cal 5435: (2012) 4 CHN 157.
216. *Ameet Lalchand Shah* v. *Rishabh Enterprises*, (2018) 15 SCC 678.
217. *Yogi Agarwal* v. *Inspiration Clothes & U*, (2009) 1 SCC 372.
218. *Niranjan Lal Todi* v. *Nandlal Todi*, 2010 SCC OnLine Cal 2120: (2011) 1 CHN 762.

supplied by the plaintiff to the defendant. The defendants made an application under Section 8, Arbitration and Conciliation Act, 1996 for referring the parties to arbitration. To show the existence of the arbitration agreement, the defendants relied upon three invoices of *Y*, a proprietary concern of the second defendant in regard to the sale of cotton fabric by *Y* to the plaintiff which contained the arbitration clause. The defendants alleged that the said invoices were accepted by the plaintiff resulting in a binding arbitration agreement. Defendants' application under Section 8 was rejected. Held, there was no arbitration agreement between the parties in regard to the suit transactions, and the aforesaid invoices related to some other transactions and not the transactions in suit. As there was no arbitration agreement with reference to the subject-matter of the suit filed by the plaintiff, rejection of the application filed by the defendants under Section 8 was proper.[219]

Where an application seeking reference to arbitration is filed, the court has to consider whether the subject-matter of the suit is the subject-matter of the arbitration.[220] Before objection to jurisdiction is raised, civil court is duty-bound to find out whether controversy is covered by the arbitration agreement.[221]

It is a legislative command to the court once it is found that there is an arbitration agreement between the parties and once an action has been brought to the court by one party to the agreement on the same subject-matter of the agreement, the other party submitted for reference to the arbitration and when a true copy of the contract containing the "arbitration agreement" is already annexed along with the petition, all the preconditions under Section 8, Arbitration and Conciliation Act, 1996 are satisfied and, therefore, the parties must refer their dispute to arbitration as per the arbitration agreement between them. Merely because the contract has come to an end by its termination, the arbitration clause does not perish nor it becomes inoperative to resolve the dispute. The parties are duty-bound to solve their dispute by mode of arbitration, as agreed by them.[222]

The trial court is statutorily obliged to refer the dispute to arbitration when such a plea is raised by the party at the earliest point of time.[223]

---

219. *Yogi Agarwal* v. *Inspiration Clothes & U*, (2009) 1 SCC 372.
220. *Master Pieces Furniture (P) Ltd.* v. *K. Lakshma Reddy*, 2013 SCC OnLine AP 286: (2014) 1 ALD 375.
221. *Bais Surgical and Medical Institute (P) Ltd.* v. *Dhananjay*, 2007 SCC OnLine Bom 46: (2007) 3 Mah LJ 377.
222. *Parcel Carriers (India) (P) Ltd.* v. *Union of India*, 2010 SCC OnLine Bom 637: (2010) 3 Mah LJ 993.
223. *Abdul Haque Abdul Aziz* v. *Mohd. Rizwan*, 2008 SCC OnLine Bom 557: (2008) 6 Mah LJ 373.

What is provided for reference to the arbitrator is dispute as to the rights of the parties arising out of the agreement. Where the plaintiff filed suit seeking injunction to ensure that any construction made by the defendant builder was in accordance with law, held the relief sought in the suit did not involve any dispute as to the rights of the parties under the agreement, order referring the parties to arbitration was unsustainable, was set aside.[224]

Application for reference of dispute to arbitration can be rejected only when there is no valid arbitration agreement. As the agreement in question contained an arbitration clause, rejection of application for referring the dispute to arbitration was not proper.[225]

Where relief sought is declaration of rights in immovable property, disputes between parties are rights *in rem*, disputes between the parties are non-arbitrable.[226]

Arbitration agreement only covered disputes as to the construction or interpretation of the document. Cause of action in the suit was founded on the dishonoured cheque, the claim did not involve the interpretation or construction of the original agreement. Prayer for reference to the arbitrator was rejected.[227]

Power of the judicial authority to refer the matter for arbitral dispute is dependent upon fulfillment of the necessary conditions precedent as laid down in Section 8. Section 8(1) does not permit dissection of the power of the judicial authority and the duty cast upon the applicant. Both are interwoven and inseparable.[228]

Arbitration agreement is a solemn agreement entered into between the parties for resolution of the dispute. The provision regarding reference of the matter pending before the civil court to the arbitration as provided for under Section 8 of the Act has got to be strictly complied with. Unless the procedural and other requirements of law as provided under Section 8 are not complied with strictly then the matter should not be referred to the arbitration and the suit should proceed before the civil court. The jurisdiction of the civil court is not completely ousted even if the matter is covered by the arbitration clause.[229]

---

224. *B. Kamala Devi* v. *Mehta Builders*, 2000 SCC OnLine AP 574: (2000) 3 AP LJ 190.
225. *H.H. Infrastructure (P) Ltd.* v. *Allan James Taylor*, 2020 SCC OnLine Bom 1746.
226. *Sharad* v. *Hemantkumar*, 2018 SCC OnLine Bom 11462: (2018) 5 Mah LJ 190.
227. *Poddar Heritage Investments* v. *Chopra Mktg.*, 2010 SCC OnLine Cal 2245: (2011) 2 CHN 1030.
228. *Union of India* v. *C & C Construction (P) Ltd.*, 2006 SCC OnLine Gau 422: (2007) 1 Gau LR 782.
229. *North Eastern Electric Power Corpn. Ltd.* v. *Jiban Kumar Saha*, 1999 SCC OnLine Gau 25: (2000) 2 Gau LR 242.

Absence of arbitration agreement—Reference to arbitration not possible

Reference to arbitration under Section 8, Arbitration and Conciliation Act, 1996 is not possible in the absence of arbitration agreement.[230] Court had no jurisdiction to refer the dispute to arbitration in the absence of an arbitration clause.

It is well settled that an agreement to refer the dispute or differences to arbitration must be expressly or impliedly spelt out from the relevant clauses in the contract. In *Durha Constructions (P) Ltd.* v. *Bateman Engg. India (P) Ltd.*[231], clause 12 of the LoI only referred to the venue of arbitration and stated that in case of any dispute, the venue of arbitration shall be Bangalore. Except this, there was no other clause which stated that the disputes have to be referred for arbitration and the decision of the arbitrator will be binding, let alone exclusion of the jurisdiction of the courts, the letter of acceptance communicated by the petitioner incorporated a mechanical expression under the head "arbitration" at clause 5 stating that it shall be applicable as per Arbitration and Conciliation Act, 1996. It was held that there was no clause incorporated in the agreement nor can it be deduced either from the LoI or the letter of acceptance to hold that the parties have agreed to refer their dispute for arbitration and that the decision of the tribunal will be binding on them. The clauses did not contain the attributes that are required to be present for an agreement to be considered as an arbitration agreement. Application filed under Section 8 was dismissed.

Absence of written arbitration agreement

Where a party has given its consent to refer disputes to arbitration before the High Court, it is estopped from contending absence of written agreement to refer parties to arbitration.[232]

Where dispute not arbitrable

Where the cause/dispute is non-arbitrable, the court where the suit is pending will refuse to refer the parties to arbitration under Section 8 of the Act, even if the parties might have agreed upon arbitration as the forum for settlement of such disputes.[233]

230. *M.P. Rural Road Development Authority* v. *L.G. Chaudhary Engineers & Contractors*, (2012) 3 SCC 495; *Kvaerner Cementation India Ltd.* v. *Bajranglal Agarwal*, (2012) 5 SCC 214; *TISCO Ltd.* v. *Standard Chrome*, 2005 SCC OnLine Cal 396: (2006) 2 CHN 378.

231. *Durha Constructions (P) Ltd.* v. *Bateman Engg. India (P) Ltd.*, 2011 SCC OnLine Kar 3409: ILR 2012 Kar 1242.

232. *MTNL* v. *Canara Bank*, (2020) 12 SCC 767.

233. *Booz Allen & Hamilton Inc.* v. *SBI Home Finance Ltd.*, (2011) 5 SCC 532.

Clause in agreement contained exception as regards matters relating to collection of royalty and imposition of penalty. It was held, the arbitrator would not have power to decide the said dispute.[234]

Dispute relating to extension or invocation of bank guarantee falls within the ambit of arbitration clause and becomes an arbitrable dispute.[235]

In cases where there is no vestige of doubt that the claims are not arbitrable or the agreement is invalid, the courts may decline to refer the parties to arbitration but not in any other case.[236]

Financial institution

A financial institution which happens to be a borrower vis-à-vis institution with which a dispute arises, cannot resort to arbitration as a remedy.[237]

Proceedings under Section 9

Proceedings under Section 9 are in aid and assistance to arbitration proceedings. Provisions of Section 8 cannot be invoked in proceedings under Section 9. Invoking the same is inconsistent and contrary to the scheme of the Act.[238]

Section 8 and Section 11

Section 8 entitled a party to an arbitration agreement to apply before the judicial authority for an action with the plea that the action is covered by an arbitration agreement. Existence of an arbitration agreement has to be conclusively decided. But under Section 11, the party might still have to satisfy the tribunal upon the claim being lodged that the entirety thereof is covered by the arbitration agreement. Application was allowed, disputes were referred to arbitration.[239]

Section 8 and Section 21

Sections 8 and 21 operate in different fields and under two distinct circumstances. An application under Section 8 is not contemplated under Section 21.[240]

---

234. *BSNL* v. *Alekya Graphic (P) Ltd.*, 2018 SCC OnLine Hyd 144: (2018) 4 ALD 312 (DB).
235. *Vijai Electricals Ltd.* v. *Transformers and Rectifiers India Ltd.*, 2022 SCC OnLine Guj 2647.
236. *Parsvnath Developers Ltd.* v. *Future Retail Ltd.*, (2022) 2 HCC (Del) 516.
237. *Bell Finvest India Ltd.* v. *A.U. Small Finance Bank Ltd.*, (2022) 6 HCC (Del) 467.
238. *Mercury Exports* v. *CLC Tanner's Assn.*, 2011 SCC OnLine Cal 73: (2011) 2 CHN 492.
239. *Rajeev Maheshwari* v. *Indu Kocher*, 2011 SCC OnLine Cal 1243: (2011) 3 ICC 176.
240. *Cash and Gain Finance and Investments* v. *Manjula Udaya Shankar*, 2008 SCC OnLine Mad 802: (2009) 2 CTC 234.

Relative scope of Sections 8 and 45

Section 8 of the 1996 Act is differently worded from Section 45 whereunder the judicial authority cannot refer the parties to arbitration in a case where it finds that the agreement is null and void, inoperative and incapable of being performed. Thus, as and when a question in regard to the validity or otherwise of the arbitration agreement arises, in a case falling under Section 8, a judicial authority would have the jurisdiction under certain circumstances to go into the said question.[241]

The Arbitration and Conciliation Act, 1996 is divided into two parts. Part I relates to domestic arbitration and Part II relates to international commercial arbitration. In respect of domestic arbitration, a person against whom a suit is brought, is entitled to file an application under Section 8 before the court, seeking a reference of the dispute to arbitration. In respect of international commercial arbitration, a person against whom a civil suit is filed, has to take out an application under Section 45, seeking a reference of the dispute to arbitration. Though Sections 8 and 45 are identical provisions, enabling the defendant in a civil suit to seek a reference of the dispute to arbitration, they are not exactly worded in pari materia. The jurisdiction of the civil court to refer parties to international commercial arbitration under Section 45, is a qualified mandate. Section 45 contains a rider which reads: "unless it finds that the said agreement is null and void, inoperative or incapable of being performed". This rider is conspicuously absent in Section 8(1). Therefore, to say that even in respect of domestic arbitrations, a reference cannot be made in terms of Section 8(1) whenever the agreement is assailed to be vitiated by fraud, would tantamount to importing the rider found in Section 45, into Section 8(1).[242]

Section 8 (Part I) of the Act, relates to domestic arbitration, Sections 45 and 54 (Part II) relate to international commercial arbitration. A comparative study of Sections 8, 45 and 54 of the Act, would show that the lawmakers made each one of them different and distinct in their scope, ambit and operation.[243]

Section 8 and Section 89 CPC

Section 89 CPC cannot be restored for interpreting Section 8, Arbitration and Conciliation Act, 1996 as it stands on a different footing and it would

241. *India Household and Healthcare Ltd.* v. *LG Household and Healthcare Ltd.*, (2007) 5 SCC 510.
242. *SBQ Steels Ltd.* v. *Goyal Gases (P) Ltd.*, 2013 SCC OnLine Mad 3658: (2014) 3 CTC 586.
243. *Kotak Mahindra Bank Ltd.* v. *Sundaram Brake Lining Ltd.*, 2008 SCC OnLine Mad 519: (2008) 4 CTC 1.

be applicable even in cases where there is no arbitration agreement for referring the dispute to arbitration. Further, for that purpose the court has to apply its mind to the conditions contemplated under Section 89 CPC and even if application under Section 8, Arbitration and Conciliation Act, 1996 is rejected, the court is required to follow the procedure prescribed under the said section.[244]

Ouster of jurisdiction of civil court under Section 8

There is no total ouster of jurisdiction of the civil court under Section 8 of the Act. Ouster is only by choice of the defending party. Judicial authority can refer parties to arbitration only upon application made by party to arbitration agreement and cannot suo motu return suit at threshold.[245]

Applicability of Section 8—Necessary conditions

For applicability of Section 8, Arbitration and Conciliation Act, 1996 the conditions which must be satisfied are:

(*a*) that there exists an arbitration agreement;
(*b*) that an action has been brought to the court by one party to the arbitration agreement against the other party;
(*c*) that the subject-matter of the suit is the same as the subject-matter of the arbitration agreement;
(*d*) that the other party before he submits his first statement of the substance of the dispute, moves the court for referring the parties to arbitration; and
(*e*) that along with the application the other party tenders the original arbitration agreement or duly certified copy thereof.[246]

What is permitted to be produced as secondary evidence, *i.e.* other than the original document in terms of para 2(*a*) of the 1996 Scheme framed under Section 11(10) of the 1996 Act is only a "certified copy" thereof as under Section 63(1) read with Section 79 of the Evidence Act, 1872 and not any other form of secondary evidence thererof.[247]

---

244. *Sukanya Holdings (P) Ltd.* v. *Jayesh H. Pandya*, (2003) 5 SCC 531.
245. *Convinio Shopping Nine 2 Nine* v. *Olympia Opaline Owners Assn.*, 2019 SCC OnLine Mad 646: (2019) 2 LW 64.
246. *Magma Leasing & Finance Ltd.* v. *Potluri Madhavilata*, (2009) 10 SCC 103; *Booz Allen & Hamilton Inc.* v. *SBI Home Finance Ltd.*, (2011) 5 SCC 532; *Bais Surgical and Medical Institute (P) Ltd.* v. *Dhananjay*, 2007 SCC OnLine Bom 46: (2007) 3 Mah LJ 377.
247. *N.N. Global Mercantile (P) Ltd.* v. *Indo Unique Flame Ltd.*, (2023) 7 SCC 1.

Section 8 can be invoked and parties directed to arbitration if 1) all the parties to the suit are parties to the arbitration agreement; and 2) the reliefs prayed for in the suit are covered by the arbitral clause.[248]

The provisions of Section 8 are mandatory.[249] If in an agreement between the parties before the civil court, there is a clause for arbitration, it is mandatory for the civil court to refer the parties to arbitration. If an objection regarding the applicability of the arbitration to the facts of the case is raised, the court should leave the question to be decided by the Arbitral Tribunal. This is very much clear from the language of Section 16 of the Act.[250]

Under Section 8, dispute can be referred to an arbitrator only if the action brought before the court is subject to an arbitration agreement. It shall refuse to refer the dispute to arbitration if it finds that prima facie no valid arbitration agreement exists. Therefore, the court under Section 8 before referring the dispute is enjoined with the duty to find out if there exists a valid arbitration agreement in respect of the dispute which is subject-matter of the suit. It cannot mechanically refer the dispute to the Arbitral Tribunal merely because the arbitration agreement provides for the dispute being referred to the Arbitral Tribunal even if the provision therefor is not valid as the dispute itself is such that is not arbitrable.[251]

Proceeding of a civil action with regard to a matter covered by arbitration agreement is a condition precedent to invoke the powers of the court under Section 8.[252]

The defendants had not moved the court to refer the parties to arbitration. There being no such application, there was no question of the court suo motu directing the parties to arbitration by invoking the arbitral clause.[253]

Situation contemplated by Section 8 can arise at the instance of the defendant or suo motu at the instance of the judicial authority when the judicial authority comes to know of the existence of an arbitration agreement.[254]

---

248. *Vijaykumar Bhogilal Patel* v. *Karim Mohammed Maredia*, 2003 SCC OnLine Bom 930: (2004) 1 Mah LJ 966.
249. *Convinio Shopping Nine 2 Nine* v. *Olympia Opaline Owners Assn.*, 2019 SCC OnLine Mad 646: (2019) 2 LW 64.
250. *Hindustan Petroleum Corpn. Ltd.* v. *Pinkcity Midway Petroleums*, (2003) 6 SCC 503; *Sundaram Finance Ltd.* v. *T. Thankam*, (2015) 14 SCC 444.
251. *U.P. Industrial Coop. Assn. Ltd.* v. *Rajendra Kumar Dhingra*, 2019 SCC OnLine All 3949: (2019) 3 All LJ 28.
252. *M.S. Rao* v. *Mangalore University*, 2001 SCC OnLine Kar 344: ILR 2001 Kar 4863.
253. *Pamvi Consultancy Services Ltd.* v. *Global Syntex (Bhilwara) Ltd.*, 2002 SCC OnLine Bom 463: (2002) 4 Mah LJ 748.
254. *Ardy International (P) Ltd.* v. *Inspiration Clothes & U*, (2006) 1 SCC 417.

In application for reference to arbitration in terms of partnership deed, objection was taken by the appellant that the partnership deed was "unregistered partnership". The High Court did not decide the issue of subject-matter and straightway dismissed the objection. The Supreme Court remanded the matter to the High Court for decision afresh on merits.[255]

When the parties have an arbitration agreement existing and are themselves willing to go to the alternative dispute redressal forum of arbitration, the court ought not to deny the same.[256]

There are some conditions for filing application for making reference to Arbitration. *First*, it is to be seen whether an application is made in a suit or proceedings, *secondly*, whether there exists an agreement, *thirdly*, whether there exists an arbitration clause in the agreement, and *lastly*, whether dispute sought to be raised in the suit is covered by the agreement. Once these conditions are satisfied, the matter has to be referred to arbitration in terms of agreement for adjudication.[257]

Section 8 peremptory in nature

Section 8 of the 1996 Act is peremptory in nature. In a case when there exists an arbitration agreement, the court is under an obligation to refer the parties to arbitration in terms of the arbitration agreement.[258]

If in agreement between the parties before the civil court, there is a clause for arbitration, it is mandatory for the civil court to refer the dispute to an arbitration. In *Hindustan Petroleum Corpn. Ltd.* v. *Pinkcity Midway Petroleums*[259], the existence of an arbitration clause in the agreement was accepted by the parties as also by the courts below. Therefore, in view of the mandatory language of Section 8 of the Act, the courts below ought to have referred the dispute to arbitration. Application filed by the defendant-appellant under Section 8 was allowed by the Supreme Court, the trial court was directed to refer the parties in the civil suit before it to arbitration.

Section 8 contemplates that judicial authority before which an action is brought in matter which is subject of an arbitration proceeding shall, if party so applied, refer parties to arbitration. Party should seek such reference

255. *Bhagwan Das Goel* v. *Pyare Kishan Agarwal*, (2019) 4 SCC 731.
256. *Rajasthan SRTC* v. *Nand Lal Saraswat*, 2004 SCC OnLine Raj 114: (2005) 2 RLW 946.
257. *Birla Global Finance Ltd.* v. *Gajra Bevel Gears Ltd.*, 2006 SCC OnLine MP 311: (2006) 4 MP LJ 566.
258. *Agri Gold Exims Ltd.* v. *Sri Lakshmi Knits & Wovens*, (2007) 3 SCC 686; *Hindustan Petroleum Corpn. Ltd.* v. *Pinkcity Midway Petroleums*, (2003) 6 SCC 503; *Sundaram Finance Ltd.* v. *T. Thankam*, (2015) 14 SCC 444; *Mahesh Agarwal* v. *Indian Oil Corpn. Ltd.*, 2008 SCC OnLine Cal 5: (2008) 2 CHN 696; *IndusInd Bank Ltd.* v. *K. Nachimuthu*, 2016 SCC OnLine Mad 5686: (2016) 2 LW 902.
259. (2003) 6 SCC 503.

not later than submitting his first statement on the substance of dispute. When an agreement contains a clause for arbitration it is mandatory to refer parties to arbitration. Employment of the word "shall" in Section 8 makes it mandatory. Suit filed ignoring such arbitration clauses is not maintainable.[260]

The language of Section 8, Arbitration and Conciliation Act, 1996 is peremptory, as such the court is under an obligation to refer the parties to arbitration in terms of their arbitration agreement. An application before a court under Section 8 merely brings to the court's notice that the subject-matter of the action before it is the subject-matter of an arbitration agreement.[261] Once requirements of Section 8, Arbitration and Conciliation Act are complied with, the judicial authority has no option but to refer the matter to arbitration.[262] Where agreement between the parties provides arbitration, civil court is under a legislative command to refer the parties to arbitration.[263] Where the subject-matter of the suit is covered by the arbitration agreement, it is necessary to refer the matter to the arbitrator. The arbitration must go on first.[264]

Where the petitioner had filed an application under Section 8, Arbitration and Conciliation Act before filing the written statement, the trial court was bound to refer the matter to the arbitrator and should not have exercised its jurisdiction to try the case between the parties.[265]

Ingredients to attract Section 8 are: (1) action is brought before judicial authority; (2) action relates to matter of arbitration agreement; (3) respondent to such action files application under Section 8 at any time before submitting first statement on substance of dispute; (4) judicial authority is satisfied that there is valid arbitration agreement. Judicial authority on being satisfied that all above requirements are present has to mandatorily refer parties to arbitration. As provided by Section 8(3), arbitration may be commenced or continued and award be made even if application under Section 8(1) is pending decision.[266] Reference of dispute to arbitration for adjudication is

---

260. *India Cements Capital Finance Ltd.* v. *Kwality Spinning Mills Ltd.*, 1999 SCC OnLine Mad 950: (2000) 2 CTC 267; *Mahesh Agarwal* v. *Indian Oil Corpn. Ltd.*, 2008 SCC OnLine Cal 5: (2008) 2 CHN 696; *Uttam Mondal* v. *Kotak Mahindra Bank Ltd.*, 2010 SCC OnLine Cal 2379: (2011) 1 ICC 106.

261. *P. Anand Gajapathi Raju* v. *P.V.G. Raju*, (2000) 4 SCC 539.

262. *Krebs Bio-Chemicals Ltd.* v. *Gayatri Sugar Complex Ltd.*, 2004 SCC OnLine AP 679: (2004) 6 ALD 430.

263. *Madhucon Projects Ltd.* v. *B. Girijapathi Reddy & Co.*, 2010 SCC OnLine AP 799: (2011) 3 ICC 124.

264. *A.B.K. Dubhash* v. *Petit Towers Coop. Housing Society Ltd.*, 2010 SCC OnLine Bom 1751: (2011) 2 Mah LJ 57.

265. *Escorts Finance Ltd.* v. *Dharambir*, 2004 SCC OnLine P&H 1112: PLR (2005) 140 P&H 57 (2).

266. *Sporting Pastime India Ltd.* v. *Kasthuri and Sons Ltd.*, 2006 SCC OnLine Mad 551: (2006) 4 CTC 377.

mandatory on the part of the civil court under the 1996 Act when the dispute is covered under an arbitration agreement between the parties.[267]

Section 8 mandates that the judicial authority before which an action has been brought in respect of a matter which is the subject-matter of an arbitration agreement, shall refer the parties to arbitration, if a party to such an agreement applies not later than when submitting his first statement of defence.[268] Section 8 is in the form of legislative command to the court and once the prerequisite conditions of the section are satisfied, the court must refer the parties to arbitration.[269]

Once, all the necessary prerequisites enshrined under Section 8 of the Act are fulfilled and there is no dispute regarding the validity of the arbitration agreement, then in such circumstances, the judicial authority ceases to exercise jurisdiction and the dispute is to be adjudicated upon by the arbitrator. Section 8 of the Act is mandatory in nature.[270]

Where an application has been filed under Section 8 praying court to refer the parties to arbitration since there is a clause in the agreement, the court should gather the intention of the parties to refer the matter to the arbitration in accordance with the procedures stipulated under the clauses of the agreement and resolution.[271]

All that is to be seen under Section 8 of the 1996 Act after its amendment is that, prima facie, a valid arbitration agreement exists. There is a sea change between Section 8 of the 1996 Act and Section 20, Arbitration Act, 1940. Post amendment, it is clear that the judicial authority before which an action is brought shall, if the other conditions of Section 8 are met, refer the parties to arbitration unless it finds that, prima facie, no valid arbitration agreement exists.[272]

Sections 8 and 11 were amended pursuant to a detailed Law Commission Report being the 246th Law Commission Report on Arbitration. The net result of the amendments and judicial interpretation thereof, is that while considering any application under Section 8 or Section 11 of the 1996 Act, the court is to confine itself to the prima facie examination of the existence of

267. *Sri Lakshmi Enterprises* v. *R. Ramakrishnan*, 2007 SCC OnLine Mad 167: (2007) 2 CTC 818.
268. *Kalpana Kothari* v. *Sudha Yadav*, (2002) 1 SCC 203.
269. *Magma Leasing & Finance Ltd.* v. *Potluri Madhavilata*, (2009) 10 SCC 103; *Rashtriya Ispat Nigam Ltd.* v. *Verma Transport Co.*, (2006) 7 SCC 275; *Agri Gold Exims Ltd.* v. *Sri Lakshmi Knits & Wovens*, (2007) 3 SCC 686.
270. *Ultra Home Constructions (P) Ltd.* v. *Choice Hotels International Inc.*, 2012 SCC OnLine Del 245: (2012) 127 DRJ 724.
271. *International Air Transport Assn. (IATA)* v. *All India Travel Agency (Madurai) (P) Ltd.*, 2012 SCC OnLine Mad 1909: (2012) 4 CTC 748.
272. *Deccan Paper Mills Co. Ltd.* v. *Regency Mahavir Properties*, (2021) 4 SCC 786.

an arbitration agreement and leave all other preliminary issues to be decided by the arbitrator. Prima facie examination of the existence of an arbitration agreement, which is what the court must restrict itself to while considering reference of the matter to arbitration under Section 8 or appointment of an arbitrator under Section 11 of the 1996 Act, is not full review but a primary first review to weed out manifestly and ex facie non-existent and invalid arbitration agreements and non-arbitrable disputes. The prima facie review at the reference stage is to cut the deadwood and trim off the side branches in straightforward cases where dismissal is barefaced and pellucid and when on the facts and law the litigation must stop at the first stage. Only when the court is certain that no valid arbitration agreement exists or the disputed subject-matter is not arbitrable, the application under Section 8 or Section 11 would be rejected. At this stage, the court should not get lost in thickets and decide debatable questions of facts. Referral proceedings are preliminary and summary and not a mini trial.[273]

Judicial authority

The term "judicial authority" is a term of wider import, it would not only include the court but it will also include all authorities which can be described as judicial authorities. The Civil Judge, Senior Division in the district can be safely described as a judicial authority for the purpose of the Arbitration Act.[274]

In Section 8, the word used is "judicial authority" which means and includes any forum exercising judicial powers. The Junior Civil Judge is a judicial authority.[275]

Application under Section 8, Arbitration and Conciliation Act is not maintainable before any other forum but only before the judicial authority before which an action is brought. Even the applications under Section 11 of the Act are also not maintainable during the pendency of civil suit before the civil court.[276]

Tribunal constituted under Section 11, Delhi School Education Act, 1973 (18 of 1973) is judicial authority. The School Tribunal hearing appeal of the teacher need not refer the dispute to arbitration.[277]

---

273. *Pravin Electricals (P) Ltd.* v. *Galaxy Infra & Engg. (P) Ltd.*, (2021) 5 SCC 671.
274. *Cotton Corpn. of India Ltd.* v. *Sharad Shetkari Soot Girni Niyamit*, 1999 SCC OnLine Bom 823: (2000) 3 Mah LJ 96.
275. *M.D., Sundaram Finance Ltd.* v. *G.S.N. Nandakumar*, 2001 SCC OnLine AP 528: (2001) 2 AP LJ 95.
276. *Sanjay Sinha* v. *Pinaki Chaudhury*, 1999 SCC OnLine Cal 615.
277. *Montfort Senior Secondary School* v. *Vijay Kumar*, (2005) 7 SCC 472.

Written application is necessary

Application contemplated by Section 8(1) of the Act is a written application and not an oral application. The party which seeks to refer the dispute to the arbitrator has to make a written application so that the other side knows exactly the grounds on which reference is fought.[278] It is mandatory for a party seeking reference to make an application in writing. Where no such application was made, the court could not have made a reference and it did not get jurisdiction to make such a reference.[279] Where application under Section 8(1) for referring the parties to the suit to arbitration is not filed, the suit cannot be referred to arbitration.[280]

Where an arbitration clause exists in the JVA, no application is filed to refer the dispute to arbitration, if parties choose to contest the suit despite arbitration agreement, Section 8 cannot be invoked.[281]

Mere disclosure of arbitration agreement in the written statement and claiming that civil court has no jurisdiction to try the suit would be of no consequence unless the written statement itself contains a prayer for referring the dispute for arbitration. In the instant case, though the defendants claimed that there is arbitration agreement between the parties and civil court has no jurisdiction in the matter, no prayer was made in the written statement to refer the disputes between the parties for arbitration. The jurisdiction of the civil court is not ousted on account of an arbitration agreement between the parties. It is ousted because of an application filed under Section 8 of the Act provided it otherwise conforms to the requirements laid down in the section.[282]

Before the court can exercise its power under Section 8, conditions to be satisfied are: (*i*) there must be an arbitration agreement; (*ii*) an action is brought by a party to the arbitration agreement against the other party before a judicial authority; (*iii*) the subject-matter of the action before the judicial authority is the subject of the arbitration agreement; and (*iv*) the other party applies before the judicial authority for referring parties to arbitration before it submits his first statement on the substance of the dispute.[283]

---

278. *Garden Finance Ltd.* v. *Prakash Industries Ltd.*, 2001 SCC OnLine Bom 351: (2001) 4 Mah LJ 425.
279. *Ganesh Trading Co.* v. *State of Maharashtra*, 2007 SCC OnLine Bom 184: (2007) 4 Mah LJ 715.
280. *Archetype India Construction Consultants (P) Ltd.* v. *Bombay Dyeing Mfg. Co. Ltd.*, 2012 SCC OnLine Bom 865: (2012) 5 Mah LJ 807.
281. *K.E. Burgmann A/S* v. *H.N. Shah*, 2011 SCC OnLine Del 2957: (2011) 124 DRJ 526.
282. *R.R. Enterprises* v. *C.M.D. of Garware-Wall Ropes Ltd.*, 2012 SCC OnLine Del 4821: ILR (2013) 1 Del 248.
283. *Sharda Raje Uday Singh Rao Gaekwar* v. *Veer Corpn.*, 2011 SCC OnLine Bom 1631: (2012) 2 Mah LJ 242.

For enabling a court to invoke the provisions of Section 8, the application seeking to get the dispute referred to arbitration must be filed before the written statement is submitted. The fact that the existence of the arbitration clause was admitted in the plaint or asserted in the written statement is immaterial inasmuch as the court, under Section 8, can refer for arbitration a dispute pending in a civil suit only when the party or parties concerned make application for getting the dispute referred to arbitration. If, despite the existence of an arbitration clause, the parties choose to contest the suit, the powers under Section 8 cannot be invoked.[284]

When no application was filed under Section 8 of the Act, before the trial court, trial court could not refer the dispute to arbitration.[285]

Necessity of existence of arbitration agreement

For application of Section 8 of the 1996 Act, it is absolutely essential that there should be an arbitration agreement between the parties. In *Atul Singh* v. *Sunil Kumar Singh*[286], neither *R* the predecessor-in-interest of the appellant-plaintiffs nor the plaintiffs were parties to the partnership deed which contained the arbitration clause. There was no document as defined in Section 7, Arbitration and Conciliation Act, 1996 containing the signatures of *R* or the plaintiffs. Similarly, there was no document as contemplated by Section 74(*b*) or (*c*) of the 1996 Act from which it could be spelled out that either of the plaintiffs were parties to the clause relating to the arbitration contained in the partnership deed. Admittedly, *R* was alive when the partnership deed was executed. It was held, on the face of it Section 8 of the 1996 Act did not apply to any dispute and the matter could not be referred to the arbitration.

Judicial authority is not divested of the powers to determine existence or non-existence of arbitration agreement before directing reference to arbitrators.[287]

In a hire purchase agreement the petitioner applicant had appended his signatures on printed forms and blank paper. Mere signing of forms and agreements would not constitute fraud. Mere allegation that the agreement contained unfilled blank space would not mean that the applicant had not consented to abide by the terms and conditions of agreement. As there was

284. *W.B. SEB* v. *Shanti Conductors (P) Ltd.*, 2003 SCC OnLine Gau 8: (2003) 2 Gau LR 76.
285. *Kanhaiya Lal Kankani* v. *Ambika Supply and Services (P) Ltd.*, 2017 SCC OnLine Gau 308: (2019) 2 Gau LR 558.
286. (2008) 2 SCC 602.
287. *Motilal* v. *Kedarmal Jainarayan Bharadiya*, 2002 SCC OnLine Bom 74: (2003) 2 Mah LJ 751.

agreement between the parties to refer the dispute to arbitrator, the order referring the parties to seek redressal under the Act was proper.[288]

In *HDFC Bank Ltd.* v. *Ashish Sheshmani Pandey*[289], plaintiff had taken a vehicle loan from defendant-bank. Bank had refused to issue a "no-objection certificate" despite payment of all dues because in some other transactions, certain amounts were due. Defendant-bank had not made any application in writing to refer the matter to the arbitration. There was no dispute between the parties in respect of that vehicle loan. Therefore, the question of referring the matter to the arbitration does not arise.

Once the defendant has itself repudiated the arbitration agreement, it does not lie in the mouth of the defendant to seek reference of the claims of the plaintiff in the suit to arbitration.[290]

In order to succeed in such an application the applicant must establish the existence of a valid arbitration agreement. If the applicant himself alleges that there is no arbitration agreement, he cannot possibly seek a reference of the disputes between himself and another to arbitration.[291]

For invoking of arbitration proceedings, what is essential is existence of an arbitration agreement, *i.e.* mandate under Section 7, Arbitration and Conciliation Act, 1996. In a given case, an arbitration clause may be provided by way of statute. The dispute resolution mechanism as provided under Section 23, Societies Registration Act, 1860 which provides a choice for dispute resolution, cannot be read into the bye-laws of the society or as forming part of bye-laws, as it only provides a choice of forum for dispute resolution, *i.e.* either arbitration or by approaching the court concerned. Where there is no arbitration clause in the agreement entered into between the parties, the question of invoking Section 8, Arbitration and Conciliation Act, 1996 does not arise.[292]

It is obligatory on the part of the court if it is brought to the notice of the court that there exists an agreement containing a clause to refer the matter for arbitration. Arbitrator has ample power to decide whether there is an existence of the arbitration clause in the agreement or he can give his own ruling about the validity of the arbitration agreement.[293]

---

288. *Ballabh Lal* v. *Kukkoo Motors Finance (P) Ltd.*, 2016 SCC OnLine All 2737: (2016) 116 ALR 111.
289. 2008 SCC OnLine Bom 159: (2008) 3 Mah LJ 865.
290. *Hindustan Steels Works Construction Ltd.* v. *Airports Authority of India*, 2007 SCC OnLine Del 1036: ILR (2008) 1 Del 233.
291. *Rajesh V. Choudhary* v. *Kshitij R. Torak*, 2010 SCC OnLine Bom 1126: (2010) 6 Mah LJ 457.
292. *Vasavi Clubs International* v. *Gella Krishna Veni*, 2021 SCC OnLine TS 3637.
293. *Railways* v. *Metal Powder Co. Ltd.*, 2006 SCC OnLine Mad 1036: (2006) 5 CTC 865.

Where the reference is made without intervention of the court, the Arbitral Tribunal can decide the question affecting its jurisdiction, one of which is the existence and validity of the arbitration agreement. But, where the intervention of the court is sought for the purpose, the court has the discretion to decide the preliminary issue of existence and validity of the arbitration agreement. The same principle will have to apply to an application for reference to arbitration made under Section 8, Arbitration and Conciliation Act.[294]

A mere writing on a piece of paper with signatures of the parties by itself cannot mean the existence of an agreement.[295]

Where an MOU which contained an arbitration clause was superseded by subsequent agreement, the question of reference of dispute to the arbitrator did not arise.[296]

When any party to the suit pending before a judicial authority raises a plea of existence of an alternate redressal forum by way of arbitration on the basis of alleged agreement in this regard, the remedy is in terms of Section 8, Arbitration and Conciliation Act.[297]

In order to constitute an arbitration agreement, a signed copy of general conditions of contract should have been attached to the signed contract and placed on record.[298]

Necessity of formal contract

General conditions of contract stipulated that once acceptance of a bid is communicated to the bidder by fax and it is followed by a letter of acceptance from the bidder, it constitutes a binding contract between both parties. Mere absence of formal contract in such a case will not render the making of reference of dispute improper.[299]

Arbitration clause—Registration not necessary

There is no requirement that an arbitration agreement should be effected by a registered instrument.[300]

---

294. *NRC Ltd.* v. *Kalyan Dombivli Municipal Corpn.*, 2014 SCC OnLine Bom 1195: (2014) 5 Mah LJ 564.
295. *Ibid.*
296. *Ceebros Property Development (P) Ltd.* v. *Vanisri*, 2008 SCC OnLine Mad 489: (2008) 4 CTC 275.
297. *Krishan Kumar Goel* v. *National Institute of Technology*, 2007 SCC OnLine P&H 672.
298. *Gayatri Engg. Co.* v. *Indian Oil Corpn. Ltd.*, 2007 SCC OnLine P&H 731: PLR (2008) 149 P&H 154.
299. *Kochi Refineries Ltd.* v. *Reva Enviro Systems (P) Ltd.*, 2016 SCC OnLine Ker 1564: (2016) 1 KLJ 774.
300. *Aspire Investments (P) Ltd.* v. *Nexgen Edusolutions (P) Ltd.*, 2009 SCC OnLine Del 3759: (2010) 114 DRJ 20.

Legality or otherwise of arbitration clause

When agreement between the parties contains an arbitration clause, it is obligatory for the court to refer the parties to arbitration, the court is not required to go into the legality or otherwise of the same.[301]

"In a matter which is the subject-matter of an arbitration agreement" [Sub-s. (1)]

The language used in Section 8 is "in a matter which is the subject of an arbitration agreement". Therefore, the suit should be in respect of "a matter" which the parties have agreed to refer to and which comes within the ambit of arbitration agreement. Where, however, a suit is commenced "as to a matter" which lies outside the arbitration agreement and is also between some of the parties who are not parties to the arbitration agreement, there is no question of application of Section 8. The words "a matter" indicates that the entire subject-matter of the suit should be subject to arbitration agreement.[302] Suit cannot be bifurcated into two parts so as to refer some part to arbitrator for adjudication and other part to be decided by civil court. Where a contract contains an arbitration agreement, subject-matter of the suit can be said to be covered by the arbitration agreement.[303]

Enquiry would be peripheral to examination of few aspects like: (*a*) existence of arbitration agreement; (*b*) whether action brought before court is by one of parties to said agreement against other party; (*c*) whether subject-matter of action before court is same as subject-matter of arbitration agreement; and (*d*) whether other party moves court seeking reference to arbitration before submitting its statement on substance of dispute. Judicial authority is not empowered under Section 8 to get into merits of case to decide whether parties should be referred or not.[304]

In *Ajoy Sankar Roy* v. *Sonar Bangla Developers (P) Ltd.*[305], subject-matter of the suit was not covered by an agreement containing an arbitration clause. It was held, suit not confined to agreement, but, related to other disputes and hence application for referring the dispute to the arbitration was dismissed.

In *Lahar Publicity Service* v. *Union of India*[306], the plaintiff filed suit for the recovery of the telecasting charges. Admittedly there was an arbitration agreement between the parties covering the suit for which suit was filed.

---

301. *Magma Leasing Ltd.* v. *Inder Pal*, 2009 SCC OnLine P&H 7727.
302. *Sukanya Holdings (P) Ltd.* v. *Jayesh H. Pandya*, (2003) 5 SCC 531.
303. *Ramdeobaba Padmavati Developers* v. *Ganesh Vitthaldas Chandak*, 2017 SCC OnLine Bom 3958: (2017) 5 Mah LJ 357.
304. *Andritz Oy.* v. *Enmas Engg. (P) Ltd.*, 2007 SCC OnLine Mad 461: (2007) 4 CTC 186.
305. 2013 SCC OnLine Cal 20796: (2014) 1 Cal LT 202.
306. 2003 SCC OnLine MP 35: (2003) 2 MP LJ 307.

Once it is held that the subject-matter of the action is covered by the arbitration agreement, then it is mandatory for the court to refer the parties to arbitration in view of the language used in Section 8 of the new Act. Parties were referred to arbitration.

It would be difficult to give an interpretation to Section 8 under which bifurcation of cause of action, *i.e.* to say, the subject-matter of the suit or in some cases bifurcation of the suit between parties who are parties to the arbitration agreement and others is possible. This would be laying down a totally new procedure not contemplated under the Arbitration Act. Such bifurcation of suit in two parts one to be decided by the Arbitral Tribunal and the other to be decided by the civil court would inevitably delay in proceedings. The whole purpose of speedy disposal of disputes and decreasing the cost of litigation would be frustrated by such a procedure. It will also increase the cost of litigation and harassment to the parties and on occasions there is possibility of conflicting judgments and orders by two different forums.[307]

Where subject-matter of suit is not covered by arbitration clause under agreement, reference to arbitration is not permissible.[308]

The phrase "matter which is the subject of an arbitration agreement" in sub-section (1) of Section 8 covers an arbitration agreement brought into existence while civil action was pending. It does not require that the arbitration agreement must be already in existence even before action is brought in court.[309]

If there is a clause for arbitration, the matter can be referred to arbitration. But when the subject-matter of the suit includes the subject-matter of the arbitration as well as the other disputes not covered under the agreement the civil court can proceed with the suit.[310]

In *Gurcharan Singh* v. *Collage Estates (P) Ltd.*[311], dispute between the parties was about maintenance charges. As there was no arbitration agreement between the parties covering the maintenance charges, reference of dispute to the arbitrator was not proper.

---

307. *Sukanya Holdings (P) Ltd.* v. *Jayesh H. Pandya*, (2003) 5 SCC 531; *Sundaram Finance Ltd.* v. *T. Thankam*, (2015) 14 SCC 444.
308. *T.A.I. Pharma Ltd.* v. *Wockhardt Ltd.*, 2016 SCC OnLine Bom 9820: (2017) 5 Mah LJ 500.
309. *P. Anand Gajapathi Raju* v. *P.V.G. Raju*, (2000) 4 SCC 539.
310. *Dhandapani Finance Ltd.* v. *Laxmi Cranes & Trailers (P) Ltd.*, 2012 SCC OnLine Mad 3220: (2013) 5 CTC 823.
311. *Gurcharan Singh* v. *Collage Estates (P) Ltd.*, 2020 SCC OnLine P&H 5355

When the plaintiff himself fails to prove that the arbitration contract is illegal or ineffective, then he has no right to object against referring the matter to arbitration.[312]

"If a party to the arbitration agreement" [Sub-s. (1)]

"Party" referred to in Section 8(1) only means a party who is entitled to make an application. A defendant who had filed a suit countering plaintiff's suit is not a party as envisaged by Section 8(1). A defendant who has preferred a suit cannot invoke agreement to refer the case to arbitration.[313]

Agreement containing arbitration clause should be between parties to dispute and such agreement should relate to or be applicable to dispute.[314] The expression "any dispute" in Section 8 *will not cover dispute against non-parties to arbitration agreement.*[315] In *Ramdeobaba Padmavati Developers* v. *Ganesh Vitthaldas Chandak*[316], partnership deed contained a clause to refer disputes regarding partnership business to sole arbitrator. Applicants/Defendants 2 to 6 deleted names of non-applicants from revenue records and sold suit properties to Applicant/Defendants 7 to 9. Applicant/Defendants 7 to 9 were not partners in the firm and had not signed an arbitration agreement. Relief sought with regard to cancellation of sale deeds executed in favour of Defendants 7 to 9 who were strangers to deed of partnership was thus non-arbitrable. In circumstances, rejection of application under Section 8 was upheld.

In *Mukesh Chandrashekhar Kumaran* v. *Suman Vitthalrao Ikhankar*[317], Defendants 2 to 5 in the suit were not parties to the arbitration agreement. Reference to arbitration by allowing application under Section 8 was not proper. Order of reference passed by the trial court was set aside.

Where one of the two defendants is not party to the arbitration agreement, the dispute cannot be referred to arbitration, though the plaintiff has cause of action against both the defendants.[318]

Third party who is not a party to the arbitration agreement cannot be referred to arbitration.[319]

---

312. *Ranwa Construction Co.* v. *Administrator*, 2005 SCC OnLine Raj 74: (2005) 4 RLW 2680.
313. *MSTC Ltd.* v. *Srinivas Smelters Ltd.*, 2010 SCC OnLine Mad 4564: (2011) 1 CTC 557.
314. *Ramdeobaba Padmavati Developers* v. *Ganesh Vitthaldas Chandak*, 2017 SCC OnLine Bom 3958: (2017) 5 Mah LJ 357.
315. *Ibid.*
316. 2017 SCC OnLine Bom 3958: (2017) 5 Mah LJ 357.
317. 2014 SCC OnLine Bom 1588: (2014) 2 Mah LJ 845.
318. *Kensoft Infotech Ltd.* v. *Sundaram BNP Paribus Home Finance Ltd.*, 2010 SCC OnLine Mad 2031: (2010) 2 LW 253.
319. *Simran Sodhi* v. *Sandeep Singh*, 2022 SCC OnLine Del 3688: (2023) 296 DLT 363.

Where the plaintiff and the defendant are not parties to the arbitration clause, the provisions of Section 8 cannot be invoked.[320]

All the parties to the suit were not party to the arbitration agreement. Subject-matter of the dispute was not covered by the suit. Reference of dispute to the arbitration was not called for.[321]

Power agents of landowners entered into MOU in individual capacity. The MOU contained an arbitration clause. The MOU would not bind the landowners and as such arbitration proceedings cannot be invoked against landowners who were not parties to MOU.[322]

Mere impleadment in suit of some defendants against whom no specific relief has been claimed cannot ensure to the benefit of the plaintiff to avoid the arbitration agreement.[323]

Stranger to arbitration agreement (Section 8 as amended by Act 3 of 2016)

Amended Section 8 makes it clear that even a stranger, person claiming through vendor, can be a party to arbitration agreement within ambit of arbitration clause. The matter was arbitrable and reference to arbitration was proper.[324]

"Submitting his first statement on the substance of the dispute" [Sub-s. (1)]

Any party who seeks to make a reference to arbitration has to apply to the court before filing of the written statement, *i.e.* in the words of that section, first statement. Once a party submits a first statement on merits, it can be assumed that the party has submitted to the jurisdiction of the court and then the court ceases to have jurisdiction to refer the dispute to arbitration.[325]

The expression "first statement on the substance of the dispute" contained in Section 8(1) of the 1996 Act must be contradinguished with the expression "written statement". It implies submission of the party to the jurisdiction of the judicial authority. What is, therefore, needed is a finding on the part

320. *Alankar Global (P) Ltd.* v. *Dinesh Kumar Mathur*, 2006 SCC OnLine Del 1512: (2007) 93 DRJ 684.
321. *Ibid.*
322. *Jain Housing & Constructions Ltd.* v. *v. Ramaiah*, 2009 SCC OnLine Mad 246.
323. *Kotak Mahindra Bank Ltd.* v. *Sundaram Brake Lining Ltd.*, 2008 SCC OnLine Mad 519: (2008) 4 CTC 1.
324. *Debasish De Bhowmick* v. *Tirupati Awas (P) Ltd.*, 2018 SCC OnLine Cal 5515: (2018) 4 CHN 443.
325. *Ganesh Trading Co.* v. *State of Maharashtra*, 2007 SCC OnLine Bom 184: (2007) 4 Mah LJ 715.

of the judicial authority that the party has waived its right to invoke the arbitration clause. If an application is filed before actually filing the first statement on the substance of the dispute, the party cannot be said to have waived its right or acquiesced itself to the jurisdiction of the court. What is, therefore, material as to whether the petitioner has filed his first statement on the substance of the dispute or not, if not, his application under Section 8 of the 1996 Act may not be held wholly unmaintainable.[326]

It is mandatory for a party seeking reference under Section 8, Arbitration and Conciliation Act, 1996 to make an application in writing before submitting his first statement on the substance of the dispute and it is only then that the judicial authority gets the jurisdiction to make reference under Section 8 of the 1996 Act. Once a party submits his first statement on the substance of the dispute, *i.e.* on merits, it can be assumed that such a party has submitted to the jurisdiction of the judicial authority and the judicial authority thereafter ceases to have jurisdiction to refer the dispute to arbitration, unless of course, both the parties consent to the making of such reference.[327] If the question of jurisdiction is not raised before or at the time of first statement, it would be deemed that the parties submitted before the jurisdiction of the court.[328] Where the defendant has filed a written statement with preliminary objection in regard to the existence of an arbitration agreement, the right to invoke an arbitration clause is not lost.[329] Mere making of application for extension of time for filing written statement does not amount to submitting to the jurisdiction of the court, nor amounts to abandonment of arbitration agreement.[330]

The expression "first statement on the substance of the dispute" is of wide import. It takes within its sweep any statement filed to join or raise issues regarding the substratum of the matter in dispute. In the context of the civil suit, it includes the written statement as required to be presented under Order 8 Rule 1 CPC.[331]

The expression "not later than" in Section 8(1), Arbitration and Conciliation Act, 1996 implies that a party is not precluded from applying under Section 8 simultaneously along with filing of a written statement or including such relief in the written statement. However, the party forfeits its

326. *Rashtriya Ispat Nigam Ltd.* v. *Verma Transport Co.*, (2006) 7 SCC 275.

327. *Harvestdeal Securities Ltd.* v. *Punjab National Bank*, 2016 SCC OnLine Bom 2631: (2016) 4 Mah LJ 273.

328. *Alok Nath Chattopadhya* v. *Anil Narain Tadvalkar*, 2010 SCC OnLine All 1915.

329. *APL Polyfab (P) Ltd.* v. *Technology Information, Forecasting and Assessment Council (TIFAC)*, 2011 SCC OnLine Del 3447: (2011) 125 DRJ 375.

330. *Emirates Grains Products Co. LLC* v. *L.M.J. International Ltd.*, 2009 SCC OnLine Cal 1761: (2009) 4 CHN 125.

331. *SPML Infra Ltd.* v. *Trisquare Switchgears (P) Ltd.*, (2022) 4 HCC (Del) 249.

right once it has filed the written statement. Once the proceedings before the court or judicial authority progress beyond the initial stage, it is not permissible for a party to then turn around and seek recourse to arbitration. A mere delay in making an application under Section 8 is not fatal to a party's right.[332]

If a party fails to file an application under Section 8(1) for referring the parties to arbitration within the time available or granted for filing the first statement on the substance of the dispute (which includes a written statement in the context of a suit), the party forfeits its right to apply under Section 8(1).[333]

The filing of a written statement without prejudice to the arbitration clause is not the equivalent to an application under Section 8 and thereby consequences of waiver of arbitration cannot be avoided.[334]

In opposing the prayer for interim injunction, the restriction contained in Section 8(1) would not be attracted. Filing of reply to the injunction application was held not sufficient ground to refuse to entertain the plea taken by the appellants that the suit should be referred to Arbitral Tribunal.[335] Unlike the Arbitration Act, 1940, under the Arbitration and Conciliation Act, 1996 a reply to an interim/interlocutory application can be construed as the first statement on the substance of the dispute. The first statement of substance of the dispute will include a written statement in a suit or a reply to an application under other proceedings before a judicial authority.[336]

Where application to refer the dispute to arbitration was filed after the written statement was filed in the suit and entire defence was disclosed, application was not maintainable, was rejected.[337]

Section 8 requires a person invoking said section to file an application for reference to arbitration not later than when submitting his "first statement" on the substance of dispute. Application for adjournment or seeking time for filing counter will not constitute "first statement". When the substance of disputes has been made clear to the opposing party who sets down his stand clearly in proceedings pending before judicial authority, he makes the first statement. "First statement" need not necessarily be a written statement, filing of counter-affidavit dealing with substances of dispute constituted

332. *Ibid.*
333. *Ibid.*
334. *Lindsay International (P) Ltd.* v. *Laxmi Niwas Mittal*, 2020 SCC OnLine Cal 1658: (2021) 1 Arb LR 137.
335. *Rashtriya Ispat Nigam Ltd.* v. *Verma Transport Co.*, (2006) 7 SCC 275.
336. *Jashu M. Patel* v. *Shivdatta R. Joshi*, 2002 SCC OnLine Bom 1168: (2003) 3 Mah LJ 487.
337. *Arti Jethani* v. *Daehsan Trading (India) (P) Ltd.*,. 2011 SCC OnLine Del 2270: ILR (2011) 6 Del 319.

first statement and application filed under Section 8 after filing of such counter-affidavit is not maintainable.[338]

In a suit for the recovery of possession of the vehicle seized by the defendant in exercise of powers under finance agreement, plaintiff's plea that the defendant has waived his claim for arbitration as the written statement has been filed was not accepted.[339]

Filing a counter to an application for temporary injunction cannot be considered as submitting the first statement on the substance of the dispute. Not only filing of the written statement in a suit but filing of any statement, application, affidavit by a defendant prior to the filing of the written statement will be considered as submission of a statement on the substance of the dispute, if by filing such statement/application/affidavit, the defendant shows his intention to submit himself to the jurisdiction of the court and waive his right to seek reference to arbitration. But filing of a reply by a defendant, to an application for temporary injunction/attachment before judgment/appointment of receiver, cannot be considered as submission of a statement on the substance of the dispute, as that is done to avoid an interim order being made against him.[340] In this case the counter affidavit filed by the appellant in reply to the notice of motion seeking appointment of receiver and grant of a temporary injunction clearly stated that the reply of affidavit was being filed for the limited purpose of opposing the interim relief. Even in the absence of such a disclaimer, filing a detailed objection to an application for interim relief cannot be considered to be submission on a statement on the substance of the dispute resulting in submitting oneself to the jurisdiction of the court.[341]

Filing of a written statement would not constitute waiver of the application under Section 8 of the Act.[342]

In *Narayana Farm Produce (P) Ltd.* v. *Jalaram Feeds*[343], records showed that applicants never insisted upon trial court to decide their objection on maintainability of suit as well as need for referring dispute to arbitration. Applicants submitted their written statement, such conduct showed their intention that civil court must decide disputes between parties on its own merits. This amounted to a waiver of the right to seek arbitration.

---

338. *Wankanner Jain S.W.S.* v. *Jugal Kishore*, 2001 SCC OnLine Mad 528: (2001) 3 CTC 656.
339. *Sugal* v. *P. Subramania Reddy*, 1999 SCC OnLine Mad 775: (2000) 1 LW 828.
340. *Booz Allen & Hamilton Inc.* v. *SBI Home Finance Ltd.*, (2011) 5 SCC 532.
341. *Ibid.*
342. *Shivangi Pharmaceuticals (P) Ltd.* v. *Anil Sharma*, 2006 SCC OnLine All 1015: (2007) 66 ALR 505.
343. 2017 SCC OnLine Bom 8483: (2018) 3 Mah LJ 292.

The expression "first statement on the substance of the dispute" refers to the submission of the party to the jurisdiction of the judicial authority by offering to defend the suit and thereby, waiving his right to invoke the arbitration clause. If the affidavit opposing the summons for judgment and seeking leave to defend objects to the jurisdiction of the court to hear the suit and indicates that the defendant does not want the civil court to adjudicate upon his rights or liabilities, but wants the domestic forum to decide that, then mere filing of a reply to the summons for judgment does not amount to making a "first statement on the substance of the dispute", even if such affidavit contains various other defences.[344]

Filing of application by the appellant seeking further time to file a written statement would not amount to making first statement on substance of defence. Rejection of application for referring the parties to arbitration on the ground that appellant had waived right to seek arbitration was found not sustainable was set aside.[345]

Where the defendant filed a written statement and participated in the trial, the right of the defendant to refer matter for arbitration in terms of Section 8(1) ceases to exist.[346]

By filing an application under Section 8, the party does not subject itself to jurisdiction of court—pecuniary, territorial or subject-matter. A party merely brings to notice of that court the existence of arbitration agreement and seeks an order referring the party bringing the action to arbitration in accordance therewith.[347]

In suit for specific performance reply opposing application for interim injunction which showed unequivocal intention to contest proceedings in suit was not treated as first statement on substance of dispute. Order of the trial court referring the dispute to the arbitrator was not interfered.[348]

Assigning the grounds in the civil revision petitions filed by the petitioners earlier before the High Court were "first statement on the substance of the dispute" since they directly pertained to the pleadings contained in the plaint, the applications filed at a later point of time after the filing of the civil revision petition were held not sustainable. By not pleading about the arbitration clause and the possible remedy under Section 8 of the Act in the

344. *Drive India Enterprise Solutions Ltd.* v. *Haier Telecom (India) (P) Ltd.*, 2018 SCC OnLine Bom 571: (2018) 3 Mah LJ 605.

345. *Greaves Cotton Ltd.* v. *United Machinery & Appliances*, (2017) 2 SCC 268.

346. *Dharmsee Parpia* v. *J.K. Leathers*, 2020 SCC OnLine Mad 28362.

347. *Conros Steels (P) Ltd.* v. *Lu Qin (Hong Kong) Co. Ltd.*, 2014 SCC OnLine Bom 2305: (2015) 1 Mah LJ 434.

348. *Navalji Cotspin Ltd.* v. *Amravati Growers Coop. Spg. Ltd.*, 2015 SCC OnLine Bom 8343: (2016) 2 Mah LJ 134.

civil revision petition, the petitioners had waived their right to the relief under this section. The defendants had subjected themselves to the jurisdiction of the court. The petitioners had already submitted their first statement on the substance of the dispute prior to the filing of the application under Section 8 of the Act.[349]

Not at a belated stage

The party is at liberty to seek a reference to the arbitrator but not at a belated stage. The party desiring a reference has to approach the court for such reference before it submits first statement on the substance of the dispute.[350]

Submission of the first statement on the substance of the dispute—Referral of dispute to arbitration when not barred

The conditions which are required to be satisfied under Section 8(1), Arbitration and Conciliation Act, 1996 before the court can exercise its powers are:

1. there is an arbitration agreement;
2. a party to the agreement brings an action in the court against the other party;
3. subject-matter of the action is the same as the subject-matter of the arbitration agreement; and
4. the other party moves the court for referring the parties to arbitration before it submits his first statement on the substance of the dispute.

The last condition creates a right in the person bringing the action to have the dispute adjudicated by the court once the other party has submitted his first statement of defence. But if the party, who wants the matter to be referred to the arbitration, applies to the court after submission of his statement and the party who has brought the action does not object, as in the instant case, there is no bar on the court referring the parties to arbitration.[351]

Defendant filed written statement and participated in the trial. Once a written statement is filed, the right of the defendant to refer matter for arbitration in terms of Section 8(1) ceases to exist. Relegating parties to pursue remedy of arbitration was not proper.[352]

349. *SBI* v. *P.R.P. Exports*, 2009 SCC OnLine Mad 369: (2009) 6 CTC 187.
350. *Motilal* v. *Kedarmal Jainarayan Bharadiya*, 2002 SCC OnLine Bom 74: (2003) 2 Mah LJ 751.
351. *P. Anand Gajapathi Raju* v. *P.V.G. Raju*, (2000) 4 SCC 539.
352. *Dharmsee Parpia* v. *J.K. Leathers*, 2020 SCC OnLine Mad 28362.

Inordinate delay in filing of written statement

Merely because there is inordinate delay in filing the written statement, it cannot in any way take away the rigour of Section 8. Law mandates whenever it is brought to the notice of the court before filing the written statement that there is an arbitral clause and the subject-matter of the suit is actually decided by the arbitrator, it has got to be referred to arbitration. Provisions pertaining to the filing of the written statement cannot be applied to the initiation of an application under Section 8. Parties were directed to approach the arbitrator as understood between them under clause 5 of the agreement.[353]

Two different causes of action—Reference to arbitration

Company *C* had entered into a contract with a partnership firm to avail its services. Company *C* terminated the contract as one of the partners of the said firm was guilty of overcharging freight by mis-presentation to *C*. Company issued a show-cause notice to blacklist the firm. The firm challenged show-cause notice by filing suit. It was held that both the causes of action, *i.e.* legal termination of contract and blacklisting of firm arose out of the terms of the contract. Section 8 was attracted. Application filed under Section 8 for referring the parties to arbitration was maintainable.[354]

Composite reference to arbitration

Composite reference for disputes and differences arising out of two separate contracts is not maintainable.[355]

Bifurcation of cause of action, not permissible

Where an application under Section 8 of the Act for referring the parties to arbitration is filed, it is obligatory for the court to refer the parties to arbitration in terms of the agreement. The language of Section 8 is peremptory.

Bifurcation of the cause of action, *i.e.* to say the subject-matter of the suit or in some cases bifurcation of the suit between the parties who are parties to the arbitration agreement and others is not possible, as this would be laying down a totally new procedure not contemplated under the Act. If the bifurcation of the subject-matter of a suit was contemplated, the legislature

353. *Ragavendra Advertising* v. *Prasar Bharati, (Broadcasting Corpn. of India)*, 2009 SCC OnLine Mad 1599: (2009) 5 LW 439.

354. *Rashtriya Ispat Nigam Ltd.* v. *Verma Transport Co.*, (2006) 7 SCC 275.

355. *Ganapati Technology Services (P) Ltd.* v. *State Fisheries Development Corpn.*, 2021 SCC OnLine Cal 4320.

would have used appropriate language to permit such a course. Since there is no such indication in the language of the section, bifurcation of the subject-matter of an action brought before a judicial authority is not allowed. Such bifurcation of suit in two parts, one to be decided by the Arbitral Tribunal and the other to be decided by the civil court would delay the proceedings frustrating the object of the 1996 Act, and complicate the matter.[356] Subject-matter of the suit included the subject-matter of the arbitration agreement as well as other disputes. As there is no provision in the Act for splitting the cause or parties, application for reference of dispute to arbitration was rejected.[357]

Arbitrable and non-arbitrable dispute cannot be bifurcated, rejection of reference was proper. Suit claims cannot be bifurcated/split up into arbitrable and non-arbitrable disputes.[358]

A suit in which a single claim is made against two defendants, if cannot be split up and dispute as against one cannot be referred to arbitration, while it is tried against another, who is not party to the arbitration agreement. In such a case, a dispute cannot be referred to arbitration.[359] In *Rita Bagga* v. *Milan Developers*[360], dispute was between the plaintiff and two defendants. Agreement entered into between the plaintiff and one defendant stipulated reference to arbitrator in case of dispute pertaining to terms and conditions of agreement. However, no such agreement was entered into between the plaintiff and the other defendant. Cause of action and relief sought could not be split so as to hit some parts by referring to Section 8 and other parts allowing suit to continue. Dispute cannot be referred to arbitration.

The court can refer the parties of a suit to arbitration only when the subject-matter of the suit and the subject-matter of the arbitration agreement are the same. Parties to the arbitration agreement and suit are to be the same for taking benefit of Section 8 of the Act. The court cannot split up the subject-matter of the suit and the parties to the suit for referring the disputes to arbitration.[361]

---

356. *Sundaram Finance Ltd.* v. *T. Thankam*, (2015) 14 SCC 444.
357. *Alankar Global (P) Ltd.* v. *Dinesh Kumar Mathur*, 2006 SCC OnLine Del 1512: (2007) 93 DRJ 684.
358. *Gujarat Composite Ltd.* v. *A. Infrastructure Ltd.*, 2018 SCC OnLine Guj 4782: (2018) 59 (4) GLR 3083.
359. *Terry Gold (India) Ltd.* v. *TCI Finance Ltd.*, 1998 SCC OnLine AP 534: (1998) 6 ALD 831; *Rita Bagga* v. *Milan Developers*, 2016 SCC OnLine All 2751: (2016) 116 ALR 192.
360. 2016 SCC OnLine All 2751: (2016) 116 ALR 192.
361. *Raman Agarwal* v. *Sadhuram Agarwal*, 2010 SCC OnLine Gau 106: (2010) 6 Gau LR 349.

Reference of two disputes to single arbitrator

If *A* has a claim against *B* and *C* and if *A* has an arbitration agreement with *B* and *A* also has a separate arbitration agreement with *C*, there is no reason why *A* cannot have a joint arbitration against *B* and *C*.[362] In *Hema Khattar* v. *Shiv Khera*[363], the respondent entered into arbitration agreement with Applicants 1 and 2 separately. Respondent was held entitled to have joint arbitration to settle the dispute with the appellants.

Issues to be decided by judicial authority prior to referring disputes to arbitration

When a suit is filed by one of the parties to an arbitration agreement against the other parties to the arbitration agreement and if the defendant(s) file application under Section 8 stating that the parties should be referred to arbitration, the judicial authority will have to decide:

(*i*) whether there is an arbitration agreement amongst the parties;

(*ii*) whether all the parties to the suit are parties to the arbitration agreement;

(*iii*) whether the disputes which are the subject-matter of the suit fall within the scope of arbitration agreement;

(*iv*) whether the defendant had applied under Section 8 of the Act before submitting his first statement on the substance of the dispute; and

(*v*) whether the reliefs sought in the suit are those that can be adjudicated and granted in an arbitration.[364]

Reference under Section 151 CPC

Where the provisions of Section 8, Arbitration and Conciliation Act, 1996 are not satisfied, reference to arbitration under Section 151 CPC would not be justified.[365]

The judicial authority, after referring the matter to arbitration under Section 8, Arbitration and Conciliation Act, has no jurisdiction to pass any order applying Section 151 CPC.[366]

---

362. *P.R. Shah, Shares & Stock Brokers (P) Ltd.* v. *B.H.H. Securities (P) Ltd.*, (2012) 1 SCC 594.
363. (2017) 7 SCC 716.
364. *Booz Allen & Hamilton Inc.* v. *SBI Home Finance Ltd.*, (2011) 5 SCC 532.
365. *Eagle Agro-Farm (P) Ltd.* v. *Eagle Soraj Townships (P) Ltd.*, 2013 SCC OnLine Bom 1614: (2014) 5 Mah LJ 330.
366. *Bosabari Tea Estates (P) Ltd.* v. *Auro Tea Co. Ltd.*, 1999 SCC OnLine Gau 252: (1999) 2 Gau LR 348.

Admitted liability

What is material for the purpose of Section 8, Arbitration Act is that there should be existence of difference or disputes with regard to a particular liability arising out of the terms of the agreement. If the liability is acknowledged and admitted, it does not come within the meaning and ambit of disputes and differences.[367]

Compromise

Where the dispute for which arbitration is sought has been compromised outside court, the court should not refer such matter to arbitration.[368]

Settled matter

Where there is full and final settlement in respect of the dispute or differences regarding matter covered by the arbitrator clause, subsequently such settled matter cannot be referred for arbitration once again.[369]

When arbitrator already appointed

When an arbitrator had already been appointed in the matter, no question of referring the dispute to arbitration arises at all.[370]

Allegations of fraud, deceit, coercion, under influence or misrepresentation, arbitrability of

In a case where the parties allege that the arbitration agreement is vitiated on account of fraud, the court may refuse to refer the parties to arbitration under Section 8. Mere allegation of fraud is no ground to nullify the effect of arbitration agreement between the parties and arbitration clause need not be avoided and the parties can be relegated to arbitration where merely simple allegations of fraud touching upon internal affairs of the parties is alleged. It is only in those cases where the court finds that there are serious allegations of fraud which make the virtual case of criminal offence and where there are complicated allegations of fraud, then it becomes necessary that such complicated issues can be decided only by the civil court on the appreciation of evidence that needs to be produced.[371] Simple allegations of fraud which

---

367. *Maruti Udyog Ltd.* v. *Mahalaxmi Motors Ltd.*, 2001 SCC OnLine Del 1291: (2002) 61 DRJ 398.
368. *Vivek Arya* v. *Economic Transport Organisation*, 2002 SCC OnLine Cal 484.
369. *S.S.M. Soundappan* v. *K.G. Balakrishnan*, 1997 SCC OnLine Mad 503: (1997) 2 CTC 385.
370. *Biplab Das* v. *Mira Sengupta*, 2013 SCC OnLine Cal 17879.
371. *Ameet Lalchand Shah* v. *Rishabh Enterprises*, (2018) 15 SCC 678.

concern internal affairs of the parties, are not sufficient to oust the jurisdiction of the tribunal. In such cases, the parties can be permitted to avoid forum of their choice, i.e. adjudication of dispute by Arbitral Tribunal.[372] In *Ameet Lalchand Shah* v. *Rishabh Enterprises*[373], both the parties have consciously proceeded with the commercial transactions to the commission of the Photovoltaic Solar Plant at Dongri, Raksha, District Jhansi, U.P. The respondent had proceeded to procure the materials, entered into agreement with Juwi India for engineering, installation and commissioning, the sale and purchase agreement with Astonfield, all the conscious steps were taken in the commercial understanding to commission of the solar plant though Juwi India and Astonfield are not parties to the main agreement. Equipment lease agreement and all the agreements/contracts contain clauses referring to the main agreement. It is the duty of the court to import the commercial understanding with a "sense of business efficacy" and not by mere averments made in the plaint. The High Court was not right in not referring the parties to arbitration merely on the ground of allegations of fraud made in the plaint.

The court must refer the parties to arbitration once the requisite conditions are satisfied. In case of serious allegations of fraud, malpractices and collusion among the members to the detriment of a party, the court may refuse to refer the issues to arbitration.[374] Claims on allegations of fraud, forgery and siphoning off of goods and monies of the firm, whereby FIR was lodged would lie in the realm of public law and cannot be referred to arbitration.[375]

"Fraud" includes fraud or cheating at stage of formation of contract and at stage of performance of contract, and is arbitrable regardless of the stage at which it is alleged.[376]

The respondent had challenged the compromise decree alleging that it had been obtained by inducement and fraud. In view of the allegations of fraud levelled by the respondent that the compromise decree is vitiated by fraud, the parties cannot be referred to arbitration. Where there are allegations of fraud which are so complicated that it becomes absolutely essential that such complex issues can be decided only by the civil court on apprehension of the evidence adduced by the parties.[377]

372. *Solitaire Ventures Pte Ltd.* v. *Vipul Ltd.*, 2020 SCC OnLine P&H 2604; *Ameet Lalchand Shah* v. *Rishabh Enterprises*, (2018) 15 SCC 678.
373. (2018) 15 SCC 678.
374. *Mahesh Kumar Sharma* v. *Badal Chandra Choudhury*, 2012 SCC OnLine Gau 773: (2013) 6 Gau LR 390.
375. *Simran Sodhi* v. *Sandeep Singh*, 2022 SCC OnLine Del 3688: (2023) 296 DLT 363.
376. *Avitel Post Studioz Ltd.* v. *HSBC PI Holdings (Mauritius) Ltd.*, (2021) 4 SCC 713.
377. *Nicholas Piramal India Ltd.* v. *Zenith Drugs and Allied Agencies (P) Ltd.*, 2007 SCC OnLine Gau 52: (2008) 2 Gau LR 418.

Those cases where there are serious allegations of fraud, they are to be treated as non-arbitrable and it is only the civil court which should decide such matters. However, where there are allegations of fraud simpliciter, and as such allegations are merely alleged, it is not necessary to nullify the effect of the arbitration agreement between the parties, such issues can be determined by the Arbitral Tribunal. In *A. Ayyasamy* v. *A. Paramasivam*[378], it was held that the allegations of purported fraud were not so serious which cannot be taken care of by the arbitrator, rejecting the application under Section 8 for referring the parties to arbitration was not proper.

In *Ram Kishan Mimani* v. *Goverdhan Das Mimani*[379], petitioners asserted that respondents have siphoned off funds of partnerships, the respondents contended that there are serious allegations pertaining to fraud and malpractice. Charges regarding malpractice were not such that the arbitrator or Arbitral Tribunal would not be able to address the same. In case of any problem, the arbitrator or the Arbitral Tribunal may seek assistance of the court in relation to evidence being received. Only where matter involves serious charges with heavy documentary and oral evidence, may not be referred to arbitration notwithstanding the disputes being covered thereby.

If fraud was alleged in the execution of the agreement, *i.e.* by forging the signature of a party, fabricating the arbitration agreement and so on the court and not the arbitrator should go into it, if raised before the court. When fraud is alleged in the performance of the agreement the arbitrator has the competence to go into it as he has competence to go into all other aspects of the contract.[380]

Dispute arose out of partnership deed between the parties. No serious question of fraud raised required evidence to be adduced at length. Matter was referred to arbitration for adjudication.[381]

The courts, while deciding an application under Section 8 of the Act, are not to go into the merits of the dispute including the ground of fraud, undue influence, misrepresentation, etc. These issues are also capable of being adjudicated by the arbitrator who is competent to decide all issues relating to the franchise as well as Hotel Operation Agreement including allegations of fraud.[382]

Where there is no dispute as to arbitrability of the dispute or existence of the arbitral clause, the duty of the court is to refer it to the arbitrator.

378. (2016) 10 SCC 386; *Ameet Lalchand Shah* v. *Rishabh Enterprises*, (2018) 15 SCC 678.
379. 2010 SCC OnLine Cal 1060: (2010) 4 CHN 527.
380. *Jessop & Co. Ltd.* v. *Tecpro Systems Ltd.*, 2012 SCC OnLine Cal 6324: (2012) 4 CHN 567.
381. *Rajia Begum* v. *Barnali Mukherjee*, 2021 SCC OnLine Cal 4281.
382. *Ultra Home Constructions (P) Ltd.* v. *Choice Hotels International Inc.*, 2012 SCC OnLine Del 245: (2012) 127 DRJ 724.

Allegation of fraud or malpractice, if made out, the arbitrator may not be competent to decide those questions. Civil court may reject application under Section 8 of the Act.[383]

Expression "shall" occurring in Section 8(1) is not mandatory and Section 8 does not deviate from time tested principles of civil court to refer or not to refer dispute to arbitrator, civil court can decline to refer dispute to arbitrator.[384] Serious allegations of fraud/misrepresentation require minute details of evidence. Application for reference to arbitrator was rejected.[385]

In view of the mandatory nature of Section 8, the contention that the party seeking reference to arbitration had fabricated the record was not accepted. The settled position of law is that it is the person against whom fraud is alleged who has an option to have the matter decided by the civil court.[386]

In application under Section 8 to refer parties to arbitration, the court cannot and need not to go into question as to whether agreement entered into between parties is vitiated by fraud, etc. Such a question can also be determined by the arbitrator himself. Judicial authority cannot go into question as to whether agreement is null and void, inoperative or incapable of being performed and these issues should be raised before the arbitrator.[387]

Allegations of fraud will be non-arbitrable only if either of the following two tests laid down are satisfied, and not otherwise, *namely*: 1) does this plea of fraud permeate the entire contract and above all, the agreement of arbitration, rendering it void; or, 2) whether the allegations of fraud touch upon the internal affairs of the parties inter se having no implication in the public domain.[388]

Following *Avitel Post Studioz Ltd.* v. *HSBC PI Holdings (Mauritius) Ltd.*[389], it was held that if the subject-matter of an agreement between the parties falls within Section 17, Contract Act, 1872 or involves fraud in the performance of the contract, which would amount to deceit, being a civil wrong, the subject-matter of such agreement would certainly be arbitrable. Further, merely because a particular transaction may have criminal overtones

383. *Shriram Transport Finance Co. Ltd.* v. *Rumasaha*, 2016 SCC OnLine Gau 184: (2016) 5 Gau LR 46.

384. *H.G. Oomor Sait* v. *O. Aslam Sait*, 2001 SCC OnLine Mad 465: (2001) 3 CTC 269.

385. *Ibid*; *GDR F.S.(P) Ltd.* v. *All Securities Ltd.*, 2001 SCC OnLine Mad 491: (2002) 1 LW 418.

386. *Bombay Gas Co. Ltd.* v. *Parmeshwar Mittal*, 1997 SCC OnLine Bom 314: (1997) 3 Mah LJ 863.

387. *Kotak Mahindra Bank Ltd.* v. *Sundaram Brake Lining Ltd.*, 2008 SCC OnLine Mad 519: (2008) 4 CTC 1.

388. *Avitel Post Studioz Ltd.* v. *HSBC PI Holdings (Mauritius) Ltd.*, (2021) 4 SCC 713.

389. *Ibid.*

as well, does not mean that its subject-matter becomes non-arbitrable so long as the dispute(s) in question are principally inter partes and do not fall in the public domain.[390]

Mere allegations of fraud will not preclude civil court from referring parties to arbitration unless those allegations are examined. Main grievance of plaintiffs was breach of contract relating to non-payment of balance consideration. Matter did not involve serious charges requiring parties to lead heavy documentary and oral evidence. The trial judge had committed serious error in dismissing the application without examining allegations of fraud made in the plaint.[391]

The same set of facts may have civil as well as criminal consequences. Hence, mere fact that criminal proceedings can or have been instituted in respect of the same allegations of fraud, coercion, undue influence, or misrepresentation, and/or tort of deceit, does not make such disputes non-arbitrable. Thus, there can be concurrent arbitration proceedings, *i.e.* civil proceedings and criminal proceedings in respect of the same set of allegations of fraud, coercion, undue influence, or misrepresentation, and/or tort of deceit.[392]

Where the main agreement has come to end, the arbitration clause being independent continues to remain in force for the purpose of resolution of all disputes between the parties arising in relation to the said agreement.[393]

Action "*in rem*"

Exclusion of actions *in rem* from arbitration, exposits the intrinsic limits of arbitration as a private dispute resolution mechanism, which is only binding on "the parties" to the arbitration agreement. The courts established by law, on the other hand, enjoy jurisdiction by default and do not require mutual agreement for conferring jurisdiction. The Arbitral Tribunals not being courts of law or established under the auspices of the State cannot act judicially so as to affect those who are not bound by the arbitration clause. Arbitration is unsuitable when it has *erga omnes* effect, *i.e.* it affects the rights and liabilities of persons who are not bound by the arbitration agreement. Equally arbitration as a decentralised mode of dispute resolution is unsuitable when the subject-matter or a dispute in the factual background, requires collective adjudication before one court or forum. Certain disputes

390. *Deccan Paper Mills Co. Ltd.* v. *Regency Mahavir Properties*, (2021) 4 SCC 786.
391. *VBHC, Mumbai Value Homes (P) Ltd.* v. *Laxman Bhoir*, 2015 SCC OnLine Bom 8273: (2015) 6 Mah LJ 385.
392. *N.N. Global Mercantile (P) Ltd.* v. *Indo Unique Flame Ltd.*, (2021) 4 SCC 379.
393. *BSNL* v. *Ashok Kumar*, 2014 SCC OnLine All 15200: (2014) 4 All LJ 506.

as a class, or sometimes the dispute in the given facts, can be efficiently resolved only through collective litigation proceedings.[394]

Multiple arbitration agreements in relation to the same transaction

Main dispute being a common one, in such case, Arbitral Tribunal consisting of same members but separately constituted in respect of each agreement, would be appropriate. Freedom would be given to such Arbitral Tribunal as to when to hold separate proceedings with regard to a particular agreement and when disputes should be clubbed.[395]

Stale claims

The reference of dispute to arbitration is not an empty or idle formality. The court has to satisfy itself about the existence of an arbitration agreement and whether the dispute referred is entertainable and not a live matter.[396]

Time barred claims

Suit cannot be referred to arbitration where the right of referring the dispute to arbitration has become time barred.[397]

Execution of contract was completed by 22 July 2011, contractor issued notice on 24 April 2014, raised claim and sought reference to arbitrator. Notice was issued within three years of the raising of claim, it was not clear on what basis the company alleged that the claim was time barred. Question of limitation is a mixed question of law and fact. Matter required reference to the Arbitral Tribunal for decision.[398]

Limitation law is procedural and normally disputes, being factual, would be for the arbitrator to decide, guided by the facts found and the law applicable. The court at the referral stage can interfere only when it is manifest that the claims are ex facie time barred and dead, or there is no subsisting dispute. All other cases should be referred to the Arbitral Tribunal for decision on merits. Similar would be the position in case of disputed "no-claim certificate" or defence on the plea of novation and "accord and satisfaction".[399]

---

394. *Vidya Drolia* v. *Durga Trading Corpn.*, (2021) 2 SCC 1.
395. *Indus Biotech (P) Ltd.* v. *Kotak India Venture (Offshore) Fund*, (2021) 6 SCC 436.
396. *Deepak Khanna* v. *Pandit Bro.*, 2008 SCC OnLine Del 394: ILR (2008) 2 Del 973.
397. *Kishan Mimani* v. *Indu Kocher*, 2011 SCC OnLine Cal 5435: (2012) 4 CHN 157.
398. *Vishwakna Enterprises* v. *Sree Rayalaseema Hi-Strength Hypo Ltd.*, 2022 SCC OnLine AP 2884.
399. *Vidya Drolia* v. *Durga Trading Corpn.*, (2021) 2 SCC 1.

Termination of agreement by mutual consent of parties—Arbitration clause remains operative

If subsequent to a written agreement containing an arbitration clause, parties enter into an oral agreement in continuation of the previous one without referring to any arbitration clause, the arbitration clause contained in previous agreement would continue to be operative. Civil court shall refer the parties to arbitration. Civil court has no jurisdiction to entertain suit after application under Section 8 is filed.[400] In *Ashapura Mine-Chem Ltd.* v. *Gujarat Mineral Development Corpn.*[401], clause 25 of the MOU to constitute a joint venture for setting up an aluminium plant provided for resolution of disputes and differences amicably and clause 27 of the MOU provided for reference of unresolved disputes or differences concerning or arising from MOU, its implementation breach or termination, interpretation of any terms of MOU to arbitrator. It was held, arbitration clause 27 was a valid arbitration agreement contained in MOU, even if MOU is terminated, continues to remain operative, appellant's application for reference of dispute to arbitration was allowed, arbitrator was appointed in the case.

Novation by fresh agreement

If previous agreements mentioning arbitration clause are superseded, novated by a fresh document creating fresh agreement with no arbitration clause then dispute cannot be referred to arbitration seeking help of previous agreement.[402]

Reference of disputes to arbitration in pending suit—Waiver of right

A party which has willingly participated in proceedings in suit and has subjected itself to jurisdiction of court cannot subsequently turn round and say that the dispute should be referred to arbitration.[403]

Once the defendant has already participated and submitted itself to the jurisdiction of the court, the subsistence of the arbitration clause cannot be taken by the defendant.[404]

---

400. *Hema Khattar* v. *Shiv Khera*, (2017) 7 SCC 716.
401. (2015) 8 SCC 193.
402. *Young Achievers* v. *IMS Learning Resources (P) Ltd.*, 2012 SCC OnLine Del 3547: ILR (2012) 5 Del 462.
403. *Booz Allen & Hamilton Inc.* v. *SBI Home Finance Ltd.*, (2011) 5 SCC 532.
404. *Deepali Designs & Exhibits (P) Ltd.* v. *Encompass Events (P) Ltd.*, (2022) 5 HCC (Del) 790.

Presence of arbitration clause in agreement does not bar continuance of civil suit

Presence of arbitration clause in arbitration agreement does not bar continuance of civil suit.[405]

Summary suits

Dispute in summary suit can be referred to arbitration, subject to satisfaction of requirements in Section 8(1). Section 8, Arbitration and Conciliation Act would cover suits under Order 37 CPC and it is not permissible to leave them out of its purview.[406]

Summary suit is based on the invoices which are not issued under the agreement entered into between the parties which records the arbitration agreement, mandatory condition under Section 8 is not satisfied. Parties to the summary suit cannot be referred to arbitration.[407]

For effectively filing an application under Section 8, Arbitration and Conciliation Act, 1996 the defendant should first be granted leave to defend the suit. A defence may include questioning the jurisdiction of the court or maintainability of the suit also. Thus, it is not necessarily to be construed that when a person seeks permission under Order 37 Rule 3(5) CPC to defend the suit, he has submitted to the jurisdiction of the court and consequently had given up his right to refer the matter to the arbitration in spite of the presence of an arbitration clause in the agreement. Filing a petition under Order 37 Rule 3(5) CPC does not mean filing of the statement as contemplated under Section 8, Arbitration and Conciliation Act, 1996.[408]

Where in a suit for recovery, the defendant files an application for leave to defend the suit, subsequent application under Section 8 for referring the matter to arbitrator is not maintainable.[409]

Reference to arbitration in pending appeal

The court, in appeal, can refer the parties to arbitration under Section 8 even where the arbitration agreement is entered into during pendency of appeal so long as the agreement meets the requirement of Section 7. Language of

---

405. *Jharna Ghosh* v. *Debibrata Chattopadhyay*, 2019 SCC OnLine Cal 1482.
406. *ION Exchange (India) Ltd.* v. *MSK Projects (India) Ltd.*, 2005 SCC OnLine Bom 928: (2005) 4 Mah LJ 921.
407. *Ruby Organics (P) Ltd.* v. *Sai Mirra Innopharm (P) Ltd.*, 2013 SCC OnLine Bom 1261: (2013) 6 Mah LJ 320.
408. *G. Rajarajan* v. *AIG Consumer Financial Services (India) Ltd.*, 2012 SCC OnLine Mad 2717: (2012) 5 CTC 313.
409. *L.D. Industries* v. *Hindustan Wires Ltd.*, 1998 SCC OnLine P&H 473: PLR (1998) 119 P&H 651.

Section 8 is peremptory and the court is under an obligation to refer parties to arbitration.[410]

The phrase "which is the subject of an arbitration agreement" in Section 8(1) does not, in the context, necessarily require that the agreement must be already in existence before the action is brought in court. The phrase also connotes an arbitration agreement being brought into existence while action is pending.[411]

Reference to arbitration on the application of the defendant

Reference to arbitration at the instance of the defendant lies.[412]

Referring a dispute to a third party/individual

There is no provision in law nor any authority that adjudication of matters before court/commission/tribunal can be entrusted to a third party/individual and the decision of the third person then made a decree or order of a court/commission/tribunal. An award made by an arbitrator can be and is made a decree of a court, but that is under the provisions of the Arbitration Act and not dehors the Act.[413]

In *Skypak Couriers Ltd.* v. *Tata Chemicals Ltd.*[414], both the parties had consented for reference to third persons. Since all the parties had participated in the proceedings and award was made, the Supreme Court found it inequitable to set aside the award. Hence, the references to third persons and awards passed were treated as references and awards made under the Arbitration Act. The parties were given liberty to challenge the awards on the grounds available under the Act.[415]

"Unless it is accompanied by the original arbitration agreement or duly certified copy thereof" [Sub-s. (2)]

The requirement of filing original arbitration agreement or certified copy thereof along with application for reference of disputes to arbitration is mandatory. The word "shall" has been used in sub-section (2) of Section 8 and it postulates that the application for reference of dispute(s) to the arbitration shall not be entertained unless it is accompanied by the original arbitration agreement or a duly certified copy thereof. In *Atul Singh* v. *Sunil*

---

410. *P. Anand Gajapathi Raju* v. *P.V.G. Raju*, (2000) 4 SCC 539.
411. *Ibid.*
412. *Damani Shipping (P) Ltd.* v. *Hindustan Zinc Ltd.*, 2018 SCC OnLine Raj 3019: (2019) 2 RLW 1141.
413. *Skypak Couriers Ltd.* v. *Tata Chemicals Ltd.*, (2000) 5 SCC 294.
414. *Ibid.*
415. *Ibid.*

Kumar Singh[416], there was no whisper in the petition filed under Section 8 that the original arbitration agreement or a duly certified copy thereof was being filed with the application. Therefore, there was a clear non-compliance with Section 8(2) of the Act which is a mandatory provision and the dispute could not have been referred to arbitration, an order for referring the dispute to arbitration could not have been passed in the suit. Where neither the original agreement nor certified copy of the original agreement was produced before the civil court, refusal to refer matter for arbitration by the civil court was held proper.[417] In *M. Venugopal* v. *Union of India*[418], the respondent took the plea that the arbitration clause was contained in the lease deed and as such the civil suit was not maintainable. However, neither original lease deed nor a duly certified copy was filed along with the application, there was non-compliance of the mandatory provisions of Section 8(2), order passed by the Single Judge referring the parties to arbitration was set aside.

In reference to arbitration, the production of original agreement or its certified copy is mandatory. In the absence thereof dispute cannot be referred to arbitration.[419]

Where a person having custody of the original document issues a duplicate declaring that it is a true copy of the original, it is a "certified copy". The declaration "true copy" by an officer of the defendant with his signatures and the stamp of the company complies with the requirement of the section.[420] The expression "duly certified copy" includes a certification made by a party that it is a true document. Filing of the copy certified by the party is adequate to satisfy the requirement of Section 8(2). Where an agreement containing an arbitration agreement is admitted and made basis of the suit itself, such a party cannot complain that there has been non-compliance with the requirement under Section 8(2).[421] Filing of the certified copy by the party is adequate, satisfying the requirement of Section 8(2).

In view of three parts of the provisions of Section 8 of the Act, it is clear that a party who wants to file an application for arbitration shall file an application accompanied by the original arbitration agreement or a duly

416. (2008) 2 SCC 602; *Kishan Mimani* v. *Indu Kocher*, 2011 SCC OnLine Cal 5435: (2012) 4 CHN 157; *Kailash Baruah* v. *Hinduja Leyland Finance Co.*, 2017 SCC OnLine Gau 1083: (2017) 5 Gau LR 571.
417. *Auto Oil Co.* v. *Indian Oil Corpn. Ltd.*, 2011 SCC OnLine All 2915; *M. Venugopal* v. *Union of India*, 2011 SCC OnLine Mad 2453: (2012) 1 MWN (Civil) 272.
418. 2011 SCC OnLine Mad 2453: (2012) 1 MWN (Civil) 272.
419. *G. TEC* v. *Koulath Kareem*, 2015 SCC OnLine Ker 20276: (2015) 3 KLJ 652.
420. *Jessop & Co. Ltd.* v. *Tecpro Systems Ltd.*, 2012 SCC OnLine Cal 6324: (2012) 4 CHN 567.
421. *Cash and Gain Finance and Investments* v. *Manjula Udaya Shankar*, 2008 SCC OnLine Mad 802: (2009) 2 CTC 234.

certified copy thereof. In sub-section (2) of Section 8 of the Act, the word used is "shall". Therefore, it is mandatory on the part of the first defendant to produce the original arbitration agreement or a duly certified copy thereof. Admittedly in the present case, the first defendant had not complied with the said provision even at the time of entertaining the application.[422]

Certifying authority is not required to be a governmental authority. Where the defendant complies with provision of Section 8(2) of the Act by filing the certified copy of the agreement certified by competent officer and later on by filing the original agreement, rejection of prayer of the defendant was held to be illegal.[423]

Section 8 is couched in mandatory language and it debars the civil court from entertaining an application under sub-section (1) unless it is accompanied by the original arbitration agreement or a duly certified copy thereof. Thus, the law requires that the application under Section 8 of the Act must be accompanied by the original arbitration agreement or a duly certified copy thereof.[424]

Section 8(2) has to be interpreted to mean that the court shall not consider any application filed by the party under Section 8(1) unless it is accompanied by the original arbitration agreement or duly certified copy thereof. The filing of the application without such original or certified copy, but bringing original arbitration agreement on record at the time when the court is considering the application shall not entail rejection of the application under Section 8(2).[425]

Where the copy of the arbitration agreement was already on record, the technical plea of the appellant of non-compliance of the provisions of sub-section (2) of Section 8 was rejected.[426] Failure of the petitioner to produce a copy of the arbitration agreement/a duly certified copy thereof was of no effect when the petitioner had produced certified copy of Passenger Sales Agency Agreement (PSSA) and Travel Agents Handbook (TAH) containing the arbitration clause. Existence of the arbitration clause was undisputed in the case. Parties were referred to arbitration.[427]

---

422. *Transvahan Technologies India (P) Ltd.* v. *Sepson India (P) Ltd.*, 2018 SCC OnLine Kar 3783: (2018) 5 Kant LJ 851.

423. *Tata Finance Ltd.* v. *Naresh Ch. Deb*, 2006 SCC OnLine Gau 58: (2007) 1 Gau LR 153.

424. *Reliance Infratel Ltd.* v. *Chanderwati*, 2011 SCC OnLine HP 2363.

425. *Ananthesh Bhakta* v. *Nayana S. Bhakta*, (2017) 5 SCC 185; *Drive India Enterprise Solutions Ltd.* v. *Haier Telecom (India) (P) Ltd.*, 2018 SCC OnLine Bom 571: (2018) 3 Mah LJ 605 [If original or copy of agreement is brought on record when the court considers reference application, application cannot be rejected under sub-section (2) of S. 8].

426. *Parampal Singh* v. *Punjab State Ware Housing Corpn.*, 1999 SCC OnLine P&H 745: ILR (2000) 1 P&H 220.

427. *International Air Transport Assn.* v. *Indrani Air Travels (P) Ltd.*, 2022 SCC OnLine Gau 324: (2022) 3 Gau LR 638.

Where the arbitration clause is reproduced by the plaintiff in the application, objection of non-filing original arbitration agreement or duly certified copy cannot be raised by the plaintiff.[428]

In *Chinoo Sarkar* v. *Vodafone Essar Spacetel Ltd.*[429], view was taken that the application must be accompanied with the original or duly certified copy of the agreement. Pre-conditions of sub-section (2) of Section 8 are mandatory, production of the original copy of the agreement at the time of hearing of the application is not sufficient compliance with Section 8(2). Order allowing the application for referring the dispute to arbitration was erroneous. Production of the original arbitration agreement or a duly certified copy thereof, is mandatory for the purpose of a judicial authority to exercise its jurisdiction under sub-section (1) of Section 8, Arbitration and Conciliation Act.[430] Application seeking an order referring the parties to arbitration was not accompanied by the original arbitration agreement or a duly certified copy thereof. No order could be passed in the suit referring the dispute to arbitration.[431]

The word "entertained" occurring in Section 8 should be given wide meaning and either original agreement or duly certified copy thereof can be filed before the court at time when application pending comes for consideration. Failure to file original arbitration agreement or duly certified copy thereof at time of filing application does not affect maintainability of such application.[432]

Application for reference of dispute to arbitration should not be rejected on the ground that the original agreement or a duly certified copy of the same was not filed by the respondents herein along with the application filed under Section 8 of the Act.[433]

Wide interpretation should be given to the word "entertainment". The expression "entertained" will include, not only to file, but also to deal with the application, till it is finally determined.[434]

428. *Manoj Makkar* v. *Neeru Bal*, 2012 SCC OnLine P&H 8679.
429. 2017 SCC OnLine Gau 1092: (2018) 1 Gau LR 139.
430. *Accounts Officer* v. *R. Sen & Co.*, 2008 SCC OnLine Cal 111: (2008) 3 CHN 935.
431. *B.L.B. Ltd.* v. *Calcutta Stock Exchange Assn. Ltd.*, 2008 SCC OnLine Cal 699: (2008) 4 Cal LT 504.
432. *Kotak Mahindra Finance Ltd.* v. *T.N. Balasubramanian*, 2004 SCC OnLine Mad 472: (2004) 5 CTC 699.
433. *Thirumuruga Kirupananda Variyar Thavathiru Sundara Swamigal Medical Educational and Charitable Trust* v. *Sahu Trust*, 2008 SCC OnLine Mad 756: (2008) 6 CTC 447.
434. *Kotak Mahindra Finance Ltd.* v. *T.N. Balasubramanian*, 2004 SCC OnLine Mad 472: (2004) 5 CTC 699.

"Certified copy" [S. 8(2)]

Only production of a certified copy of the arbitration agreement satisfies the requirement of Section 8(2).[435]

Original or certified copy of arbitration agreement though not accompanied with application is filed at time of consideration of such application by court, it does not entail rejection of application under Section 8(2).[436]

Filing of original deed is mandatory

Notwithstanding subsistence of arbitral dispute, non-filing of original deed disentitles reference to arbitration. The court is not empowered to refer parties to arbitration if procedural requirements in Section 8(2) of the Act are not complied with.[437]

Where the document is in custody of the adversary or with the third party [Sub-s. (2), proviso]

Production of original partnership deed or arbitration agreement is not necessary in the case of a private document, if it is not in the custody of the applicant but with the adversary or with the third party.[438]

Photocopies of original arbitration agreement—Consideration of

In *Bharat Sewa Sansthan* v. *U.P. Electronics Corpn. Ltd.*[439], there was a dispute between the lessor and the lessee. Lessee had filed an application under Section 8 for reference of the dispute to arbitration. Both the lessor and the lessee denied the possession of the original lease agreement. In such a case, the photocopies of the original arbitration agreement could be taken on record under Section 8, Arbitration and Conciliation Act, 1996 for ascertaining the existence of the arbitration clause. Xerox copies of the agreement containing arbitration clause were annexed with the application. It was held, there was sufficient compliance of the provisions of Section 8(2) of the Act.[440]

---

435. *Transvahan Technologies India (P) Ltd.* v. *Sepson India (P) Ltd.*, 2018 SCC OnLine Kar 3783: (2018) 5 Kant LJ 851.
436. *Ananthesh Bhakta* v. *Nayana S. Bhakta*, (2017) 5 SCC 185.
437. *N. Radhakrishnan* v. *Maestro Engineers*, (2010) 1 SCC 72.
438. *Vivek Arya* v. *Economic Transport Organisation*, 2002 SCC OnLine Cal 484.
439. (2007) 7 SCC 737.
440. *ITC Classic Finance Ltd.* v. *Grapco Mining and Co. Ltd.*, 1997 SCC OnLine Cal 123; *Motilal* v. *Kedarmal Jainarayan Bharadiya*, 2002 SCC OnLine Bom 74: (2003) 2 Mah LJ 751.

Calling upon the opposite party to produce the original arbitration agreement/certified copy before court

New proviso to Section 8(2) has been added by the Amendment Act (3 of 2016). The proviso envisages provision that where the original arbitration agreement/certified copy thereof is not available with the applicant applying for referring the parties to the arbitration and the original arbitration agreement/certified copy has been retained by the other party to the agreement, then the party so applying shall file an application along with a copy of the arbitration agreement praying the court to call upon the other party to produce the original arbitration agreement or its duly certified copy before that court.

Hire purchase agreement containing arbitration clause not registered

Where the hire purchase agreement containing the arbitration clause is not registered, the question of submitting a certified copy of the agreement from a registering authority does not arise. Photocopy of the original agreement certified by the officer of the defendant was filed in the court; the original was also submitted later on. Submission that the original of the agreement should only be adhered to was not accepted.[441]

Pendency of injunction order

The pendency of the injunction order is not a bar to the invocation of the arbitration proceedings. Section 8(1) application is filed only when an action is brought before a judicial authority regarding a matter covered by the arbitration clause.[442]

Right to seek reference of dispute to arbitration—Waiver of

Though Section 8 does not prescribe any time-limit for filling an application under that section, and only states that the application under Section 8 of the Act should be filed before submission of the first statement on the substance of the dispute, the scheme of the Act and the provisions of the section clearly indicate that the application thereunder should be made at the earliest. Obviously, a party who willingly participates in the proceedings in the suit and subjects himself to the jurisdiction of the court cannot subsequently turn around and say that the parties should be referred to arbitration in view of the existence of an arbitration agreement. The defendant petitioner participated in the arbitration proceedings, it is only at the stage of producing

441. *Tata Finance Ltd.* v. *Naresh Ch. Deb*, 2006 SCC OnLine Gau 58: (2007) 1 Gau LR 153.
442. *Hindustan Petroleum Corpn. Ltd.* v. *Sri Prabh Transport*, 2001 SCC OnLine Mad 363: (2001) 2 LW 583.

its witnesses that the petitioner sought to file the present application under Section 8. It was held, the conduct of the petitioner reveals that it has subjected itself to the jurisdiction of the court and waived its right to seek reference of the dispute to arbitration. Reference of dispute to arbitration was not allowed.[443]

Pending application under sub-section (1), arbitration may be commenced/continued [Sub-s. (3)]

The intention of Section 11 is that neither the filing of any suit by any party to the arbitration agreement nor any application being made by the other party under Section 8 to the court, should obstruct or preclude a party from initiating any proceeding for the appointment of an arbitrator or proceeding with the arbitration before the Arbitration Tribunal. The specific provision in Section 8(3) provides that the pendency of an application under Section 8(1) will not come in the way of the arbitration being commenced or continued.[444] Section 8(3) contains the expression "may" which means that it is only optional contrary to mandate under Section 8(1) to court to make reference to arbitration.[445]

Arbitration can be commenced without the intervention of the court when even a suit is pending covering the subject-matters of the arbitration before a court even without making an application.[446]

Non-production of agreement between the parties along with application under Section 8(3) will not disentitle the petitioner from claiming relief under the Act.[447]

An application filed under Section 11 or Section 15(2) of the 1996 Act for the appointment of an arbitrator will not be barred by mere pendency of an application under Section 8 of the Act in any suit, nor will designate of the Chief Justice be precluded from considering and disposing of an application under Section 11 or Section 5(2) of the Act. It necessarily follows that if an arbitrator is appointed by the designate of the Chief Justice under Section 11 of the Act, nothing prevents the arbitrator from proceeding with the arbitration proceedings.[448]

---

443. *Aid et Action* v. *Kolleru Rural Development Service Organization*, 2021 SCC OnLine AP 3950: (2022) 1 ALD 422.
444. *Vijay Kumar Sharma* v. *Raghunandan Sharma*, (2010) 2 SCC 486.
445. *Cash and Gain Finance and Investments* v. *Manjula Udaya Shankar*, 2008 SCC OnLine Mad 802: (2009) 2 CTC 234.
446. *Maheswari Steel (P) Ltd.* v. *Aravali Leasing Ltd.*, 2001 SCC OnLine Cal 685: (2001) 3 ICC 568.
447. *Railways* v. *Metal Powder Co. Ltd.*, 2006 SCC OnLine Mad 1036: (2006) 5 CTC 865.
448. *Vijay Kumar Sharma* v. *Raghunandan Sharma*, (2010) 2 SCC 486.

Service of notice on other party

Service of notice on the other party under the arbitration agreement is not mandatory for the maintainability of application filed under Section 8. What is necessary at this stage is the existence of an arbitration.[449]

Time-limit for filing application under Section 8

In *Booz Allen & Hamilton Inc.* v. *SBI Home Finance Ltd.*[450], though Section 8 does not prescribe any time-limit for filing an application, however, such an application has to be made at the earliest. Appellant had filed an application for referring the dispute to arbitration long after contesting supplementary proceedings in pending suit. Appellant having contested the supplementary proceedings alone, held, mere passage of time would not lead to the inference that the defendant had subjected himself to the jurisdiction of the court for adjudication of main dispute and had thus lost the right to seek reference to arbitration. Talks were in progress for arriving at a settlement out of court. Only when such talks failed, the appellant had filed an application under Section 8. Appellant's application was not rejected on the ground of delay.

Pendency of civil suit

Even if the civil suit is pending in civil court, yet the matter can be referred to the arbitrator, the arbitrator can proceed with the arbitration proceedings, the aggrieved party has the remedy to challenge the award under Section 34 of the Act.[451]

A defendant is entitled to file the application under Section 8 at any point of time before filing the written statement. If any such application is so filed by fulfilling the mandatory requirements as contemplated under sub-clause (2) of Section 8, the courts are duty-bound to refer the matter to the arbitration without resorting to proceed with the matter thereby compelling the parties to agitate the dispute within the civil court's jurisdiction.[452]

Ex parte decree

In *Union of India* v. *Rajesh Damani*[453], an application filed by the defendant under Section 8 for referring the dispute to arbitration was rejected. The

449. *Rashtriya Ispat Nigam Ltd.* v. *Verma Transport Co.*, (2006) 7 SCC 275.
450. (2011) 5 SCC 532.
451. *Punjab State Coop. Supply and Mktg. Federation Ltd.* v. *Shiv Rice and General Mills*, 2000 SCC OnLine P&H 606: ILR (2001) 1 P&H 511.
452. *G. Rajarajan* v. *AIG Consumer Financial Services (India) Ltd.*, 2012 SCC OnLine Mad 2717: (2012) 5 CTC 313.
453. 2012 SCC OnLine Mad 2718: (2012) 5 CTC 426; *H.J. Hansen Recycling Industry Ltd.* v. *Shree Ganesh Steel Rolling Mills (P) Ltd.*, 2013 SCC OnLine Mad 3622: (2014) 1 LW 811.

defendant filed revision, meanwhile ex parte decree was passed against the defendant. The revisional court allowed revision, application under Section 8 and matter was referred to arbitration. The court held, (*i*) when the civil revision petition itself was allowed thereby referring the matter for arbitration, the decree passed in the meantime either ex parte or on merits by the civil court cannot be sustained, as the same has to be treated as the one passed without jurisdiction; (*ii*) when the civil court's jurisdiction is taken away by referring the matter to the Arbitral Tribunal, the decree passed by the trial court either ex parte or on merits should necessarily be set aside as it should not stand in the way of getting the matter decided by the Arbitral Tribunal.

Winding up of company—Dispute cannot be referred to arbitration

Section 8(1), Arbitration and Conciliation Act, 1996 provides that the judicial authority before whom an action is brought in a matter will refer the parties to arbitration the said matter in accordance with the agreement. This, however, postulates that what can be referred to the arbitrator is only that dispute or matter which the arbitrator is competent or empowered to decide.[454] A claim in a petition for winding up is not for money. A petition filed under the Companies Act, 1956 would be to the effect that the company has become commercially insolvent, and therefore, should be wound up. The power to order winding up of a company is contained under the Companies Act, and is conferred on the court. An arbitrator, notwithstanding any agreement between the parties, would have no jurisdiction to order winding up of a company.[455]

Companies Act, 1956

In *Das Lagerway Wind Turbines Ltd.* v. *Cynosure Investments (P) Ltd.*[456], a petition for oppression and mismanagement was filed against the company and several reliefs were sought. Company invoked Section 8, Arbitration and Conciliation Act and relied on agreement containing arbitration clause and prayed for referring the matter to the arbitrator. Company had pleaded that agreement containing arbitration clause got extinguished and petition to refer parties to arbitration could not be ordered. Reliefs to be granted in petition for oppression and mismanagement cannot be granted by an arbitrator. Order of Company Law Board dismissing petition invoking arbitration clause upheld.

---

454. *Haryana Telecom Ltd.* v. *Sterlite Industries (India) Ltd.*, (1999) 5 SCC 688.
455. *Ibid.*
456. 2007 SCC OnLine Mad 280: (2007) 3 CTC 524; see also, *Sporting Pastime India Ltd.* v. *Kasthuri and Sons Ltd.*, 2006 SCC OnLine Mad 551: (2006) 4 CTC 377.

Lease deed

Arbitration clause finding place in earlier lease deeds already expired cannot be invoked by a tenant.[457]

In *Roshin Lal Gupta & Sons (P) Ltd.* v. *Delhi Tourism & Transportation Development Corpn.*[458], lease came to an end and the tenancy stood terminated. Question whether there has been a breach by one side or the other, or as to whether circumstances have arisen which have discharged one or both parties from further performance, such differences should be regarded as differences which have arisen "in respect of", or "with regard to", or "under" the contract. Arbitration clause contained in a contract constitutes a separate agreement. It has an independent existence. Application deserved to be allowed.

In *Eigen Technical Services (P) Ltd.* v. *Vatika Ltd.*[459], there was a suit for possession by way of ejectment, and recovery of rent and mesne profits. Lease was for a period of three years, was not renewed, hence stood extinguished by efflux of time. The possession of the tenant was unauthorised after the lease period. The lease deed did not provide for reference of future disputes to arbitration. The court cannot refer to arbitration clause for the disputes other than those specifically referred to in the arbitration agreement/clause unless the parties agreed to refer to such disputes.

Purchase order

Section 8 of 1996 Act mandates judicial authority to refer parties to arbitration if pending action is subject of arbitration agreement. Arbitration clause mentioned in contract document to purchase order established fact that arbitration agreement exists between parties. Trial court rightly referred parties to arbitration.[460]

Arbitration agreement contained in unregistered insufficiently stamped lease deed

In *Naina Thakkar* v. *Annapurna Builders*[461], the period of lease was five years. While pressing the application under Section 8, the petitioner did not show intention to pay the penalty as may be imposed by the Collector, if the document was impounded and stamp duty payable thereon was determined.

457. *National Textile Corpn. Ltd.* v. *Ashval Vaderaa*, 2008 SCC OnLine Del 1201: (2009) 107 DRJ 637.
458. 2009 SCC OnLine Del 502: (2009) 109 DRJ 456.
459. 2013 SCC OnLine P&H 12364: PLR (2013) 172 P&H 27.
460. *Anik Industries Ltd.* v. *DCM Shriram Consolidated Ltd.*, 2018 SCC OnLine MP 1923.
461. (2013) 14 SCC 354.

Rejection of the application made under Section 8 by the trial court was held proper.

Suit for recovery of possession, mesne profit and permanent injunction

In *A.K. Jaju* v. *Avni Kumar*[462], there was a suit for recovery of possession, mesne profits and permanent injunction under Order 39 Rule 7 CPC. Defendant filed application for reference of dispute to arbitration under Section 8 of the Act. First agreement contained an arbitration clause and the second agreement was not in supersession of the first agreement. Dispute was referable to arbitration, sole arbitrator was appointed.

Mortgage suit—Arbitrability of dispute

An agreement to sell or an agreement to mortgage does not involve any transfer of right *in rem* but creates only a personal obligation. Therefore, if specific performance is sought either in regard to an agreement to sell or an agreement to mortgage, the claim for specific performance will be arbitrable.[463]

Mortgage is a transfer of a right *in rem*. A mortgage suit for sale of mortgaged property is an action *in rem*, for the enforcement of a right *in rem*. A suit on a mortgage is not a mere suit for money. A suit for enforcement of a mortgage being the enforcement of a right *in rem* will have to be decided by the court of law and not by Arbitration Tribunal.[464] A decree for sale of a mortgaged property as in the case of a decree for order for winding up, requires the court to protect the intents of persons other than the parties to the suit/petition and empowers the court to entertain and adjudicate upon the rights and liabilities of third parties (other than those who are parties to the arbitration agreement). Therefore, a suit for sale, foreclosure or redemption of the mortgaged property should only be tried by a public forum, and not by an Arbitral Tribunal. The court should not refer the parties to arbitration.[465]

SBI had filed suit to enforce the mortgage, and had also sought delivery of vacant possession. The enforcement of the charge/mortgage over the flat, realisation of sale proceeds therefrom and the right of the appellant to stay in possession till the entire deposit was repaid, were all matters which were mentioned in the agreement as matters to be settled by arbitration. It was held, subject-matter of the suit fell within the scope of the arbitration agreement. Dispute was referred to arbitration.[466]

462. 2003 SCC OnLine Del 401: (2003) 68 DRJ 523.
463. *Booz Allen & Hamilton Inc.* v. *SBI Home Finance Ltd.*, (2011) 5 SCC 532.
464. *Ibid.*
465. *Ibid.*
466. *Ibid.*

Disputes within the purview of RDB Act, 1993 and SARFAESI Act, 2002

Claims covered by the Recovery of Debts Due to Banks and Financial Institutions Act, 1993 and Securitisation and Reconstruction of Financial Assets and Enforcement of Security Interest Act, 2002 are non-arbitrable as there is a prohibition against waiver of jurisdiction of Debt Recovery Tribunal (DRT) by necessary implication and the legislation has overwritten the contractual right to arbitration. Furthermore, even prior arbitration proceedings are not a bar to proceedings under the SARFAESI Act, the said Act sets out an expeditious, procedural methodology enabling financial institutions to take possession and sell secured properties for non-payment of dues. Such powers, it is obvious, cannot be exercised through arbitral proceedings.[467]

Matters which came within the scope and jurisdiction of DRT are arbitrable.[468]

Disputes relating to sovereign and public interest functions of the State

Sovereign functions of the State being inalienable and non-delegable are non-arbitrable as the State alone has the exclusive right and duty to perform such functions. For example, it is generally accepted that monopoly rights can only be granted by the State. Correctness and validity of the State or sovereign functions cannot be made a direct subject-matter of a private adjudicatory process. Sovereign functions for the purpose of the Arbitration and Conciliation Act would extend to exercise of executive power in different fields including commerce and economic legislations in all forms, taxation, eminent domain and police powers which includes maintenance of law and order, internal security, grant of pardon, etc. as distinguished from commercial activities, economic adventures and welfare activities. Similarly, decisions and adjudicatory functions of the State that have public interest element like the legitimacy of marriage, citizenship, winding up of companies, grant of patents, etc. are non-arbitrable, unless the statute in relation to a regulatory or adjudicatory mechanism either expressly or by clear implication permits arbitration. In these matters the State enjoys monopoly in dispute resolution.[469]

---

467. *Vidya Drolia* v. *Durga Trading Corpn.*, (2021) 2 SCC 1.

468. *HDFC Bank Ltd.* v. *Satpal Singh Bakshi*, 2012 SCC OnLine Del 4815: (2013) 134 DRJ 566; *M.D. Frozen Foods Exports (P) Ltd.* v. *Hero Fincorp Ltd.*, (2017) 16 SCC 741; *Indiabulls Housing Finance Ltd.* v. *Deccan Chronicle Holdings Ltd.*, (2018) 14 SCC 783.

469. *Vidya Drolia* v. *Durga Trading Corpn.*, (2021) 2 SCC 1.

Landlord and tenant disputes, if arbitrable

Landlord–tenant disputes governed by the Transfer of Property Act, 1882 are arbitrable as they are not actions *in rem* but pertain to subordinate rights *in personam* that arise from rights. Such actions normally would not affect third party rights or have *erga omnes* affect or require centralised adjudication. An award passed deciding landlord-tenant disputes can be executed and enforced like a decree of the civil court. Landlord-tenant disputes do not relate to inalienable and sovereign functions of the State. The provisions of the Transfer of Property Act do not expressly or by necessary implication bar arbitration. The Transfer of Property Act, like all other Acts, has a public purpose, *i.e.* to regulate landlord-tenant relationships and the arbitrator would be bound by the provisions, including provisions which ensure and protect the tenants.

Landlord–tenant disputes are arbitrable as the Transfer of Property Act does not forbid or foreclose arbitration. However, landlord-tenant disputes covered and governed by rent control legislation would not be arbitrable when a specific court or forum has been given exclusive jurisdiction to apply and decide special rights and obligations. Such rights and obligations can only be adjudicated and enforced by the specified court/forum, and not through arbitration.[470]

Suit for possession of tenanted premises is not governed by the provisions of Rajasthan Rent Control Act, 2001. Dispute can be referred to an arbitrator.[471]

Insofar as eviction or tenancy relating to matters governed by special statutes where the tenant enjoys statutory protection against eviction, whereunder the court/forum is specified and conferred jurisdiction under the statute alone can adjudicate such matters. Hence, in such cases, the dispute is non-arbitrable. If the special statutes do not apply to the premises/property and the lease/tenancy created thereunder as on the date when the cause of action arises to seek for eviction or such other relief and in such transaction if the parties are governed by an arbitration clause; the dispute between the parties is arbitrable and there shall be no impediment whatsoever to invoke the arbitration clause.[472]

In *Himangni Enterprises* v. *Kamaljeet Singh Ahluwalia*[473], suit for eviction and recovery of rent was filed. Lease deed entered into between the parties contained an arbitration clause for resolution of disputes by referring

---

470. *Ibid.*
471. *Magma Fincorp Ltd.* v. *Kamal Kumari*, 2018 SCC OnLine Raj 3596.
472. *Suresh Shah* v. *Hipad Technology (India) (P) Ltd.*, (2021) 1 SCC 529.
473. (2017) 10 SCC 706.

them to arbitration. Tenants sought resolution of disputes by reference to arbitration. Lease period had come to an end by the efflux of time. Disputes relating to eviction of tenants and recovery of arrears of rent are subject-matter of civil suit, and cannot be referred to an arbitrator.

Lease deed contained an arbitration clause. Suit was filed for recovery of possession on the basis of service of notice under Section 106, Transfer of Property Act , 1882. The issue of eviction is essentially an issue which could be adjudicated and/or decided by the court as it involved various questions relating to the granting of the relief under the different provisions of the 1882 Act. It was held, the eviction or a recovery proceeding under the special statute or where the express power is conferred upon the court which necessarily implies the exclusion of the private fora.[474]

In *V.S. Enterprises* v. *B.R. Sharma*[475], the landlord was seeking ejectment of the tenant. Arbitration clause in the lease agreement did not cover this dispute. Dispute between the parties was not referred to the arbitration.

Lease deed contained an arbitration clause. Relationship of landlord and tenant was disputed by the party. Lease deed was unregistered and, hence, could not be considered in evidence. Arbitrator was not appointed in the case.[476] There was no agreement or contract of tenancy between the parties containing arbitration agreement. Arbitration clause contained in rules and regulations of the society was a unilateral document to which the defendant was not a party. Rejection of applications seeking reference to arbitration was proper.[477]

The language of Section 8 though peremptory and an obligation is cast on the court to refer the dispute to arbitration, the court can still decline to exercise power under Section 8, if it is shown to the satisfaction of the court that the person moving the court is disentitled to the relief claimed by him and that the whole idea in moving the application for referring the matter to arbitration is to prolong the issue and to deny the other party the relief to which he is rightfully entitled to. In *Ramakrishna Theatre Ltd.* v. *General Investments and Commercial Corpn. Ltd.*[478], the petitioner, who had the right to seek for adjudication of his rights under the agreement in an arbitration proceedings, waived that right when he rejected the offer made by the plaintiff-respondent to subject the dispute to arbitration proceedings.

---

474. *Fingertips Solutions (P) Ltd.* v. *Dhanashree Electronics Ltd.*, 2011 SCC OnLine Cal 4974.
475. 2011 SCC OnLine P&H 13638.
476. *Chemical Sales Agencies* v. *Naraini Newar*, 2004 SCC OnLine Del 753: (2004) 77 DRJ 224.
477. *Krishna Premmai Devidasi* v. *International Society for Krishna Consciousness*, 2012 SCC OnLine All 2167: (2012) 94 ALR 833.
478. 2003 SCC OnLine Kar 465: ILR 2003 Kar 3463.

Tortious liability—Reference of dispute to arbitration

Where a suit is filed by a party for damages under tort and beyond the terms of condition of the contract, the matter cannot be referred to the arbitrator under the terms of the agreement.[479]

In *T.N. Electricity Board* v. *Sumathi*[480], the respondents were legal heirs of persons whose deaths had been caused by electrocution. They filed writ petitions before the High Court under Article 226 of the Constitution, claiming compensation. Appreciating that questions of fact were involved in the writ petition, the High Court appointed an arbitrator to decide the question of compensation. The arbitrator gave his awards, which were made the rule of the court after objections were heard and the High Court had examined the evidence recorded by the arbitrator. The appellant-Electricity Board filed an appeal. The Supreme Court held that since the disputed questions of fact arose in the present appeals, the High Court should not have entertained writ petitions under Article 226 of the Constitution and then referred the matter to arbitration in violation of the provisions of the new Arbitration and Conciliation Act, 1996. There was no arbitration agreement within the meaning of Section 7 of the new Act. Under the new Act, award can be enforced as if it is a decree of a court and yet the High Court passed a decree in terms of the award which is not warranted by the provisions of the new Act. Exercise of jurisdiction by the High Court in entertaining the petitions was not proper and the High Court, in any case, could not have proceeded to have the matter adjudicated in violation of the provisions of the new Act. In the circumstances of the case, however, the appellant was restrained from recovering from any of the respondents, any amount which had been paid to them in terms of the impugned judgments of the High Court.

Purchase order

Arbitration clause was incorporated in the purchase order. Parties had acted on the purchase order, arbitration agreement existed between the parties. Order of the trial court rejecting the application of the petitioners for reference of dispute between the parties was improper, was quashed and set aside.[481]

---

479. *Bougainvillea Multiplex and Entertainment Center (P) Ltd.* v. *Shankar Rai*, 2008 SCC OnLine Del 1182: (2008) 154 DLT 687.
480. (2000) 4 SCC 543.
481. *Saiwardha Power Ltd.* v. *Goyal Dhatu Udyog (P) Ltd.*, 2015 SCC OnLine Bom 6313: (2016) 2 Mah LJ 356.

Suit for recovery of money on a Bill of Lading

Amount released by the insurance company was sought to be recovered under a letter of subrogation in suit. Cause of action was only a Bill of Lading and letter of subrogation, and indemnification by the insurer was not material to decide the issue. The Bill of Lading contained an arbitration clause, the provisions of Arbitration and Conciliation Act, 1996 were applicable, and the civil suit was not maintainable. When the parties have agreed to take recourse to a particular procedure to resolve their disputes, they cannot be permitted to approach the civil court bypassing the remedies agreed to by them.[482]

Specific performance of an agreement to sell or agreement to mortgage—Arbitrable

An agreement to sell or mortgage does not involve any transfer of right *in rem* but creates only a personal obligation. Hence, a claim for specific performance of agreement to sell or agreement to mortgage is arbitrable.[483]

Agreement for sale contained an arbitration clause which provided that if there is any dispute or difference between the parties with reference to the completion of transaction, then the matter is to be referred to "arbitrator". The contention that dispute can be referred to arbitrator only when it pertains to payment of consideration amount was not tenable. Once parties have made their intention clear to refer the dispute to the arbitrator for resolving the same, the court should direct parties to the arbitrator instead of interpreting relevant clause to decide whether only part of the dispute was to be referred and in case of certain eventuality only. Order of trial court rejecting application for reference to arbitrator, deserved to be quashed and was set aside.[484]

Dealership agreement

If an agreement contains a clause for reference of dispute to arbitration, it is mandatory for the civil court to refer the same to the arbitrator. Clause 37 of the dealership agreement couched in mandatory form stated "dispute shall be referred to arbitration". Parties were directed to approach the Arbitral Tribunal in consonance with clause 37 of the dealership agreement.[485]

---

482. *Sanco Trans Ltd.* v. *Addison & Co. Ltd.*, 2009 SCC OnLine Mad 1069: (2009) 4 CTC 569.
483. *Booz Allen & Hamilton Inc.* v. *SBI Home Finance Ltd.*, (2011) 5 SCC 532; *Deccan Paper Mills Co. Ltd.* v. *Regency Mahavir Properties*, (2021) 4 SCC 786.
484. *Suman Baburao Thapa* v. *Jigar K. Mehta*, 2018 SCC OnLine Bom 377: (2018) 5 Mah LJ 260.
485. *Escorts Ltd.* v. *Subhash Manakchand Zambad*, 2011 SCC OnLine Bom 492: (2011) 6 Mah LJ 18.

Cancellation of written instrument/agreement under Section 31, Specific Relief Act, 1963

Cancellation of written instrument/agreement under Section 31 of the Specific Relief Act. Adjudication of the same is arbitrable and relief of cancellation of written instrument is grantable by Arbitral Tribunal, as proceedings under Section 31, Specific Relief Act, 1963 are *in personam* in nature.[486]

Petroleum dealership agreement—Reference to arbitration

Allegations were of short supply of petroleum products and tampering with weights and measure seals by the respondent-dealer. The allegations constituted violation of the provisions of Weights and Measures (Enforcement) Act, 1985 as well misconduct under the terms of the agreement. If the appellant-Petroleum Corporation was satisfied that the respondent was indulging in short supply or tampering with the seals, it was entitled to initiate such action as is contemplated under the agreement like suspending or stopping the supply of petroleum products to such erring dealer. If in that process any dispute arose between the parties between the appellant and such dealer, the same was required to be referred to the arbitration as contemplated under the arbitration clause of the dealership agreement. The dispute was referred to arbitration.[487]

The trial judge and the Additional District Judge were manifestly in error in not referring the parties to arbitration in terms of the arbitration clause contained in the dealership agreement.[488]

Petitioner-public corporation (HPC) had entered into contract with the successful tenderer (respondent) for supply of petroleum products. The petitioner suspended the supply of products on the ground that the respondent-company was guilty of malpractices, and was supplying adulterated products. The respondent filed a civil suit and challenged the act of the petitioner as unlawful, and also prayed for injunction restraining the petitioner, HPC from giving effect to the order and preventing the plaintiff from participating in the future tenders. Clause 51 of the agreement contained an arbitration clause. On application filed under Section 8 of the Act by the HPC, the dispute between the parties was referred to arbitration.[489]

---

486. *Deccan Paper Mills Co. Ltd.* v. *Regency Mahavir Properties*, (2021) 4 SCC 786.
487. *Hindustan Petroleum Corpn. Ltd.* v. *Pinkcity Midway Petroleums*, (2003) 6 SCC 503.
488. *Hindustan Petroleum Corpn. Ltd.* v. *Parshwa Auto Center*, 2006 SCC OnLine Bom 421: (2006) 4 Mah LJ 111.
489. *Hindustan Petroleum Corpn. Ltd.* v. *Sri Prabh Transport*, 2001 SCC OnLine Mad 363: (2001) 2 LW 583.

Representative suit against society—Dispute referred to arbitration

A dispute arose between plaintiffs, owners and occupiers of society and defendants and executive committee members of society. Plaintiffs filed a representative suit seeking various reliefs including framing of scheme to convene and conduct free and fair election of society on the ground that the issue of election is an action *in rem* and is independent of the arbitration clause provided in rules and regulations of the memorandum of society, and hence, should be decided in the representative suit. Reliefs sought by plaintiffs in suit are regarding administration and management of society which are sufficiently covered by the arbitration clause. The application of the defendants to refer the matter to arbitration was allowed.[490]

Hire purchase agreement cases

As per clause of the loan agreement, on the failure to pay installments, the financier seized the hypothecated vehicles. A suit was filed questioning the seizure of the vehicle. Seizure of the vehicle does not amount to waiver of the arbitration clause in the loan agreement. All disputes, differences and all claims arising out of loan agreement required to be adjudicated by the arbitrator.[491]

Dispute arose between the purchaser of the car and finance company over repayment of installments of loan. Suit was filed by the purchaser for declaration and injunction. During pendency of suit, the finance company moved the court for referring clause in hire purchase agreement to arbitration. The provisions of Section 8 are mandatory, it was obligatory on the part of the trial court to refer the parties to arbitration. Even if a civil suit is pending in civil court, the matter can be referred to the arbitration.[492]

Dispute arising of insurance claim—Whenever an insurance company admits a claim which is not acceptable to the claimant and a dispute is raised, such a dispute has to be referred to the arbitrator.[493]

Literary work—Motion picture

As per the terms of the MOU, the rights for creating a motion picture from the literary work of the plaintiff were assigned to the defendants. Parties

490. *Rajda Industries and Exports (P) Ltd.* v. *Mahesh Kumar Prahladka*, 2018 SCC OnLine Cal 16988.
491. *Kotak Mahindra Primus Ltd.* v. *S. Laxman Rao*, 2004 SCC OnLine AP 1060: (2004) 3 APLJ 51 (SN).
492. *Ashok Leyland Finance Ltd.* v. *Ramchandra*, 2002 SCC OnLine Bom 1093: (2003) 1 Mah LJ 536; *Punjab State Coop. Supply and Mktg. Federation Ltd.* v. *Shiv Rice and General Mills*, 2000 SCC OnLine P&H 606: ILR (2001) 1 P&H 511.
493. *Compack Foam (P) Ltd.* v. *National Insurance Co. Ltd.*, 2022 SCC OnLine Utt 1852.

themselves incorporated the arbitration clause in the agreement. It was held, subject-matter was arbitrable.[494]

Maintenance charges

Where the arbitration agreement between parties did not cover maintenance charges, reference of dispute to arbitration was not proper.[495]

Complicated matter involving various questions and issues—Relegation to arbitrator not warranted

Where a dispute requires detailed investigation and production of elaborate evidence, it must be tried by a court. In the present dispute of partnership, the appellant had made serious allegations against the respondents alleging that they have committed malpractices in the account books and manipulated the finances of the partnership firm, which cannot be properly dealt with by the arbitrator. Petition of the appellant under Section 8 to refer the matter to the arbitrator was not warranted.[496]

Jurisdiction of civil court

Once an application under Section 8 for reference to arbitration is filed, the civil court has no jurisdiction to continue with suit.[497]

The bar of jurisdiction of civil court would come into play if the application for referring the dispute to arbitration is made by any of the parties to the arbitration agreement and in accordance with the procedure prescribed therein.[498]

The civil court has jurisdiction to decide whether an arbitration clause exists or has been waived.[499]

Jurisdiction of the civil court to entertain a suit is not barred only because there is an arbitration clause in the agreement. Court shall refer the parties to arbitration only on filing of an application under Section 8 of the Act. Order VII Rule 11(*d*) CPC providing that the plaint shall be rejected where the suit appears from the statement in the plaint to be barred by any law is not applicable.[500]

---

494. *Earth and Air Films (P) Ltd.* v. *M.T. Vasudevan Nair*, 2019 SCC OnLine Ker 4701.
495. *Gurcharan Singh* v. *Collage Estates (P) Ltd.*, 2020 SCC OnLine P&H 5355.
496. *N. Radhakrishnan* v. *Maestro Engineers*, (2010) 1 SCC 72.
497. *Indian Oil Corpn. Ltd.* v. *J. Lal Filling Station*, 2021 SCC OnLine All 1274.
498. *Indian National Trade Union Congress* v. *Hiranya Bora*, 2015 SCC OnLine Gau 937: (2016) 2 Gau LR 499.
499. *Lindsay International (P) Ltd.* v. *Laxmi Niwas Mittal*, 2020 SCC OnLine Cal 1658: (2021) 1 Arb LR 137.
500. *Maa Sarada and Co.* v. *Sahidul Hoque*, 2018 SCC OnLine Gau 2102: (2019) 2 Gau LR 494; *Assam State Transport Corpn.* v. *Ghosh Bros. Motors (P) Ltd.*, 2018 SCC OnLine Gau 2081: (2019) 2 Gau LR 317.

Mere existence of arbitration clause does not create an embargo on civil court to continue proceeding pending before such court. Power of civil court to refuse stay of suit in view of arbitration clause on existence of certain grounds available under 1940 Act continues to be available under 1996 Act. Civil court is not prevented from proceeding with suit despite an arbitration clause if dispute involves serious questions of law or complicated questions of fact, adjudication of which would depend upon detailed or a land documentary evidence.[501]

There is no total embargo on the civil court to continue the proceedings before it on the mere existence of an arbitration clause. Discretion of civil court to proceed with suit is only narrowed down. Civil court can refuse to stay the suit and can proceed with it under certain circumstances. Shortcomings and deficiencies of enquiry before an arbitrator are well known. Cases requiring serious consideration of evidence relating to fraud, misrepresentation, etc. are best left to the civil court and the arbitrator will not be competent to go into said issues. Where dispute involves substantial questions of law and contested allegations of mala fide, fraud, etc. which depend on oral and documentary evidence, civil court will be justified in ignoring arbitration clause.[502]

Territorial jurisdiction

Where the cause of action takes place within the jurisdiction of the subordinate office, it is only the court situated at that place where the suit can be brought.[503]

Jurisdiction of court

By specific agreement between the parties, parties had restricted the jurisdiction to the courts at Delhi. The courts at Hyderabad will not have jurisdiction to entertain arbitration application(s) just due to the mere fact that the cause of action or a part thereof had arisen within the jurisdiction of the court at Hyderabad.[504]

Reference to arbitration under Section 8—Effect on civil suit

Once matter is referred to arbitration, proceedings in civil suit are disposed of. There is no question of stay of civil proceedings pending the conclusion

501. *H.G. Oomor Sait* v. *O. Aslam Sait*, 2001 SCC OnLine Mad 465: (2001) 3 CTC 269.
502. *Ibid.*
503. *NTPC* v. *A.P. Singh*, 2008 SCC OnLine Del 1343: (2009) 107 DRJ 276.
504. *A. Contractors (I) Ltd.* v. *National Buildings Construction Corpn. Ltd.*, 2021 SCC OnLine TS 3648.

of arbitration. After reference all rights, obligations and remedies of parties would be governed by the provisions of Arbitration and Conciliation Act, 1996 including the right to challenge the award.[505]

Estoppel

A right once waived by a party in respect of the course to be adopted for settlement of a dispute between himself and the other side is lost forever and cannot be reclaimed or re-agitated later on, on being visited by the consequences that followed such waiver of the right to a specific course to which he was entitled to as a matter of right. This is so because when a party to an arbitration agreement gives up his right to refer the dispute to arbitration, a right comes to vest on the other party to take recourse to other remedies that are open to him in law and when such a course is resorted to by the other party, the party who had waived the right to settle the dispute in an arbitration proceedings cannot be permitted to turn around and contend that he is entitled to the remedy of arbitration and the recourse to the suit by the other party under the common law is bad.[506]

Where in a suit for dissolution of partnership firm and for rendition of accounts under Section 44(*g*), Partnership Act, 1932, an application of appellants for stay of suit under Section 34, Arbitration Act, 1940 had been allowed but during appeal stage upon repeal of the 1940 Act, the appellant got the application dismissed as not pressed, the appellants were not precluded from seeking to have civil proceedings before the trial court stayed under Section 8 of the 1996 Act. The High Court erred in dismissing the appellants' application under Section 8 of the Act.[507]

Waiver

Dispute arose due to a development agreement. Parties to the agreement must apply for reference not later than the date of submission of their first statement on the substance of the dispute before the court. No such application was filed by the owner. Held, owner had waived such right.[508]

In the written statement there was no prayer for referring parties to arbitration. Defendants also filed an application under Section 9-A CPC for dismissal of suit. There was no unequivocal attempt to see that parties are referred to arbitration. Intention was to get suit terminated rather than seeing to it that parties are referred to arbitration. Application under Section 9-A

505. *P. Anand Gajapathi Raju* v. *P.V.G. Raju*, (2000) 4 SCC 539.
506. *Ramakrishna Theatre Ltd.* v. *General Investments and Commercial Corpn. Ltd.*, 2003 SCC OnLine Kar 465: ILR 2003 Kar 3463.
507. *Kalpana Kothari* v. *Sudha Yadav*, (2002) 1 SCC 203.
508. *Shyamal Kumar Roy* v. *Sushil Kumar Agarwal*, 2023 SCC OnLine Cal 525.

indicated that Defendants 3 to 5 had waived their right to be referred to arbitration. Rejection of application under Section 8 was justified.[509]

Res judicata

Application under Section 34, Arbitration Act, 1940 was dismissed in the year 1995, the dismissal was affirmed in 2000 by the High Court in 2001 and had attained finality. Subsequent attempt by the appellants by application under Section 8 of the 1996 Act was rightly negated by the trial court and the High Court.[510]

Once the decision of the judicial authority rejecting the reference of dispute to arbitration becomes final, application under Section 11(6) before the Chief Justice/his designate for appointment of arbitrator is not maintainable at the instance of either party, since it is hit by principles of res judicata and issue estoppel. In the present case the order of the civil court that it has jurisdiction to try the suit became final and the parties participated in proceedings by examining all the witnesses. Respondent's application filed under Section 11(6) before the Chief Justice for appointment of the arbitrator was nothing but abuse of the process of the court. Designate judge erred in appointing arbitrator, order was set aside.[511]

Order restraining arbitration proceedings

An order under Section 8 restraining arbitration proceedings, from commencing or continuing cannot be passed.[512]

Injunction restraining a party from proceeding with the arbitration

There is nothing in the Act which suggests that the court can restrain a party from proceeding with the arbitration when the arbitration clause exists with a forum selected by the parties and the subject-matter is an arbitrable one.[513]

"Any dispute" between the parties referred to arbitration (MOU)

Dispute and differences had arisen between the parties and after the death of MD of the respondent-company, the successor MD had assured the appellant that the commitments and obligations would be met by the respondents.

---

509. *Nirmal Lifestyle (Kalyan) (P) Ltd.* v. *Hendrya*, 2015 SCC OnLine Bom 1796: (2015) 2 Mah LJ 772.
510. *H. Srinivas Pai* v. *H.V. Pai*, (2010) 12 SCC 521.
511. *Anil* v. *Rajendra*, (2015) 2 SCC 583.
512. *Ardy International (P) Ltd.* v. *Inspiration Clothes & U*, (2006) 1 SCC 417.
513. *JSW Steel Ltd.* v. *JFE Shoji Trade Corpn.*, 2009 SCC OnLine Bom 2069: (2010) 3 Mah LJ 165.

Section 8 of the 1996 Act is peremptory in nature. In case where there exists an arbitration agreement, the court is under obligation to refer the parties to arbitration in terms of the arbitration agreement. Existence of the arbitration agreement was not disputed in the case. Application under Section 8 was allowed, dispute between the parties was referred to arbitration.[514]

Reference to arbitration can be with respect to parties to arbitration agreement and not non-parties

There can be reference to arbitration only if there is an arbitration agreement between the parties. If there is a dispute between a party to an arbitration agreement with the other parties, as also non-parties to the arbitration agreement, reference to arbitration or appointment of arbitrator can be only with respect to the parties to the arbitration agreement and not the non-parties.[515] Loan agreement amongst the first respondent (lender) and third respondent (guarantor) contained a provision for arbitration. But the appellant was not a party to the same. Appellant's letter of guarantee was given prior to the dates of the two loan agreements which did not contain a provision for arbitration. An arbitration agreement between the lender, the borrower and one of the guarantors cannot be deemed or construed to be an arbitration agreement as defined under Section 7(4)(*a*) or (*b*) of the Act insofar as the appellant was concerned. As the letter of guarantee given by the appellant did not refer to any document containing an arbitration clause, there was also no arbitration agreement between the first respondent and the appellant as contemplated under Section 7(5) of the Act. When the appellant gave the guarantee letter, he could not be imputed with knowledge that the loan agreements which were to be executed in future would contain an arbitration clause. Further, the appellant had not stated in his letters of guarantee that he would be bound by the terms of the loan agreement(s) that may be executed by the borrower. The question of the appellant impliedly agreeing to the arbitration clause did not arise. The appellant who had not signed the loan agreement(s) containing the arbitration clause could not be deemed to be a party to the arbitration and bound by the award. As there was no arbitration agreement between the appellant, the impleading of the appellant as a respondent in the arbitration proceedings and the award against the appellant in the arbitration proceedings was not sustained, the award of the arbitrator in part against the appellant was set aside.[516]

---

514. *Agri Gold Exims Ltd.* v. *Sri Lakshmi Knits & Wovens*, (2007) 3 SCC 686.
515. *S.N. Prasad* v. *Monnet Finance Ltd.*, (2011) 1 SCC 320.
516. *Ibid.*

Application under Section 8 can be filed by a party to arbitration agreement

Application under Section 8 can be filed only by a party to the arbitration.[517] The order by which disputes of non-party to the arbitration agreement is sought to be referred to invoking Section 8, Arbitration and Conciliation Act, 1996 is not an order under the Arbitration and Conciliation Act.[518]

Government-company supplying defective/sub-standard seeds to farmers—Remedy of arbitration optional

When a government-company supplies defective/substandard seeds to farmers, the remedy of arbitration available to the farmers is optional in addition to compensatory relief under Consumer Protection Act, 1986. The remedy of arbitration is not the only remedy available to a grower. Rather it is an optional remedy. He can either seek reference to an arbitrator or file complaint under the Consumer Protection Act. If the grower opts for remedy of the arbitrator, then it may be possible to say that he cannot subsequently file a complaint under the Consumer Protection Act. However, if he chooses to file a complaint in the first instance before the competent consumer forum, then he cannot be denied relief by invoking Section 8, Arbitration and Conciliation Act, 1996.[519]

Partnership Act, 1932

Where the partnership deed contains an arbitration clause, to which the parties are signatories, on application filed under Section 8, the parties have to be sent to the arbitration. Where the arbitration clause in the partnership deed is couched in wide terms, the arbitrator will be competent to decide all the questions thereto, including the question of whether or not the partnership shall be dissolved. There is no other option left for the court but to refer the matter to arbitration.[520] Reference of dispute to arbitration by virtue of arbitration clause in the partition deed was proper.[521] Dispute arose out of partnership deed containing arbitration clause. Objection by the opposite party alleging partnership deed to be forged, also making allegations against working of partnership firm. Allegations did not fall into the category of "serious allegation" but were made without any substantial basis, only for the purpose of avoiding reference of dispute to arbitration.

---

517. *Supreme Mega Construction LLP* v. *Symphony Coop. Housing Society Ltd.*, 2014 SCC OnLine Bom 4624: (2015) 2 Mah LJ 776.
518. *Kishan Mimani* v. *Indu Kocher*, 2011 SCC OnLine Cal 5435: (2012) 4 CHN 157.
519. *National Seeds Corpn. Ltd.* v. *M. Madhusudhan Reddy*, (2012) 2 SCC 506.
520. *Navin Kumar* v. *Standard Restaurant*, 2003 SCC OnLine Del 82: (2003) 68 DRJ 702.
521. *Rakesh Sethi* v. *Rajeev Sethi*, 2019 SCC OnLine Cal 974.

Dispute was referred to arbitration.[522] Bar imposed under Section 59(3), Partnership Act, 1932 has no application to the arbitration proceedings as well as arbitration award.[523]

In *Mukesh Singh Tomar* v. *Rakesh*[524], plaintiff and defendants were carrying on business under a registered partnership deed dated 5 May 2008. Plaintiff pleaded that defendants prepared forged and fabricated agreement on 26 August 2011 and also prepared an unregistered partnership deed. Documents were neither signed by the plaintiff nor they were prepared with his consent. Prayer by plaintiff was that forged documents be declared as null and void and registered partnership deed dated 5 May 2008 be enforced. It was held that subject-matter of the suit is capable of adjudication by the civil court and the relief claimed can only be granted by the civil court.

Partnership deed executed much after the enactment of Arbitration and Conciliation Act, 1996 provided for reference of disputes to arbitration as per provisions of 1940 Act. Such reference to arbitration under Act of 1940 would be of no consequence after coming into force of new Act of 1996. Reference would be governed by the provisions of 1996 Act.[525]

Unregistered partnership firm

Partners can file application under Section 8 for reference. Since the partnership deed is not a compulsorily registrable document, its non-registration cannot bar the court from referring the dispute to arbitration.[526]

Dissolution of partnership

It cannot be said that arbitrator can only resolve disputes in respect of partnership accounts and not dissolve the firm. Dissolution of a partnership cannot be equated with winding up of a company. Dissolution of the firm is a private action between the partners.[527] Where an arbitrator clause provides that all disputes and questions whatsoever arise can be decided by the arbitrator, the dissolution of partnership can be decided by the arbitrator. The word "Court" in Section 44, Partnership Act, 1932 includes arbitrator.[528]

522. *Ramadhar Singh* v. *Raj Mangal Singh*, 2017 SCC OnLine Pat 3726; *A. Ayyasamy* v. *A. Paramasivam*, (2016) 10 SCC 386 relied on.
523. *Umesh Goel* v. *H.P. Coop. Group Housing Society Ltd.*, (2016) 11 SCC 313; *Ananthesh Bhakta* v. *Nayana S. Bhakta*, (2017) 5 SCC 185.
524. 2012 SCC OnLine MP 9605: (2013) 1 MP LJ 233.
525. *Purushottam* v. *Anil*, (2018) 8 SCC 95.
526. *Ajay Tiwari* v. *Vijayendra Bajpai*, 2020 SCC OnLine TS 3403: (2020) 6 ALT 361; see also, *Tapadiya Construction Ltd.* v. *Sanjay Suganchand Kasliwal*, 2015 SCC OnLine Bom 6781: (2016) 6 Mah LJ 768.
527. *Mahendra Kumar Poddar* v. *Bansal Builders*, 2001 SCC OnLine Cal 687: (2001) 4 ICC 140.
528. *Ibid.*

There was dispute between parties whether the respondent had retired or whether accounts were settled or whether the firm was liable to be dissolved and were liable for rendition of accounts. Dispute between the parties as per clause 11 of partnership deed would be decided by the arbitrator and referred to the arbitrator.[529]

Suit arose from a partnership deed. Arbitration clauses continue to have effect on partners even after retirement from partnership. Merely because partners retired from partnership firm, does not mean that issue cannot be referred to arbitration. Moreover, Section 8 of 1996 Act makes it mandatory that when there exists a clause of arbitration, dispute should be referred to arbitration. Reference to arbitration was proper.[530]

Partnership deed superseded by compromise agreement

The partnership deed contained an arbitration clause. Disputes arose between partners and after discussions, some partners entered into compromise. Compromise evidenced that business had been closed and partnership had come to an end and partnership had been superseded by compromise agreement and amount due to bank was agreed to be paid by plaintiff and defendants in specified ratio. Plaintiff claimed the amount on the basis of compromise. Compromise did not contain any arbitration clause and evidence prima facie disclosed that compromise was acted upon. Order of subordinate judge in referring parties to arbitration on basis of clause contained in partnership deed set aside as partnership had been superseded by compromise agreement.[531]

Unregistered partnership firm

Arbitration clause in agreement of an unregistered firm of partnership can be invoked for referring the dispute to arbitration.[532]

Reference to arbitration after dissolution of partnership firm

Partnership deed stated that the plaintiff and the defendant were two partners who entered into a deed of partnership for carrying out business. Partnership deed contained an arbitration clause which included all disputes, controversies and differences between parties relating to partnership deed, the deed did not indicate that the parties intended to exclude post-dissolution disputes

529. *Tejinder Pal Grover* v. *Murari Lal Gupta*, 2007 SCC OnLine P&H 454: PLR (2008) 149 P&H 368.
530. *Savitha* v. *Dineshkumar*, 2021 SCC OnLine Mad 16962.
531. *Rajendran* v. *Rama Chidambaram*, 2005 SCC OnLine Mad 535: (2005) 4 CTC 736.
532. *Manoj Makkar* v. *Neeru Bal*, 2012 SCC OnLine P&H 8679.

from arbitral reference. In the absence of an embargo to refer post-dissolution dispute to arbitration, the plea that the arbitration clause ceased to exist with the dissolution of partnership firm was not accepted. Reference to arbitration was proper.[533] Petitioners can seek reference of the disputes relating to partnership firm to arbitration.

Agreement contained an arbitration clause which empowered the parties to refer disputes to arbitrator "during continuance of partnership". Such a clause becomes inoperative in the event of dissolution and parties cannot seek reference to an arbitrator after dissolution. Application filed under Section 8, Arbitration and Conciliation Act, 1996 was dismissed.[534]

Civil suit for dissolution of the firm and rendition of accounts was filed. Clause 22 of partnership deed provided that anything not specifically mentioned in this deed shall be settled by mutual discussion and in case the dispute remains unsolved, the same shall be referred to the arbitration. Clause 17 provided that there was no fixed duration of partnership but any of the partners could retire from the partnership after giving three-months notice in writing to remaining partners and on expiry of such period, partnership shall be terminated. Clause 22 was not a general arbitration clause pertaining to all disputes arising between the parties, only such matters not specifically mentioned in the deed of partnership required to be referred to arbitration. Clause 17 specifically dealt with the question of retirement of a partner on serving of requisite notice. Dispute between parties was not covered under clause 22, hence was not referable for adjudication to the arbitrator.[535]

Societies Registration Act, 1860 (21 of 1860)

For invoking of arbitration proceedings, what is essential is the existence of an arbitration agreement, *i.e.* mandate under Section 7, Arbitration and Conciliation Act, 1996. In a given case, an arbitration clause may be provided by way of statute. The dispute resolution mechanism as provided under Section 23, Societies Registration Act which provides a choice for dispute resolution cannot be read into the bye-laws of the society or as forming part of bye-laws, as it only provides a choice of forum for dispute resolution, *i.e.* either by arbitration or by approaching the court concerned. There was no arbitration clause in the agreement entered into between the parties, the

533. *Ankit Vijaykumar Khandelwal* v. *Aarti Rajkumar Khandelwal*, 2021 SCC OnLine Bom 642: (2021) 6 Mah LJ 550; see also, *Ram Kishan Mimani* v. *Goverdhan Das Mimani*, 2010 SCC OnLine Cal 1060: (2010) 4 CHN 527.

534. *H.G. Oomor Sait* v. *O. Aslam Sait*, 2001 SCC OnLine Mad 465: (2001) 3 CTC 269.

535. *Ahluwalia & Co.* v. *Surinder Mohan*, 2004 SCC OnLine P&H 91: PLR (2004) 137 P&H 684.

question of invoking Section 8, Arbitration and Conciliation Act, 1996 did not arise. Application for reference to arbitration was rejected.[536]

Hire purchase agreement

Where the plaintiff had purchased a car under hire purchase agreement and the defendant had taken forcible possession of the car, as the hire purchase agreement contained an arbitration clause, in plaintiff's suit for possession and other consequential relief on application of the financier defendant, dispute was referred to arbitration. The basic principle is whether parties contracted to go to arbitration. The court must be lenient towards directing parties to seek redressal through arbitration once they have chosen for that course. Section 8(1) says that the court shall refer parties to arbitration and has no discretion in that matter.[537] There was an arbitration clause in the hire purchase agreement. The trial court rejected the request for reference to arbitration as the agreement was not sustainable in law. Held, it was not open to the court to go into the merits of the case as all the disputes concerning the hire purchase agreement between the parties were to be decided by the arbitrator to be appointed out of the panel. Order was set aside and request for reference was allowed.[538]

Concluded contract

Since there was no concluded contract between the parties containing the arbitration clause, the matter could not be referred to the arbitrator.[539] When there is no concluded contract containing an arbitration clause, matter cannot be referred to the arbitrator.[540] Petitioners had filed an application under Section 8 of the Act for reference of dispute to the arbitrator. The tender of the plaintiff was not accepted, as such no contract came into being.

Wakf property

Where the dispute involves wakf property, the jurisdiction of the Wakf Tribunal is not ousted. Reference to arbitration cannot be made.[541]

---

536. *Vasavi Clubs International* v. *Gella Krishna Veni*, 2021 SCC OnLine TS 3637.
537. *Sugal & Damani Finlease Ltd.* v. *P. Subramania Reddy*, 1999 SCC OnLine Mad 773: (2000) 2 CTC 74; *S. Sakthivel* v. *Vijay Hemant Finances Estate Ltd.*, 2013 SCC OnLine Mad 1201: (2013) 3 LW 579.
538. *Sant Finance Co.* v. *Darshan Singh*, 2006 SCC OnLine P&H 1105: PLR (2007) 145 P&H 74 (2).
539. *Food Corporation of India* v. *P.K. Co.*, 2000 SCC OnLine P&H 1294.
540. *Ibid.*
541. *Namira Construction (P) Ltd.* v. *Fazal Imam Public Charitable and Religious Trust*, 2019 SCC OnLine Pat 3409: (2019) 3 PLJR 223.

Dispute arising out of work contract

Dispute as to works contract can be referred to the Arbitral Tribunal even after the completion of the contract.[542]

Dispute was covered by the arbitration clause in the agreement. Application for referring the dispute to the arbitrator was allowed.[543]

Arbitration clause provided that any dispute or difference arising between the parties out of or relating to the construction, meaning, scope, operation or effect of the contract or the validity or breach thereof would be settled by way of arbitration in accordance with the rules of arbitration. Question as to whether a particular claim falls within the contract or beyond the contract is a matter for resolution by way of arbitration.[544]

Election

Respondent was elected Secretary of respondent-Association but was not a member of the Association. Petitioner was aggrieved by the election of the respondent. Dispute was not an arbitrable dispute, hence was not referred to arbitration.[545]

Cases arbitrable/non-arbitrable—Law summarised

1. The legislature amended sub-section (1) of Section 8 to provide that a judicial authority shall refer the parties to arbitration, "unless it finds that prima facie no valid agreement exists". Section 8 mandates reference to arbitration, unless the arbitration agreement is found to be invalid. It has been recognised that certain categories of disputes which are of public nature, are not capable of adjudication and settlement by arbitration, which is a private forum constituted by consent of parties.
2. All civil or commercial disputes, either contractual or non-contractual, which can be adjudicated upon by a civil court, in principle, can be adjudicated and resolved through arbitration, unless it is excluded either expressly by statute, or by necessary implication. The Arbitration and Conciliation Act, 1996 does not exclude any category of disputes as being non-arbitrable. Section 2(3) of the Arbitration and Conciliation Act, 1996 however recognises that certain categories of disputes by

542. *M.P. Rural Road Development Authority* v. *L.G. Chaudhary Engineers and Contractors*, (2018) 10 SCC 826; *M.P. Rural Road Development Authority* v. *L.G. Chaudhary Engineers & Contractors*, (2012) 3 SCC 495, *followed*.
543. *BHEL* v. *Kalpana Gears (P) Ltd.*, 2003 SCC OnLine MP 327: (2003) 4 MPLJ 473.
544. *Philip Vanlalmawia John* v. *State of Mizoram*, 2012 SCC OnLine Gau 488: (2013) 3 Gau LR 877.
545. *Madras Sporting Youngsters Football Club* v. *T.N. Football Assn.*, 2022 SCC OnLine Mad 460.

law may not be submitted to arbitration. In all jurisdictions, certain categories of disputes are reserved by the legislature, as a matter of public policy, to be adjudicated by a court of law.

3. Traditionally, disputes relating to rights *in rem* are required to be adjudicated by courts and/or statutory tribunals. A right *in rem* is a right exercisable against the world at large. Actions *in rem* refer to actions which create a legal status such as citizenship, divorce, testamentary and probate issues, etc. A *lis in rem* is not arbitrable by a private tribunal constituted by the consent of parties. Actions *in personam* determine the rights and interests of parties to the subject-matter of the dispute, which are arbitrable.
4. The broad categories of disputes which are considered to be non-arbitrable are penal offences which are visited with criminal sanction; offences pertaining to bribery/corruption; matrimonial disputes relating to divorce, judicial separation, restitution of conjugal rights, child custody and guardianship matters, which pertain to the status of a person; testamentary matters which pertain to disputes relating to the validity of a will, grant of probate, letters of administration, succession, which pertain to the status of a person, and are adjudicated by civil courts.
5. Certain categories of disputes such as consumer disputes; insolvency and bankruptcy proceedings; oppression and mismanagement, or winding up of a company; disputes relating to trusts, trustees and beneficiaries of a trust are governed by special enactments.
6. The well-recognised examples of non-arbitrable disputes are: (*i*) disputes relating to rights and liabilities which give rise to or arise out of criminal offences; (*ii*) matrimonial disputes relating to divorce, judicial separation, restitution of conjugal rights, child custody; (*iii*) guardianship matters; (*iv*) insolvency and winding up matters; (*v*) testamentary matters (grant of probate, letters of administration and succession certificate); and (*vi*) eviction or tenancy matters governed by special statutes where the tenant enjoys statutory protection against eviction and only the specified courts are conferred jurisdiction to grant eviction or decide the disputes.[546]

Tender form

Tender form which contained a clause for referring dispute to arbitrator was duly accepted by tenderer. Absence of formally signed agreement between parties would not affect acceptance of clause by tenderer and its implication. Plea of tenderer that application for reference is not maintainable in absence

546. *N.N. Global Mercantile (P) Ltd.* v. *Indo Unique Flame Ltd.*, (2021) 4 SCC 379.

of any formal agreement is not tenable, was rejected. Dispute regarding payment of bill was referred to arbitration.[547]

There was a tender for construction of a dwelling unit. Dispute arose between the parties. Clause 29 of the agreement provided that in case of any dispute arising between the parties, the same will be decided by the Chief Engineer. The Chief Engineer of the Corporation did not decide the dispute. Clause 29 was treated as an arbitration clause. A retired judge of the High Court was decided as arbitrator in the case.[548]

Section 8—Application verification

Order 29 Rule 1 CPC provides that a pleading by the corporation can be signed and verified on its behalf by the Secretary or by any Director or the principal officer. The court should not be too technical. When the Board of Directors has authorised *S*, it is to be deemed that the petition has been signed and affirmed with the sanction of the Board. The description of *S* as a "Senior Manager" complies with such requirement.[549]

Reversal of proceedings to civil court after reference to arbitration

The scheme of the Arbitration and Conciliation Act does not contemplate reversal of the proceedings to the civil court for its adjudication under any circumstances once the matter is referred to the arbitration from civil court.[550]

Bombay Municipal Corporation Act, 1886 (3 of 1888)—Reference to arbitration

In cases of disputes between Municipal Corporation and Contractor, clause 96 of the General Conditions of Contract provides for resolution of dispute between Engineer and Contractor by referring matter to the Municipal Commissioner. Clause 97 of General Conditions of Contract is an arbitration clause, covering every facet of arbitration. Clause 96 does not mention that clause 97 would only be in respect of matters which have arisen under clause 96. Clause 97 encompasses all disputes and differences arising before or after completion of work. Invocation of clause 96 is not precursor to invocation of clause 97. Disputes can be referred to arbitrator by following the procedure laid down in clause 97.[551]

---

547. *Satya Paul Sharma* v. *BSNL*, 2015 SCC OnLine J&K 24.
548. *Bharat Drilling and Foundation Treatment (P) Ltd.* v. *Ranchi Municipal Corpn.*, 2014 SCC OnLine Jhar 1115: (2014) 3 JLJR 624.
549. *Jessop & Co. Ltd.* v. *Tecpro Systems Ltd.*, 2012 SCC OnLine Cal 6324: (2012) 4 CHN 567.
550. *Union of India* v. *Rajesh Damani*, 2012 SCC OnLine Mad 2718: (2012) 5 CTC 426.
551. *S. Kumar Construction Co.* v. *Municipal Corpn. of Greater Bombay*, 2017 SCC OnLine Bom 130 (FB).

Gujarat Public Works Contracts Disputes Arbitration Tribunal Act, 1992 (4 of 1992)

A dispute arising out of a public works contract is to be adjudicated by the Arbitration Tribunal under the Act of 1992 and not under the Arbitration and Conciliation Act, 1996.[552]

Letters Patent Appeal

No appeal lies under clause 15 of the Letters Patent from an order passed by the Single Judge on an application under Section 8, Arbitration and Conciliation Act, as it is not covered by Section 37(1) of the Act.[553]

Rejection of plaint

Section 8, Arbitration and Conciliation Act, 1996 does not empower the court to reject the plaint.[554]

Writ petition

As no appeal is provided in the Arbitration and Conciliation Act, 1996 against an order passed under Section 8 of the Act and as the trial court where the suit is filed is subordinate to the High Court, certainly, petition under Article 227 of the Constitution of India is maintainable before the High Court.[555]

Where an application filed under Section 8 of the Act is rejected, no appeal is provided under the Act, and therefore, the aggrieved party is entitled to seek redress of his grievance by knocking the doors of a writ court under Article 227 of the Constitution of India.[556]

Reference of dispute to arbitration—Refusal—No appeal lies

Section 37(1)(*a*) was incorporated in the principal Act of 1996 w.e.f. 25 October 2015. Before 25 October 2015, no right existed to file an appeal

552. *Vijay Construction Co. Consulting Engineers & Contractors* v. *Sardar Sarovar Narmada Nigam Ltd.*, 2018 SCC OnLine Guj 203: (2018) 59 (3) GLR 1809; *Sardar Sarovar Narmada Nigam* v. *Bhaven Construction*, 2012 SCC OnLine Guj 6499.
553. *Sureka Steel Ltd.* v. *Union of India*, 1997 SCC OnLine Cal 279: (1998) 1 CHN 13; *Conros Steels (P) Ltd.* v. *Lu Qin (Hong Kong) Co. Ltd.*, 2014 SCC OnLine Bom 2305: (2015) 1 Mah LJ 434; *TISCO Ltd.* v. *Standard Chrome*, 2005 SCC OnLine Cal 396: (2006) 2 CHN 378; *Rites Ltd.* v. *JMC Projects (I) Ltd.*, 2009 SCC OnLine Del 532: (2009) 109 DRJ 577; *Kotak Mahindra Investment Ltd.* v. *Kitply Industries Ltd.*, 2011 SCC OnLine Cal 2736: (2012) 5 CHN 489.
554. *M. Shankara Reddy* v. *Amara Ramakoteswara Rao*, 2017 SCC OnLine Hyd 426: (2018) 1 ALD 220.
555. *G.R. Amarnath* v. *M.N. Narasimlia Murthy Naik*, 2015 SCC OnLine Kar 8607: ILR 2016 Kar 20.
556. *M.M.C. (India) (P) Ltd.* v. *Nitesh Estates Ltd.*, 2022 SCC OnLine Kar 1836.

against the order refusing to refer the parties to arbitration under Section 8 of the Act of 1996. The date of commencement of court proceedings was 10 July 2015, when the application under Section 8 of the Act of 1996 was filed. The appellant had no right to file an appeal at the time of the commencement of court proceedings on 10 July 2015. The appeal against refusal to refer parties to arbitration was not maintainable.[557]

INTERIM MEASURES, ETC. BY COURT [S. 9]

9. *Interim measures, etc. by Court.*—[558][(1)] A party may, before or during arbitral proceedings or at any time after the making of the arbitral award but before it is enforced in accordance with Section 36, apply to a Court:—

(*i*) for the appointment of a guardian for a minor or a person of unsound mind for the purposes of arbitral proceedings; or

(*ii*) for an interim measure of protection in respect of any of the following matters, namely:—

(*a*) the preservation, interim custody or sale of any goods which are the subject-matter of the arbitration agreement;

(*b*) securing the amount in dispute in the arbitration;

(*c*) the detention, preservation or inspection of any property or thing which is the subject-matter of the dispute in arbitration, or as to which any question may arise therein and authorising for any of the aforesaid purposes any person to enter upon any land or building in the possession of any party, or authorising any samples to be taken or any observation to be made, or experiment to be tried, which may be necessary or expedient for the purpose of obtaining full information or evidence;

(*d*) interim injunction or the appointment of a receiver;

(*e*) such other interim measure of protection as may appear to the Court to be just and convenient,

and the Court shall have the same power for making orders as it has for the purpose of, and in relation to, any proceedings before it.

[559][(2) Where, before the commencement of the arbitral proceedings, a court passes an order for any interim measure of protection under sub-section (1), the arbitral proceedings shall be commenced within a period of ninety days from the date of such order or within such further time as the court may determine.

(3) Once the arbitral tribunal has been constituted, the court shall not entertain an application under sub-section (1), unless the court finds that circumstances exist which may not render the remedy provided under Section 17 efficacious.]

557. *Graviss Foods (P) Ltd.* v. *Ice Cream Garden*, 2023 SCC OnLine HP 1032.
558. Section 9 *renumbered* as sub-section (1) by Act 3 of 2016, S. 5 (w.r.e.f. 23-10-2015).
559. *Ins.* by Act 3 of 2016, S. 5 (w.r.e.f. 23-10-2015).

COMMENTS

Corresponding old law

Section 9 corresponds to Sections 18, 41(*b*) and Second Schedule of the Arbitration Act, 1940.

18. *Power of Court to pass interim orders.*—(1) Notwithstanding anything contained in Section 17, at any time after the filing of the award, whether notice of the filing has been served or not, upon being satisfied by affidavit or otherwise that a party has taken or is about to take steps to defeat, delay or obstruct the execution of any decree that may be passed upon the award, or that speedy execution of the award is just and necessary, the Court may pass such interim orders as it deems necessary.

(2) Any person against whom such interim orders have been passed may show cause against such orders, and the Court, after hearing the parties, may pass such further orders as it deems necessary, and just.

41. *Procedure and powers of Court.*—Subject to the provisions of this Act and of rules made thereunder—

(*a*) the provisions of the Code of Civil Procedure, 1908 (5 of 1908), shall apply to all proceedings before the Court, and to all appeals, under this Act; and

(*b*) the Court shall have, for the purpose of, and in relation to, arbitration proceedings, the same power of making orders in respect of any of the matters set out in the Second Schedule as it has for the purpose of, and in relation to, any proceedings before the Court:

Provided that nothing in clause (*b*) shall be taken to prejudice any power which may be vested in an arbitrator or umpire for making orders with respect to any of such matters.

UNCITRAL Model Law

Article 9. *Arbitration agreement and interim measures by court*

It is not incompatible with an arbitration agreement for a party to request, before or during arbitral proceedings, from a court an interim measure of protection and for a court to grant such measure.

Legislative changes

Arbitration and Conciliation (Amendment) Act, 2015 (3 of 2016)

Section 9 of the principal Act shall be renumbered as sub-section (1) thereof, and after sub-section (1) as so renumbered, the following sub-sections shall be *inserted*, namely—

"(2) Where, before the commencement of the arbitral proceedings, a court passes an order for any interim measure of protection under sub-section (1), the arbitral proceedings shall be commenced within a period of ninety days from the date of such order or within such further time as the court may determine.

(3) Once the arbitral tribunal has been constituted, the court shall not entertain an application under sub-section (1), unless the court finds that circumstances exist which may not render the remedy provided under Section 17 efficacious.".

NOTES ON CLAUSES

Clause 5 of the Bill seeks to amend Section 9 of the principal Act to provide that where the court passes an order for any interim measure under sub-section (1) before the commencement of the arbitral proceedings, the arbitral proceedings shall be commenced within a period of 90 days from the date of such order. It further provides that once the Arbitral Tribunal is constituted, the court shall not entertain an application for interim measures unless it finds that circumstances which may not render the remedy provided under Section 17 efficacious.

Object of the section

The object and intent of the interim order passed under Section 9 is to protect the rights of both the parties till a final decision is taken by the arbitrator.[560]

Scope and application

Section 9 provides for passing of interim orders by the court in respect of arbitration proceedings initiated on the application filed by a party before or during the arbitration proceedings or at any time after the making of the award but before it is enforced under Section 36 of the Act. The court may pass the following orders:

(*i*) For the appointment of a guardian for a minor or a person of unsound mind where a minor or a person of unsound mind is a party to the arbitration proceedings. Order 32, Rule 1 CPC lays down that every suit by a minor shall be instituted in his name by a person who in such a suit shall be called the next friend of the minor. Order 32, Rule 2 provides that where the suit by a minor plaintiff is instituted without next friend, the suit shall be taken off the file. Likewise Order 32, Rule 3 provides that the court shall appoint a guardian for the minor defendant in the suit.

(*ii*) Interim measure/order for the preservation, interim custody or sale of the property/subject-matter of the arbitration agreement.

560. *Suresh Dhanuka* v. *Sunita Mohapatra*, (2012) 1 SCC 578.

(*iii*) Interim injunction.
(*iv*) Appointment of a receiver.
(*v*) Any other interim measure of protection which the court finds just and convenient.

Section 9 does not permit any or all applications. It only permits applications for interim measures mentioned in clauses (*i*) and (*ii*) thereof. There cannot be applications under Section 9 for stay of the arbitral proceedings or to challenge the existence or validity of the arbitration agreements or the jurisdiction of the arbitral jurisdiction. All such applications would have to be made before the Arbitral Tribunal under the relevant provisions of the Act.[561]

The court should, before entertaining application under Section 9, satisfy itself that (*a*) there exists arbitration agreement; (*b*) that applicant intends to take dispute to arbitration; (*c*) subject-matter of arbitration comes within pecuniary and territorial civil jurisdiction of the court which is approached by applicant.[562]

An application under Section 9 of the Act cannot be rejected on the ground that the respondent has disclosed before the High Court that it does not have any asset other than one asset that is also fully encumbered. The court is not precluded under Section 9 of the Act to pass an equitable order by securing the claim of the applicant by directing the opponent to deposit such amount, to furnish bank guarantee once the applicant proves prima facie case in his favour.[563]

Where the existence of an arbitration agreement is disputed, the High Court has jurisdiction to determine the existence of a valid arbitration agreement.[564] Where dispute arises about the fulfillment of the conditions of escrow, jurisdiction of the question is not excluded.[565]

While considering the prayers for interim measures under Section 9, Arbitration and Conciliation Act, 1996, the court has to be guided by the principles governing the exercise of powers under Order 39 Rules 1 and 2 CPC 1908, and the principles analogous thereto. The equitable consideration and the aspect of conduct of the parties, as are relevant for seeking the equitable relief of injunction, are also germane in considering the grant or otherwise of interim measures under Section 9. The conduct of the party

561. *Bhatia International* v. *Bulk Trading S.A.*, (2002) 4 SCC 105.
562. *Hairtha Finance Ltd.* v. *ATV Projects India Ltd.*, 2003 SCC OnLine Mad 265: (2003) 2 CTC 226.
563. *Essar House (P) Ltd.* v. *Arcellor Mittal Nippon Steel India Ltd.*, 2022 SCC OnLine SC 1219.
564. *Jeweltouch (India) (P) Ltd.* v. *Naheed Hafeez Quraishi (Patrawala)*, 2008 SCC OnLine Bom 82: (2008) 3 Mah LJ 54.
565. *Ibid.*

becomes a relevant consideration in weighing the prayers for grant of interim measures under Section 9, Arbitration and Conciliation Act, 1996.[566]

The power of the court under Section 9, Arbitration and Conciliation Act, 1996 does not depend on filing of suit like Order 39 CPC. Hence, application under Order 39, Rules 1 and 2 cannot be treated as an application under Section 9, Arbitration and Conciliation Act, 1996.[567]

There was agreement between the parties which contained an arbitration clause. Simply because some parties have joined in the suit is no ground for granting injunction from proceeding further with the arbitration.[568]

In the absence of any concluded contract between the parties, the arbitration clause in the draft agreement cannot be made operational, application under Section 9 of the Act for interim relief is not maintainable.[569]

Sections 9 and 8 are independent provisions.[570]

Section 9, Arbitration and Conciliation Act, 1996 is a power in the court to grant interim injunction even before the constitution of the Arbitral Tribunal, in the course of the proceedings and till the award becomes executable. Then, Section 8, even if invoked, will not apply to proceedings under Section 9 of the Act.[571]

Provisions of Sections 9 and 11 are required to be invoked simultaneously.[572] The court has powers to pass appropriate orders under Section 9 of the Act notwithstanding the pendency of arbitral proceedings, especially since the Act preserves the power of the court and bestows restricted jurisdiction on the arbitrator.[573]

Section 9, Arbitration and Conciliation Act, 1996 clearly indicates that even before or during arbitration proceedings, a party is entitled to apply to a court for an interim measure of protection in respect of the preservation, interim custody or sale of any goods which are the subject-matter of the arbitration agreement for securing the amount in dispute in the arbitration,

566. *Time Cinemas & Entertainment (P) Ltd.* v. *Venus Infrastructure & Developers (P) Ltd.*, 2022 SCC OnLine Guj 2651.
567. *Krebs Bio-Chemicals Ltd.* v. *Gayatri Sugar Complex Ltd.*, 2004 SCC OnLine AP 679: (2004) 6 ALD 430.
568. *JSW Steel Ltd.* v. *JFE Shoji Trade Corpn.*, 2009 SCC OnLine Bom 2069: (2010) 3 Mah LJ 165.
569. *Forum Projects (P) Ltd.* v. *Berhampur Development Authority*, 2020 SCC OnLine Ori 925: (2021) 131 CLT 261.
570. *Mercury Exports* v. *CLC Tanner's Assn.*, 2011 SCC OnLine Cal 73: (2011) 2 CHN 492.
571. *Qassim Mohd. Yousuf Aquil Bastaki* v. *Sultana Abdul Ahad Narvel*, 2003 SCC OnLine Bom 330: (2003) 3 Mah LJ 373.
572. *Atul Resorts and Hospitality India (P) Ltd.* v. *Lucky Developers*, 2012 SCC OnLine Bom 535: (2012) 5 Mah LJ 567.
573. *MMTC Ltd.* v. *Priyanka Overseas Ltd.*, 2004 SCC OnLine Del 1122: ILR (2004) 2 Del 683.

for the detention, preservation or inspection of any property or thing which is the subject-matter of the dispute in arbitration. It also entitles a party to obtain interim injunction or appointment of a receiver from a civil court.[574] Power under Section 9 cannot be exercised to oust any party of its legitimate entitlement. In a partnership business jointly started by the parties, the appellant had the right to take part in the conduct of the business and share the property till the partnership was continuing. The court was not justified in passing an order restraining the appellant from participating in the day-to-day management of the business of the firm. No provision was made in the order for the withdrawal of the share of the profit of the appellant. The order was set aside and a receiver was appointed in the case.[575]

Section 9, Arbitration and Conciliation Act, 1996, confers wide powers to the courts in granting an appropriate interim order based on the relevant sets of the case at all stages of the arbitration proceedings, *namely*, before, during or after the arbitration proceedings. Court's jurisdiction under Section 9 is to support the arbitration and to ensure that if an award is passed by the arbitrator, it is executable and is not rendered infructuous. Though exercise of such powers is premised on the underlying principles of Orders 47 and 39 CPC, yet the court is not absolutely bound by the text of these provisions.[576]

The purpose of Section 9 is to seek an interim measure/protection pending the arbitration proceedings.[577]

Unless a strong prima facie case is made out, the ad interim injunction so as to stall the re-development of the land cannot be granted.[578]

Under Section 9 where power has been conferred upon the court to put in place certain measures on a party approaching the court prior to the proceedings under the 1996 Act reaching the stage of enforcement as envisaged under Section 36, the court is conferred with all such powers for making orders as envisaged in Section 9 as it would be in "any" proceedings before it.[579]

---

574. *Chandra Shipping and Trading Services* v. *Beerapalli Chenchu Subba Reddy*, 2003 SCC OnLine AP 513: (2003) 4 ALD 572; *Prakash Boolu Kundar* v. *Shankar Aithu Poojari*, 2006 SCC OnLine Bom 611: (2006) 5 Mah LJ 453.
575. *Prakash Boolu Kundar* v. *Shankar Aithu Poojari*, 2006 SCC OnLine Bom 611: (2006) 5 Mah LJ 453.
576. *Savita Jain Sole Proprietor of M.S. Navkar Sales* v. *Krishna Packaging*, (2021) 2 HCC (Del) 197.
577. *Tata Capital Ltd.* v. *Maven Industries Ltd.*, 2012 SCC OnLine Bom 240: (2012) 4 Mah LJ 376.
578. *Middle Income Group Coop. Society Ltd.* v. *L&T Bombay Developers (P) Ltd.*, 2010 SCC OnLine Bom 648: (2010) 7 Mah LJ 785.
579. *NHAI* v. *Oriental Structure Engineers Ltd.-Gammon India Ltd. (JV)*, 2012 SCC OnLine Del 4787: (2012) 132 DRJ 769.

Section 9 applies to the proceedings under Part II of the Act.[580]

The civil court is empowered to grant interim relief during pendency of arbitration proceedings.[581]

The court may not necessarily consider the prayers in the manner made by the petitioner in the petition, but on a finding of prima facie case, irreparable injury and balance of convenience grant, pending adjudication of the disputes in the prospective arbitration proceedings between the petitioner and respondent, such reliefs as deemed appropriate.[582]

Section 9 contemplates a provision for interim measures. But in any case any award has been passed and an aggrieved party wants to challenge the same, that can only be done by way of making an application under Section 34 for setting aside the award.[583] Section 9 envisages movement of application for interim measure/protection before a court not only during the arbitration proceedings or after the declaration of the arbitral award but also before the initiation of such arbitral proceedings which are in contemplation.[584]

Interim relief—Scope

The relief which the petitioner seeks is for withdrawal of the amount deposited by the respondent upon furnishing appropriate security by the petitioner. The scope of Section 9 of the Act cannot be extended to enforcement of the award or granting the fruits of the award to the award holder as an interim measure. The order sought for by the petitioner goes beyond the realm of securing the petitioner and shifts to encashment of the security or equitably dealing with the same. This is not permissible even on the broadest interpretation of Section 9 of the Act.[585]

An interim measure/relief cannot be of such a nature which amounts to granting final relief, and cannot be granted.[586]

---

580. *Hindustan Copper Ltd.* v. *Centrotrade Minerals & Metals Inc.*, 2004 SCC OnLine Cal 22; *LML Ltd.* v. *Union of India*, 1998 SCC OnLine All 810: (1999) 35 ALR 199.
581. *LML Ltd.* v. *Union of India*, 1998 SCC OnLine All 810: (1999) 35 ALR 199.
582. *Mohit Saraf* v. *Rajiv K. Luthra*, (2021) 1 HCC (Del) 478.
583. *Rajesh Kumar Agrawal* v. *Manish Sharma*, 2008 SCC OnLine All 499: (2008) 72 ALR 92.
584. *N.K.C. Projects (P) Ltd.* v. *Utility Energytech & Engineers (P) Ltd.*, 2009 SCC OnLine All 296: (2009) 75 ALR 397.
585. *Satyen Construction* v. *State of W.B.*, 2022 SCC OnLine Cal 708.
586. *Adarsh Gas Service Basti* v. *Bharat Petroleum Corpn. Ltd.*, 2021 SCC OnLine All 1159: (2022) 1 All LJ 120.

Interim order

The words "any measure" appearing in Section 37(1)(*b*) after the Amendment of 2015 are of widest amplitude which would obviously include an interim order passed by the court while exercising its powers under Section 9. The power to grant a temporary injunction would also include the power to pass an interim order.[587]

Wide power is given to the court under Section 9, Arbitration and Conciliation Act to pass interim orders of protection.[588] The court is competent to pass an appropriate protection under interim measure outside the provisions of Order 38 Rule 5 CPC.[589]

Ex parte interim order

When an application under Section 9 is made and during pendency of such application, an ex parte ad interim order becomes imperative, in the facts and circumstances of the case, it is open to the court to pass an ad interim ex parte order based on well recognised principles contemplated by the provisions of Order XXXIX, Rules 1 and 2 CPC governing the grant of interim injunction or the appointment of a receiver. The power to grant an ex parte interim order is derived by a court under the principle that every court has the power to pass an order, which it must pass so as to ensure that the application, made before it, does not become infructuous merely because of the fact that no specific provision has been made dispensing, in an emergent situation.[590]

Sections 9 and 17

Section 9 provides for taking of interim measures by the court in certain matters, Section 17 provides for taking of interim measures in respect of the subject-matter of the dispute by the Arbitral Tribunal. The power available to the Arbitral Tribunal is narrower than that vested in the court under Section 9. The exercise of power by the court under Section 9 is no way controlled by the power exercisable by the Arbitral Tribunal under Section 17. Even assuming that the power under Section 17 to direct interim

---

587. *Road Infrastructure Development Co. of Rajasthan Ltd.* v. *IVRCL Ltd.*, 2014 SCC OnLine Raj 6524: (2014) 4 RLW 3660; *Larsen and Toubro Ltd.* v. *T.N. Minerals Ltd.*, 1998 SCC OnLine Mad 159: (1998) 1 CTC 524.

588. *Hairtha Finance Ltd.* v. *ATV Projects India Ltd.*, 2003 SCC OnLine Mad 265: (2003) 2 CTC 226.

589. *National Shipping Co. of Saudi Arabia* v. *Sentrans Industries Ltd.*, 2004 SCC OnLine Bom 25: (2004) 2 Mah LJ 696.

590. *East India Udyog Ltd.* v. *Maytas Infra Ltd.*, 2015 SCC OnLine Hyd 214: (2015) 4 CTC 593; *Yassh Deep Builders* v. *Sushil Kumar Singh*, (2023) 2 HCC (Del) 69.

measures is in certain respects and limited to certain area concurrent with the power vested in the court under Section 9, the very fact that the Arbitral Tribunal could also be approached for a proper interim measure would not deprive the civil court of its jurisdiction under Section 9 to make an appropriate direction in an appropriate case brought before it.[591]

The existence of power under Section 17 with the Arbitral Tribunal would not deny to the civil court the power to exercise its jurisdiction under Section 9 of the Act.[592]

In Section 17, the power has been given for taking interim measures by the Arbitral Tribunal. Section 17 is applicable when the arbitration proceeding has been initiated, meaning thereby when the Arbitral Tribunal is seisin over the matter, then in aid and assistance of the original proceeding Arbitral Tribunal can take interim measure at the request of any of the parties. It is, thus, clear that the scope and purview of Section 9 vis-à-vis the power of the court for passing interim measure is wider as far as the stage and time factor are concerned. Language of both the aforesaid sections imply that during pendency of the arbitration proceeding both the fora can exercise such power on the request of the parties and these provisions are not intended to apply to mutually oust the jurisdiction of each forum.[593]

Application for interim relief before the court under Section 9, post-constitution of Arbitral Tribunal

Section 9(3) has two limbs: the first limb prohibits an application under Section 9(1) from being entertained once an Arbitral Tribunal has been constituted while the second limb carves out an exception to that prohibition, if the court finds that circumstances exist, which may not render the remedy provided under Section 17 efficacious. Held, there is no reason why the court should continue to take up applications for interim relief, once the Arbitral Tribunal is constituted and is in seisin of the dispute between the parties, unless there is some impediment in approaching the Arbitral Tribunal, or the interim relief sought cannot expeditiously be obtained from the Arbitral Tribunal.

Section 9(1) enables the parties to an arbitration agreement to approach the appropriate court for interim measures before the commencement of arbitral proceedings, during arbitral proceedings or at any time after the making of an arbitral award but before it is enforced and in accordance with Section

591. *Yenepoya Minerals & Granites Ltd.* v. *Maharastra Apex Corpn. Ltd.*, 2004 SCC OnLine Kar 2: ILR 2004 Kar 1008.
592. *Ibid.*
593. *Krishna Motor Finance (P) Ltd.* v. *Iltush Ahammed*, 2011 SCC OnLine Cal 1367: (2011) 4 CHN 394.

36, Arbitration and Conciliation Act, 1996. The bar of Section 9(3) operates where the application under Section 9(1) had not been entertained till the constitution of the Arbitral Tribunal. Of course, even if an application under Section 9 had been entertained before the constitution of the tribunal, the court always has the discretion to direct the parties to approach the Arbitral Tribunal, if necessary, by passing a limited order of interim protection, particularly when there has been a long time-gap between hearings and the application has for all practical purposes, to be heard afresh, or the hearing has just commenced and is likely to consume a lot of time.[594]

Sections 9 and 21

There is no bar for the court from granting interim order under Section 9 even when no notice has been issued under Section 21, Arbitration and Conciliation Act.[595] Making of application under Section 9, Arbitration and Conciliation Act without recourse to arbitral proceedings either by issuing notice under Section 21 of the Act or by making a specific averment in the application itself that the applicant would be issuing such notice is not ruled out.[596]

Jurisdiction of the court to grant reliefs under Section 9—Source and nature

The purpose of enacting Section 9 read in the light of the Model Law and UNCITRAL Rules is to provide "interim measures of protection". The order passed by the court should fall within the meaning of the expression "an interim measure of protection" as distinguished from an all time or permanent protection. The court under Section 9 only formulates interim measures so as to protect the right under adjudication before the Arbitral Tribunal from being frustrated.[597]

The reliefs which the court may allow to a party under clause (*i*) and (*ii*) of Section 9 flow from the power vesting in the court exercisable by reference to "contemplated", "pending" or "completed" arbitral proceedings. The court is conferred with the same power of making the specified orders as it has for the purpose of and in relation to any proceedings before it, though the venue

---

594. *Arcelor Mittal Nippon Steel (India) Ltd.* v. *Essar Bulk Terminal Ltd.*, (2022) 1 SCC 712.

595. *Gour Chakraborty* v. *Chandra Nath Dutta*, (2004) 3 ICC 312 (Cal) (DB); *Tata Finance Ltd.* v. *Pragati Paribahan*, 2000 SCC OnLine Cal 158: (2000) 2 CHN 72.

596. *Gour Chakraborty* v. *Chandra Nath Dutta*, (2004) 3 ICC 312 (Cal) (DB).

597. *Firm Ashok Traders* v. *Gurumukh Das Saluja*, (2004) 3 SCC 155.

of the proceedings in relation to which the power under Section 9 is sought to be exercised is the Arbitral Tribunal.[598]

The court referred to in Section 9 of the Act is the court having Principal Original Jurisdiction in the District, *i.e.* the Principal District Court.[599] The term "court" means only the court of principal civil original jurisdiction in a District and it is only the court of "District Judge" in a District which is such a "court" of principal civil jurisdiction. Therefore, the District Court has jurisdiction to decide applications under Section 9, Arbitration and Conciliation Act, 1996.[600]

Application made under Section 9, Arbitration and Conciliation Act, 1996 filed before the Court of Civil Judge (Senior Division) is not maintainable since the Court of District Judge is the principal civil court within the meaning of Section 2(1)(*e*), of the 1996 Act.[601] All the city civil courts constituted under the Act are deemed to be the principal city civil court of original jurisdiction of the District and each of the judges has the jurisdiction to receive, try and dispose of all suits and proceedings of a civil nature arising within the city of Bangalore. Therefore, all the city civil courts have jurisdiction to entertain an application under Section 9, Arbitration and Conciliation Act, 1996.[602]

Application for interim relief before the commencement of the arbitration proceedings

A glance at Section 9 would show that an application for interim order/measures can be filed before or during arbitral proceedings or at any time after the making of an arbitral award, but before it is enforced in accordance with Section 36. The arbitral proceedings, contemplated by Section 9, commences on the date on which a request for a particular dispute is received by the respondent for its reference to arbitration, as provided for in Section 21 of the Act. An application for interim relief can be considered by the court even before commencement of arbitral proceedings. However, the court cannot dispose of such application ex parte without giving notice to the respondents.[603]

598. *Ibid.*
599. *M.D., Sundaram Finance Ltd.* v. *G.S.N. Nandakumar*, 2001 SCC OnLine AP 528: (2001) 2 AP LJ 95
600. *Fun N. Fund* v. *GLK Associates*, 2019 SCC OnLine Guj 4236: (2020) 1 GCD 154.
601. *Kapil Kumar Katyal* v. *Praveen Chandra Bhanjdeo*, 2010 SCC OnLine Cal 1486: (2010) 3 CHN 767.
602. *Valliappa Software Technologies Part (P) Ltd.* v. *C. Sundaram*, 2001 SCC OnLine Kar 652.
603. *East India Udyog Ltd.* v. *Maytas Infra Ltd.*, 2015 SCC OnLine Hyd 214: (2015) 4 CTC 593.

Jurisdiction to entertain application under Section 9

An application under Section 9 of the Act by way of interim measure can be filed before the court which has jurisdiction to decide the subject-matter involved in the arbitration agreement in the absence of an arbitration clause. Section 9 uses the word "Court".

In *Kirloskar Construction and Engineer Ltd.* v. *Fast Track Associates*[604], the place of arbitration as agreed by the parties was Chennai. The applicant had its branch office at Panipat, Haryana, respondent was residing in Uttar Pradesh, subject-matter of the arbitration agreement related to laying of road in Haryana and Uttar Pradesh, parties had signed the contract at Panipat. It was held, parties' decision to have arbitration at Chennai could not confer jurisdiction on the Madras High Court under Section 9. As the subject-matter of arbitration agreement related to laying of road in Haryana and Uttar Pradesh, the arbitration award can be challenged only in the courts at Haryana and Uttar Pradesh, where subject-matter of arbitration agreement would have been otherwise decided by competent civil court in absence of arbitration clause.

Ordinarily, a court having jurisdiction over the seat of arbitration, fixed by contract, is competent to exercise jurisdiction under Sections 9, 11 and 34, Arbitration and Conciliation Act, 1996. Where the exclusive jurisdiction clause confers exclusive jurisdiction in respect of arbitral proceedings on a court located elsewhere, Section 11 petition has also to be filed in the High Court having jurisdiction over that place.[605]

If the petitioner cannot make a claim for substantial relief or other ancillary reliefs at Mumbai and can claim only at Chennai, the application for interim measures cannot be filed in the High Court at Mumbai.[606] In view of the fact that the suit agreement was entered into at Mumbai and the dispute had arisen in respect of such agreement for which specific performance was sought before the Arbitral Tribunal, the High Court at Mumbai had jurisdiction to entertain, try and dispose of the petition.[607]

Once the seat of arbitration has been fixed, it would be in the nature of an exclusive jurisdiction clause as to the courts which exercise supervisory jurisdiction over the arbitration. In the present case, the parties have agreed to the venue of arbitration as Chennai and also that the competent courts in Chennai would have exclusive jurisdiction. Even assuming that no part of cause of action has arisen in Chennai, the courts at Chennai would

---

604. 2009 SCC OnLine Mad 1151: (2009) 5 CTC 97:.
605. *Hunch Circle (P) Ltd.* v. *Futuretimes Technology India (P) Ltd.*, (2022) 2 HCC (Del) 6.
606. *Roman Tarmat Ltd.* v. *Indukuru Venku Reddy Constructions (IVRCL)*, 2012 SCC OnLine Bom 1553: (2012) 6 Mah LJ 905.
607. *Navin Makhija* v. *Tulsibhimjiyani*, 2012 SCC OnLine Bom 1551: (2013) 1 Mah LJ 173.

have exclusive jurisdiction to entertain any proceedings arising under the Arbitration and Conciliation Act, 1996.[608]

In *Kotak Mahindra Bank Ltd.* v. *Sharma Crane Service*[609], the petitioner in view of the binding contract between the parties filed an arbitration petition before Bombay High Court when an arbitration dispute arose between the parties. The fact that the arbitration proceedings had commenced, pending and stay was obtained from the Andhra Pradesh High Court would not bar grant of protective order under Section 9 of the Mumbai High Court.[610] Agreement executed at Raipur contained an arbitration clause. As the respondent office was executed at Raipur and the branch concerned of the petitioner was also situated at Raipur, city court of Raipur had jurisdiction to grant interim relief under Section 9, the petition under Section 9 filed at Mumbai was not maintainable.[611]

The court within the meaning of Section 2(1)(*e*) of the Act is only the court which would have jurisdiction with regard to the subject-matter of the arbitration if the disputes were sought to be adjudicated by way of a suit. If the court does not have jurisdiction to entertain such a suit equally the court is not competent to entertain the petition under Section 9 of the Act.[612]

Loan was granted in Chennai, agreement was also entered into at Chennai. It is that place where cause of action has arisen shall be deemed the place where business was being carried on. Application filed under Section 9 of the 1996 Act before the Bombay High Court was held not tenable.[613]

For determining the issue with regard to jurisdiction of courts to entertain a petition under Section 9 of the Act, one has to answer the question as to which court would have jurisdiction had it been a civil suit? If the subject-matter of a petition and the issues arising therein can be adjudicated upon in a civil suit by court at a particular place, then the court defined under Section 2(1)(*e*) of the Act of that place is eligible to entertain a petition under Section 9 of the Act. Thus, the court referred to in Section 9 of the Act would be a court having jurisdiction to decide the questions forming subject-matter of arbitration if the same had been subject-matter of a civil suit.[614]

608. *Sikka Motors (P) Ltd.* v. *Hyundai Motor India Ltd.*, (2022) 2 HCC (Del) 559.
609. 2009 SCC OnLine Bom 1871: (2010) 1 Mah LJ 814.
610. *Networth Stock Broking Ltd.* v. *Madhava Rao Nadella*, 2009 SCC OnLine Bom 1711: (2010) 1 Mah LJ 582.
611. *Kotak Mahindra Bank Ltd.* v. *Sharma Crane Service*, 2009 SCC OnLine Bom 1871: (2010) 1 Mah LJ 814.
612. *Liberty Commodities Ltd.* v. *Reliance Trade Corpn. PLC.*, 2005 SCC OnLine AP 490.
613. *Kotak Mahindra Finance Ltd.* v. *T. Thomas Educational Trust*, 2003 SCC OnLine Bom 347: (2004) 1 Mah LJ 1112.
614. *Ladakh Road Lines* v. *UT of J&K*, 2020 SCC OnLine J&K 730.

District Court alone has original civil jurisdiction to entertain application for interim relief/measures under the Arbitration Act. The Manipur High Court does not exercise ordinary original civil jurisdiction and does not fall within the definition of court under Section 2(1)(*e*). By agreement, the parties cannot confer jurisdiction upon the High Court.[615]

Assets in India—Passing of interim orders under Section 9 does not presuppose the existence of assets in India. The High Court cannot refuse to entertain a petition under Section 9 of the Act on the ground that the foreign parties do not have assets in India.[616]

Where the parties in the arbitration agreement clearly stipulated and agreed that no other court other than at New Delhi will have jurisdiction to try/decide any dispute arising out of agreement, such an agreement would not be void or against public policy. The court at New Delhi alone would have jurisdiction to try and decide applications filed under Arbitration Act.[617]

Merely fixing the place of arbitration in Mumbai in the agreement did not take away the power of the court at Chennai under Section 9, Arbitration and Conciliation Act, 1996. In the absence of any evidence to show that any part of cause of action had arisen at Mumbai, it could not be held that the courts at Mumbai alone could have any jurisdiction in the matter.[618]

By the agreement the parties had agreed to resolve their dispute at Mumbai through an Arbitral Tribunal. They specifically agreed for ordinary original civil jurisdiction of the High Court, Mumbai, being court as defined under Section 2(1)(*e*), Arbitration Act. The leave as contemplated under clause 12 of the Letters Patent of Bombay High Court to file petition under Section 9 of the 1996 Act on the original side of the Bombay High Court is not necessary/mandatory.[619]

Application under Section 9 lies before the principal civil court of original jurisdiction, *i.e.* District Judge. Pendency of application under Section 11 before High Court is immaterial.[620]

615. *Simplex Projects Ltd.* v. *State of Manipur*, 2020 SCC OnLine Mani 66.

616. *Goodwill Non-Woven(P) Ltd.* v. *Xcoal Energy & Resources LLC*, 2020 SCC OnLine Del 631: (2020) 270 DLT 337.

617. *Ashok Kumar Ajmera* v. *Hindustan Petroleum Corpn. Ltd.*, 2010 SCC OnLine All 1760: (2011) 84 ALR 80.

618. *Tata Capital Ltd.* v. *Rani*, 2009 SCC OnLine Mad 977: (2010) 1 CTC 176.

619. *Vodafone Spacetel Ltd.* v. *S Tel (P) Ltd.*, 2012 SCC OnLine Bom 480: (2012) 6 Mah LJ 931; *L&T Finance Ltd.* v. *Duplex Industries Ltd.*, 2013 SCC OnLine Bom 530: (2013) 3 Mah LJ 864.

620. *Payal Enterprises* v. *Union of India*, 2002 SCC OnLine All 1012: 2003 All LJ 1395.

Arbitration clause stipulated that the place of arbitration shall be at Delhi. Held, the Delhi High Court shall have jurisdiction to decide applications filed under Sections 7 and 11 of the Act.[621]

Non-existence of arbitral dispute

In the absence of any arbitral dispute, no interim measure can be passed by the commercial court.[622]

"Before or during arbitral proceedings" [Sub-s. (1)]

The time or the stage for invoking the jurisdiction of the court under Section 9 can be:

(*i*) before, or
(*ii*) during arbitral proceedings, or
(*iii*) at any time after the making of the award but before it is enforced in accordance with Section 36.[623]

Parties to arbitration agreement can approach court for interim measures if dispute arises between them. Application for interim orders can be filed either before or during arbitral award but before it is enforced in accordance with Section 36.[624] Under Section 9 of the Act, the court is competent to pass an interim order which may appear to the court to be just and convenient even after the making of the arbitral award and before it is enforced.[625] The power vested in the court may be exercised when the proceedings before the arbitrator are either "contemplated", "pending" or even "completed". As the award of the arbitrator was not enforced in accordance with Section 36, the period for filing petition under Section 34 had not expired. The court had power to grant interim relief.[626]

Application for interim measures would be maintainable before or during arbitral proceedings or at any time after making an arbitral award but before

621. *Associates India Financial Services (P) Ltd.* v. *Jairaj Shetty*, 2004 SCC OnLine Del 43: (2004) 73 DRJ 53.
622. *Tourism and Civil Aviation Deptt.* v. *Brij Raj Oberoi*, 2021 SCC OnLine Sikk 201.
623. *Firm Ashok Traders* v. *Gurumukh Das Saluja*, (2004) 3 SCC 155; *Mahendra R. Saraf* v. *Goldstone Technologies Ltd.*, 2002 SCC OnLine AP 24: (2002) 1 AP LJ 65.
624. *Hairtha Finance Ltd.* v. *ATV Projects India Ltd.*, 2003 SCC OnLine Mad 265: (2003) 2 CTC 226.
625. *Inderjit Goel* v. *Punjab Reliable Investment (P) Ltd.*, 2005 SCC OnLine P&H 124: PLR (2005) 140 P&H 598.
626. *Delhi Metro Rail Corpn. Ltd.* v. *Delhi Airport Metro Express (P) Ltd.*, 2017 SCC OnLine Del 8868.

award is enforced. However, the party invoking Section 9 of the Act of 1996 must be ready and willing to go to arbitration.[627]

Section 9 permits the filing of an application before the commencement of the arbitration proceedings, but does not give any indication of how much before. The word "before", means, inter alia, "ahead of"; in the presence or sight of; under the consideration or cognizance of". The two events sought to be interconnected by the use of the term "before" must have proximity of relationship by reference to occurrence; the later event closely following the precedent event as a foreseeable or "within sight" certainty. The party invoking Section 9 may not have actually commenced the arbitral proceedings but must be able to satisfy the court that the arbitral proceedings were actually contemplated or manifestly intended to and were positively going to commence within a reasonable time. What is a reasonable time will depend on the facts and circumstances of each case and the nature of the interim relief sought for would itself give an indication thereof. The distance of time must not be such as would destroy the proximity of relationship of the two events between which it exists and elapses.[628]

The court approached by a party with an application under Section 9 is justified in asking the party and being told how and when that party proposes to commence the arbitration proceedings. Rather, the scheme in which Section 9 is placed obliges the court to do so. The applicant was awaiting the orders of the court under Section 9 of the Act is hardly an explanation. Commencement of the arbitral proceedings is not dependent on the interim relief being allowed or denied. The court may also, while passing an order under Section 9, put the party on the terms and may recall the order if the party commits the breach of the terms.[629]

New sub-section (2) in Section 9 inserted by the Amendment Act 3 of 2016 (w.e.f. 23 October 2015) provides that where the court has passed order for any interim measure of protection under sub-section (1), the arbitral proceedings shall be commenced within a period of 90 days from the date of the order or within such further time as the court may determine. *See*, comments under sub-section (2). Where the court is not satisfied that arbitral proceedings were actually contemplated or manifestly intended and positively going to commence within reasonable time, interim relief cannot be granted.[630]

---

627. *HBA Offshore Pte. Ltd.* v. *Samsung Heavy Industries India (P) Ltd.*, 2022 SCC OnLine All 996.
628. *Firm Ashok Traders* v. *Gurumukh Das Saluja*, (2004) 3 SCC 155.
629. *Ibid.*
630. *Railway Electrification* v. *Awadh Transformers (P) Ltd.*, 2010 SCC OnLine All 2183: (2011) 84 ALR 112.

Interim relief—Remedy under Section 9 can be availed only when arbitration proceedings are initiated soon

A party seeking an interim relief must also satisfy the court that it intends to initiate arbitration proceedings at the earliest and its failure to do so may result in denial of any interim relief from the court. No sooner an arbitration dispute has arisen between the parties, the party concerned must proceed for appointment of the arbitrator or should take necessary steps for the same and if it is found that the steps to appoint an arbitrator have not been taken within the reasonable period of time, it would disentitle the party to claim any interim measure.[631]

Where application by petitioner under Section 11 for constitution of Arbitral Tribunal is dismissed, there is no question of "proximately contemplated or manifestly intended arbitral proceedings". Petitioner is not entitled to interim relief in the appeal.[632]

Under Arbitration and Conciliation Act, 1996 the court can pass interim orders under Section 9. The material words occurring in Section 9 are "before or during the arbitral proceedings". This clearly contemplates two stages when the court can pass interim orders, *i.e.* during the arbitral proceedings or before the arbitral proceedings. There is no reason why Section 9 of the Act should not be liberally construed. Meaning has to be given to the word "before" occurring in the said section. The only interpretation that can be given is that the court can pass interim orders before the commencement of arbitration proceedings. The court has jurisdiction to entertain an application under Section 9 either before arbitral proceedings or during arbitration proceedings or after the making of the arbitral award but before it is enforced in accordance with Section 36 of the Act.[633] Section 9, Arbitration and Conciliation Act, 1996 provides for interim protection before or after publishing of the award.[634]

Any party to an arbitration agreement can before or at any time after the making of the arbitral award, but before its enforcement, apply to a court for any one or more of the directions envisaged therein. The nature of the power reserved with the court under Section 9 is such that it can be invoked by a party before, during or after the making of the arbitral award.[635]

631. *Fortune Builders* v. *Hansraj Kamdar*, 2021 SCC OnLine MP 3129: (2022) 1 MP LJ 80; *HBA Offshore Pte. Ltd.* v. *Samsung Heavy Industries India (P) Ltd.*, 2022 SCC OnLine All 996.
632. *Masood Mohmmed Husain* v. *Gulam Rasul Mohammedali Shaikh*, 2006 SCC OnLine Bom 1239: (2007) 2 Mah LJ 116.
633. *Sundaram Finance Ltd.* v. *NEPC India Ltd.*, (1999) 2 SCC 479.
634. *Partha Sarathi Ghosh* v. *Maa Construction*, 2008 SCC OnLine Cal 327: (2008) 3 CHN 72.
635. *M.S. Rao* v. *Mangalore University*, 2001 SCC OnLine Kar 344: ILR 2001 Kar 4863.

The power under Section 9, Arbitration and Conciliation Act in all its force must be available to the extent applicable till the award becomes enforceable. After the award becomes enforceable the provisions of Order 21 CPC are applicable, as the award becomes a decree and can be executed as a decree. Thus, Section 9(1)(*i*) and 9(1)(*ii*) would be applicable even if the award has been passed but before it becomes enforceable, though the arbitral process terminates except in cases covered by Section 32(3). Parliament when it conferred power in the court under Section 9 to grant interim relief, recognised situations that will arise on the termination of the arbitral proceedings and the need to protect the subject-matter of the dispute by using the expression till the award can be enforced as the award till it becomes enforceable does not become a decree.[636] The court can grant interim measures either before or during arbitral proceedings or at any time after making of arbitral award but before it is enforced in accordance with Section 36 of the Act.[637] Under Section 9, Arbitration and Conciliation Act, 1996 an application can be made before or during the arbitral proceeding and at any time after making of the arbitral award but before it is enforced in accordance with the provisions of Section 36, Arbitration and Conciliation Act, it does not postulate that such an application could be made only during the arbitral proceedings. It can be made even before. There is nothing to indicate that before Section 9 application is disposed of, a party is bound to make the reference to arbitration.[638]

Once an arbitral award becomes enforceable, the authority to entertain a petition under Section 9 of the Act or to continue with the same or pass any orders thereon, vanishes. Section 9 of the Act permits a post award petition for interim measures to be relevant till such time that the award becomes enforceable. Though the relevant words used in the provision are "but before it is enforced in accordance with Section 36", such expression read in the context of Section 36 of the Act that provides for enforcement implies that a party may apply to a court for interim measures only till such time that the arbitral award becomes enforceable. Interim orders passed under Section 9 of the Act, after the passing of the award are not sustainable, are liable to be set aside.[639]

---

636. *Delta Construction Systems Ltd.* v. *Narmada Cement Co. Ltd.*, 2001 SCC OnLine Bom 630: (2002) 1 Mah LJ 684.
637. *Mineira Nacional Limitada* v. *Hardesh Ores (P) Ltd.*, 2017 SCC OnLine Bom 2604: (2017) 5 Mah LJ 611.
638. *Mahendra Prasad Gupta* v. *Vijay Gaurav Rasayan (P) Ltd.*, 2003 SCC OnLine Cal 109: (2003) 1 Cal LJ 634.
639. *Gopuram Enterprises Ltd.* v. *Integrated Finance Co. Ltd.*, 2021 SCC OnLine Mad 16559: (2021) 1 LW 929.

When a party applies under Section 9 of the 1996 Act, it is implicit that it accepts that there is a final and binding arbitration agreement in existence. It is also implicit that a dispute must have arisen which is referable to the Arbitral Tribunal. Section 9 further contemplates arbitration proceedings taking place between the parties. When an application under Section 9 is filed before the commencement of the arbitral proceedings, there has to be manifest intention on the part of the applicant to take recourse to the arbitral proceedings if, at the time when the application under Section 9 is filed, the proceedings have not commenced under Section 21 of the 1996 Act.[640]

Plea that application for interim relief can only be made before the arbitrator, under Section 17 of the Act and not under Section 9, was rejected. A party even during the subsistence of the arbitral proceedings can make an application for interim reliefs under Section 9 of the Act.[641]

In Section 17, the power has been given for taking interim measures by the Arbitral Tribunal. Section 17 is applicable when the arbitration proceeding has been initiated, meaning thereby when the Arbitral Tribunal is seisin over the matter, then in aid and assistance of the original proceeding Arbitral Tribunal can take interim measure at the request of any of the parties. It is, thus, clear that the scope and purview of Section 9 vis-à-vis the power of the court for passing interim measure is wider as far as the stage and time factor are concerned. Language of both the aforesaid sections during pendency of the arbitration proceeding, both the fora can exercise such power on the request of the parties and these provisions are not intended to apply to mutually oust the jurisdiction of each forum.[642]

Any party to an arbitration agreement can before or during arbitration proceedings or at any time after the making of an arbitration award, but before its enforcement, apply to the court for any one or more of the interim directions. Application under Section 9, Arbitration and Conciliation Act, 1996 cannot be rejected merely because the petition under Section 8 was not maintainable.[643]

"Once the Arbitral Tribunal has been constituted" [Sub-s. (3)]

Sub-section (3) of Section 9, Arbitration and Conciliation Act, 1996 now clearly spells out that once the Arbitral Tribunal has been constituted, the court shall not entertain an application under sub-section (1), unless

640. *Sundaram Finance Ltd.* v. *NEPC India Ltd.*, (1999) 2 SCC 479.
641. *Ashok Leyland Finance Ltd.* v. *Sanatan Transport Co. (P) Ltd.*, 2005 SCC OnLine Bom 280: (2005) 2 Mah LJ 850.
642. *Krishna Motor Finance (P) Ltd.* v. *Iltush Ahammed*, 2011 SCC OnLine Cal 1367: (2011) 4 CHN 394.
643. *M.S. Rao* v. *Mangalore University*, 2001 SCC OnLine Kar 344: ILR 2001 Kar 4863.

the court finds that circumstances exist which may not render the remedy provided under Section 17 efficaciously. Interim measure can be granted by the Arbitral Tribunal. Application under Section 9 for interim measure filed before the court was dismissed, the parties were given option to approach the Arbitral Tribunal.[644] In *S. Ramesh* v. *Kotak Mahindra Bank Ltd.*[645], the Arbitral Tribunal had already been constituted and entered upon reference. The remedy open to the applicant was to seek interim relief before the tribunal under Section 17. Application for interim relief under Section 9(1) filed before the High Court was not maintainable.

Even though an earlier application for interim relief may have been filed in court, once arbitral proceedings have commenced and an Arbitral Tribunal has been appointed, interim relief would have to be sought before the arbitrator. The court would be denuded of its power to grant interim relief unless the court is satisfied that circumstances exist, which may not render the remedy provided under Section 17 efficacious.[646]

Delay in agreeing to an arbitrator—Does not disentitle a party from interim relief under Section 9

Mere delay in agreeing to an arbitrator does not disentitle a party from relief under Section 9, Arbitration and Conciliation Act, 1996. Section 11, Arbitration and Conciliation Act, 1996 itself provides a remedy in case of delay of any party to the arbitration agreement to appoint an arbitrator.[647]

Existence of arbitration "sine qua non"

For filing an application for interim protection/measure existence of an arbitration agreement between the parties is a sine qua non to the maintainability of such an application. Where neither agreement in writing was entered into between the parties in pursuance of the auction nor arbitration agreement was pleaded in the application and there was no pleading that the applicant had any intention to draw arbitral proceedings, power under Section 9 could not be invoked. Interim intention sought was based on the highest bid which too was not accepted, application was not at all maintainable, was rightly rejected.[648]

In the absence of arbitration agreement, interim relief cannot be granted.[649]

644. *Mohd. Rashid* v. *Mohd. Arif*, 2020 SCC OnLine Cal 2382.
645. 2019 SCC OnLine Mad 39253: (2020) 2 CTC 307.
646. *Tufan Chatterjee* v. *Rangan Dhar*, 2016 SCC OnLine Cal 483.
647. *Arcelor Mittal Nippon Steel (India) Ltd.* v. *Essar Bulk Terminal Ltd.*, (2022) 1 SCC 712.
648. *Raj Kumar* v. *Union of India*, 2009 SCC OnLine All 158: (2009) 75 ALR 422.
649. *South Eastern Coalfields Ltd.* v. *CART Roadwings JV*, 2018 SCC OnLine Cal 16987.

Where there is no valid arbitration agreement duly executed between the parties, there is no question of invoking Section 9 for granting relief.[650]

It is necessary for the court to hold/observe prima facie that there is an arbitration agreement or not before passing order under Section 9. The requirement is that there should be written agreement between the parties.[651]

Written arbitration clause

The power to grant interim reliefs under Section 9 of the Act of 1996 in respect of any dispute under an agreement cannot be exercised unless the agreement in issue has a written arbitrable clause within the meaning of Section 7 of the Act of 1996. Where the sale deeds whereby the appellant had transferred its rights in suit plots to the respondents did not include a written arbitration clause within the scope of Section 7(4)(*b*), injunction could not be granted.[652]

Party to arbitration agreement

For invoking the jurisdiction of the court under Section 9, Arbitration and Conciliation Act, 1996, the person should be a party to an arbitration agreement. Thus, a person not a party to the arbitration agreement cannot invoke the jurisdiction of the court for the interim relief under Section 9 of the 1996 Act.[653]

Interim injunction—Relevant factors—Prima facie case—Balance of convenience, irreparable loss, conduct of parties, etc.

The interim direction ordinarily would precede finding of a prima facie case. When the existence of a prima facie case is established, the court should consider other factors, *namely*, balance of convenience and irreparable injuries.[654] It is not possible to keep out the concept of balance of convenience, prima facie case, irreparable injury and concept of just and convenient while passing interim measures under Section 9 of the Act.[655] The rule that

650. *Rajesh Construction Co. Ltd.* v. *Ravilal Nanji Dedhia*, 2008 SCC OnLine Bom 1052: (2009) 1 Mah LJ 950.
651. *Ravinder Singh Ahluwalia* v. *Kuljinder Singh Ahluwalia*, 2009 SCC OnLine Bom 712: (2009) 5 Mah LJ 170.
652. *S.N.G. Real Estate (P) Ltd.* v. *Ghanshyam Surajmal Singhal*, 2019 SCC OnLine Raj 7823.
653. *Mohd Yusuf* v. *Ashish Aggarwal*, 2021 SCC OnLine Utt 1274: (2022) 150 ALR 27.
654. *Transmission Corpn. of A.P. Ltd.* v. *Lanco Kondapalli Power (P) Ltd.*, (2006) 1 SCC 540.
655. *Adhunik Steels Ltd.* v. *Orissa Manganese and Minerals (P) Ltd.*, (2007) 7 SCC 125; *Meenakshi Energy Ltd.* v. *PTC India Ltd.*, (2021) 4 HCC (Del) 511; *Essar House (P) Ltd.* v. *Arcellor Mittal Nippon Steel India Ltd.*, 2022 SCC OnLine SC 1219.

the court before granting interim relief must satisfy itself that the petitioner has a prima facie case, does not mean that the court should examine the merits of the case closely and come to a conclusion that the petitioner has a case in which he must succeed.[656] The procedural provisions under the CPC not provided in the Arbitration Act or the rules framed which are not inconsistent and are required for the purpose of effectively disposing of the proceedings before the competent court would be applicable.[657] Without a case of irreparable loss being made out, an injunction could not be granted merely on the ground of the legal proceedings likely to take a long time.[658]

The principles which are embodied in Section 14(*d*) read with Section 41(*e*), Specific Relief Act, 1963 are applicable even when the court considers an application under Section 9 of the Act for interim measures. It is a settled principle of law that although Section 9 is a remedy available to the parties having an arbitration agreement between them, however, when a relief for grant of an injunction is prayed for certainly, the court would be guided by the principles as contained in the Specific Relief Act read with the provisions of Order 39 CPC.[659]

It is now well settled that powers under Section 9, Arbitration and Conciliation Act, 1996 are required to be exercised on the lines of recognised principles applicable to exercise general powers to grant interim injunction under Order 39 CrPC. Therefore, the celebrated principles for grant of interim injunction, *namely*, that prima facie case, balance of convenience and irreparable injury are relevant considerations also in respect of passing orders for interim measures under Section 9, Arbitration and Conciliation Act, 1996. Interim injunction is an equitable remedy, so would be the consideration in granting interim measures under Section 9, Arbitration and Conciliation Act. It is trite principle that interim injunction of nature amounting to granting of principal relief, could not be granted. In proceedings under Section 9 final relief cannot be granted.[660]

While exercising jurisdiction under Section 9, Arbitration and Conciliation Act, 1996 the court should forbear from entering into merits of the dispute or interpreting the covenants of the contract. The limited exercise of appreciation of the merits of the controversy between the parties by a Section 9 court is restricted to satisfying that a prima facie case for consideration exists. If

656. *Newage Fincorp (India) Ltd.* v. *Asia Corp Securities Ltd.*, 2000 SCC OnLine Bom 281: (2000) 4 Mah LJ 134.
657. *Delta Construction Systems Ltd.* v. *Narmada Cement Co. Ltd.*, 2001 SCC OnLine Bom 630: (2002) 1 Mah LJ 684.
658. *Veda Research Laboratories Ltd.* v. *Survi Prosects*, 2009 SCC OnLine Del 2298: (2009) 111 DRJ 566.
659. *Chetan Iron LLP* v. *NRC Ltd.*, 2022 SCC OnLine Bom 159: (2022) 6 Mah LJ 21.
660. *Kanhai Foods Ltd.* v. *A and HP Bakes*, 2022 SCC OnLine Guj 2650.

the dispute is found to be wholly unsubstantial, or moonshine, the court would decline to exercise Section 9 jurisdiction, as cumulative satisfaction of the troika of a prima facie case, balance of convenience and irreparable loss, are required for the court exercising Section 9 jurisdiction. These principles are required to be applied only to the extent they satisfy the court that a dispute deserving a resolution by arbitration exists. Once that is established, the concern of the court is whether a case for protecting the arbitral corpus so as to ensure that the arbitral proceedings are not frustrated, does or does not exist. The respondent was restrained, pending disposal of the arbitral proceedings from using the prohibitions trade mark.[661]

Applications for interim relief are inherently applications which are required to be disposed of urgently. Interim relief is granted in aid of final relief. The object is to ensure protection of the property being the subject-matter of arbitration and/or otherwise ensure that the arbitration proceedings do not become infructuous and the arbitral award does not become an award on paper, of no real value. The principles for grant of interim relief are *(i)* good prima facie case; *(ii)* balance of convenience in favour of grant of interim relief; and *(iii)* irreparable injury or loss to the applicant for interim relief.[662] Unless applications for interim measures are decided expeditiously, irreparable injury or prejudice may be caused to the party seeking interim relief.[663]

The subject-matter of dispute was tea lying in the godown of the respondent. The commodity in question is a perishable item and its price also fluctuates. The plaintiff had a strong prima facie case regarding ownership and possession of the tea lying in the godown of the respondent. Interim relief restraining the respondent from interfering with the petitioner's right to lift tea in question was granted.[664]

Respondent had provided shares as security for loan, interim injunction was passed restraining the respondent from selling pledged shares.[665]

Where the court finds that money is adequate compensation, the court would be justified in refusing an interim injunction.[666]

661. *Vidya Mandir Classes Ltd.* v. *Harsh Tiwary*, (2021) 3 HCC (Del) 587.
662. See also *Union of India* v. *Nayak Infrastructure (P) Ltd.*, 2022 SCC OnLine Gau 2176: (2023) 1 Gau LR 241.
663. *Arcelor Mittal Nippon Steel (India) Ltd.* v. *Essar Bulk Terminal Ltd.*, (2022) 1 SCC 712.
664. *Kanoi Tea (P) Ltd.* v. *Octavius Tea and Industries Ltd.*, 2021 SCC OnLine Cal 1659.
665. *Jayneer Infra Power and Multiventures (P) Ltd.* v. *Hero Fincorp Ltd.*, 2020 SCC OnLine Del 2023.
666. *Quippo Infrastructure Ltd.* v. *AZZ Infraservices Ltd.*, 2021 SCC OnLine Cal 102: (2021) 2 Cal LT 127.

Civil court has jurisdiction to entertain civil suit and pass necessary orders even in cases where there is an arbitration agreement

The civil court has jurisdiction to entertain a civil suit even in cases where there is an arbitration agreement and pass necessary orders as an interim measure of protection as may be found just and convenient. If either of the parties to any contract with an arbitration clause does not refer or take steps to refer the dispute to arbitration, the law does not bar either of them to have recourse to a civil court and seek appropriate remedies.[667]

If the respondents create third party rights in the property and if the petitioner succeeds in the arbitration proceedings, the petitioner would not be able to recover any amount from the respondent, a case for grant of interim measures in favour of the petitioner is made out.[668]

Application was filed seeking restraint on society to appoint a new developer for re-development of the dilapidated property. Since balance of convenience was in favour of the society, interim relief restraining the society for appointing new developer was not granted.[669]

Conduct of the parties is also a relevant factor. If the parties had been acting in a particular manner for a long time upon interpreting the terms and conditions of the contract, if pending determination of the *lis*, an order is passed that parties would continue to do so, the same would not render the decision as an arbitrary one.[670]

Interim measure—Nature of

The interim measure should be of such nature as may preserve the subject-matter of the arbitration agreement, or secure the amount, or the property by such measure as may appear to be just and convenient. While exercising power under Section 9, the court cannot decide the claim on merits, or pass an order which has the effect of decreeing the claim of one party or the other. At best, the court could issue a direction to secure the amount that may prima facie appear to be due or payable to a party and for such purpose, it is vested with power to issue necessary directions.[671]

667. *Chandra Shipping and Trading Services* v. *Beerapalli Chenchu Subba Reddy*, 2003 SCC OnLine AP 513: (2003) 4 ALD 572
668. *Badal Mittal* v. *Lakadawala Developers (P) Ltd.*, 2013 SCC OnLine Bom 610: (2013) 5 Mah LJ 185.
669. *Heritage Lifestyle and Developers Ltd.* v. *Cool Breeze Coop. Housing Society Ltd.*, 2014 SCC OnLine Bom 99: (2014) 3 Mah LJ 376.
670. *Transmission Corpn. of A.P. Ltd.* v. *Lanco Kondapalli Power (P) Ltd.*, (2006) 1 SCC 540.
671. *U.P. SRTC* v. *Krishna Bros.*, 2022 SCC OnLine All 995: (2023) 1 All LJ 368.

An interim measure/relief cannot be of such a nature which amounts to granting final relief and cannot be granted.[672]

Interim measures—Principles of CPC to be followed

The grant of an interim prohibitory or mandatory injunction is governed by the well known rules and it is difficult to imagine that the legislature, while enacting Section 9 of the Act, intended to make a provision which dehors the accepted principles that governed the grant of an interim injunction. Same is the position with regard to the appointment of receivers. Section 9 itself brings in the concept of "just and convenient" while speaking of passing any interim measures of protection. The concluding words of Section 9, "and the Court shall have the same power for making order as it has for the purpose and in relation to any proceedings before it" also suggest that the normal rules that govern the court in grant of interim orders are not sought to be jettisoned by the provision. Moreover, when a party is given a right to approach an ordinary court of the country without providing a special procedure or a special set of rules in that behalf, the ordinary rules followed by that court would govern the exercise of power conferred by the Act. On that basis also, it is not possible to keep out the concept of balance of convenience, prima facie case, irreparable injury and the concept of just and convenience while passing interim measures under Section 9.[673] General principles governing grant of temporary injunction under Order 39 CPC apply.[674]

Grant of injunction or interim order of protection by way of restraint order pending disposal of arbitral proceedings to be passed in careful manner keeping in mind the principles of granting injunction under Order 39, Rules 1 and 2 CPC. Restraint order passed without disclosing reasons falls short of judicial order and will not be sustainable.[675]

Section 9, Arbitration and Conciliation Act, 1996 does not specifically require any specific averment in any particular form as contemplated under Order 38 Rule 5 or under Section 18 of the 1940 Act.[676]

No doubt, Section 9 gives wide powers to the court including the same power for making orders as it has for the purpose of and in relation to any

672. *Adarsh Gas Service Basti* v. *Bharat Petroleum Corpn. Ltd.*, 2021 SCC OnLine All 1159: (2022) 1 All LJ 120.
673. *Adhunik Steels Ltd.* v. *Orissa Manganese and Minerals (P) Ltd.*, (2007) 7 SCC 125.
674. *Orissa Concrete & Allied Industries Ltd.* v. *Union of India*, 2017 SCC OnLine Chh 1903.
675. *Indian Railway Catering and Tourism Corpn. Ltd.* v. *Alak Kumar Ghose*, 2006 SCC OnLine Gau 59: (2007) 2 Gau LR 521.
676. *Ganesh Benzoplast Ltd.* v. *Sundaram Finance Ltd.*, 2002 SCC OnLine Mad 231: (2002) 2 CTC 238.

proceeding before it. Nevertheless, the discretion is not to be exercised lightly. Court must be satisfied that essential conditions for grant of such relief have been met by the party seeking it.[677] Exercise of power under Section 9(1)(*ii*)(*b*) of the Act is controlled by the provisions of the CPC.[678]

Notice to other party

The general procedure under CPC cannot be dispensed with.[679]

Ex parte interim orders

While granting interim relief under Section 9, Arbitration and Conciliation Act, 1996, the court shall have the same power for making orders, as it has for purpose of, and in relation to any proceeding before it. Section 9 is a self-contained Code, does not mandate application of the entire gamut of Order 39 CPC, more particularly Rule 3 when it passes ex parte interim orders.[680]

Equitable considerations

The court has to be guided by equitable considerations keeping in mind that the award to be passed by the Arbitral Tribunal is capable of enforcement.[681]

Dispute not arbitrable

Where allegations are of fraud and cheating and dispute is non-arbitrable in nature, application under Section 9 for interim nature would not be maintainable.[682]

Section 9 and Specific Relief Act, 1963

The power under Section 9, Arbitration and Conciliation Act, 1996 is not independent of the Specific Relief Act, 1963 the restrictions imposed

---

677. *Lalea Trading Ltd.* v. *Anant Raj Projects (P) Ltd.*, 2013 SCC OnLine Del 149: ILR (2013) 3 Del 1679.

678. *Nimbus Communications Ltd.* v. *Board of Control for Cricket in India*, 2012 SCC OnLine Bom 287: (2013) 1 Mah LJ 39. For detailed discussion, see, Suranjan Chakravarti and Bholeswar Nath, *Cases and Materials on Code of Civil Procedure* (5th Edn.) and C.K. Thakker, *Code of Civil Procedure* (EBC).

679. *IndBharath Power (Madras) Ltd.* v. *ICOMM Tele Ltd.*, 2017 SCC OnLine Hyd 609: (2017) 3 ALD 33.

680. *Sree Venkataraya Builders (P) Ltd.* v. *Kausalya Shelters Ltd.*, 2022 SCC OnLine TS 3476.

681. *Girish Mulchand Mehta* v. *Mahesh S. Mehta*, 2009 SCC OnLine Bom 1986: (2010) 2 Mah LJ 657; *Cinemas & Entertainment (P) Ltd.* v. *Venus Infrastructure and Developers (P) Ltd.*, 2022 SCC OnLine Guj 2651.

682. *Asgar Ali* v. *Nipani Advaita Developers LLP*, 2023 SCC OnLine MP 6940.

by the Specific Relief Act control the exercise of powers under Section 9, Arbitration and Conciliation Act, 1996. The Arbitration and Conciliation Act, 1996 does not prima facie purport to keep out of the provision of the Specific Relief Act from consideration.[683]

No special condition is contained in Section 9, Arbitration and Conciliation Act, 1996. No special procedure is indicated. When the grant of relief by way of injunction is, in general, governed by the provisions of the Special Relief Act, and Section 9, Arbitration and Conciliation Act, 1996 provides for an approach to the court for an interim injunction, the relevant provisions of the Special Relief Act cannot be kept out of consideration. For, the grant of that interim injunction has necessarily to be based on the principles governing its grant emanating from the relevant provisions of the Specific Relief Act and the law bearing on the subject. Under Section 28 of the 1996 Act, even the Arbitral Tribunal is enjoined to decide the dispute submitted to it in accordance with the substantive law for the time being in force in India, if it is not an international commercial arbitration.[684]

When the petitioner is statutorily barred from seeking specific performance of the collaboration agreement, the petitioner cannot be held entitled to claim interim relief under Section 9, Arbitration and Conciliation Act, 1996.[685]

"Arbitral proceedings shall be commenced within a period of ninety days" [Sub-s. (2)]

New sub-section (2) added by the Amendment Act 3 of 2016 provides that where the court has passed order for any interim measures of protection under sub-section (1), the arbitral proceedings shall be commenced within a period of 90 days from the date of the order or within such further time as the court may determine.

Issuance of notice by one party to another party is sufficient to disclose intention to have recourse to arbitration. Issuing notice as contemplated in Section 21 invoking arbitration clause is not mandatory to invoke Section 9. Circumstances could establish the manifest intention of the applicant to have recourse to arbitration or resolve dispute.[686]

---

683. *Arvind Constructions Co. (P) Ltd.* v. *Kalinga Mining Corpn.*, (2007) 6 SCC 798.
684. *Adhunik Steels Ltd.* v. *Orissa Manganese and Minerals (P) Ltd.*, (2007) 7 SCC 125. See also, *Chetan Iron LLP* v. *NRC Ltd.*, 2022 SCC OnLine Bom 159: (2022) 6 Mah LJ 21.
685. *Yassh Deep Builders* v. *Sushil Kumar Singh*, (2023) 2 HCC (Del) 69.
686. *Hairtha Finance Ltd.* v. *ATV Projects India Ltd.*, 2003 SCC OnLine Mad 265: (2003) 2 CTC 226.

Provisions of Section 9 cannot be invoked by a party which has no intention to approach the arbitrator.[687] A party, who has no intention to ultimately refer dispute to arbitration and seek final relief, cannot be permitted to seek interim relief. Interim relief is no aid of final relief. In *Minochar* v. *Deenyar Sheriar Jehani*[688], the petitioner had not taken any steps to appoint an arbitrator though notice invoking an arbitration agreement which was given as far back as on 30 January 2008. The petitioner was held not entitled to any interim measures.

In the absence of any material showing intention of the contractor for invocation of the arbitration clause, the contractor was held disentitled to get any indulgence of the court under Section 9 of the Act.[689]

Attachment of property pending arbitration proceedings

Just because the amount is due, "attachment before judgment" cannot be sought. There must be definite evidence that the respondent is trying to dispose of property with a view to defeat the rights of the creditor. In *Cholamandalam Investment & Finance Co. Ltd.* v. *Philomina George*[690], apart from mechanical pleadings, no positive evidence was shown by the appellant. Application for attachment of property pending arbitration proceedings was not allowed.

The principles regarding injunction restraining the encashment of bank guarantee are well settled. Only in rare circumstances, the court will issue an order of injunction restraining the bank in performance of bank guarantee. Of the two known exceptions to otherwise embargo are: fraud and special equity. If, however, there is fraud committed by the parties and that the bank has notice of the fraud, then the court may issue an order of injunction. In *Mercator Oil and Gas Ltd.* v. *ONGC Ltd.*[691], several breaches of contract had been committed by the applicant seeking interim injunction. The beneficiary, Oil and Natural Gas Corporation had not made any false representation to the bank. No fraud was shown. Injunction restraining invocation of bank guarantee was not granted. Commitment of banks must be honoured free from interference by the courts, otherwise trust in internal and international commerce, damages. Injunction ought not be used as an instrument to mulling a contract agreement or undertaking which is lawfully

687. *Anil Constructions* v. *Vidarbha Irrigation Development Corpn.*, 1999 SCC OnLine Bom 485: (2000) 1 Mah LJ 838.
688. 2014 SCC OnLine Bom 901: (2015) 3 Mah LJ 173.
689. *Railway Electrification* v. *Awadh Transformers (P) Ltd.*, 2010 SCC OnLine All 2183: (2011) 84 ALR 112.
690. 2014 SCC OnLine Mad 670: (2014) 2 MWN (Civil) 188.
691. 2019 SCC OnLine Bom 1378: (2020) 4 Mah LJ 521.

enforceable.[692] Hence, in this case the injunction order was found unsustainable and was set aside.

Bank guarantee is a separate and independent contract between bank and the respondent, and is governed by its own terms. Where a bank guarantee is unconditional, the bank cannot refuse to encash it. The court while deciding the question of encashment of bank guarantees will not interpret the breach or compliance of the terms of the contract.[693] In this case, an interim injunction was refused. Bank guarantee is an independent contract, the bank is not to the terms of the underlying or the main contract entered into between the contractor and the beneficiary. The examination by the court has to be from the point of view of the bank concerned furnishing bank guarantee and not independent to it. The bank guarantee was unconditional, injunction restraining encashment of bank guarantee was refused.[694] Where the bank guarantee was not legally discharged, an injunction restraining the encashment of bank guarantee was refused.[695] Merely because the respondent-company was likely to be declared a sick industrial undertaking, it was not a ground of a special equity or an irretrievable injustice, injunction was refused.[696]

Section 9, Arbitration and Conciliation Act, 1996 does not confer any wider powers on the court in the matter of grant of bank guarantees than those under Order 39 Rules 1, 2 CPC.[697]

Injunction restraining termination of contract

At this stage, granting stay of termination would necessarily entail the court first forming an opinion, albeit a prima facie one, that the termination effected by the respondent-corporation was misconceived and contrary to the terms of the agreement. Considering the nature and scope of the present proceedings under Section 9, Arbitration and Conciliation Act, 1996, such an exercise cannot be undertaken by the court, particularly in light of the settled position of law that it is not permissible for any party to seek an injunction on the termination of an agreement.[698]

---

692. *Road Infrastructure Development Co. of Rajasthan Ltd.* v. *IVRCL Ltd.*, 2014 SCC OnLine Raj 6524: (2014) 4 RLW 3660.
693. *Larsen & Toubro Ltd.* v. *Experion Developers (P) Ltd.*, 2019 SCC OnLine Del 11549: (2020) 266 DLT 70.
694. *Indu Projects Ltd.* v. *Union of India*, 2013 SCC OnLine Del 4601: (2013) 139 DRJ 260.
695. *Kamal Virdichandji Garg* v. *Fiat India (P) Ltd.*, 2004 SCC OnLine Bom 250: (2004) 4 Mah LJ 233.
696. *Ibid.*
697. *Binny Ltd.* v. *Nizam Sugars Ltd.*, 1996 SCC OnLine AP 725: (1996) 4 ALT 100.
698. *Shubham HP Security Force (P) Ltd.* v. *Central Warehousing Corpn.*, (2022) 2 HCC (Del) 264.

Interim injunction against public interest

Appellant sought injunction restraining respondent authority from awarding contract of providing sewerage facilities to third person. Authority executed contract work in larger public interest. Applicant, if aggrieved, can be compensated monetarily. Grant of injunction, against public interest was declined.[699]

Injunction restraining encashment of bank guarantee

Sum claimed by the respondent did not relate to the contract for which bank guarantee had been furnished. Arbitration proceedings in relation to that other contract were pending. Sum claimed by the respondent was in the nature of damages in relation to another contract which was yet to be adjudicated/determined in arbitration proceedings. Bank guarantee in question was a performance guarantee furnished for execution of the work contract. Since the works contract was completed to the satisfaction of the respondents, therefore, the respondents had no right to encash bank guarantee. Injunction restraining the respondents from encashing the bank guarantee was granted.[700] There was nothing on the record to show that the invocation of bank guarantee by the State was vitiated by fraud. Injunction against invocation of bank guarantee was refused.[701]

It is settled that bank guarantee is an independent contract between the bank and the beneficiary thereof, therefore, the bank is always obliged to honour the guarantee if it is unconditional and irrevocable. The dispute between the beneficiary and the party at whose instance bank guarantee is given is of no consequence and has no effect on the right relating to the encashment of the bank guarantee. It is also settled that the bank guarantee which provides that the amount is payable by the guarantor on demand is considered to be the unconditional bank guarantee and that once the unconditional bank guarantee in course of commercial dealing is given, the beneficiary is entitled to realise the bank guarantee as per the terms contained therein.[702]

Unconditional bank guarantee permits the beneficiary to receive payments on first demand without reference to the person furnishing it cannot be

---

699. *Vishwa Infrastructure & Services (P) Ltd.* v. *Chennai Metropolitan Water Supply and Sewerage Board*, 2017 SCC OnLine Mad 20078.
700. *Gangotri Enterprises Ltd.* v. *Union of India*, (2016) 11 SCC 720.
701. *Techma Engg. Enterprise (P) Ltd.* v. *Union of India*, 2017 SCC OnLine Cal 15983.
702. *Cobra-CIPL JV* v. *Chief Project Manager*, 2021 SCC OnLine MP 609; *Vinitec Electronics (P) Ltd.* v. *HCL Infosystems Ltd.*, (2008) 1 SCC 544; *U.P. State Sugar Corpn.* v. *Sumac International Ltd.*, (1997) 1 SCC 568; *Vinitec Electronics (P) Ltd.* v. *HCL Infosystems Ltd.*, (2008) 1 SCC 544; *U.P. State Sugar Corpn.* v. *Sumac International Ltd.*, (1997) 1 SCC 568.

turned into conditional guarantee by introducing any clauses. Presence of an element of prejudice that party has suffered or is likely to suffer can never be a ground for unconditional bank guarantee to be interdicted with.[703]

If by the terms of bank guarantee, the bank/guarantor is precluded from questioning or enquiring into the beneficiary's decision to invoke the guarantee, the beneficiary necessarily would become the sole judge in deciding whether the right to invoke guarantee has accrued or not.[704]

In a case relating to a works contract, the respondent contractor had furnished a performance bank guarantee of ₹39 crores in favour of the appellant. The appellant, however, established a claim of ₹7,85,77,581 only. After considering the balance of convenience, a limited prohibitory order restraining invocation of bank guarantee for more than the claim of the appellant was granted.[705]

Interim relief of injunction restraining the encashment of bank guarantee can be granted only in limited cases where there is fraud or irretrievable harm and injury is likely to the applicant. Mere financial hardship is not irretrievable harm or injury. Injunction shall not be granted in the absence of harm and injury to the applicant.[706] Contractor failed to complete work within the target time and as such bank guarantee was invoked by the opposite party. No case of fraud or irretrievable damage was alleged/made by the contractor. Interim stay against the encashment of bank guarantee was refused.[707] Vague allegations of fraud cannot form basis for grant of an injunction. Fraud which vitiates contract must have nexus to acts of parties prior to entering contract.[708]

Unconditional bank guarantee

Dispute arose between the parties on termination of contract. Case of fraud was neither pleaded nor proved. Existence of dispute between the parties was held, no ground to grant injunction. Injunction restraining the invocation of bank guarantee was refused.[709]

---

703. *North Eastern Electric Power Corpn. Ltd. (NEEPCO)* v. *Patel Unity Joint Venture*, 2022 SCC OnLine Megh 701.
704. *Felguera Gruas India Pvt. Ltd, Vishakhapatnam* v. *Tuticorin Coal Terminal Pvt. Ltd.*, Mumbai, AIR 2018 Bom 153 (DB).
705. *Rajiv Gandhi Institute of Petroleum Technology (RGIPT)* v. *Punj Lloyd Ltd.*, 2013 SCC OnLine All 14061: (2014) 2 All LJ 529.
706. *ABG Shipyard Ltd.* v. *Shipping Corpn. of India Ltd.*, 2013 SCC OnLine Bom 1412: (2014) 3 Mah LJ 670.
707. *ISGEC Heavy Engg. Ltd.* v. *Cavite Biofuel Producers Inc.*, 2018 SCC OnLine P&H 6914: (2019) 1 BC 105.
708. *ICICI Bank Ltd.* v. *IVRCL Ltd.*, 2015 SCC OnLine Hyd 311: (2015) 6 ALD 486.
709. *Supreme Infrastructure India Ltd.* v. *NTPC Ltd.*, 2023 SCC OnLine HP 1821.

Once it is found that a bank guarantee is unconditional and irrevocable, it is not open to the bank or principal debtor to raise any objection whatsoever to pay the amount under guarantee. The State beneficiary in whose favour the guarantee is furnished cannot be prevented from the bank guarantee on the pretext that the letter of invocation must state what monies are payable by the contractor. The contractor has its remedy to include all its claims in arbitration proceedings. The contractor is not entitled to an order of injunction.[710]

Once an unconditional bank guarantee warrants payment to beneficiary without any demur or protest, the bank is bound to honour bank guarantees irrespective of any dispute raised by the petitioner.[711]

Mandatory injunction

No irreparable loss would be caused to the appellant if the respondent is permitted to remove the machinery. The respondent is only seeking to exercise its lien over the machinery to secure its claim. The contention that mandatory injunction cannot be granted except to maintain status quo was found unmerited. The plain language of Section 17(1)(*ii*)(*e*), Arbitration and Conciliation Act, 1996 is of a wide import. It enables the Arbitral Tribunal to pass such orders as may be passed by the court for the purposes of proceedings before it. Section 17(1)(*ii*)(*e*) cannot be read restrictively that the Arbitral Tribunal must follow the settled principles while passing an order of mandatory injunction. The decision of the Arbitral Tribunal could not be faulted.[712]

Suit for specific performance of contract—Status quo order

The respondent had executed an agreement for sale in favour of the appellant and had received an advance of ₹2 crores. Dispute arose between the parties and as per agreement dispute was referred to the arbitrator. The respondent took the plea that time was the essence of the contract and appellant had failed to perform his part of the contract. It is well settled that even if an agreement ceases to exist, the arbitration clause remains in force and any dispute pertaining to the agreement ought to be resolved according to the conditions mentioned in the arbitration clause. Pending disposal of the arbitration proceeding interim measures to safeguard the interest were required to be taken. Since the respondent was trying to transfer the property

---

710. *BHEL* v. *W.B. State Electricity Distribution Co. Ltd.*, (2022) 1 HCC (Cal) 10.

711. *Hindustan Construction Co. Ltd.* v. *National Hydro Electric Power Corpn. Ltd.*, 2020 SCC OnLine Del 2777.

712. *Supertech Ltd.* v. *B.E. Billimoria and Co. Ltd.*, (2021) 2 HCC (Del) 231.

to a third person, order of status quo passed by the trial court was held proper.[713]

Mining lease rights

O had assigned mining rights to *A*. On the termination of the said contract of assignment by *O*, *A* could be compensated in terms of money. *A* was not granted injunction for keeping alive the assignment agreement with *A* during the pendency of the arbitration proceedings. Though it was unjust to permit *O* to enter into an arrangement for raising the ore with any other party other than *A*, there was no reason to injunct *O* from raising the ore itself pending the arbitral proceedings. Hence, limited injunction was granted and *O* was restrained from entering into any arrangement for raising ore with any party other than *A*.[714]

In *Arvind Constructions Co. (P) Ltd.* v. *Kalinga Mining Corpn.*[715], the respondent had entered into an agreement with the respondent-company for the purpose of raising iron ore from the area covered by the mining lease. The term of the original agreement expired and this was followed by two extensions for three years each. Thereafter the respondent had refused to extend the agreement and claimed that it wanted to do the mining itself. Appellant-company moved application under Section 9 seeking interim relief essentially to permit it to carry on mining operations and to restrain the respondent from interfering with it. The High Court did not grant interim relief. The Supreme Court held that the High Court did not commit an error in refusing to grant the interim injunction. The Supreme Court declined to interfere.

Power of the court to arrest ship or keep ship under arrest

Section 9 deals with interim measures in arbitration proceedings. Arrests of ships often affect the interest of third parties like charterer, cargo owners and persons having maritime claims. Such persons are permitted to intervene in action *in rem* and it cannot be done in Section 9 application which owes its origin to arbitration agreement. Application under Section 9 is not maintainable for arrest of vessel for obtaining security of award that may be made in arbitration proceedings.[716]

713. *N. Srinivasa* v. *Kuttukaran Machine Tools Ltd.*, (2009) 5 SCC 182.
714. *Adhunik Steels Ltd.* v. *Orissa Manganese and Minerals (P) Ltd.*, (2007) 7 SCC 125.
715. (2007) 6 SCC 798
716. *J.S. Ocean Liner LLC* v. *M.V. Golden Progress*, 2007 SCC OnLine Bom 69: (2007) 2 Mah LJ 410.

Trade mark

A joint venture agreement (JVA) to market and distribute products was entered into between the petitioner and the respondent. By deed of assignment the respondent had assigned 50 per cent of right, title and interest in the trade mark "Naturoma Herbal" along with proportional good will in appellant's favour permanently and forever. Negative stipulation in the assignment deed restrained assignor or assignee on termination of JVA from using or registering such trade mark in its own name/jointly with some other party.

Appellant subsequently floated the company under the name of "Naturoma Herbals (P) Ltd" and also applied for registration of trade mark in said company's name. The respondent cancelled JVA purporting to revoke the deed of assignment. Deed of assignment contained an arbitration clause. The appellant filed an application for interim injunction restraining respondent from selling her products under the trade mark "Naturoma Herbal" except through the appellant. It was held that provisions of the deed of assignment were yet to be adjudicated upon and decided as to whether by the purported revocation of the deed of assignment, appellant was no longer entitled to the benefits of the trade mark which had been transferred to him to the extent of 50 per cent absolutely and forever. Hence, the order passed by the District Judge restraining respondent from marketing her products through any person other than the appellant was justified as rights of both the parties stood protected till a final decision could be taken in the arbitration proceedings which is the object and intention of Section 9 of the 1996 Act.[717]

Assets of the firm—Protection of

A party to arbitration agreement can invoke Section 9 even before invoking an arbitration clause for protection of the assets of the firm.[718]

Unregistered firms—Bar of Section 69, Partnership Act, 1932

An application for interim measure under Section 9, Arbitration and Conciliation Act, 1996 filed by a partner of an unregistered person or by a person not shown as a partner in the Registrar of Firms is not barred by Section 69, Partnership Act. Such an application is not a suit. Undoubtedly, such an application results in the initiation of civil proceedings but the relief sought for in an application under Section 9, Arbitration and Conciliation Act is neither that in a suit nor under a right arising from the contract. The right arising from the partnership deed or conferred by the Partnership Act is being enforced in the Arbitral Tribunal.[719]

717. *Suresh Dhanuka* v. *Sunita Mohapatra*, (2012) 1 SCC 578.
718. *T. Vaithilingam* v. *S. Selvaraj*, 2015 SCC OnLine Mad 10359: (2015) 4 LW 455.
719. *Firm Ashok Traders* v. *Gurumukh Das Saluja*, (2004) 3 SCC 155.

Application under Section 9, Arbitration and Conciliation Act, 1996 by a partner of an unregistered firm is maintainable.[720] Application under Section 9 by petitioner of an unregistered firm is maintainable when there exists an arbitration agreement between the parties.[721]

Interim application for appointment of receiver was filed. Property was situated outside the jurisdiction of the original side of the High Court. It was held that the High Court lacked territorial jurisdiction, as such, application for appointment of receiver was rejected.[722]

Interim relief restraining partner from carrying rival business, granted

Conduct of partner amounted to breach of conditions in terms of Section 9, Partnership Act. Order restraining the partner from carrying on rival business was granted.[723]

Interim injunction against invocation of bank guarantee, refused

There were work contracts between the parties, the petitioner had given unconditional bank guarantee in favour of the respondent. As the petitioner failed to perform work and was overpaid, the respondent invoked bank guarantee. Petitioner also filed criminal complaints and also an injunction application on the ground of fraud. Criminal complaints were dismissed. Injunction restraining invocation of bank guarantee was also refused. Ground of special equities raised by the petitioner before the Supreme Court was not considered by the Supreme Court as such ground was not raised earlier. Even otherwise also, the respondent was entitled to receive the amount in partial award made in its favour which was not challenged by the petitioner.[724]

In the instant case, the bank unconditionally and irrevocably promised to pay, on demand, the amount of liability undertaken in the guarantee without any demur or dispute in terms of the bank guarantee, provided the invocation is done in terms with the bank guarantee. Order restraining the government from encashing the bank guarantee was set aside.[725]

---

720. *Masood Mohmmed Husain* v. *Gulam Rasul Mohammedali Shaikh*, 2006 SCC OnLine Bom 1239: (2007) 2 Mah LJ 116.
721. *Ravinder Singh Ahluwalia* v. *Kuljinder Singh Ahluwalia*, 2009 SCC OnLine Bom 712: (2009) 5 Mah LJ 170.
722. *Zoom Developers (P) Ltd.* v. *Small Tools Mfg. Co. of India Ltd.*, 2006 SCC OnLine Cal 629: (2007) 2 Cal LJ 312.
723. *Mukhtar Alam* v. *Yasmin Khalique*, 2018 SCC OnLine Cal 16986 .
724. *Yograj Infrastructure Ltd.* v. *Ssang Yong Engg. & Construction Co. Ltd.*, (2012) 3 SCC 425.
725. *Union of India* v. *Nayak Infrastructure (P) Ltd.*, 2022 SCC OnLine Gau 2176: (2023) 1 Gau LR 241.

Stay of arbitral proceedings

On application under Section 9, arbitral proceedings cannot be stayed.[726]

Interim relief restraining government undertaking from withdrawing work allotted to bidder/issuing new tender

The contract given to the petitioner was delayed as it did not complete the work in terms of the time schedule given in the tender, when there was no pandemic due to COVID-19. It was held that the petitioner was not entitled to resist withdrawal of work when opportunity had already been given by the government to execute the work. The petitioner was not going to suffer irreparable loss which could not be compensated in money terms. Interim injunction for restraining the respondent from withdrawing the work allotted to the petitioner was refused.[727]

Interim relief restraining the respondent from terminating the contract

Since the contract in *Inter Ads Exhibition (P) Ltd.* v. *Busworld International Coop. Vennootschap Met Beperkte Anasprakelijkheid*[728], was terminable and as the issue of the legality of the action of termination has yet to be determined and further, since wrongful termination can be restituted by awarding of damages, in the event the applicant is able to establish that the said termination was illegal and invalid, the Single Judge rightly declined the reliefs prayed for by the appellant in the Section 9 petition.

Case of termination of services—Injunction refused

The respondent-university had been dispensed with services of the appellant. Allowing appellant to continue imparting teaching on (Presentation, Practice, and Production) mode irrespective of termination of MOU would amount to granting of entire relief claimed by appellant in arbitration proceedings. "Irreparable loss" if any caused by termination/discontinuance of MOU's could be adequately compensated in terms of money. Order declining grant of injunction was proper.[729]

Stay of recovery of licence fee from the contractor

A contract for the entry of vehicles in Nainital was awarded to the petitioner on licence fee of ₹1,85,40,000 for the period 1 April 2009 to 31 March 2010.

---

726. *Bhatia International* v. *Bulk Trading S.A.*, (2002) 4 SCC 105.
727. *Golden Edge Engg. (P) Ltd.* v. *BHEL*, 2020 SCC OnLine Cal 996.
728. 2020 SCC OnLine Del 2649.
729. *Heritage Vision Education Trust* v. *Ravenshaw University*, 2014 SCC OnLine Ori 293.

A contract was executed and under the terms of the contract, 50 per cent of the licence fee was required to be paid by the petitioner at the time of the execution of the contract. He invoked an arbitration clause and pleaded that the licence fee was liable to be adjusted in damages sought by the petitioner. Interim injunction staying recovery of balance amount till the conclusion of the arbitration proceedings was refused.[730]

Inspection of property [Sub-s. (1)(*ii*)(*c*)]

Section 9 expressly permits inspection of property which is subject-matter of dispute for obtaining full information or evidence and even permits obtaining of evidence. There was a dispute pertaining to construction of work, denial of appointment of local commissioner in respect of construction was improper.[731]

"Appointment of a receiver" [Sub-s. (1)(*d*)]

Section 9(1)(*d*) provides that a party may apply to the court for the appointment of receiver and the court shall have the same power for making orders as it has for the purpose or in relation to any proceedings before it. The most basic principle governing the discretion of the court in appointing a receiver is whether it is "just and convenient" to do so. In *Firm Ashok Traders* v. *Gurumukh Das Saluja*[732], the Supreme Court observed that except bald and general allegations of mismanagement and siphoning off of funds, nothing concrete was alleged much less demonstrated to give real colour to the averments made. It is a serious matter to appoint a receiver over a running business. The respondent had obtained a loan for acquiring the asset, hypothecated the assets in favour of the petitioner. As the respondent failed to pay the monthly instalments, the petitioner terminated the loan agreement, the court appointed a receiver to take possession of the hypothecated assets. Under an agreement, property (Mill) was leased out to the respondent.[733] There was default in making payment as required under the said agreement, hence the agreement was terminated. The respondent expressed willingness to make payment, on failure the receiver was to take possession of the Mill.[734]

---

730. *Singla Realters Ltd.* v. *Municipal Board, Parishad*, 2011 SCC OnLine Utt 299: (2011) 4 All LJ 189.
731. *Prima Developers* v. *Lords Coop. Group Housing Society Ltd.*, 2009 SCC OnLine Del 504: (2009) 110 DRJ 293.
732. (2004) 3 SCC 155.
733. *SREI Equipment Finance Ltd.* v. *Pankaj Kumar Yadav*, 2020 SCC OnLine Cal 3294.
734. *Kotak Mahindra Finance Ltd.* v. *Rajinder Steels Ltd.*, 1998 SCC OnLine Bom 498: (1999) 2 Mah LJ 586.

A partnership firm conducted business of liquor vend during the years 2002–2003 and 2003–2004. Partners were divided into groups A, B and C. Group A had 20 per cent shares while groups B and C held 80 per cent shares. Group B ran the business of the firm upto nine months in the year 2003–2004. Group A made bald allegations of mismanagement and siphoning off the funds against Group B and sought appointment of receiver of the business of the firm. Group A had not filed an application for appointment of receiver. After the year 2002–2003, no fresh partnership deed was entered into between the parties. On the facts of the case, the Supreme Court directed the business of the firm to be run by Group B but as a receiver.[735]

Relief of appointment of receiver to take possession of property of a third party cannot be granted. Interim order in respect of the property of the appellant third party was not proper.[736] Where firms were not party to the arbitration agreement with the petitioners, relief of appointment of court receiver/injunction could/was not to be granted against those third parties in the proceedings.[737]

Under the loan agreement the respondent had taken loan in respect of vehicle and hypothecated the same in favour of the applicant. The respondent had defaulted in repayment of the vehicle loan, the applicant alleged that there was every likelihood of the respondent disposing of the vehicle. Balance of convenience was in favour of the creditor, receiver was appointed.[738]

Defendant had taken a loan for purchasing hypothecated assets, and was refusing to pay instalments. Receiver was appointed to take possession of hypothecated assets.[739]

An arbitrator cannot appoint a court receiver.[740]

Security

Application was filed by Madras Aluminium Co. Ltd. for directing the respondent TCS to furnish security before the Court of Subordinate Judge. The court while granting or refusing to grant injunction or issuing direction to furnish security should exercise sound judicial discretion to find out the

---

735. *Firm Ashok Traders* v. *Gurumukh Das Saluja*, (2004) 3 SCC 155.
736. *Md. Ghufran* v. *Varun Finance Corporation Ltd.*, AIR 2016 Cal 197 (DB).
737. *Minochar* v. *Deenyar Sheriar Jehani*, 2014 SCC OnLine Bom 901: (2015) 3 Mah LJ 173.
738. *Cholamandalam Investment and Finance Co. Ltd.* v. *Sobhana NC*, 2020 SCC OnLine Mad 20780.
739. *Tata Capital Financial Services Ltd.* v. *Teju Khan*, 2018 SCC OnLine Cal 4127; *Srei Equipment Finance Ltd.* v. *Martha Rodrigues*, 2018 SCC OnLine Cal 4123.
740. *Aditya Birla Finance Ltd.* v. *Carnet Elias Fernandes*, 2015 SCC OnLine Bom 4774: (2015) 5 Bom CR 649.

amount of substantial mischief or injury which is likely to be caused to the parties if interim order is granted and compare it with that which is likely to be caused otherwise if injunction is refused.[741] Intention of the respondent is sine qua non. The court is to see if there is real danger of the respondent defeating, delaying or obstructing the execution of the award. In *Global Co.* v. *National Fertilizers Ltd.*[742], respondent was a Government of India undertaking, there was no necessity for directing the respondent to furnish security.

If the petitioner succeeds in arbitration proceedings against the respondent, petitioner would not be able to recover any amount from the respondents unless the respondents are directed to secure the claim of the petitioner, in such a case it would be proper to direct the respondents to furnish the security.[743]

Dispute arose from shareholders agreement and share purchase agreement containing arbitration clause. Interim protection was sought to secure the amount of petitioners' investment in the joint venture company. Relief sought is similar to attachment before judgment under Order 38 Rule 5 CPC. Petitioner failed to prove general apprehension that respondent will divert the assets during pendency of proceedings. Direction was given to petitioners to formally invoke arbitration clause and to the respondent to make deposit of ₹23 crores and title deed of project land with the registrar of the court subject to final orders.[744]

Dispute was between the parties regarding payment of outstanding amount as per contract. Balance of convenience was in favour of the applicant. Respondent was directed to furnish sufficient security for the amount in dispute failing which attachment shall be made as prayed for in the application.[745]

The court under Section 9 cannot direct a party to furnish security in the form of a bank guarantee in relation to a speculative claim for damages.[746] Respondent had not averred nor produced any material to show that there was an apprehension or danger that the amount could not be recovered by them from the appellant, nor there was any averment that there was an

741. *Techmo Car SPA* v. *Madras Aluminium Co. Ltd.*, 2004 SCC OnLine Mad 246: (2004) 3 CTC 754.
742. 1998 SCC OnLine Del 387: (1998) 47 DRJ 144.
743. *L&T Finance Ltd.* v. *Duplex Industries Ltd.*, 2013 SCC OnLine Bom 530: (2013) 3 Mah LJ 864.
744. *Lalea Trading Ltd.* v. *Anant Raj Projects (P) Ltd.*, 2013 SCC OnLine Del 149: ILR (2013) 3 Del 1679.
745. *Spack Matrix Design Consultants (P) Ltd.* v. *C.S.S. Corpn. (P) Ltd.*, 2011 SCC OnLine Mad 1525: (2012) 1 MWN (Civil) 696.
746. *Intertoll Ics Cecons O & M Co. (P) Ltd.* v. *NHAI*, 2013 SCC OnLine Del 447: (2013) 135 DRJ 160.

attempt to defect the award, interim direction to the appellant to furnish security was not justified.[747]

Injunction cannot be granted under Section 9 restraining the respondent-contractor from claiming the amount deposited in respect of earlier contract.[748]

Government's right to move for security in respect of the claim pending before the arbitration is always available, but that does not mean that an amount lying in the court of competent jurisdiction, before whom the government, being an obliged party, has voluntarily deposited the amount can be directed to be kept to the credit of the government.[749]

A direction to the respondent to furnish security is not antithesis to the concept enshrined under Section 9 of the Act.[750]

Deposit of amount—Respondent, a private limited company, was facing proceedings under the Insolvency and Bankruptcy Code 2016. Petitioner, a non-banking financer, had sanctioned a loan to the respondent with which the respondent had purchased machinery and equipment. Respondent had defaulted in repayment of loan. To safeguard the interest of the petitioner, the respondent was directed to deposit a specified amount with the Prothonotary and Senior Master of Court.[751]

Bank guarantee for the admitted amount

Where the respondents in their own balance sheet and statement of account had admitted liability, the respondents were directed to furnish bank guarantee of this admitted amount. Held, the order was proper.[752]

Territorial jurisdiction

Only that court in whose jurisdiction the "cause of action" did arise will have jurisdiction to entertain an application either under Section 9 or under Section 11 of the Act. The overall circumstances on record and the nature of business that is being carried on and also the terms and conditions between the parties have to be taken into consideration for the purpose of "cause of

747. *C.S.S. Corpn. (P) Ltd.* v. *Space Matrix Design Consultants (P) Ltd.*, 2011 SCC OnLine Mad 2413: (2012) 1 CTC 225.
748. *Union of India* v. *Saravana Constructions (P) Ltd.*, 2009 SCC OnLine Mad 1073: (2009) 4 LW 62385.
749. *Ibid.*
750. *Ibid.*
751. *Tata Capital Financial Service Ltd.* v. *Tahsildar*, 2020 SCC OnLine Bom 11728.
752. *Savita Jain Sole Proprietor of M.S. Navkar Sales* v. *Krishna Packaging*, (2021) 2 HCC (Del) 197.

action".[753] Tender was invited in Punjab, address in letter enclosing the bid was of Punjab. There was nothing in the agreement or the correspondence to suggest/support that the agreement was made, signed or executed at Delhi. Deposit of tax in Delhi does not form part of cause of action. Mere existence of an office within the jurisdiction of the court which is called upon to exercise jurisdiction, anything more, by itself, would not be sufficient to permit the court to exercise jurisdiction over the subject-matter of the litigation, petition filed in Delhi was dismissed.[754]

Clause of the purchase contract provided that in case of dispute between the parties, the court at Jaipur would have jurisdiction where the contract was signed. Part of the cause of action arose at Jaipur. The court at Calcutta had no jurisdiction to entertain application under Section 9 of the Act.[755]

Plaintiff had filed suit for dissolution of firm and rendition of accounts. Partnership firm had its registered office at Bhopal. A part of cause of action in the present case relating to rendition of accounts had arisen in the territory of commercial court, Bhopal. The court below has certainly erred in dismissing the application filed under Section 9, Arbitration and Conciliation Act, 1996 for want of jurisdiction.[756]

Where the jurisdiction clause in the agreement indicates that the parties agree to conduct arbitration proceedings at Court A, Court A has territorial jurisdiction to entertain application under Section 9.[757]

Commercial disputes involving arbitration dispute

The term "Court" means only the court of the principal civil original jurisdiction in a District and it is only the court of "District Judge" in a District which is such a "Court" of principal civil jurisdiction. Therefore, the District Court has jurisdiction to decide application under Section 9 of the Act.[758]

International commercial arbitration—Jurisdiction of Indian courts

Where the parties had agreed to govern by the laws of England, it implies that the parties have agreed to exclude the provisions of Part I of the Arbitration and Conciliation Act, the Delhi High Court would have no jurisdiction to entertain a petition under Section 9 of the Act. The mere fact that the

---

753. *Iron & Steel Co. Ltd. v. Tiwari Road Lines*, (2007) 5 SCC 703.
754. *Rattan Singh Associates (P) Ltd.* v. *Gill Power Generation Co. (P) Ltd.*, 2007 SCC OnLine Del 19.
755. *Techma Engg. Enterprises (P) Ltd.* v. *Union of India*, 2022 SCC OnLine Cal 4565.
756. *Ratan Lalchandani* v. *Gopaldas Kukreja*, 2023 SCC OnLine MP 415: (2023) 2 MP LJ 376.
757. *Kanhai Foods Ltd.* v. *A and HP Bakes*, 2022 SCC OnLine Guj 2650.
758. *Fun N. Fund* v. *GLK Associates*, 2019 SCC OnLine Guj 4236: (2020) 1 GCD 154.

appellant had earlier filed similar petitions would not clothe the Delhi High Court with jurisdiction to entertain a petition filed by the respondent.[759] In spite of the fact that the arbitrator clause in the agreement between the parties provided that the venue of arbitration shall be London, unless there was implied consent for excluding jurisdiction of the court in India, it could not be said that Section 9 would not apply.[760]

Issuance of notice invoking arbitration clause to the opposite party is not a condition precedent for filing application under Section 9 for interim order

In order to give full effect to the words "before or during arbitral proceedings" occurring in Section 9, it would not be necessary that a notice invoking arbitration cause must be issued to the opposite party before an application under Section 9 can be filed. The issuance of a notice may, in a given case, be sufficient to establish the manifest intention to have the dispute referred to an Arbitral Tribunal. But a situation may demand that a party may choose to apply before issuing a notice under Section 21 of the Act. If an application is made, the court will first have to be satisfied that there exists a valid arbitration agreement and the applicant intends to take the dispute to arbitration. Once it is so satisfied, the court will have the jurisdiction to pass orders under Section 9 giving such interim protection as the facts and circumstances of the case warrant.[761]

While passing such an order and in order to ensure that effective steps are taken to commence the arbitration proceedings, the court while exercising jurisdiction under Section 9 can pass a conditional order to put the applicant to such terms as it may deem fit with a view to see that effective steps are taken by the applicant for commencing the arbitral proceedings. What is apparent, however, is that the court is not debarred from defeating an application under Section 9 merely because no notice has been issued under Section 21.[762]

Ex parte measure/protection

The legislature never intended to confer powers on a court to make interim measures under Section 9, Arbitration and Conciliation Act dehors the accepted principles that govern the grant of an interim injunction. Upon Section 9 application, the court has power to grant an ex parte order or make an ex parte measure. However, the court has an obligation to direct

759. *Videocon Industries Ltd.* v. *Union of India*, (2011) 6 SCC 161.
760. *National Aluminium Co. Ltd.* v. *Gerald Metals SA*, (2004) 9 SCC 307.
761. *Sundaram Finance Ltd.* v. *NEPC India Ltd.*, (1999) 2 SCC 479.
762. *Ibid.*

notice to opposite party in all cases when it makes such an order and it can make exception to the normal rule on the grounds indicated in Order 39 Rule 3 CPC, so also the judge not ruling out the applicability of Order 39 Rule 3 CPC, then it is inconceivable that the proviso would not be attracted. The court shall in all cases before granting an injunction direct notice of the application to be given to the opposite party. However, at the same time, if the object of granting the injunction is being defeated by the delay and that appears to be the position before the court, then it has to record reasons/ opinion as contemplated by the proviso.[763]

Interim relief against non-party to arbitration agreement

Under Section 9, the court has power to issue interim directions to non-parties to arbitration.[764]

Financier—Proceedings under Section 9 of the Act are maintainable only between parties to arbitration agreement. A financier cannot be said to be a party to arbitration agreement between opposite parties, and cannot seek impleadment or protection of his right under Section 9 of the Act.[765]

The jurisdiction under Section 9 can be invoked only by a party to the arbitration agreement. Section 9, however, does not limit the jurisdiction of the court to pass an order of interim measures only against a party to an arbitration agreement or arbitration proceedings.[766]

International Chamber of Commerce Rules (ICC Rules)

Rule 3 of ICC Rules does not exclude the powers of the civil court to entertain applications under Section 9, Arbitration and Conciliation Act, 1996.[767]

"Locus standi" for filing application under Section 9—Third party cannot apply

The right conferred by Section 9 is on a party to an arbitration agreement. A third person not party to an arbitration agreement cannot enter the court for protection under Section 9.[768]

763. *Vascon Engineers Ltd.* v. *Sansara Hotels India (P) Ltd.*, 2009 SCC OnLine Bom 638: (2009) 4 Mah LJ 859.
764. *Sterling and Wilson International FZE* v. *Sunshakti Solar Power Projects (P) Ltd.*, 2020 SCC OnLine Del 2414.
765. *SREI Infrastructure Finance Ltd.* v. *Bhageeratha Engg. Ltd.*, 2009 SCC OnLine Gau 30: (2009) 6 Gau LR 828.
766. *Girish Mulchand Mehta* v. *Mahesh S. Mehta*, 2009 SCC OnLine Bom 1986: (2010) 2 Mah LJ 657.
767. *LML Ltd.* v. *Union of India*, 1998 SCC OnLine All 810: (1999) 35 ALR 199.
768. *Firm Ashok Traders* v. *Gurumukh Das Saluja*, (2004) 3 SCC 155; *Girish Mulchand Mehta* v. *Mahesh S. Mehta*, 2009 SCC OnLine Bom 1986: (2010) 2 Mah LJ 657.

Under Section 9, an interim measure can be allowed in favour of a party who moves such application either before the commencement of the arbitration proceedings or during the pendency of the arbitral proceedings, and even after the making of the arbitral award but before it is enforced in accordance with Section 36. Thus, an interim arrangement can be made under Section 9 not only before or during the pendency of the arbitration proceedings but also after the arbitral award has been pronounced.[769]

The respondent had terminated a lease agreement for operation and management of a luxury tourist train, which it had with a joint venture (JV) company. The petitioner, one of the shareholders of JV company, filed an application under Section 9 seeking stay of the termination of the lease and allow it to operate the said train service. It was held that the petitioner had no locus standi to question the termination of the lease with JV company as it was not a party to the lease agreement. Further, mere investment of a large sum of money in the project was no ground to entitle the petitioner to obtain mandatory order of injunction to operate the train once lease agreement/arrangement had been terminated. Remedy open to the petitioner was an action for damages against the terms and conditions of the JV agreement.[770]

A person not a party to an arbitration agreement cannot invoke the jurisdiction of the court for interim relief under Section 9, Arbitration and Conciliation Act, 1996.[771]

Third party—Impleadment of

Section 9 does not recognise inclusion of third party, who may be independently claiming rights against parties to arbitration. A person who is not party to arbitration agreement, would remain stranger to proceedings under Section 9, for such third party no *lis* would be created. Even if parties to arbitration and third party have some inter se rights and obligations to be enforced vis-à-vis each other, it would be a separate course of action. Application for impleadment of third party was rejected.[772]

---

769. *Ultratech Cement Ltd.* v. *Rajasthan Rajya Vidyut Utpadan Nigam Ltd.*, (2018) 15 SCC 210.
770. *Cox & Kings India Ltd.* v. *Indian Railways Catering & Tourism Corpn. Ltd.*, (2012) 7 SCC 587.
771. *Mohd Yusuf* v. *Ashish Aggarwal*, 2021 SCC OnLine Utt 1274: (2022) 150 ALR 27.
772. *Vijay Arvind Jariwala* v. *Umang Jatin Gandhi*, 2022 SCC OnLine Guj 2648: (2023) 1 GLH 140.

Anti-arbitration injunction

Arbitration clause specifically stated the venue of arbitration. Parties to the contract had agreed to the arbitration clause. Parties are to abide by the arbitration agreement. Anti-arbitration injunction cannot be granted.[773]

Document containing arbitration clause unstamped/insufficiently stamped

The court can entertain applications under Section 9 and grant interim relief even if a document containing arbitration clause is not stamped or insufficiently stamped.[774]

Order of blacklisting

When the contractor has been blacklisted, his remedy is to file an application under Section 9 or Section 17 before the arbitrator or before the civil court, writ petition under Article 226 of the Constitution is not maintainable.[775]

The Commercial Court in its jurisdiction under Section 9 of the Act of 1996 would have jurisdiction to pass interim injunction or such other interim measure of protection as may appear to it to be just and convenient, but certainly, it would not include to quash the order of blacklisting and the Commercial Court would have no jurisdiction to quash the order of blacklisting proceeding under Section 9 of the Act of 1996 in the garb of granting interim injunction as it is absolutely without jurisdiction and beyond the scope of power under Section 9 of the Act of 1996.[776]

Proceedings under Section 9 dismissed for non-prosecution

An order dismissing proceedings under Section 9, Arbitration and Conciliation Act, 1996 is not appealable under Section 37(1)(*a*). Filing of application under Section 151(1) CPC does not revive proceedings under Section 9 nor are continuation or extended limb of the section of proceedings.[777]

Successive applications for interim measures

Once the application under Section 9, Arbitration and Conciliation Act seeking interim measures filed with similar prayers and the same has been

---

773. *Siddhi Vinayak Industries (P) Ltd.* v. *Virgoz Oils & Fats PTE Ltd.*, 2010 SCC OnLine Cal 1982: (2011) 1 Cal LT 110.
774. *Gautam Landscapes (P) Ltd.* v. *Shailesh S. Shah*, 2019 SCC OnLine Bom 563: (2019) 3 Mah LJ 231.
775. *S.G.S. India (P) Ltd.* v. *Indian Institute of Management*, 2019 SCC OnLine Utt 1895.
776. *South Eastern Coalfields Ltd.* v. *Sadbhav Engg. Ltd.*, 2021 SCC OnLine Chh 3978.
777. *Ambika Enterprises* v. *Trishna Bose*, 2003 SCC OnLine Cal 85: (2003) 2 CHN 335.

disposed of by granting the prayers either fully or in part, subsequent similar application making prayers on the same lines which were dealt with in the earlier proceedings, would not be maintainable.[778]

Setting aside the award of arbitrator

In an application filed under Section 9(1)(*ii*)(*d*) of the Act, the court dealing with such an application would be competent to set at naught an award otherwise validly made under the provisions of the Arbitration and Conciliation Act, 1996. The impugned order of the Principal District Judge setting aside the award of the arbitrator was set aside.[779]

Interim order—Effect on where mandate of arbitrators coming to an end

Interim reliefs are always granted only in aid of and as an ancillary to, the main relief which may be available to the party on the final determination of his right in a suit or proceedings. Interim order passed during arbitral proceedings does not come to end where arbitral proceedings are still pending and mandate of arbitrations is terminated.[780]

Expiry of contract containing arbitration clause—Interim relief

Contract which contained an arbitration clause was never renewed after its expiry. Arbitration clause was automatically terminated at the end of the agreement period. In the absence of an arbitration clause, application under Section 9 for interim relief was not maintainable.[781]

Interim measure cannot go beyond final relief

Grant of interim measure though independent to the arbitral proceedings cannot go beyond the final relief which is likely to be claimed, or likely to be awarded.[782]

Principal relief cannot be granted at interim stage

The relief which could be granted by the arbitrator only at the end of the arbitral proceedings, would ordinarily and in normal circumstances not be

778. *Cinemas & Entertainment (P) Ltd.* v. *Venus Infrastructure and Developers (P) Ltd.*, 2022 SCC OnLine Guj 2651.
779. *Sri Swaminathan Construction* v. *Sri Thirunavukkarasu Dhanalakshmi*, 2007 SCC OnLine Mad 984: (2008) 4 LW 956.
780. *Kifayatullah Haji Gulam Rasool* v. *Bilkish Ismail Mehsania*, 2000 SCC OnLine Bom 260: (2000) 4 Mah LJ 341.
781. *G. Radha Madhavi* v. *Indian Oil Corpn. Ltd.*, 2017 SCC OnLine Hyd 329: (2017) 6 ALD 406.
782. *Samay Singh* v. *Hindustan Petroleum Corpn. Ltd.*, 2012 SCC OnLine All 1253: (2012) 94 ALR 16.

granted as an interim measure on the footing of the principle that principal relief cannot be granted at the interim stage and that grant of interim directions of the nature granting main relief is not permissible in law.[783]

The lessee petitioner made a prayer for directing the lessor to operationalise facilities for running a cinema theatre. By such prayer the lessee sought to revive the lease agreement which was already terminated. Allowing such prayer would result in granting principal relief which is impermissible. Prayer was rejected.[784]

Presidency Small Cause Courts Act, 1882

Relief under Section 9 can be granted by the court when dispute arising out of the agreement falls within the ambit of Section 41, Presidency Small Courts Act, 1882.[785]

Recovery proceedings under Maharashtra Co-operative Societies Act, 1960

Section 9 of the 1996 Act cannot be permitted to be invoked for halting the statutory proceedings initiated under Section 101, Maharashtra Co-operative Societies Act, 1960. Such a petition under Section 9 of the Act is not maintainable.[786]

Two separate arbitration agreements—Single application for interim relief

Two separate arbitration agreements, single application for both the agreements for interim relief is not maintainable.[787]

Jurisdiction of the High Court

In the absence of any exclusive clause in the agreement for the purpose of Section 9 petition, the High Court has jurisdiction to grant interim relief as prayed on the basis of averments made by the petitioner.[788]

---

783. *Cinemas & Entertainment (P) Ltd.* v. *Venus Infrastructure and Developers (P) Ltd.*, 2022 SCC OnLine Guj 2651.
784. *Ibid.*
785. *Genesis Colors (P) Ltd.* v. *Anil Ramlabhaya Suri*, 2009 SCC OnLine Bom 1631: (2010) 1 Mah LJ 231.
786. *Kail Ltd.* v. *Sahebrao Deshmukh Coop. Bank Ltd.*, 2012 SCC OnLine Bom 357: (2012) 3 Mah LJ 320.
787. *H.P. SEB Ltd.* v. *Ahluwalia Contracts (India) Ltd.*, 2015 SCC OnLine HP 3122: (2015) 6 Arb LR 279.
788. *Indusind Bank Ltd.* v. *Quality Fabricators and Erectors*, 2009 SCC OnLine Bom 1360: (2009) 6 Mah LJ 543.

Commercial Courts Act, 2015 (4 of 2016)

In cases of commercial dispute, the commercial court alone has jurisdiction to deal with applications filed under Section 9, Arbitration and Conciliation Act, 1996. Order of the civil court allowing applications filed under Section 9 was set aside.[789]

Grant of interim relief—Jurisdiction of civil court

Arbitral Tribunal, whether it is functional or whether its mandate stands terminated, was uncertain. Due to the said uncertainty, civil court can entertain application under Section 9, Arbitration and Conciliation Act, 1996 to grant interim relief.[790]

Wakf Act, 1995 (43 of 1995)—Bar on jurisdiction of civil court

No provision in the 1996 Act creates exception to jurisdiction of arbitration in respect of valid agreement relating to wakf property. The civil court is competent to entertain an application for grant of interim relief under Section 9.[791]

Sick Industrial Companies (Special Provisions) Act, 1985

For the purpose of execution and/or for taking any action under Section 22 of the 1985 Act, merely because the properties are mortgaged cannot be the reason to permit the petitioner to take steps as prayed. It is necessary for them to take necessary permission from the Sick Industrial Companies Authority before taking any proceedings for recovery of loan or for appointment of receiver as contemplated under Section 9 of the 1996 Act.[792]

Initiation of proceedings under SARFAESI Act, 2002

SARFAESI Act overrides other provisions of law which are inconsistent therewith. SARFAESI Act shall prevail over provisions of all other statutes. Proceedings under Section 14 of the SARFAESI Act cannot be said to be illegal on account of appointment of court receiver under Arbitration Act.[793]

---

789. *K. Srimannarayana Murthy* v. *V. Agastya Sagar*, 2022 SCC OnLine TS 3469.
790. *Bishnu Kumar Yadav* v. *M.L. Soni & Sons*, 2016 SCC OnLine Cal 1420.
791. *Sayed Hassan Ali* v. *Mohd. Sahidul Islam*, 2016 SCC OnLine Cal 4276.
792. *Tata Capital Ltd.* v. *Maven Industries Ltd.*, 2012 SCC OnLine Bom 240: (2012) 4 Mah LJ 376.
793. *Aditya Birla Finance Ltd.* v. *Carnet Elias Fernandes*, 2018 SCC OnLine MP 1317: (2019) 1 MP LJ 471.

Pending execution of award, it is permissible to grant protective and security order

Pending the execution of the award, it is possible to grant protective and security order to avoid further complication.[794]

MOU containing arbitration clause insufficiently stamped—Interim measures not granted

MOU containing arbitration clause insufficiently stamped cannot be admitted/read in evidence. The District Judge could not have granted interim measures on the basis of such MOU, order granting interim measures was set aside.[795]

Loan was granted on the hypothecation of movables and agreement contained an arbitration clause. Plea raised was that interim relief under Section 9 cannot be granted as agreement was unstamped. Plea was rejected as hypothecation is charge on property and not transfer of property, hence not required to be stamped.[796]

Appeal

Appeal lies against an order granting or refusing to grant any measure under Section 9. [S. 37(1)(*b*)]. Appeal against the grant/refusal of temporary injunction, lies under Section 37.[797] No appeal is maintainable against the order issuing notice on the application for grant of injunction.[798] Against the order passed under Section 9 of the Act, whether an ad interim or ex parte or regular, appeal is maintainable.[799]

Ex parte order of interim injunction—Appeal lies

Grant or refusal of an interim measure of protection, by way of an ex parte ad interim order under Section 9 of the Act, is an appealable order under Section 37 thereof.[800]

794. *Sahyadri Earthmovers* v. *L and T Finance Ltd.*, 2012 SCC OnLine Bom 1861: (2013) 2 Mah LJ 302.
795. *Jayraj Devidas* v. *Nilesh Shantilal Tank*, 2014 SCC OnLine Bom 900: (2014) 6 Mah LJ 156.
796. *Saumya Mining Ltd.* v. *Srei Equipment Finance Ltd.*, 2016 SCC OnLine Cal 78: (2016) 2 CHN 345.
797. *Orissa Concrete & Allied Industries Ltd.* v. *Union of India*, 2017 SCC OnLine Chh 1903.
798. *Felguera Gruas India (P) Ltd.* v. *R.V.R. Projects (P) Ltd.*, 2015 SCC OnLine Hyd 376: (2016) 2 ALD 518.
799. *State Council for IT & E Governance* v. *Karnataka State Electronics Development Corpn. Ltd.*, 2012 SCC OnLine Gau 908: (2014) 4 Gau LR 452.
800. *Perin Hoshang Davierwalla* v. *Kobad Dorabji Davierwalla*, 2014 SCC OnLine Bom 534: (2014) 3 Bom CR 551; *Sati Oil Udyog Ltd.* v. *Avanti Projects and Infrastructure*

An order refusing to grant interim relief on application filed under Section 9 is an order under Section 9 of the Act, and not under Order 39, Rules 1, 2, 3, and is not appealable under Order 43, Rule 1(*r*).[801]

Order of injunction passed under Section 9 of the Act is appealable order under Section 37(1)(*a*) of the Act irrespective of the fact as to whether such an order is passed ex parte or upon hearing of the parties concerned.[802]

Writ petition

The High Court in writ jurisdiction will not interfere in an interlocutory order passed by the arbitrator in the pending arbitral proceeding; the party aggrieved may reserve its right to lay a challenge to such an interlocutory order, if and when it suffers an adverse award.[803]

Interim relief—Contract was entered in Nepal, for works to be executed in Nepal—Courts in India have no jurisdiction

Contract between the parties was entered in Nepal for the works to be executed. Contractual clauses stipulate that laws of Nepal govern contracts, contractual disputes are to be settled under UNCITRAL Rules, and the judicial seat of arbitration is in Nepal. Applicability of Part 1 of Act was ruled out by conscious decision. It was held, Section 9 cannot be invoked, courts in India had no jurisdiction to entertain application under Section 9 of the Act.[804]

Ltd., 2009 SCC OnLine Gau 85: (2010) (1) 2 Gau LR 512; *Aventis Pasteur S.A.* v. *Cadila Pharmaceuticals Ltd.*, 2002 SCC OnLine Guj 288: (2003) 2 Arb LR 259; *ICICI Bank Ltd.* v. *IVRCL Ltd.*, 2015 SCC OnLine Hyd 311: (2015) 6 ALD 486.

801. *Sai Concrète Pavers (P) Ltd.* v. *National Alluminum Co. Ltd.*, 2016 SCC OnLine Ori 132.

802. *Sati Oil Udyog Ltd.* v. *Avanti Projects and Infrastructure Ltd.*, 2009 SCC OnLine Gau 85: (2010) 2 Gau LR 512. An order granting or refusing to grant any measure under S. 9, Arbitration and Conciliation Act is appealable. [*Sundaram Finance Ltd.* v. *Radhamma*, 2003 SCC OnLine Ker 338: (2003) 3 KLT 289.] The scope of interference is very limited. [*Sterling Tree Magnum India Ltd.* v. *G.A.M. Thandapani*, 2011 SCC OnLine Mad 423: (2011) 4 LW 91.]

803. *Radiant Infosystems Ltd.* v. *Karnataka SRTC Ltd.*, 2018 SCC OnLine Kar 1209: ILR 2018 Kar 4873.

804. *ICICI Bank Ltd.* v. *IVRCL Ltd.*, 2015 SCC OnLine Hyd 311: (2015) 6 ALD 486.

CHAPTER III
Composition of Arbitral Tribunal

NUMBER OF ARBITRATORS [S. 10]

10. *Number of arbitrators.*—(1) The parties are free to determine the number of arbitrators, provided that such number shall not be an even number.

(2) Failing the determination referred to in sub-section (1), the arbitral tribunal shall consist of a sole arbitrator.

COMMENTS

Corresponding old law

Sub-section (2) of this section corresponds to Rules 1 and 2 of the First Schedule of the Arbitration Act, 1940. The said Rules 1 and 2 provided as under:

1. Unless otherwise expressly provided, the reference shall be to a sole arbitrator.

2. If the reference is to an even number of arbitrators the arbitrators shall appoint an umpire not later than one month from the latest date of their respective appointments.

UNCITRAL Model Law

Article 10. *Number of arbitrators*

(1) The parties are free to determine the number of arbitrators.

(2) Failing such determination, the number of arbitrators shall be three.

Scope and application

Section 10 of the Act deals with the number of arbitrators to be appointed in the case. It has been left at the option of the parties to determine the number of arbitrators to be appointed in the case, subject to the rider that the number of arbitrators appointed in a case shall not be an even number. When the parties fail to determine the number of the arbitrators to be appointed in a case, the Arbitral Tribunal shall consist of a sole arbitrator.

Where an arbitration agreement specifies even number of arbitrators, it could not be a ground to render an arbitration agreement invalid.[1]

Section 10 and UNCITRAL Model Law on International Commercial Arbitration, 1985

Section 10 of the 1996 Act has close similarity with Article 10 of UNCITRAL Model Law on International Commercial Arbitration, 1985. Section 10 of the 1996 Act deviates from Article 10 of the UNCITRAL Model Law only in the sense that Section 10 of the 1996 Act provides that despite the freedom given to the parties to determine the number of arbitrators, such numbers shall not be an even number. But in default of determination of the number, Section 10(2) provides that the tribunal is to consist of a sole arbitrator. Therefore, the scheme of 1996 Act is virtually similar to Article 10(2) of the UNCITRAL Model Law.[2]

"Number (of arbitrators) shall not be an even number" [Sub-s. (1)]

Section 10 provides that the number of arbitrators shall not be "even". In *Groupe Chimique Tunisien SA* v. *Southern Petrochemicals Industries Corpn. Ltd.*[3], the arbitration clause provided that the dispute shall be referred to two arbitrators and in the event of arbitrators not agreeing, then an umpire shall be appointed by the arbitrators in writing before proceeding to the reference. It was held that having regard to Section 10 of the Act, the Arbitral Tribunal in this case shall consist of three arbitrators (one to be appointed by each of the two parties and the presiding arbitrator).

Where the Arbitral Tribunal is not constituted in accordance with the procedure under Section 10 of the 1996 Act, the award of the tribunal is liable to be set aside in terms of Section 34(2)(*a*)(*v*) of the Act. The tribunal cannot assure jurisdiction in contravention of Section 10 merely because no objection was raised by the party.[4] However, Ahmedabad Stock Exchange Rules and Regulations provide for appointment of even number of arbitrators. As the bye-laws framed under the regulations prevail over Section 10, Arbitration and Conciliation Act, the award passed by the two arbitrators cannot be set aside.[5]

---

1. *MMTC Ltd.* v. *Sterlite Industries (India) Ltd.*, (1996) 6 SCC 716.
2. *Sime Darby Engg. SDN. BHD.* v. *Engineers India Ltd.*, (2009) 7 SCC 545.
3. (2006) 5 SCC 275.
4. *Atul R. Shah* v. *V. Vrijlal Lalloobhai and Co.*, 1998 SCC OnLine Bom 403: (1999) 1 Mah LJ 629.
5. *Gautam Sarabhai* v. *Navinbhai R. Thakker*, 2011 SCC OnLine Guj 7769: (2011) 2 GCD 1259.

Where the arbitration agreement prescribed appointment of two arbitrators, appointment of even numbers being inconsistent with Section 10(1), appointment of third arbitrator as presiding officer was ordered.[6] An agreement to appoint two arbitrators is not an agreement under Section 10(1).[7]

Where the arbitration clause provides for appointment of even number of arbitrators, the Arbitral Tribunal shall be constituted by a sole arbitrator.[8]

Arbitration clause provided for three arbitrators. However, the words "two arbitrators appointed by the parties shall appoint the third arbitrator" were missing. To ensure workability of arbitration clause, the missing line that the "two arbitrators appointed by the parties shall appoint the third arbitrator" can be read into the arbitration clause.[9]

Arbitration agreement specifying even number of arbitrators does not make arbitration agreement invalid.[10]

In the agreement, the number of arbitrators to be appointed had not been specifically mentioned. Procedure for appointment of arbitrator was not provided. Appointment of arbitrators in the case was patently illegal.[11]

Appointment of two arbitrators by agreement of parties — Agreement not invalid

Section 10, Arbitration and Conciliation Act, 1996 provides that the number of arbitrators shall not be an even number. However, if the parties provide for appointment of only two arbitrators, the agreement does not become invalid. Under Section 11(3), the two arbitrators should then appoint a third arbitrator who shall act as the presiding arbitrator. Such an appointment should preferably be made at the beginning. However, there is no reason why the two arbitrators cannot appoint a third arbitrator at a later stage, *i.e.* if and when they agree. This would ensure that on a difference of opinion the arbitration proceedings are not frustrated.[12] Where an arbitration agreement provides for an even number of arbitrators to be appointed by each party, the agreement would not become invalid on that ground, in such a case, dispute

6. *B.T. Patil and Sons Belgaum (Construction) (P) Ltd.* v. *Konkan Railway Corpn. Ltd.*, 1997 SCC OnLine Bom 545: (1998) 1 Mah LJ 502.
7. *Deepashree* v. *Sultan Chand*, 2008 SCC OnLine Del 1078: (2008) 106 DRJ 457.
8. *Venkateswara Construction Co.* v. *Union of India*, 2001 SCC OnLine AP 116: (2001) 1 AP LJ 141.
9. *Enercon (India) Ltd.* v. *Enercon Gmbh*, (2014) 5 SCC 1.
10. *Jagnesh Castor Industries* v. *Devi Leasing and Financing*, (1998) 1 WN 142 (MP).
11. *Unit Head, National Jute Manufacturers Corpn. Ltd.* v. *Saroj Agarwal*, 2007 SCC OnLine Pat 30.
12. *Narayan Prasad Lohia* v. *Nikunj Kumar Lohia*, (2002) 3 SCC 572.

has to be adjudicated by a sole arbitrator to be appointed by the procedure provided under Section 11(6) of the Act.[13]

If the two arbitrators agree and give a common award there is no frustration of the proceedings. In such a case their common opinion will prevail, even if the third arbitrator, presuming there was one, had differed. No party should be permitted to resile from such a common award.[14]

Where only two arbitrators have been appointed in the case and they deliver a common award, such a common award is valid, no party should be permitted to resile from such a common award.[15]

Parties have freedom to change the number of arbitrators

The parties have freedom to change the number of arbitrators even after the contract has been entered and by mutual consent the parties may amend the contract.[16]

Where the number of arbitrators not determined [Sub-s. (2)]

Section 10(2) makes it very clear that where the number of arbitrators is not determined, the Arbitral Tribunal shall consist of a sole arbitrator.[17]

Appointment of sole arbitrator

In *National Aluminium Co. Ltd.* v. *Metalimpex Ltd.*[18], an international arbitration agreement envisaged appointment of two arbitrators one by each party who, in turn, had to appoint an umpire. The respondent failed to nominate its arbitrator. The Supreme Court, having regard to the provisions of Sections 10 and 34(2)(*v*) of the Act, did not find it proper to appoint sole arbitrator in the absence of respondent's, representation before the court, and appointed a retired judge of the High Court as arbitrator in the case.

Where parties are not able to arrive at an understanding to identify a person to act as arbitrator, in view of the provision in sub-section (2) of Section 10 of the Act, sole arbitrator can be appointed by the court to resolve the inter se disputes arising out of the employment agreement.[19]

---

13. *National Council of Y.M.C. of India* v. *Sudhir Chandra Datt*, 2012 SCC OnLine MP 7880: (2013) 2 MP LJ 684.
14. *Narayan Prasad Lohia* v. *Nikunj Kumar Lohia*, (2002) 3 SCC 572.
15. *Ibid.*
16. *Sime Darby Engg. SDN. BHD.* v. *Engineers India Ltd.*, (2009) 7 SCC 545.
17. *Ibid*; *Citibank, N.A.* v. *TLC Mktg. PLC*, (2008) 1 SCC 481.
18. (2001) 6 SCC 372; see also, *National Aluminium Co. Ltd.* v. *Metalimpex Ltd.*, (2001) 6 SCC 372.
19. *Weiss Technik India (P) Ltd.* v. *Bollupalli Madhavilatha*, 2021 SCC OnLine TS 644.

Panel of three arbitrators appointed

The arbitration agreement contained a clause for appointment of a panel of three arbitrators if the claim was for more than ₹1 crore. In view of the clause, a panel of three arbitrators was appointed.[20]

Appointment of five or seven or more arbitrators—Procedure under Section 11 applicable "mutatis mutandis"

By agreement parties may provide for appointment of five or seven arbitrators. If they do not provide for a procedure for their appointment or there is failure of the agreed procedure, the agreement of the parties is not invalid. The procedure provided in Section 11 will apply *mutatis mutandis* for appointment of five or seven more arbitrators.[21]

Appointment of arbitrator at the instance of a party not covered by the arbitration clause

Where the arbitration clause in contract provided for resolution of commercial disputes between the public sector enterprises inter se and between public sector enterprises and government departments but one of the parties to contract was a private one, appointment of arbitrator at the instance of such private party was improper.[22]

Nationality of arbitrator(s) [Sub-s. (1) of S. 11]

The Arbitration and Conciliation Act, 1996 does not put any restriction on the nationality of the arbitrator to be appointed in the case. A person of any nationality may be an arbitrator, unless otherwise agreed by the parties.

"Procedure for appointing the arbitrator or arbitrators" [Sub-s. (2) of S. 11]

Subject to the provisions of sub-section (6) of Section 11, the parties are free to agree on a procedure for appointing the arbitrator or arbitrators. Where no agreement has arrived at between the parties, each party shall appoint one arbitrator and the two arbitrators, so appointed, shall appoint the third arbitrator who shall act as the presiding arbitrator. [Sub-Ss. (2) & (3)]

---

20. *GCC JV AEC* v. *Rajasthan Urban Infrastructure Development Program*, 2020 SCC OnLine Raj 2894.
21. *Narayan Prasad Lohia* v. *Nikunj Kumar Lohia*, (2002) 3 SCC 572.
22. *Eastern Coalfields Ltd.* v. *Sanjay Transport Agency*, (2009) 7 SCC 345.

Application for appointment of arbitrator by the LRs of the deceased partner—Maintainable

Application for appointment of arbitrator by the legal representative (son) of the deceased partner is maintainable in view of Section 40, Arbitration and Conciliation Act, 1996 and Sections 46 and 48, Partnership Act, 1932, more so, when the dispute had arisen before the death of the deceased partner. Merely because the Will was not probated would not affect the maintainability of the application.[23]

Appointment of arbitrator—Existence of arbitration agreement precedent

The existence of an arbitration agreement as defined in Section 7, Arbitration and Conciliation Act, 1996 is a condition precedent for the exercise of power to appoint an arbitrator/Arbitral Tribunal under Section 11 of the Act by the Chief Justice on his designate. It is not permissible to appoint an arbitrator to adjudicate the disputes between the parties in the absence of an arbitration agreement or mutual consent.[24] Clause in partition deed used the words "the dispute shall be referred for arbitration if the parties so determine", which meant that it is not an arbitration agreement as defined under Section 7 of the Act. The said clause required the consent of the parties before the dispute could be referred to arbitration.[25]

Award signed by even number of arbitrators

Award was signed by an even number of arbitrators. Objection was raised for the first time, in appeal. Objection was not taken before the Single Judge that the award could not have been signed in terms of Section 10(2), hence the Division Bench of the High Court declined to entertain the objection.[26]

APPOINTMENT OF ARBITRATORS [S. 11]

11. *Appointment of arbitrators.*—(1) A person of any nationality may be an arbitrator, unless otherwise agreed by the parties.

(2) Subject to sub-section (6), the parties are free to agree on a procedure for appointing the arbitrator or arbitrators.

(3) Failing any agreement referred to in sub-section (2), in an arbitration with three arbitrators, each party shall appoint one arbitrator, and the two appointed

23. *Ravi Prakash Goel* v. *Chandra Prakash Goel*, (2008) 13 SCC 667.
24. *Jagdish Chander* v. *Ramesh Chander*, (2007) 5 SCC 719.
25. *Ibid.*
26. *P.D. Khanna* v. *Ashwani Khanna*, 2008 SCC OnLine Del 875: (2008) 152 DLT 544.

arbitrators shall appoint the third arbitrator who shall act as the presiding arbitrator.

[27][(3-A) The Supreme Court and the High Court shall have the power to designate, arbitral institutions, from time to time, which have been graded by the Council under Section 43-I, for the purposes of this Act:

Provided that in respect of those High Court jurisdictions, where no graded arbitral institution are available, then, the Chief Justice of the concerned High Court may maintain a panel of arbitrators for discharging the functions and duties of arbitral institution and any reference to the arbitrator shall be deemed to be an arbitral institution for the purposes of this section and the arbitrator appointed by a party shall be entitled to such fee at the rate as specified in the Fourth Schedule:

Provided further that the Chief Justice of the concerned High Court may, from time to time, review the panel of arbitrators.]

(4) If the appointment procedure in sub-section (3) applies and—

(*a*) a party fails to appoint an arbitrator within thirty days from the receipt of a request to do so from the other party; or

(*b*) the two appointed arbitrators fail to agree on the third arbitrator within thirty days from the date of their appointment,

[28][the appointment shall be made, on an application of the party, by the arbitral institution designated by the Supreme Court, in case of international commercial arbitration, or by the High Court, in case of arbitrations other than international commercial arbitration, as the case may be.]

(5) Failing any agreement referred to in sub-section (2), in an arbitration with a sole arbitrator, if the parties fail to agree on the arbitrator within thirty days from receipt of a request by one party from the other party to so agree [29][the appointment shall be made on an application of the party in accordance with the provisions contained in sub-section (4).]

(6) Where, under an appointment procedure agreed upon by the parties,—

(*a*) a party fails to act as required under that procedure; or

(*b*) the parties, or the two appointed arbitrators, fail to reach an agreement expected of them under that procedure; or

---

27. *Ins.* by Act 33 of 2019, S. 3(*i*) (w.e.f. the date to be notified).

28. *Subs.* by Act 33 of 2019, S. 3(*ii*) (w.e.f. the date to be notified). Prior to substitution it read as:

"the appointment shall be made, upon request of a party, by the Supreme Court or, as the case may be, the High Court or any person or institution designated by such court".

29. *Subs.* by Act 33 of 2019, S. 3(*iii*) (w.e.f. the date to be notified). Prior to substitution it read as:

"the appointment shall be made, upon request of a party, by the Supreme Court or, as the case may be, the High Court or any person or institution designated by such court".

(*c*) a person, including an institution, fails to perform any function entrusted to him or it under that procedure,

[30][the appointment shall be made, on an application of the party, by the arbitral institution designated by the Supreme Court, in case of international commercial arbitration, or by the High Court, in case of arbitrations other than international commercial arbitration, as the case may be] to take the necessary measure, unless the agreement on the appointment procedure provides other means for securing the appointment.

(6-A) [31][* * *]

[32][(6-B) The designation of any person or institution by the Supreme Court or, as the case may be, the High Court, for the purposes of this section shall not be regarded as a delegation of judicial power by the Supreme Court or the High Court.]

(7) [33][* * *]

[34][(8) [35][The arbitral institution referred to in sub-sections (4), (5) and (6)], before appointing an arbitrator, shall seek a disclosure in writing from the prospective arbitrator in terms of sub-section (1) of Section 12, and have due regard to—

(*a*) any qualifications required for the arbitrator by the agreement of the parties; and

---

30. *Subs.* by Act 33 of 2019, S. 3(*iv*) (w.e.f. the date to be notified). Prior to substitution it read as:

"a party may request the Supreme Court or, as the case may be, the High Court or any person or institution designated by such court".

31. *Omitted* by Act 33 of 2019, S. 3(*v*) (w.e.f. the date to be notified). Prior to omission it read as:

"(6-A) The Supreme Court or, as the case may be, the High Court, while considering any application under sub-section (4) or sub-section (5) or sub-section (6), shall, notwithstanding any judgment, decree or order of any court, confine to the examination of the existence of an arbitration agreement."

32. *Ins.* by Act 3 of 2016, S. 6(*ii*) (w.r.e.f. 23-10-2015).

33. *Omitted* by Act 33 of 2019, S. 3(*v*) (w.e.f. the date to be notified). Prior to omission it read as:

"(7) A decision on a matter entrusted by sub-section (4) or sub-section (5) or sub-section (6) to the Supreme Court or, as the case may be, the High Court or the person or institution designated by such court is final and no appeal including Letters Patent Appeal shall lie against such decision."

34. *Subs.* by Act 3 of 2016, S. 6(*iv*) (w.r.e.f. 23-10-2015). Prior to substitution it read as:

"(8) The Chief Justice or the person or institution designated by him, in appointing an arbitrator, shall have due regard to—

(*a*) any qualifications required of the arbitrator by the agreement of the parties; and

(*b*) other considerations as are likely to secure the appointment of an independent and impartial arbitrator."

35. *Subs.* by Act 33 of 2019, S. 3(*vi*) (w.e.f. the date to be notified). Prior to substitution it read as:

"The Supreme Court or, as the case may be, the High Court or the person or institution designated by such court".

(*b*) the contents of the disclosure and other considerations as are likely to secure the appointment of an independent and impartial arbitrator.]

(9) In the case of appointment of sole or third arbitrator in an international commercial arbitration, [36][the arbitral institution designated by the Supreme Court] may appoint an arbitrator of a nationality other than the nationalities of the parties where the parties belong to different nationalities.

(10) [37][* * *]

[38][(11) Where more than one request has been made under sub-section (4) or sub-section (5) or sub-section (6) to different arbitral institutions, the arbitral institution to which the request has been first made under the relevant sub-section shall be competent to appoint.

(12) Where the matter referred to in sub-sections (4), (5), (6) and (8) arise in an international commercial arbitration or any other arbitration, the reference to

---

36. *Subs.* by Act 33 of 2019, S. 3(*vii*) (w.e.f. the date to be notified). Prior to substitution it read as:

"the Supreme Court or the person or institution designated by that court.

37. *Omitted* by Act 33 of 2019, S. 3(*viii*) (w.e.f. the date to be notified). Prior to omission it read as:

"(10) The Supreme Court or, as the case may be, the High Court, may make such scheme as the said court may deem appropriate for dealing with matters entrusted by sub-section (4) or sub-section (5) or sub-section (6), to it."

38. Sub-sections (11) to (14) *subs.* by Act 33 of 2019, S. 3(*ix*) (w.e.f. the date to be notified). Prior to substitution they read as:

"(11) Where more than one request has been made under sub-section (4) or sub-section (5) or sub-section (6) to different High Courts or their designates, the High Court or its designate to whom the request has been first made under the relevant sub-section shall alone be competent to decide on the request.

(12)(*a*) Where the matters referred to in sub-sections (4), (5), (6), (7), (8) and sub-section (10) arise in an international commercial arbitration, the reference to the "Supreme Court or, as the case may be, the High Court" in those sub-sections shall be construed as a reference to the "Supreme Court"; and

(*b*) where the matters referred to in sub-sections (4), (5), (6), (7), (8) and sub-section (10) arise in any other arbitration, the reference to "the Supreme Court or, as the case may be, the High Court" in those sub-sections shall be construed as a reference to the "High Court" within whose local limits the principal civil court referred to in clause (*e*) of sub-section (1) of Section 2 is situate, and where the High Court itself is the court referred to in that clause, to that High Court.

(13) An application made under this section for appointment of an arbitrator or arbitrators shall be disposed of by the Supreme Court or the High Court or the person or institution designated by such court, as the case may be, as expeditiously as possible and an endeavour shall be made to dispose of the matter within a period of sixty days from the date of service of notice on the opposite party.

(14) For the purpose of determination of the fees of the arbitral tribunal and the manner of its payment to the arbitral tribunal, the High Court may frame such rules as may be necessary, after taking into consideration the rates specified in the Fourth Schedule.

Explanation.—For the removal of doubts, it is hereby clarified that this sub-section shall not apply to international commercial arbitration and in arbitrations (other than international commercial arbitration) in case where parties have agreed for determination of fees as per the rules of an arbitral institution".

the arbitral institution in those sub-sections shall be construed as a reference to the arbitral institution designated under sub-section (3-A).

(13) An application made under this section for appointment of an arbitrator or arbitrators shall be disposed of by the arbitral institution within a period of thirty days from the date of service of notice on the opposite party.

(14) The arbitral institution shall determine the fees of the arbitral tribunal and the manner of its payment to the arbitral tribunal subject to the rates specified in the Fourth Schedule.

Explanation.—For the removal of doubts, it is hereby clarified that this sub-section shall not apply to international commercial arbitration and in arbitrations (other than international commercial arbitration) where parties have agreed for determination of fees as per the rules of an arbitral institution.].

COMMENTS

Corresponding old law

Sub-section (3) corresponds to Section 10(1), Arbitration Act, 1940.

Sub-section (4) corresponds to Section 8(1)(*c*) and Rule 2 of the First Schedule of the Arbitration Act, 1940.

UNCITRAL Model Law

Article 11. *Appointment of arbitrators*

(1) No person shall be precluded by reason of his nationality from acting as an arbitrator, unless otherwise agreed by the parties.

(2) The parties are free to agree on a procedure of appointing the arbitrator or arbitrators, subject to the provisions of paragraphs (4) and (5) of this article.

(3) Failing such agreement,

(*a*) in an arbitration with three arbitrators, each party shall appoint one arbitrator, and the two arbitrators thus appointed shall appoint the third arbitrator; if a party fails to appoint the arbitrator within thirty days of receipt of a request to do so from the other party, or if the two arbitrators fail to agree on the third arbitrator within thirty days of their appointment, the appointment shall be made, upon request of a party, by the court or other authority specified in article 6;

(*b*) in an arbitration with a sole arbitrator, if the parties are unable to agree on the arbitrator, he shall be appointed, upon request of a party, by the court or other authority specified in Article 6.

(4) Where, under an appointment procedure agreed upon by the parties,

(*a*) a party fails to act as required under such procedure, or (*b*) the parties, or two arbitrators, are unable to reach an agreement expected of them under such procedure, or

(*c*) a third party, including an institution, fails to perform any function entrusted to it under such procedure,

any party may request the court or other authority specified in article 6 to take the necessary measure, unless the agreement on the appointment procedure provides other means for securing the appointment.

(5) A decision on a matter entrusted by paragraph (3) or (4) of this article to the court or other authority specified in article 6 shall be subject to no appeal. The court or other authority, in appointing an arbitrator, shall have due regard to any qualifi cations required of the arbitrator by the agreement of the parties and to such considerations as are likely to secure the appointment of an independent and impartial arbitrator and, in the case of a sole or third arbitrator, shall take into account as well the advisability of appointing an arbitrator of a nationality other than those of the parties.

Legislative changes

Arbitration and Conciliation (Amendment) Act, 2015 (3 of 2016)

In Section 11 of the principal Act,—

(*i*) in sub-sections (4), (5) and (6), for the words "the Chief Justice or any person or institution designated by him" wherever they occur, the words "the Supreme Court or, as the case may be, the High Court or any person or institution designated by such court" shall be *substituted*;

(*ii*) after sub-section (6), the following sub-sections shall be *inserted*, namely—

"(6-A) The Supreme Court or, as the case may be, the High Court, while considering any application under sub-section (4) or sub-section (5) or sub-section (6), shall, notwithstanding any judgment, decree or order of any court, confine to the examination of the existence of an arbitration agreement.

(6-B) The designation of any person or institution by the Supreme Court or, as the case may be, the High Court, for the purposes of this section shall not be regarded as a delegation of judicial power by the Supreme Court or the High court.";

(*iii*) in sub-section (7), for the words "the Chief Justice or the person or institution designated by him is final", the words "the Supreme Court or, as the case may be, the High Court or the person or institution designated by such Court is final and no appeal including Letters Patent Appeal shall lie against such decision" shall be *substituted*;

(*iv*) for sub-section (8), the following sub-section shall be *substituted*, namely—

"(8) The Supreme Court or, as the case may be, the High Court or the person or institution designated by such Court, before appointing an arbitrator, shall seek a disclosure in writing from the prospective arbitrator in terms of sub-section (1) of Section 12, and have due regard to—

(*a*) any qualifications required for the arbitrator by the agreement of the parties; and

(*b*) the contents of the disclosure and other considerations as are likely to secure the appointment of an independent and impartial arbitrator.";

(*v*) in sub-section (9), for the words "the Chief Justice of India or the person or institution designated by him", the words "the Supreme Court or the person or institution designated by that court" shall be *substituted*;

(*vi*) for sub-section (10), the following sub-section shall be *substituted*, namely—

"(10) The Supreme Court or, as the case may be, the High Court, may make such scheme as the said court may deem appropriate for dealing with matters entrusted by sub-section (4) or sub-section (5) or sub-section (6), to it.";

(*vii*) in sub-section (11), for the words "the Chief Justices of different High Courts or their designates, the Chief Justice or his designate to whom the request has been first made", the words "different High Courts or their designates, the High Court or its designate to whom the request has been first made" shall be *substituted*;

(*viii*) for sub-section (12), the following sub-section shall be *substituted*, namely—

'(12)(*a*) Where the matters referred to in sub-sections (4), (5), (6), (7), (8) and sub-section (10) arise in an international commercial arbitration, the reference to the "Supreme Court or, as the case may be, the High Court" in those sub-sections shall be construed as a reference to the "Supreme Court"; and

(*b*) where the matters referred to in sub-sections (4), (5), (6), (7), (8) and sub-section (10) arise in any other arbitration, the reference to "the Supreme Court or, as the case may be, the High Court" in those sub-sections shall be construed as a reference to the "High Court" within whose local limits the principal civil court referred to in clause (*e*) of sub-section (1) of Section 2 is situate, and where the High Court itself is the court referred to in that clause, to that High Court.';

(*ix*) after sub-section (12), the following sub-sections shall be *inserted*, namely—

"(13) An application made under this section for appointment of an arbitrator or arbitrators shall be disposed of by the Supreme Court or the High Court or the person or institution designated by such court, as the case may be, as expeditiously as possible and an endeavour shall be made to dispose of the matter within a period of sixty days from the date of service of notice on the opposite party.

(14) For the purpose of determination of the fees of the arbitral tribunal and the manner of its payment to the arbitral tribunal, the High Court may frame such rules as may be necessary, after taking into consideration the rates specified in the Fourth Schedule.

Explanation.—For the removal of doubts, it is hereby clarified that this sub-section shall not apply to international commercial arbitration and in arbitrations (other than international commercial arbitration) in case where parties have agreed for determination of fees as per the rules of an arbitral institution.".

NOTES ON CLAUSES

Clause 6 of the Bill seeks to amend Section 11 of the principal Act to provide that the appointment of arbitrator shall be made by the Supreme Court or the High Court as the case may be instead of the Chief Justice of India or the Chief Justice of the High Court. Sub-section (6-A) is inserted to provide that the Supreme Court or the High Court while considering application under sub-section (4) to 6 shall confine to the examination of an arbitration agreement. In sub-section (7) it is clarified that the decision on a matter entrusted under sub-section (4) to (6) shall be final and no appeal including Letters Patent Appeal shall lie against such decision. A new sub-section (13) is inserted to provide that an application for appointment of arbitrator(s) shall be disposed of as expeditiously as possible and an endeavour shall be made to dispose of the matter within a period of sixty days from the date of service of notice on the opposite party. A new sub-section (14) is inserted to empower the High Court to frame rules for the purpose of determination of fees of the arbitral tribunal and the manner of such payment. The High Court while framing the rules shall take into account the rates of the fees specified in the Fourth Schedule.

Arbitration and Conciliation (Amendment) Act, 2019 (33 of 2019)

In Section 11 of the principal Act,—

(*i*) after sub-section (3), the following sub-section shall be inserted, namely:—

"(3-A) The Supreme Court and the High Court shall have the power to designate, arbitral institutions, from time to time, which have been graded by the Council under Section 43-I, for the purposes of this Act:

Provided that in respect of those High Court jurisdictions, where no graded arbitral institution are available, then, the Chief Justice of the concerned High Court may maintain a panel of arbitrators for discharging the functions and duties of arbitral institution and any reference to the arbitrator shall be deemed to be an arbitral institution for the purposes of this section and the arbitrator appointed by a party shall be entitled to such fee at the rate as specified in the Fourth Schedule:

Provided further that the Chief Justice of the concerned High Court may, from time to time, review the panel of arbitrators.";

(*ii*) in sub-section (4), in the long line, for the portion beginning with "the appointment shall be made" and ending with "designated by such Court", the following shall be substituted, namely:—

"the appointment shall be made, on an application of the party, by the arbitral institution designated by the Supreme Court, in case of international commercial arbitration, or by the High Court, in case of arbitrations other than international commercial arbitration, as the case may be";

(*iii*) in sub-section (5), for the portion beginning with "the appointment shall be made" and ending with "designated by such Court", the following shall be substituted, namely:—

"the appointment shall be made on an application of the party in accordance with the provisions contained in sub-section (4)";

(*iv*) in sub-section (6), in the long line, for the portion beginning with "party may request" and ending with "designated by such Court", the following shall be substituted, namely:—

"the appointment shall be made, on an application of the party, by the arbitral institution designated by the Supreme Court, in case of international commercial arbitration, or by the High Court, in case of arbitrations other than international commercial arbitration, as the case may be";

(*v*) sub-sections (6-A) and (7) shall be omitted;

(*vi*) in sub-section (8), for the words "The Supreme Court or, as the case may be, the High Court or the person or institution designated by such Court", the words, brackets and figures "The arbitral institution referred to in sub-sections (4), (5) and (6)" shall be substituted;

(*vii*) in sub-section (9), for the words "the Supreme Court or the person or institution designated by that Court", the words "the arbitral institution designated by the Supreme Court" shall be substituted;

(*viii*) sub-section (10) shall be omitted;

(*ix*) for sub-sections (11) to (14), the following sub-sections shall be substituted, namely:—

"(11) Where more than one request has been made under sub-section (4) or sub-section (5) or sub-section (6) to different arbitral institutions, the arbitral institution to which the request has been first made under the relevant sub-section shall be competent to appoint.

(12) Where the matter referred to in sub-sections (4), (5), (6) and (8) arise in an international commercial arbitration or any other arbitration, the reference to the arbitral institution in those sub-sections shall be construed as a reference to the arbitral institution designated under sub-section (3-A).

(13) An application made under this section for appointment of an arbitrator or arbitrators shall be disposed of by the arbitral institution within a period of thirty days from the date of service of notice on the opposite party.

(14) The arbitral institution shall determine the fees of the arbitral tribunal and the manner of its payment to the arbitral tribunal subject to the rates specified in the Fourth Schedule.

Explanation.—For the removal of doubts, it is hereby clarified that this sub-section shall not apply to international commercial arbitration and in arbitrations (other than international commercial arbitration) where parties have agreed for determination of fees as per the rules of an arbitral institution.".

Amendment Act (33 of 2019)—Enforcement

Section 11(6-A) amended by the Amending Act 33 of 2019 has not yet come into force as its coming into force has not been notified.[39]

Scope and application

Section 11 deals with the appointment of arbitrator(s). This is the most important section as with the appointment of arbitrators, the process of arbitration starts.

Unless otherwise agreed by the parties, a person of any nationality may be an arbitrator [S. 11(1)].

The parties are free to agree on a procedure for appointing the arbitrator or arbitrators [S. 11(2)].

The Supreme Court and the High Court shall have the power to designate arbitral institutions from time to time which have been graded by the Arbitral Council of India. In respect of those High Court jurisdictions where

39. *R.K. Construction India (P) Ltd.* v. *Hindustan Steel Works Construction Ltd.*, 2022 SCC OnLine All 1312: (2022) 6 All LJ 313.

no graded arbitral institution are available, the Chief Justice of the High Court concerned may maintain a panel of arbitrators for discharging the functions and duties of the arbitral institution. The Chief Justice may from time to time review the panel of arbitrators [S. 11(3-A)].

If a party fails to appoint an arbitrator within 30 days from the receipt of a request to do so from other party or the two appointed arbitrators fail to agree on the third arbitrator within 30 days from the date of their appointment, the appointment shall be made on the application of the party:

1. by the arbitral institution designated by the Supreme Court in the case of international commercial arbitration; or
2. by the High Court in the case of arbitrations other than international commercial arbitration as the case may be [S. 11(4)].

The same procedure would apply in the case of arbitration by a sole arbitrator [S. 11(5)].

Where (*a*) a party fails to act as required under the agreed procedure; or (*b*) the parties or the two appointed arbitrators fail to reach an agreement expected of them under that procedure; or (*c*) a person including an institution fails to perform any function entrusted to him or it under that procedure, the appointment shall be made, on an application of the party by the arbitral institution designated by the Supreme Court, in the case of international commercial arbitration, or by the High Court in case of arbitrations other than international commercial arbitration, to take the necessary measure, unless the agreement on the appointment procedure provides other means for securing the appointment [S. 11(6)].

In order to constitute a valid binding and enforceable arbitration agreement, the requirements contained in Section 7 have to be satisfied strictly. These requirements apart from others are: 1) there has to be an agreement; 2) it has to be in writing; 3) parties must sign such agreement, in other words, the agreement must bear the signatures of the parties concerned; and 4) such agreement must contain an arbitration clause. Failure to satisfy any of the four conditions would render the arbitration agreement invalid and unenforceable, and in consequence would result in dismissal of the application filed under Section 11, Arbitration and Conciliation Act, 1996 at its threshold.[40]

While dealing with petition under Section 11, the court by default would refer the matter when contentions relating to non-arbitrability are plainly arguable and in such case, the issue of non-arbitrability is left open to be decided by the Arbitral Tribunal.[41]

40. *Vimal Kishor Shah* v. *Jayesh Dinesh Shah*, (2016) 8 SCC 788.
41. *Mohd. Masroor Shaikh* v. *Bharat Bhushan Gupta*, (2022) 4 SCC 156.

Power exercised by the Chief Justice of India or his designate under Section 11(6) is not an administrative power.[42] Going by the general principles of law, the scheme of Section 11, the scheme of the Act as a whole and the object with which it was enacted replacing the Arbitration Act of 1940, it is difficult to call the order of the Chief Justice under Section 11(6), merely an administrative order.[43]

Under Section 7 of the 1996 Act, the parties to an arbitration agreement must agree to submit their disputes to arbitration. What is contemplated under the "solutions programme" is a mere possibility of the employee seeking arbitration as opposed to an obligation to refer all disputes to arbitration. An integral element of Section 7 of the 1996 Act is the agreement of the parties to be bound by the decision of the arbitrator. The same is not found in "solutions programme" which leaves the employee with an option to accept or reject the decision of the arbitrator. The petitioner was held not entitled to invoke the Supreme Court's jurisdiction under Section 11(6) of the 1996 Act.[44]

Sections 8 and 11

Sections 8 and 11, Arbitration and Conciliation Act are complementary provisions. The object and purpose behind the two provisions is identical to compel and force parties to abide by their contractual understanding. This being so, the two provisions should be read as laying down similar standards and not as laying down different and separate parameters. Section 11 does not prescribe any standard of judicial review by the court for determining whether an arbitration agreement is in existence. Section 8 states that the judicial review at the stage of reference is prima facie and not final. Prima facie standard equally applies when the power of judicial review is exercised by the court under Section 11, Arbitration and Conciliation Act. Therefore, we can read the mandate of valid arbitration agreement in Section 8 into the mandate of Section 11, *i.e.* "existence of an arbitration agreement".[45]

The law can be summarised as follows:

1. Sections 8 and 11, Arbitration and Conciliation Act have the same ambit with respect to judicial interference.
2. Usually, subject-matter arbitrability cannot be decided at the stage of Section 8 or Section 11 of the Act, unless it is a clear case of deadwood.

---

42. *Nandan Biomatrix Ltd.* v. *D 1 Oils Ltd.*, (2009) 4 SCC 495.
43. *SBP & Co.* v. *Patel Engg. Ltd.*, (2005) 8 SCC 618.
44. *Payal Chawla Singh* v. *Coca-Cola Co.*, (2015) 13 SCC 699.
45. *Vidya Drolia* v. *Durga Trading Corpn.*, (2021) 2 SCC 1.

3. The court, under Sections 8 and 11, has to refer a matter to arbitration or to appoint an arbitrator, as the case may be, unless a party has established a prima facie (summary findings) case of non-existence of valid arbitration agreement, by summarily portraying a strong case that he is entitled to such a finding.
4. The court should refer a matter if the validity of the arbitration agreement cannot be determined on a prima facie basis, as laid down above, *i.e.* "when in doubt, do refer".[46]

Modes of appointment of arbitrator

There are only two modes of appointment of a sole arbitrator: 1) by express agreement in writing between the parties, post the dispute, agreeing to waive the applicability of Section 12 of the Act; or 2) by order of appointment by the High Court under Section 11, Arbitration and Conciliation Act, 1996. If the appointment of a sole arbitrator is made other than by the above two modes, the appointment is ex facie bad and is in contravention of the provisions of the Act, which goes to the root of the matter, and the arbitrator becomes de jure ineligible to act as an arbitrator by the operation of law.[47]

Nomination of arbitrator

Arbitration clause in the agreement did not provide for appointment with the consent or consultation with parties to dispute. It contemplated one arbitrator to be appointed on nomination by the employer, one by contractor and third by the President of the International Chamber of Commerce. Appointment of another arbitrator in vacancy caused by the resignation of the first arbitrator appointed by the company was proper.[48] As the respondents failed to honour the agreement for referring the disputes to the arbitrator, application for appointment of arbitrator was allowed.[49]

Section 11 cannot be interpreted on the basis of UNCITRAL Model Law

The UNCITRAL Model Law was only taken into account in the drafting of the Arbitration and Conciliation Act, 1996 is apparent from the Statement of Objects and Reasons of the Act. The Act and the Model Law are not identically drafted. Under Section 11 the appointment of an arbitrator, in

46. *Ibid.*
47. *Hedge Finance (P) Ltd.* v. *Bijish Joseph*, 2022 SCC OnLine Ker 11064.
48. *State of U.P.* v. *Coromandal Engg. Co. Ltd.*, 2013 SCC OnLine All 13622: (2013) 3 All LJ 746.
49. *P. Jeevanandam C.P. Ponnurangam* v. *Union of India*, 1999 SCC OnLine AP 768: (2000) 1 AP LJ 510.

the event of a party to the arbitration failing to carry out his obligation to appoint an arbitrator, is to be made by the Chief Justice or any person or institution designated by him; under clause 11 of the Model Law it is to be made by a court. Section 34 of the Act is altogether different from clause 34 of the Model Law. The Model Law and judgments and literature thereon are, therefore, not a guide to the interpretation of the Act and especially Section 11 thereof.[50]

Territorial jurisdiction

Application under Section 11(6) for appointment of arbitrator to a court having no jurisdiction on the subject-matter of dispute is not maintainable.[51] Arbitration agreement between the parties executed at Lucknow, companies of the parties were established in Uttar Pradesh and the site of work was located outside Chennai. No part of cause of action arose to invoke the jurisdiction of the High Court at Chennai. It was held that the High Court at Lucknow had jurisdiction to appoint an arbitrator.[52]

Where, by the specific clause, parties conferred exclusive jurisdiction on the Delhi High Court for resolution of disputes, application for appointment of arbitrator is maintainable before the Delhi High Court, and not before the Gujarat High Court.[53]

Dispute arose between the parties about dealership agreement. Agreement between the parties conferred exclusive jurisdiction on court at Lucknow. Once an exclusive jurisdiction clause exists whether any objection is raised or not will not confer any jurisdiction upon any other court. Courts mentioned in the agreement clause alone shall have jurisdiction to try the case.[54] In cases where the seat of arbitration is mentioned under the arbitration clause, it is akin to exclusive jurisdiction clause. Clause in the arbitration agreement specified the place of arbitration to be Pune, Maharashtra. It was held, the Orissa High Court had no jurisdiction to appoint arbitrators under Section 11(6) of the Act.[55] The agreement provided that the seat of arbitration shall be at Patna in the State of Bihar. No part of cause of action had arisen within the territories of Telangana. Application under Section 11

---

50. *Konkan Railway Corpn. Ltd.* v. *Rani Construction (P) Ltd.*, (2002) 2 SCC 388.
51. *Project Engg. Corpn. Ltd.* v. *Doshion (P) Ltd., Gujarat*, 2020 SCC OnLine Ker 1822: (2020) 3 KLT 43.
52. *Sikta Inc.* v. *Mahindra Holidays & Resorts (P) Ltd.*, 2013 SCC OnLine All 1679: (2013) 4 All LJ 143.
53. *Unique Optical Fiber & Telecom Services (P) Ltd.* v. *Telecomunications Consultancy India Ltd.*, 2018 SCC OnLine Guj 316.
54. *Jain Automobiles H.P.C. Dealer* v. *Hindustan Petroleum Corpn. Ltd.*, 2020 SCC OnLine All 2242.
55. *SJ Biz Solution (P) Ltd.* v. *Sany Heavy Industry India (P) Ltd.*, 2020 SCC OnLine Ori 958: (2020) 130 CLT 890.

for appointment of arbitrator before the Telangana High Court was rejected.[56] Agreement was executed in Hyderabad and parties by agreement had conferred jurisdiction upon Hyderabad court. It was held, the courts at Hyderabad alone would have jurisdiction to appoint arbitrators, the jurisdiction of Uttarakhand High Court would be excluded.[57]

On review of the contract and the work order, it was found that the parties agreed to Delhi as the seat of arbitration. Gurugram courts were for the subject-matter of the dispute. In view of specific provision for arbitration, the Delhi court had territorial jurisdiction to exercise power under Section 11(6).[58]

Parties substituted a new contract and agreed to have their dispute resolved at Chennai excluding all other courts. It was held, High Court at Madras would have jurisdiction to entertain a petition for appointment of the arbitrator.[59]

Where the contract specifies the jurisdiction of the court at a particular place, only such court will have the jurisdiction to deal with the matter and parties intended to exclude all other courts. In the present case when the parties have agreed to have the "venue" of arbitration at Bhubaneswar, the Madras High Court erred in assuming the jurisdiction under Section 11(6) of the Act, since only Orissa High Court will have the jurisdiction to entertain the petition filed under Section 11(6) of the Act.[60]

Where the parties had not only expressly subjected themselves to "arbitration in accordance with the Arbitration and Conciliation Act, 1996" but also that "the place of the arbitration shall be New Delhi, India". Held, High Court Delhi has jurisdiction to appoint an arbitrator under Section 11(4).[61]

The Chief Justice or his designate will not allow any protracted argument on the question of territorial jurisdiction, unless, serious injustice occurred to the respondent by continuing the matter in a particular forum. Question of territorial jurisdiction is unimportant in context of Section 11 of the 1996 Act.[62]

---

56. *Indian Oil Corpn. Ltd.* v. *M. Kishore*, 2019 SCC OnLine TS 2083: (2019) 4 ALT 331.
57. *Shobit Enterprises* v. *Vijai Electricals Ltd.*, 2008 SCC OnLine Utt 146: (2009) 1 All LJ 349.
58. *S & S Technocrats (P) Ltd.* v. *Classic Infrasolutions (P) Ltd.*, (2021) 1 HCC (Del) 212.
59. *Jyoti Ltd.* v. *Marg Ltd.*, 2020 SCC OnLine Mad 28366.
60. *Brahmani River Pellets Ltd.* v. *Kamachi Industries Ltd.*, (2020) 5 SCC 462.
61. *Huawei Telecommunications (India) Co. (P) Ltd.* v. *WIPRO Ltd.*, (2022) 1 HCC (Del) 186.
62. *Sunrise Ore & Minerals (P) Ltd.* v. *Ore Cast (India)*, 2012 SCC OnLine Cal 8778: (2012) 4 Cal LT 250.

Only that court in whose jurisdiction the "cause of action" did arise will have jurisdiction to entertain an application either under Section 9 or under Section 11 of the Act. The overall circumstances on record and the nature of business that is being carried on and also the terms and conditions between the parties have to be taken into consideration for the purpose of "cause of action".[63] Tender was invited in Punjab, address in letter enclosing in bid was of Punjab. There was nothing in the agreement or the correspondence to suggest/support that the agreement was made, signed or executed in Delhi. Deposit of tax in Delhi does not form part of cause of action. Mere existence of an office within the jurisdiction of the court which is called upon to exercise jurisdiction, anything more, by itself, would not be sufficient to permit the court to exercise jurisdiction over the subject-matter of the litigation. Petition was dismissed.[64]

Sections 11 and 8, compared

While considering an application under Section 11, Chief Justice/designate does not embark upon "arbitrability" or appropriateness of adjudication by a private forum once he finds that there exists an arbitration agreement, and leaves the issue of arbitrability for decision of the Arbitral Tribunal. Whereas in a pending suit, in an application under Section 8, the court has to decide all aspects of arbitrability. It cannot be left to the decision of the arbitrator.[65]

Section 11(6) and Section 8—Relative scope

The expression used in Section 8 is "shall" and the judicial authority is bound to refer the matter to arbitration once the existence of a valid arbitration clause is established. Thus, the judicial authority is entitled to, has to and is bound to decide the jurisdictional issue raised before it, before making or declining to make a reference under Section 8. Section 11 only covers another situation: where one of the parties has refused to act in terms of the arbitration agreement, the other party moves the Chief Justice under Section 11 of the Act to have an arbitrator appointed and if the first party objects, it would be incongruous to hold that the Chief Justice cannot decide the question of his own jurisdiction to appoint an arbitrator when in a parallel situation, the judicial authority has to decide that question and his competence to decide cannot be questioned. If it is held that the Chief Justice had no right or duty to decide the question or cannot decide the question, it will lead to an anomalous situation in that a judicial authority

---

63. *Iron & Steel Co. Ltd.* v. *Tiwari Road Lines*, (2007) 5 SCC 703.
64. *Rattan Singh Associates (P) Ltd.* v. *Gill Power Generation Co. (P) Ltd.*, 2007 SCC OnLine Del 19.
65. *Booz Allen & Hamilton Inc.* v. *SBI Home Finance Ltd.*, (2011) 5 SCC 532.

under Section 8 can decide, but not a Chief Justice under Section 11, though the nature of the objection is the same and the consequence of accepting the objection in one case and rejecting it in the other is also the same, *namely*, sending the parties to arbitration.[66]

Application under Section 8 is for referring parties to arbitration whereas application under Section 11(6) is for appointment of arbitrator. Both provisions are independent and distinct for different causes of action.[67]

Appointment of arbitrator—Section 11 not governed by Section 42

Section 11 cannot be governed by Section 42. Section 42 of the Act will have no manner of operation on situs of subsequent request under Section 11 of the Act, since request has to be carried to High Court and not to District Court.[68]

It is inconceivable that when a request is taken to the High Court of a State where such High Court does not exercise original jurisdiction, that by virtue of Section 42 of the Act, future petitions and applications pertaining to the arbitration agreement have per force to be carried to such High Court.[69]

Notice under Section 21

Objection was raised that application under Section 11 for appointment of arbitrator cannot be allowed since the petitioner has not served any notice under Section 21 of the 1996 Act on the respondent. The objection was rejected. Section 21 merely lays down as to when the arbitral proceedings in respect of a particular dispute will be deemed to have commenced, which is when a request for dispute to be referred to the arbitration is received by the respondent. One cannot read into Section 21 any mandate to the effect that Section 11 application will not be maintainable unless a notice under Section 21 has been served by the petitioner on the respondent. An application under Section 11 of the 1996 Act is itself a request by the petitioner for arbitration.[70] Issuance of a valid notice under Section 21 for referring the dispute(s) between the parties to arbitration is a condition precedent for the commencement of the valid arbitral proceedings. There was unilateral

66. *SBP & Co.* v. *Patel Engg. Ltd.*, (2005) 8 SCC 618.
67. *Raman Feedmills* v. *Japfa Comfeeed India Ltd.*, 2013 SCC OnLine Bom 1493: (2014) 1 Mah LJ 356.
68. *Tapas Kumar Bhunia* v. *Jagadish Patra*, 2018 SCC OnLine Cal 15013: (2018) 5 CHN 85.
69. *Ibid.*
70. *Universal Consortium of Engineers (P) Ltd.* v. *Kanak Mitra*, 2021 SCC OnLine Cal 1425.

appointment of the arbitrator, arbitration proceedings held by the arbitrator were invalid.[71]

In terms of Section 21, Arbitration and Conciliation Act, 1996, the commencement of arbitral proceedings is incumbent on the receipt of request or notice. If no notice is received by the respondent concerned, there is no commencement of arbitral proceedings at all. The notice should not only be sent but also that the notice should be received.[72]

The purpose of notice under Section 21, Arbitration and Conciliation Act, 1996 is that the party to the arbitration agreement against whom a claim is made should know what the claims are. The notice under Section 21 provides an opportunity to such party to point out if some of the claims are time-barred or barred by law or untenable in fact or if there are counterclaims.[73]

After appointment of arbitrator, procedure is governed by Section 23. Objection by the opposite party that notice under Section 21 is mandatory, in the absence of notice petition under Section 11(6) was not maintainable, and was not tenable, hence was rejected.[74]

This section and Section 89 CPC

Section 89 has no application to proceedings under Section 11, Arbitration and Conciliation Act, 1996.[75]

Application for appointment of arbitrator filed prior to commencement of 1996 Act

In *U.P. State Sugar Corpn. Ltd.* v. *Jain Construction Co.*[76], disputes and differences between the parties arose in the year 1991. The respondent filed an application under Section 20 of the 1940 Act on 1 May 1991. It invoked the arbitration agreement. The arbitral proceeding was, therefore, set in motion within the meaning of Section 21 of the 1996 Act. In respect of the arbitral proceedings commenced before coming into force of the 1996 Act, the provisions of the 1940 Act shall apply. Therefore, in view of Section 85(2)(*a*) of the 1996 Act, the decision of the High Court that remedy under 1996 Act was available to the applicant was not sustainable, was set aside.

---

71. *Arun Kumar Bhunia* v. *Badal Midya*, 2019 SCC OnLine Cal 9410: (2019) 4 Cal LT 545.
72. *Shriram Transport Finance Co. Ltd.* v. *Narender Singh*, (2022) 6 HCC (Del) 275.
73. *Ibid.*
74. *Globe Detective Agencies (P) Ltd.* v. *Gammon India Ltd.*, 2019 SCC OnLine Mad 39355.
75. *Jagdish Chander* v. *Ramesh Chander*, (2007) 5 SCC 719.
76. (2004) 7 SCC 332.

Pendency of application under Section 8 before civil court

Mere pendency of an application under Section 8 before a civil court would not disentitle an application to have an arbitrator appointed in terms of Section 11, if the facts and circumstances of the case so warrant.[77]

Appointment of arbitrator—Jurisdiction of High Court

Cause of action arose within the State of Orissa, merely because the place of arbitration is referred as Bangalore, would not oust the jurisdiction of the Orissa High Court.[78]

Pendency of criminal case against petitioner—No embargo to appoint arbitrator

Mere fact of registration of a criminal case against the petitioner cannot act as an embargo on the adjudication of entitlement of petitioner for payment so as to hold up arbitration proceedings indefinitely. Arbitration proceedings can be conducted by taking into account the issue of registration of criminal cases in addition to any other issues that may legitimately arise.[79] After the amendment to Section 11, Arbitration and Conciliation Act, 1996 by Act 3 of 2016, the scope of inquiry under Section 11 is limited to whether there is an arbitration agreement between the parties and whether the dispute is manifestly non-arbitrable. In the case in hand, the parties admitted the existence of an arbitration agreement. The registration of a criminal case against the petitioner does not lead to the inference that the dispute between the parties is manifestly non-arbitrable. Arbitrator was appointed in the case.[80]

Filing of civil suit—Waiver of right to appoint arbitrator

Merely because a civil suit for partition of properties is pending, it would not amount to waiver of right to resolve partnership disputes through arbitration where there is partnership agreement between the parties for settlement of partnership disputes between the parties by resort to arbitration.[81]

---

77. *Akla Builders (P) Ltd.* v. *Cityscape Developers (P) Ltd.*, 1999 SCC OnLine Cal 608: (2000) 2 ICC 470.
78. *Ridhi Sidhi* v. *Levis Strauss (India) (P) Ltd.*, 2019 SCC OnLine Ori 358.
79. *China Railway Shisiju Gr. Corpn.* v. *NDMC*, (2015) 16 SCC 258.
80. *T.S. Thamilan* v. *R. Sampathkumar*, 2022 SCC OnLine Mad 155.
81. *Rekha Sebi* v. *Rosalind John*, 2022 SCC OnLine Ker 11061.

Pendency of proceedings under Insolvency and Bankruptcy Code, 2016 (IBC)

Mere pendency of proceedings under IBC cannot be treated as an embargo on court exercising jurisdiction under Section 11 of the Act of 1996.[82]

Pendency of proceedings before NCLT

Pendency of proceedings at the instance of minority shareholders for oppression and mismanagement before the National Company Law Tribunal (NCLT) is no bar in the appointment of arbitrators under Section 11(6).[83]

Pendency of vigilance inquiry no bar

Dispute was between parties as to non-payment of contractual amount by Railways to contractor. Vigilance inquiry was initiated regarding contracted work. Pendency of vigilance enquiry would not bar reference to arbitrator.[84]

Bar imposed under Section 59(3), Partnership Act, 1932 has no application to the arbitration proceedings as well as arbitration award.[85]

Partnership Act, 1932 [S. 69]

Section 69, Partnership Act, 1932 has no application to the proceedings of the arbitration as arbitral proceedings will not come under the expression "other proceedings" of Section 69(3), Partnership Act. The ban imposed under the said section can have no application to arbitration proceedings as well as arbitration award.[86] Arbitration proceedings do not fall within the bar contained in Section 69(3), Partnership Act and therefore Section 69 shall have no application to the arbitral proceeding. Application for appointment of arbitrator by the members of an unregistered partnership firm is maintainable, and not barred.[87]

Dispute arose between the parties as the respondents had acted in contravention of the conditions of partnership deed. Respondents disputed every execution of the partnership deed. It was held, arbitrator cannot be appointed in such cases, the proper remedy is to approach the civil court and establish the execution of partnership deed.[88]

82. *Jasani Realty (P) Ltd.* v. *Vijay Corpn.*, 2022 SCC OnLine Bom 879: (2022) 6 Mah LJ 240.
83. *VGP Marine Kingdom (P) Ltd.* v. *Kay Ellen Arnold*, (2023) 1 SCC 597.
84. *Girraj Ji Stone Crushers (P) Ltd.* v. *Union of India*, 2016 SCC OnLine Raj 9234: (2017) 2 WLC 120.
85. *Umesh Goel* v. *H.P. Coop. Group Housing Society Ltd.*, (2016) 11 SCC 313; *Ananthesh Bhakta* v. *Nayana S. Bhakta*, (2017) 5 SCC 185.
86. *Umesh Goel* v. *H.P. Coop. Group Housing Society Ltd.*, (2016) 11 SCC 313.
87. *Vishal Bhavan* v. *H.N. Jayashankar*, 2019 SCC OnLine Kar 2181: ILR 2020 Kar 111.
88. *Narendra Singh* v. *Ashendra Mishra*, 2020 SCC OnLine MP 3204: (2020) 4 MP LJ 169.

Where the partnership firm was not registered, disputes raised were not between the parties to arbitration agreement alone, were much beyond scope of the arbitration clause of the partnership deed, application for appointment of arbitrator was held hit by Section 69, Partnership Act, 1932.[89]

Unregistered firm—Appointment of arbitrator

Suit for dissolution of a firm or for accounts of a dissolved firm is saved from bar under Section 69(3), Partnership Act, 1932 and is maintainable. Arbitrator can be appointed for adjudication of disputes.[90]

Non-registration of the petitioner firm would not be a bar under Section 69, Partnership Act for institution of proceedings under Section 11 of the 1996 Act. Arbitrator was appointed in the case.[91]

District Judges may not be designated to perform functions under Section 11(6)

Designation of a District Judge as the authority under Section 11(6) of the Act by the Chief Justice of the High Court is not warranted on the scheme of the Act. Where District Judges had been designated by the Chief Justice of the High Court under Section 11(6) of the Act, the appointment orders thus far made by them will be treated as valid; but applications, if any, pending before them as on this date will stand transferred, to be dealt with by the Chief Justice of the High Court concerned or a designated judge of that court by the Chief Justice.[92]

The Chief Justice of the High Court cannot designate District Judge to perform functions under Section 11(6).[93]

"Locus standi" to file application under Section 11(6)

Party *M* originally was not party to the arbitration agreement, nor was made party thereto as per procedure prescribed in the agreement. *M* had later acquired some shareholding which was bought by the party objecting to the *locus standi* of *M*. *M* having acquired and becoming wholly owned subsidiary of one of the original parties to the contract and which was one of

89. *Kiran Agrawal* v. *Ashok Kr. Agrawal*, 2013 SCC OnLine All 13334: (2013) 100 ALR 482.
90. *Jagdish Chandra Gupta* v. *Kajaria Traders (India) Ltd.*, 1964 SCC OnLine SC 50; *Monojit Das* v. *Sujit Roy Chowdhury*, 2017 SCC OnLine Cal 3781, relied on.
91. *Jayamurugan Granite Exports* v. *SQNY Granites*, 2015 SCC OnLine Mad 6848: (2015) 4 LW 385.
92. *SBP & Co.* v. *Patel Engg. Ltd.*, (2005) 8 SCC 618.
93. *Ibid.*

the co-applicants in application under Section 11(6), had *locus standi* to file application under Section 11(6) for appointment of the arbitrator.[94]

Petitioner-company had entered into a distributorship agreement for supply of prawn feed to the respondent-company. Arbitration clause in the agreement required the petitioner-company only refer disputes to arbitration and no liberty to seek adjudication of disputes by arbitration was granted to the respondent-company. In view of the arbitration clause, respondent-company had no locus to refer matter to arbitration for adjudication of dispute. Order of the High Court appointing arbitrator on the behest of the respondent was set aside.[95]

On the death of the deceased partner who was signatory to the partnership agreement, his son being his heir and legal representative was held legally competent to enforce the said agreement and raise dispute for reference to arbitration. Objection as to the locus of the son to raise dispute/demand arbitration was rejected.[96]

Right of legal representative to invoke arbitration clause on the death of member of firm

Deceased had executed a registered Will leaving his assets and properties to his legal representatives. Arbitration agreement is not discharged by the death of any party, can be enforced by his/her legal representative. Death of parties does not end the provision pertaining to arbitration. Legal representative can invoke an arbitration clause.[97]

Arbitration agreement is not discharged by death of any party and is enforceable by or against legal representatives of the deceased. Arbitration agreement in the form of partnership deed existed and legal representatives of the deceased are bound by it as per Section 40. Arbitrator was appointed by the court.[98]

"Failing any agreement referred to in Sub-s. (2)" [Sub-s. (3)]

The opening part of Section 11(3) and (5) use the expression "failing any agreement referred to in sub-section (2)". Therefore, Section 11(3) and (5) will come into play only when there is no agreement between the parties as is referred to in Section 11(2), *viz.* that the parties have not agreed on a

94. *Tata Industries Ltd.* v. *Grasim Industries Ltd.*, (2008) 10 SCC 187.
95. *Sundarban Marine Products (P) Ltd.* v. *Waterbase Ltd.*, (2017) 14 SCC 182.
96. *Sushil Kumar Ojha* v. *Shesh Narayan Tripathi*, 2014 SCC OnLine All 15226: (2014) 4 All LJ 734; *Parwati Devi* v. *Kesarwani & Co.*, 2011 SCC OnLine All 786: (2011) 4 All LJ 463. (Legal representation can invoke arbitration clause.)
97. *Parwati Devi* v. *Kesarwani & Co.*, 2011 SCC OnLine All 786: (2011) 4 All LJ 463.
98. *Papiya Mukherjee* v. *Aruna Banerjea*, 2022 SCC OnLine Cal 595.

procedure for appointing the arbitrator or arbitrators. If the parties have agreed on a procedure for appointing arbitrator or arbitrators, Section 11(3) and (5) can have no application.[99]

International arbitrations—Application if to be heard by two judges of Supreme Court

Order 7 Rule 1 of the Supreme Court Rules, 1966 is inapplicable and applications are not to be heard by a Bench of two judges of the Supreme Court. The power under Section 11(6) exercisable by the Chief Justice under Section 11(6) of the 1996 Act is not the power of the Supreme Court under the Constitution.[100]

Appointment of arbitrator by court—Matters to be considered

Before appointment of arbitrator, the Chief Justice or his designate has to consider: 1) whether the party making application approached the appropriate court; and 2) existence of arbitration agreement and whether the party that has applied for appointment of arbitrator is party to such agreement. However, said proceedings before Chief Justice or his designate being summary in nature, wider examination of the matters is not warranted.[101]

It is well settled that the power under Section 11(6) of the Act is judicial power. The designated judge has to consider the claim of both the parties to the matter and pass a reasoned order. Existence of arbitration agreement is a condition precedent before exercise of powers under Section 11(6) of the Act. The preliminary matters to be considered by the court are: 1) existence of arbitration agreement; 2) territorial jurisdiction; 3) whether there are live issues to be referred to the arbitrator; and 4) whether application is filed within the period of limitation prescribed by the law. If the court finds that the arbitration agreement does not exist or is rescinded, then the prayer for referring the dispute to the arbitrator will have to be rejected.[102]

The scope of Section 11 petition is limited to testing the existence of an arbitration agreement. No party can be compelled to enter into a contract. The court cannot rewrite a contract either. The court cannot bring into existence an arbitration agreement, which is otherwise not in existence between the parties, much less in a petition under Section 11, Arbitration and Conciliation Act.[103]

---

99. *Iron & Steel Co. Ltd.* v. *Tiwari Road Lines*, (2007) 5 SCC 703.
100. *Rodemadan India Ltd.* v. *International Trade Expo Centre Ltd.*, (2006) 11 SCC 651.
101. *Indowind Energy Ltd.* v. *Wescare (I) Ltd.*, (2010) 5 SCC 306.
102. *Speech and Software Technologies (India) (P) Ltd.* v. *Neos Interactive Ltd.*, (2009) 1 SCC 475.
103. *S.M.R. Nagarajan* v. *N. Navamani*, 2020 SCC OnLine Mad 28224: (2020) 2 CTC 710.

In deciding an application under Section 11(6), Arbitration and Conciliation Act, 1996 what the Chief Justice or his designate does is to put the arbitration proceedings in motion by appointing an arbitrator and it is for that purpose that the finding is given in respect of the existence of the arbitration clause, the territorial jurisdiction, live issue and the limitation. Unless there is a finding given on these issues, there would be no question of proceeding with the arbitration.[104] For the purpose of deciding whether the arbitral procedure is to be set into motion or not, the Chief Justice or his designate has to examine and record his satisfaction that an arbitration agreement exists between the parties and that in respect of the agreement a live issue, to be decided between the parties, still exists. On being so satisfied, he may allow the application and appoint an Arbitral Tribunal or a sole arbitrator, as the case may be. However, if he finds and is convinced that the claim is a dead one or is patently barred by time, he may hold so and decline the request for appointment of an arbitrator.[105] Where the Chief Justice comes to a finding that there exists a live issue, then naturally this finding would include a finding that the respective claims of the parties have not become barred by limitation.[106]

In exercising jurisdiction under Section 11, the court has to only examine if there is an existence of the arbitration agreement, and whether there exist arbitral disputes which are required to be adjudicated. The court cannot, at this preliminary stage, venture into deciding the disputes arising between the parties.[107] Where the High Court did not hold preliminary inquiry on whether the dispute was arbitrable or not, the Supreme Court remitted the matter to the High Court for deciding the application under Section 11(5) and (6) afresh.[108]

The filing of a petition before the NCLT by the petitioner's Directors alleging oppression and mismanagement, does not mean that contractual disputes cannot be submitted to arbitration. Equally misconceived is the objection that allegations against the respondent's Directors permeates the memorandum of understanding (MOU) and renders it void. The court is not evaluating the contentions relating to the merits of the dispute at this stage. The respondent is free to urge all pleas/objections relating to such claims before the arbitrator in accordance with law.[109]

---

104. *Shree Ram Mills Ltd.* v. *Utility Premises (P) Ltd.*, (2007) 4 SCC 599.
105. *DHV BV* v. *Tahal Consulting Engineers Ltd.*, (2007) 8 SCC 321.
106. *Shree Ram Mills Ltd.* v. *Utility Premises (P) Ltd.*, (2007) 4 SCC 599.
107. *IMZ Corporate (P) Ltd.* v. *MSD Telematics (P) Ltd.*, (2021) 2 HCC (Del) 414.
108. *Emaar (India) Ltd.* v. *Tarun Aggarwal Projects LLP*, 2022 SCC OnLine SC 1328.
109. *IMZ Corporate (P) Ltd.* v. *MSD Telematics (P) Ltd.*, (2021) 2 HCC (Del) 414.

The court while appointing the arbitrator is not concerned with the allegations or controversies in the dispute and does not adjudicate them. Those are the matters to be raised before the Arbitral Tribunal.[110]

Even if a contract is void, or even if a contract/agreement is terminated or even if an agreement is invalid or even if the arbitration clause itself is invalid, the jurisdiction to appoint arbitrator vested in the Chief Justice or his designate is not taken away. The construction of an arbitration clause should start from the assumption that the parties are likely to have intended that any dispute arising out of the relationship into which they have entered or purported to enter, has to be decided by the same tribunal.[111]

Once the existence of an arbitration agreement itself is questioned by the party to proceeding under Section 11, the Chief Justice/designate should decide about the existence of a valid arbitration agreement between parties as well.[112]

Once an arbitration clause is incorporated in the agreement, the High Court is only required to confine its consideration as to whether an arbitration agreement exists. If a dispute arises between the parties and there is difference of opinion between the parties on who should be arbitrator, the High Court should step in and appoint an arbitrator.[113]

Recourse to Section 11(6) can be had only where the parties have agreed on a procedure for appointment of an arbitrator and if the conditions enumerated in clause (*a*) or (*b*) or (*c*) of this sub-section are satisfied. In *Iron & Steel Co. Ltd.* v. *Tiwari Road Lines*[114], there being an agreed procedure for resolution of disputes by arbitration in accordance with the Rules of Arbitration of the Indian Council of Arbitration, Section 11(3), (4) and (5) can have no application. Furthermore, the respondent did not make any effort to have the dispute settled by arbitration in accordance with the Rules of Arbitration of the Indian Council of Arbitration. On the contrary, it straightway moved an application under Section 11. The application moved by the respondent was clearly not maintainable and the court had no jurisdiction to entertain such an application and pass any order.

Sections 8 and 11 were amended pursuant to a detailed Law Commission Report being the 246th Law Commission Report on Arbitration. The net result of the amendments and judicial interpretation thereof, is that while considering any application under Section 8 or Section 11 of the 1996 Act,

110. *Pothens Vehicles & Service (P) Ltd.* v. *Honda Cars India Ltd.*, (2021) 2 HCC (Del) 515.
111. *Krebs Biochemicals & Industries Ltd.* v. *Nannapaneni Venkatrao Coop. Sugars Ltd.*, 2009 SCC OnLine AP 391: (2009) 3 AP LJ 220.
112. *Reva Electric Car Co. (P) Ltd.* v. *Green Mobil*, (2012) 2 SCC 93.
113. *Weiss Technik India (P) Ltd.* v. *Bollupalli Madhavilatha*, 2021 SCC OnLine TS 644.
114. (2007) 5 SCC 703.

the court is to confine itself to the prima facie examination of the existence of an arbitration agreement and leave all other preliminary issues to be decided by the arbitrator. Prima facie examination of the existence of an arbitration agreement, which is what the court must restrict itself to while considering reference of the matter to arbitration under Section 8 or appointment of an arbitrator under Section 11 of the 1996 Act, is not full review but a primary first review to weed out manifestly and ex facie non-existent and invalid arbitration agreements and non-arbitrable disputes. The prima facie review at the reference stage is to cut the deadwood and trim off the side branches in straightforward cases where dismissal is barefaced and pellucid and when on the facts and law the litigation must stop at the first stage. Only when the court is certain that no valid arbitration agreement exists or the disputed subject-matter is not arbitrable, the application under Section 8 or Section 11 would be rejected. At this stage, the court should not get lost in thickets and decide debatable questions of facts. Referral proceedings are preliminary and summary and not a mini trial.[115]

The court is not supposed to undertake a meager cosmetic exercise to examine the existence and/or validity of an arbitration agreement and simply refer the matter to arbitration just because the arbitration clause is valid. If it is manifestly evident on face of contract/agreement that issues purported to be referred to arbitration are hopelessly time barred and/or are non-arbitrable, courts can intervene and decline reference to arbitration in such cases. Application for reference of dispute to arbitration was rejected.[116]

Invocation of arbitration clause

Section 11 shows that the appointment of an arbitrator designated by the Chief Justice can only be resorted to when one of the parties fail to appoint an arbitrator on the demand being made by the other party or when they do not agree for the arbitrator. Thus, for the appointment of the arbitrator by the Chief Justice or his designate, invocation of the arbitration clause is necessary.[117] In the absence of invocation of an arbitration clause, it is not within the domain of the Chief Justice or the person designated to refer the dispute to an arbitrator or to appoint an arbitrator, the petition seeking an arbitrator to the Chief Justice/person designate would not be maintainable.[118]

115. *Pravin Electricals (P) Ltd.* v. *Galaxy Infra & Engg. (P) Ltd.*, (2021) 5 SCC 671.
116. *B.K. Consortium Engineers (P) Ltd.* v. *Indian Institute of Management*, 2023 SCC OnLine Cal 124.
117. *Abdul Rashid* v. *National Building Construction Corpn.*, 2012 SCC OnLine All 730: (2012) 5 All LJ 370; *Shyam Kishor Gupta* v. *Bharat Sarkar*, 2020 SCC OnLine All 2185: (2020) 3 All LJ 499 (All).
118. *Abdul Rashid* v. *National Building Construction Corpn.*, 2012 SCC OnLine All 730: (2012) 5 All LJ 370.

In *Abdul Rashid* v. *National Building Construction Corpn.*[119], the petitioner directly filed an application before the Chief Justice/person designated for the appointment of the arbitrator without invoking the arbitration clause. Application for appointment of arbitrator was not maintainable, was dismissed.

Necessity of full compliance with the procedure provided for the agreement

An application for appointment of an arbitrator is not maintainable unless the procedure and mechanism agreed to by and between the parties is complied with. The applicant had not appointed its arbitrator, the respondent had also not been called upon to appoint its arbitrator by notice or otherwise. It was held, the applicant's application for appointment of arbitrator was not maintainable as such was dismissed.[120] The petitioner had not averred that he had given notice to the opposite party for the appointment of the arbitrator and that the opposite party had not agreed to appointment of named arbitrator. Rather on the date of filing of petition, the opposite party had already appointed the arbitrator. The court held, the condition precedent for the appointment of the arbitrator did not exist as such the application for the appointment of the arbitrator was not maintainable.[121] In *Municipal Corpn., Jabalpur* v. *Rajesh Construction Co.*[122], the arbitration clause provided for deposit of security amount with the appointing authority before the Arbitration Board would be constituted by it. The applicant had not deposited the said security, thus had not complied with the procedure for appointment of arbitrator fully, application for appointment of arbitrator was liable to be rejected.

Where the petitioner files a petition under Section 11 for appointment of arbitrator without exhausting the procedure contained in the arbitration agreement, by seeking appointment of arbitrator by the nominated authority, the arbitration petition shall be rejected.[123]

---

119. 2012 SCC OnLine All 730: (2012) 5 All LJ 370.
120. *India Household and Healthcare Ltd.* v. *LG Household and Healthcare Ltd.*, (2007) 5 SCC 510; *Municipal Corpn., Jabalpur* v. *Rajesh Construction Co.*, (2007) 5 SCC 344; *Iron & Steel Co. Ltd.* v. *Tiwari Road Lines*, (2007) 5 SCC 703.
121. *Kanpur Development Authority* v. *U.P. Builders*, 2011 SCC OnLine All 368: (2011) 4 All LJ 407.
122. (2007) 5 SCC 344.
123. *Wipra Finance Ltd.* v. *SRG Infotech (India) Ltd.*, 2005 SCC OnLine Del 1303: (2005) 85 DRJ 530.

Unilateral appointment of arbitrator

There cannot be unilateral appointment of an arbitrator and in case, if other party is objecting to the name of an arbitrator appointed by one of the parties, then the arbitrator is not competent to enter the reference. According to agreement, dispute was to be resolved through arbitration process by appointing a sole arbitrator. On filing of applications under Section 11 by both parties, sole arbitrator was appointed by the court.[124]

Existence of arbitration agreement/arbitration clause, necessary

Reference to arbitration under Section 7, Arbitration and Conciliation Act, 1996 is not possible in the absence of arbitration agreement.[125] Where no arbitration clause exists between the parties though recommendation is made for appointment of arbitrator which is not accepted by the opposite party, the arbitrator cannot be appointed by the court.[126] Where the arbitration clause is not in existence as contemplated under Section 7, arbitrator cannot be appointed.[127]

Written agreement containing arbitration clause

An application under sub-section (6) of Section 11 shall be maintainable only in a case where there is a contract between the parties containing the arbitration agreement and the appointment procedure is prescribed and is agreed upon in writing. In the present case, the sole arbitrator was appointed by the parties themselves by mutual consent and in the absence of any written contract containing the arbitration agreement. Therefore, application under Section 11(6) of the Act, 1996 in absence of any written agreement containing arbitration agreement was not maintainable at all.[128]

Mere use of the word "arbitration" in the heading in a clause of the agreement between the parties in the present proceedings would not lead to the inference that there exists an agreement between the parties seeking resolution of disputes through arbitration.[129] In one of the clauses of agreement in the bracket portion, arbitration was mentioned. It was held,

---

124. *Deekshaa Infosystems (P) Ltd.* v. *AGS Transact Technologies Ltd.*, 2023 SCC OnLine Bom 2892.
125. *M.P. Rural Road Development Authority* v. *L.G. Chaudhary Engineers & Contractors*, (2012) 3 SCC 495; *Kvaerner Cementation India Ltd.* v. *Bajranglal Agarwal*, (2012) 5 SCC 214; *R.D. Builders (P) Ltd.* v. *Kanpur Development Authority*, 2020 (6) All LJ 349 (All).
126. *Ibid.*
127. *Ritika Agencies* v. *Add Corpn. Ltd.*, 2012 SCC OnLine All 664: (2012) 5 All LJ 51; *Mahanadi Coalfields Ltd.* v. *IVRCL AMR Joint Venture*, 2022 SCC OnLine SC 960.
128. *Swadesh Kumar Agarwal* v. *Dinesh Kumar Agarwal*, (2022) 10 SCC 235.
129. *Foomill (P) Ltd.* v. *Affle (India) Ltd.*, (2022) 2 HCC (Del) 98.

the clause was not an arbitration clause. Application for appointment of arbitrator was rejected.[130]

The question whether there exists an arbitration agreement cannot be decided in a vacuum and without reference to the subject disputes. In one sense, if it is found that the disputes are outside the scope of the arbitration clause, an arbitration agreement for adjudicating the disputes in question, the arbitration clause can be considered to be not in existence. The standards of examination under Section 11, Arbitration and Conciliation Act, 1996 are limited. The limited scope of examination under Section 11, Arbitration and Conciliation Act, 1996, also includes an ex facie view on the question whether the disputes are arbitrable and whether the parties are required to be relegated to arbitration.[131]

Whether or not the disputes alleged fall within the scope of arbitration agreement can be seen by a referring court but purely on a prima facie basis, addressing the following questions: (*i*) Is the arbitration agreement restricted only to certain specified disputes or is it worded in a manner so as to include within its fold any and all disputes arising from an agreement? (*ii*) Do the contentions and counter-contentions raised by the parties emanate from their relationship under the agreement or outside of it? (*iii*) Are the disputes per se non-arbitrable, which would be so if the disputes are such that they are required to be dealt with *in rem* and not *in personam*?[132]

An application under sub-section (6) of Section 11 shall be maintainable only in a case where there is a contract between the parties and containing the arbitration agreement and the appointment procedure is prescribed and is agreed upon in writing.[133]

Where the commercial offer of the petitioner containing arbitration clause for resolution of disputes was accepted by the respondent through email and correspondence exchanged between the parties and finally charter party agreement was entered into by them, arbitration clause did not suffer from vice of being unclear, absence of formal signed agreement was not significant.[134]

Clause 12 of the MOU between the parties provided that any decision to be taken by the specified mediators/arbitrators during the period of the entire transaction in the event of any breaches committed by either of the

---

130. *Contec Airflow (I) (P) Ltd.* v. *Rajasthan Drags and Pharmaceuticals Ltd.*, 2018 SCC OnLine Raj 3450: (2018) 2 WLC 633.
131. *Avantha Holdings Ltd.* v. *CG Power & Industrial Solutions Ltd.*, (2021) 4 HCC (Del) 267.
132. *Epsilon Eduventures (P) Ltd.* v. *Nikhil Goel*, (2022) 3 HCC (Del) 455.
133. *Swadesh Kumar Agarwal* v. *Dinesh Kumar Agarwal*, (2022) 10 SCC 235.
134. *Trimex International FZE Ltd.* v. *Vedanta Aluminium Ltd.*, (2010) 3 SCC 1.

parties shall be final and binding on all the parties. The court analysed the various clauses of the MOU and held that the specified persons though styled as mediators/arbitrators were escrow agents who had been appointed to ensure a successful completion of the transaction contained in MOU. The language used in the MOU was loose. The two escrow agents were not persons who had to decide disputes after hearing the parties and observing the principles of natural justice. The wording of the agreement was inconsistent with the view that the agreement intended that the disputes be decided by arbitration.[135]

It was clear from a reading of the arbitration clause that the parties were ad-idem to amicably settle their disputes or settle the disputes through an arbitrator in India/UAE. There was apparently some ambiguity caused by the language of the arbitration clause. Once the correspondence between the parties and the attendant circumstances are read conjointly with the petition of the petitioner and with particular reference to the purchase contract, it becomes evident that the parties had an agreement in writing and were ad-idem in their intention to refer these matters to an arbitrator in accordance with the provisions of the Act. Petition for appointment of arbitrator was allowed, a retired High Court judge was appointed arbitrator in the case.[136]

Where an arbitration clause exists in the partnership deed, in considering application for appointment of arbitrator, the court cannot go beyond examination of case for determining existence of arbitration agreement. Arbitrator was appointed in the case.[137]

The court has to consider that prima facie, there exists an arbitration agreement in writing. If there is any challenge to the genuineness of the document or any issue of threat and coercion in signing the documents, the parties are at liberty to raise these issues before the arbitrator.[138]

Dispute handling clause between the parties provided that the disputes should be settled through consultation and if the consultation fails "by treatment of to the arbitration body for arbitration or the court". It was held that the dispute handling clause referred to arbitration or court and thus there was an option, *i.e.* either to go for arbitration or for litigation in a court of law. Petitioner invoked arbitration, sole arbitrator was appointed in the case.[139]

---

135. *Shyam Sunder Agarwal* v. *P. Narotham Rao*, (2018) 8 SCC 230.
136. *Powertech World Wide Ltd.* v. *Delvin International General Trading LLC*, (2012) 1 SCC 361.
137. *Mohd. Ahmed Ali Khan* v. *Candy Children's Hospital*, 2019 SCC OnLine TS 3672.
138. *Esha Kedia* v. *Milan R. Parekh*, (2022) 6 HCC (Del) 184.
139. *Zhejiang Bonly Elevator Guide Rail Manufacture Co. Ltd.* v. *Jade Elevator Components*, (2018) 9 SCC 774.

Dispute between the parties relating to and arising of four purchase orders, was covered by the arbitration clause contained in the first purchase order between the company and the contractor. Arbitrator was appointed in the case.[140]

In a petition under Section 11 for appointment of arbitrator, dispute regarding existence and validity of arbitration agreement cannot be adjudicated upon by a Single Judge of the High Court as designate of the Chief Justice acting administratively under Section 11 and by Division Bench of the High Court exercising powers under Article 226. Section 16 empowers the Arbitral Tribunal to decide the question of existence and validity of the arbitration agreement.[141] These are the questions that must be left to be decided by the arbitrator.[142]

There was a dispute between the petitioner, a foreign company and the respondent, and therefore, an "international commercial arbitration" within the meaning of Section 2(1)(*f*) of the Act. There was a dispute between the parties where both parties were subject to an arbitration agreement. The appointed arbitrators had failed to reach an agreement upon a Chairperson/presiding arbitrator of the Arbitral Tribunal. Hence, all the preliminary conditions specified in Section 11(6) and the *SBP case*[143] had been met. A retired judge of the Supreme court was appointed as Chairman/presiding judge of the Arbitral Tribunal.[144]

Where both the development agreement and the MOU between the developer and the owner of the land provided an arbitration clause, an arbitrator was appointed by the court.[145]

First arbitrator appointed by the party having the right to appoint arbitrators under the agreement had resigned. Respondent filed application in the High Court for the appointment of the new arbitrator. During pendency of the said application, the appellant had appointed a new arbitrator. The High Court passed an order on respondent's application and appointed a new arbitrator. Order of appointment of arbitrator by the High Court was set aside as it violated the provisions of the agreement which clearly said that the arbitrator must be appointed by the competent authority, and the competent authority had already appointed an arbitrator who had already entered appearance and proceeded with the arbitration.[146]

---

140. *Techno Electric & Engg. Co. Ltd.* v. *Bengal Energy Ltd.*, 2019 SCC OnLine Cal 9420.
141. *Hythro Power Corpn. Ltd.* v. *Delhi Transco Ltd.*, (2003) 8 SCC 35.
142. *Maharshi Dayanand University* v. *Anand Coop. L/C Society Ltd.*, (2007) 5 SCC 295.
143. *SBP & Co.* v. *Patel Engg. Ltd.*, (2005) 8 SCC 618.
144. *Rodemadan India Ltd.* v. *International Trade Expo Centre Ltd.*, (2006) 11 SCC 651.
145. *Sree Neelalohita Associates* v. *M.A. Aleem*, 2020 SCC OnLine TS 3429.
146. *Union of India* v. *Premier Files Ltd.*, (2009) 9 SCC 384.

Section 11 of the Act only deals with the procedure to be followed by the party for getting an Arbitral Tribunal constituted. It does not prescribe that where there is no arbitration agreement between the parties, still a party could approach the courts for getting an arbitrator appointed. Existence of an arbitral agreement is a *sine qua non* for invoking Section 11 of the Act. Since there was no arbitration clause in the work order, application under Section 11 for appointment of the arbitrator was dismissed.[147] There was no arbitration clause for settlement of the dispute. The fact that the parties failed to adhere to terms of dispute redressal system envisaged under the agreement would not confer jurisdiction upon the High Court for settlement by way of arbitration. Arbitrator was not appointed in the case.[148]

The essence of arbitration is adjudication of disputes by independent/ neutral person/body. There was a licence agreement between the allottee of land and India Trade Promotion Organisation (ITPO). Clause in the agreement provided that disputes arising between the parties shall be referred to sole arbitration of the Chairman of the ITPO or his nominee whose decision shall be binding on the parties. It was held that it was not an arbitration clause, appointment of the arbitrator by the nominee of the Chief Justice was set aside.[149]

In the absence of the same, the court has no power to compel any party to get a dispute settled through arbitration unless they voluntarily agree for the same. In *Saraf Raj Mohammad* v. *Chairman*[150], there was no arbitration clause in the work order in relation to which arbitration was being sought. Section 11 only deals with the procedure to be followed by a party for getting an Arbitral Tribunal constituted. It does not anywhere prescribe that where there is no arbitration agreement between the parties, still a party can approach the court for getting an arbitrator appointed. Application filed under Section 11 for appointment of arbitrator was rejected.

Expiry of lease agreement—Appointment of arbitrator

Mere expiry of the lease agreement which contained the arbitration clause does not lead to the inference of non-existence of the arbitration clause. The arbitrator was appointed.[151]

147. *Saraf Raj Mohammad* v. *Chairman*, 2020 SCC OnLine All 1925: (2020) 4 All LJ 127.
148. *Sadanand Singh Construction (P) Ltd.* v. *Managing Director*, 2020 SCC OnLine Pat 704.
149. *International Amusement Ltd.* v. *India Trade Promotion Organisation*, (2015) 12 SCC 677; *P. Dasaratharama Reddy Complex* v. *State of Karnataka*, (2014) 2 SCC 201, followed.
150. 2020 SCC OnLine All 1925: (2020) 4 All LJ 127.
151. *Ayesha Oman* v. *Trend World*, 2018 SCC OnLine Hyd 323: (2018) 6 ALT 223.

Contingencies for appointment of arbitrator [Sub-s. (6)]

Section 11(6) sets out the contingencies when a party may request the Chief Justice or any person or institution designated by him to take necessary measures unless the agreement on the appointment procedure provides other means for securing the appointment. The contingencies contemplated in Section 11(6) statutorily are:

(*i*) a party fails to act as required under agreed procedure; or

(*ii*) the parties or the two appointed arbitrators fail to reach an agreement expected of them under that procedure; or

(*iii*) a person including an institution fails to perform any function entrusted to him or it under the procedure.

The third contingency does not relate to the parties to the agreement or the appointed arbitrators.[152]

In *You One Engg. & Construction Co. Ltd.* v. *National Highways Authority of India (NHAI)*[153] neither of the three conditions mentioned in clause (*a*), (*b*) and (*c*) of sub-section (6) of Section 11 were satisfied. The two arbitrators failed to reach a consensus within a period of 30 days. There was no appointment of the presiding arbitrator within 30 days from the appointment of the arbitrator appointed subsequently. Thus, under the appointment procedure contemplated by the contract, the president of Indian Roads Congress was required to appoint the presiding arbitrator. This was done by IRC. In the circumstances the contention that the situation was one contemplated by Section 11(6)(*c*), *viz.* that the institution failed to perform any function entrusted to it under the procedure, was not accepted. Thus, the cause of action for moving an application under Section 11(6) of the Act did not exist, since the presiding officer was appointed by IRC in accordance with the contract. The appointment of the presiding officer by IRC was perfectly valid and justified, and no occasion had arisen for the petitioner to move the Chief Justice of India under Section 11(6) of the Act.

Where on notice sent by the applicant, an arbitrator was appointed by the authority, the applicants did not appear before the arbitrator, no circumstances were disclosed which might indicate that the arbitrator was biased, application for appointment of independent arbitrator could not be allowed.[154]

Under the clause of the general conditions of contract in the event of dispute or difference, the contractor could refer the dispute to the Railways

152. *Northern Railway Admn.* v. *Patel Engg. Co. Ltd.*, (2008) 10 SCC 240.
153. (2006) 4 SCC 372.
154. *Nampa Electrical (P) Ltd.* v. *G.M. Central Org. for Railway Electrification*, 2014 SCC OnLine All 16107: (2015) 2 All LJ 478.

and if the Railway fails to make a decision within the reasonable time, the matter may be referred to the arbitrator for the resolution of the disputes. Despite request, the Railways did not refer the dispute to arbitrator. In such a situation, the application for referring the dispute to arbitrator was allowed.[155]

In terms of the parent agreement before initiating arbitration proceedings, parties were required to attempt amicable settlement of the dispute, the parties, *viz.* the contractor and the Project Manager made efforts for amicable settlement but the efforts failed, the arbitrator was appointed in the case.[156]

The respondents did not appoint arbitrator according to the arbitration clause contained in the agreement/contract bond within a period of 30 days of demand of appointment of arbitrator, the respondents forfeited their right to appoint arbitrator. In such a case, the Chief Justice/his designate has power to appoint sole arbitrator. A retired judge of the High Court was appointed arbitrator in the case.[157]

The contract expressly prescribes a period of 30 days, from the date of receipt of notice invoking arbitration by one party, for the other party to appoint the arbitrator. That period having elapsed, and the respondent having failed to appoint the arbitrator, Section 11(6) comes into operation.[158]

When the notice/recommendation of the respondents with regard to the arbitrator was not confirmed, the respondents should have approached the court under Section 11, Arbitration and Conciliation Act, 1996 seeking an appointment of an arbitrator. In view of the arbitration clause, the appointment made by the respondent was non-est, and needs to be ignored. When the appointment is non-est, being not in accordance with the agreed procedure, the petitioner was within its right to approach the court for appointment of an arbitrator under Section 11.[159]

There was no dispute about the legality, validity and binding effect of the agreement entered into between the parties and the arbitration clause contained therein, an arbitrator was appointed in the case.[160]

---

155. *P. Jeevanandam C.P. Ponnurangam* v. *Union of India*, 1999 SCC OnLine AP 768: (2000) 1 AP LJ 510.
156. *S & S Technocrats (P) Ltd.* v. *Classic Infrasolutions (P) Ltd.*, (2021) 1 HCC (Del) 212; see also, *Kunwar Narayan* v. *MS Ozone Overseas (P) Ltd.*, (2021) 1 HCC (Del) 372.
157. *Satya Prakash & Bros. (P) Ltd.* v. *State of U.P.*, 2010 SCC OnLine All 267: (2010) 79 ALR 275.
158. *Valecha Engg. Ltd.* v. *DMRC Ltd.*, (2021) 1 HCC (Del) 15.
159. *Oyo Hotels & Homes (P) Ltd.* v. *Rajan Tewari*, (2021) 1 HCC (Del) 225.
160. *Prince Mini Rice Mill* v. *Bihar State Food and Civil Supplies Corpn. Ltd.*, 2020 SCC OnLine Pat 4033.

Absence of consensus ad-idem

A petition under Section 11, Arbitration and Conciliation Act, 1996 for appointment of an arbitrator was filed by the petitioner. The respondent raised an objection that there was no concluded contract between the parties, and hence, no arbitration agreement as well. In absence of any prima facie material or evidence of an agreement, the provisions of Section 11(6) could not be invoked.[161]

Where both the parties do not agree for arbitration

If both the parties do not agree to refer their dispute to arbitration, application for appointment of arbitrator would be dismissed.[162]

One of the parties not agreeing on the name of the arbitrator

The respondent was not agreeing on the name of the arbitrator proposed by the applicant. The High Court appointed a retired judge of the court as arbitrator in the case.[163]

Existence of arbitration agreement in some other contract between the same parties—Arbitrator cannot be appointed

It is well settled that an arbitrator can be appointed only if there is an arbitration agreement in regard to the contract in question. If there is an arbitration agreement in regard to contract *A* and no arbitration agreement in regard to contract *B*, obviously a dispute relating to contract *B* cannot be referred to arbitration on the ground that contract *A* has an arbitration agreement. Therefore, where there is an arbitration agreement in one partnership deed, but the dispute is raised and appointment of an arbitrator is sought not with reference to the said partnership deed, but with reference to a subsequent partnership deed, unless the party filing the application under Section 11 of the Act is able to make out that there is a valid arbitration clause as per the subsequent contract, there can be no appointment of an arbitrator.[164]

Existence of arbitration dispute/enforceable claim

Before exercising power under Section 11(6) to make appointment of arbitrator, the court will have to decide on the existence of an arbitrable

161. *Angang Group Intnl. Trade Corpn.* v. *Pipavav Railway Corpn. Ltd.*, (2003) 10 SCC 51.
162. *Quick Heal Technologies Ltd.* v. *NCS Computech (P) Ltd.*, 2020 SCC OnLine Bom 687.
163. *Tdb Spinners (P) Ltd.* v. *Parasram Puria Internatin*, 2016 SCC OnLine MP 7804.
164. *Bharat Rasiklal Ashra* v. *Gautam Rasiklal Ashra*, (2012) 2 SCC 144.

dispute/enforceable claim by and between the parties to the contract. The existence of a claim and denial thereof giving rise to a dispute is required to be determined on the basis of what the parties had agreed upon as embodied in the terms of the contract and only for the purpose of a decision on the question of arbitrability and nothing beyond.[165]

In *KSS KSSIIPL Consortium* v. *GAIL (India) Ltd.*[166], under the terms of the agreement contractor-claimant quoted "NIL" against the compensation for extended stay in its bid. It meant that he had agreed to forgo its claim to extended stay compensation in the event, period of performance of contract was extended as had happened in the instant case. He cannot subsequently claim extended stay compensation which he had agreed to be foregone. Therefore, the claim against the extended stay compensation did not give rise to an arbitrable dispute which required reference to the arbitrator. However, the agreement clause contemplated making/raising of claims by the contractor for additional works and consideration thereof by the Engineer-in-Chief. The decision of the Engineer-in-Chief was final and binding. The finality attached to such a decision cannot be an unilateral act beyond the pale of security. Such a view would negate the arbitration clause in the agreement. Accordingly, the claims made by the petitioner-contractor for payment of additional works under the two contracts raised by arbitrable disputes, were referred to the arbitrator. Chief Justice (retired) of the High Court was appointed sole arbitrator in the case.

Earlier arbitration proceedings pending—Fresh arbitrator cannot be appointed

Where earlier arbitration proceedings started between the parties were abandoned, the parties did not approach the court for the termination of the mandate of the arbitrator; fresh arbitrator could not be appointed on petition filed under Section 11(6-A) of the Act.[167] When an earlier Arbitration Tribunal was in existence, appointment of a fresh arbitrator under Section 11 of the Act was erroneous, and the award of the arbitrator was set aside.[168]

165. *KSS KSSIIPL Consortium* v. *GAIL (India) Ltd.*, (2015) 4 SCC 210.
166. *Ibid.*
167. *Vidhyawati Construction Co. Builders and Govt. Contractors* v. *Allahabad Development Authority*, 2020 SCC OnLine All 1331: (2020) 143 ALR 560.
168. *Vidyawati Construction Co.* v. *Union of India*, 2020 SCC OnLine All 1371: (2021) 2 All LJ 114.

Appointment of arbitrator — Agreement and arbitration clause alleged to be obtained by fraud

Where underlying agreements including arbitration clauses are alleged to have been obtained by fraud, in such a case an arbitrator cannot be appointed and left to decide as to the existence of an arbitration agreement.[169]

Allegation of fraud, forgery and fabrication

Existence of a valid and enforceable arbitration agreement is a condition precedent before an arbitrator can be appointed under Section 11 of the Act. When serious allegations of fraud and fabrication are made, it is not possible for the court to proceed to appoint an arbitrator without deciding the said issue which relates to the very validity of the arbitration agreement. Therefore, the fact that the allegations of fraud, forgery and fabrication are likely to involve recording of evidence or involve some delay in disposal, are not grounds for refusing to consider the existence of a valid arbitration agreement. If a party is found to have falsely contended that the contract was forged/fabricated, the Chief Justice or his designate may subject such party to heavy costs so that such false claims are discouraged.[170] Appointment made ignoring objections raised that there was no dispute to be referred to arbitrator in view of full and final settlement between the parties, was held not sustainable. The High Court was directed to go into the dispute and then dispose of the application for appointment of arbitrator in accordance with law.[171]

A mere plea of fraud, coercion or undue influence in itself is not enough and the party who alleged the same is under obligation to prima facie establish it by placing satisfactory material on record before the Chief Justice or his designate to exercise power under Section 11(6) of the Act.[172]

Order of the High Court appointing the arbitrator was set aside, matter was remanded to the High Court for deciding questions whether the

---

169. *India Household and Healthcare Ltd.* v. *LG Household and Healthcare Ltd.*, (2007) 5 SCC 510.

170. *Bharat Rasiklal Ashra* v. *Gautam Rasiklal Ashra*, (2012) 2 SCC 144.

171. *Union of India* v. *Talson Builders*, (2008) 14 SCC 502.

172. *United India Insurance Co. Ltd.* v. *Antique Art Exports (P) Ltd.*, (2019) 5 SCC 362; *New India Assurance Co. Ltd.* v. *Genus Power Infrastructure Ltd.*, (2015) 2 SCC 424. This has been overruled by the Supreme Court in its subsequent decision in *Mayavati Trading (P) Ltd.* v. *Pradyuat Deb Burman*, (2019) 8 SCC 714. After the introduction of S. 11(6-A by Amending Act 3 of 2016, the jurisdiction of the Supreme/High Court while considering application for appointment of arbitrator is confined to examination of existence of arbitration agreement. *Mayavati Trading (P) Ltd.* v. *Pradyuat Deb Burman*, (2019) 8 SCC 714.

subsequent deed of partnership was forged or fabricated and whether there was a valid and enforceable arbitration agreement between the parties.[173]

Parties provided conciliation as the first step towards dispute resolution and also provided for arbitration as next or last step in that direction. If conciliation is avoided by one of the parties, the other party is not rendered a helpless spectator and would be justified in calling upon them to appoint the arbitrator.[174]

Question regarding legality and genuineness of arbitration agreement to be decided by court and not by arbitrator

The question whether there is an arbitration agreement is a jurisdictional issue and unless there is a valid arbitration agreement, application under Section 11 will not be maintainable and Chief Justice/his designate will have no jurisdiction to appoint an arbitrator under Section 11. Appellant contested the petition filed under Section 11(5) and (6) by the respondent and inter alia, contended that the MOU containing arbitration clause was a forged and fabricated document as he had never signed any such document. It was held that the High Court ought to have decided the questions itself and recorded a finding as to validity and genuineness of the document and depending on the findings, appropriate directions could have been given for the disposal of the application. The High Court had no jurisdiction to ask an arbitrator to decide such a question. The case was remanded to the designated judge to decide the question of legality, validity and genuineness of the agreement (MOU).[175]

Allegations of material alterations in arbitration agreement

An MOU was entered into between the petitioner and Respondent 1 and Respondent 2 for sale of helicopter to the petitioner, Respondent 1 resisted the appointment of arbitrator on grounds that certain clauses of MOU had been materially altered by changing the period of one month, the power of attorney in favour of Respondent 2 was also forged one. It was held, such questions cannot be gone into by the court in exercise of powers under Section 11(6), they can be raised before and decided by the Arbitral Tribunal in view of the provisions of Section 16. Arbitrator was appointed in the case and all disputes and questions raised by Respondent 1 were referred to the arbitrator.[176]

173. *Bharat Rasiklal Ashra* v. *Gautam Rasiklal Ashra*, (2012) 2 SCC 144.
174. *Tulip Hotels (P) Ltd.* v. *Trade Wings Ltd.*, 2009 SCC OnLine Bom 1222: (2010) 1 Mah LJ 73.
175. *Velugubanti Hari Babu* v. *Parvathini Narasimha Rao*, (2016) 14 SCC 126.
176. *Sanghi Bros. (Indore) (P) Ltd.* v. *Muktinath Airlines (P) Ltd.*, (2015) 16 SCC 471.

Preliminary matters to be determined—Bar of res judicata, jurisdiction and limitation if can be considered

The question whether a claim is barred by res judicata, does not arise for consideration in a proceedings under Section 11 of the Act. Such an issue will have to be examined by the Arbitral Tribunal. A decision on res judicata requires consideration of the pleadings as also the claims/issues/points and the award in the first round of arbitration, in juxtaposition with the pleadings and the issues/points/claims in the second arbitration. The limited scope of Section 11 of the Act does not permit such examination of the maintainability or tenability of a claim either on facts or in law. It is for the Arbitral Tribunal to examine and decide whether the claim was barred by res judicata. There can be no threshold consideration and rejection of a claim on the ground of res judicata, while considering an application under Section 11 of the Act. The designate had exceeded his limited jurisdiction under Section 11 of the Act, by deciding that the claim for extra cost, though covered by the arbitration agreement, was barred by limitation and by the principles of res judicata. He was also not justified in terming the application under Section 11 of the Act as "misconceived and mala fide".[177]

Where the arbitration agreement between the parties contains an arbitration clause, an arbitrator shall be appointed, whether the claim is barred by limitation or not is to be decided by the arbitrator. Arbitrator was appointed in the case.[178]

While functioning under Section 11(6) of the Act, a Chief Justice or the person or institution designated by him, is bound to decide whether he has jurisdiction to entertain the request, in the sense, whether the party making the motion has approached the right High Court, whether there is a valid arbitration agreement in terms of Section 7 of the Act and whether the person before him with the request is a party to the arbitration agreement or whether there was no dispute subsisting which was capable of being arbitrated upon. The Chief Justice can also decide the question whether the claim was a dead one; or a long barred claim that was sought to be resurrected and whether the parties have concluded the transaction by recording satisfaction of their mutual rights and obligations or by receiving the final payment without objection. It may not be possible at that stage to decide whether a live claim made is one which comes within the purview of the arbitration clause. It will be appropriate to leave that question to be decided by the Arbitral Tribunal on taking evidence, along with the merits of the claims involved in the arbitration. On coming to a conclusion on these aspects, the Chief

177. *Indian Oil Corpn. Ltd.* v. *SPS Engg. Ltd.*, (2011) 3 SCC 507.

178. *Suresh Kumar Kothari* v. *State of Rajasthan*, 2019 SCC OnLine Raj 3870; *Wexford Financial Inc. Panama* v. *BHEL*, (2016) 8 SCC 267.

Justice has to enquire whether the conditions for exercise of his power under Section 11(6) of the Act have been fulfilled; and if an arbitrator is to be appointed, who is the fit person, in terms of the provision. The Chief Justice or the designated judge would be entitled to seek the opinion of an institution in the matter of nominating an arbitrator qualified in terms of Section 11(8) of the Act if the need arises, but the order appointing the arbitrator could only be that of the Chief Justice or the designated judge. These are all adjudications which affect the rights of parties. He cannot constitute an Arbitral Tribunal without considering these questions.[179]

Preliminary objection as to existence/validity of arbitration agreement, etc.

Preliminary objection as to existence/validity of arbitration agreement should be decided by Chief Justice or his designate before making appointment of arbitrator. This case, being pre-*SBP & Co.* v. *Patel Engg. Ltd.*[180], it was held that the arbitrator had to decide all objections including existence or validity of the arbitration agreement.[181]

Once the existence of an arbitration agreement itself is questioned by the party to proceedings under Section 11, the Chief Justice/designate should decide about the existence of a valid arbitration agreement between parties as well.[182]

Dispute with respect to arbitrability

Unless on the face of it, it is found that dispute is not arbitrable and if it requires further/deeper consideration, dispute with respect to arbitrability should be left to the arbitrator.[183]

Issue of non-arbitrability can be raised at three stages: *First*, before the court on an application for reference under Section 11 or for stay of pending judicial proceedings and reference under Section 8, Arbitration and Conciliation Act; *secondly*, before the Arbitral Tribunal during the course of the arbitration proceedings; or *thirdly*, before the court at the stage of the challenge to the award or its enforcement.[184]

179. *SBP & Co.* v. *Patel Engg. Ltd.*, (2005) 8 SCC 618.
180. *Ibid.*
181. *A.P. Tourism Development Corpn. Ltd.* v. *Pampa Hotels Ltd.*, (2010) 5 SCC 425.
182. *Reva Electric Car Co. (P) Ltd.* v. *Green Mobil*, (2012) 2 SCC 93.
183. *VGP Marine Kingdom (P) Ltd.* v. *Kay Ellen Arnold*, (2023) 1 SCC 597.
184. *Vidya Drolia* v. *Durga Trading Corpn.*, (2021) 2 SCC 1.

Pre-condition of conciliation

Where the petitioner has not fulfilled the pre-condition of conciliation before invoking the arbitration clause in the work order, he has no right to invoke arbitration at this stage, petition filed under Section 11(6) for appointment of arbitrator being premature was rejected.[185]

Jurisdiction under Section 11—Limited jurisdiction—Findings on the merits of the case

Jurisdiction of the court under Section 11 is limited one, and confined to the examination of issue whether there is an arbitration agreement between the parties, and if so whether any dispute has arisen between them out of such agreement which may call for appointment of arbitrator to decide such dispute. Where the court elaborately discusses issues touching the merits of the controversy, relating to agreement, it exceeds jurisdiction.[186]

Appointment of arbitrator—Decision on contentious issues

Section 5 of the 1996 Act clearly indicates the legislative intent to minimise supervisory role of courts to ensure that the intervention of the court is minimal. The consistent view taken by the Supreme Court is that contentious issues should not be gone into or decided at the stage of appointment of an arbitrator and no time should be wasted in such an exercise. The remedy of the aggrieved party is to raise an objection before the Arbitral Tribunal, as under Section 16 of the Act it is empowered to rule about its own jurisdiction.[187]

Admission of debt/liability by the respondent

Even if the respondent has admitted the claim of the applicant, it needs to be seen whether such admission is bona fide or not. Where admission by respondent of claim of applicant is not bona fide and is only to dodge and avoid payment of money to applicant, applicant cannot be left without any remedy and even if claim of applicant is admitted, but without bona fides, then same would constitute a dispute, which requires to be adjudicated before an arbitrator in view of agreement between parties. Application for appointment of arbitrator would be allowed.[188]

---

185. *Sobha Ltd.* v. *Nava Vishwa Shashi Vijaya Krishna Properties (P) Ltd.*, 2022 SCC OnLine Kar 1708: (2022) 4 Kant LJ 460.
186. *Rajesh Verma* v. *Ashwani Kumar Khanna*, (2016) 12 SCC 678; *Arasmeta Captive Power Co. (P) Ltd.* v. *Lafarge India (P) Ltd.*, (2013) 15 SCC 414.
187. *Shree Subhlaxmi Fabrics (P) Ltd.* v. *Chand Mal Baradia*, (2005) 10 SCC 704.
188. *Dell International Services India Ltd.* v. *Analogics Tech India Ltd.*, 2022 SCC OnLine TS 3470.

Existence of arbitration agreement and not defence on merits, material

In proceedings under Section 11 what is relevant is the existence of the arbitration agreement and not the defence on merits.[189]

Live dispute necessary

On application under Section 11 for appointment of arbitrator, the court must determine the existence of live dispute between the parties to the agreement and then the arbitrator must be appointed as per terms and conditions of the agreement and the need of the dispute. Order of the High Court for appointment of arbitrator without considering whether any dispute existed between the parties was not justified, was set aside.[190]

Where substantive claim is ex facie time barred, the court shall not refer the dispute to the arbitration.[191]

Where the non-applicant contended that by virtue of a termination agreement, the claims of the applicant stood extinguished but the applicant contended that the alleged agreement was a forged document, held, there did exist a live claim between the parties. Dispute was referred to the arbitrator.[192]

There was agreement between the parties for the supply of the materials. The goods supplied by the petitioner were faulty, the respondent invoked bank guarantee as dispute could not be resolved. The petitioner filed an application under Section 11(6) before the Supreme Court for appointment of arbitrator. It was held that there was a live dispute between the parties, the Supreme Court allowed the application and appointed an arbitrator to resolve the dispute between the parties.[193]

From the facts as pleaded and as well as from the exchange of correspondence between the parties, it was amply clear that there was no mutual satisfaction arrived at between the parties as regard the present dispute. The claims were obviously not barred by any limitation. It was thus clear that there was a live issue subsisting between the parties requiring its resolution. A clear case for appointment of arbitrator was made out, an arbitrator was appointed in the case.[194]

---

189. *S.N. Prasad* v. *Monnet Finance Ltd.*, (2011) 1 SCC 320.
190. *Union of India* v. *Onkar Nath Bhalla & Sons*, (2009) 7 SCC 350; *P.K. Ramaiah & Co.* v. *NTPC*, 1994 Supp (3) SCC 126.
191. *BSNL* v. *Nortel Networks (India) (P) Ltd.*, (2021) 5 SCC 738.
192. *Nandan Biomatrix Ltd.* v. *D 1 Oils Ltd.*, (2009) 4 SCC 495.
193. *TBEA Shenyang Transformers Group Co. Ltd.* v. *Alstom Projects India Ltd.*, (2016) 15 SCC 722.
194. *Visa International Ltd.* v. *Continental Resources (USA) Ltd.*, (2009) 2 SCC 55.

Agency agreement between applicant and respondent containing arbitration clause provided for settlement of dispute between the parties through arbitration. Applicant acted as agent of respondent for secured contract from a foreign company, A.A. Turki Corporation (AATC). Respondent raised dispute, contending that applicant had unauthorisedly opened sealed price offer submitted by respondent for AATC whereby it lost confidentiality, that it withheld respondent's offer from AATC and that it represented a Chinese company which was a competitor of respondent on the same project, and hence, agency agreement was terminated. Dispute also existed between the parties on the question as to whether the contract was awarded by AATC to respondent subsequent to the alleged termination of the agency agreement and on account of respondent's own efforts or applicant had rendered any services in terms of the agreement in the matter of award of the contract to respondent. In view of the existence of a dispute, held, the same has to be resolved through arbitration. Accordingly, a former Chief Justice of India was nominated as sole arbitrator to decide the dispute between the parties.[195]

In *Tata Industries Ltd.* v. *Grasim Industries Ltd.*[196], live issue was found to exist, as such an Arbitral Tribunal was appointed in the case.

The respondent had not issued shares to the applicant as the applicant was not a member of *E*. The grievance of the applicant related to non-payment of consideration for supply of equipment to *E* under shareholders' agreement (SHA). Further, the dispute raised by applicant related to non-issuance of shares by respondent in terms of amalgamation scheme entered into between *E* and the respondent-company. The disputes were very much live and surviving. The procedure for appointment of arbitrator was agreed upon between the parties in the arbitration clause of SHA. The respondent failed to act as required under that procedure in spite of service of notice of the applicant. The agreement on the appointment procedure did not provide other means for securing the appointment of a sole arbitrator. Therefore, the conditions precedent set out in Section 11(6) of the Act were completely satisfied and the applicant was entitled to approach the court for securing appointment of sole arbitrator for resolution of the disputes, which had arisen between the parties. A retired judge of the High Court was appointed sole arbitrator in the case.[197]

195. *Vigil Marine Services* v. *Cochin Shipyard Ltd.*, (2004) 13 SCC 465.
196. (2008) 10 SCC 187.
197. *Geo-Group Communications Inc.* v. *IOL Broadband Ltd.*, (2010) 1 SCC 562.

Live issues — Limitation

Where the Chief Justice comes to a finding that there exists a live issue, then naturally this finding would include a finding that the respective claims of the parties have not become barred by limitation.[198]

Once it is concluded that the designated judge was right in holding that there was a live issue, the question of limitation automatically gets resolved. Till such time as the settlement talks are going on directly or by way of correspondence, no issue arises, with the result the clock of limitation does not start ticking. Where the negotiations were still on, there would be no question of the limitation period starting. In *Shree Ram Mills Ltd.* v. *Utility Premises (P) Ltd.*[199], things did not seem to have settled even by 19 January 2005, but that would be for the Arbitral Tribunal to decide. At this stage it could not be said that the claim of the respondent could not be said to have become dead firstly because of the settlement or because of lapse of limitation. The question of limitation was also left open for the Arbitral Tribunal to decide. The Chief Justice or his designate is not expected to go into merits of claim or examine maintainability or tenability of claims either on facts or law in an application under Section 11. He can decide on an apparent dead claim (long time barred) which is evidently and patently long time barred and where there is no need for detailed consideration of evidence. The court will not enter into the disputed question whether a claim was barred by limitation or not. Such issues shall be left for the decision of the arbitrator.[200]

While considering application under Section 11(6) for appointment of arbitrator, the Chief Justice/his designate will not ordinarily consider the issue of limitation. However, in appropriate cases, he may consider whether an application was on the face of it so hopelessly barred by time that it was already a dead/stale claim which did not deserve to be resurrected and referred to arbitration.[201] It is optional for the Chief Justice or his designate to decide whether the claim is dead or time barred. Chief Justice or his designate would do so only when the claim is evidently and patently a long time barred claim. However, when delay in making the petition is not apparent but based on disputed facts, the court will not enter into the said disputed question but leave it to be decided by the Arbitral Tribunal.[202]

198. *Shree Ram Mills Ltd.* v. *Utility Premises (P) Ltd.*, (2007) 4 SCC 599.
199. (2007) 4 SCC 599.
200. *Indian Oil Corpn. Ltd.* v. *SPS Engg. Ltd.*, (2011) 3 SCC 507.
201. *State of Goa* v. *Praveen Enterprises*, (2012) 12 SCC 581.
202. *Schlumberger Asia Services Ltd.* v. *ONGC Ltd.*, (2013) 7 SCC 562.

Plea of limitation is a mixed question of law and fact. Court cannot undertake any detailed adjudication and give any definite finding in order to non-suit claimant at very threshold.[203]

Claim whether alive

In order to set into motion the arbitral procedure, the Chief Justice or his designate has to decide the issues, if raised, regarding territorial jurisdiction and existence of an arbitration agreement between the parties. In addition thereto, he can also decide the question whether the claim was a dead one in the sense that the parties have already concluded the transaction by recording satisfaction of their mutual rights and obligations or have recorded satisfaction regarding their financial claims. Nevertheless, at that stage it may not be possible to decide whether a live claim made, is one which comes within the purview of the arbitration clause and this question should be left to be decided by the Arbitral Tribunal on taking evidence. In the instant case head contract provided for payment of taxes by head contractor on behalf of sub-contractor. Sub-contractor raised a claim of reimbursement of certain taxes paid by him after final payments had been made. It was held, prima facie claim was alive as the tax demand was raised by the Revenue Department subsequent after the final payments. Arbitrator was appointed in the case.[204]

In order to set into motion the arbitral procedure, the Chief Justice or his designate has to decide the issue, if raised, regarding whether the claim made by the applicant was a dead one in the sense that the parties have already concluded the transaction by recording satisfaction of their mutual rights and obligations or have recorded satisfaction regarding their financial claims. In *Anil Kumar* v. *B.S. Neelkanta*[205], the Supreme Court, being satisfied that the disputes raised between the parties could not be resolved without evidence, arbitrator was appointed in the case.

Claim ex facie time barred

In rare and exceptional cases, where the claims are ex facie time barred, and it is manifest that there is no subsisting dispute, the court may refuse to make the reference.[206] When an arguable case is made out and issue as to whether a claim is barred by limitation or not calls for an inquiry, in view of primacy

203. *Rajalaxmi Mckenna* v. *Sankaran Raghunathan*, 2021 SCC OnLine Mad 16581.
204. *DHV BV* v. *Tahal Consulting Engineers Ltd.*, (2007) 8 SCC 321.
205. (2010) 5 SCC 407.
206. *BSNL* v. *Nortel Networks (India) (P) Ltd.*, (2021) 5 SCC 738; *Bizibi Infotech (P) Ltd.* v. *HCL Infosystem Ltd.*, (2022) 5 HCC (Del) 429. (Deadwood claims—Petition for appointment of arbitrator was rejected.)

given to Arbitral Tribunal, the Chief Justice or his designate should yield to such authority and allow objection to be decided in accordance with law by Arbitral Tribunal. In this case, objection was to be decided by the Arbitral Tribunal. Request for setting up an Arbitral Tribunal was allowed.[207]

Cause of action for invoking an arbitration clause arose in the year 2011 when the contract was terminated. Application for appointment of arbitrator filed in the year 2022 was barred by limitation, hence was rejected.[208]

In this case of a works contract, all the claims in the contract were settled, and a final bill was passed which was accepted by the contractor. The contractor did not adduce any evidence to show that payment under final bill was accepted under duress or cocrcion. Subsequent demand letters by the contractor did not make a reference to coercion or duress. Notice of arbitration under Section 21 issued after six years was patently barred by limitation. Claim was ex facie time barred and fell within the limited category of deadwood. Application for reference of dispute to arbitration was rejected.[209]

Ex facie time barred claims need not be referred for arbitration by the court.[210] Work order was issued in the year 1982 and work/excess work was completed in the year 1986. Legal notice invoking arbitration clause seeking amount due was issued 32 years thereafter. No cause of action accrued to the appellant in the year 2018/2019. Application seeking appointment of arbitrator was barred by time, and was rejected.[211] There was a tender for procurement of sub-machine guns under the fast track procedure. A dispute arose between the parties over the wrongful encashment of the warranty bond issued by the Defence Ministry. The Ministry deducted the amount towards recovery of liquidated damages on 26 September 2016; the amount was credited into the government account and the matter ended at that time only. Merely because the petitioner kept negotiating with the Ministry thereafter in anticipation of some amicable settlement would not save period of limitation. The claim of the petitioner was hopelessly time-barred. The application for appointment of arbitrator was rejected.[212]

It is open to the Chief Justice or his designate to consider whether the claim is barred by limitation or is alive. The issue of limitation, though a mixed question of fact and law, in a case on available evidence, the Chief Justice comes to the conclusion that the claim is time barred, then it is within

207. *Maya Construction* v. *Union of India*, 2022 SCC OnLine Megh 138.
208. *Brave Lions India Security Services* v. *SAIL*, 2023 SCC OnLine AP 710.
209. *B.K. Consortium Engineers (P) Ltd.* v. *Indian Institute of Management*, 2023 SCC OnLine Cal 124.
210. *Secunderabad Cantonment Board* v. *B. Ramachandraiah & Sons*, (2021) 5 SCC 705.
211. *Vishram Varu & Co.* v. *Union of India*, 2022 SCC OnLine SC 487.
212. *B & T AG* v. *Ministry of Defence*, (2024) 5 SCC 358.

his jurisdiction to decide. In *Sheodhan Singh* v. *Union of India*[213], from the pleadings of the parties itself it was clear that the claim was time barred. There could be no arbitral dispute, application for appointment of arbitrator was dismissed on the ground of limitation. The contractor had completed the work in February 2007. The petitioner demanded payment from the respondent Corporation on 31 August 2019 more than 12 years thereafter. There was no acknowledgement by the Corporation in the meanwhile. Claim of the petitioner was hopelessly time barred. Arbitrator was not appointed in the case.[214]

The court is not required to undertake any adjudicatory exercise to decide whether the disputes are barred by limitation. However, in cases where it is ex facie apparent and is established that the disputes are either not arbitrable or barred by limitation, the court would not appoint an arbitrator as that would be an exercise in futility.[215]

The demand for arbitration was made by a letter dated 7 November 2006, the demand was reiterated through a letter dated 13 January 2007. As no arbitrator was appointed, cause of action accrued from 13 January 2007. Final rejection of request for appointment of arbitrator on 10 November 2010 would not give any fresh start to the limitation period. Applications filed on 6 November 2013 under Section 11 for appointment of arbitrator were barred by time. The High Court was in error in holding that the applications filed were within the limitation period. Applications under Section 11 being time barred, claims made on merits also being time barred, arbitrator could not be appointed.[216] Request for appointment of arbitrator was made after a lapse of 6/8 years for the first time. Application for appointment of arbitrators was barred by limitation.[217]

Merely because for the claim/alleged dues of the year 1985/1986, the legal notice calling upon the respondent to pay the amount due and payable or to refer the dispute to the arbitrator is made after a period of 32 years; the appellant cannot be permitted to say that the cause of action to file an application under Section 11(6) had accrued in the year 2018/2019. The application filed under Section 11(6) was rejected.[218]

The demand for final judgment by the appellant company was raised in the year 2007. For settlement of the demand, the appellant filed an application

213. 2010 SCC OnLine All 2308: (2011) 85 ALR 683.
214. *Kamalakanta Engg. & Construction Co. (P) Ltd.* v. *National Projects Construction Corpn. Ltd.*, 2021 SCC OnLine Ori 2487.
215. *G4S Secure Solutions (India) (P) Ltd.* v. *LI Consulting (P) Ltd.*, (2021) 3 HCC (Del) 92.
216. *Secunderabad Cantonment Board* v. *B. Ramachandraiah & Sons*, (2021) 5 SCC 705.
217. *Bimla Halan* v. *Chandulal Patodia*, 2014 SCC OnLine Ori 849.
218. *Vishram Varu & Co.* v. *Union of India*, 2022 SCC OnLine SC 487.

under Section 11 after an inordinate delay of 13 years in the year 2020. The application being clearly barred by limitation was rejected.[219]

The contractor had completed the work in February 2007. The petitioner demanded payment from the respondent Corporation on 31 August 2019, more than 12 years thereafter. There was no acknowledgement by the Corporation in the meanwhile. The claim of the petitioner was hopelessly time-barred. An arbitrator was not appointed in the case.[220]

No claim pending—Appointment of arbitrator erroneous—Set aside

Bank guarantees were released by the employer on the issuance of completion certificate. There was no pending claim between the parties. Claims raised subsequently were afterthought and not bona fide. The appointment of the arbitrator under Section 11(6), Arbitration and Conciliation Act was erroneous, and was set aside.[221]

Application for appointment of arbitrator after long delay

Application for appointment of arbitrator filed after enormous delay of more than 10 years after company petition was rejected.

Dead claim—Powers of the Chief Justice

The Chief Justice exercises the judicial power while passing an order under Section 11 of the Act thus can examine the question as to whether the claim which has been raised before him survives and needs to be adjudicated. If the Chief Justice finds that claim is a dead claim, he can exercise jurisdiction in rejecting the application. According to the contract there was a two years' period for effecting any recovery from the contractor. No claim was raised during aforesaid defect liability period. Claim for disputed amount was raised after expiry of said period of two years, which was not adjudicated upon, cannot be held to be "dead" claim.[222]

Objection on the ground of limitation can be raised by the contractor in proceedings under Section 11 of the Act.[223]

---

219. *Kamla Construction Co.* v. *State of Rajasthan*, 2023 SCC OnLine Raj 5338.
220. *Kamalakanta Engg. & Construction Co. (P) Ltd.* v. *National Projects Construction Corpn. Ltd.*, 2021 SCC OnLine Ori 2487.
221. *NTPC Ltd.* v. *SPML Infra Ltd.*, (2023) 9 SCC 385.
222. *EMM ENN Associates* v. *Commander Works Engineer*, (2016) 13 SCC 61.
223. *Chief Engineer* v. *Roman Tarmat Ltd.*, 2021 SCC OnLine Mad 2467: (2021) 5 CTC 1.

Chief Justice/his designate is not required to identify disputes for reference to arbitrator

Section 11 of the Act requires the Chief Justice or his designate to either appoint the arbitrator(s) or to take necessary measures in accordance with the appointment procedure contained in the arbitration agreement. The Chief Justice or his designate is not required to draw up a list of disputes and refer them to arbitration. The appointment of the Arbitral Tribunal is an implied reference in terms of the arbitration agreement.[224]

Chief Justice/his designate is not to decide the arbitrability of the dispute

The issues that the Chief Justice/his designate has to decide does not include issue about arbitrability of the dispute. He need not also decide whether controversy raised falls in excepted matters.[225]

Appointment of arbitrator—Power of court

Clause in the arbitration agreement provided for reference of dispute to the Arbitral Tribunal constituted by the State Government. The tribunal constituted under the Arbitration Act, 1940 could not decide disputes relating to agreements entered after its repeal. In the absence of an Arbitral Tribunal, the High Court is competent to appoint the arbitrator. Arbitrator was appointed in the case.[226]

Petitioner was given 30 days time but he failed to appoint an arbitrator during the said period. The respondent approached the court for the same. The appointment of the arbitrator by the court was proper.[227]

A dispute arose between parties regarding alleged breach of engagement letter. The respondent was called upon to name an arbitrator for adjudication of the said disputes between them but he failed to do the needful. An application was allowed, and an arbitrator was appointed by the court.[228]

Where the parties failed to appoint an arbitrator, a sole arbitrator was appointed in the case.[229]

---

224. *State of Goa* v. *Praveen Enterprises*, (2012) 12 SCC 581.
225. *Arasmeta Captive Power Co. (P) Ltd.* v. *Lafarge India (P) Ltd.*, (2013) 15 SCC 414.
226. *Mahipatlal Patel* v. *Chief Engineer*, (2008) 12 SCC 64.
227. *Indian Drug and Pharmaceutical Ltd.* v. *Arundhati Manna*, 2020 SCC OnLine Cal 392.
228. *Purple India Holdings Ltd.* v. *Drilling & Offshore (P) Ltd.*, (2016) 7 SCC 583.
229. *R. Vedagiri* v. *K. Rajakumari*, 2022 SCC OnLine Mad 9017.

Appointment of substitute arbitrator by court

Arbitration agreement provided for appointment of arbitrator by the Indian Roads Congress (IRC). It was not shown that IRC had failed to exercise its jurisdiction. The respondent-contractor unilaterally approached the High Court under Section 11(6) for appointing presiding officer of the Arbitral Tribunal. Order of the High Court appointing the presiding officer of the Arbitral Tribunal was found against the express provisions of the contract, and was set aside. The Supreme Court held that the appointment of the presiding officer shall be made as per the procedure contemplated under the contract, the IRC should be approached for this purpose.[230]

In this case, the arbitrator appointed in the year 2008 failed to fix any date for arbitration, and the matter was still pending. Application for appointment of substitute arbitrator was allowed. Substitute arbitrator was appointed in the case.[231]

Failure/gross neglect of the arbitrator in concluding the arbitration proceedings—Court appointed fresh arbitrator

Arbitration proceedings between the parties pending for the last six years at the same stage. Fresh arbitrator was appointed in the case.[232]

Vice-Chancellor of University was arbitrator in the case

Allegation of mala fide bias has to be established by cogent evidence. There was a dispute between the parties regarding the cancellation of agreement between the respondent-university and the company. In terms of the agreement, the Vice-Chancellor was the sole arbitrator. The fact that he had called for explanation from the Registrar for non-receipt of relevant examination material could not lead to the presumption that he was biased against the university. The company failed to establish that he would not act independently as arbitrator in the case. Appointment of arbitrator was delivered under Section 11 of the Act.[233]

Arbitration clause in the arbitration agreement provided that the Vice-Chancellor of the university shall be appointed arbitrator in the case. But with the consent of the parties an independent arbitrator was appointed in the case. Appointment of the arbitrator in the case was held valid.[234]

230. *NHAI* v. *Bumihiway DDB Ltd. (JV)*, (2006) 10 SCC 763.
231. *B. Engineers & Builders Ltd.* v. *State of Odisha*, 2019 SCC OnLine Ori 435.
232. *Karuppudayar* v. *Union of India*, 2015 SCC OnLine Mad 14284.
233. *Leelajay Technologies (P) Ltd.* v. *Dr Bhimrao Ambedkar University*, 2011 SCC OnLine All 1399: (2011) 89 ALR 83.
234. *Bundelkhand University Jhansi* v. *Woodfun A Registered Partnership Firm*, 2022 SCC OnLine All 994: (2022) 5 All LJ 26.

A plea raised was that the arbitration clause provided for the appointment of Vice-Chancellor as the arbitrator, and no other person could be appointed as the arbitrator. With the consent of the parties, an independent arbitrator was appointed in the case.[235]

Factors relevant in deciding number of arbitrators and their qualifications

Dispute arose between collaborators in the project for exploration, extraction and production of crude oil. Dispute was covered by the arbitration clause but parties disagreed on the name of sole arbitrator. In view of the said fact and also that the subject-matter of dispute involved complicated issues, parties suggested appointment of Arbitration Tribunal with a retired judge nominated by the Supreme Court as Chairman and one Geophysics expert nominated by each of the two parties as member. Suggestion was accepted and order was passed accordingly. There was no legal impediment for accepting the suggestions made by the parties.[236]

Death of named arbitrator(s) prior to appointment—Appointment of substitute arbitrator

Arbitration clause subsists so long as any dispute or difference between the parties exist, despite death of the named arbitrator(s), unless language of the arbitration clause clearly expresses an intention to the contrary. In *ACC Ltd.* v. *Global Cements Ltd.*[237], arbitration clause provided for appointment of named arbitrator(s), if any question, difference or dispute arose between the parties "at any time". It was held, expression "at any time" used in the arbitration clause has no nexus with the lifetime of named arbitrators. It does not mean that dispute shall be adjudicated only by the named arbitrators at any time. The arbitration clause did not prohibit nor debar appointment of substitute arbitrator in case of death of named arbitrator(s) or their non-availability. The plea of the opposition that the arbitration clause did not subsist since both the named arbitrators had died was rejected. Thus, the High Court was justified in appointing a sole arbitrator to adjudicate disputes between the parties.

Whenever parties agree for mediation, and even name a specific arbitrator with no specific provision for appointment of another arbitrator on the recusal/withdrawal of the said arbitrator, the said omission is made up by Section 15(2) of the Act. Unless arbitration agreement between the parties

---

235. *Ushadevi* v. *Cotton Corpn. of India Ltd.*, 2019 SCC OnLine MP 6113: (2020) 1 MP LJ 200.
236. *Geophysical Institute of Israel* v. *Geoenpro Petroleum Ltd.*, (2009) 17 SCC 18.
237. (2012) 7 SCC 71.

provides a categorical prohibition or debarment in resolving a question or dispute or difference between the parties by a substitute arbitrator in case of death of the named arbitrator, courts have the power to appoint a substitute arbitrator. This power is given by Section 15(2) of the Act and this provision is to be given a liberal interpretation so as to apply to all possible circumstances under which the mandate of the earlier arbitrator may be terminated.[238]

Successor arbitrator if, must not be lesser in rank than his predecessor

Arbitrator, a retired Chief Justice of India had resigned. When the parties failed to select the successor, the appointing authority in terms of arbitration clause appointed a retired judge of the High Court as arbitrator in the case. The objection of the opposite party that a retired judge of the High Court in replacement of the arbitrator (CJI) could not be appointed, was found not sustainable and rejected. More so, when the opposite party had not challenged the credibility of the person so appointed as sole arbitrator as in this case.[239]

Each party shall appoint one arbitrator, the two appointed arbitrators shall appoint presiding arbitrator [Sub-s. (3)]

Section 11(3) requires the two arbitrators to appoint the third arbitrator or the umpire. In the present case, the arbitration clause provided that each party shall nominate one arbitrator and the two arbitrators shall then appoint an umpire before proceeding with the case. In *MMTC Ltd.* v. *Sterlite Industries (India) Ltd.*[240], the respondent invoked arbitration clause in the agreement between the parties by letter dated 19 January 1996 which was received by the appellant on 31 January 1996. On 7 February 1996, the respondent appointed former Chief Justice of the Madras High Court as arbitrator in the case. The appellant contended that arbitration could not be restored to, and therefore, it did not name its arbitrator. The respondent filed an application in Bombay High Court for appointing an arbitrator in accordance with the provisions of the Act. It was held that the said case was governed by Section 11 of the new Act. Section 11(3) was attracted in the case. Since the two arbitrators had not appointed the third arbitrator within 30 days from the date of their appointment, the Supreme Court directed the Chief Justice of the High Court to appoint the third arbitrator under Section 11(4) of the Act.

---

238. *Shailesh Dhairyawan* v. *Mohan Balkrishna Lulla*, (2016) 3 SCC 619.
239. *Balli Petrochemicals Ltd.* v. *National Aluminium Co. Ltd.*, (2009) 2 SCC 558.
240. (1996) 6 SCC 716.

Party having right to appoint arbitration under the agreement when loses such right [Sub-s. (4)]

Once a minimum of 30 days, as prescribed under the Act concerned, has expired and a petition for appointment of an arbitrator is filed in the court, the appointing authority loses the right to make the appointment. The appointing authority, CGM Kerala, in *BSNL* v. *Motorola India (P) Ltd.*[241], did not respond to the notice requiring the appointment of an arbitrator within the time prescribed under the Arbitration and Conciliation Act, 1996. Since the appointing authority did not appoint the arbitrator, the respondent filed a petition under Section 11 of the Act before the High Court. It was held, the appellants had lost their right to appoint an arbitrator for settling the disputes under the agreement.

The opposite party had failed to act as per the appointment procedure agreed upon by the parties and it was open for the petitioner to invoke Section 11 of the Act to take necessary measures as stipulated therein. The right of the opposite party to appoint an arbitrator is lost once an application for appointment of arbitrator is made to the court.[242]

Respondent did not select name from amongst the panel of the arbitrators sent by the appellant. Subsequent nomination of the arbitrator by the respondent was not proper.[243]

If one parity demands the opposite party to appoint an arbitrator and the opposite party does not make an appointment within 30 days of the demand, the right to appointment does not get automatically forfeited after the expiry of 30 days. If the opposite party makes an appointment even after 30 days of the demand but *before the first party has moved the court under Section 11*, that would be sufficient. Only then the right of the opposite party ceases. In other words, in cases arising under Section 11(6), if the opposite party has not made an appointment within 30 days of demand, the right to make appointment is not forfeited but continues, but an appointment has to be made before the former files application under Section 11 seeking appointment of an arbitrator.[244] In *Datar Switchgears Ltd.* v. *Tata Finance Ltd.*[245], the respondent made the appointment before the appellant filed the application under Section 11(6) though it was beyond 30 days from the date of the demand. It was held, the appointment of arbitrator by the respondent

241. (2009) 2 SCC 337; *Datar Switchgears Ltd.* v. *Tata Finance Ltd.*, (2000) 8 SCC 151; *Punj Lloyd Ltd.* v. *Petronet MHB Ltd.*, (2006) 2 SCC 638.
242. *Jagannathdham Superstructures (P) Ltd.* v. *General Manager*, 2015 SCC OnLine Ori 607.
243. *GAIL* v. *Keti Construction (I) Ltd.*, (2007) 5 SCC 38.
244. *Datar Switchgears Ltd.* v. *Tata Finance Ltd.*, (2000) 8 SCC 151.
245. (2000) 8 SCC 151.

was valid, the right of the respondent was not forfeited after the expiry of 30 days from the date of demand.

Appointment of arbitrator by Chief Justice or designated judge—Party when loses right to appoint arbitrator

Once notice period (30 days in *Punj Lloyd Ltd.* v. *Petronet MHB Ltd.*)[246] had lapsed and the applicant had moved Chief Justice under Section 11(6), a party having right to appoint arbitrator under arbitral agreement loses the right to do so. Appellant's application under Section 11(6) was restored for fresh consideration for appointment of arbitrator in accordance with Section 11(6). Once a party files an application under Section 11(6) of the Act, the other party extinguishes its right to appoint an arbitrator in terms of the clause of the agreement thereafter. The other party also cannot resurrect the clause of the agreement dealing with the appointment of the arbitrator.[247]

In *Shin Satellite Public Co. Ltd.* v. *Jain Studios Ltd.*[248], the respondent had the right to appoint arbitrator but did not appoint arbitrator despite service of notice on him by the petitioner. Thereafter, the petitioner filed an application under Section 11(6) before the Chief Justice for the appointment of the arbitrator. The respondent resisted the application and took plea that it had questioned the enforceability of the arbitration agreement itself, and prayed that it should be given time for appointment of arbitrator. The court held, at this belated stage, the respondent could not be permitted to take advantage of its own default. There was failure on the part of the respondent in making appointment of arbitrator in accordance with the agreement, the prayer could not be granted.

Dispute arose between the parties, but the respondent instead of seeking arbitration pursued remedy of civil suit which culminated in court's direction to the parties to refer the dispute to arbitrator as per arbitration within the time specified. Respondent, instead of referring the dispute to the designated person or calling upon the appellant to do so, issued notice to the appellant to agree upon an independent arbitrator. It was held, the respondent and not the applicant had failed to act in terms of procedure contained in the arbitration clause as he had not taken steps for invoking arbitration in terms of the arbitration clause. Non-compliance of the respondent's notice by the appellant did not entitle the Chief Justice to appoint an independent arbitrator at the instance of the respondent. Hence, a person named as arbitrator in the arbitration clause was appointed as arbitrator.[249]

246. (2006) 2 SCC 638.
247. *Union of India* v. *Bharat Battery Mfg. Co. (P) Ltd.*, (2007) 7 SCC 684.
248. (2006) 2 SCC 628.
249. *Indian Oil Corpn. Ltd.* v. *Raja Transport (P) Ltd.*, (2009) 8 SCC 520.

Where there was delay on the part of the Railways in appointing arbitrator(s) due to frequent transfers of officers and the arbitration proceedings were pending for more than seven years, the order of the High Court for appointing judge of the High Court as arbitrator in the case was held proper.[250]

Where the parties fail to agree between themselves, then the Chief Justice or any person or institution designated by him has the jurisdiction to appoint an arbitrator.[251]

Appointment of third arbitrator [S. 11(3)]

Primarily, it is for the parties to agree upon a procedure for appointing the arbitrator or arbitrators. Failing such agreement, sub-section (3) of Section 11, Arbitration and Conciliation Act, 1996 provides that in an arbitration with three arbitrators, each party shall appoint one arbitrator, and the two appointed arbitrators shall appoint the third arbitrator who shall act as the presiding arbitrator. The law nowhere contemplates such appointments being necessarily in writing. The requirement of the law is that there should be an appointment and the appointment should be by the two appointed arbitrators.[252]

It is not necessary within the meaning of Section 11(3) that the presiding arbitrator must be appointed by the two appointed arbitrators in writing nor is it necessary that the two appointed arbitrators must necessarily sit at one place, deliberate jointly and take a decision in the presence of each other in regard to the appointment of the presiding arbitrator. It is enough if they have actually consulted or conferred with each other and if both or any of them communicates to the parties the appointment of the presiding arbitrator as having taken place by the joint deliberation of the two.[253]

Extinguishment of right of a party to appoint arbitrator under arbitration agreement

Where a party declines to appoint an arbitrator in terms of an arbitration agreement, it amounts to failure to appoint arbitrator. Hence, the right of the party under the arbitration agreement to appoint arbitrators gets extinguished. The designated court did not commit an error in appointing the arbitrator. The plea of the petitioner that the designated judge ought to have

250. *Union of India* v. *Singh Builders Syndicate*, (2009) 4 SCC 523.

251. *Jharna Sarkar* v. *Nitish Mohan Sanyal*, 2012 SCC OnLine Cal 5722: (2012) 5 CHN 713.

252. *Grid Corpn. of Orissa Ltd.* v. *AES Corpn.*, (2002) 7 SCC 736.

253. *Ibid.*

been given an opportunity to nominate its arbitrator was held tenable.[254] Where party fails to appoint arbitrator as per agreement procedure within 30 days from the receipt of request from the other party to do so, the right of said party to appoint arbitrator subsequently does not automatically cease after the expiry of the period of 30 days, but continues till application under Section 11(6) is filed by the other party. The 30 days' limitation cannot be invoked as a mandatory period under Section 11(6).[255]

Party failing to appoint arbitrator within 30 days [S. 11(4)]

In *Groupe Chimique Tunisien SA* v. *Southern Petrochemicals Industries Corpn. Ltd.*[256], the party concerned did not appoint the arbitrator as it was under the bona fide impression that there cannot be arbitration in the case; however, nominated the arbitrator before the Supreme Court. The said nomination was accepted.

Opposite party failed to appoint arbitrator despite lapse of 30 days from date of receipt of notice invoking arbitration clause; independent arbitrator was appointed to adjudicate and decide dispute between parties including their claims, counterclaims and objections. Retired judge of the High Court was appointed as arbitrator.[257] Arbitration agreement clearly stated that if respondent fails to nominate arbitrator within 30 days of notice by claimant, arbitrator nominated by the claimant shall become the sole arbitrator. As the respondent failed to nominate arbitrator in terms of notice, nomination of arbitrator by the claimant was held proper. It was not necessary for the claimant to approach the High Court under Section 11(4).[258] Where the employer fails to appoint an arbitrator in terms of the arbitration clause within time after receipt of notice from the contractor, the contractor is justified in invoking Section 11(6). A case is made out for appointment of arbitrator, and an arbitrator was appointed in the case.[259]

The petitioner firm had entered into agreement with the contractor for development and construction of property. Where the contractor failed to appoint an arbitrator within the period of 30 days after multiple notice sent by the firm, the court had ample jurisdiction to appoint arbitrator. Retired judge of the High Court was arbitrator in the case.[260]

---

254. *Dakshin Shelters (P) Ltd.* v. *Geeta S. Johari*, (2012) 5 SCC 152.
255. *BSNL* v. *Dhanurdhar Champatiray*, (2010) 1 SCC 673.
256. (2006) 5 SCC 275.
257. *National Associates* v. *North Eastern Indira Gandhi Regional Institute of Health and Medical Sciences*, 2019 SCC OnLine Megh 301.
258. *Power Grid Corpn. of India Ltd.* v. *B.C. Enterprise*, 2020 SCC OnLine Megh 206.
259. *Shree Laxmi Iron & Steel Works (P) Ltd.* v. *Railways*, 2022 SCC OnLine Cal 144.
260. *Bihar Home Developers and Builders* v. *Narendra Prasad Gupta*, 2021 SCC OnLine Pat 1355: (2021) 3 PLJR 385.

A vacancy arose as one nominated arbitrator from the side of the petitioner reclused himself. The agreement provided for constituting Arbitral Tribunal consisting of three arbitrators. The appointing authority did not adhere to the request of the petitioner to fill the vacancy by appointing an arbitrator and a period of 30 days expired. The appointing authority ceased to have jurisdiction to appoint arbitrator. The court alone in exercise of jurisdiction under Section 11(6) can fill the vacancy by appointing an arbitrator. Retired judge of the High Court was appointed as arbitrator in the case.[261]

Arbitrators appointed by parties failing to agree on presiding officer [Sub-s. (4)]

When the arbitrators appointed by the parties failed to agree on the presiding arbitrator as per the terms of the agreement, the Supreme Court with the consent of both the parties appointed sole arbitrator in the case.[262]

Ruling in *SBP & Co.* v. *Patel Engg. Ltd.*[263], relating to exercise of power under Section 11(6), apply equally to exercise of power under Section 11(4).[264]

Nomination of arbitrator by Chief Justice or his designate before expiry of 30 days period [Sub-s. (4)]

Where the arbitrator is nominated by Chief Justice or his designate before expiry of 30 days period, such an Arbitral Tribunal would be improperly constituted, and thus, without jurisdiction. Aggrieved party would have the right to require the tribunal to rule on its jurisdiction under Section 16.[265]

Even if a contract is void, or even if a contract/agreement is terminated or even if an agreement is invalid or even if the arbitration clause itself is invalid, the jurisdiction to appoint arbitrator vested in the Chief Justice or his designate is not taken away. The construction of an arbitration clause should start from the assumption that the parties are likely to have intended that any dispute arising out of the relationship into which they have entered or purported to enter, has to be decided by the same tribunal.[266]

Appointment of arbitrator—Right when lost

Applicant requested the Engineer-in-Chief to appoint an arbitrator. The Engineer-in-Chief failed to act as per procedure, however, appointed

261. *V.K. Gupta and Associates* v. *Superintending Engineer*, 2023 SCC OnLine All 2949.
262. *Arvind Constructions Co. (P) Ltd.* v. *Kalinga Mining Corpn.*, (2007) 6 SCC 798.
263. (2005) 8 SCC 618.
264. *Punjab Agro Industries Corpn. Ltd.* v. *Kewal Singh Dhillon*, (2008) 10 SCC 128.
265. *Konkan Railway Corpn. Ltd.* v. *Rani Construction (P) Ltd.*, (2002) 2 SCC 388.
266. *Krebs Biochemicals & Industries Ltd.* v. *Nannapaneni Venkatrao Coop. Sugars Ltd.*, 2009 SCC OnLine AP 391: (2009) 3 AP LJ 220.

arbitrator only after application under Section 11 of the Act was filed. The appointment of arbitrator by the Engineer-in-Chief was of no consequence. The right of the Engineer-in-Chief to appoint an arbitrator was lost after an application under Section 11 for appointment of arbitrator was filed in court.[267]

Forfeiture of right to appoint arbitrator

The applicant requested the opposite party to appoint an arbitrator as per agreed procedure. The opposite party did not appoint arbitrator as per agreed procedure but appointed arbitrator after the appellant had filed an application under Section 11(6) for the appointment of the arbitrator. It was held, right of the opposite party to appoint an arbitrator was lost after the application for appointment of arbitrator was made to the court. Appointment of arbitrator by the opposite party was of no consequence.[268] Where the respondent failed to appoint arbitrator within 30 days, his right to appoint arbitrator stood forfeited, the court appointed substitute arbitrator.[269]

In event of forfeiture of right of a party to nominate its nominee on Arbitral Tribunal would not render court powerless to appoint appropriate Arbitral Tribunal or to appoint only a sole arbitrator on insistence of petitioner.[270]

Not mandatory to appoint named arbitrator [Sub-s. (6)]

It is true that it is not mandatory for the Chief Justice or any person or institution designated by him to appoint named arbitrator or arbitrators. But at the same time, due regard has to be given to the qualifications required by the agreement and other considerations.[271]

"To take the necessary measure" [Sub-s. (6)]

The crucial expression in Section 11(6) is "a party may request the Chief Justice or any person or institution designated by him *to take the necessary measure*". The expression "necessary" as a general rule can be broadly stated to be those things which are reasonably required to be done or legally ancillary to the accomplishment of the intended act. Necessary measures can be stated to be the reasonable steps required to be taken. This expression has to be read along with requirement in Section 11(8) that the Chief Justice or

267. *Sunil Sharma* v. *Union of India*, 2017 SCC OnLine Megh 152: (2017) 3 Civ LT 368.
268. *Deep Trading Co.* v. *Indian Oil Corpn.*, (2013) 4 SCC 35.
269. *Wig Bros. (India) (P) Ltd.* v. *Devi Shakuntala Thakral Charitable Foundation*, 2014 SCC OnLine MP 8621: (2015) 1 MP LJ 596.
270. *PSP Projects Ltd.* v. *Bhiwandi Nizampur City Municipal Corpn.*, 2023 SCC OnLine Bom 230: (2023) 4 Mah LJ 517.
271. *Northern Railway Admn.* v. *Patel Engg. Co. Ltd.*, (2008) 10 SCC 240.

the person or an institution designated by him to appointing an arbitrator shall have "due regard" to the two cumulative conditions contained in Section 11(8)(*a*) and (*b*) relating to qualifications and other considerations as are likely to secure the appointment of an independent and impartial arbitrator. The expression "due regard" in Section 11(8) means that proper attention to several circumstances have been focused.[272] In appointment of arbitrator under Section 11(6), there is obligation to give due regard to the twin requirements under Section 11(8), *i.e.* the qualifications required of an arbitrator by the agreement concerned and other considerations necessary to secure the appointment of an independent and impartial arbitrator.[273]

Appointment of arbitrator—Proper procedure [S. 11(6)]

The scheme of the Act is that under Section 11(2), the parties are free to agree on a procedure for appointing an arbitrator subject to the provisions of Section 11(6). A petition under Section 11(5) of the Act would not lie if there is any agreement between the parties providing for the procedure for appointment of an arbitrator. In *Standard Corrosion Controls (P) Ltd.* v. *Sarku Engg. Services SDN BHD*[274], the parties had agreed that any dispute between them shall be settled as far as possible by mutual consultation and consent failing which by arbitration to be held at Mumbai by applying the Arbitration Rules of the International Chamber of Commerce. It was held, the applicant, therefore, has to apply to the Secretariat of ICC as provided in the Arbitration Rules of the ICC, applicant cannot directly approach the court by application under Section 11(5) for appointment of arbitrator. Section 11(6) was not attracted in the case, the procedure for appointment of arbitrator as agreed up by the parties would be applicable. Petition under Section 11(6) for appointment of arbitrator cannot be allowed when procedure prescribed in the arbitration clause of agreement has not been exhausted.[275]

An application under Section 11(6) for appointment of arbitrator is not maintainable when notice requiring invocation of an arbitration clause has not been sent and served on the opposite party.[276]

Only Chief Justice of India or Chief Justice of the High Court have been conferred exclusive power under Section 11(6) of the Act to appoint

---

272. *Ibid.*
273. *BSNL* v. *Dhanurdhar Champatiray*, (2010) 1 SCC 673; *Everest Holding Ltd.* v. *Shyam Kumar Shrivastava*, (2008) 16 SCC 774.
274. (2009) 1 SCC 303.
275. *Ohm Construction* v. *State of Bihar*, 2020 SCC OnLine Pat 4615.
276. *Shyam Kishor Gupta* v. *Bharat Sarkar*, 2020 SCC OnLine All 2185: (2020) 3 All LJ 499 (All); *Abdul Rashid* v. *National Building Construction Corpn.*, 2012 SCC OnLine All 730: (2012) 5 All LJ 370.

arbitrators. Order passed by the Additional District Judge directing the parties to suggest names of arbitrators was without jurisdiction.[277]

Scope of judicial inquiry

The scope of judicial inquiry in appointment of arbitrator under Section 11(6) extends to the legal perimeter of examining the existence of an arbitration agreement.[278]

If an arbitration agreement exists, the court is only required to consider the appointment of an arbitrator and leave it to the Arbitral Tribunal to decide all issues. Issue regarding non-arbitrability of disputes can also be considered and decided by the Arbitral Tribunal. As both the parties agreed that there were disputes and agreed to invoke the arbitration clause, but there was no consensus as to who should be arbitrator, a retired judge of the High Court was appointed arbitrator in the case.[279]

Qualification of arbitrators [Sub-s. (6)]

Objection was that the person appointed as per procedure in the agreement was not qualified for adjudicating the dispute in question. It was held that there was no requirement as to the qualification of arbitrator to resolve the dispute in question, in the agreement. If the parties have entered into the arbitration agreement with open eyes, and there is no failure of the procedure for appointment of arbitrator(s) as provided for therein, it was not open to them to ignore it and invoke Section 11(6). In *You One Engg. & Construction Co. Ltd.* v. *NHAI*[280], the arbitration agreement clearly envisaged the appointment of the presiding officer by Indian Roads Congress (IRC). There was no qualification that the arbitrator had to be a different person depending on the nature of the dispute. Objection was rejected.

Appointment of another arbitrator

Arbitrator had made an award without notice to the objectors. Service of notice on the objectors was found manipulated. The court set aside the arbitrator's award and appointed another arbitrator in the case.[281]

---

277. *Ballabh Lal* v. *Kukkoo Motors Finance (P) Ltd.*, 2016 SCC OnLine All 2737: (2016) 116 ALR 111.
278. *Mayavati Trading (P) Ltd.* v. *Pradyuat Deb Burman*, (2019) 8 SCC 714; *R. Vedagiri* v. *K. Rajakumari*, 2022 SCC OnLine Mad 9017, followed.
279. *Subba Reddy Badwelu* v. *Aditya Vamsiram Homes LLP*, 2021 SCC OnLine TS 3646.
280. (2006) 4 SCC 372.
281. *Taruna Vaid* v. *Rakesh Kumar*, (2005) 12 SCC 235.

Decision of the earlier arbitrator that it has no jurisdiction to entertain application is no ground to appoint another arbitrator.[282]

When a dispute arises out of similar work and between the same parties, there cannot be two litigations for the same contract, second arbitration is not permissible.[283]

Non-referral of dispute(s) to Arbitral Tribunal as per procedure—High Court's power to appoint arbitrator

Railways and public institutions are very slow in reacting to the request made by a contractor for appointment of the arbitrator. Therefore, in case the appointment is not made in time on the request made by the contracting party, then in that case, the power of the High Court to appoint an arbitrator under Section 11 of the Act will not be denuded. Administrative authorities cannot be allowed to sleep over the matter and leave the citizens without any remedy.[284]

Designation of any person or institution by Supreme Court is not delegation of judicial power [Sub-s. (6-B)]

Sub-section (6-B) is newly added by the Amendment Act 3 of 2016. It has been categorically provided in sub-section (6-B) that the designation of any person or institution by the Supreme Court shall not be construed as delegation of judicial power. The order passed by a designated person or institution would continue to be regarded as a judicial order.[285]

Appointment of arbitrator—Scope [S. 11(6) vis-a-vis S. 11(4), S. 11(5)]

The Supreme Court has summarised the scope of Section 11(6) thus:

> (*iv*) While failure of the other party to act within 30 days will furnish a cause of action to the party seeking arbitration to approach the Chief Justice or his designate in cases falling under sub-sections (4) and (5), such a time-bound requirement is not found in sub-section (6) of Section 11. The failure to act as per the agreed procedure within the time-limit prescribed by the arbitration agreement, or in the absence of any prescribed time-limit, within a reasonable time, will enable the aggrieved party to file a petition under Section 11(6) of the Act.
>
> (*v*) Where the appointment procedure has been agreed between the parties, but the cause of action for invoking the jurisdiction of the Chief Justice or

---

282. *Technofab Engg. Ltd.* v. *National Aluminium Co. Ltd.*, 2019 SCC OnLine Ori 105.
283. *Ibid.*
284. *Union of India* v. *V.S. Engg. (P) Ltd.*, (2006) 13 SCC 240.
285. *Duro Felguera, S.A.* v. *Gangavaram Port Ltd.*, (2017) 9 SCC 729.

his designate under clauses (*a*), (*b*) or (*c*) of sub-section (6) has not arisen, then the question of the Chief Justice or his designate exercising power under sub-section (6) does not arise. The condition precedent for approaching the Chief Justice or his designate for taking necessary measures under sub-section (6) is that

(*i*) a party falling to act as required under the agreed appointment procedure; or

(*ii*) the parties (or the two appointed arbitrators) falling to reach an agreement expected of them under the agreed appointment procedure; or

(*iii*) a person/institution who has been entrusted with any function under the agreed appointment procedure, failing to perform such function.

(*vi*) The Chief Justice or his designate while exercising power under sub-section (6) of Section 11 shall *endeavour to give effect to the appointment procedure prescribed in the arbitration clause.*

(*vii*) If circumstances exist, giving rise to justifiable doubts as to the independence and impartiality of the person nominated, or if other circumstances warrant appointment of an independent arbitrator by ignoring the procedure prescribed, the Chief Justice or his designate may, for reasons to be recorded ignore the designated arbitrator and appoint someone else.[286]

Distinction between Section 11(5) and 11(6)

1. There is a difference and distinction between Section 11(5) and 11(6), Arbitration and Conciliation Act, 1996.
2. In a case where there is no written agreement between the parties on the procedure for appointing an arbitrator or arbitrators, parties are free to agree on a procedure by mutual consent and/or agreement, and the dispute can be referred to a sole arbitrator/arbitrators who can be appointed by mutual consent and failing any agreement referred to Section 11(2), Section 11(5), Arbitration and Conciliation Act, 1996 shall be attracted and in such a situation, the application for appointment of arbitrator or arbitrators shall be maintainable under Section 11(5), Arbitration and Conciliation Act, 1996 and not under Section 11(6), Arbitration and Conciliation Act, 1996.
3. In a case where there is a written agreement and/or contract containing the arbitration agreement and the appointment or procedure is agreed upon by the parties, an application under Section 11(6), Arbitration and Conciliation Act, 1996 shall be maintainable and the High Court or its nominee can appoint an arbitrator or arbitrators in case any of the eventualities occurring under Section 11(6)(*a*) to (*c*) of the Arbitration and Conciliation Act, 1996.

---

286. *Indian Oil Corpn. Ltd.* v. *Raja Transport (P) Ltd.*, (2009) 8 SCC 526.

4. Once the dispute is referred to arbitration, and the sole arbitrator is appointed by the parties by mutual consent, and the arbitrator/arbitrators is/are so appointed; the arbitration agreement cannot be invoked for the second time.
5. In a case where there is a dispute/controversy on the mandate of the arbitrator being terminated on the ground mentioned in Section 14(1)(*a*), such a dispute has to be raised before the "court", defined under Section 2(1)(*e*), Arbitration and Conciliation Act, 1996 and such a dispute cannot be decided on an application filed under Section 11(6), Arbitration and Conciliation Act, 1996.[287]

Appointment of arbitrator(s) by court dehors arbitration agreement—When warranted

When a party having responsibility to appoint arbitrator(s) in terms of the agreement does not appoint arbitrator(s) within 30 days of demand made by the other party, arbitrator(s) should be appointed by the court keeping in mind the mandate of Section 11(8). In order to allay any apprehensions in the minds of the applicants and to ensure fairness, appointment procedure given in the arbitration agreement was not followed. One arbitrator was nominated from the panel suggested by the applicants and one arbitrator from the panel given in the arbitration agreement. The two appointed arbitrators would choose the third arbitrator from the panel so prepared, who would act as presiding arbitrator of the Arbitral Tribunal.[288]

Powers of the court to appoint arbitrator(s) of its own choice

In *Union of India* v. *U.P. State Bridge Corpn. Ltd.*[289], since the Arbitral Tribunal consisting of three arbitrators appointed by the department did not conclude the proceedings despite the direction given by the High Court, the appointment of sole arbitrator in the case by the High Court was upheld.

Provision in arbitration clause for reference to named arbitrator when can be ignored

If circumstances exist, giving rise to justifiable doubts as to the independence and impartiality of the person nominated, or if other circumstances warrant appointment of an independent arbitrator by ignoring the procedure prescribed, the Chief Justice or his designate may, for reasons to be recorded, ignore the designated arbitrator and appoint someone else.[290]

287. *Swadesh Kumar Agarwal* v. *Dinesh Kumar Agarwal*, (2022) 10 SCC 235.
288. *Kumagai Gumi Co. Ltd.* v. *Delhi Metro Rail Corpn. Ltd.*, (2004) 13 SCC 22.
289. (2015) 2 SCC 52.
290. *Indian Oil Corpn. Ltd.* v. *Raja Transport (P) Ltd.*, (2009) 8 SCC 520.

Where the application under Section 11(6) for appointment of arbitrator contains name of sole arbitrator, the arbitrator did not show any inclination to adjudicate party's claim as there was failure of the sole arbitrator to perform his function, appointment of arbitrator by the Chief Justice was proper.[291]

Power of Chief Justice/designate to appoint arbitrator other than named in arbitration clause

The Chief Justice or his designate has the power to appoint a person other than the named arbitrator upon examination of the relevant facts which would tend to indicate that the named arbitrator is not likely to be impartial. Hence, the petition could not be rejected merely on the ground that the Chief Justice or his designate would have no power to make an appointment of an arbitrator other than the Chairman-cum-Managing Director (CMD) or his designate.[292] In this case the petitioner clearly pleaded that the named arbitrator was a direct subordinate of the CMD and an employee of the respondent. CMD is the controlling authority of the employees, who had been dealing with the subject-matter in the present dispute and also the controlling authority of the respondent. Further, CMD himself would not be able to act independently and impartially, being amenable to the directions issued by the Ministry of Defence. Hence, a retired Chief Justice of the High Court was appointed arbitrator in the case.[293]

"Within thirty days of demand"

The period of 30 days is not mentioned in sub-section (6) of Section 11. The period of limitation of 30 days is only provided under sub-sections (4) and (5) of Section 11. As such as per statute, the period of limitation of 30 days cannot be invoked under sub-section (6) of Section 11.[294]

Non-appointment of arbitrator within 30 days from the receipt of notice from the opposite party—Effect

Dispute arose between the parties, a letter dated 21 July 2005 was written by the appellant to the Director (Marketing) of the respondent, the appointing authority under the arbitration clause, invoking the arbitration clause and requesting him to refer the matter to arbitration for resolving the differences.

291. *Aargee Engg. & Co.* v. *Era Infra Engg. Ltd.*, 2017 SCC OnLine All 3929: (2017) 122 ALR 179.
292. *Bipromasz Bipron Trading Sa* v. *Bharat Electronics Ltd.*, (2012) 6 SCC 384.
293. *Ibid.*
294. *ACE Pipeline Contracts (P) Ltd.* v. *Bharat Petroleum Corpn. Ltd.*, (2007) 5 SCC 304; *Datar Switchgears Ltd.* v. *Tata Finance Ltd.*, (2000) 8 SCC 151.

No one was appointed as arbitrator. Therefore, on 22 August 2005, the appellant filed an application before the High Court for appointment of arbitrator under Section 11(5) and (6) of the Arbitration and Conciliation Act, 1996. It was held, the right of the appointing authority to appoint the arbitrator was not automatically forfeited in such a case. The limitation period of 30 days is only provided under Section 11(4) and (5), and could not be invoked in a case under Section 11(6).[295]

Where the opposite party fails to appoint an arbitrator within 30 days of the notice, the court is empowered to appoint arbitrator.[296]

Where the employer fails to appoint an arbitrator in terms of the arbitration clause within time after receipt of notice from the contractor, the contractor is justified in invoking Section 11(6). Case is made out for appointment of arbitrator, arbitrator was appointed in the case.[297]

Appointment of arbitrator by Chief Justice/his designate—Object of the provision

The only function of the Chief Justice or his designate under Section 11 is to fill up the gap left by a party to the arbitration agreement or by two of the arbitrators appointed by the parties and nominate an arbitrator. This is to enable the Arbitral Tribunal to be expeditiously constituted and the arbitration in proceedings to commence. The function has been left to the Chief Justice or his designate advisedly, with a view to ensure that the nomination of the arbitrator is made by a person occupying high judicial office or his designate, who would take due care to see that a competent, independent and impartial arbitrator is nominated.[298]

Indian Council of Arbitration (ICA) taking long time in appointment of arbitrator

The underlying principle of the Arbitration and Conciliation Act, 1996 is to strive for efficient and expeditious disposal of disputes between the parties by a forum of their own choice. Considering urgency of the matter as well as the fact that if ICA takes unduly long time in appointing the arbitrator, it will defeat the purpose of approaching the forum and in the meantime the purpose to set the adjudication mechanism in motion may become redundant, a retired judge of the High Court was appointed arbitrator in the case.[299]

---

295. *ACE Pipeline Contracts (P) Ltd.* v. *Bharat Petroleum Corpn. Ltd.*, (2007) 5 SCC 304.
296. *KMC Construction Ltd.* v. *State of Chhattisgarh*, 2017 SCC OnLine Chh 1905.
297. *Shree Laxmi Iron & Steel Works (P) Ltd.* v. *Railways*, 2022 SCC OnLine Cal 144.
298. *Konkan Railway Corpn. Ltd.* v. *Rani Construction (P) Ltd.*, (2002) 2 SCC 388.
299. *Jindal Steel and Power Ltd.* v. *State Trading Corpn. of India Ltd.*, 2020 SCC OnLine Del 620.

Contract entered into between the parties to appoint arbitrator. Where no arbitrator is appointed by the respondent within time stipulated in notice served by the applicant, the court gets jurisdiction to appoint arbitrator under Section 11(6). The court appointed an arbitrator in the case.[300]

Existence of arbitration agreement—Finding by the Chief Justice/his designate

The Chief Justice or his designate is required to decide the existence of arbitration agreement between parties finally. Prima facie finding as to existence of arbitration agreement is not contemplated by the Act. Once the Chief Justice or his designate has held that there is an arbitration agreement between the parties, the arbitrator is precluded from considering the issue and recording a contrary finding.[301]

The court should and need only look into one aspect, the existence of an arbitration agreement. After the 2015 Amendment, all that the courts need to see is whether an arbitration agreement exists, nothing more, nothing less. The legislature's policy and purpose is to minimise the court's intervention at the stage of appointing the arbitrator and this intention as incorporated in Section 11(6-A) ought to be respected.[302]

Dispute/differences arose between parties with regard to payment of bills raised by the petitioner. Clause of the supply agreement provided for reference of all disputes and differences to the Arbitration Authority under 1996 Act. Petition for appointment of arbitrator was allowed, arbitrator was appointed in the case.[303]

Clause in the arbitration agreement executed between the parties provided for determination of disputes by arbitration in accordance with the governing law being law of India. The petitioner-company sent an arbitration notice to the respondent to nominate the arbitrator within 15 days of the receipt of the notice. Since the respondent did not respond, the petitioner by petition under Section 11(9) prayed for appointment of arbitrator. Petitioner's assertions were that disputes had arisen and remained unsettled. Application was allowed, a former judge of the Supreme Court was appointed arbitrator in the case.[304] (Legal notice invoking arbitration clause not replied, none appeared on behalf of respondent before the court, arbitrator appointed in the case.)

---

300. *RCM Infrastructure Ltd.* v. *State Highway Authority of Jharkhand*, 2022 SCC OnLine Jhar 418: (2022) 3 JBCJ 208.
301. *Indowind Energy Ltd.* v. *Wescare (I) Ltd.*, (2010) 5 SCC 306.
302. *Duro Felguera, S.A.* v. *Gangavaram Port Ltd.*, (2017) 9 SCC 729.
303. *Suprema Inc.* v. *4G Identity Solutions (P) Ltd.*, (2015) 13 SCC 122.
304. *Trans Asian Shipping Services (P) Ltd.* v. *Beacon Shipping Lines Ltd.*, (2018) 10 SCC 521; *Fugro Survey (India) (P) Ltd.* v. *Ramunia International Services Ltd.*, (2012) 10 SCC 752.

When consensus not reached between parties—Jurisdiction of court to appoint arbitrator

When consensus is not reached between parties for making reference of disputes to arbitration as per terms of the arbitration clause, either of the parties can invoke Section 11 and seek reference of dispute to arbitration. When one of the parties as required per the arbitration clause does not concur with the arbitrator appointed by the other party and the parties fail to appoint arbitrator under the agreed procedure, the court is required to appoint arbitrator.[305]

Appointment of presiding officer

Where two nominated arbitrators are required to appoint the presiding officer of the tribunal by mutual consent and no consensus on the name of the presiding officer is arrived at by the two nominated arbitrators despite mutual consultation, the Supreme Court can appoint the presiding officer.[306]

Appointment of arbitrator by court under Section 11(6) even where procedure exists for appointment of named arbitrator

In normal circumstances while exercising jurisdiction under Section 11(6), the court would adhere to the terms of the agreement as closely as possible. But if the circumstances warrant, the Chief Justice or the nominee of the Chief Justice is not debarred from appointing an independent arbitrator other than the named arbitrator. In the peculiar facts and circumstances of this case, it would be necessary and advisable to appoint an independent arbitrator. In this case, the contact was with the Ministry of Defence. The arbitrator, *S* had been nominated by the Director General, Ordnance Factories, Government of India, who was bound to accept the directions issued by the Union of India. *S* was an employee within the same organisation. The attitude of the arbitrator *S* was found not independent and impartial. Hence, in exercise of powers under Section 11(4) and (6) of the Arbitration and Conciliation Act, 1996 read with para 2 of the Appointment of Arbitrators by the Chief Justice of India Scheme, 1996, sole arbitrator other than the named arbitrator was appointed to adjudicate the disputes between the parties.[307]

Power of Chief Justice to appoint independent arbitrator is not confined to those persons who have been named in an arbitration agreement, particularly

305. *Ashapura Mine-Chem Ltd.* v. *Gujarat Mineral Development Corpn.*, (2015) 8 SCC 193.

306. *ONGC Petro Additions Ltd.* v. *Daelim Industrial Co. Ltd.*, (2015) 13 SCC 176.

307. *Denel (Pty) Ltd.* v. *Ministry of Defence*, (2012) 2 SCC 759.

when, in facts and circumstances of case, named persons in an arbitration agreement are working under control of authority who has appointed them as such. Prayer made by the petitioner to appoint an independent arbitrator other than one named in the arbitration agreement was allowed.[308]

Apprehension of petitioners about the named arbitrator not being impartial, was a reasonable apprehension. Order of the High Court which directed the Municipal Commissioner, named as arbitrator, to expedite consideration of dispute raised by the petitioners, and to decide on their claim as well as counter claim was not implemented. The High Court appointed an independent arbitrator to arbitrate upon the dispute.[309]

Procedure prescribed in arbitration clause not exhausted

A petition under Section 11(6) for appointment of arbitrator cannot be allowed when the procedure prescribed in the arbitration clause of the agreement has not been exhausted.[310]

Where named arbitrator refuses to act as arbitrator

Where a named arbitrator refused to act as an arbitrator, refusal does not extinguish the arbitration agreement. Arbitration clauses become exhausted if named arbitrator refuses to act, but the provisions of Section 15, Arbitration and Conciliation Act, 1996 would then be attracted and appointment of a substitute arbitrator shall be made by the court, unless bar of appointment of any other arbitrator except named arbitrator is specifically provided for in the arbitration clause/agreement.[311]

Appointment of person other than designated arbitrator

Appellant's demand was that some retired judge of the Supreme Court be appointed arbitrator in the case as the arbitrator nominated in the agreement may suffer from bias, and may not take independent decisions in the case. Once a party has entered into an agreement with eyes wide open it cannot wriggle out of the situation that if any officer of the respondent is appointed as arbitrator, as provided for in the arbitration clause, he will not be impartial or objective. However, if the appellant feels that the arbitrator has not acted independently or impartially or he has suffered from any bias, it will always be open to the party to make an application under Section 34 of the Act to

308. *Tramboo Joinery Mill (P) Ltd.* v. *State of J&K*, 2014 SCC OnLine J&K 55: (2015) 3 Civ LT 315.
309. *B.R. Ganesh* v. *Commr., Bruhat Bangalore Mahanagara Palike*, 2015 SCC OnLine Kar 8169: ILR 2015 Kar 2130.
310. *Ohm Construction* v. *State of Bihar*, 2020 SCC OnLine Pat 4615.
311. *San-A Tradubg Co. Ltd.* v. *I.C. Textiles Ltd.*, (2012) 7 SCC 192.

set aside the award on the ground that arbitrator acted with bias or malice in law or fact. Hence, there was no reason to interfere with the order passed by the Single Judge dismissing the application for appointment of arbitrator.[312]

Employee of company appointed arbitrator

In *Aravali Power Co. (P) Ltd.* v. *Era Infra Engg. Ltd.*[313], the employee, the Chief Executive Officer, appellant of the company was appointed arbitrator in the case. The arbitrator (employee) was neither the dealing authority in regard to the contract nor was directly subordinate to the officer whose decision was subject-matter of the dispute. Thus, there could be no justifiable apprehension about his independence or impartiality. Arbitrator had dealt with contracts of similar nature. There was no reason to challenge the validity of the appointment of the arbitrator. The High Court was not justified in interfering with the process and progress of arbitration.

Indian Railway Standard Contract (para 2900)

Conditions of standard conditions of contract are binding on the parties. In accordance with para 2900 the respondent, Railways could appoint Gazetted Railway Officer as sole arbitrator after satisfying conditions of para 2900.[314] On the date of agreement, General Conditions of Contract (GCC) (2010) alone was in existence. Hence, the award of GCC (2016) and (2019) did not have enforceability to the contract. Applicant had not waived its right to object to serving Railway officers to be appointed as arbitrators and proposed to appoint an independent arbitrator, there was no defect in applicant approaching the court for appointment of independent arbitrator. A retired judge of the High Court was appointed arbitrator in the case.[315]

General conditions of contract (GCC)

Dispute submitted by contractor to appropriate authority was not resolved within 45 days as per terms of GCC. Former High Court judge was appointed as arbitrator.[316]

Dispute arose between the parties, the appellant invoked arbitration clause, but the respondent Railways did not respond, hence forfeited its right to appoint arbitrator. The High Court exercising powers under Section 11(6)

---

312. *ACE Pipeline Contracts (P) Ltd.* v. *Bharat Petroleum Corpn. Ltd.*, (2007) 5 SCC 304.
313. (2017) 15 SCC 32.
314. *Sight Sound Electronics (India) (P) Ltd.* v. *Central Organisation Railway*, 2011 SCC OnLine All 1843: (2012) 1 All LJ 599.
315. *Tata Projects Ltd.* v. *Central Organization for Railway Electrification*, 2021 SCC OnLine All 122: (2021) 3 All LJ 558.
316. *GSR Venture (P) Ltd.* v. *State of Mizoram*, 2020 SCC OnLine Gau 5015.

directed the constitution of the Arbitration Tribunal in terms of GCC. GCC was not signed by the parties, nor was made part of the arbitration agreement. Order of the High Court directing the constitution of the Arbitration Tribunal in terms of GCC was erroneously set aside. A former judge of the Supreme Court was appointed arbitrator in the case.[317]

Clause 63 of Northern Railways General Conditions of Contractor Regulations and Instructions (GCC) require submission of all disputes arising out of contract to the General Manager within 120 days. A grievance contractor can demand appointment of an arbitrator under clause 64 of GCC. Straightway making a claim for appointment of arbitrator without following the said procedure is premature and unsustainable, was rejected.[318]

Chief Justice or his designate does not discharge judicial function under Section 11(6)

The Chief Justice or his designate does not discharge any judicial function under Section 11(6). The Chief Justice or his designate, though a judge, does not sit as a court.[319]

Government contracts—Appointment of arbitrator(s)

The power of appointment of arbitrator under government contracts casts an onerous and responsible duty upon personal designate to appoint such persons/officers as arbitrators who are not only able to function independently and impartially but are in position to devote adequate time in conducting arbitration. Appointing authorities should be more vigilant and more responsible in choosing arbitrators who are in a position to conduct the arbitration proceedings in an efficient manner, without compromising with their other duties, failing which the courts are not powerless to remedy such situations in exercising their powers under Section 11 to constitute Arbitral Tribunal to protect the interest of other side. If the government has appointed officers as arbitrators who are not able to devote time to the arbitration proceedings or become incapable of acting as arbitrators because of frequent transfers, etc., then the principle of "default procedure" at least in the cases where the government has assumed the role of appointment of arbitrators to itself, has to be applied in the case of substitute arbitrators as well and the court will step in to appoint the arbitrators by keeping aside the procedure which is agreed to between the parties.[320]

---

317. *Continental (India) (P) Ltd.* v. *Railways*, 2022 SCC OnLine SC 922.
318. *Dharam Pal Maddar and Sons* v. *Union of India*, 2018 SCC OnLine P&H 6924.
319. *Grid Corpn. of Orissa Ltd.* v. *AES Corpn.*, (2002) 7 SCC 736.
320. *Union of India* v. *U.P. State Bridge Corpn. Ltd.*, (2015) 2 SCC 52.

Works contract

On the completion of the work contract, final dues were not paid to the contractor. The contractor raised his first claim within the period stipulated in the contract. Despite service of notice, the respondents failed to appoint the arbitrator. Arbitrator was appointed by the court.[321] Works contract contained an arbitration clause, the only remedy available to the contractor is to seek arbitration as per arbitration clause under the contract, arbitrator was appointed in the case.[322]

One of the parties appointed the same person as arbitrator, who was appointed during finalisation of tender. Appointing the same person will lead to conflict of interest. With consent of parties, former judge of the High Court was appointed as sole arbitrator.[323]

Development agreement—Arbitrator appointed

Dispute between the parties arose out of a development agreement. Court is only required to examine the existence of arbitration clause in agreement. Development agreement contained an arbitration clause, and an arbitrator was appointed.[324]

The contractor had failed to execute the work within the stipulated time. The Joint Development Agreement between the parties contained an arbitration clause. The contractor did not respond to the notice sent by the petitioner for the appointment of the arbitrator. Contractor thereby waived his right of appointment of independent arbitrator of his choice and impliedly consented to appointment of sole arbitrator named in notice. Sole arbitrator was appointed in the case.[325]

Security services

There was an agreement for providing security services between the company and the security agency. Clause 27 of agreement provided that parties shall refer all disputes or differences to arbitration and the same shall be adjudicated by a single arbitrator appointed by the company. Company failed to

---

321. *Goel Construction Co.* v. *Union of India*, 2003 SCC OnLine Del 283: (2003) 68 DRJ 312.
322. *Consolidated Construction Consortium Ltd.* v. *Blue Horizon Hotels (P) Ltd.*, 2019 SCC OnLine Kar 2097.
323. *Swarna Techno Constructions (P) Ltd.* v. *Hubli-Dharwad BRTS Co. Ltd.*, 2020 SCC OnLine Kar 5266: (2021) 2 KCCR 1107.
324. *Rajsheel Builders and Developers* v. *Shakuntla Bai*, 2022 SCC OnLine MP 6013.
325. *Mohd. Gafoorur Rahman* v. *J.M. Associates*, 2020 SCC OnLine Kar 1353: (2020) 5 KCCR 302.

refer matter to arbitration by nominating/appointing sole arbitrator, security agency invoked Section 11(6).[326]

Appointment of arbitrator—Bifurcation of causes of action or parties

Parties concerned formed a new company pursuant to joint venture agreement (JVA), which contained an arbitration clause. On failure of the said company to function due to dispute arising between the parties, one of the parties filed the present petition seeking appointment of an arbitrator for adjudication of its claim regarding refund of the money paid/deposited pursuant to and in execution of the JVA and also amount paid towards working expenses of the said company together with interest thereon. Objection was raised by the respondents that certain claims mentioned in the said petition pertained to dealings between the sister concerns of the petitioner and sister concerns of the respondents, and therefore, those claims could not be said to be a part of the disputes arising out of the JVA between the parties, and consequently, the said petition could not be entertained in view of impermissibility of bifurcation of the parties or of the matter under the Arbitration Act concerned. It was held that under the JVA, it was agreed by the parties that equity shares of the joint venture company (JVC) could be subscribed to by either of the parties or by their affiliates and that shareholdings of its affiliates should be considered as shareholdings of the party to the extent it was recognised. Affiliates were also bound by terms and conditions of the JVA. Hence, in such circumstances present matter, if referred to arbitrator, would not in any manner amount to bifurcation of the causes of action or of the parties.[327]

Piecemeal consideration of application under Section 11(6), impermissible

In *Hindustan Copper Ltd.* v. *Monarch Gold Mining Co. Ltd.*[328], one designated judge adjudicated as to the existence of live dispute between the parties and then referred the matter to another designated judge for appointment of arbitrator. Piecemeal consideration of the application under Section 11(6) by the designated judge and another designated judge or the Chief Justice, as the case may be, is not contemplated by Section 11. The function of the Chief Justice or designated judge in consideration of the application under Section 11 is judicial and such application has to be dealt with in its entirety

326. *Globe Detective Agencies (P) Ltd.* v. *Gammon India Ltd.*, 2019 SCC OnLine Mad 39355.
327. *Everest Holding Ltd.* v. *Shyam Kumar Shrivastava*, (2008) 16 SCC 774.
328. (2012) 10 SCC 167.

by either the Chief Justice himself or the designated judge nor by the two designated judges by making it a two tier procedure.

Power of Chief Justice/his designate—Judicial power

Power of the Chief Justice/his designate is not an administrative power but judicial power. The reason is that adjudication is involved in the constitution of an Arbitral Tribunal.[329]

Appointment of an arbitrator is a judicial power and is not a mere administrative function leaving some degree of judicial intervention; when it comes to the question to examine the existence of a prima facie arbitration agreement, it is always necessary to ensure that the dispute resolution process does not become unnecessarily protracted.[330]

The role of Chief Justice of India or his nominee under Section 11 although might only be administrative and not adjudicatory, nevertheless he has to apply his mind to determine the fitness of the case for the exercise of power under Section 11. On the facts of the case, it was found a fit case for the exercise of power under Section 11. Arbitrator was appointed in the case.[331]

The designation of any person or institution by the Supreme Court, or as the case may be, the High Court for the purpose of Section 11 is not delegation of judicial power by the Supreme Court or the High Court [S. 13(6B)].

It is now settled that the power exercised by the Chief Justice of India or the designated judge under Section 11(6), Arbitration and Conciliation Act, 1996 is not an administrative power. It is a judicial power. While exercising the power or performing the duty under Section 11(6) of the Act, the Chief Justice or the designated judge has to consider whether the conditions laid down by the section for the exercise of that power or the performance of that duty, exist. The Chief Justice or the designated judge, as the case may be, is bound to decide whether he has jurisdiction to entertain the request, in the sense, whether there is a valid arbitration agreement in terms of Section 7 of the Act and whether the person before him with a request is a party to the arbitration agreement or whether there was no dispute subsisting which was capable of being arbitrated upon.[332]

329. *SBP & Co.* v. *Patel Engg. Ltd.*, (2005) 8 SCC 618.
330. *United India Insurance Co. Ltd.* v. *Antique Art Exports (P) Ltd.*, (2019) 5 SCC 362.
331. *Glencore International AG* v. *Hindustan Zinc Ltd.*, (2005) 7 SCC 99.
332. *Visa International Ltd.* v. *Continental Resources (USA) Ltd.*, (2009) 2 SCC 55.

Issues that Chief Justice or his designate has to decide

While considering an application under Section 11, the Chief Justice or his designate would not embark upon an examination of the issue of "arbitrability" or appropriateness of adjudication by a private forum, once he finds that there was an agreement between or among the parties, and would leave the issue of the arbitrability for the decision of the Arbitral Tribunal. If the arbitrator wrongly holds that the dispute is arbitrable, the aggrieved party will have to challenge the award by filing an application under Section 34 of the 1996 Act relying upon sub-section (2)(*b*)(*i*) of that section. In *Arasmeta Captive Power Co. (P) Ltd.* v. *Lafarge India (P) Ltd.*[333], the designated judge, while dealing with an application under Section 11(6) on an issue raised with regard to the excepted matters, was not justified in addressing the same on merits whether it was a dispute relating to excepted matters under the agreement in question or not, the same should have been left to be adjudicated by the arbitrator.

Appointment of technical person as arbitrator

Respondent raised a plea that the issue being technical in nature as such, a technical person should be appointed as arbitrator. It was held, the dispute involved in the case was an arbitrable issue which can be adjudicated by any retired High Court judge. Former judge of the High Court was appointed as arbitrator in the case.[334]

Appointment of independent arbitrator by court

The Chief Justice or his designate while exercising power under sub-section (6) of Section 11 *shall endeavour to give effect* to the appointment procedure prescribed in the arbitration clause.

However, if circumstances exist, giving rise to justifiable doubts as to the independence and impartiality of the person nominated, or if other circumstances warrant appointment of an independent arbitrator by ignoring the procedure prescribed, the Chief Justice or his designate may, for the reasons to be recorded, ignore the designated arbitrator and appoint someone else.[335]

District Collector was appointed as arbitrator by parties. He, being employee of organisation, had business relationship and interested in dispute between parties, was not eligible to act as arbitrator considering need for

333. (2013) 15 SCC 414.
334. *S.P. Singla Constructions (P) Ltd.* v. *Chief Engineer*, 2021 SCC OnLine HP 1.
335. *Union of India* v. *BESCO Ltd.*, (2017) 14 SCC 187.

neutrality, impartiality and independence of arbitrators. Application for appointment of independent arbitrator was allowed.[336]

The arbitration clause provided that the dispute be referred to authority for amicable settlement; if not amicably settled, either party may refer the dispute to the arbitrator. The clause provided that Principal Secretary, UDH and LSG shall be the sole arbitrator to decide the dispute. It was held that independence and impartiality of the arbitrator was the paramount consideration, and Principal Secretary, UDH and LSG cannot act as an arbitrator in the case.[337]

Removal of arbitrator under Section 11

Section 11 does not provide for removal of arbitrator(s). The Chief Justice or his designate cannot remove the arbitrator even if wrongly nominated once he assumed jurisdiction or his appointment itself was a nullity at law.[338]

Provision in arbitration clause for reference to named arbitrator, when can be ignored

Where there is a provision in the arbitration clause for reference to a named arbitrator (by designation or name) such a provision should normally be given effect to. Only where there is material to create a reasonable apprehension that the named arbitrator is not likely to act independently or impartially or he is not available, then only an independent arbitrator can be appointed in accordance with the provisions of Section 11(8), after recording reasons.[339] The court emphasised that referring the dispute to a named arbitrator shall be the rule. Ignoring the named arbitrator/Arbitral Tribunal and nominating an independent arbitrator shall be an exception to the rule, to be restored for recording reasons. However, where an arbitration clause refers to a person not by designation but by name, then his non-availability would be fatal to the arbitration agreement itself.[340]

336. *Sadhna Kumari* v. *Bihar State Food & Civil Supplies Corpn. Ltd.*, 2017 SCC OnLine Pat 3707.

337. *A2Z Waste Management (Jaipur) Ltd.* v. *Jaipur Municipal Corpn.*, 2016 SCC OnLine Raj 5353: (2017) 1 RLW 426.

338. *Kanpur Development Authority* v. *U.P. Builders*, 2011 SCC OnLine All 368: (2011) 4 All LJ 407; *Rakesh Jain* v. *Wellwon Builders (India)(P) Ltd.*, 2011 SCC OnLine All 291: (2011) 85 ALR 406.

339. *Indian Oil Corpn. Ltd.* v. *Raja Transport (P) Ltd.*, (2009) 8 SCC 520.

340. *Ibid.*

Breakdown of procedure agreed by parties—Third arbitrator appointed by Chief Justice of India

Under the arbitration agreement, after the two parties had appointed one arbitrator each, the two arbitrators thus appointed had to jointly appoint a third arbitrator to act as a presiding arbitrator. On failure to appoint the third arbitrator, the said arbitrator was to be appointed by the International Chamber of Commerce (ICC). Petitioner and respondent nominated their arbitrators but the nominee arbitrators failed to appoint the presiding arbitrator. Hence, petitioner approached ICC for the said appointment but ICC refused the said request without assigning any reason. In these circumstances, held, the procedure agreed upon by the parties to constitute the Arbitration Tribunal having broken down, the petitioner was justified in approaching the Chief Justice of India for appointment of the third/presiding arbitrator. The court directed the parties to submit an agreed name, if they do not agree, to submit two names each, for being considered for appointment as Chairman of the Arbitral Tribunal.[341]

Appointment of arbitrator contrary to procedure agreed in arbitration agreement, impermissible

Unless the appointment of the arbitrator is ex facie valid and satisfies the requirement of Section 11(6), such appointment as *fait accompli* is not acceptable and does not bar the court from exercising jurisdiction under Section 11(6).[342] Clause in agreement provided for appointment of one arbitrator by each party, and on failure of one of the parties to do so within 30 days, International Centre for Alternative Dispute Resolution in India (ICADR) shall appoint the arbitrator. On the failure of the respondent to appoint its arbitrator, ICADR called upon the respondent to appoint its arbitrator or choose one from amongst a panel of three arbitrators. On the said communication respondent appointed its arbitrator. It was held, option given to the respondent to go beyond the panel submitted by ICADR and to appoint any person of its choice was not the procedure agreed upon. Appointment of arbitrator by the respondent was invalid in law and hence does not bar the Supreme Court from exercising powers under Section 11(6) to appoint arbitrator on behalf of the respondent.[343]

341. *Delta Mechcons (India) Ltd.* v. *Marubeni Corpn.*, (2008) 15 SCC 772.
342. *Walter Bau AG* v. *Municipal Corpn. of Greater Mumbai*, (2015) 3 SCC 800.
343. *Ibid.*

Appointment of arbitrator by Chief Justice/his designate—Power to decide question of jurisdiction

Application filed by contractor for appointment of arbitrator was opposed by the petitioner on the ground that the main contract and the arbitration agreement were fraudulently entered and as such were void. The court appointed arbitrator, left the issue for the determination by the arbitrator. It was held, course adopted by the court was improper. The impugned order was set aside and the matter was remitted for a fresh decision in keeping with the decision of the seven-judge Bench in the *SBP case.*[344]

Arbitrable dispute—Full and final settlement of contractor's claim under contract

The conduct of the contractor showed that "no-claim certificates" were given by it voluntarily and it had accepted the amount voluntarily. Financial duress/coercion was not established prima facie. No arbitrable dispute existed between the parties, and appointment of the arbitrator in the case was improper.[345]

Respondent (contractor) was awarded a contract by the appellant, Union of India. The agreement between the parties contained an arbitration clause. As the work was completed by the contractor, a completion certificate was issued. The contractor furnished three no-claim certificates on three dates and the final bill was released to the contractor. Therefore, the bank guarantee was also released. On that same day the contractor wrote to the appellants withdrawing "no-claim certificates" and lodged certain claims. The Chief Engineer of the appellant declined to entertain the claims of the contractor on the ground that the final bills had been accepted by the contractor after furnishing the "no-claim certificates" and no claim under the contract remained. As no arbitrator was appointed by the appellant, the respondent-contractor filed an application under Section 11 for appointment of the arbitrator before the civil judge, which was dismissed, appeal against the said order was dismissed by the High Court. On the direction of the Supreme Court when the matter was placed before the Chief Justice of the High Court for appropriate orders, the Chief Justice of the High Court appointed sole arbitrator in the case. In appeal, the Supreme Court held that in view of the facts of the case after the contractor had submitted "no-claim certificates" and received payments of the final bill, no arbitral dispute between the parties survived. The "no-claim certificates" leave no doubt that

344. *SBP & Co.* v. *Patel Engg. Ltd.*, (2005) 8 SCC 618 followed in *Ludhiana Improvement Trust* v. *Today Homes and Infrastructure (P) Ltd.*, (2008) 10 SCC 715.
345. *Union of India* v. *Master Construction Co.*, (2011) 12 SCC 349.

upon the receipt of the payment, there has been a full and final settlement of the contractor's claim. The payment of the final bill to the contractor was not in dispute. After the receipt of the payment, no grievance was raised or lodged by the contractor immediately. The authority concerned thereafter, released the bank guarantee. It was then, on that day itself, the contractor lodged further claims. The present case appears to be a case falling in the category of exception noted in the *Boghara Polyfab (P) Ltd. case*[346]. As to the financial duress or coercion, without there being anything more to suggest that does not lead to an arbitrable dispute. The conduct of the contractor clearly shows that "no-claim certificates" were given by it voluntarily; the contractor accepted the amount voluntarily and the contract was discharged voluntarily. Hence, no arbitrable dispute remains between the parties. The appointment of the arbitrator made by the High Court was set aside.[347]

The petitioner received the amount in full and final settlement of its claim. The parties had fully and finally settled the matter. There was no arbitrable dispute which could be referred to the arbitrator. No reference to arbitration was warranted.[348]

Moving of application under Section 9 of the 1996 Act, filing of writ petition, then entering into MOU and then repudiating the same, were all in respect of subject-matter of claim. It was held, the facts in the present case did not suggest that there was a full and final settlement between the parties in respect of the claim in question. Designated judge appointing the arbitrator under Section 11(6) had correctly recorded his satisfaction that the parties had not concluded their claims.[349]

A claim for arbitration cannot be rejected solely on the ground that a settlement agreement or discharge voucher had been executed by the claimant if its validity is disputed by the claimant. As the applicant had not issued a discharge voucher of its own free will and volition but while he was acting under economic duress, dispute is arbitrable.[350] The applicant had received full and final payment and had signed the document. On the completion of the work, the right to get further payment gets weakened but whether the claim subsists or not is a matter which is arbitrable. Arbitrator was appointed to resolve the dispute.[351]

---

346. *National Insurance Co. Ltd.* v. *Boghara Polyfab (P) Ltd.*, (2009) 1 SCC 267.
347. *Union of India* v. *Master Construction Co.*, (2011) 12 SCC 349.
348. *Prime Engineers* v. *Punjab National Bank*, 2002 SCC OnLine Del 1313: (2003) 67 DRJ 376.
349. *Shree Ram Mills Ltd.* v. *Utility Premises (P) Ltd.*, (2007) 4 SCC 599.
350. *Mirc Electronics Ltd.* v. *Oriental Insurance Co. Ltd.*, 2016 SCC OnLine Bom 1054: (2016) 3 Mah LJ 933.
351. *Krishna Kumari Rathore* v. *Kusum Punia*, 2006 SCC OnLine Raj 591: (2007) 1 RLW 654; *Niranjan Lal Joshi* v. *Pramod Kumar*, 2006 SCC OnLine Raj 593: (2007) 1 RLW 662.

Plea of settlement between parties—Appointment of sole arbitrator

Dispute between the parties related to the cancellation of agreement for sale and forfeiture of advance amount paid. Plea was taken of the settlement of dispute between the parties. The alleged settlement was not reduced into writing. There was no definite material on record to indicate that there was a concluded settlement between the parties, as such, there was no reason to hold that there was no dispute which required resolution through arbitration. A retired Chief Justice of the High Court was appointed arbitrator in the case.[352]

Discharge of insurance claim—Appointment of arbitrator set aside

In the instant case, prima facie no dispute subsisted after the discharge voucher being signed by the respondent without any demur or protest and claim being finally settled with accord and satisfaction and after 11 weeks of the settlement of claim a letter was sent on 27 July 2016 for the first time raising a voice in the form of protest that the discharge voucher was signed under undue influence and coercion with no supportive prima facie evidence being placed on record in absence thereof, it must follow that the claim had been settled with accord and satisfaction leaving no arbitral dispute subsisting under the agreement to be referred to the arbitrator for adjudication. Appointment of the arbitrator made by the High Court was set aside.[353]

Accord and satisfaction—Survival/extinguishment of arbitration agreement

A bald plea of fraud, coercion, duress or undue influence is not enough and the party who sets up such plea must prima facie establish the said allegation by placing material before the Chief Justice/his designate. In *New India Assurance Co. Ltd.* v. *Genus Power Infrastructure Ltd.*[354], the respondent-claimant, after receiving payment under the insurance policy and signing letter of subrogation in favour of insurance company in full and final settlement of its claim under the policy, sought appointment of arbitrator on the ground that it signed said letter due to extreme financial difficulties and under duress, coercion and undue influence exercised by appellant. On the facts of the case, it was held that the plea raised by the respondent was bereft of any details and particulars and was a bald assertion. The respondent never made any protest or demur when the letter of subrogation was signed

352. *V. Sreenivasa Reddy* v. *B.L. Rathnamma*, 2021 SCC OnLine SC 294.
353. *United India Insurance Co. Ltd.* v. *Antique Art Exports (P) Ltd.*, (2019) 5 SCC 362.
354. (2015) 2 SCC 424.

but issued notice only after three weeks. The financial condition of the respondent was not so precarious as to suggest that discharge and signing of a letter of subrogation was because of exercise of undue influence. The discharge and execution of letter of subrogation was voluntary and free from any coercion or undue influence, upon execution of letter of subrogation there was full and final settlement of the claim and no arbitrable dispute existed for exercising power under Section 11 of the Act, the Chief Justice of the High Court was not justified in appointing arbitrator.

In a case where the claimant contends that a discharge voucher or no-claim certificate has been obtained by fraud, coercion, duress or undue influence and the other side contests the correctness thereof the Chief Justice/his designate must look into this aspect to find out, at least prima facie, whether or not the dispute is bona fide and genuine. Where the dispute raised by the claimant with regard to validity of the discharge voucher or no-claim certificate or settlement agreement, prima facie, appears to be lacking in credibility, there may not be a necessity to refer the dispute to arbitration at all. A bald plea of fraud, coercion, duress or undue influence is not enough and the party who sets up such a plea must prima facie establish the same by placing material before the Chief Justice/his designate. In the present case the contractor alleged that he had issued "no-dues certificate" under coercion/undue influence and raised a claim of ₹98.88 crores as losses sustained by him. Facts of the case showed that the contractee-company issued a certificate after receiving the final bill, mutually signed by both the parties. Certificate was issued voluntarily by the contractor. No rights/obligations remained between the parties. Power under Section 11 was not exercised.[355] Land owner had entered into a development agreement with the developer firm. As the developer firm did not complete the project in time, the owner suffered losses giving rise to dispute. Subsequently, the parties also entered into the supplementary agreement and rectification deed which recorded full and final satisfaction between the parties. No arbitral dispute existed between the parties, the application for appointment of arbitrator was rejected.[356]

A notice invoking the arbitration clause was issued prior to the Amendment Act, 2015 and an application under Section 11(6) of the Act was filed after the Amendment Act, 2015 came into force. Held, the law prevailing prior to the Amendment Act, 2015 shall be applicable. Dismissal of application filed under Section 11(6) on considering the ground of accord and satisfaction by applying the Act of 1996 was held proper.[357]

---

355. *ONGC Mangalore Petrochemicals Ltd.* v. *ANS Constructions Ltd.*, (2018) 3 SCC 373.
356. *A. Raghunandan Raj* v. *Fortune Monarch Associates*, 2020 SCC OnLine TS 3401: (2020) 6 ALT 333.
357. *Shree Vishnu Constructions* v. *Military Engg. Service*, (2023) 8 SCC 329.

Even though plea of "accord and satisfaction" of the claims may/can be considered by the court at the stage of deciding Section 11 application, it is always advisable and appropriate that in cases of debatable and disputable facts, good reasonably arguable case, the same should be left to the Arbitral Tribunal.[358]

Submission of final bill

Final bill made to the contractor was duly accepted by him. There was no material placed on record to show that the final bill was accepted under protest. Even after submitting no-claim certificate and accepting final bill payment, the contractor remained silent for six months before raising a plea that said certificate was issued under duress. Mere allegation that the discharge voucher or no-claim certificate was obtained by fraud, coercion or undue influence is not sufficient to accept the plea for appointment of arbitrator, but the party seeking appointment of arbitrator is required to produce prima facie evidence to substantiate the plea of fraud, coercion or undue influence. In the present case, no such prima facie evidence was produced. Arbitrator was not appointed in the case.[359]

Plea of full and final discharge/settlement/voucher/no dues certificate

Where allegations of forgery/fabrication are made in regard to the document recording discharge of contract by full and final settlement, it would be appropriate if the Chief Justice/his designate decides the issue. If the Chief Justice/his designate exercising jurisdiction under Section 11 of the Act finds that there was really accord and satisfaction or discharge of contract by performance, he will refuse to refer the dispute to arbitration. On the other hand, if the Chief Justice/his designate comes to the conclusion that the full and final settlement receipt or discharge voucher was the result of any fraud/coercion/undue influence, he will have to hold that there was no discharge of the contract, and consequently, refer the dispute to arbitration. Alternatively, where the Chief Justice/his designate is satisfied prima facie that the discharge voucher was not issued voluntarily and the claimant was under some compulsion or coercion, and that the matter deserved detailed consideration, he may instead of deciding the issue himself, refer the matter to the Arbitral Tribunal with a specific direction that the said question should be decided in the first instance.[360]

---

358. *Indian Oil Corpn. Ltd.* v. *NCC Ltd.*, (2023) 2 SCC 539.
359. *Hindusthan Builders* v. *Ircon International Ltd.*, 2022 SCC OnLine Cal 197.
360. *National Insurance Co. Ltd.* v. *Boghara Polyfab (P) Ltd.*, (2009) 1 SCC 267.

Whether a contract has been discharged by performance is a mixed question of fact and law, and if there is a dispute in regard to that question, that is arbitrable. If the party which has executed the discharge agreement/voucher alleges fraud/coercion/undue influence practiced by the other party and is able to establish the same, then obviously the discharge of such contract by such agreement/voucher is rendered void and cannot be acted upon. Consequently, any dispute raised by the executor of the discharge agreement/voucher would be arbitrable. Non-exhaustive illustrations of cases as to when claims are arbitrable and when they are not, when discharge of contract by accord and satisfaction are disputed, given. In this case, it being found that discharge voucher prima facie had not been obtained validly and voluntarily, the High Court's order appointing arbitrator was affirmed.[361]

Application for appointment of arbitrator was rejected. Payment with regard to the final bill was made to the contractor. Due to illegal deductions, the contractor invoked arbitration clause and requested that the issue be referred to arbitration. Contractor had voluntarily accepted the amount. Alleged dispute subsequently raised cannot be entertained after submission of "no claim certificate".[362]

Plea of the respondent was that the termination of the agreement granted full and final discharge from all claims as such there was no subsisting arbitrable dispute in view thereof. However, the respondent consented for the appointment of arbitrator. The petition for appointment of arbitrator was allowed and all disputes including the disputes regarding interpretation and effect of termination of agreement were referred for adjudication by arbitration.[363]

Payment received under protest

Applicant contradict alleged that final bill was not prepared in accordance with agreement, and applicant received payment under protest. Invocation of arbitral agreement was within the period of limitation. However, issues of limitation can be left for adjudication by the Arbitral Tribunal. Arbitrator was appointed by the court.[364]

If full and final settlement of a claim under the contract is itself in dispute arising "upon" or "in relation to" or "in connection with" the contract then dispute exists between the parties which as per terms of the contract have

361. *Ibid.*
362. *Rakesh Kumar Jain* v. *Railways*, 2022 SCC OnLine Chh 2748.
363. *OMNIA Technologies (P) Ltd.* v. *W.M.A. Van Loosbroek*, (2011) 3 SCC 682.
364. *Telecommunication Consultants India Ltd.* v. *Border Road Organization*, 2022 SCC OnLine Utt 1856.

to be referred to the arbitrator for settlement. Appointment of an arbitrator was proper.[365]

Conclusion/discharge of contract—Appointment of arbitrator

Merely because a contract containing arbitration clause comes to an end by efflux of time, the same would not itself put an end to the arbitration clause. In *Lufthansa German Airlines* v. *Airport Authority of India*[366], disputes arose during subsistence of agreement which were found prima facie arbitrable which required to be referred to arbitration. Arbitrator was appointed with liberty to the parties to raise further/additional issues before the arbitrator.

Discharge of contract by release/mutual agreement—Reference to arbitration not permissible

Where a contract has been discharged by release/mutual agreement reference to arbitration is not permissible. As the contract is concluded, the question of appointment of arbitrator does not arise.[367]

Sole arbitrator appointed

The parties were governed by the terms of an agreement, which provided for referring the disputes or differences arising between the parties, to a sole arbitrator in accordance with and subject to the provisions of the Act. Since the respondent-company had admitted the existence of disputes and differences arising between the parties which were the subject-matters to be referred to a sole arbitrator and the respondent-company had no objection for appointment of an arbitrator. A sole arbitrator was appointed in the case.[368]

One of the parties to agreement disentitled to sole arbitrator on its own

As per arbitration clause each of the parties were to appoint one independent arbitrator and then two arbitrators so appointed were required to select the presiding arbitrator. Instead of having arbitration by three members, the

---

365. *Ahmedabad Urban Development Authorities (Auda)* v. *M.C. Dalal and Co.*, 2022 SCC OnLine Guj 2649.
366. (2012) 11 SCC 554; see also, *National Insurance Co. Ltd.* v. *Boghara Polyfab (P) Ltd.*, (2009) 1 SCC 267.
367. *Cauvery Coffee Traders* v. *Hornor Resources (International) Co. Ltd.*, (2011) 10 SCC 420.
368. *Shristi Infrastructure Development Corpn. Ltd.* v. *Sunway Construction SDN BHD*, (2008) 5 SCC 222.

parties agreed for arbitration of dispute by sole arbitrator. As such, a sole arbitrator was appointed in the case.[369]

One of the parties to agreement is disentitled to appoint sole arbitrator on its own as it is having interest in dispute and there is possibility of bias due to exclusivity in determining the course of dispute resolution.[370]

Preference to retired judges in appointment of sole arbitrator

Clause in the arbitration agreement provided for the constitution of three members Arbitral Tribunal. Irrespective of clause, parties are free to determine the number of arbitrators and to agree on procedure for appointing arbitrator and to appoint sole arbitrator with mutual consent. Parties arrived at consensus to appoint only a single member Arbitral Tribunal, proper. Appointment of sole arbitrator was proper.[371]

The High Court had appointed a lawyer as arbitrator in the case. On the submission of the appellant, the Supreme Court appointed a retired judge as arbitrator in the case.[372]

Challenge to appointment of sole arbitrator

The appointment of the sole arbitrator was challenged on the ground that the arbitrator was appointed unilaterally and, therefore, the appointment was invalid, non-est in the eye of law. The petitioner expressly consented to the appointment of the sole arbitrator and also expressly consented to make payment of 50 per cent of the fees of the said arbitrator. Such consent on the part of the petitioner was nothing but consent to waive the applicability of Section 12(5). It could not be said that the appointment of the arbitrator is unilateral, invalid or non-est in the eye of law. The petitioner also participated in the proceedings, and the appointment of the arbitrator could not be challenged.[373]

Fixation of time limit by court for concluding arbitration proceedings

Where the arbitration process remained pending for a very long period (over nine years in this case) despite successive appointments of sole arbitrators, the High Court while directing the authority concerned to appoint a new

---

369. *Anandini Village Resorts* v. *Nibaana*, 2022 SCC OnLine HP 115.
370. *Perkins Eastman Architects DPC* v. *HSCC (India) Ltd.*, (2020) 20 SCC 760.
371. *HCL Infotech Ltd.* v. *H.P. SEB*, 2017 SCC OnLine HP 2669.
372. *Rajesh Verma* v. *Ashwani Kumar Khanna*, (2016) 12 SCC 678.
373. *Escort Security & Personnel Services* v. *Deendayal Port Trust*, 2021 SCC OnLine Guj 3038: (2022) 63 (2) GLR 966.

arbitrator, correctly fixed a time limit (of six months) for such new arbitrator to conclude the arbitration proceedings.[374]

Where the High Court has fixed time limit for concluding arbitration proceedings, and a party has not challenged the said order, the party is estopped from raising objection there against in appeal and challenging subsequent order of the High Court terminating mandate of arbitrator on the ground of his failure to make and publish award within said time limit.[375]

Appointment of sole arbitrator by the Supreme Court

The arbitration clause provided for appointment of arbitrator by each party and for appointment of third arbitrator by them, failing which recourse to be taken to Section 11(6) of the 1996 Act. As the respondent failed to appoint an arbitrator, application was filed under Section 11(6) for appointment of arbitrator. In the absence of any counter from the respondent as to referability of dispute to arbitration, averments made in the application for appointment of arbitrator were taken as correct, the Supreme Court allowed the application and appointed a retired judge of the High Court as a sole arbitrator to adjudicate upon disputes between the parties.[376]

Jurisdiction of Chief Justice of India/his designate [S. 11(6)]

It is implied that if an objection is raised by the respondent before the Chief Justice of India or his designate that the so-called arbitration clause is not at all an arbitration clause falling within Section 7, such a question will have to be decided in the proceedings under Section 11 of the Act. Even if the Chief Justice of India or his designate is to be treated as an administrative authority, the position is that when the said authority is approached seeking appointment of an arbitrator/Arbitral Tribunal under Section 11 and a question is raised that there is to start with, no arbitration clause at all between the parties, the Chief Justice of India or his designate has to decide that question.[377]

When arbitration agreement cannot be invoked

An arbitration agreement contained in a contract cannot be invoked to seek reference of any dispute to arbitration in the following circumstances *when the contract is discharged* on account of

1. performance; or
2. accord; or

374. *NBCC Ltd.* v. *J.G. Engg. (P) Ltd.*, (2010) 2 SCC 385.
375. *Ibid.*
376. *Purple India Holdings Ltd.* v. *Drilling & Offshore (P) Ltd.*, (2016) 7 SCC 583.
377. *Wellington Associates Ltd.* v. *Kirit Mehta*, (2000) 4 SCC 272.

3. mutual agreement; and
4. the same is reduced to writing (and signed by both parties) or by the party seeking the arbitration:
   (*a*) where the obligations under a contract are fully performed and discharge of the contract by performance is acknowledged by a full and final discharge voucher/receipt. Nothing survives in regard to such a discharged contract;
   (*b*) where the parties to the contract, by mutual agreement, accept performance of the altered modified and substituted obligations and confirm in writing the discharge of contract by performance of the altered, modified or substituted obligations;
   (*c*) where the parties to a contract by mutual agreement, absolve each other from the performance of their respective obligations (either on account of frustration or otherwise) and consequently cancel the agreement and confirm that there are no outstanding claims or disputes.[378]

Signing of final Bill, no further claim certificate—Further claims, whether arbitrable

The appellants had made full and final payment of the final bill, the respondent has certified by signing the bill without any protest or reservation. The respondent with the intention of receiving further payments after two years raised yet another claim and tried to bring up a dispute. The appellants specifically pleaded that the respondent could not have raised yet another claim as the respondent after signing the final bill without any protest or reservation had waived its rights as per the conditions of the contract. It was held, no dispute existed between the parties, appointment of arbitrator by the High Court was not justified, order of appointment of arbitrator passed by the High Court was set aside.[379]

No claim certificate after arbitration proceedings have commenced

Contract agreement between the parties contained an arbitration clause. Contractor had not waived its right of seeking arbitration prior to invocation of arbitration clause. Once arbitral proceedings have commenced, signing of "No-Claim Certificate" would be immaterial to affect progress of proceedings.[380]

---

378. *National Insurance Co. Ltd.* v. *Boghara Polyfab (P) Ltd.*, (2009) 1 SCC 267.
379. *Union of India* v. *Onkar Nath Bhalla & Sons*, (2009) 7 SCC 350.
380. *Rama Kishan Ashok Kumar* v. *Union of India*, 2023 SCC OnLine Raj 4758: (2023) 2 RLW 1607.

Joint venture agreement—Disputes arising—Arbitrator appointed

In pursuance of JVA, a JVC was formed which, due to disputes arising between the parties, could not function. Petition was filed for appointment of arbitrator for adjudication of claim regarding refund of money paid/deposited pursuant to and in execution of JVA and also amount paid towards working expenses of JVC together with interest thereon. It was held, all such disputes relating to the payments concerned were to be decided and adjudicated upon through the process of arbitration as agreed upon by parties in JVA. Contributions made towards execution of JVA and functioning of JVC on behalf of the party by its affiliates, whether to be treated as contributions made by the party, were also matters to be adjudicated upon by the arbitrator. Petition was allowed, arbitrator was appointed and matter was referred to arbitration for decision on the issues concerned.[381]

Single application for appointment of presiding arbitrator in four cases—Maintainable

In four sub-contracts, one application for appointment of presiding officer was filed. The application was allowed. Objection of the opposite party, that single application in four cases was not maintainable, was held devoid of merit was rejected.[382]

Government contract—No arbitration agreement—Preference of dispute to arbitrator not proper

Clause in government contract provided that the decision of the Superintending Engineer of the department with regard to the rates of non-tendered work shall be final. The clause, operated in a limited sphere, did not provide for reference of dispute between the parties to arbitration. The clause also did not provide that the decision of the Superintending Engineer would be binding on the parties or that the Superintending Engineer had to act judicially. It was held, the clause was not an arbitration agreement, reference of dispute between the parties to arbitration was not proper.[383]

Development agreement

Development agreement between the developer and the owner of the property contained an arbitration clause. Existence of the arbitration clause was established. Arbitrator was appointed in the case.[384]

---

381. *Everest Holding Ltd.* v. *Shyam Kumar Shrivastava*, (2008) 16 SCC 774.
382. *Delta Mechcons (India) Ltd.* v. *Marubeni Corpn.*, (2008) 15 SCC 772.
383. *State of Orissa* v. *Bhagyadhar Dash*, (2011) 7 SCC 406.
384. *Sree Neelalohita Associates* v. *M.A. Aleem*, 2020 SCC OnLine TS 3429.

Partnership firm [S. 11(5)]

Partnership firm is a registered firm, the partnership deed contained an arbitration agreement. The High Court cannot go beyond examination of the case for determining the existence of an arbitration agreement. A retired Chief Justice of the Delhi High Court was appointed arbitrator in the case.[385]

Mortgage suit(s)—Arbitration of dispute(s)

See, under Section 8 ante.

Claim for recovery of lease amount

Petitioner only sought for recovery of arrears of lease amount in terms of agreement, was not seeking ejectment of respondent. Dispute does not fall within exclusive jurisdiction of Rent Controller rather it can be adjudicated by an arbitrator. Arbitrator was appointed by the court.[386]

Non-renewal of lease—Appointment of arbitrator

Suit property was leased out to the appellant by the respondent-State for a stipulated period. Offer of the lessee for renewal of the lease was rejected by the State. Clause in lease deed stipulated that dispute about quantum of rent or period of lease could be referred to arbitration. As lessee offered for renewal within stipulated time and dispute arose out of non-renewal of lease, dispute is clearly arbitrable. Dismissal of application for appointment of arbitrator was not proper. Arbitrator was appointed.[387]

Fees to be taken as a composite amount and not to be paid separately and individually to each arbitrator.[388]

Counterclaim by the respondents

Where the arbitration agreement provides for referring all disputes between the parties (whether without any exceptions or subject to exceptions), the arbitrator will have jurisdiction to entertain any counterclaim, even though it was not raised at a stage prior to the stage of pleadings before the arbitrator. When an arbitrator is appointed under Section 11(6) of the Act who is requested to decide all disputes, the arbitrator would be authorised to decide the claim of the petitioner as well as the counterclaim of the respondent, if so raised. There is no fetter on powers of the court while making an

---

385. *Mohd. Ahmed Ali Khan* v. *Candy Children's Hospital*, 2019 SCC OnLine TS 3672.
386. *Rohit Sawhney* v. *DLF Power and Services Ltd.*, 2022 SCC OnLine P&H 4271.
387. *Brij Raj Oberoi* v. *Tourism & Civil Aviation Deptt.*, 2022 SCC OnLine SC 1033.
388. *State of U.P.* v. *Shyam Lal*, 2021 SCC OnLine All 514: (2021) 148 ALR 344.

appointment under Section 11(6) of the Act to require the arbitrator to decide both the claims and the counterclaim.[389]

Where, however, the arbitration requires specific disputes to be referred to arbitration and provides that the arbitrator will have the jurisdiction to decide only the disputes so referred, the arbitrator's jurisdiction is controlled by the specific reference and he cannot travel beyond the reference, nor entertain any additional claims or counterclaims which are not part of the disputes specifically referred to arbitration.[390]

The respondent had the choice of raising a dispute by way of counterclaim in pending arbitration proceedings or resort to independent arbitration proceedings by issuing notice to the claimant.[391]

Vague arbitration clause

Arbitration clause stated that any dispute between the parties shall be referred to arbitration under bye-laws of the Companies Act, 1956 as amended upto date. However, no such bye-laws were ever framed. It was held, the arbitration clause being vague, no arbitrator could be appointed. Appointment of the arbitrator was refused.[392]

Arbitration clause whether once invoked can/cannot be invoked for future disputes arising under the same contract

Arbitration clause in the agreement provided for settlement of "all disputes under the agreement". It was held, the arbitration clause in the agreement can only mean all disputes that might be in existence when the arbitration clause is invoked and one of the parties gives the arbitration notice to the other. The arbitration cannot be said to be a one-time measure, it cannot be held that once the arbitration clause is invoked, the remedy of arbitration is no longer available in regard to other disputes that might arise in future. Arbitration clauses in the agreement cannot be restricted as a one-time measure.[393] If a cause of action arose after completion of pleadings and commencement of the first round of arbitration proceedings, the claimant can make a separate claim by initiating second arbitration.[394]

389. *Ashes Deb* v. *State of Tripura*, 2021 SCC OnLine Tri 661.
390. *State of Goa* v. *Praveen Enterprises*, (2012) 12 SCC 581.
391. *Ibid.*
392. *System for International Agencies* v. *Rahul Coach Builders (P) Ltd.*, (2015) 13 SCC 436.
393. *Dolphin Drilling Ltd.* v. *ONGC Ltd.*, (2010) 3 SCC 267.
394. *Indian Oil Corpn. Ltd.* v. *SPS Engg. Ltd.*, (2011) 3 SCC 507.

Appointment of arbitrator when earlier application dismissed pre-mature

Dismissal of earlier application for appointment of arbitrator, as being premature cannot be ground for dismissal of subsequent application for appointment of arbitrator.[395]

Whether rights of parties under agreement superseded by subsequent settlement agreement—Arbitrable

Whether rights of parties under agreement were superseded by subsequent settlement agreement may be an arbitrable issue and the issue can be examined by the arbitrator. Application for appointment of arbitrator was allowed.[396]

Specific performance of an agreement to sell or agreement to mortgage—Arbitrable

An agreement to sell or mortgage does not involve any transfer of right *in rem* but creates only a personal obligation. Hence, a claim for specific performance of agreement to sell is, or agreement to mortgage is, arbitrable.[397]

Dispute whether arbitrable or to be adjudicated under Companies Act, 1956, Section 111-A

A foreign company under agreement containing arbitration clause supplied goods to an Indian company, *E* for equity shares to be issued by *E*. Under the amalgamation scheme sanctioned by the High Court, liabilities of *E* devolved on the latter (successor) company. However, promised equity shares were not issued to the foreign company by Indian company *E* or by successor company. In such circumstances, foreign company's claim against the successor company under the said arbitration clause was not a dispute arising out of the amalgamation scheme. Hence, it was arbitrable under Section 11(6) of the 1996 Act and was not referable to the Company Tribunal under Section 111-A, Companies Act, 1956.[398]

---

395. *Simpark Infrastructure (P) Ltd.* v. *Jaipur Municipal Corpn.*, 2017 SCC OnLine Raj 4455.
396. *Sirajuddin Kasim* v. *Paramount Investments Ltd.*, (2010) 8 SCC 557.
397. *Booz Allen & Hamilton Inc.* v. *SBI Home Finance Ltd.*, (2011) 5 SCC 532.
398. *Geo-Group Communications Inc.* v. *IOL Broadband Ltd.*, (2010) 1 SCC 562.

Nomination power in arbitration clause

Nomination power given in arbitration clause does not imply requirement of concurrence of other party unless so specified. Nomination amounts to selection of the arbitrator.[399]

Section 11(6-A) (omitted)

As per Section 11(6-A), the power of the court has now been restricted only to the examination of the existence of the arbitration agreement. Earlier the Chief Justice had been given the power to examine the other aspects as well, *i.e.* the limitation, whether the claims were referable for arbitration, etc. in terms of the judgments of the Supreme Court in *SBP & Co.* v. *Patel Engg. Ltd.*[400] and *National Insurance Co. Ltd.* v. *Boghara Polyfab (P) Ltd.*[401]. Section 11(6-A) has now been omitted by Act 33 of 2019. Now all preliminary issues have been left for the Arbitral Tribunal to decide in terms of Section 16 of the Act.[402] In application for appointment of arbitrator, the court cannot embark on examination of "arbitrability" of matter, when arbitration agreement exists between parties. The court is only required to see if the arbitration agreement contains a clause which provides for arbitration, pertaining to disputes arising between the parties.[403]

In terms of Section 11(6-A), Arbitration and Conciliation Act, 1996 the scope of examination under Section 11 is limited to the existence of an arbitration agreement between the parties. Notwithstanding the same, in cases where it is ex facie clear that the disputes cannot be entertained, the courts would refrain from entertaining the petition to appoint an arbitrator as it would be an exercise in futility. It is only in exceptional cases where it is clear that the disputes cannot be entertained that the court will decline to entertain a petition under Section 11. The standards of examination under Section 11 do not permit the court to carry out any adjudicatory exercise in respect of any contentious issue.[404]

The court is only required to look into the existence of an arbitration agreement, nothing more nothing less. In view of the existence of the arbitration agreement between the parties, a former judge of the High Court was appointed arbitrator in the case.[405]

---

399. *Datar Switchgears Ltd.* v. *Tata Finance Ltd.*, (2000) 8 SCC 151.
400. (2005) 8 SCC 618.
401. (2009) 1 SCC 267.
402. *Duro Felguera, S.A.* v. *Gangavaram Port Ltd.*, (2017) 9 SCC 729.
403. *Swatantra Properties (P) Ltd.* v. *Airplaza Retail Holdings (P) Ltd.*, 2018 SCC OnLine All 5952: (2019) 1 All LJ 409.
404. *Bharat Petroresources Ltd.* v. *JSW Ispat Special Products Ltd.*, (2022) 1 HCC (Del) 512.
405. *Raw Edge Industrial Solutions Ltd.* v. *Hindustan Zinc Ltd.*, 2019 SCC OnLine Raj 7828.

The existence of the arbitration agreement was not disputed by the parties. However, the respondent-State urged that there was nothing which was required to be arbitrated. Under Section 11(6-A), the High Court while considering any application under Section 11(6) must confine its examination only to the existence of an arbitration agreement. Since the existence of the arbitration agreement was not disputed by the respondent, an arbitrator was appointed in the case.[406]

Sub-section (6-A) was inserted by the Amendment Act of 2015. Certain provisions of the Act were again sought to be amended by Amending Act 33 of 2019. Along with amendments to other provisions, Section 3 of the said Amending Act seeks to omit Section 11(6-A). However, in the Government Notification dated 30 August 2019 whereby other provisions of the said Amending Act were notified, Section 3 of the Amending Act which seeks to omit Section 11(6-A) of the Act has not been notified. It follows from that as of today. Section 11(6-A) of the Act continues to remain in the statute book and is in force and consequently, the decision of the Supreme Court in the *Uttrakhand case*[407], reiterating its earlier decisions qua Section 11(6-A) would continue to be applicable to the facts of the instant case. The effect/impact of omission of Section 11(6-A) of the Act by Amending Act 33 of 2019 also came up for consideration before a three-judge Bench of the Supreme Court in *Mayavati Trading (P) Ltd.* v. *Pradyuat Deb Burman*[408], where it was held that omission of Section 11(6-A) would not be to resuscitate the law that was prevailing prior to Amendment Act of 2015; rather, the entire scheme of 2019 Amendment is to strengthen and deepen what was sought to be achieved by insertion of Section 11(6-A), *i.e.* to confine power of court to examination of existence of arbitration agreement, nothing less by leaving all other preliminary issues to be decided by Arbitral Tribunal; omission of Section 11(6-A) will not alter this position in any way which would be squarely applicable to facts of instant case. The result is that under these circumstances, by virtue of Section 11(6-A) of the Act as well as the decisions of the Supreme Court in the *Uttrakhand case* and *Mayavati Trading case* (supra), the scope of application for the court in the petition under Section 11(6-A) is restricted/confined/limited to examining whether there exists an arbitration agreement between the parties and all and every other issues/contention of any of the parties will have to necessarily be decided by the Arbitral Tribunal.[409]

406. *Sundar Singh Bora* v. *State of Uttarakhand*, 2020 SCC OnLine Utt 1343.
407. *Uttarakhand Purv Sainik Kalyan Nigam Ltd.* v. *Northern Coal Field Ltd.*, (2020) 2 SCC 455.
408. (2019) 8 SCC 714.
409. *Royal Orchid Hotels Ltd.* v. *Rock Reality (P) Ltd.*, 2020 SCC OnLine Kar 3414: ILR 2021 Kar 2373; *Vidya Drolia* v. *Durga Trading Corpn.*, (2021) 2 SCC 1.

Sub-section (6-A) was inserted by Act 3 of 2016 in Section 11 with retrospective effect from 23 October 2015 and omitted by Act 33 of 2019. Section 11(6) requires the court to appoint an arbitrator on an application made by a party. Section (6-A) to Section 11 stipulates that the court shall, at the stage of appointment under sub-sections (4), (5) or (6), confine itself to the examination of the existence of an arbitration agreement. Sub-section (6-A) was omitted by Act 33 of 2019, but the omission is in view of the introduction of a new regime of institutionalised arbitration. Sections 8 and 11 are complementary in nature as both relate to reference to arbitration. Section 8 applies when judicial proceeding is pending and an application is filed for stay of judicial proceeding and for reference to arbitration. Amendments to Section 8 *vide* Act 3 of 2016 have not been omitted. Section 11 covers the situation where the parties approach a court for appointment of an arbitrator. *Mayavati Trading (P) Ltd.* v. *Pradyuat Deb Burman*[410], rightly holds that *SBP & Co.* v. *Patel Engg. Ltd.*[411] has been legislatively overruled, and hence, would not apply even post-omission of sub-section (6-A) to Section 11 of the Arbitration and Conciliation Act. The *Mayavati Trading case* has elaborated upon the object, purposes and history of the amendment to Section 11, with reference to sub-section (6-A) to elucidate that the section, as originally enacted, was facsimile with Article 11 of the UNCITRAL Model of Law of Arbitration on which the Arbitration and Conciliation Act was drafted and enacted. Referring to the legislative scheme of Section 11, different interpretations, and the Law Commission's Reports, it has been held that the omitted sub-section (6-A) to Section 11, Arbitration and Conciliation Act would continue to apply and guide the courts on its scope of jurisdiction at Stage one, that is the pre-arbitration stage.[412]

A deeper consideration of whether an arbitration agreement exists between the parties must be left to an arbitrator who is to examine the documentary evidence produced before him in detail after witnesses are cross-examined on the same.[413]

Omission of sub-section (6-A) of Section 11 (post-Act 33 of 2019) does not affect the restrictive role of courts as envisaged prior to its deletion.[414]

According to Section 11(6-A) as inserted by the Amendment Act, 2015, a duty is cast upon the referral court to consider the dispute/issue regarding existence of an arbitration agreement. A party raised objection regarding the existence of arbitration clause. The order vide which the High Court/referral

410. (2019) 8 SCC 714.
411. (2005) 8 SCC 618.
412. *Vidya Drolia* v. *Durga Trading Corpn.*, (2021) 2 SCC 1.
413. *Pravin Electricals (P) Ltd.* v. *Galaxy Infra & Engg. (P) Ltd.*, (2021) 5 SCC 671.
414. *Vidya Drolia* v. *Durga Trading Corpn.*, (2021) 2 SCC 1.

court did not decide the said issue conclusively and finally and left it to be decided by the sole arbitrator was set aside.[415]

Whether agreement time barred

A plea that the claim in the arbitration is time barred must be taken before the arbitrator and not before the court at stage of Section 11.[416] The Supreme Court held that the deletion by the 2019 Amendment of this section would not operate to resuscitate the law prevailing prior to that amendment. The omission of Section 11(6-A) would not alter the position that the power of court under Section 11 is confined to an examination of the existence of the arbitration agreement, nothing more, nothing less. All other preliminary issues are to be decided by the arbitrator.

Section 11(6-A), as inserted by (Amendment) Act 3 of 2016—Novation—Dispute relating to transfer of share holding—Appointment of arbitrator

The dispute related to transfer of share holding. Objection raised was that the MOU was novated by Shareholders' Agreement (SHA), as such the arbitration clause contained in MOU was not applicable. Issue whether MOU has been novated by SHA required examination of the clauses of agreement and surrounding circumstances which cannot be decided by court in petition under Section 11 of the Act. The Supreme Court held thus:

> Judged by the aforesaid tests, it is obvious that whether the MoU has been novated by the SHA dated 12-4-1996 requires a detailed consideration of the clauses of the two agreements, together with the surrounding circumstances in which these agreements were entered into, and a full consideration of the law on the subject. None of this can be done given the limited jurisdiction of a court under Section 11 of the 1996 Act. As has been held in para 148 of *Vidya Drolia*[417], detailed arguments on whether an agreement which contains an arbitration clause has or has not been novated cannot possibly be decided in exercise of a limited prima facie review as to whether an arbitration agreement exists between the parties. Also, this case does not fall within the category of cases which ousts arbitration altogether, such as matters which are in rem proceedings or cases which, without doubt, concern minors, lunatics or other persons incompetent to contract. There is nothing vexatious or frivolous in the plea taken by the appellant. On the contrary, a Section 11 court would refer the matter when contentions relating to non-arbitrability are plainly arguable, or when facts are contested. The court cannot, at this

415. *Magic Eye Developers (P) Ltd.* v. *Green Edge Infrastructure (P) Ltd.*, (2023) 8 SCC 50.
416. *C. Shamsuddin* v. *Now Realty Ventures LLP*, 2020 SCC OnLine Bom 100: (2020) 6 Mah LJ 108. See also, *Mayavati Trading (P) Ltd.* v. *Pradyuat Deb Burman*, (2019) 8 SCC 714.
417. *Vidya Drolia* v. *Durga Trading Corpn.*, (2021) 2 SCC 1.

stage, enter into a mini trial or elaborate review of the facts and law which would usurp the jurisdiction of the Arbitral Tribunal.

Order of the High Court declining appointment of the arbitrator was set aside. Parties were referred to arbitration.[418]

Sub-section (7) (Omitted)

Originally sub-section (7) provided as under:

> (7) A decision on a matter entrusted by sub-section (4) or sub-section (5) or sub-section (6) to the Chief Justice or the person or institution designated by him is final.

Sub-section (7) was amended by Amendment Act 3 of 2016. The amended sub-section (7) provides as under:

> (7) A decision on a matter entrusted by sub-section (4) or sub-section (5) or sub-section (6) to the Supreme Court, or as the case may be, the High Court or the person or institution designated by such Court is final and no appeal including letters patent appeal shall lie against such decision.

It was provided in sub-section (7), that the order passed under this section shall not be appealable. This change meant that finality is attached to the order passed under Section 11 and it would not be subject to further examination by an appellate court.[419]

Insurance claim—Appointment of arbitrator

Clause of the agreement between the parties postulated that if the insurer had disputed or not accepted the liability, no difference/dispute shall be referred to in arbitration. The claim of the respondent was disputed by the appellate insurer, in its communication on the premise that 1) the alleged loss of imported coal was an inventory shortage; 2) there was no actual loss of stock in process; 3) the damage to the sponge iron was due to inherent vice; and 4) the loss towards buildings/sheds, etc. were exaggerated to cover the insured maintenance. It was held, the communication was nothing but denial of liability by the insurer in toto and not a dispute pertaining to quantum. Language used in the second part of the arbitration clause was absolutely categorical and unequivocal that no difference/disputes shall be referable to arbitration if the company has disputed or not accepted the liability. The remedy open to the respondent was to institute a civil suit for mitigation

418. *Sanjiv Prakash* v. *Seema Kukreja*, (2021) 9 SCC 732.
419. *Duro Felguera, S.A.* v. *Gangavaram Port Ltd.*, (2017) 9 SCC 729.

of the grievances. The impugned order of the High Court appointing the arbitrator was set aside.[420]

Dispute arose out of an insurance agreement. Notice invoking the arbitration clause with respect to disputes arising out of agreement was duly issued to the insurance company by insured hospital. Notice was duly received by the insurance company through counsel and was responded to. Insured hospital sought initiation of the process of settlement within 15 days. Despite that, the arbitrator was not appointed. There was no legal impediment in the appointment of arbitrator. A retired District and Sessions Judge was appointed arbitrator in the case.[421]

Applicant cannot make bald allegations regarding fraud and coercion just to get an arbitrator appointed. There was an unexplained delay of five years in disputing alleged coercion/duress on part of the insurer in discharging fire insurance claim. No assurances were proved to be given by the insurer regarding payment of any remaining amounts after issuance of discharge voucher. Discharge voucher fully settled claims between parties and no arbitral disputes existed. In absence of any prima facie proof regarding duress/coercion, the court rightly refused to appoint an arbitrator.[422]

Fire and special perils policy

Parties entered into an agreement styled as "Standard Fire and Special Perils Policy", which contained an arbitration clause for settlement of disputes with regard to the quantum of claim to be paid under said policy. Applicant had claimed that settlement agreement executed between parties was vitiated by coercion. A business enterprise had suffered a huge fire in its factory, leading to losses. The surveyor and assessor had assessed the loss at ₹11–12 crores, but only a sum of ₹2 crores had been paid. Records showed that allegation of coercion required adjudication. It was not a case of accord and satisfaction. Sole arbitrator was appointed in the case.[423]

Dispute arose out of insurance for Standard Fire and Special Perils Policy. Major fire accident took place in the cold storage unit of the petitioner. Dispute arose with regard to the method to be adopted for calculation of

420. *Oriental Insurance Co. Ltd.* v. *Narbheram Power and Steel (P) Ltd.*, (2018) 6 SCC 534; *United India Insurance Co. Ltd.* v. *Hyundai Engg. & Construction Co. Ltd.*, (2018) 17 SCC 607.
421. *Bapu Jan Kalyan Sansthan Hospital* v. *E. Meditek (T.P.A) Service Ltd.*, 2021 SCC OnLine Pat 5496.
422. *Agastya Agro Ltd.* v. *United India Insurance Co. Ltd.*, 2022 SCC OnLine TS 1323: (2022) 6 ALD 514.
423. *Ashoka Foam Multiplast (P) Ltd.* v. *New India Assurance Co. Ltd.*, 2023 SCC OnLine Utt 167: (2023) 2 Arb LR 230.

claim. Existence of the arbitration clause was not disputed, a retired judge was appointed arbitrator in the case.[424]

Compensation for land acquired

Dispute about compensation for land acquired for National Highway. Land owner sought appointment of arbitrator to adjudicate dispute between parties regarding fixation of compensation for acquired land. As the State failed to appoint an arbitrator, the court appointed arbitrator on a petition filed under Section 11 of the Act.[425]

Delay in appointment of arbitrator—Power of High Court to appoint arbitrator

Railways and public institutions are very slow in reacting to the request made by a contractor for appointment of the arbitrator. Therefore, in case appointment is not made in time on the request made by the contracting party, then in that case the power of the High Court to appoint arbitrator under Section 11 of the Act will not be denuded. Administrative authorities cannot be allowed to sleep over the matter and leave the citizens without any remedy. The High Court appoints any arbitrator according to the given situation.[426]

Government contract—Panel of arbitrators of the department

Provision for arbitration in contracts entered by government, statutory authorities and government companies, invariably require that the arbitrators should be their own serving officers. Such a provision has to be given effect to, subject to requirement of independence and impartiality. Where arbitration clause requires arbitrators to be appointed from serving gazetted railway officers, one, by the contractor from a panel to be proposed by the Railways and the other, by the Railways, in such circumstances, inclusion in the panel, of names of officers due for transfer shortly or posted at far-away places, should be avoided so that arbitration proceedings might not be dragged on for long periods. As the matter was pending for the last 10 years, a retired judge of the High Court was appointed arbitrator in the case.[427]

---

424. *V.B. Cold Storage (P) Ltd.* v. *Bajaj Allianz General Insurance Co. Ltd.*, 2021 SCC OnLine AP 2958: (2022) 1 ALD 267.
425. *Prakash Chand Pradhan* v. *Union of India*, 2017 SCC OnLine Sikk 94.
426. *Union of India* v. *V.S. Engg. (P) Ltd.*, (2006) 13 SCC 240.
427. *Union of India* v. *Singh Builders Syndicate*, (2009) 4 SCC 523.

Government/statutory bodies, public sector undertaking—Arbitration by employee arbitrators

A person being an employee of one of the parties (which is the State or its instrumentality) cannot per se be a bar to his acting as an arbitrator. However, it is a ground reality that contractors in their anxiety to secure contracts from government/statutory bodies/public sector undertakings agree to arbitration clauses providing for employee arbitrators. But when subsequent disputes arise, they baulk at the idea of arbitration by such employee arbitrators and tend to litigate to secure an "independent" arbitrator. It will be appropriate if government/statutory authorities/public sector undertakings reconsider their policy providing for arbitration by employee arbitrators in deference to the specific provisions of the new Act reiterating the need for independence and impartiality in arbitrators. A general shift may in future be necessary for understanding the word "independent" as referring to someone not connected with either party. That may improve the credibility of arbitration as an alternative dispute resolution process.[428]

There must be reasonable apprehension of the biased disposition

There must be reasonable apprehension of the biased predisposition. Mere imagination of a ground/reason cannot be an excuse in apprehending bias in the mind of chosen/named arbitrator.[429]

Government contracts—Provision for appointment of serving officers of one party as arbitrator

A provision for serving officers of one party being appointed as arbitrator(s) brings out considerable resistance from the other party, when disputes arise. Having regard to the emphasis on independence and impartiality in the new Act, government, statutory authorities and government companies should think of phasing out arbitration clauses providing for serving officers and encourage professionalism in arbitration.[430]

Purchase order

Dispute between the parties arising of four purchase orders was covered by the arbitration clause in the first purchase order. An arbitrator was appointed in the case.[431]

---

428. *Indian Oil Corpn. Ltd.* v. *Raja Transport (P) Ltd.*, (2009) 8 SCC 520.
429. *Larsen & Toubro Ltd.* v. *Fertilizer & Chemicals Travancore Ltd.*, (2008) 1 SCC 252; *Nampa Electrical (P) Ltd.* v. *G.M. Central Org. for Railway Electrification*, 2014 SCC OnLine All 16107: (2015) 2 All LJ 478.
430. *Union of India* v. *Singh Builders Syndicate*, (2009) 4 SCC 523.
431. *Techno Electric & Engg. Co. Ltd.* v. *Bengal Energy Ltd.*, 2019 SCC OnLine Cal 9420.

Works contract—Appointment of arbitrator

Arbitration clause in work contract prohibited reference to arbitrator of a claim of more than 20 per cent of the value of the work. Original work order was followed by several supplementary work orders issued from time to time. In such circumstances, for determining whether the claim exceeded the said percentage, held, the value of the original work order should have been taken into account along with the value of supplementary work orders. The High Court erred in rejecting the application for appointment of arbitrator merely because the claim exceeded the prohibited percentage of the original work order. Matter was remanded to High Court for appointing an arbitrator.[432]

Existence of lease deed—Arbitrator appointed

Lease deed executed between the parties contained an arbitration clause. Dispute arose between the parties. Applicant had invoked the arbitration agreement. Dispute whether on merits or with regard to limitation falls for consideration by Arbitral Tribunal and that cannot be a reason to deny appointment of arbitrator as per agreement of parties. Claim was in the range of ₹5 lakhs, practicing advocate appointed as arbitrator in the case.[433]

Service provider agreement

Dispute arose between the parties. Only method for determination of such disputes is by way of arbitration, questions whether said services were adequate and satisfactory and whether claim made by petitioner is time barred are matters that can be examined by arbitrator alone, sole arbitrator was appointed for adjudication of disputes.[434]

Dealership agreement—Appointment of arbitrator

Retail outlet dealership agreement provided for arbitration of dispute relating to or arising out of said agreement. Dealership agreement was terminated on account of variance in physical stock at time of inspection. Dealer filed an application for appointment of arbitrator to resolve the dispute. Non-applicant, Corporation had no objection to appointment of arbitrator. Arbitrator was appointed in the case.[435]

---

432. *Deepak Kumar Bansal* v. *Union of India*, (2009) 3 SCC 223.
433. *Devendra Singh Sahdev* v. *Reliance Jio*, 2022 SCC OnLine Utt 1003.
434. *Wexford Financial Inc. Panama* v. *BHEL*, (2016) 8 SCC 267.
435. *Roopal Indian Oil* v. *Indian Oil Corpn. Ltd.*, 2019 SCC OnLine Raj 7905.

Development agreement

Development agreement which contained an arbitration clause was signed by all the three owners of the land. Agreed procedure for appointment of arbitrator failed. Arbitrator was appointed in the case.[436]

Trust deed

Settler had executed a trust deed in favour of the beneficiaries, the deed was signed by the settler alone. Beneficiaries cannot be regarded as party to the deed. It was held, trust deed including the arbitration clause does not satisfy the requirements of Section 2(1)(*b*) and 2(1)(*h*) read with Section 7, Arbitration and Conciliation Act, 1996, hence trust deed cannot be construed as an "arbitration agreement" within the meaning of Section 7, Arbitration and Conciliation Act, 1996. Application of the respondent filed under Section 11 for appointment of the arbitrator was dismissed.[437]

Lease and licence agreement

It is settled law that dispute between licensor and licensee falls under the category of non-arbitrable dispute. Dispute cannot be referred to arbitration.[438]

Issue of payment of interest

There was communication between the parties by virtue of electronic mode about the payment of interest, parties had agreed for payment of 9 per cent interest for lapses on their part. Respondent disputed the payment of interest. Prima facie case for appointment of arbitrator was made out. Arbitrator was appointed in the case.[439]

Memorandum of Understanding (MOU) contained arbitration clause—Arbitrator appointed

MOU entered between parties contained arbitration clause. Disputes arose between parties with regard to certain communication whereby purchase order in favour of petitioner, executed in furtherance of MOU, was kept in abeyance. Intention of the parties to refer the dispute to the arbitration was clear. Arbitrator was appointed in the case.[440]

---

436. *Santosh Pandey* v. *Felicity Estate (P) Ltd.*, 2019 SCC OnLine Raj 2094.
437. *Vimal Kishor Shah* v. *Jayesh Dinesh Shah*, (2016) 8 SCC 788.
438. *Allied Digital Services Ltd.* v. *XL Dynamics India (P) Ltd.*, 2023 SCC OnLine Bom 2890.
439. *R. Sivasankaran* v. *Harmony Residences (P) Ltd.*, 2023 SCC OnLine Mad 1248.
440. *Nirmal Software Services (P) Ltd.* v. *Dr Babasaheb Ambedkar Marathwada University*, (2019) 7 SCC 356.

International commercial arbitration [Sub-s. (9)]

In *Dolphin International Ltd.* v. *Ronak Enterprises Inc.*[441], the plaintiff-company was incorporated in America while the defendant-company was incorporated in India, as such an arbitrator whose nationality would be other than that of either party, *viz.* neither Indian nor American was required to be appointed. International Chamber of Commerce, Paris, suggested by the respondent was found too expensive for the parties, hence a retired Chief Justice of Pakistan suggested by the petitioner was found suitable, hence was appointed arbitrator in the case.

Where one of the parties to the agreement is a company incorporated in a country other than India, it is an international commercial arbitration, the petitioner has to approach the Chief Justice of India for appointment of arbitrator, application filed in the High Court would not be maintainable.[442]

The words in the clause of MOU that "arbitration administered in Hong Kong" indicated the seat of arbitration at Hong Kong. Since the parties had chosen "Hong Kong" as the place of arbitration, the laws of Hong Kong would govern the arbitration. Indian courts had no jurisdiction for the appointment of the arbitrator. Section 11 has no application to "international commercial arbitrations" seated outside India.[443]

International commercial agreement governed by laws of foreign country—Jurisdiction of Supreme Court to appoint arbitrator

Terms stipulated in agreement (signed in India) between Indian company and foreign company provided for agreement to be governed by and interpreted in accordance with laws of the State of California, US. Having regard to binding law laid down in the *Bhatia International case*[444], the *Indtel Technical Services (P) Ltd. case*[445] and the *Venture Global Engg. case*[446], held, in absence of any express or implied exclusion of provisions of Part I of the 1996 Act by agreement between the parties concerned, the Supreme Court had jurisdiction to appoint an arbitrator in this case.

In the *Indtel Technical Services (P) Ltd. case*[447], the Supreme Court specifically held that unless the provisions of Part I of the Arbitration and Conciliation Act, 1996 are excluded by agreement between the parties either

441. (1998) 5 SCC 724.
442. *Dr Reddy's Laboratories Ltd.* v. *Bombay Trading Co. (1993) (P) Ltd.*, 2004 SCC OnLine AP 598: (2004) 3 AP LJ 35.
443. *Mankastu Impex (P) Ltd.* v. *Airvisual Ltd.*, (2020) 5 SCC 399.
444. *Bhatia International* v. *Bulk Trading S.A.*, (2002) 4 SCC 105.
445. *Indtel Technical Services (P) Ltd.* v. *W.S. Atkins Rail Ltd.*, (2008) 10 SCC 308.
446. *Venture Global Engg.* v. *Satyam Computer Services Ltd.*, (2008) 4 SCC 190.
447. *Indtel Technical Services (P) Ltd.* v. *W.S. Atkins Rail Ltd.*, (2008) 10 SCC 308.

expressly or by implication, Part I of the Act including Section 11 would be applicable even where the international commercial agreements are governed by the laws of another country. It may be that the arbitrator might be required to take into account the applicable laws which may be the foreign laws but that does not affect the jurisdiction under Section 11 which falls in Part I which has been specifically held applicable in the *Bhatia International case*[448]. Application under Section 11(5) was allowed. Ex-Chief Justice of the Supreme Court was appointed arbitrator in the case.[449]

Appointment of third arbitrator of another nationality [S. 11(9)]

Section 11(9) of the Act is not mandatory, the word "may" therein cannot be read as "shall", to appoint an arbitrator not belonging to the nationality of either of the parties is not mandatory. However, there is nothing wrong in the two arbitrators having formed an opinion in consultation with each other that a person of a third nationality would be preferable as presiding arbitrator.[450]

In *Indtel Technical Services (P) Ltd.* v. *W.S. Atkins Rail Ltd.*[451], clause in the agreement provided that validity and performance of the agreement shall be governed by and construed in accordance with the laws of England and Wales. But the venue for such adjudication was not stipulated in the agreement. As held in *Bhatia International*[452], even in respect of international commercial agreements which are to be governed by the laws of another country, the party would be entitled to invoke the provisions of Part I of the Arbitration and Conciliation Act, 1996 and consequently application filed under Section 11 thereof would be maintainable. Clauses in the arbitration agreement in the instant case showed that the parties to the memorandum intended to have their disputes resolved by arbitration. Application under Section 11 was allowed. A retired judge of the Supreme Court was appointed as arbitrator in the case.[453]

Respondent, a British national, a profession expert entered into an MOU with the appellant-company for providing technical "know-how" and expert advice to the appellant, for which the appellant-company was required to pay fees. The respondent was also made a "Director (Technical)" and CEO of the subsidiary company of the appellant and 40 per cent equity shares in the subsidiary company were also allotted to him. It was held that a Director is

448. *Bhatia International* v. *Bulk Trading S.A.*, (2002) 4 SCC 105.
449. *Citation Infowares Ltd.* v. *Equinox Corpn.*, (2009) 7 SCC 220.
450. *Grid Corpn. of Orissa Ltd.* v. *AES Corpn.*, (2002) 7 SCC 736.
451. (2008) 10 SCC 308.
452. *Bhatia International* v. *Bulk Trading S.A.*, (2002) 4 SCC 105.
453. *Indtel Technical Services (P) Ltd.* v. *W.S. Atkins Rail Ltd.*, (2008) 10 SCC 308.

not a mere employee or servant of the company. The respondent was working in dual or double capacity, *i.e.* (*i*) as an employee, and (*ii*) as a Director. The functions to be performed by him were supervisory and related to policy-making decisions in the affairs of the company. Any dispute between the appellant-company and the respondent would, therefore, be covered by the clause in question of the arbitration agreement which provided for arbitration. Application filed before the Supreme Court for the appointment of the arbitrator was found maintainable. Sole arbitrator was appointed in the case to decide the dispute which had arisen between the parties.[454]

Appointment of arbitrator by Singapore International Arbitration Centre (SIAC)—Award passed by arbitrator cannot be questioned in proceedings under Section 11(6)

Appointment of arbitrator by SIAC and partial award passed cannot be questioned in proceedings under Section 11(6), as it would amount to sitting in appeal over the decision of SIAC in appointing arbitrator and award passed by the arbitrator which is not permissible under Section 11(6). Section 11(6) empowers the Chief Justice or his nominee only to appoint arbitrators in case(s), the parties fail to do so in accordance with the terms agreed upon by them.[455]

Frustration of arbitration clause

Arbitration clause provided that no person other than the named officer Executive Director (Northern Region) of the respondent-Corporation or his delegate shall act as arbitrator. The office of the named arbitrator (NR) ceased to exist, held the arbitration clause did not survive and has to be treated as having worked its course. Appointment of the Director (Marketing) as sole arbitrator in place of ED (NR) by the Corporation was unsustainable, the proceedings carried by him had no legal consequence. Sections 11(6)(*c*), 13 and 15 had no application in the circumstances of the case. Appointment of sole arbitrator was set aside.[456]

Expiry of lease agreement containing arbitration clause—Arbitrator can be/was appointed

In case of expiry of lease agreement between parties which contained an arbitration clause, mere expiry of lease agreement does not lead to

---

454. *Comed Chemicals Ltd.* v. *C.N. Ramchand*, (2009) 1 SCC 91.
455. *Pricol Ltd.* v. *Johnson Controls Enterprise Ltd.*, (2015) 4 SCC 177; *Purple Medical Solutions (P) Ltd.* v. *MIV Therapeutics Inc.*, (2015) 15 SCC 622.
456. *Newton Engg. & Chemicals Ltd.* v. *Indian Oil Corpn. Ltd.*, (2013) 4 SCC 44.

the inference of non-existence of arbitration clause. An arbitrator was appointed.[457]

Application for appointment of arbitrator—Held not premature

Arbitration clause in the agreement provided that disputes arising out of the agreement "which cannot be settled amicably shall be finally settled in accordance with the 1996 Act". Correspondence exchanged between the parties showed total absence of any scope for amicable settlement. It also showed that attempts for amicable settlement, although made, had remained without any result. In such circumstances, respondent's contention that the precondition for amicable settlement was not exhausted and that the application for appointment of arbitrator was premature, rejected. Application for appointment of arbitrator was allowed.[458]

Appointment of arbitrator by court on behalf of non-signatory to arbitration agreement

Petitioner applied for appointment of arbitrator on behalf of both R1 and R2 since R1 was only a corporate veil of R2 and all the acts/deeds/transactions were performed by R2 on behalf of R1, also signed agreement. Clauses in the agreements provided for reference to arbitration in case of dispute/differences arising between the parties. Petitioner had appointed arbitrator but the respondents did not make appointment of arbitrator as per agreements. Lapse/failure on the part of the respondents conferred jurisdiction on the court to appoint arbitrator under Section 11(6). Facts of the case showed the involvement of R2 also. Application for appointment of arbitrator was allowed, arbitrator was appointed on behalf of both the respondents.[459]

Withdrawal of application for appointment of arbitrator before High Court, subsequent filing of application before Supreme Court on same cause of action—Maintainability of

Applicant had filed application for appointment of arbitrator before the High Court. Subsequent withdrawal of the same and refiling of the same before the Supreme Court on the same cause of action was held not barred. Dispute had arisen between the parties which needed adjudication. Retired judge of the Supreme Court was appointed arbitrator in the case.[460]

---

457. *Ayesha Oman* v. *Trend World*, 2018 SCC OnLine Hyd 323: (2018) 6 ALT 223.
458. *Visa International Ltd.* v. *Continental Resources (USA) Ltd.*, (2009) 2 SCC 55.
459. *Purple Medical Solutions (P) Ltd.* v. *MIV Therapeutics Inc.*, (2015) 15 SCC 622.
460. *Vanna Claire Kaura* v. *Gauri Anil Indulkar*, (2009) 7 SCC 541.

Person disqualified to act as arbitrator cannot nominate another arbitrator

By virtue of amended Section 12(5), if any person who falls under any of the categories specified in the Seventh Schedule of the Arbitration and Conciliation Act, 1996 shall be ineligible to be appointed as arbitrator in the case. The Managing Director of a Corporation becomes ineligible to be appointed as arbitrator in the case. A person disqualified to act as arbitrator cannot nominate another arbitrator.[461]

Appointment of new arbitrator after the appointed arbitrator rescues himself from the proceedings

In a case where the original arbitrator had rescued himself, the substitute or new arbitrator is required to be appointed according to the rules that were applicable to the appointment of the original arbitrator. This is the mandate of Section 15(2). It was, therefore, incumbent on the petitioner to give notice and explore the possibility of naming an arbitrator by mutual consent and only on failure thereof, the application under Section 11(6) for appointment of arbitrator would be filed.[462]

Appointment of presiding officer [S. 11(9)]

Under the arbitration agreement, the presiding arbitrator has to be a nationality different from the nationality of the contracting parties. Contention that since the arbitrator was being appointed by the Chief Justice of India or his nominee, the said restriction as to nationality would not apply. Held, the part of the agreement dealing with nationality of presiding arbitrator must also be given effect to. Presiding arbitrator would be of a nationality different from the nationality of either of the parties.[463]

Scheme made by Chief Justice [Sub-s. (10)] (Now repealed)

If provisions of such schemes go beyond the terms of Section 11, they are vitiated and have to be amended. Therefore held, Clause 7 of the Appointment of Arbitrators by CJI Scheme, 1996, stipulating the service of notice to the other party to show cause why arbitrator should not be nominated, as requested, was bad and must be amended. Other parties must be given notice only of the request itself.[464]

---

461. *TRF Ltd.* v. *Energo Engg. Projects Ltd.*, (2017) 8 SCC 377.
462. *Huawei Technologies Co. Ltd.* v. *Sterlite Technologies Ltd.*, (2016) 1 SCC 721.
463. *Delta Mechcons (India) Ltd.* v. *Marubeni Corpn.*, (2008) 15 SCC 772.
464. *Konkan Railway Corpn. Ltd.* v. *Rani Construction (P) Ltd.*, (2002) 2 SCC 388.

Appointment of arbitrator by Supreme Court

Agreement provided for reference to named arbitrator for resolution of dispute outside India. Arbitrator at Singapore passed the award. Award was set aside by the court at Singapore with liberty to apply for fresh arbitration. Appellant did not file a fresh application for appointment of arbitrator at Singapore, but filed an application before the Supreme Court in India for appointment of arbitrator. It was held, award of the arbitrator was passed at Singapore, it was set aside by the High Court of Singapore and, therefore, the court at Singapore, which alone shall have jurisdiction over the arbitral proceedings and all applications arising out of that agreement shall be made in that court and no other court. Having mutually agreed to have the dispute referred to an arbitrator in Singapore, the applicant is not permitted to turn around and say that the Supreme Court in India should appoint an arbitrator. Application for appointment of arbitrator filed before the Supreme Court in India was rejected.[465]

Reference when a third party is impleaded as party in petition under Section 11

If a person who is not a party to the arbitration agreement is impleaded as a party to the petition under Section 11 of the Act, the court should either delete such party from the array of parties, or when appointing an arbitrator make it clear that the arbitrator is appointed only to decide the disputes between the parties to the arbitration agreement.[466] Construction agreement, in *Deutsche Post Bank Home Finance Ltd.* v. *Taduri Sridhar*[467], was between developer, owner of land and purchaser. Appellant-bank was not party to that agreement. Agreement between the bank and purchaser was a separate agreement. Arbitration clause of the construction agreement was invoked by the purchaser. Bank was not party to the construction agreement, could not be impleaded as party-respondent in the case.

There can be reference to arbitration only if there is an arbitration agreement between the parties. If there is a dispute between a party to an arbitration agreement, with other parties to the arbitration agreement as also non-parties to the arbitration agreement, reference to arbitration or appointment of arbitrator can be only with respect to the parties to the arbitration agreement and not the non-parties.[468] If "X" enters into two contracts, one with "M" and another with "D", each containing an

465. *Shivnath Rai Harnarain (India) Ltd.* v. *Abdul Ghaffar Abdul Rehman*, (2008) 5 SCC 135.
466. *Deutsche Post Bank Home Finance Ltd.* v. *Taduri Sridhar*, (2011) 11 SCC 375.
467. *Ibid.*
468. *S.N. Prasad* v. *Monnet Finance Ltd.*, (2011) 1 SCC 320.

arbitration clause providing for settlement of disputes arising under the respective contract, in a claim for arbitration by "X" against "M" in regard to the contract with "M", "X" cannot impaled "D" as a party on the ground that there is an arbitration clause in the agreement between "X" and "D".[469]

Guarantor of loan not party to loan agreement containing arbitration clause

A guarantor was not party to the loan agreement executed between the principal borrower and the finance company. It was held, as there was no arbitration agreement between the parties, the impleading of the appellant-guarantor in the arbitration proceedings and the award against him in such arbitration was not sustained, the part of the award so far as it related to the guarantor was set aside.[470]

Arbitration agreement not binding on non-party

W applied for appointment of arbitrator for resolution of disputes with company *I* on the strength of the arbitration agreement which *W* had with *S*, on allegations that both *S* and *I* had common Directors and correspondence from *I* was signed by the same person who was a signatory on behalf of *S* in the agreement. It was held, *S* and *I* are two independent companies having separate and different legal entities. Mere common shareholders or common Board of Directors neither makes the two companies a single entity nor leads to an inference that one company will be bound by the acts of the other. Further, there was no correspondence between *W* and *I* which proved on record any arbitration agreement between the parties. In the absence of any arbitration agreement between *W* and *I*, no claim or dispute of *W* with *I* can be the subject-matter of reference to an arbitrator. Application for appointment of arbitrator was rejected.[471]

Plea that applicant is not party to arbitration agreement—Rejected

Respondent's plea was that two of the sub-agreements were between Taiyo Membrane Corporation (India) and the respondent and the applicant, Taiyo Membrane Corporation Pty. Ltd. was not a party to any of the said two sub-agreements. Letters of intent issued in respect of the works and the correspondences exchanged between the parties showed that the applicant Taiyo Membrane Corporation Pty. Ltd. and Taiyo Membrane Corporation (India) are one and the same entity and the works under the sub-agreements were

469. *Deutsche Post Bank Home Finance Ltd.* v. *Taduri Sridhar*, (2011) 11 SCC 375.
470. *S.N. Prasad* v. *Monnet Finance Ltd.*, (2011) 1 SCC 320.
471. *Indowind Energy Ltd.* v. *Wescare (I) Ltd.*, (2010) 5 SCC 306.

allotted by the respondent to the said entity. Further, under the Australian Corporations Act, 2001 [S. 57-A], a corporation includes a company and a proprietary company limited by shares is incorporated as a Pty. Ltd. It was held that it was a case of misdescription and did not affect the maintainability of the application under Section 11(6).[472]

Appointment of sole arbitrator by one party

A party to the agreement would be disentitled to make any appointment of an arbitrator on its own, a party or an official or an authority having interest in the dispute would be disentitled to make appointment of an arbitrator. In a case where only one party has a right to appoint a sole arbitrator, its choice will always have an element of exclusivity in determining or charting the course for dispute resolution. Naturally, the person who has an interest in the outcome or decision of the dispute must not have the power to appoint a sole arbitrator.[473]

Arbitration clause in purchase contract

Arbitration clause in the purchase contract between the petitioner and the respondent was unambiguous. In reply to the petitioner's letter for invoking the arbitration clause, the respondent did not deny the existence of the arbitration clause. It was held, considering correspondence between the parties and attendant circumstances with particular reference to the purchase contract, there was a valid arbitration agreement between the parties. Arbitrator was appointed in the case.[474]

Where the main agreement, *i.e.* pricing agreement contained arbitration clause and there was consensus ad-idem to terms and conditions contained therein, which was different from the one contained in purchase order, the arbitration agreement contained in the main agreement would govern parties, it would not be appropriate for the parties to invoke clause in the purchase orders for the appointment of the arbitrator.[475]

Excepted matters—Failure of supplier to deliver goods within agreed period

Clause in the agreement provided for decision by the purchaser regarding quantification of liquidated damages in case the supplier failed to deliver

---

472. *Taiyo Membrane Corpn. Pty. Ltd.* v. *Shapoorji Pallonji & Co. Ltd.*, (2016) 1 SCC 736.
473. *Perkins Eastman Architects DPC* v. *HSCC (India) Ltd.*, (2020) 20 SCC 760.
474. *Powertech World Wide Ltd.* v. *Delvin International General Trading LLC*, (2012) 1 SCC 361.
475. *Balasore Alloys Ltd.* v. *Medima LLC*, (2020) 9 SCC 136.

goods within the agreed period. Purchaser imposed liquidated damages alleging that there was delay in delivery of goods. The supplier objected and sought reference of dispute to arbitration. Purchaser filed an objection that the dispute was beyond the purview of the arbitration agreement. The court held, the arbitration clause was to come into operation only after a finding was entered into that the supplier was liable for liquidated damages on account of delay in making delivery. The relevant agreement did not provide for any adjudicatory process regarding the fixing the liability of the supplier. The present matter involved a clear dispute as to fact whether there was any delay/breach on the part of the supplier, the said dispute was not excepted from the scope of arbitration. The order of the High Court allowing appointment of arbitrator at the instance of the respondent-supplier and directing the parties to submit their disputes to arbitration was upheld.[476]

Part of arbitration clause invalid—Doctrine of severability can be applied

Partial invalidity in contract will not *ipso facto* make the whole contract void or unenforceable. Wherever a contract contains legal as well as illegal parts and objectionable parts can be severed, effect be given to legal and valid parts striking out the offending parts. The objectionable part in the arbitration clause stated that the arbitrator's decision shall be "final and binding between the parties" and the parties had waived "all rights of appeal or objection in any jurisdiction". It was held, the objectionable part is clearly severable as it is independent of the dispute being referred to and resolved by an arbitrator. Hence, even in the absence of any other clause, the part as to referring the dispute to an arbitrator can be given effect to and enforced. By implementing that part, it cannot be said that the court is doing something which is not contemplated by the parties or by "interpretative process", the court is re-writing the contract which is in the nature of *novatio*. The intention of the parties is explicitly clear and they have agreed that the dispute, if any, would be referred to an arbitrator. To that extent, therefore, the agreement is legal, lawful and the offending part as to the finality and restraint in approaching a court of law can be separated and severed by using "a blue pencil".[477]

476. *BSNL* v. *Motorola India (P) Ltd.*, (2009) 2 SCC 337.
477. *Shin Satellite Public Co. Ltd.* v. *Jain Studios Ltd.*, (2006) 2 SCC 628.

Notice to opposite party

In case of exercise of power by Chief Justice/his designate, notice to the opposite party is necessary.[478]

In the present case, service of the advocate's, notice of the petition under Section 11, Arbitration and Conciliation Act on the appellant was found sufficient.[479]

Hearing of opposite party

It is fundamental to procedural jurisprudence that the right of no person shall be affected without being heard. This necessarily imposes an obligation on the Chief Justice to issue notice to the opposite party when he is moved under Section 11 of the Act. The notice to the opposite party cannot be considered to be merely an intimation to that party for the filing of the arbitration application and the passing of an administrative order appointing an arbitrator or an Arbitral Tribunal. It is really the giving of an opportunity of being heard. An opportunity of hearing to both the parties is a must. Even in administrative functions if rights are affected, rules of natural justice stated in the doctrine of "duty to act fairly" applies and the Chief Justice must issue notice to the person or persons likely to be affected by the decision under sub-section (6) of Section 11. Basic procedural fairness requires such notice to the opposite party.[480]

Communication of appointment of arbitrator to party necessary

Where an arbitrator is appointed in the case, communication thereof to the party concerned is necessary. Mere drafting of the letter is not enough.[481]

Appointment of arbitrator—Reasoned order

An order passed under Section 11(6) for appointment of arbitrator is a judicial order. It is incumbent on the part of the Chief Justice or designated judge to consider the claim of both the parties to the matter and pass a reasoned order. In *Rameshwar Das Agrawal* v. *Kiran Agrawal*[482], as Chief Justice of the High Court passed order under Section 11(6) without assigning reasons, the order was set aside and the matter was remanded to the High Court for passing fresh order in the light of decision of the Supreme Court in the *SBP case*.

478. *SBP & Co.* v. *Patel Engg. Ltd.*, (2005) 8 SCC 618.
479. *Mohd. Masroor Shaikh* v. *Bharat Bhushan Gupta*, (2022) 4 SCC 156.
480. *SBP & Co.* v. *Patel Engg. Ltd.*, (2005) 8 SCC 618.
481. *BSNL* v. *Subash Chandra Kanchan*, (2006) 8 SCC 279.
482. (2008) 2 SCC 155.

Finality of orders [Sub-s. (7)]

Finality attached to the decision of the Chief Justice under Section 11(4), (5) and (6) attaches to all preliminary matters needed to be adjudicated upon by the Chief Justice to exercise power under Section 11(4), (5) and (6) in addition to the finality that attaches to the decisions under the said sub-sections pre se.[483]

Appointment of arbitrator—Challenge by third party—Writ petition

Only a party to the arbitration agreement can challenge the appointment of an arbitrator and none else. Writ petition filed by a third person, who is challenging the appointment of arbitrator, is not maintainable.[484]

Appointment of arbitrator—Applicability of Section 14, Limitation Act, 1963

Section 14, Limitation Act has wider amplitude and provides that the time spent in prior proceedings is liable to be excluded provided the proceedings relating to the same matter were in issue and prosecuted in good faith and the court was unable to entertain it. The earlier proceedings before the Chief Justice of the Madras High Court by the petitioner were in good faith. The petitioner might have realised later that the application is to be filed under Section 11 of the Act before the Chief Justice of India. The respondent could not show willful negligence or lack of good faith on the part of the petitioner in having filed the application before the Chief Justice of the Madras High Court. Plea of limitation raised by the respondent was rejected, an arbitrator was appointed in the case.[485]

In *Sundarban Marine Products (P) Ltd.* v. *Waterbase Ltd.*[486], respondent had been wrongly pursuing for appointment of arbitrator for its claim ever since issuance of legal notice. The High Court has held in favour of the respondent but the said order was set aside by the Supreme Court, liberty was given to the respondent to raise its claim before the appropriate forum. In the circumstances of the case, the respondent was also granted the right to seek benefits available to it under Section 14, Limitation Act.

---

483. *SBP & Co.* v. *Patel Engg. Ltd.*, (2005) 8 SCC 618.
484. *Pandit Dwarka Prasad Mishra* v. *Director General (Works)*, 2021 SCC OnLine MP 6048.
485. *HBM Print Ltd.* v. *Scantrans India (P) Ltd.*, (2009) 17 SCC 338.
486. (2017) 14 SCC 182.

Reference to second arbitration

If cause of action arises after completion of pleadings and commencement of the first round of arbitration, claimants can make a separate claim by initiating second arbitration. However, making new claims by amendment to pending proceedings is untenable.[487]

Once a dispute is referred to arbitration and the sole arbitrator is appointed by parties by mutual consent and the arbitrator is so appointed, the arbitration agreement cannot be invoked for the second time.[488]

Subsistence/survival of arbitration agreement after termination/ discharge of main contract

MOU was entered into between the parties for distribution of cars manufactured by the appellant in Europe by the respondent initially valid upto 31 December 2007. The appellant terminated MOU on 25 September 2009 for unsatisfactory progress by the respondent. The respondent claiming damages initiated legal proceedings before the court in Belgium. The appellant obtained injunction from the court in India under Section 9, Arbitration and Conciliation Act, 1996 restraining the respondent's legal proceedings before Belgium court and also invoked arbitration clause contained in MOU, which was resisted on the ground that the arbitration clause ceased to exist on the termination of MOU, and the disputes were beyond the purview of arbitration since the arbitration clause did not cover disputes/claims related to the period beyond 31 December 2007. It was held, the disputes that had arisen were in relation to the termination of MOU and the consequences thereof. Such disputes would be clearly covered under an arbitration clause which provided that in the event of any dispute/difference arising at any time between the parties in relation to the agreement, it shall be referred to a sole arbitrator. As the disputes, which had arisen between the parties related to the subject-matter of MOU, the termination of MOU did not affect the arbitration clause in MOU. Since the parties had failed to appoint an arbitrator as per agreed procedure, sole arbitrator was appointed in the case.[489]

The law is settled that even if the whole agreement is terminated, the arbitration agreement would still remain. In *Tata Industries Ltd.* v. *Grasim Industries Ltd.*[490], dispute had arisen between the parties in relation to SHA. SHA contained an arbitration clause that on a party's share below 15 per

487. *Indian Oil Corpn. Ltd.* v. *SPS Engg. Ltd.*, (2011) 3 SCC 507.
488. *Swadesh Kumar Agarwal* v. *Dinesh Kumar Agarwal*, (2022) 10 SCC 235.
489. *Reva Electric Car Co. (P) Ltd.* v. *Green Mobil*, (2012) 2 SCC 93.
490. (2008) 10 SCC 187.

cent, rights of such party under SHA would not survive. The share of a party fell below 15 per cent. The right of such a party to seek arbitration did not perish. It was held, reduction in the shareholding below 15 per cent of the party did not nullify its right to seek arbitration as the arbitration clause in the contract was clearly autonomous of the contract. Arbitrator was appointed in the case.

Inaction, delay by Arbitral Tribunal

The object of the alternative dispute resolution process of arbitration is to have expeditious and effective disposal of disputes through a private forum of the parties, choice. If the Arbitral Tribunal consists of serving officers of one of the parties to the dispute, as members in terms of arbitration agreement and such tribunal is made non-functional on account of the action or inaction or delay of such party, either by frequent transfers of such members of the tribunal or by failing to take steps expeditiously to replace the arbitrators in terms of the arbitration agreement, the Chief Justice or his designate, required to exercise powers under Section 11 of the Act, can step in and pass appropriate orders.[491]

Appointment of arbitrator—Period of limitation

The period of limitation for filing an application under Section 11 would be governed by Article 137 of the First Schedule of the Limitation Act, 1963. The period of limitation begins to run from the date when there is failure to appoint the arbitrator.[492] No limitation period is prescribed in the Limitation Act for filing an application for appointment of arbitrator. Residuary Article 137, Limitation Act, 1963 would apply. Application filed within three years was not barred by limitation.[493]

In view of the provisions of Section 16, and the legislative policy to restrict judicial intervention at the pre-reference stage, the issue of limitation would require to be decided by the arbitrator. Sub-section (1) of Section 16 provides that the Arbitral Tribunal may rule on its own jurisdiction, "including any objections" with respect to the existence or validity of the arbitration agreement. Section 16 is an inclusive provision which would comprehend all preliminary issues touching upon the jurisdiction of the Arbitral Tribunal. The issue of limitation is a jurisdictional issue, which would be required to be decided by the arbitrator under Section 16, and not the High Court at the pre-reference stage under Section 11 of the Act. Once the existence of

491. *Union of India* v. *Singh Builders Syndicate*, (2009) 4 SCC 523.
492. *BSNL* v. *Nortel Networks (India) (P) Ltd.*, (2021) 5 SCC 738.
493. *Shridhar Dubey* v. *Union of India*, 2016 SCC OnLine MP 8013: (2016) 3 MP LJ 369.

the arbitration agreement is not disputed, all issues, including jurisdictional objections are to be decided by the arbitrator.[494]

Objection on ground of limitation

Objection on the ground of limitation can be raised by the contractor in proceedings under Section 11.[495]

Joinder/striking off parties to arbitration—Forum competent

Forum competent to determine joinder/striking off of parties to the arbitration is the arbitrator under Section 16 and not the Chief Justice making reference under Section 11.[496]

General conditions of contract providing for arbitration clause

See, under Section 7 under the same synopsis.

In the instant case, the High Court had directed the constitution of the Arbitral Tribunal in terms of the general conditions of contract (GCC), but the GCC was neither signed by the parties, nor made a part of the agreement between the parties. It was held that the parties were not governed by GCC, and the order of the High Court was illegal.[497]

Arbitration agreement—Supply agreement

The applicant was engaged in the business of seed cloning, production, nursery development, etc. The applicant and the non-applicant entered into a seed supply agreement through which the applicant agreed to establish nurseries and prepare seedlings (seeds) catering to the requirement of the non-applicant. The supply agreement contained a clause that any dispute arising between the parties should be resolved by submitting the same to the institutional arbitration in India under the provisions of the Arbitration and Conciliation Act, 1996. The applicant claimed compensation for breach of obligations by the non-applicant under the supply agreement. The applicant called upon the non-applicant to appoint an arbitrator. As the non-applicant did not agree, the applicant filed an application under Section 11(5) and (9) seeking appointment of arbitrator in terms of the relevant clause of the supply agreement. The non-applicant opposed the application contending

---

494. *Uttarakhand Purv Sainik Kalyan Nigam Ltd.* v. *Northern Coal Field Ltd.*, (2020) 2 SCC 455.
495. *Chief Engineer* v. *Roman Tarmat Ltd.*, 2021 SCC OnLine Mad 2467: (2021) 5 CTC 1.
496. *BHEL* v. *Bayer Shipping and Trading Ltd.*, (2005) 12 SCC 188.
497. *Continental (India) (P) Ltd.* v. *Railways*, 2022 SCC OnLine SC 922.

that the alleged supply agreement did not contain any arbitration clause. The expression "institutional arbitration" used in the clause, in question, was vague and/or uncertain and void under Section 29, Contract Act, 1872. The Supreme Court rejected the contentions of the non-applicant and allowed application for appointment of arbitrator. The court held that the 1996 Act does not prescribe any forum for an arbitration agreement. What is required is to gather the intention of the parties as to whether they have agreed for resolution of disputes through arbitration. The name of a specific institution was not indicated in the relevant clause of the arbitration agreement. However, parties unequivocally agreed for resolution of disputes through institutional arbitration and there existed a valid arbitration clause between the parties in the supply agreement entered into between the parties.[498]

Special terms in addition to general/standard terms—Effect of

Appellant L&T had entered into contract with respondent Fertilizer & Chemicals Travancore Ltd. The arbitration clause in Article 26 of the standard conditions of the contract provided that the Chairman/MD (CMD) of the respondent (FCTL) shall be the arbitrator in case of dispute between the parties. As the dispute arose between the parties, L&T invoked arbitration clause, suggested the name of three persons and called upon FCTL to name one of them as sole independent arbitrator. FCTL declined the request on the ground that only its CMD could be appointed as an arbitrator as per Article 26 of the contract. L&T filed an application under Section 11 of the Act before the High Court, the application was rejected by the High Court on the ground that there was no failure of agreed procedure. In an appeal filed before the Supreme Court, L&T contended that the special conditions attached to the contract replaced earlier Article 26 and CMD of FCTL cannot be treated as an independent arbitrator. The Supreme Court held that there was addition and not substitution of the old contract. The addition only provided the procedure to be adopted in the arbitration proceedings, venue of arbitration, language of the proceedings, etc. The mere fact that the arbitrator was named does not render the proceeding invalid. Appeal was dismissed.[499]

Condition precedent for deposit of disputed amount—Invalid

Clause in the arbitration agreement provided for constitution of Dispute Resolution Committee with stipulation that before availing of dispute resolution, disputed amount shall be deposited. It was held, the clause of

---

498. *Nandan Biomatrix Ltd.* v. *D 1 Oils Ltd.*, (2009) 4 SCC 495.
499. *Larsen & Toubro Ltd.* v. *Fertilizer & Chemicals Travancore Ltd.*, (2008) 1 SCC 252.

the arbitration agreement restricted the right of the petitioner to arbitration which is a statutory right. While making a claim it would be difficult for the petitioner to determine disputed amount since it may be partially admitted or entirely denied. Held, such a condition was invalid.[500]

Application under Section 11—Necessary pleadings and details

An application under Section 11 of the Act is expected to contain pleadings about the existence of a dispute and the existence of an arbitration agreement to decide such dispute. The applicant is not expected to justify the claim or plead exhaustively in regard to limitation or produce documents to demonstrate that the claim is within time in a proceeding under Section 11. That issue should normally be left to the Arbitral Tribunal.[501]

Rejection of claim on the ground of res judicata

The question whether a claim is barred by res judicata does not arise for consideration in proceedings under Section 11 of the Act. Such an issue will have to be examined by the Arbitral Tribunal. The limited scope of Section 11 does not permit such examination of the maintainability or tenability of a claim either on facts or in law. It is for the Arbitral Tribunal to examine and decide whether the claim was barred by res judicata. There can be no threshold consideration and rejection of a claim on the ground of res judicata while considering an application under Section 11 of the Act.[502]

Agreement containing arbitration clause insufficiently stamped

Where the agreement containing the arbitration clause is insufficiently stamped, application under Section 11, Arbitration and Conciliation Act, 1996 is not maintainable and shall be rejected. However, the petitioner can file a fresh application under Section 11 of the Act if he/she gets the agreement duly stamped making the actual stamp duty payable in accordance with law.[503]

A five-judge Bench of the Supreme Court has held that non-payment or deficient payment of stamp duty on substantive contract comprising or containing an arbitration clause or on standalone arbitration agreement, in cases where payment of stamp duty is mandatory, renders such arbitration agreement as non-existent pending payment of (the balance) stamp duty.

---

500. *Amazing India Contractors (P) Ltd.* v. *Airport Authority of India*, 2023 SCC OnLine Cal 1704.
501. *Indian Oil Corpn. Ltd.* v. *SPS Engg. Ltd.*, (2011) 3 SCC 507.
502. *Ibid.*
503. *Sukanti Barik* v. *Bedabyas Bank*, 2020 SCC OnLine Ori 982.

In such cases, the appointment of the arbitrator by a court or reference to arbitration is impermissible until the deficiency in stamp duty is made good in accordance with law.[504]

Having regard to larger ramifications of the *N.N. Global*[505], the Supreme Court viewed that proceedings should be placed before a seven-judge Bench to reconsider the correctness of the view by the five-judge Bench. In *Interplay between Arbitration Agreements under the Arbitration and Conciliation Act, 1996 and the Indian Stamp Act, 1899, re,*[506] the seven-judge Bench observed that agreements which are not stamped or are inadequately stamped are not rendered void or void ab initio or unenforceable. Non-stamping or inadequate stamping is a curable defect. The decisions in *N.N. Global* (five-judge Bench) and *SMS Tea Estates (P) Ltd.* v. *Chandmari Tea Co. (P) Ltd.*[507], were overruled.

Arbitration agreement contained in letters or correspondence can fall within the umbrage of the stamp duty.[508]

The plea of the agreement being unstamped does not prevent the court in appointing an arbitrator while exercising jurisdiction under Section 11 of the Act.[509]

The court would not refuse to consider application for ad interim injunction merely on the ground that the agreement in question needs to be adjudicated on the issue of payment of stamp duty.[510]

Order appointing arbitrator has no precedential value

Section 11 essentially confers on the Chief Justice of India/Chief Justice of the High Court to appoint an arbitrator whose power may be exercised by another judge as delegatee of the Chief Justice. This power of appointment of an arbitrator under Section 11, notwithstanding the fact that it has been held in *SBP*[511], as a judicial power, cannot be deemed to have precedential value.[512]

504. *N.N. Global Mercantile (P) Ltd.* v. *Indo Unique Flame Ltd.*, (2023) 7 SCC 1.
505. *Ibid.*
506. 2023 SCC OnLine SC 1666.
507. (2011) 14 SCC 66.
508. *N.N. Global Mercantile (P) Ltd.* v. *Indo Unique Flame Ltd.*, (2023) 7 SCC 1.
509. *IMZ Corporate (P) Ltd.* v. *MSD Telematics (P) Ltd.*, (2021) 2 HCC (Del) 414.
510. *Universals Enterprises* v. *Deluxe Laboratories (P) Ltd.*, 2016 SCC OnLine Bom 3963: (2016) 5 Mah LJ 623; *IMZ Corporate (P) Ltd.* v. *MSD Telematics (P) Ltd.*, (2021) 2 HCC (Del) 414.
511. *SBP & Co.* v. *Patel Engg. Ltd.*, (2005) 8 SCC 618.
512. *A. Ayyasamy* v. *A. Paramasivam*, (2016) 10 SCC 386.

Arbitral award set aside by civil court—Fresh arbitrator can be appointed

Arbitral award set aside by the civil court is non-est in law. Parties can apply for initiation of fresh arbitration proceedings. Fresh arbitrator can be appointed.[513]

Appointment of arbitrator in international commercial arbitration [Sub-s. (9)]

Application for appointment of arbitrator would be maintainable before the Supreme Court and not before the High Court.[514]

In case(s) of appointment of arbitrator in international commercial arbitration, the arbitrator's nationality has to be kept in mind having regard to the nationality of the respective parties.[515]

The key word in Section 11(9), Arbitration and Conciliation Act, 1996 is "may" which leaves a discretion in the Chief Justice or his nominee in this behalf and it is not mandatory that the sole arbitrator should be of a nationality other than the nationalities of the parties to the agreement. The word "may" in Section 11(9) of the Act is not indicated to be read as "must" or "shall". The Chief Justice or his nominee acting under Section 11 of the 1996 Act is not bound to appoint a sole arbitrator having neutral nationality. A retired justice of the Supreme Court was appointed as arbitrator.[516]

Where both the petitioners, husband and wife applied to become distributors of company as sole proprietorship concern with Code of Ethics with central management and control of association or body of individuals only exercised in India, both the petitioners were nationals of and habitually resident in US, it was held that arbitration becomes an international commercial arbitration notwithstanding fact that the individual, body corporate or government of a foreign country referred to in Section 2(1)(*f*) carry on business in India. The Delhi High Court had no jurisdiction to appoint an arbitrator.[517]

513. *J.K. Cold Tyre Retraders* v. *United India Insurance Co. Ltd.*, 2018 SCC OnLine Hyd 376: (2019) 1 ALD 74.
514. *Ibid.*
515. *TDM Infrastructure (P) Ltd.* v. *UE Development India (P) Ltd.*, (2008) 14 SCC 271.
516. *MSA Nederland B.V.* v. *Larsen & Toubro Ltd.*, (2005) 13 SCC 719.
517. *Amway (India) Enterprises (P) Ltd.* v. *Ravindranath Rao Sindhia*, (2021) 8 SCC 465.

International commercial arbitration—Appointment of outside arbitrator despite provision in arbitration clause for reference to a named arbitrator

In *Denel (Proprietary) Ltd.* v. *Bharat Electronics Ltd.*[518], appointment of arbitrator was rejected by the respondent (a Government of India Undertaking enterprise) in view of the direction of the Ministry of Defence, though the arbitration clause provided for appointment of MD of the respondent or his nominee as arbitrator. It was held, failure of a party concerned to appoint an arbitrator requires the Chief Justice or his nominee to come to the rescue of the parties. Norms of appointment of arbitration agreed to by the parties can be deviated from where independence of arbitrator is in question. In this case, the appointment of the named arbitrator MD of the respondent would not be proper as he was bound by the directions of the Ministry of Defence and might not decide independently. A retired judge of the Supreme Court was appointed as arbitrator in the case.

International commercial arbitration—Juridical seat of arbitration

Where the agreement provided that the agreement was governed by the laws of the Republic of Korea and all disputes shall be settled by arbitration in Seoul (Korea) (or such other place as the parties may agree in writing), it was held that on the facts of the case, Part I stood excluded. The Supreme Court had no jurisdiction to entertain an application under Section 11(6) for appointment of the arbitrator. There will be no question of applicability of Section 11(6) in such a case.[519]

Bihar Public Works Contracts Disputes Arbitration Tribunal Act, 2008 (21 of 2008), Sections 8, 9 and 22

Clause of general conditions of contract provided for settlement of dispute through Central Act, *viz.*, Arbitration and Conciliation, 1996 and not through State Act. It was held, State Arbitration Tribunal would have no jurisdiction to appoint an arbitrator to resolve the dispute.[520]

Electricity Act, 2003

Section 86(1)(*f*), Electricity Act, 2003 is a special provision which overrides the general provisions contained in Section 11, Arbitration and Conciliation Act, 1996. Section 86(1)(*f*) vests a statutory jurisdiction with the State Electricity Commission to adjudicate disputes between the licensees and

518. (2010) 6 SCC 394.
519. *Dozco India (P) Ltd.* v. *Doosan Infracore Co. Ltd.*, (2011) 6 SCC 179.
520. *Kamladitya Construction (P) Ltd.* v. *State of Bihar*, 2016 SCC OnLine Pat 2326.

generating companies and to refer any dispute for arbitration. Order of the High Court under Section 11(6) of the 1996 Act appointing an arbitrator was unsustainable, and was set aside.[521]

Consumer Protection Act, 1986

Pendency of proceedings before the National Consumer Commission cannot be a ground for disallowing an application filed under Section 11(6) for appointment of arbitrator. Arbitrator was appointed in the case.[522]

Micro, Small and Medium Enterprises Development Act, 2006 (27 of 2006)

Where the respondent, registered under the provisions of the MSMED Act has already made a reference to the Council, i.e. prior to present the application under Section 11(6), the jurisdiction of the Council had been invoked, and it would have exclusive jurisdiction. An application under Section 11(6), Arbitration and Conciliation Act, 1996 is not maintainable.[523]

Micro, Small and Medium Enterprises Development Act, 2006 (27 of 2006)—Appointment of arbitrator

To seek benefit of provisions under Micro, Small and Medium Enterprises Development Act, 2006, seller should have been registered under provisions of 2006 Act, as on date of entering into contract. No acceptable material was produced to show that supply of goods had taken place or any services were rendered, subsequent to registration of the supplier as a unit under the 2006 Act. The supplier cannot become a micro or small enterprise or supplier, to claim benefits within the meaning of the 2006 Act, by submitting memorandum to obtain registration subsequent to entering into contract and supply of goods and services. Supplier had abandoned incomplete work and made deficient and defective supplies. Supplier was not entitled to invoke provision of the 2006 Act. Arbitration agreement was existing between parties. Appointment of the arbitrator was proper.[524]

There was a development agreement between the parties, dispute relating to outstanding dues of the contractor arose. Counterclaims were filed against the supplier contractor before the Facilitation Council. There is no provision for raising counterclaim under the Micro, Small and Medium Enterprises

521. *M.P. Power Trading Co. Ltd.* v. *Narmada Equipments (P) Ltd.*, (2021) 14 SCC 548.
522. *Universal Consortium of Engineers (P) Ltd.* v. *Kanak Mitra*, 2021 SCC OnLine Cal 1425.
523. *H.P. SEB Ltd.* v. *Suri Electricals & Ceramics*, 2023 SCC OnLine HP 5.
524. *Silpi Industries* v. *Kerala SRTC*, (2021) 18 SCC 790.

Development Act, 2006. In the development agreement parties had agreed to refer their disputes to an arbitrator. A former judge of the High Court was appointed arbitrator in the case.[525]

Micro, Small and Medium Enterprises Development Act, 2006 (27 of 2006), Section 18(2)

The Facilitation Council under had itself chosen to act as Arbitral Tribunal, which it was empowered to do under Section 18(2), Micro, Small and Medium Enterprises Development Act, 2006. Since dispute between parties were already pending in arbitration before the Facilitation Council, no arbitrator to be appointed. Application under Section 11(6) for appointment of arbitrator was rejected.[526]

Micro, Small and Medium Enterprises Development Act, 2006 (27 of 2006), Sections 18(2), (3), 24—Facilitation Council

Facilitation Council can act in dual capacity, in the event of failure of conciliation proceedings, it can act as arbitrator.[527]

Micro, Small and Medium Enterprises Development Act, 2006 (27 of 2006)—Arbitration and Conciliation Act, 1996, Section 11

Facilitation Council has jurisdiction to act as arbitrator in disputes between suppliers located within its jurisdiction and buyers located anywhere in India. Provisions of Section 18, Micro, Small and Medium Enterprises Development Act, 2006 will prevail over individual arbitration clauses.[528]

Sick Industrial Company (Special Provisions) Act, 1985 —Appointment of arbitrator

Where there is no clash between scope of proceedings under Section 11, Arbitration and Conciliation Act, 1996 and Section 22, Sick Industrial Company (Special Provisions) Act, 1985, an arbitrator may be appointed.[529]

---

525. *GR Green Life Energy (P) Ltd.* v. *Leitwind Shriram Mfg. (P) Ltd.*, 2021 SCC OnLine SC 133.
526. *Mondrian High* v. *Pranav Doors & Windows (P) Ltd.*, 2023 SCC OnLine Utt 457.
527. *Best Towers (P) Ltd.* v. *Reliance Communications Ltd.*, 2019 SCC OnLine Pat 3357: (2019) 3 PLJR 486.
528. *Reliance Life Science (P) Ltd.* v. *Klenzaids Contamination Controls (P) Ltd.*, 2017 SCC OnLine Bom 9999.
529. *Agio Countertrade Pte. Ltd.* v. *Punjab Iron & Steel Co. Ltd.*, (1999) 5 SCC 734.

SARFAESI Act—Appointment of arbitrator

Dispute arose due to the failure of the petitioner to repay the loan. Dispute was already the subject-matter of proceedings before the Debt Recovery Tribunal. Arbitrator was not appointed.[530]

Gujarat Public Works Contracts Disputes Arbitration Tribunal Act, 1992 (4 of 1992)—Appointment of arbitrator

General conditions of contract of the Engineering Department of Ahmedabad Municipal Corporation provided for reference of disputes relating to the contract to the Arbitration Tribunal, Gujarat State. As the Gujarat Municipal Corporation had not been notified as public undertaking, as such was outside the purview of the State Act governing the reference to the Arbitration Tribunal, the aggrieved party could file application under Section 11(5) before the Chief Justice or his designate for appointment of arbitrator. Rejection of application on the ground that the arbitration agreement did not lay down any procedure for appointment of arbitrator was not proper.[531]

National Highways Act, 1956 (48 of 1956)

Parties cannot make an application under Section 11, Arbitration and Conciliation Act, 1996 for appointment of arbitrator. Section 3-G(6) cannot be construed to make provision of Section 11 of Act of 1996 applicable for appointment of arbitrator.[532]

U.P. Co-operative Societies Act, 1965 (11 of 1966)

There was an agreement between the parties to sell and dispose of sugar to the best advantage of the factories concerned for maximum price obtainable. Dispute arose between Factories Federation and its agents, which had to be referred to Registrar, Cooperative Societies as provided under Section 70, U.P. Co-operative Societies Act, 1965. Provisions of Section 11(6) of the 1996 Act were not attracted; application under Section 11, Arbitration and Conciliation Act, 1996 for appointment of arbitrator was rejected.[533]

---

530. *Bell Finvest India Ltd.* v. *A.U. Small Finance Bank Ltd.*, (2022) 6 HCC (Del) 467.
531. *Om Construction Co.* v. *Ahmedabad Municipal Corpn.*, (2009) 2 SCC 486.
532. *Vishwasrao Dattatray Kachare* v. *Union of India*, 2017 SCC OnLine Bom 451: (2017) 6 Mah LJ 85.
533. *Motilal & Sons* v. *M.D. U.P. Coop. Sugar Factories Federation Ltd.*, 2020 SCC OnLine All 1323: (2020) 143 ALR 666.

Rajasthan Co-operative Societies Act, 2001 (16 of 2002)—Appointment of arbitrator under Arbitration and Conciliation Act, 1996

In the distribution agreement for distribution of milk and buttermilk for a period of two years, there was a provision to resolve disputes through arbitration. Despite Section 58, Rajasthan Co-operative Societies Act, 2001, there was an agreement between parties to resolve disputes through arbitrator Chairman. Parties are bound by agreement and arbitration clause contained in agreement. Therefore, Section 58, Rajasthan Co-operative Societies Act, should not be applicable at all nor should the same come in the way of appointing arbitrator under Arbitration and Conciliation Act.[534]

Real Estate (Regulation and Development) Act, 2016

A petitioner who has filed a complaint before the Real Estate Regulatory Authority under the Real Estate (Regulation and Development) Act, 2016 is not barred from seeking arbitration as the object of the two Act is different.[535]

Non-service of notice invoking arbitration clause

Objection was raised as to the non-service of notice invoking arbitration clause; track result was brought on the record regarding delivery of registered post under which notice invoking arbitration clause was sent to the respondent. The track result showed that the notice sent was delivered to the respondent. Objection raised by the respondent was rejected.[536]

Appointment of arbitrator—Pleadings and proof

The Chief Justice can either proceed on the basis of affidavits and documents produced or take such evidence or get such evidence recorded, as may be necessary.[537]

Oral evidence is not necessary to determine the issue involved. In any case even if the power under Section 11(6) is judicial in the sense of requiring a judicial determination by the designate of the Chief Justice, it surely does not render the designate of the Chief Justice into a trial court.[538]

---

534. *Jaipur Zila Dugdh Utpadak Sahkari Sangh Ltd.* v. *Ajay Sales & Suppliers*, (2021) 17 SCC 248.
535. *Nageshwar Singh Swaraj* v. *Rukmani Buildtech (P) Ltd.*, 2020 SCC OnLine Pat 925.
536. *Sushil Kumar Ojha* v. *Shesh Narayan Tripathi*, 2014 SCC OnLine All 15226: (2014) 4 All LJ 734.
537. *SBP & Co.* v. *Patel Engg. Ltd.*, (2005) 8 SCC 618.
538. *Rodemadan India Ltd.* v. *International Trade Expo Centre Ltd.*, (2006) 11 SCC 651.

Amendment of plaint

The provisions of CPC are applicable to achieve the object of resolution of disputes unless its applicability is excluded by the 1996 Act. Amendment of a plaint can be allowed to avoid multiplicity of litigation.[539]

Application for revocation of mandate of arbitrator

Where dispute is raised about the impartiality of the arbitrator, invocation of Section 11 is improper. Section 11 can be invoked only when there is vacancy. For challenging the continuance of the arbitrator, the party must file application under Sections 12(3), (4), 13(2), 13(3) of the Act before the Arbitral Tribunal.[540]

Redetermination of fee of arbitrator [Sub-s. (14)]

Section 11(14) and the Fourth Schedule relatable to it, are applicable to even Arbitral Tribunal appointed by the parties themselves in terms of their agreement.[541]

Once a dispute is referred to arbitration and a sole arbitrator is appointed by parties by mutual consent and the arbitrator is so appointed, the arbitration agreement cannot be invoked for a second time.[542]

Fees to be taken as a composite amount and not to be paid separately and individually to each arbitrator.[543]

Initially the sole arbitrator had determined his fee. On the quantification of interest as claimed in the statement of claim the arbitrator re-determined his fee and the petitioner participated in the proceedings. At the final stage of arguments, the petitioner was estopped from challenging order of re-determination of fees.[544]

Limitation for filing application under Section 11

Section 11 does not prescribe any time period for filing an application under sub-section (6) for appointment of an arbitrator. Since there is no provision in the 1996 Act specifying the period of limitation for filing

539. *Aargee Engg. & Co.* v. *Era Infra Engg. Ltd.*, 2017 SCC OnLine All 3929: (2017) 122 ALR 179.
540. *S.K. and Associates* v. *Indian Farmer and Fertilizers Coop. Ltd.*, 2010 SCC OnLine All 1620: (2010) 6 All LJ 664.
541. *State of U.P.* v. *Shyam Lal*, 2021 SCC OnLine All 514: (2021) 148 ALR 344.
542. *Swadesh Kumar Agarwal* v. *Dinesh Kumar Agarwal*, (2022) 10 SCC 235.
543. *State of U.P.* v. *Shyam Lal*, 2021 SCC OnLine All 514: (2021) 148 ALR 344.
544. *Project Director* v. *Electrosteel Casting Ltd.*, 2021 SCC OnLine Raj 4358: (2021) 2 WLC (UC) 19.

an application under Section 11, one would have to take recourse to the Limitation Act, 1963, as per Section 43, Arbitration and Conciliation Act, which provides that the Limitation Act shall apply to arbitrations, as it applies to proceedings in court. The provisions of the Limitation Act, 1963 apply to all proceedings under the Arbitration and Conciliation Act, both in court and in arbitration, except to the extent expressly excluded by the provisions of the Arbitration and Conciliation Act. Since none of the articles in the Schedule to the Limitation Act, 1963 provide a time period for filing an application for appointment of an arbitrator under Section 11, it would be covered by the residual provision Article 137 of the Limitation Act, 1963. The period of limitation for filing an application under Section 11 would be governed by Article 137 of the First Schedule of the Limitation Act, 1963.[545]

The limitation for filing an application under Section 11 would arise upon the failure to make the appointment of the arbitrator within a period of 30 days from issuance of the notice invoking arbitration. In other words, an application under Section 11 can be filed only after a notice of arbitration in respect of the particular claim(s)/dispute(s) to be referred to arbitration as contemplated by Section 21 of the 1996 Act is made, and there is failure to make the appointment. The period of limitation for filing a petition seeking appointment of an arbitrator(s) cannot be confused or conflated with the period of limitation applicable to the substantive claims made in the underlying commercial contract. The period of limitation for such substantive claims is prescribed under various articles of the Limitation Act, 1963. The limitation for deciding the underlying substantive disputes is necessarily distinct from that of filing an application for appointment of an arbitrator.[546]

A claim crystallises upon the issuance of final bill. The final bill was issued by the contractor on 14 December 1992. The contractor's complaint with respect to payment was first made to the Executive Engineer (EE) in 1988. Its rejection resulted in an appeal before the Superintending Engineer SE who never gave his opinion or decision. Even in 1993 after the final bill was drawn, the SE's decision was not given. It was held, the application before the civil court for the appointment of the arbitrator made in January 1995 was to be within the period of limitation.[547]

---

545. *BSNL* v. *Nortel Networks (India) (P) Ltd.*, (2021) 5 SCC 738.
546. *Secunderabad Cantonment Board* v. *B. Ramachandraiah & Sons*, (2021) 5 SCC 705.
547. *S.D. Shinde Tr. Partner* v. *State of Maharashtra*, 2023 SCC OnLine SC 1045.

Recall of order of appointment of arbitrator [S. 11(5)]

The High Court has enough power to recall any order appointing an arbitrator which appears to be incorrect, especially when the proceedings before the arbitrator have not yet been initiated.[548]

As the petitioner stated that he did not want to pursue arbitration proceedings and sought recall of his petition, the order of appointment of arbitrator was recalled.[549]

Review

The Arbitration and Conciliation Act, 1996 is a complete Code which does not specifically confer any power upon the court to review an application under the statute which is Section 11 of the Act and consequently, a review in the instant case was not maintainable.[550]

Review of the order passed by Chief Justice of India/his designate

An order passed by the Chief Justice of India or his nominee under Section 11(6) of the Act is indeed an "order" within the meaning of Article 137 of the Constitution and is subject to review under the aforesaid provision.[551]

An order under Section 11 for appointment of arbitrator can be reviewed under Article 215 of the Constitution of India.[552]

Appeal

In matters of appointment of arbitrator by the court, no statutory right of appeal lies against the decision under Section 11.[553]

Appeal against the order passed by the Chief Justice of the High Court or his designate under Section 11(6) lies only under Article 136 of the Constitution. Order passed by the Chief Justice of India/judge of the Supreme Court under Section 11(6) is not appealable.[554]

548. *Resident Engg. Raj. Division II* v. *LP. Singh Construction Co.*, 2018 SCC OnLine Raj 3590.
549. *Shiva Sanjaya Enterprises* v. *Tamura Electric Works Ltd.*, (2002) 10 SCC 495.
550. *Sarada Construction* v. *Bhupendra Pramanik*, 2023 SCC OnLine Cal 342.
551. *Jain Studios Ltd.* v. *Shin Satellite Public Co. Ltd.*, (2006) 5 SCC 501.
552. *Pushpalata Jain* v. *Raj Enterprises*, 2020 SCC OnLine MP 4694.
553. *A.P. Tourism Development Corpn. Ltd.* v. *Pampa Hotels Ltd.*, (2010) 5 SCC 425.
554. *SBP & Co.* v. *Patel Engg. Ltd.*, (2005) 8 SCC 618.

Order appealable under Article 136 of the Constitution

An order passed by the High Court that the dispute is not arbitrable, is an adjudicatory order and is appealable under Article 136 of the Constitution.[555]

Order of designate of Chief Justice of High Court, not being a judge of High Court under Section 11(4), (5), (6)—Remedy of appeal/writ

The Act does not provide for an appeal against the order of the Chief Justice or his designate made under Section 11(4), (5) or (6). On the other hand, Section 11(7) makes it clear that a decision of the designate under Section 11(4), (5) or (6) is final. As no appeal is maintainable against the order of the designate and as his order has been made final, the only course available to the appellant was to challenge the order, even if it is a judicial order, by a writ petition under Article 227 of the Constitution of India. The decision in the *SBP case*[556], does not bar such a writ petition. The observation of the Supreme Court in the *SBP case* that against an order under Section 11 of the Act, only an appeal under Article 136 of the Constitution would lie, is with reference to the orders made by the Chief Justice of a High Court or by the designated judge of that High Court. The said observations do not apply to a subordinate court functioning as designate of the Chief Justice.[557]

Writ

An order passed by the High Court under Section 11(6) being an administrative order is amenable to writ jurisdiction under Article 226 of the Constitution subject to rule of alternative remedy.[558]

The power of the Chief Justice or his designate in making appointment of arbitrators is not administrative action but judicial in nature which could be assailed only before the Supreme Court by recourse of Article 136 of the Constitution, therefore, writ petition would not be maintainable there against.[559]

There is hardly any area of dispute which cannot be decided by the arbitrator appointed by the designated judge. So, since an efficacious alternative remedy is available before the arbitrator, a writ court normally would not entertain a challenge to an order of the designated judge made under

555. *Food Corporation of India* v. *Indian Council of Arbitration*, (2003) 6 SCC 564.
556. *SBP & Co.* v. *Patel Engg. Ltd.*, (2005) 8 SCC 618.
557. *Punjab Agro Industries Corpn. Ltd.* v. *Kewal Singh Dhillon*, (2008) 10 SCC 128.
558. *State of Orissa* v. *Gokulananda Jena*, (2003) 6 SCC 465.
559. *RIICO Ltd.* v. *Manoj Ajmera*, 2007 SCC OnLine Raj 98: (2008) 1 RLW 473.

Section 11(6) of the Act which includes considering the question of jurisdiction of the arbitrator himself. Therefore, even though a writ petition under Article 226 of the Constitution is available to an aggrieved party, ground available for challenge in such a petition is limited because of the alternative remedy available under the Act itself.[560]

Special leave to appeal under Article 136 of the Constitution

An order passed by the Chief Justice of India or his designate under Section 11 nominating an arbitrator is not an adjudicatory order; the Chief Justice or his designate is not a tribunal. Such an order cannot be made the subject of a petition for special leave to appeal under Article 136 of the Constitution.[561]

A petition under Article 136 of the Constitution can lie for challenging a judgment, decree, determination, sentence or order in any cause or matter passed or made by any court or tribunal in the territory of India. As the Chief Justice of the High Court or his designate under Section 11(6) of the Act acts in administrative capacity, an order of the Chief Justice is not passed by any court exercising any judicial function nor is it a tribunal having the trappings of a judicial authority. It was held, orders by the Chief Justice under Section 11(6) of the Act being of an administrative nature cannot be subjected to any challenge directly under Article 136 of the Constitution.[562]

The nature of the function performed by the Chief Justice being essentially to aid the constitution of Arbitral Tribunal immediately and the legislature having consciously chosen to confer the power on the Chief Justice and not a court, it is apparent that the order by the Chief Justice or his nominee is an administrative order.[563] Even an order refusing to appoint an arbitrator will not be amenable to the jurisdiction of the Supreme Court under Article 136 of the Constitution. However, an order of refusal which has decided contentious issues would be an act of non-performance of duty and the authority concerned could be directed by mandamus to perform its duty.[564]

Alternative remedy under Section 7 of M.P. Madhyastham Adhikaran Adhiniyam, 1983

Where alternative remedy under Section 7 of the Madhya Pradesh Madhyastham Adhikaran Adhiniyam to refer dispute to tribunal is available,

560. *State of Orissa* v. *Gokulananda Jena*, (2003) 6 SCC 465.

561. *Konkan Railway Corpn. Ltd.* v. *Rani Construction (P) Ltd.*, (2002) 2 SCC 388, affirmed.

562. *Ador Samia (P) Ltd.* v. *Peekay Holdings Ltd.*, (1999) 8 SCC 572; *Datar Switchgears Ltd.* v. *Tata Finance Ltd.*, (2000) 8 SCC 151 (Question left open); *Konkan Railway Corpn. Ltd.* v. *Mehul Construction Co.*, (2000) 7 SCC 201.

563. *Konkan Railway Corpn. Ltd.* v. *Mehul Construction Co.*, (2000) 7 SCC 201.

564. *Ibid.*

application under Section 11(3), Arbitration and Conciliation Act, 1996 is not maintainable.[565]

Miscellaneous

Clause in the agreement provided for resolution of dispute by arbitration. The contractor appointed an arbitrator and communicated it to the State. The State failed to object within 30 days. As the State had given deemed consent, it was stopped from challenging the appointment of the arbitrator.[566]

POWER OF CENTRAL GOVERNMENT TO AMEND FOURTH SCHEDULE [S. 11-A]

[567][**11-A.** *Power of Central Government to amend Fourth Schedule.*—(1) If the Central Government is satisfied that it is necessary or expedient so to do, it may, by notification in the Official Gazette, amend the Fourth Schedule and thereupon the Fourth Schedule shall be deemed to have been amended accordingly.

(2) A copy of every notification proposed to be issued under sub-section (1), shall be laid in draft before each House of Parliament, while it is in session, for a total period of thirty days which may be comprised in one session or in two or more successive sessions, and if, before the expiry of the session immediately following the session or the successive sessions aforesaid, both Houses agree in disapproving the issue of the notification or both Houses agree in making any modification in the notification, the notification shall not be issued or as the case may be, shall be issued only in such modified form as may be agreed upon by the both Houses of Parliament.]

NOTES ON CLAUSES

Clause 7 of the Bill seeks to insert a new Section 11-A in the principal Act to empower the Central Government to amend the Fourth Schedule by notification in the Official Gazette after having the same in draft form before each House of Parliament.

COMMENTS

Corresponding old law

Section 11-A is new section inserted in the Act by the Amending Act 3 of 2016 (w.e.f. 23 October 2015).

565. *Kes International Ltd.* v. *M.P. Madhya Kshetra Vidyut Vitaran Co. Ltd.*, 2019 SCC OnLine MP 2275: (2019) 2 MP LJ 618.
566. *State of H.P.* v. *Bmd (P) Ltd.*, 2022 SCC OnLine HP 6824.
567. *Ins.* by Act 3 of 2016, S. 7 (w.r.e.f. 23-10-2015).

Scope

Section 11-A empowers the Central Government to amend the Fourth Schedule of the Act by Official Gazette after laying the same in draft before each House of Parliament.

GROUNDS FOR CHALLENGE [S. 12]

12. *Grounds for challenge.*—[568][(1) When a person is approached in connection with his possible appointment as an arbitrator, he shall disclose in writing any circumstances,—

(*a*) such as the existence either direct or indirect, of any past or present relationship with or interest in any of the parties or in relation to the subject-matter in dispute, whether financial, business, professional or other kind, which is likely to give rise to justifiable doubts as to his independence or impartiality; and

(*b*) which are likely to affect his ability to devote sufficient time to the arbitration and in particular his ability to complete the entire arbitration within a period of twelve months.

Explanation 1.—The grounds stated in the Fifth Schedule shall guide in determining whether circumstances exist which give rise to justifiable doubts as to the independence or impartiality of an arbitrator.

Explanation 2.—The disclosure shall be made by such person in the form specified in the Sixth Schedule.]

(2) An arbitrator, from the time of his appointment and throughout the arbitral proceedings, shall, without delay, disclose to the parties in writing any circumstances referred to in sub-section (1) unless they have already been informed of them by him.

(3) An arbitrator may be challenged only if—

(*a*) circumstances exist that give rise to justifiable doubts as to his independence or impartiality; or

(*b*) he does not possess the qualifications agreed to by the parties.

(4) A party may challenge an arbitrator appointed by him, or in whose appointment he has participated, only for reasons of which he becomes aware after the appointment has been made.

[569][(5) Notwithstanding any prior agreement to the contrary, any person whose relationship, with the parties or counsel or the subject-matter of the

---

568. *Subs.* by Act 3 of 2016, S. 8(*i*) (w.r.e.f. 23-10-2015). Prior to substitution it read as:
"(1) When a person is approached in connection with his possible appointment as an arbitrator, he shall disclose in writing any circumstances likely to give rise to justifiable doubts as to his independence or impartiality."

569. *Ins.* by Act 3 of 2016, S. 8(*ii*) (w.r.e.f. 23-10-2015).

dispute, falls under any of the categories specified in the Seventh Schedule shall be ineligible to be appointed as an arbitrator:

Provided that parties may, subsequent to disputes having arisen between them, waive the applicability of this sub-section by an express agreement in writing.]

COMMENTS

Corresponding old law

Section 12 is new, and did not find place in the Arbitration Act, 1940.

UNCITRAL Model Law

Article 12. *Grounds for challenge*

(1) When a person is approached in connection with his possible appointment as an arbitrator, he shall disclose any circumstances likely to give rise to justifiable doubts as to his impartiality or independence. An arbitrator, from the time of his appointment and throughout the arbitral proceedings, shall without delay disclose any such circumstances to the parties unless they have already been informed of them by him.

(2) An arbitrator may be challenged only if circumstances exist that give rise to justifiable doubts as to his impartiality or independence, or if he does not possess qualifications agreed to by the parties. A party may challenge an arbitrator appointed by him, or in whose appointment he has participated, only for reasons of which he becomes aware after the appointment has been made.

Legislative changes

Arbitration and Conciliation (Amendment) Act, 2015 (3 of 2016)

In Section 12 of the principal Act,—

(*i*) for sub-section (1), the following sub-section shall be *substituted*, namely—

"(1) When a person is approached in connection with his possible appointment as an arbitrator, he shall disclose in writing any circumstances,—

(*a*) such as the existence either direct or indirect, of any past or present relationship with or interest in any of the parties or in relation to the subject-matter in dispute, whether financial, business, professional or other kind, which is likely to give rise to justifiable doubts as to his independence or impartiality; and (*b*) which are likely to affect his ability to devote sufficient time to the arbitration and in particular his ability to complete the entire arbitration within a period of twelve months.

Explanation 1.—The grounds stated in the Fifth Schedule shall guide in determining whether circumstances exist which give rise to justifiable doubts as to the independence or impartiality of an arbitrator.

Explanation 2.—The disclosure shall be made by such person in the form specified in the Sixth Schedule.";

(*ii*) after sub-section (4), the following sub-section shall be *inserted*, namely—

"(5) Notwithstanding any prior agreement to the contrary, any person whose relationship, with the parties or counsel or the subject-matter of the dispute, falls under any of the categories specified in the Seventh Schedule shall be ineligible to be appointed as an arbitrator:

Provided that parties may, subsequent to disputes having arisen between them, waive the applicability of this sub-section by an express agreement in writing."

NOTES ON CLAUSES

Clause 8 of the Bill seeks to amend Section 12 of the principal Act to ensure neutrality of arbitrators. When a person is approached in connection with possible appointment of arbitrator, he is required to disclose in writing regarding existence of any relationship or interest of any kind which is likely to give rise to justifiable grounds. He is also required to disclose any circumstances which are likely to affect his ability to devote sufficient time to the arbitration and complete the arbitration within the specified period. A new sub-section (5) is inserted to the effect that a person having relationship as specified in the Seventh Schedule shall be ineligible to be appointed as an arbitrator.

Scope and application

Section 12 lays down provisions to ensure neutrality, independence and impartiality of the arbitrator(s) proposed to be appointed in the case. Section 12 has been amended by Amending Act 3 of 2016 to ensure neutrality and impartiality of the arbitrator(s) proposed to be appointed in the case. The provisions of Section 12(5) and Schedule 7 are applicable to arbitration agreements entered into even prior to insertion of the said provisions.[570]

Both the parties approached S.P. Kurdukar (a retired judge of the Supreme Court) and requested him to act as arbitrator in disputes arising between the

570. *Jaipur Zila Dugdh Utpadak Sahkari Sangh Ltd.* v. *Ajay Sales & Suppliers*, (2021) 17 SCC 248.

parties. S.P. Kurdukar pointed out that he had been a member of the Bench which had earlier passed an order in the case. Both the parties reiterated before the Supreme Court that they still had no objection to him acting as arbitrator. It was held, the said retired judge could be appointed as an arbitrator in the matter, the Supreme Court appointed him as arbitrator in the case.[571]

Section 12 has been amended by the Amendment Act, 2015 based on the recommendations of the Law Commission, which specifically dealt with the issue of "neutrality of arbitrators". To achieve the main purpose for amending the provision, *namely*, to provide for "neutrality of arbitrators", sub-section (5) of Section 12 lays down that notwithstanding any prior agreement to the contrary, any person whose relationship with the parties or counsel or the subject-matter of the dispute falls under any of the categories specified in the Seventh Schedule, he shall be ineligible to be appointed as an arbitrator. In such an eventuality, *i.e.* when the arbitration clause is found to be foul with the amended provision, the appointment of the arbitrator would be beyond the pale of the arbitration agreement, empowering the court to appoint such an arbitrator as may be permissible. That would be the effect of the non-obstante clause contained in sub-section (5) of Section 12 and the other party cannot insist upon the appointment of the arbitrator in terms of the arbitration agreement.[572]

In the present case, the Stationery Purchase Committee-Arbitral Tribunal comprising of officers of the respondent-State are all ineligible to become and/or to continue as arbitrators in view of the mandate of sub-section (5) of Section 12 read with Seventh Schedule. Therefore, by operation of law and by amending Section 12 and bringing on statute sub-section (5) of Section 12 read with Seventh Schedule, the earlier Arbitral Tribunal-Stationery Purchase Committee comprising of the Additional Secretary, Department of Revenue as President, and: (*i*) Deputy Secretary, Department of Revenue; (*ii*) Deputy Secretary, General Administration Department; (*iii*) Deputy Secretary, Department of Finance; (*iv*) Deputy Secretary/Under-Secretary, General Administration Department, and (*v*) Senior Deputy Controller of Head Office, Printing as Members, has lost its mandate and such an Arbitral Tribunal cannot be permitted to continue and therefore a fresh arbitrator has to be appointed as per the Arbitration and Conciliation Act, 1996.[573]

There are certain minimum levels of independence and impartiality that should be required of the arbitral process regardless of the parties' apparent agreement. A sensible law cannot, for instance, permit appointment of an

571. *Renuka Anantrai Vora* v. *Kirtikumar Fulchand Vora*, (2000) 9 SCC 414.
572. *Ellora Paper Mills Ltd.* v. *State of M.P.*, (2022) 3 SCC 1.
573. *Ibid*.

arbitrator who is himself a party to the dispute, or who is employed by (or similarly dependent on) one party, even if this is what the parties agreed. Where, under any agreement between the parties, a person falls within any of the categories set out in the Seventh Schedule, he is, as a matter of law, ineligible to be appointed as an arbitrator. The only way in which this ineligibility can be removed, again, in law, is that parties may, *after* disputes have arisen between them, waive the applicability of this sub-section by an "express agreement in writing". The "express agreement in writing" has reference to a person who is interdicted by the Seventh Schedule, but who is stated by parties (after the disputes have arisen between them) to be a person in whom they have faith notwithstanding the fact that such person is interdicted by the Seventh Schedule.[574]

The grounds of holding an arbitrator to be de jure or de facto ineligible to act as an arbitrator vis-à-vis unilateral appointment cannot be taken in instances where the proceedings commenced prior to the Amendment Act of 2015.[575]

Arbitration clause provided that respondent Corporation would make a panel of five arbitrators, amongst whom both parties would nominate one arbitrator each and the two arbitrators would choose the third arbitrator. Choice of petitioner stood restricted to choose an arbitrator from a panel of names forwarded by respondent. Hence, the arbitration clause was hit by Section 12(5) read with the Seventh Schedule.[576]

Disclosure in writing by arbitrator existence of past or present relationship or interest with parties [Sub-s. (1)(2)]

Section 12 requires that when a person is approached in connection with his possible appointment as an arbitrator in a case, he shall disclose in writing existence of direct/indirect of any past or present relationship/interest with any of the parties, subject-matter in dispute whether financial, business, professional or other kind which is likely to give rise to justifiable doubts as to his independence or impartiality and which are likely to affect his ability to complete the entire arbitration within a period of 12 months. This obligation to furnish disclosure shall remain on the arbitrator throughout the arbitral proceedings.

The grounds stated in the Fifth Schedule shall be relevant and give rise to justifiable doubts as to the independence/impartiality of the arbitrator.

---

574. *Ibid.*
575. *Gammon Engineers & Contractors (P) Ltd.* v. *State of W.B.*, 2023 SCC OnLine Cal 2326.
576. *PSP Projects Ltd.* v. *Bhiwandi Nizampur City Municipal Corpn.*, 2023 SCC OnLine Bom 230: (2023) 4 Mah LJ 517.

Such disclosure shall be made in the form specified in the Sixth Schedule.

The requirement of furnishing disclosure is the most healthy provision to ensure the independence and impartiality of the arbitrator.

Where the arbitrator had not made disclosure as mandated by Section 12 of the Act, the award rendered by the arbitrator was not sustained.[577]

If a party has doubts as regards the impartiality or independence of the arbitrator, he has to challenge the appointment of the arbitrator within 15 days after becoming aware of the constitution of the Arbitration Tribunal. Where an arbitrator does not make a declaration that by itself does not offend Section 12.[578]

If agreement specifies the period within which award has to be passed, the arbitrator is duty-bound to comply with the same, and has no power or mandate to extend time suo moto.[579]

Bias, malice of arbitrator

Once a party has entered into an agreement with eyes wide open, it cannot wriggle out of the situation that if any person of the respondent was appointed as arbitrator, he will not be impartial or objective. However, if the party feels that the arbitrator has not acted independently or impartially, or has suffered from any bias, it will be open to the party to make an application under Section 34 of the Act to set aside the award on the ground that the arbitrator acted with bias or malice in law or fact.[580] Allegations of mala fide/bias are required to be established by cogent evidence.[581]

Where a person appointed by the Central Government as arbitrator is not connected with acquisition proceedings, the question of bias does not arise.[582]

When the parties themselves have chosen a person as arbitrator, they being the best judges of the person, the presumption is that the selection was made upon consideration of the pros and cons. However, having specifically agreed to his appointment knowingly what the arbitrator is, the parties shall be deemed to have waived the objection of bias, if any.[583]

---

577. *Shriram Transport Finance Co. Ltd.* v. *Narender Singh*, (2022) 6 HCC (Del) 275.
578. *Vijayakumar Raju* v. *Indus Ind Bank Ltd.*, 2009 SCC OnLine Mad 885: (2009) 4 LW 86.
579. *Nitya Nand and Sons* v. *Union of India*, 2019 SCC OnLine P&H 7921.
580. *ACE Pipeline Contracts (P) Ltd.* v. *Bharat Petroleum Corpn. Ltd.*, (2007) 5 SCC 304.
581. *Leelajay Technologies (P) Ltd.* v. *Dr Bhimrao Ambedkar University*, 2011 SCC OnLine All 1399: (2011) 89 ALR 83.
582. *Ibid.*
583. *Essel Shyam Communication Ltd.* v. *Union of India*, 2000 SCC OnLine Del 2: ILR (2000) 1 Del 313.

Independence, impartiality of arbitrator

The officer of the appellants who had already taken a decision that the appellants were right in imposing the liquidated damages upon the respondent (the very issue in dispute), held, cannot become an arbitrator in the matter as it would not satisfy the test of impartiality and independence as required under Section 12. Moreover, his appointment as an arbitrator would also defeat the principles of natural justice wherein it has been recognised that a party cannot be a judge in his own cause.[584]

Where the arbitrator had represented the opposite party in the same case and had issued legal notice to the applicant, there was justifiable doubt about the independence and impartiality of the arbitrator. The appointment of the arbitrator was set aside, a fresh arbitrator was appointed in the case.[585]

Independence as used in the statute means nothing more than deciding for oneself. Impartiality is lack of bias: the ability to decide without tilting to one side on considerations other than the merits of the case. A counsel having accepted a brief from a particular attorney, advocate-on-record or lawyer for some other client is not per se a disqualification or ineligibility. The disqualification connection must be between the arbitrator-counsel and the litigant.[586]

Once arbitration agreement indicates a mechanism for appointment of arbitrator, mere fact that the arbitrator was an employee of one of the parties shall be of no reference.[587]

It is not open to a party to challenge the appointment of the arbitrator on the ground that there are justifiable doubts as to his independence and impartially in terms of the guidelines, in collateral proceedings. The contention that the petitioner is deemed to have concurred with the arbitrator's appointment as it participated in the arbitral proceedings without any protest, is unpersuasive. Once it is held that the arbitrator's appointment is unilateral, the appointment becomes void ab initio.[588]

---

584. *BSNL* v. *Motorola India (P) Ltd.*, (2009) 2 SCC 337.
585. *V. Balakrishnan* v. *Capital First Ltd.*, 2019 SCC OnLine TS 1290: (2019) 5 ALD 414.
586. *Sheetal Maruti Kurundwade* v. *Metal Power Analytical (I) (P) Ltd.*, 2017 SCC OnLine Bom 251: (2017) 6 Mah LJ 642.
587. *NRP Projects (P) Ltd.* v. *Bharat Petroleum Corpn. Ltd.*, 2021 SCC OnLine Mad 2889: (2021) 4 LW 487.
588. *Delhi Integrated Multi Modal Transit Systems Ltd.* v. *Delhi Jal Board*, (2021) 4 HCC (Del) 25

Impartiality of the arbitrator—Arbitrator had acted as counsel for the party in another case—Award set aside

Record showed that the arbitrator had acted as a counsel in another case for one of the parties to dispute in instant case. Despite objection taken with regard to his appointment, arbitrator proceeded with the matter without disclosing facts within his knowledge as per Section 12. Award passed by the arbitrator was found unsustainable, was set aside.[589]

Decision of the arbitrator rejecting objection of party as to independence or impartiality of arbitrator under Sections 12 and 13 and to proceed further with proceedings can be challenged while challenging final award under Section 34.[590]

Apprehension of bias against person designated in arbitration clause

Fanciful apprehension of bias against the designated arbitrator is not enough. Vague and general objections/allegations that the arbitrator was biased and had predisposition to decide against the appellant are not sufficient to prove the bias of the arbitrator. Where the bias of the adjudicator is alleged, it has to be established in the facts and circumstances of each case.[591] In *Ladli Construction Co. (P) Ltd.* v. *Punjab Police Housing Corpn. Ltd.*[592], the appellant had consciously agreed to refer disputes to the Chief Engineer of the respondent with full knowledge that he was in control of the affairs of the respondent-organisation. No allegation of bias or hostility was made against the said named arbitrator, in application for appointment of arbitrator and appellant rather prayed for his appointment as arbitrator in terms of arbitration clause. Even after the appointment of the said arbitrator, the appellant could not refer to any incident which prompted the appellant to say that it had lost faith in the arbitrator. It was held, in the absence of any material, mere passing of award a day before next date of hearing fixed by the court, or concluding arbitration proceedings within a short span of 49 days that too when proceedings for removal of arbitrator were pending in court, it could not be said that the arbitrator was biased, especially when there was no stay order from the court restraining him from passing the award. Full opportunity of hearing was given to the appellant but appellant failed to avail of that opportunity. The award passed by the arbitrator did

589. *Vinod Bhaiyalal Jain* v. *Wadhwani Parmeshwari Cold Storage (P) Ltd.*, (2020) 15 SCC 726.

590. *Winsome International Ltd.* v. *New India Assurance Co. Ltd.*, 2023 SCC OnLine Cal 2090.

591. *Ladli Construction Co. (P) Ltd.* v. *Punjab Police Housing Corpn. Ltd.*, (2012) 4 SCC 609.

592. *Ibid.*

not show that the arbitrator had misconducted himself, the test of reasonable apprehension of bias was not satisfied in the situation of the case.

Appointment of officer of department as arbitrator

Plea that the appointment of officer of department would be against the principles of natural justice as he was obliged to follow the instructions of the superiors and cannot act against the Union of India was rejected.[593]

The arbitration agreement provided for appointment of sole arbitrator by the Managing Director of the respondent-organisation. Held, normally an arbitration agreement prevails but in view of the possibility that departmental nominee may not be unbiased, the court invoked its power to appoint an arbitrator.[594]

Appointment of the arbitrator was challenged on the ground that he was an employee of the respondent employer, hence was unable to act. Appointment of arbitrator was completed long before the insertion of Section 12(5), by Amendment Act, 2015. It was held, it could not be said that the Arbitral Tribunal was improperly constituted.[595]

There was agreement for purchase of stationary. By order dated 3 May 2000 the dispute was referred to the arbitration by the Stationary Purchase Committee which consisted of officers of the respondent State. Therefore, as per Amendment Act, 2015—sub-section (5) of Section 12 read with Seventh Schedule, all of them have become ineligible to become arbitrators and to continue as arbitrators. Fresh arbitrator was appointed in the case.[596]

Appointment of retired employees of the Railways as arbitrators—No bar

In *State of Haryana* v. *G.F. Toll Road (P) Ltd.*[597], the Supreme Court held that the appointment of a retired employee of a party to the agreement cannot be assailed on the ground that he is a retired/former employee of one of the parties to the agreement. There is no bar under Section 12(5), as inserted by, Arbitration and Conciliation (Amendment) Act, 2015 for appointment of a retired employee to act as an arbitrator. As such there is no bar for the retired employees to act as arbitrators. In *Bishambar Dayal Sinsinwar*

593. *Denel (Pty.) Ltd.* v. *Ministry of Defence*, (2012) 2 SCC 759.
594. *SRICO Projects (P) Ltd.* v. *Central Railside Warehouse Co. Ltd.*, (2022) 1 HCC (Del) 321.
595. *NRP Projects (P) Ltd.* v. *Bharat Petroleum Corpn. Ltd.*, 2021 SCC OnLine Mad 2889: (2021) 4 LW 487.
596. *Ellora Paper Mills Ltd.* v. *State of M.P.*, (2022) 3 SCC 1.
597. (2019) 3 SCC 505.

v. *Railways*[598], there was a dispute between the appellant-company and the Railways. Appointment of retired employees of the Railways as arbitrators was upheld. Application for appointment of independent arbitrator was rejected.

The contractor-applicant had not waived off the applicability of Section 12(5), the opposite party Railways would be justified in forwarding the panel of three retired officers of Railways to the applicant, calling upon him to choose two of them, out of which one will be chosen as nominee arbitrator of the applicant.[599]

As per arbitration clause, the respondent, a Central Public Sector Enterprises with Ministry of Railways suggested the name of five arbitrators to the petitioner to choose from the panel. The suggested five names were retired Indian Railway personnel, and had no connection with the respondent with regard to the contract in question. The embargo put under Fifth and Seventh Schedule was not attracted in the case. The petitioner was at liberty to select an arbitrator from the panel suggested by the respondent.[600]

Appointment of whole time government employee as arbitrator

Where a person in whole time government employment is appointed arbitrator, this may affect his employment but does not disqualify him as arbitrator if he is otherwise qualified.[601]

Managing Director of company

Managing Director of the company cannot be appointed as arbitrator in the case.

General conditions of contract—Eligibility of arbitrator

Dispute arose regarding execution of work between contractor and Railways. General conditions of contract provided that the General Manager may appoint retired Railway officers as arbitrators. Amended Section 12(5) provides that any person whose relationship with parties or subject-matter of dispute falls under any of the categories specified in Seventh Schedule shall be ineligible to be appointed as arbitrator. Contractors had not waived

---

598. 2020 SCC OnLine All 1926: (2020) 5 All LJ 204.

599. *Vijay Energy Equipments* v. *Railways*, 2021 SCC OnLine MP 2237: (2021) 2 MP LJ 443.

600. *ITD-ITD CEM Joint Venture* v. *Kolkata Metro Rail Corpn. Ltd.*, 2021 SCC OnLine Cal 2337: (2021) 1 Cal LT 348.

601. *Delhi Integrated Multi Modal Transit Systems Ltd.* v. *Delhi Jal Board*, (2021) 4 HCC (Del) 25.

applicability of Section 12(5). Liberty was granted to contractor to choose Railway officers as arbitrators.[602]

Serving officers of Railway

By virtue of Section 12(5) of amended Act read with Fifth Schedule, serving officer of Railways cannot be appointed as arbitrator.[603]

Provision in arbitration clause for appointment of Secretaries/Directors of government/statutory corporations or their nominee—Validity/binding effect of

The fact that the named arbitrator is an employee of one of the parties is not *ipso facto* a ground to raise a presumption of bias or partiality or lack of independence on his part. There can, however, be a justifiable apprehension about the independence or impartiality of an employee arbitrator, if such person was the controlling or dealing authority in regard to the subject contract or if he is a direct subordinate (as contrasted from an officer of an inferior rank in some other department) to the officer whose decision is the subject-matter of the dispute. Where, however, the named arbitrator, though a senior officer of the government/statutory body/government company, had nothing to do with the execution of the subject contract, there can be no justification for anyone doubting his independence or impartiality, in the absence of any specific evidence. Therefore, senior officer(s) (usually Head of Department or equivalent) of a government/statutory corporation/public sector undertaking, not associated with the contract, are considered to be independent and impartial and are not barred from functioning as arbitrators merely because their employer is a party to the contract. The position may be different where the person named as the arbitrator is an employee of a company or body or individual other than the State and its instrumentalities. In such cases, if any circumstance exists to create a reasonable apprehension about the impartiality or independence of the agreed or named arbitrator, then the court has the discretion not to appoint such a person.[604]

Section 12(5) read with the Seventh Schedule is a mandatory and non-derogable provision of the Act. In the facts of *Haryana Space Application Centre* v. *Pan India Consultants (P) Ltd.*[605], the Principal Secretary to the Government of Haryana would be ineligible to be appointed as an arbitrator, since he would have a controlling influence on the appellant-company being

602. *Udit Prasad Babu* v. *Union of India*, 2020 SCC OnLine Ori 993.
603. *J.K. Agarwala* v. *Union of India*, 2017 SCC OnLine Chh 1906.
604. *Indian Oil Corpn. Ltd.* v. *Raja Transport (P) Ltd.*, (2009) 8 SCC 520.
605. (2021) 3 SCC 103.

a nodal agency of the State. A retired judge of the Supreme Court was appointed as sole arbitrator to complete the arbitral proceedings.

Chairman of the Zila Dugdh Utpadak Sahakari Sangh

The Chairman who is elected member/Director of the Sangh can certainly be said to be "ineligible" to become an arbitrator as per sub-section (5) of Section 12 read with Seventh Schedule to the Act. Therefore, the High Court exercising powers under Section 11 read with Section 14 appointed a former District and Sessions Judge as arbitrator in the case.[606]

Chairman and Managing Director of Corporation cannot appoint arbitrator

Section 12(5) read with Section 14 clearly shows that the Chairman and Managing Director of Corporation being ineligible to act as arbitrator cannot appoint another arbitrator. The appointment made by him is void ab initio.[607]

Appointment of arbitrator by the Chief Engineer of the Department

In the instant case, clause in the agreement reserved the right of appointing arbitrator only to the Chief Engineer. Section 12(5) was inserted in the Act of 1996 by way of the Amendment Act 3 of 2016 and it provides that, notwithstanding any prior agreement to the contrary, any person whose relationship with the parties or counsel or the subject-matter of the dispute, falls under any of the categories specified in the Seventh Schedule shall be ineligible to be appointed as an arbitrator. Category 5 of the Seventh Schedule to the Act of 1996 bars a Manager, Director or part of the management or a person, who has a similar controlling influence, from being an arbitrator. Therefore, the arbitrator can no longer be an internal arbitrator from within the organisation or someone who has a direct link with it or with the matter in dispute. It is no longer open to the Chief Engineer of the PWD of the State to assert any right to unilaterally appoint an arbitrator. The court appointed a retired judge of the High Court as arbitrator in the case.[608]

Arbitration clause authorised the Secretary, Ministry of Home Affairs, whose relationship with Union of India was that of an employee, to nominate an officer of the Ministry of Law and Justice to act as sole arbitrator. Arbitration clause would fall within the expressly ineligible category provided in Paragraph 1 of Seventh Schedule, read with Section 12(5) of

606. *Rites Ltd.* v. *Subrata Kumar Ghose*, 2019 SCC OnLine Del 8605.
607. *Bharat Broadband Network Ltd.* v. *United Telecoms Ltd.*, (2019) 5 SCC 755.
608. *Simplex Projects Ltd.* v. *State of Manipur*, 2021 SCC OnLine Mani 482.

the Act. Appointment of officer of Ministry of Law and Justice as arbitrator under said clause could not be given effect to. A retired judge of the Supreme Court was appointed arbitrator in the case.[609]

As per terms of the agreement, the Secretary to the Department of Revenue of the government was appointed sole arbitrator in the case. Though amended Section 12(5) came into effect in 2015, the same was not noticed by either of the parties, there was no impediment to appoint the Secretary to the Department of Revenue as sole arbitrator in the case.[610]

"Business relationship"

The words "any other" in Item 1 of Seventh Schedule, confines "advisor" to "business relationship". Professional relationship cannot be equated to a business relationship in its widest sense. Legal advice rendered by the arbitrator cannot be included in "business relationship". In the instant case, the arbitrator had given professional advice to the respondent GAIL earlier, which had no concern with the present dispute between the parties, was not disqualified under Item 1 of Seventh Schedule of the Act.[611]

Merely because the arbitrator was appointed by the respondent in the past did not amount to business relationship between the parties. Mandate of the arbitrator was not terminated.[612]

Pendency of another arbitration case between the same parties before the arbitrator

There is no clause in Seventh Schedule which renders appointment of arbitrator as void because he/she is already dealing with another dispute between the same parties. Pendency of another arbitration proceedings before the same sole arbitrator cannot render appointment of sole arbitrator as void. Mandate of the arbitrator cannot be terminated.[613]

Reasonable likelihood of bias—Delivery of award in another case between the parties

Appointment of arbitrator was challenged on the ground that the arbitrator previously rendered an award between the parties in an earlier arbitration concerning the same disputes. The arbitrator appointed did not have previous

609. *Glock Asia-Pacific Ltd.* v. *Union of India*, (2023) 8 SCC 226.
610. *Bharath Enterprises Halahalli* v. *Deptt. of Revenue Survey Settlement and Land Records*, 2020 SCC OnLine Kar 5375: (2020) 5 KCCR 92.
611. *HRD Corpn.* v. *GAIL (India) Ltd.*, (2018) 12 SCC 471.
612. *HRD Corpn.* v. *Gail (India) Ltd.*, 2017 SCC OnLine Del 8034: (2017) 240 DLT 132.
613. *Reliance Infrastructure Ltd.* v. *State of Haryana*, 2020 SCC OnLine P&H 5145: PLR (2020) 199 P&H 386.

involvement in the very dispute contained in the present arbitration. Delivery of award providing expert "opinion", *i.e.* advice to a party is not covered by Item 15 of the Seventh Schedule. Merely because the arbitrator had already rendered an award in previous arbitration between the parties would not render him ineligible to be arbitrator in subsequent arbitration.[614]

Power of the court to appoint arbitrator where arbitrator agreed by parties falls in any category of Schedule 7

Section 12(5) lays down that notwithstanding any prior agreement to the contrary, any person whose relationship with the parties or counsel or the subject-matter of the dispute falls under any of the categories specified in the Seventh Schedule, he shall be ineligible to be appointed as arbitrator. In such an eventuality, *i.e.* when the arbitration clause finds foul with the amended provisions, the appointment of an arbitrator would be beyond the pale of the arbitration agreement, empowering the court to appoint such arbitrator(s) as may be permissible. This is the effect of non-obstante clause contained in Section 12(5) and the other party cannot insist on the appointment of arbitrator in terms of the arbitration agreement.[615]

The arbitration clause provided for appointment of sole arbitrator by the Chairman of the respondent-authority. The provision was held invalid, the High Court appointed a former judge of the Supreme Court as sole arbitrator to resolve the dispute.[616]

Waiver of bar—Express agreement in writing necessary [S. 12(5) (Proviso)]

With regard to waiver of bar contained in Section 12(5) of the Act, it cannot be said that the applicant waived bar under Section 12(5) of Act. A retired judge of the High Court was appointed as arbitrator in the case.[617]

Appointment of arbitrator by court/Chief Engineer

Contract was entered into between parties for construction of a bridge containing a clause providing to refer dispute between parties to the Chief Engineer of the department concerned or arbitrator appointed by him. A person who has become ineligible by law cannot nominate an arbitrator. It was held, arbitrator can be appointed by the court and not by the Chief Engineer.[618]

---

614. *HRD Corpn.* v. *GAIL (India) Ltd.*, (2018) 12 SCC 471.
615. *Voestalpine Schienen GmbH* v. *DMRC Ltd.*, (2017) 4 SCC 665.
616. *Ibid.*
617. *Virendra Singh Rawat* v. *Cantonment Board*, 2021 SCC OnLine Utt 902: (2021) 5 Arb LR 339.
618. *Ashes Deb* v. *State of Tripura*, 2019 SCC OnLine Tri 489.

Arbitrator contesting case filed against arbitration award—Inference of bias

Merely because the arbitrator is contesting the case for setting aside award does not reflect bias of arbitrator since he has no choice but to rebut allegations made against him as he was made one of the parties to the appeal.[619]

Government contract or contract of its instrumentalities—Panel of arbitrators

In government contracts or contracts of its instrumentalities, it is imperative that the panel should be broad based. Apart from serving or retired engineers of government departments and public sector undertakings, engineers of prominence and high repute from the private sector should also be included. Panel should also comprise persons with legal background like judges and lawyers of repute as it is not necessary that all disputes that arise, would be of technical nature. Some disputes may have the dimension of accountancy, etc. It would be appropriate to include persons from this field as well.[620]

Government contract or contract of its instrumentalities—Past, present employees of government, corporations or PSUs

In government contracts or of its instrumentalities, Section 12(5) does not debar all past or present employees of government, statutory corporations or PSUs from being appointed as arbitrators. Only such employees, who fall in the categories mentioned in Seventh Schedule cannot, be appointed arbitrators.[621]

Contracts entered into in the name of the President of India

Contracts entered into in the name of the President of India are not immune to restrictions/bar contained in Section 12(5).[622]

CHALLENGE PROCEDURE [S. 13]

13. *Challenge procedure.*—(1) Subject to sub-section (4), the parties are free to agree on a procedure for challenging an arbitrator.

(2) Failing any agreement referred to in sub-section (1), a party who intends to challenge an arbitrator shall, within fifteen days after becoming aware of

619. *Ladli Construction Co. (P) Ltd.* v. *Punjab Police Housing Corpn. Ltd.*, (2012) 4 SCC 609.
620. *Voestalpine Schienen GmbH* v. *DMRC Ltd.*, (2017) 4 SCC 665.
621. *Ibid.*
622. *Glock Asia-Pacific Ltd.* v. *Union of India*, (2023) 8 SCC 226.

the Constitution of the arbitral tribunal or after becoming aware of any circumstances referred to in sub-section (3) of Section 12, send a written statement of the reasons for the challenge to the arbitral tribunal.

(3) Unless the arbitrator challenged under sub-section (2) withdraws from his office or the other party agrees to the challenge, the arbitral tribunal shall decide on the challenge.

(4) If a challenge under any procedure agreed upon by the parties or under the procedure under sub-section (2) is not successful, the arbitral tribunal shall continue the arbitral proceedings and make an arbitral award.

(5) Where an arbitral award is made under sub-section (4), the party challenging the arbitrator may make an application for setting aside such an arbitral award in accordance with Section 34.

(6) Where an arbitral award is set aside on an application made under sub-section (5), the Court may decide as to whether the arbitrator who is challenged is entitled to any fees.

COMMENTS

Corresponding old law

Section 13 is new, and did not find place in the Arbitration Act, 1940.

UNCITRAL Model Law

Article 13. *Challenge procedure*

(1) The parties are free to agree on a procedure for challenging an arbitrator, subject to the provisions of paragraph (3) of this article.

(2) Failing such agreement, a party who intends to challenge an arbitrator shall, within fifteen days after becoming aware of the constitution of the arbitral tribunal or after becoming aware of any circumstance referred to in article 12(2), send a written statement of the reasons for the challenge to the arbitral tribunal. Unless the challenged arbitrator withdraws from his office or the other party agrees to the challenge, the arbitral tribunal shall decide on the challenge.

(3) If a challenge under any procedure agreed upon by the parties or under the procedure of paragraph (2) of this article is not successful, the challenging party may request, within thirty days after having received notice of the decision rejecting the challenge, the court or other authority specified in article 6 to decide on the challenge, which decision shall be subject to no appeal; while such a request is pending, the arbitral tribunal, including the challenged arbitrator, may continue the arbitral proceedings and make an award.

Scope and application

Section 13 of the Act lays down the procedure for challenging the appointment of arbitrator(s). As provided by Section 13 the parties are free to agree on a procedure for challenging an arbitrator in the case. The petitioner should challenge the appointment of arbitrator on the ground of independence and impartiality within a period of 15 days after becoming aware of the constitution of the Arbitral Tribunal. Challenge cannot be made after the expiry of the period of 15 days.[623]

FAILURE OR IMPOSSIBILITY TO ACT [S. 14]

14. *Failure or impossibility to act.*—(1) [624][The mandate of an arbitrator shall terminate and he shall be substituted by another arbitrator, if]—

(*a*) he becomes *de jure* or *de facto* unable to perform his functions or for other reasons fails to act without undue delay; and

(*b*) he withdraws from his office or the parties agree to the termination of his mandate.

(2) If a controversy remains concerning any of the grounds referred to in clause (*a*) of sub-section (1), a party may, unless otherwise agreed by the parties, apply to the Court to decide on the termination of the mandate.

(3) If, under this section or sub-section (3) of Section 13, an arbitrator withdraws from his office or a party agrees to the termination of the mandate of an arbitrator, it shall not imply acceptance of the validity of any ground referred to in this section or sub-section (3) of Section 12.

COMMENTS

Corresponding old law

Section 14(1)(*a*) corresponds to Section 8(1)(*b*), Arbitration Act, 1940.

Section 14(2) corresponds to Section 11(1), Arbitration Act, 1940.

UNCITRAL Model Law

Article 14. *Failure or impossibility to act*

(1) If an arbitrator becomes *de jure* or *de facto* unable to perform his functions or for other reasons fails to act without undue delay, his mandate terminates if he

623. *Novel Granites Ltd.* v. *Lakshmi General Finance Ltd.*, 2003 SCC OnLine Mad 365: (2003) 3 CTC 148. The tribunal may condone the delay in appropriate cases. [*SKF India Ltd.* v. *MGP Associates (P) Ltd.*, 2009 SCC OnLine Mad 391: (2009) 6 CTC 723.]

624. *Subs.* for "The mandate of an arbitrator shall terminate if" by Act 3 of 2016, S. 9 (w.r.e.f. 23-10-2015).

withdraws from his office or if the parties agree on the termination. Otherwise, if a controversy remains concerning any of these grounds, any party may request the court or other authority specified in Article 6 to decide on the termination of the mandate, which decision shall be subject to no appeal.

(2) If, under this article or article 13(2), an arbitrator withdraws from his office or a party agrees to the termination of the mandate of an arbitrator, this does not imply acceptance of the validity of any ground referred to in this article or Article 12(2).

Legislative changes

Arbitration and Conciliation (Amendment) Act, 2015 (3 of 2016)

In Section 14 of the principal Act, in sub-section (1), in the opening portion, for the words "The mandate of an arbitrator shall terminate if", the words "The mandate of an arbitrator shall terminate and he shall be substituted by another arbitrator, if" shall be *substituted.*

NOTES ON CLAUSES

Clause 9 of the Bill seeks to amend sub-section (1), Section 14 of the principal Act to provide that on the termination of mandate of an arbitrator, he is to be substituted by another arbitrator.

Scope and application

Section 14 enumerates the circumstances in which the mandate of an appointed arbitrator shall terminate and a substituted arbitrator replacing him shall be appointed. No provision contained in the Arbitration and Conciliation Act permits the court to terminate the mandate of the arbitrator on the challenge by a party.[625] The respondent sought termination of mandate of the arbitrator on the ground that the arbitrator was not impartial, there was real likelihood of bias and no one can be permitted to be a judge of his own cause. Held, challenge to the authority of the arbitrator by way of application under Section 14(2) of the Act was in substance made on the grounds enumerated in Section 12(3) of the Act, which is impermissible in law as Sections 13 and 14 of the Act operate in different fields.[626]

A contract was awarded to the petitioner. As the dispute arose between the parties, as per clauses of the general conditions of contract relating to settlement of disputes/arbitration, ex-Chief Secretary of the State of Haryana

625. *Ahluwalia Contracts (India) Ltd.* v. *Housing & Urban Development Corpn.*, 2007 SCC OnLine Del 1593: (2008) 100 DRJ 461.

626. *State of M.P.* v. *Vayam Technologies Ltd.*, 2014 SCC OnLine MP 5358: (2014) 2 MP LJ 641.

was appointed sole arbitrator in the case. The sole arbitrator appointed in the case was neither a party nor a signatory to contract or agreement. Merely because the State has financial interest in setting up sole arbitrator would not *ipso facto* mean that it has any interest in the arbitration proceedings. The material on the record did not show that the sole arbitrator was in any manner interested in the outcome of the arbitration. Pendency of another arbitration proceedings before the same sole arbitrator cannot render the appointment of sole arbitrator as void. There is no clause in the Seventh Schedule which renders appointment of arbitrator as void because he/she is already dealing with another dispute between the parties. Mandate of the arbitrator was not terminated.[627] Where the respondent invoked arbitration clause, unilaterally appointed the arbitrator, the petitioner had conveyed his objection to the appointment of the arbitrator even before the first sitting was held by him, mandate of the arbitrator was liable to be terminated.[628] Dispute as to termination of arbitration proceedings cannot be decided under Section 14(2) of the Act.[629]

Conjoint petition under Section 11(6) and Section 14

The Chief Justice or his designate does not discharge any judicial function under Section 11(6). The Chief Justice or his designate, though a judge, does not sit as a court. The two fora, contemplated by Section 11(6) and Section 14(2) are different, and therefore, no single forum can grant such reliefs as are contemplated by the two provisions.[630]

Arbitrator appointed unilaterally

Arbitrator was appointed unilaterally by the respondent to adjudicate the disputes that have arisen between the parties in connection with a partnership deed. It is an attempt to subvert the arbitral process. The mandate of the arbitrator stood terminated. Another Senior Advocate was appointed arbitrator.[631]

627. *Reliance Infrastructure Ltd.* v. *State of Haryana*, 2020 SCC OnLine P&H 5145: PLR (2020) 199 P&H 386.
628. *Omcon Infrastructure (P) Ltd.* v. *Indiabulls Investment Advisors Ltd.*, 2020 SCC OnLine Del 2793.
629. *S.K. and Associates* v. *Indian Farmer and Fertilizers Coop. Ltd.*, 2010 SCC OnLine All 1884: (2011) 1 All LJ 43.
630. *Grid Corpn. of Orissa Ltd.* v. *AES Corpn.*, (2002) 7 SCC 736.
631. *Mohd. Tariq Usmani* v. *Jeetender Pal*, 2022 SCC OnLine Del 4799: (2022) 289 DLT 520.

Claimant's failure to file statement

Failure of the claimant to file a statement within reasonable time can be a ground for the arbitrator to terminate the proceedings. However, it is not open for the arbitrator to remain inactive and not conclude the arbitral proceedings.[632]

The provisions of Section 15(2) of the Act provide for appointment of a substitute arbitrator in cases where the mandate of the arbitrator terminates. It is only once the finding regarding the termination of mandate of arbitrator is recorded by the jurisdictional court that proceedings for substitution of the arbitrator can be initiated and not prior to that and a combined application in this regard based on the opening words of section cannot be maintained.[633]

Termination of mandate of arbitrator on the arbitrator's failure to conclude proceedings within the fixed time

Where the arbitrator fails to conclude the proceedings within time limit, the mandate of the arbitrator is liable to be terminated. On the expiry of the term mandate of the arbitrator expires.[634]

Where time-limit fixed by court for concluding arbitration proceedings was extended by parties in accordance with procedure provided therefor in arbitration clause but was not further extended and arbitrator, without any concrete reasons, failed to conclude his proceeding within the extended time, his mandate was liable to be terminated under Section 14(1)(*b*). Hence, the aggrieved party rightly approached court for termination of mandate of arbitrator and High Court acted within its jurisdiction in deciding accordingly.[635]

After waiver of the original time stipulation, the arbitrator was required to act and make and publish the award within reasonable time. There is no evidence on record to suggest that the petitioner delayed the proceedings or expressed an unwillingness to participate before the arbitrator. The arbitrator did nothing. Not a meeting was convened. Not even a letter or a notice was issued. After four years, in 2010 there was a flurry of activity on the part of the arbitrator to revive the proceedings. Well before those four years expired, that reasonable time expired. The mandate of the arbitrator stood terminated. The court never terminates the mandate of an arbitrator.

---

632. *International Engineers and Project Consultants Ltd.* v. *Union of India*, 2017 SCC OnLine Del 8348.
633. *Doshion (P) Ltd.* v. *Hindustan Zinc Ltd.*, 2018 SCC OnLine Raj 949: (2018) 3 WLC 510.
634. *NBCC Ltd.* v. *J.G. Engg. (P) Ltd.*, (2010) 2 SCC 385 relied on.
635. *Ibid.*

It stands terminated on the happening of an event or events. The court only declares it.[636]

Arbitrator de jure

Efflux of time limit fixed for conclusion of arbitration proceedings will not make arbitrator *de jure* incapable to complete proceedings. The Chief Justice of the High Court while appointing the arbitrator made a statement that arbitration proceedings to be conducted "preferably" within four weeks and six months and that was not a mandatory direction but a judicial wish.[637]

Termination of mandate of arbitrator on the ground of fees charged by the arbitrator

The petitioner sought termination of the mandate of the arbitrator on the ground of excessive fee charged by the arbitrator. On the date of the agreement, the petitioner did not insist on the incorporation therein of condition regarding fees payable in arbitration proceedings, nor insisted on any fee being fixed. It was, therefore, not open to the petitioner to seek termination of mandate of the arbitrator on sole ground of fees of the arbitrator. Application for termination of the mandate of the arbitrator was rejected.[638]

Termination of mandate of arbitrator appointed by Chief Justice or his designate—Court where application for termination lies

The word "Court" occurring in Section 14(2) is defined in Section 2(1)(*e*). Application for termination of mandate would, therefore, lie to "Court" as defined in Section 2(1)(*e*), *namely*, principal civil court of original jurisdiction and not to Supreme Court even though an arbitrator was appointed under Section 11(5) or 11(6) by Chief Justice or his designate. Once an arbitrator is nominated, Chief Justice or his designate does not retain any further jurisdiction. It becomes *functus officio* except in matters relating to exercise of jurisdiction under constitutional provisions or Supreme Court Rules.[639]

Mandate of an arbitrator can be terminated on an application to be moved before the court, *i.e.* principal civil court of original jurisdiction in the District High Court of Allahabad is not court within the meaning of Section 2(1)(*e*) of the Act, application before the High Court is not maintainable.[640]

---

636. *Ram Chandra Rungta* v. *Ram Swarup Rungta*, 2014 SCC OnLine Cal 19408: (2015) 1 CHN 17.
637. *SAIL* v. *Pratima Kanungo*, 2019 SCC OnLine Ori 460: (2019) 128 CLT 223.
638. *Entertainment City Ltd.* v. *Aspek Media (P) Ltd.*, 2020 SCC OnLine Del 2648.
639. *Nimet Resources Inc.* v. *Essar Steels Ltd.*, (2009) 17 SCC 313.
640. *B.M.G. Construction* v. *National Small Industries Corpn. Ltd.*, 2012 SCC OnLine All 1042: (2012) 93 ALR 831.

Administrative Mechanism and Resolution of Disputes (AMRD)

The Administrative Mechanism for Resolution of Disputes (AMRD) provided in the Office Memorandum dated 30 March 2020 is only a mechanism for possible settlement of disputes inter se governmental organisations, to obviate need for more expensive and time-consuming adjudicatory mechanisms. The AMRD is not a substitute for arbitration in cases where there is an arbitration agreement between the parties. No ground was made out for termination of arbitrator's mandate when he is seized of the proceedings in the matter, least of all as contemplated in Section 14(1), Arbitration and Conciliation Act, 1996.[641]

Termination of mandate of arbitrator—Writ petition not proper remedy

Plea raised about the termination of mandate of the arbitrator has to be resolved by the court under Section 14(2). Petition in this regard under Article 227 of the Constitution is not the proper remedy.[642]

The petitioner is required to approach the competent court for termination of the arbitrator in terms of Section 2(1)(*e*); he cannot invoke jurisdiction of the High Court under Article 226.[643]

TERMINATION OF MANDATE AND SUBSTITUTION OF ARBITRATOR [S. 15]

15. *Termination of mandate and substitution of arbitrator.*—(1) In addition to the circumstances referred to in Section 13 or Section 14, the mandate of an arbitrator shall terminate—

(*a*) where he withdraws from office for any reason; or

(*b*) by or pursuant to agreement of the parties.

(2) Where the mandate of an arbitrator terminates, a substitute arbitrator shall be appointed according to the rules that were applicable to the appointment of the arbitrator being replaced.

(3) Unless otherwise agreed by the parties, where an arbitrator is replaced under sub-section (2), any hearings previously held may be repeated at the discretion of the arbitral tribunal.

(4) Unless otherwise agreed by the parties, an order or ruling of the arbitral tribunal made prior to the replacement of an arbitrator under this section shall

641. *Prasar Bharti* v. *National Brain Research Centre*, (2022) 6 HCC (Del) 302.
642. *Surinder Pal Singh* v. *HPCL*, 2006 SCC OnLine Del 1214: (2006) 92 DRJ 537.
643. *Frank Airways (P) Ltd.* v. *Airports Authority of India*, 2019 SCC OnLine MP 7175.

not be invalid solely because there has been a change in the composition of the arbitral tribunal.

COMMENTS

Corresponding old law

Section 15 is new, and did not appear in the Arbitration Act, 1940.

UNCITRAL Model Law

Article 15. *Appointment of substitute arbitrator*

Where the mandate of an arbitrator terminates under article 13 or 14 or because of his withdrawal from office for any other reason or because of the revocation of his mandate by agreement of the parties or in any other case of termination of his mandate, a substitute arbitrator shall be appointed according to the rules that were applicable to the appointment of the arbitrator being replaced.

Scope and application

Section 15 lays down that in addition to the circumstances mentioned in Section 13 or Section 14, the mandate of an arbitrator shall terminate—

(*a*) where the arbitrator withdraws from office for any reasons; or

(*b*) by agreement or pursuant to agreement between the parties.

On the termination of the mandate of the arbitrator, a substitute arbitrator shall be appointed in the case.

Where parties agree for mediation and even name a specific arbitrator with no specific provision for appointment of another arbitrator on the rescual/withdrawal of the said arbitrator, the said omission is made up by Section 15(2) of the Act and unless arbitration agreement between the parties provides a categorical prohibition or debarment in resolving a question or dispute or difference between the parties by a substitute arbitrator in case of death of the named arbitrator, courts have the power to appoint a substitute arbitrator which power is given by Section 15(2) of the Act as this provision is to be given a liberal interpretation so as to apply to all possible circumstances under which the mandate of the earlier arbitrator may be terminated.[644]

644. *Shailesh Dhairyawan* v. *Mohan Balkrishna Lulla*, (2016) 3 SCC 619.

Termination of mandate of arbitrator

Where the arbitrator failed to take any action despite service of legal notice by the contractor, the mandate of the arbitrator was terminated.[645]

Application for termination of the mandate of the arbitrator lies before the principal civil court of original jurisdiction and those High Courts who exercise ordinary original civil jurisdiction. The High Court of Chhattisgarh does not have jurisdiction of "ordinary civil court", and cannot entertain application. Party can approach the principal civil court concerned having original jurisdiction for relief of termination of the mandate of the arbitrator.[646]

Termination of mandate of arbitrator where arbitrator failed to act

The Chief Engineer of the Electricity Board appointed arbitrator in the case failed to act without undue delay which indicated failure on the part of the Arbitral Tribunal to perform its function *de jure* or *de facto*. Mandate of the arbitrator was terminated, and the Senior Advocate of the High Court was appointed arbitrator by the Board.[647]

Where the original arbitrator withdrew from arbitration on health grounds, no provision existed in the arbitration agreement for appointment of substitute arbitrator in such contingency, appointment of substitute arbitrator by the Managing Director of the respondent-company who was authorised to originally appoint arbitrator was held valid in view of Section 15(2). This omission in the arbitration agreement is made up by the specific provision contained in Section 15(2) of the Act.[648]

When named arbitrator refuses to act—Appointment of substitute arbitrator

When a named arbitrator refuses to act, it does not extinguish the arbitration agreement. Arbitration clause becomes exhausted if the named arbitrator refuses to act, but then provisions of Section 15 would be attracted, court shall appoint substitute arbitrator, unless bar of appointment of any other arbitrator is specifically provided for in the arbitration clause/agreement. In the present case, there was no specific condition barring appointment of fresh arbitrator. The plea that the arbitration clause stood obliterated on refusal to act by the named arbitrator was rejected. The named arbitrator,

645. *State of Punjab* v. *Subhash Chander Garg*, 2018 SCC OnLine P&H 8283.
646. *J.B. Construction Co.* v. *Railways*, 2020 SCC OnLine Chh 1704: (2020) 3 CGLJ 518.
647. *Ranjeet Singh & Co.* v. *H.P. SEB Ltd.*, 2018 SCC OnLine HP 2033.
648. *Yashwith Constructions (P) Ltd.* v. *Simplex Concrete Piles India Ltd.*, (2006) 6 SCC 204.

who had initially refused to act but later agreed to take up arbitrator, was appointed arbitrator in the case.[649]

Delay by Railways in appointment of arbitrator on transfer of officer, termination of arbitration proceedings

Delay by itself may not be a necessity for invoking the provisions of Section 15(2) but at the same time, if delay goes unexplained and is not bona fide but reflects slackness on the part of the authorities, then the powers for appointment of a substitute arbitrator can be exercised in terms of Section 15(2), but there is no reason to terminate the arbitral proceedings.[650]

Where the arbitrator appointed in the case failed to proceed in spite of a lapse of five years from the date of the reconstitution of the Arbitration Tribunal, there was loss of mandate on account of extraordinary delay, and a fresh arbitrator was appointed in the case. The mode and manner in which the respondent has been appointing arbitrators from the department and they being transferred and the replacements not being provided, requires appointment of an arbitrator by the court, as there is loss of mandate on account of extraordinary delay in the present case.[651]

Death of third arbitrator

The award was passed by only two arbitrators after the death of the third arbitrator. The Arbitral Tribunal became *functus officio* after the death of the third arbitrator, the award passed was null and void, and liable to be set aside.[652]

Death of named arbitrator—Appointment of substitute arbitrator

The legislative policy embodied in Sections 14 and 15 of the Act is to facilitate the parties to resolve the dispute by way of arbitration. The arbitration clause if clearly spells out any prohibition or debarment, the court has to keep its hands off and there is no question of persuading or pressurising the parties to resolve the dispute by a substitute arbitrator. Generally, this stands out as an exception and that should be discernible from the language of the arbitration clause and the intention of the parties. The court can appoint an arbitrator on the death of a named arbitrator.[653]

---

649. *San-A Tradubg Co. Ltd.* v. *I.C. Textiles Ltd.*, (2012) 7 SCC 192.
650. *Trishul Construction* v. *Union of India*, 2019 SCC OnLine Pat 1933.
651. *A. Chockalingam* v. *Union of India*, 2015 SCC OnLine Mad 1785.
652. *S.A. Fasludeen* v. *Siyauddin*, 2017 SCC OnLine Mad 11917: (2018) 1 LW 233.
653. *ACC Ltd.* v. *Global Cements Ltd.*, (2012) 7 SCC 71; *Shailesh Dhairyawan* v. *Mohan Balkrishna Lulla*, (2016) 3 SCC 619; *Enarch Consultants (P) Ltd.* v. *Lalji Superspeciality Hospital & Research*, (2021) 3 HCC (Del) 268.

Pending adjudication case would be covered by Section 15 of the Act. Application for appointment of arbitrator filed directly before the High Court would be maintainable, the applicant was not required to follow the mandate of the agreement which was followed while appointing arbitrator at the initial stage.[654]

Appointment of substitute arbitrator—Factors to be considered

Before appointing an arbitrator under Section 11(6) of the Act, the High Court had failed to take into consideration the effect of Section 11(8) of the Act. Therefore, the impugned order was set aside and the case was remanded back to the High Court for fresh decision of the application under Section 11(6) of the Act. While considering the application afresh, the High Court was directed to take into consideration the decision in the *Northern Railway Admn. case*[655].

"Substitute arbitrator shall be appointed according to rules" [S. 15(2)]

The term "rules" in Section 15(2) obviously refers to the provision for appointment contained in the arbitration agreement or any rules of any institution under which the disputes were referred to arbitration. Section 11(6) of the Act has application only when a party or the person concerned had failed to act in terms of the arbitration agreement. When Section 15(2) says that a substitute arbitrator can be appointed according to the rules that were applicable for the appointment of the arbitrator originally, it is not confined to an appointment under any statutory rule or rule framed under the Act or under the scheme. It only means that the appointment of the substitute arbitrator must be done according to the original agreement or provision applicable to the appointment of the arbitrator at the initial stage.[656]

In the relevant provisions (Sections 11, 14 and 15) of the 1996 Act, the legislature has repeatedly laid emphasis on the necessity of adherence to the terms of agreement between the parties in the matter of appointment of arbitrators and procedure to be followed for such appointment. Even Section 15(2) of the said Act, which regulates appointment of a substitute arbitrator, requires that such an appointment shall be made according to the rules which were applicable to the appointment of an original arbitrator. The term "rules" used in Section 15(2) is not confined to statutory rules or the rules framed by the competent authority in exercise of the power of

---

654. *Central Coalfields Ltd.* v. *Eastern India Powertech Ltd.*, 2022 SCC OnLine Jhar 1533.
655. *Northern Railway Admn.* v. *Patel Engg. Co. Ltd.*, (2008) 10 SCC 240, considered.
656. *Yashwith Constructions (P) Ltd.* v. *Simplex Concrete Piles India Ltd.*, (2006) 6 SCC 204.

delegated legislation but also includes the terms of agreement entered into between the parties.[657]

The High Court becomes *functus officio* with the appointment of the arbitrator and ceases to have any power either to entertain challenge to the jurisdiction of the arbitrator or to terminate his challenge on any ground. The High Court in the exercise of inherent powers cannot appoint substitute arbitrator. The remedy is to apply before the Arbitral Tribunal.[658]

When an arbitrator is substituted, the jurisdiction of the arbitrator is not enhanced or reduced by the court or the judicial authority.[659]

"A substitute arbitrator shall be appointed" [S. 15(2)]

Section 15(2) of the 1996 Act does not per se apply to a case where an arbitrator appointed by a party to the agreement declines to accept the appointment or refuses to arbitrate in the matter. In *SBP & Co. (2)* v. *Patel Engg. Ltd.*[660], the agreements entered into between the appellant and Respondent 1 did not contain a provision for appointment of a substitute arbitrator in case the arbitrator appointed by either party was to decline to accept appointment or refuse to arbitrate in the matter. There was nothing in the relevant arbitration clause from which it could be inferred that in the event of refusal of an arbitrator to accept the appointment or arbitrate in the matter, the party appointing such arbitrator has an implicit right to appoint a substitute arbitrator. Thus, in terms of the agreement entered into between the parties, Respondent 1 could not appoint *SL* as a substitute arbitrator simply because *SN* declined to accept the appointment as an arbitrator.

Appointment of new arbitrator on termination of mandate of arbitrator

The mandate of the previous arbitrator was terminated on account of virtual withdrawal from the office. The arbitrator did not deny the allegation of partial behaviour against him. New arbitrator was appointed in the case.[661]

No notice was issued by the arbitrator despite being aware of his appointment. Arbitrator refused to act as he was posted at a disputed site

657. *SBP & Co. (2)* v. *Patel Engg. Ltd.*, (2009) 10 SCC 293.
658. *Suresh Chand Agarwal* v. *Mahesh Kumar Agarwal*, 2013 SCC OnLine All 13884: (2013) 4 All LJ 50.
659. *Indian Oil Corpn. Ltd.* v. *Artson Engg. Ltd.*, 2006 SCC OnLine Bom 1106: (2007) 1 Mah LJ 825.
660. (2009) 10 SCC 293.
661. *Gopalram Gumaniram Choudhury* v. *State of Rajasthan*, 2019 SCC OnLine Raj 7904.

at the relevant time. Mandate of the arbitrator stood terminated on his withdrawal. Substitute arbitrator was appointed.[662]

Where no procedure was agreed in the arbitration agreement for appointment of substitute arbitrator and no agreement was reached between the parties before the expiry of statutory limit, the authority to appoint consented arbitrators lost by parties vested in the court. The parties cannot regain such authority to appoint arbitrator. Only court could exercise power to appoint an independent arbitrator.[663]

Appointment of new arbitrator after the appointed arbitrator recuses himself from the proceedings

In a case where the original arbitrator had recused himself, the substitute or new arbitrator is required to be appointed according to the rules that were applicable to the appointment of the original arbitrator. This is the mandate of Section 15(2). It was, therefore, incumbent on the petitioner to give notice and explore the possibility of naming an arbitrator by mutual consent and only on failure thereof, the application under Section 11(6) for appointment of arbitrator would be filed.[664]

Failure of arbitrator to conclude hearing over period of three years—Mandate of arbitrator terminated

The arbitrator did not conclude hearing on a single claim despite a period of three years having elapsed after the arbitrator entered into reference. The arbitrator was not able to devote sufficient time for arbitration and he was not able to complete the arbitration proceedings within a reasonable time and as such, the mandate of the learned arbitrator deserves to be terminated. Fresh arbitrator was appointed in the case.[665]

Time for making, publishing award—Extension by court

The court, in exercise of inherent powers, cannot extend time for making and publishing award fixed by the parties in the absence of consent of either of the parties.[666]

---

662. *Kalwanoo Rice Mills* v. *Punjab Warehousing Corpn. Ltd.*, 2023 SCC OnLine P&H 6693.
663. *Basant Ispat Udyog (P) Ltd.* v. *Basant Industries*, 2019 SCC OnLine All 4905: (2020) 1 All LJ 262.
664. *Huawei Technologies Co. Ltd.* v. *Sterlite Technologies Ltd.*, (2016) 1 SCC 721.
665. *Five Star Builders* v. *State of H.P.*, 2019 SCC OnLine HP 3611.
666. *NBCC Ltd.* v. *J.G. Engg. (P) Ltd.*, (2010) 2 SCC 385.

Resignation by arbitrator—Appointment of substitute arbitrator

Vacancy arose on the resignation of the arbitrator. In spite of the fact that the arbitration clause does provide for the appointment of a substitute arbitrator in the event of occurrence of vacancy, appointment of the substitute arbitrator under Section 15 would be valid, application under Section 11(6) would not lie.[667]

Termination of mandate of arbitrator—Excess fee charged by arbitrator

Where the parties resented to excessive fee of the arbitrator, the arbitrator closed evidence and listed the dispute for final argument though matter was pending before the commercial court and passed ex parte award. The arbitrator was rendered *de jure* or *de facto* unable to perform his functions. Mandate of the arbitrator was terminated.[668]

Application for termination of the mandate of the arbitrator—Jurisdiction of the court

Application for termination of mandate of the arbitrator lies before the principal civil court of the district as per the provisions of Section 2(1)(*e*) and the petition filed before the High Court was not maintainable.[669]

---

667. *Yashwith Constructions (P) Ltd.* v. *Simplex Concrete Piles India Ltd.*, 2005 SCC OnLine AP 166: (2005) 2 AP LJ 64.
668. *Doshion (P) Ltd.* v. *Hindustan Zinc Ltd.*, 2019 SCC OnLine Raj 6.
669. *Doshion (P) Ltd.* v. *Hindustan Zinc Ltd.*, 2018 SCC OnLine Raj 949: (2018) 3 WLC 510.

Chapter IV
Jurisdiction of Arbitral Tribunals

COMPETENCE OF ARBITRAL TRIBUNAL TO RULE ON ITS JURISDICTION [S. 16]

16. *Competence of arbitral tribunal to rule on its jurisdiction.*—(1) The arbitral tribunal may rule on its own jurisdiction, including ruling on any objections with respect to the existence or validity of the arbitration agreement, and for that purpose,—

(*a*) an arbitration clause which forms part of a contract shall be treated as an agreement independent of the other terms of the contract; and

(*b*) a decision by the arbitral tribunal that the contract is null and void shall not entail *ipso jure* the invalidity of the arbitration clause.

(2) A plea that the arbitral tribunal does not have jurisdiction shall be raised not later than the submission of the statement of defence; however, a party shall not be precluded from raising such a plea merely because that he has appointed, or participated in the appointment of, an arbitrator.

(3) A plea that the arbitral tribunal is exceeding the scope of its authority shall be raised as soon as the matter alleged to be beyond the scope of its authority is raised during the arbitral proceedings.

(4) The arbitral tribunal may, in either of the cases referred to in sub-section (2) or sub-section (3), admit a later plea if it considers the delay justified.

(5) The arbitral tribunal shall decide on a plea referred to in sub-section (2) or sub-section (3) and, where the arbitral tribunal takes a decision rejecting the plea, continue with the arbitral proceedings and make an arbitral award.

(6) A party aggrieved by such an arbitral award may make an application for setting aside such an arbitral award in accordance with Section 34.

COMMENTS

Corresponding old law

Section 16 is new, and did not appear in the Arbitration Act, 1940.

UNCITRAL Model law

Article 16. *Competence of arbitral tribunal to rule on its jurisdiction*

(1) The arbitral tribunal may rule on its own jurisdiction, including any objections with respect to the existence or validity of the arbitration agreement. For that purpose, an arbitration clause which forms part of a contract shall be treated as an agreement independent of the other terms of the contract. A decision by the arbitral tribunal that the contract is null and void shall not entail *ipso jure* the invalidity of the arbitration clause.

(2) A plea that the arbitral tribunal does not have jurisdiction shall be raised not later than the submission of the statement of defence. A party is not precluded from raising such a plea by the fact that he has appointed, or participated in the appointment of, an arbitrator. A plea that the arbitral tribunal is exceeding the scope of its authority shall be raised as soon as the matter alleged to be beyond the scope of its authority is raised during the arbitral proceedings. The arbitral tribunal may, in either case, admit a later plea if it considers the delay justified.

(3) The arbitral tribunal may rule on a plea referred to in paragraph (2) of this article either as a preliminary question or in an award on the merits. If the arbitral tribunal rules as a preliminary question that it has jurisdiction, any party may request, within thirty days after having received notice of that ruling, the court specified in article 6 to decide the matter, which decision shall be subject to no appeal; while such a request is pending, the arbitral tribunal may continue the arbitral proceedings and make an award.

Scope and application

This section deals with the competency of the Arbitral Tribunal to rule on its own jurisdiction including ruling on any objection(s) with respect to the existence of the validity of the arbitration agreement. Such a provision did not exist in the Arbitration Act, 1940.

Section 16, Arbitration and Conciliation Act, 1996 necessarily mandates that the issue of jurisdiction must be dealt first by the tribunal, before the court examines the same under Section 34, Arbitration and Conciliation Act, 1996.[1] The objection that Arbitral Tribunal had no jurisdiction cannot be raised at the time of setting aside the award; also, an objection after filing defence statement is prohibited by Section 16.[2]

Where a valid arbitration clause exists, objections challenging the jurisdiction of the Arbitral Tribunal must be raised before the arbitrators. Such

1. *Bhaven Construction* v. *Sardar Sarovar Narmada Nigam Ltd.*, (2022) 1 SCC 75.
2. *MSP Infrastructure Ltd.* v. *M.P. Road Development Corpn. Ltd.*, (2015) 13 SCC 713.

objection is not a matter for decision by the Chief Justice or his designate under Section 11.[3]

The questions relating to the relevant scope, meaning, purport and effect of the arbitration clause in the agreement between the parties and the legality or propriety of the constitution of an Arbitral Tribunal, in the teeth of Rules 21 and 22 of the ICA Rules as well as the question relating to alleged contradictions or inconsistencies among those provisions are matters which go to the jurisdiction of the Arbitral Tribunal. The question as to the existence or validity of the arbitration agreement itself also, as enjoined under Section 16 of the 1996 Act, falls within the jurisdiction of the Arbitral Tribunal constituted, which has been enabled to adjudicate on such questions also before embarking upon an exercise to decide the dispute between the parties or decide them simultaneously. The legislative intent underlying the 1996 Act is to minimise the supervisory roles of the courts in the arbitral process and nominate/appoint the arbitrator without wasting time, leaving all contentious issues to be urged and agitated before the Arbitral Tribunal itself.[4]

Whether a particular dispute comes within purview of the arbitration clause as incorporated (in the Conditions of Carriage of Bills of Lading in this case), is a matter to be decided by the arbitrator or the court.[5]

Arbitral Tribunal's authority under Section 16 is not confined to the width of its jurisdiction but goes to the very root of it. It can decide whether it has been improperly constituted by such a nomination.[6]

The arbitrator can rule on his own jurisdiction and can also record findings regarding arbitrability of the dispute.[7]

Determination of question as to whether satisfactory service of notice under Section 21 and whether giving of such notice was a condition precedent for the exercise of jurisdiction by the Arbitral Tribunal are matters to be determined by the Arbitral Tribunal itself.[8]

Section 16 covers all possible objections with respect to the existence/validity of arbitration agreement.[9]

It is settled law that the Arbitral Tribunal, if constituted, in accordance with the agreement between the parties without having recourse to Section 11(6)

3. *Viatra A.G.* v. *State Trading Corpn. of India Ltd.*, (2002) 10 SCC 74.
4. *Food Corporation of India* v. *Indian Council of Arbitration*, (2003) 6 SCC 564.
5. *Vessel M.V. "Baltic Confidence"* v. *STC*, (2001) 7 SCC 473.
6. *Niko Resources Ltd.* v. *Gujarat State Petroleum Corpn.*, (2002) 10 SCC 71.
7. *India Pistons Ltd.* v. *Ganapathi Chandrasekar*, 2021 SCC OnLine Mad 5729.
8. *Secur Industries Ltd.* v. *Godrej & Boyce Mfg. Co. Ltd.*, (2004) 3 SCC 447.
9. *Sita Holiday Resorts Ltd.* v. *Mohan Lal Harbans Lal Bhayana & Co.*, 1999 SCC OnLine Del 314: (1999) 50 DRJ 336.

of the Act, will have jurisdiction to decide all matters as contemplated by Section 16 of the Act.[10]

The issue as to whether the claim was arbitrable or fell within the scope of an excepted matter must be left to the Arbitral Tribunal. Neither the Chief Justice nor his designate under Section 11 of the Act can decide an issue that pertains to the third category enlisted in the decision in *Boghaara Polyfab*[11]. Similarly, where a reference to arbitration has taken place outside the court, a party to the arbitral agreement cannot preclude the Arbitral Tribunal from deciding as to whether the claim is arbitrable or whether it pertains to an excepted matter. That issue has to be determined by the Arbitral Tribunal.[12]

Section 16 cannot be held to empower an Arbitral Tribunal to ignore the decision given by the judicial authority or the Chief Justice before the reference to it was made. Arbitral Tribunal can decide on its jurisdiction only when parties have gone to the Arbitral Tribunal without recourse to either Section 8 or Section 11 of the Act.[13]

The power conferred on the arbitrator under Section 16 of the Act to rule on its own jurisdiction including the existence or validity of the arbitration agreement is not subject to the agreement of the parties which is evident from the absence of the expression "unless otherwise agreed by the parties", which precedes most of the non-mandatory provisions of the Act. So the parties to the arbitration, by agreement, cannot exclude the arbitrator's competence to decide on its own jurisdiction including the existence or validity of the arbitration agreement. The arbitration clause has to be treated as an agreement independent of the other terms of the contract and so the arbitrator has power to rule on its own jurisdiction including the existence and validity of the arbitration agreement. This is a departure from the 1940 Act under which the arbitrator has no power and it will be decided only by the court. Section 16 of the Act gives power to the arbitrator to decide even the validity of the agreement.[14]

Competence of Arbitral Tribunal to rule on existence of arbitration clause

Once the Chief Justice or his designate has appointed arbitrator in an application under Section 11. The Arbitral Tribunal cannot go behind the said

10. *BPL Ltd.* v. *Morgan Securities & Credits (P) Ltd.*, 2008 SCC OnLine Del 339: (2008) 149 DLT 610.
11. *National Insurance Co. Ltd.* v. *Boghara Polyfab (P) Ltd.*, (2009) 1 SCC 267.
12. *Agarwal Co.* v. *Union of India*, 2014 SCC OnLine All 16110: (2015) 2 All LJ 553.
13. *G.G. Transport (P) Ltd.* v. *Bhupendra Singh Ananda*, 2017 SCC OnLine Gau 1070: (2017) 5 Gau LR 39.
14. *NIIT Ltd.* v. *Ashish Deb*, 2004 SCC OnLine Mad 112: (2004) 2 LW 244.

decision to rule on its own jurisdiction or on the existence of an arbitration clause.[15]

Power of the arbitrator to rule on its jurisdiction can happen only when the parties have gone for arbitration without recourse to Section 8 or Section 11.[16]

Nature and scope of authority of arbitrator under Section 16

Under the 1996 Act, the Arbitral Tribunal has been given a very wide and deep area of operation and it is the court's powers which have been statutorily curtailed. The Arbitral Tribunal's authority under Section 16 of the 1996 Act is not confined to the width of its jurisdiction but goes to the very root of its jurisdiction. The scope of the authority of the Arbitral Tribunal under Section 16 is not a matter which the court can adjudicate upon. It is incumbent on the court to refer the parties to arbitration under Section 8(1) of the Act if a suit is filed in a matter which is the subject-matter of an arbitration agreement. Even when this question is pending before a court, the Arbitral Tribunal may proceed with the arbitration under Section 8(3) and make its award.[17]

No dispute can be referred for arbitration in the absence of any arbitration clause in the agreement. However, once arbitration proceedings are initiated, Section 16 confers power on the arbitrator to rule on its own jurisdiction, including ruling on any objection with respect to the existence or validity of the arbitration agreement. Hence, the civil court does not have jurisdiction to go into said questions. In the instant case, the appellant being party to said arbitral proceedings, questions as to jurisdiction of the arbitrator and the non-existence of the arbitration agreement have to be raised before the arbitrator and the same are required to be determined as preliminary issues. The order of the arbitrator on the issue of its jurisdiction can be challenged under Section 34.[18]

Jurisdiction of arbitrator can be extended by consent

The jurisdiction of an arbitrator depends upon the dispute referred to him for arbitration. However, the scope of arbitration is not always conferred to the initial dispute referred to arbitration. By consent, either expressly or impliedly, it can be extended in the course of the proceedings before the

15. *APS Kushwaha* v. *Municipal Corpn., Gwalior*, (2011) 13 SCC 258.
16. *State of W.B.* v. *Sarkar & Sarkar*, (2018) 12 SCC 736.
17. *Secur Industries Ltd.* v. *Godrej & Boyce Mfg. Co. Ltd.*, (2004) 3 SCC 447.
18. *Kvaerner Cementation India Ltd.* v. *Bajranglal Agarwal*, (2012) 5 SCC 214.

arbitrator, *firstly* at the time of filing of the statement of claim and that of defence by the parties and, *secondly*, by way of amendment.[19]

"Arbitral Tribunal may rule on its own jurisdiction" [S. 16(1)]

The expression used in Section 16(1) that the "Arbitral Tribunal may rule on its own jurisdiction including on any objection with respect to the existence or validity of the arbitration agreement" shows that the Arbitral Tribunal's authority under Section 16 is not confined to the width of its jurisdiction, but goes to the very root of its jurisdiction and there is no impediment in contending before the Arbitral Tribunal that it had been wrongly constituted.[20] The Arbitral Tribunal's authority under Section 16 of the 1996 Act is not confined to the width of its jurisdiction but goes to the very root of its jurisdiction. In *Aurohill Global Commodities Ltd.* v. *Maharashtra STC Ltd.*[21], questions as to whether the draft purchase order acquired the character of a concluded contract or not, whether the contract was non est, and whether a necessary and proper party had not been joined can only be decided by the arbitrator.

The word "jurisdiction" in Section 16 has reference to three things: 1) whether there is existence of a valid arbitration agreement; 2) whether the Arbitral Tribunal is properly constituted; and 3) matters submitted to arbitration should be in accordance with the arbitration agreement.[22]

Under Section 16(1), the Arbitral Tribunal is invested with the power to rule on its own jurisdiction, including ruling on any objection with respect to the existence or validity of the arbitration agreement. For that purpose, the arbitration clause which forms part of the contract is to be treated as an agreement independent of other terms of the contract.[23] The Arbitral Tribunal is endorsed with ample power and jurisdiction to rule on its own jurisdiction, and it would not, therefore, be open to the civil court to pass an injunction against an arbitral proceeding in the teeth of the provisions of Sections 5 and 16, Arbitration and Conciliation Act, 1996.[24]

---

19. *Ganesh Benzoplast Ltd., Mumbai* v. *Saf Yeast Co. Ltd.*, 2007 SCC OnLine Bom 323: (2007) 5 Mah LJ 230.
20. *GAIL* v. *Keti Construction (I) Ltd.*, (2007) 5 SCC 38.
21. (2007) 7 SCC 120.
22. *IFFCO Ltd.* v. *Bhadra Products*, (2018) 2 SCC 534.
23. *Olympus Superstructures (P) Ltd.* v. *Meena Vijay Khetan*, (1999) 5 SCC 651.
24. *Handicrafts & Handlooms Exports Corpn. of India Ltd.* v. *Ashok Metal Corpn.*, 2010 SCC OnLine Del 2099: (2010) 117 DRJ 370; see also, *GKC Projects Ltd.* v. *Unitech Machines Ltd.*, (2014) 1 HCC (Del) 556.

All obligations regarding existence and validity of the arbitration agreement coupled with objection as to the constitution of the Arbitral Tribunal can be gone into by the arbitrator.[25]

No dispute can be referred for arbitration in the absence of any arbitration clause in the agreement. However, once arbitration proceedings are initiated, Section 16 confers power on the arbitrator to rule on its own jurisdiction with respect to existence or validity of the arbitration agreement. However, the civil court has no jurisdiction to go into the said questions.[26]

The question as to the existence or validity of the arbitration agreement itself also, as enjoined under Section 16, falls within the jurisdiction of the Arbitral Tribunal constituted, which has been enabled to adjudicate upon such questions also before embarking upon an exercise to decide the dispute between the parties or to decide them simultaneously.[27] The legislative intent underlying the Act of 1996 is to minimise the supervisory role of the courts in the arbitral process and nominate/appoint the arbitrator without wasting time, leaving all contentious issues to be urged and agitated before the Arbitral Tribunal itself.[28]

By majority, a Bench of seven judges in the well-known case of *SBP & Co.* v. *Patel Engg. Ltd.*[29] held that authorities under the Arbitral Tribunal do not have exclusive jurisdiction to decide the question of existence or validity of an arbitration agreement and the same can be decided by the authorities.

The arbitrator has jurisdiction to decide about the arbitrability of the dispute.[30]

Authority of the arbitrator under Section 16 is not confined to the width of its jurisdiction but goes to the very root of it. Arbitrator can decide whether it has been improperly constituted by nomination made by the Chief Justice/ his designate.[31]

Arbitrator can go into the matter whether the entire contract is vitiated by alleged commission of any fraud on the part of either parties to the contract.[32]

---

25. *Ruchi Strips & Alloys Ltd.* v. *Tata South East Asia Ltd.*, (2004) 13 SCC 470; *Secur Industries Ltd.* v. *Godrej & Boyce Mfg. Co. Ltd.*, (2004) 3 SCC 447.
26. *Kvaerner Cementation India Ltd.* v. *Bajranglal Agarwal*, (2012) 5 SCC 214.
27. *Food Corporation of India* v. *Indian Council of Arbitration*, (2003) 6 SCC 564.
28. *Ibid.*
29. (2005) 8 SCC 618; see also, *Vipin Kumar Gadhok* v. *Ravinder Nath Khanna*, (2007) 10 SCC 623.
30. *Vipin Kumar Gadhok* v. *Ravinder Nath Khanna*, (2007) 10 SCC 623.
31. *Niko Resources Ltd.* v. *Gujarat State Petroleum Corpn.*, (2002) 10 SCC 71.
32. *Meguin GmbH & Co.* v. *Nandan Petrochem Ltd.*, (2016) 10 SCC 422.

Whether the claim falls within the excepted matter under agreement?

On the issue as to whether the claim was arbitrable or fell within the scope of the Arbitral Tribunal, the competent authority cannot refuse to refer the dispute to the Arbitral Tribunal on the ground that it relates to an excepted matter or concluded from the purview of arbitrability.[33]

Existence/validity of arbitration agreement—Determination —Exclusive jurisdiction of Arbitral Tribunal

By majority it has been held that the Arbitral Tribunal does not have exclusive jurisdiction to decide the existence/validity of the arbitration agreement. The same can be decided by authorities concerned under Sections 8, 9 and 11.[34]

Doctrine of kompetenz-kompetenz

The doctrine of kompetenz-kompetenz implies that the Arbitral Tribunal has the competence to determine and rule on its own jurisdiction, including objections with respect to the existence, validity, and scope of the arbitration agreement, in the first instance, which is subject to judicial scrutiny by the courts at a later stage of the proceedings. The doctrine of kompetenz-kompetenz has evolved to minimise judicial intervention at the pre-reference stage, and reduce unmeritorious challenges raised on the issue of jurisdiction of the Arbitral Tribunal. The doctrine of kompetenz-kompetenz is based on the premise that the arbitration agreement is separate and independent from the substantive underlying contract in which it is embedded. Equally, an arbitration agreement exists and can be acted upon irrespective of whether the main substantive contract is valid or not.[35]

Objections regarding validity/existence of arbitration, constitution of Arbitral Tribunal—Powers of arbitrator

All objections regarding validity and existence of arbitration agreement coupled with objection as to constitution of the Arbitral Tribunal can be gone into by the arbitrator.[36]

Power of arbitrator—Issue of limitation

Limitation is an issue that can be considered and decided by an arbitration.[37]

33. *Aargee Engg. & Co.* v. *Era Infra Engg. Ltd.*, 2017 SCC OnLine All 3929: (2017) 122 ALR 179.
34. *SBP & Co.* v. *Patel Engg. Ltd.*, (2005) 8 SCC 618.
35. *N.N. Global Mercantile (P) Ltd.* v. *Indo Unique Flame Ltd.*, (2021) 4 SCC 379.
36. *Ruchi Strips & Alloys Ltd.* v. *Tata South East Asia Ltd.*, (2004) 13 SCC 470.
37. *Groupe Chimique Tunisien SA* v. *Southern Petrochemicals Industries Corpn. Ltd.*, (2006) 5 SCC 275.

"Not later than the submission of statement of defence" [S. 16(2)]

Section 16(2) mandates that a plea that the tribunal does not have jurisdiction shall not be raised later than the submission of the statement of defence. There is a prohibition on the party from raising a plea that the tribunal does not have jurisdiction after the party has submitted its statement of defence. The scheme of the Act is very clear. All objections to jurisdiction whatever nature must be taken at the stage of the submission of the statement of defence and must be dealt with under Section 16, Arbitration and Conciliation Act, 1996. However, if one of the parties seeks to contend that the subject-matter of the dispute is such that it cannot be dealt with by arbitration, it may be dealt with under Section 34 by the court.[38] Objection to jurisdiction before arbitrator after filing of statement of defence when a special leave petition challenging jurisdiction already stands filed prior to the statement of defence held permissible.[39]

There is nothing to warrant the inference that all objections to the jurisdiction of the tribunal cannot be raised under Section 16 and that the tribunal does not have the power to rule on its own jurisdiction.[40] Where the award has already been made and no objection to the jurisdiction of the arbitrator was taken at the relevant stage, the award of the arbitrator cannot be annulled only on that ground.[41] Decision of the Arbitral Tribunal on limitation is not a ruling by the tribunal on its own jurisdiction. Not all "errors of law" are "errors of jurisdiction". An erroneous decision on a question of termination or res judicata would not oust the jurisdiction of the court/Arbitral Tribunal in the primitive sense of the term and render the decision or the decree embodying the decision a nullity liable to collateral attack.[42]

Where a party raised plea that the Arbitral Tribunal has not been properly constituted or has no jurisdiction, it must do so at the threshold before the Arbitral Tribunal so that remedial measures may be immediately taken and time and expenses involved in hearing of the matter before the Arbitral Tribunal, which may ultimately be found to be either not properly constituted or lacking in jurisdiction, in proceedings for setting aside the award may be avoided. Such a plea may be raised before the Arbitral Tribunal right

38. *MSP Infrastructure Ltd.* v. *M.P. Road Development Corpn. Ltd.*, (2015) 13 SCC 713.
39. *M.P. Rural Road Development Authority* v. *L.G. Chaudhary Engineers and Contractors*, (2018) 10 SCC 826.
40. *Ibid.*
41. *Ibid.*
42. *IFFCO Ltd.* v. *Bhadra Products*, (2018) 2 SCC 534.

at the beginning and normally not later than the filing of the statement of defence.[43]

Dispute as to terms of arbitration agreement—Arbitrator competent to decide

When parties during negotiations contemplate the execution of a formal agreement incorporating the terms of the bargain, so long as a formal agreement has not been entered into, it may be open to contend that there was no concluded contract between the parties. In *Maharshi Dayanand University* v. *Anand Coop. L/C Society Ltd.*[44], the tender of the respondent was accepted, the work was to commence on the basis of the said acceptance but payment was not to be paid until a formal contract was signed. The question raised in the case whether the respondent was precluded from seeking arbitrator under a clause of the tender can be decided by the arbitrator under Section 16.

Determination of proper law applicable to arbitration as a preliminary question

Where parties to a substantive contract in a cross-border transaction agree to the resolution of the dispute through arbitration without specifying the governing law, it is the duty of the arbitrator to ascertain "proper law" applicable to the case in terms of the established principles of law.[45]

Where Arbitral Tribunal has been constituted by parties without having recourse to Section 11(6)

In a case where an Arbitral Tribunal has been constituted by the parties without having recourse to Section 11(6) of the Act, the Arbitral Tribunal will have the jurisdiction to decide all matters as contemplated by Section 16 of the Act.[46]

Necessary/unnecessary party to the arbitration proceedings

Arbitrator already in seisin of the disputes between the parties; all contentions including whether a respondent (R3) is a necessary party or not are to be decided by the arbitrator.[47]

---

43. *GAIL* v. *Keti Construction (I) Ltd.*, (2007) 5 SCC 38.
44. (2007) 5 SCC 295.
45. *Sasan Power Ltd.* v. *North American Coal Corpn. (India) (P) Ltd.*, (2016) 10 SCC 813.
46. *SBP & Co.* v. *Patel Engg. Ltd.*, (2005) 8 SCC 618.
47. *Rajindra Kumar Tekriwal* v. *Unique Construction (P) Ltd.*, (2016) 16 SCC 93.

The presence of the petitioner was required to decide the dispute between the parties. Non-signatory or third party can be subjected to arbitration without their prior consent in exceptional cases. Impleadment of the petitioner as party in arbitration proceedings was found proper.[48]

Jurisdiction of arbitrator—Challenge to, when to be raised

Under Section 16, Arbitration and Conciliation Act, 1996, the party questioning the jurisdiction of the arbitrator has an obligation to raise the said question before the arbitrator. Such a question of jurisdiction could be raised if it is beyond the scope of his authority. It is required to be raised during arbitration proceedings or soon after initiation thereof; such a jurisdictional question is required to be determined as a preliminary ground. A decision taken thereon by the arbitrator would be subject-matter of challenge under Section 34 of the Act. In the event the arbitrator opines that he has jurisdiction in relation thereto, an appeal there-against is provided for under Section 37 of the Act.[49]

There is no bar to the plea of jurisdiction under Section 34 of the Act, even if no such objection was raised under Section 16.[50] Jurisdiction of the Arbitral Tribunal can be challenged after the passing of the award.[51]

Under Section 16 of the Act, the party questioning the jurisdiction of the arbitrator has an obligation to raise the said question before the arbitrator. Such a question of jurisdiction could be raised if it is beyond the scope of his authority. It is required to be raised during arbitration proceedings or soon after initiation thereof. The jurisdictional question is required to be determined as a preliminary ground. A decision taken thereupon by the arbitrator would be the subject-matter of challenge under Section 34 of the Act. In the event the arbitrator opined that he had no jurisdiction in relation thereto, an appeal there-against is provided for under Section 37 of the Act.[52] Where a party raises a plea that the Arbitral Tribunal has not been properly constituted or has no jurisdiction, it must do so at the threshold before the Arbitral Tribunal so that remedial measures may be immediately taken and time and expense involved in hearing of the matter before the Arbitral Tribunal which may ultimately be found to be either not properly constituted or lacking in jurisdiction, in proceedings for setting aside the award, may be avoided. Such

48. *Ashokbhai Raisingbhai Parmar* v. *Kumar Neetaben V. Patel*, 2021 SCC OnLine Guj 3178.

49. *McDermott International Inc.* v. *Burn Standard Co. Ltd.*, (2006) 11 SCC 181; *GAIL* v. *Keti Construction (I) Ltd.*, (2007) 5 SCC 38.

50. *Lion Engg. Consultants* v. *State of M.P.*, (2018) 16 SCC 758.

51. *Falcon Progress Ltd.* v. *Sara International Ltd.*, 2017 SCC OnLine Del 6989: (2017) 238 DLT 565.

52. *McDermott International Inc.* v. *Burn Standard Co. Ltd.*, (2006) 11 SCC 181.

a plea must be raised before the Arbitral Tribunal right at the beginning and normally not later than in the statement of defence.[53] Objection regarding the applicability of the arbitration clause on the facts of the case, though goes to the roots of the jurisdiction, must be raised before the arbitrator for decision.[54]

Preliminary issues that may be decided by the arbitrator

Where a contract contains an arbitration clause and any dispute in respect of the said contract is referred to arbitration without the intervention of the court, the Arbitral Tribunal can decide the following questions affecting its jurisdiction:

1. whether there is an arbitration agreement;
2. whether the arbitration agreement is valid;
3. whether the contract in which the arbitration clause is found is null and void and if so, whether the invalidity extends to the arbitration clause also.[55]

Objection regarding the applicability of arbitration clause in arbitration agreement

As the objection regarding the applicability of arbitration clause to the facts of the given case goes to the very root of jurisdiction, it cannot be said that this question will have to be decided by the civil court before referring the matter to arbitration. Where there is admittedly an arbitration clause, Section 16 of the Act is very much clear that such a question to be raised before the Arbitral Tribunal concerned. Therefore, in *Hindustan Petroleum Corpn. Ltd.* v. *Pinkcity Midway Petroleums*[56], the courts below without examining the question of applicability of the arbitration clause to the facts of the case ought to have referred the parties to arbitration as required by Section 8, Arbitration and Conciliation Act, 1996. If in an agreement between the parties before the civil court, there is a clause for arbitration, it is mandatory for the civil court to refer the dispute to arbitration.

Arbitration agreement—Prima facie finding by the Chief Justice/his designate

The Chief Justice or his designate is required to decide the existence of an arbitration agreement between parties finally. Prima facie finding as to

53. *GAIL* v. *Keti Construction (I) Ltd.*, (2007) 5 SCC 38.
54. *Hindustan Petroleum Corpn. Ltd.* v. *Pinkcity Midway Petroleums*, (2003) 6 SCC 503.
55. *National Insurance Co. Ltd.* v. *Boghara Polyfab (P) Ltd.*, (2009) 1 SCC 267.
56. (2003) 6 SCC 503.

existence of arbitration agreement is not contemplated by the Act. Once the Chief Justice or his designate has held that there is an arbitration agreement between the parties, the arbitrator/Arbitral Tribunal is precluded from considering the issue and recording a contrary finding.[57]

Existence of arbitration agreement—Question raised before Arbitral Tribunal may be decided by the tribunal under Section 16 but jurisdiction of CJI/CJ or their designate to decide such question at the stage of Section 11 application, not excluded

Section 16 has conferred jurisdiction on the Arbitral Tribunal to decide whether there is in "existence" an arbitral clause. Section 16 is only an enabling provision. Section 16 does not take away the jurisdiction of the Chief Justice of India or his designate, if need be, to decide the question of the "existence" of the arbitration agreement. Section 16 does not declare that except the Arbitral Tribunal none else can decide this question. Merely because the new Act permits the arbitrator to decide this question, it does not necessarily follow that at the stage of Section 11, the Chief Justice of India or his designate cannot decide a question as to the existence of the arbitration clause.[58]

"Decision by the Arbitral Tribunal that the contract is null and void" [S. 16(1)(*b*)]

As provided by Section 16(1)(*b*), any decision by the Arbitral Tribunal that the contract is null and void shall not entail ipso jure the invalidity of the arbitration clause.[59]

Participation in proceedings before arbitrator [Sub-s. 16(2)]

The language of Section 16(2) of the 1996 Act leaves no room for doubt that mere participation in the proceedings would not tantamount to an acceptance of the jurisdiction of the arbitrator to arbitrate disputes between the parties.[60]

Section 16(2) of the Act of 1996 stipulates that a plea that the Arbitral Tribunal does not have jurisdiction shall be raised not later than the submission of the statement of defence. However, the parties shall not be precluded from raising such a plea only on the ground that he has appointed or participated in the appointment of the arbitrator. So mere participation

57. *Indowind Energy Ltd.* v. *Wescare (I) Ltd.*, (2010) 5 SCC 306.
58. *Wellington Associates Ltd.* v. *Kirit Mehta*, (2000) 4 SCC 272.
59. *Olympus Superstructures (P) Ltd.* v. *Meena Vijay Khetan*, (1999) 5 SCC 651.
60. *Travancore Devaswom Board* v. *Panchamy Pack (P) Ltd.*, (2004) 13 SCC 510.

in the appointment of the arbitrator cannot be a ground deterring the respondent Board to raise the issue that the Arbitral Tribunal had no jurisdiction to decide the dispute referred to it.[61]

Doubt as to existence of arbitration agreement

Under Section 7, Arbitration and Conciliation Act, 1996, if the contract is in writing and reference is made to a document containing an arbitration clause as a part of the transaction, it would mean that the arbitration agreement is a part of the contract. Therefore, in a matter where there has been some transaction between the parties and the existence of the arbitration agreement is in challenge, the proper course for the parties is to thrash out such a question under Section 16 of the Act and not under Section 11 of the Act.[62]

It is permissible under Section 11 of the Act to decide a question as to the existence or otherwise of the arbitration agreement, but when the correspondence or exchange of documents between the parties is not clear as to the existence or non-existence of an arbitration agreement in terms of Section 7 of the Act, the appropriate course would be that the arbitrator should decide such a question under Section 16 of the Act rather than the Chief Justice of India or his nominee under Section 11 of the Act.[63]

Existence of arbitration agreement—Decision by the arbitrator

It is clear from Section 33 of the 1940 Arbitration Act that any question as to the "existence" of the arbitration agreement was to be decided only by application to the court and not by the arbitrator. This disability on the part of the arbitrator has now been removed by Section 16, Arbitration and Conciliation Act, 1996. Now Section 16 has conferred power on the Arbitral Tribunal to decide there is in "existence" an arbitration clause. However, language of Section 16 of the new Act shows that the said provision is only an enabling one, which, unlike Section 33 in the old Act of 1940, now permits the Arbitral Tribunal to decide a question relating to the "existence" of the arbitration clause. This section corresponds to Article 16 of the UNCITRAL Model Law and Article 21 of the UNCITRAL Arbitration Rules. While Article 16 of the Model Law says that the Arbitral Tribunal may rule on its own jurisdiction, Article 21 of the Rules states that the "Arbitral Tribunal shall have the power to rule" on these questions. Such powers given to the Arbitral Tribunal are also referred to as "Kompetenz".[64]

61. *Subhash Projects and Mktg. Ltd.* v. *Assam Urban Water Supply and Sewerage Board*, 2019 SCC OnLine Gau 3510: (2019) 5 Gau LR 625.
62. *Nimet Resources Inc.* v. *Essar Steels Ltd.*, (2000) 7 SCC 497.
63. *Ibid.*
64. *Wellington Associates Ltd.* v. *Kirit Mehta*, (2000) 4 SCC 272.

Res judicata

Where arbitrability of the issue is decided in proceedings for appointment of the arbitrator and the said determination has attained finality, the jurisdiction of the arbitrator in respect of the said issue cannot be challenged in the arbitration proceedings themselves, and the principle of res judicata is attracted.[65]

Whether contract has been discharged by performance or by accord and satisfaction not vitiated by fraud/undue influence/coercion

If the respondent before the Arbitral Tribunal contends that the contract has been discharged by reason of the claimant accepting the payment made by the respondent in full and final settlement, and if the claimant counters it by contending that the discharge order was extracted from him by practicing fraud, undue influence or coercion, the Arbitral Tribunal shall decide whether the discharge of the contract was vitiated by any circumstance which renders the contract voidable at the instance of the claimant. If the Arbitral Tribunal comes to the conclusion that there was valid discharge by voluntary execution of discharge, it will refuse to examine the claim on merits and reject the claim as not maintainable. On the other hand if the Arbitral Tribunal comes to the conclusion that the such discharge of contract was vitiated by any circumstance which rendered it void, it will ignore the same and proceed to decide the claim on merits.[66]

Mortgage cases

If the arbitrator has to adjudicate issues relating to a mortgage, he would also have jurisdiction to adjudicate the claims for the amounts due by a mortgagee for wrongful occupation of the mortgaged property after the mortgagee's right to continue in possession thereof ceases. The monetary claims would form a part of and represent the rights of the parties in the property itself.[67]

Jurisdiction of arbitrator—Lease and licence agreement [S. 16(2)]

Dispute arose between the licensor and licensee for refund of security deposit. Peaceful possession of licensed premises was already handed over to the licensor. Demand of licence fee at enhanced rate by the licensor could

65. *Food Corporation of India* v. *A.M. Ahmed & Co.*, (2006) 13 SCC 779.
66. *National Insurance Co. Ltd.* v. *Boghara Polyfab (P) Ltd.*, (2009) 1 SCC 267; *NTPC Ltd.* v. *Siemens Atkeingesellschaft*, (2007) 4 SCC 451.
67. *Veena* v. *Seth Industries Ltd.*, 2010 SCC OnLine Bom 1707: (2011) 2 Mah LJ 226.

be adjusted against security deposit and balance security deposit could be paid to the licensee. The dispute did not relate to recovery of possession. Provisions of Section 41, Presidency Small Cause Courts Act, 1882 were not attracted. Arbitrator has jurisdiction to decide the said dispute.[68]

"Shall" [S. 16(5)]

Under Section 16(5), the Arbitral Tribunal has the obligation to decide the plea referred to in Section 16(2) or (3) and where it rejects the plea, it could continue with arbitral proceedings and make the award.[69]

Objection as to constitution of Arbitral Tribunal—Power of Arbitral Tribunal to decide

All objections as to the constitution of the Arbitral Tribunal can be gone into by the arbitrator. The Supreme Court confirmed the nominations of arbitrators made by the applicants and non-applicants and directed the Arbitral Tribunal to proceed with the matter.[70]

Objection as to territorial jurisdiction

In the application for setting aside the award of the Arbitral Tribunal, the petitioner raised an objection as to territorial jurisdiction in a petition under Section 34 of the Act and had not raised any such objection before the Arbitral Tribunal. The petitioner had fully participated in the proceedings before the arbitrator and had not raised any objection within the time limit specified under Section 16(2). It was held that the petitioner cannot be allowed to raise any such objection directly under Section 34.[71]

Powers of arbitrator in relation to company—Companies Act, 1956

It is true that the arbitrator would have no power to order for winding up of a company as such power is conferred on and vested with the court as envisaged under the Companies Act. But in terms of the arbitration agreement, the court can always find and adjudicate as to whether or not a company is functional, and if it was not functional, in that event it could

68. *A.S. Patel Trust* v. *Wall Street Finance Ltd.*, 2019 SCC OnLine Bom 1328: (2020) 1 Mah LJ 381.
69. *NTPC Ltd.* v. *Siemens Atkeingesellschaft*, (2007) 4 SCC 451.
70. *Ruchi Strips & Alloys Ltd.* v. *Tata South East Asia Ltd.*, (2004) 13 SCC 470. S. 16(1) opens with words "the arbitral tribunal may rule on its own jurisdiction". *Secur Industries Ltd.* v. *Godrej & Boyce Mfg. Co. Ltd.*, (2004) 3 SCC 447; *Kvaerner Cementation India Ltd.* v. *Bajranglal Agarwal*, (2012) 5 SCC 214.
71. *Engg. Projects India Ltd.* v. *Balaji Projects*, 2021 SCC OnLine Mad 409.

always find out the nature and status of its assets and can also issue direction and pass orders regarding its dues and also for taking recourse to appropriate remedy.[72]

Section 16, Arbitration and Conciliation Act, 1996 and Section 10-A, Industrial Disputes Act, 1947

The provisions of Section 10-A, Industrial Disputes Act, 1947 are entirely different from the provisions of Section 16 of the 1996 Act.[73]

Joinder/striking off parties to arbitration—Forum competent

The forum competent to determine joinder/striking off parties to arbitration is the arbitrator and not the Chief Justice making reference under Section 11.[74]

Proceedings before Uttar Pradesh Industry Facilitation Council under Interest on Delayed Payments to Small Scale and Ancillary Industrial Undertakings Act, 1993

The proceedings pending before the Uttar Pradesh Industry Facilitation Council set up under the Industrial Act are proceedings under the Arbitration and Conciliation Act, 1996. The validity of the proceedings or whether the giving of notice under Section 21 of the 1996 Act is a condition precedent for the exercise of jurisdiction by the Council are questions to be decided by the Council. The court has no jurisdiction to stay proceedings before the Council.[75]

Waiver of right to object to the composition of Arbitral Tribunal

Unless an objection as to the composition of the Arbitral Tribunal is made before the Arbitral Tribunal within the time prescribed under Section 16(2), there would be deemed waiver of objection under Section 4. Sections 10 and 16 read together clearly indicate that the parties may derogate from the provisions of Section 10. Where the parties have appointed two arbitrators to resolve their differences, had participated in the arbitral proceedings and an award was then passed, the objection raised by the respondents that arbitration by two arbitrators was not permitted under Section 10 and, therefore, the award was unenforceable and not binding would be deemed to have been waived. Section 34 does not permit challenge to an arbitral award merely on the ground that the composition of the Arbitral Tribunal was in

72. *Everest Holding Ltd.* v. *Shyam Kumar Shrivastava*, (2008) 16 SCC 774.
73. *Secur Industries Ltd.* v. *Godrej & Boyce Mfg. Co. Ltd.*, (2004) 3 SCC 447.
74. *BHEL* v. *Bayer Shipping and Trading Ltd.*, (2005) 12 SCC 188.
75. *Secur Industries Ltd.* v. *Godrej & Boyce Mfg. Co. Ltd.*, (2004) 3 SCC 447.

conflict with the provisions of Part I of the Act. The respondents had not raised an objection as to the composition of the tribunal as provided under Section 16; they were held to have waived their right to object. The order of the High Court setting aside the award was reversed.[76]

Locus standi to challenge the jurisdiction of arbitrator

A challenge made to the jurisdiction of an arbitrator by the opposite party before filing its statement of defence is valid. The mere fact that till then it had participated in the arbitration proceedings did not tantamount to its acceptance of, and would not stop it from challenging the arbitrator's jurisdiction.[77]

Appeal

A decision taken thereupon by the arbitrator would be the subject-matter of challenge under Section 34 of the Act. In the event the arbitrator opined that he had no jurisdiction in relation thereto, an appeal thereagainst is provided for under Section 37 of the Act.[78]

When the issue of jurisdiction is raised before an Arbitral Tribunal and it ruled that it has jurisdiction, arbitral proceedings would continue and culminate into an award. The decision of jurisdiction can be challenged when the final award is challenged under Section 34. When the Arbitral Tribunal rules that it has no jurisdiction, an appeal under Section 37 would lie against that order.[79]

Section 16 stipulates that where the tribunal rejects a plea of a lack of jurisdiction, it must continue with the arbitral proceedings and make an award and the remedy of a challenge to the award would lie under Section 34. However, if the Arbitral Tribunal accepts a plea that it lacks jurisdiction, the order of the tribunal is amenable to a challenge in appeal under Section 37(2)(*a*). In the exercise of the appellate jurisdiction, the court must have due deference to the grounds which have weighed with the tribunal in holding that it lacks jurisdiction having regard to the object and spirit underlying the statute which entrusts the Arbitral Tribunal with the power to rule on its own jurisdiction. The decision of the tribunal that it lacks jurisdiction is not conclusive because it is subject to an appellate remedy under Section 37(2)(*a*). However, in the exercise of this appellate power, the

76. *Narayan Prasad Lohia* v. *Nikunj Kumar Lohia*, (2002) 3 SCC 572.
77. *Travancore Devaswom Board* v. *Panchamy Pack (P) Ltd.*, (2004) 13 SCC 510.
78. *McDermott International Inc.* v. *Burn Standard Co. Ltd.*, (2006) 11 SCC 181; *Centrotrade Minerals & Metals Inc.* v. *Hindustan Copper Ltd.*, (2006) 11 SCC 245; *M.S. Commercial* v. *Calicut Engg. Works Ltd.*, (2004) 10 SCC 656.
79. *Shailendra Bhadauria* v. *Matrix Partners India Investment*, 2019 SCC OnLine Bom 1.

court must be mindful of the fact that the statute has entrusted the Arbitral Tribunal with the power to rule on its own jurisdiction with the purpose of facilitating the efficacy of arbitration as an institutional mechanism for the resolution of disputes.[80]

Writ petition

An application was filed against the District Judge against the partial award under Section 16, Arbitration and Conciliation Act. A writ petition against the order of the District Judge was not maintainable.[81]

Intervention by the High Court with orders passed by the Arbitral Tribunals in exercise of powers under Article 227 of the Constitution is not permissible.[82]

INTERIM MEASURES ORDERED BY ARBITRAL TRIBUNAL [S. 17]

[83][**17.** *Interim measures ordered by arbitral tribunal.*—(1) A party may, during the arbitral proceedings [84][* * *], apply to the arbitral tribunal—

(*i*) for the appointment of a guardian for a minor or person of unsound mind for the purposes of arbitral proceedings; or

(*ii*) for an interim measure of protection in respect of any of the following matters, namely—

(*a*) the preservation, interim custody or sale of any goods which are the subject-matter of the arbitration agreement;

(*b*) securing the amount in dispute in the arbitration;

(*c*) the detention, preservation or inspection of any property or thing which is the subject-matter of the dispute in arbitration, or as to which any question may arise therein and authorising for any of the aforesaid purposes any person to enter upon any land or building in the possession of any party, or authorising any samples to be taken,

---

80. *ONGC Ltd.* v. *Discovery Enterprises (P) Ltd.*, (2022) 8 SCC 42.

81. *SBP & Co.* v. *Patel Engg. Ltd.*, (2005) 8 SCC 618; *Sterling Industries* v. *Jayprakash Associates Ltd.*, (2021) 18 SCC 367.

82. *CNG Trading Co. (P) Ltd.* v. *H.P. SEB Ltd.*, 2017 SCC OnLine HP 49.

83. *Subs.* by Act 3 of 2016, S. 10 (w.r.e.f. 23-10-2015). Prior to substitution it read as:

"17. *Interim measures ordered by arbitral tribunal.*—(1) Unless otherwise agreed by the parties, the arbitral tribunal may, at the request of a party, order a party to take any interim measure of protection as the arbitral tribunal may consider necessary in respect of the subject-matter of the dispute.

(2) The arbitral tribunal may require a party to provide appropriate security in connection with a measure ordered under sub-section (1)."

84. *Omitted* by Act 33 of 2019, S. 4 (w.e.f. 30-8-2019). Prior to omission it read as:

"or at any time after the making of the arbitral award but before it is enforced in accordance with Section 36".

or any observation to be made, or experiment to be tried, which may be necessary or expedient for the purpose of obtaining full information or evidence;

(*d*) interim injunction or the appointment of a receiver;

(*e*) such other interim measure of protection as may appear to the arbitral tribunal to be just and convenient, and the arbitral tribunal shall have the same power for making orders, as the court has for the purpose of, and in relation to, any proceedings before it.

(2) Subject to any orders passed in an appeal under Section 37, any order issued by the arbitral tribunal under this section shall be deemed to be an order of the court for all purposes and shall be enforceable under the Code of Civil Procedure, 1908 (5 of 1908), in the same manner as if it were an order of the court.]

COMMENTS

Corresponding old law

Section 17 is a new; the Arbitration Act, 1940 did not confer any specific powers on arbitrators to take interim measures. It was, however, open to the parties to confer such powers on arbitrators.

UNCITRAL Model Law

Article 17. *Power of arbitral tribunal to order interim measures*

(1) Unless otherwise agreed by the parties, the arbitral tribunal may, at the request of a party, grant interim measures.

(2) An interim measure is any temporary measure, whether in the form of an award or in another form, by which, at any time prior to the issuance of the award by which the dispute is finally decided, the arbitral tribunal orders a party to:

(*a*) Maintain or restore the status quo pending determination of the dispute;

(*b*) Take action that would prevent, or refrain from taking action that is likely to cause, current or imminent harm or prejudice to the arbitral process itself;

(*c*) Provide a means of preserving assets out of which a subsequent award may be satisfied; or

(*d*) Preserve evidence that may be relevant and material to the resolution of the dispute.

Legislative changes

Arbitration and Conciliation (Amendment) Act, 2015 (3 of 2016)

For Section 17 of the principal Act, the following section shall be *substituted*, namely:

17. *Interim measures ordered by arbitral tribunal.*— (1) A party may, during the arbitral proceedings or at any time after the making of the arbitral award but before it is enforced in accordance with Section 36, apply to the arbitral tribunal—

(*i*) for the appointment of a guardian for a minor or person of unsound mind for the purposes of arbitral proceedings; or

(*ii*) for an interim measure of protection in respect of any of the following matters, namely—

(*a*) the preservation, interim custody or sale of any goods which are the subject-matter of the arbitration agreement;

(*b*) securing the amount in dispute in the arbitration;

(*c*) the detention, preservation or inspection of any property or thing which is the subject-matter of the dispute in arbitration, or as to which any question may arise therein and authorising for any of the aforesaid purposes any person to enter upon any land or building in the possession of any party, or authorising any samples to be taken, or any observation to be made, or experiment to be tried, which may be necessary or expedient for the purpose of obtaining full information or evidence;

(*d*) interim injunction or the appointment of a receiver;

(*e*) such other interim measure of protection as may appear to the arbitral tribunal to be just and convenient, and the arbitral tribunal shall have the same power for making orders, as the court has for the purpose of, and in relation to, any proceedings before it.

(2) Subject to any orders passed in an appeal under Section 37, any order issued by the arbitral tribunal under this section shall be deemed to be an order of the court for all purposes and shall be enforceable under the Code of Civil Procedure, 1908 (5 of 1908), in the same manner as if it were an order of the Court.

Objects and reasons

Clause 10 of the Bill seeks to amend Section 17 of the principal Act to prove that the Arbitral Tribunal shall have the power to grant all kinds of interim measures that the court is empowered to grant under Section 9. It further provides that such interim measures can be granted by the Arbitral Tribunal during the arbitral proceedings or at any time after making the arbitral award but before it is enforced under Section 36. Sub-section (2) is amended to provide that any order issued by the Arbitral Tribunal for the grant of interim measures shall be deemed to be an order of the court for all purposes and shall be enforceable under the CPC in the same order of the court.

Section 17 has been extensively amended by Amendment Act 3 of 2016. Section 17 has been amended to provide that the Arbitral Tribunal shall have the power to pass all kinds of interim measures for the preservation, interim custody or sale of goods which are the subject-matter of the arbitration agreement, for securing the amount in dispute in arbitration, interim injunction, appointment of receiver, etc.

Section 17(2) provides that any order passed by the Arbitral Tribunal for the grant of interim measures shall be deemed to be an order of the court for all purposes and shall be enforceable under the CPC in the same manner as if it were an order of the court.

In Section 17 of the principal Act, in sub-section (1), the words and figures "or at any time after the making of the arbitral award but before it is enforced in accordance with Section 36" shall be omitted.

Scope and application

Section 17 contains provisions for passing of interim measures which can be passed by the Arbitral Tribunal on the application filed by a party to arbitral proceedings. This section is similar to Section 9 which provides for passing of interim measures/order to be passed by the court. Section 17 describes powers of the Arbitral Tribunal only with respect to the subject-matter of dispute, while Section 9 does not contemplate any such restriction.[85]

The power of the Arbitral Tribunal under Section 17 and the power of the court under Section 9, Arbitration and Conciliation Act, 1996 Act are coextensive and coequal in character. The power of the Arbitral Tribunal for making an order under Section 17 is the same as the court's power in relation to proceedings before it. The Arbitral Tribunal, exercising jurisdiction under Section 17, is required to bear in mind the provisions of Orders 38 and 39 CPC.[86]

Views expressed by arbitrators while deciding applications under Section 17 are interlocutory. They are not final expressions of opinion on the merits of the case. They are subject to modification or review at the stage of final award. They do not, in most cause, irreparably prejudice either party to the arbitration. Section 17 like Section 9 is intended to be a protective

---

85. *Hairtha Finance Ltd.* v. *ATV Projects India Ltd.*, 2003 SCC OnLine Mad 265: (2003) 2 CTC 226.
86. *Augmont Gold (P) Ltd.* v. *One97 Communication Ltd.*, (2021) 4 HCC (Del) 642.

measure, to preserve the sanctity of the arbitral process. The pre-eminent consideration which weighs with the arbitrator while examining a Section 17 application is the necessity to preserve the arbitral process and ensure that the parties before it are placed on an equitable scale.[87]

The lease was terminated. A suit was filed for payment of rent. Lessee was directed to pay the entire amount of rent after excluding the period of lockdown. The amount for the period of lockdown will be subject to the outcome of the arbitration proceedings.[88]

Interim orders can be passed by arbitrator

Under Section 17, Arbitration and Conciliation Act, 1996, interim orders can be passed by the arbitrator.[89] When the proceedings are pending before the Arbitral Tribunal, the tribunal has wide powers to pass the interim order.[90]

The two conditions that come into play for passing an interim measure or protection are:

1. there should not be an exclusion by mutual agreement between the parties and such an order of protection must have nexus with the subject-matter of the dispute; and
2. a condition can be attached to the said order and such a direction is discretionary.[91]

"Measures of protection" contemplated under Section 17 has to be a measure of protection, *i.e.* with a view to preserve the situation prevailing and to keep property available to answer final adjudication as and when the final order is passed by the arbitrator. The arbitrator issued directions to Nagpur Improvement Trust to issue necessary no-objection certificate in favour of Contractor to enable him to mortgage the project to obtain financial assistance. The interim order issued was found not covered by Section 17, Arbitration and Conciliation Act, 1996 and was set aside.[92]

An order for securing the subject-matter of arbitral proceedings, under Section 17(1)(*ii*)(*b*), Arbitration and Conciliation Act, 1996, can be passed only where there is positive evidence to indicate that if the amount is not secured, the arbitral proceedings would be frustrated. This in turn requires

87. *World Window Infrastructure (P) Ltd.* v. *Central Warehousing Corpn.*, (2021) 3 HCC (Del) 731.
88. *Evergreen Land Mark (P) Ltd.* v. *John Tinson & Co. (P) Ltd.*, (2022) 7 SCC 757.
89. *GAIL (I) Ltd.* v. *Bal Kishan Agarwal Glass Industries Ltd.*, (2008) 8 SCC 161.
90. *NHAI* v. *China Coal Construction Group Corpn.*, 2006 SCC OnLine Del 115: (2006) 87 DRJ 225.
91. *Asian Electronics Ltd.* v. *M.P. SEB*, 2007 SCC OnLine MP 179: (2007) 3 MP LJ 203.
92. *Indo Pacific Software & Entertainment Ltd.* v. *Nagpur Improvement Trust*, 2010 SCC OnLine Bom 1745: (2011) 1 Mah LJ 869.

the applicant seeking Section 17(1)(*ii*)(*b*) order to demonstrate that the respondent is in such financially impecunious circumstances as would frustrate the final arbitral award, even if it were to be passed in the applicant's favour. Else the applicant has to demonstrate that the respondent is dissipating its assets with a view to frustrate the arbitral proceedings and the awaited award. No such case has even been pleaded by the appellant in this case. It can hardly be said that the respondent is in such straitened circumstances as would justify an order for security under Section 17(1)(*ii*)(*b*).[93]

The Arbitral Tribunal has no jurisdiction and authority to interfere with the order and action taken by the court receiver to any aspect of the matter even by consent or without consent.[94]

Mere allegation of fraud is not enough to issue an injunction against the invocation of bank guarantee. As there was no possibility of the respondents suffering any irreparable injury, there was no justification for making an order restraining the appellant-firm invoking the bank guarantee; the order was set aside.[95]

Sections 17 and 9

Section 9 provides for taking of interim measures by the court in certain matters, while Section 17 provides for taking of interim measures in respect of the subject-matter of the dispute by the Arbitral Tribunal. The power available to the Arbitral Tribunal is narrower than that vested in the court under Section 9. The exercise of power by the court under Section 9 is in no way controlled by the power exercisable by the Arbitral Tribunal under Section 17. Even assuming that the power under Section 17 to direct interim measures is in certain respects and limited to certain area concurrent with the power vested in the court under Section 9, the very fact that the Arbitral Tribunal could also be approached for a proper interim measure would not deprive the civil court or its jurisdiction under Section 9 to make an appropriate direction in an appropriate case brought before it.[96]

The court under Section 9 or the Arbitral Tribunal under Section 17 is also empowered to grant interim protection where any possibility of the arbitral proceedings being frustrated is found to exist, whether such frustration be

93. *World Window Infrastructure (P) Ltd.* v. *Central Warehousing Corpn.*, (2021) 3 HCC (Del) 731.
94. *Radio Restaurant* v. *Jabbir Gulam Rasool Jamal*, 2011 SCC OnLine Bom 1246: (2012) 4 Mah LJ 232.
95. *ONGC Ltd.* v. *Jagson International Ltd.*, 2005 SCC OnLine Bom 814: (2005) 3 Mah LJ 1141.
96. *Yenepoya Minerals & Granites Ltd.* v. *Maharastra Apex Corpn. Ltd.*, 2004 SCC OnLine Kar 2: ILR 2004 Kar 1008; *Hairtha Finance Ltd.* v. *ATV Projects India Ltd.*, 2003 SCC OnLine Mad 265: (2003) 2 CTC 226.

before the arbitral process is initiated, during the arbitral process or even after the passing of the award. If, therefore, before a statement of claim is filed, the situation that presents itself is such that interim protection has to be granted, to ensure the preservation of the arbitral process, the court under Section 9 and the Arbitral Tribunal under Section 17 is empowered to grant such protection. In view of this peculiar dispensation, unique to arbitration, the filing of statement of claim under Section 23 cannot be treated as a *sine qua non* for the maintainability of an application for interim protection under Section 17.[97]

The existence of power under Section 17 with the Arbitral Tribunal would not deny to the civil court the power to exercise its jurisdiction under Section 9 of the Act.[98]

Calling of records

Section 17 does not prescribe any scope for calling any records from the opposite party. An appeal against the order of rejection is not maintainable.[99]

Interim measures, restraint orders against third party

The Arbitral Tribunal passed an order under Section 17 restraining the claimants and their heirs from alienating, encumbering, transferring any of their assets without the permission of the Arbitral Tribunal. The order of the tribunal was upheld by the High Court. It was held that the appellant's secured creditors were not parties before the Arbitral Tribunal, and their rights were affected by the order. The Arbitral Tribunal has no jurisdiction to affect the rights and remedies of the third-party secured creditors in the course of determining the disputes pending before it. The impugned orders were set aside.[100]

Interim award on admitted/undisputed facts

The power of the Arbitral Tribunal to pass interim awards on the basis of apparent and explicit admissions by a party is undisputed. However, the admission has to be specific and categorical. The relief based upon disputed admission, that too without trial, cannot be permitted on the basis of piecemeal consideration of a document.[101]

97. *Sanjay Arora* v. *Rajan Chadha*, (2021) 3 HCC (Del) 654.
98. *Yenepoya Minerals & Granites Ltd.* v. *Maharastra Apex Corpn. Ltd.*, 2004 SCC OnLine Kar 2: ILR 2004 Kar 1008.
99. *Pennar Aluminium Co. Ltd.* v. *National Aluminium Co. Ltd.*, 2019 SCC OnLine Ori 370.
100. *SBI* v. *Ericsson (India) (P) Ltd.*, (2018) 16 SCC 617.
101. *Vijay Shukla* v. *Career Launcher Infrastructure (P) Ltd.*, (2021) 4 HCC (Del) 72.

Emergency award

There is nothing in the Arbitration and Conciliation Act, 1996 that prohibits contracting parties from agreeing to a provision providing for an award being made by an Emergency Arbitrator. Further, sections of the Arbitration and Conciliation Act, 1996 which speak of party autonomy in choosing to be governed by institutional rules make it clear that the said rules would apply to govern the rights between the parties. An Emergency Arbitrator's "award", *i.e.* order, would undoubtedly be an order which furthers the objectives to decongest the court system and to give the parties urgent interim relief in cases which deserve such relief. In arbitral proceedings with their juridical seat in India, Amazon initiated arbitration proceedings and filed an application seeking emergency interim relief under applicable Arbitration Rules of the Singapore International Arbitration Centre (SIAC Rules), asking for injunctions against certain transactions and an "award" was delivered by an Emergency Arbitrator. Held, full party autonomy is given by the Arbitration and Conciliation Act, 1996 to have a dispute decided in accordance with institutional rules which can include Emergency Arbitrators delivering interim orders, described as "awards". No appeal lies under Section 37, Arbitration and Conciliation Act, 1996 against an order of enforcement of an Emergency Arbitrator's order made under Section 17(2), Arbitration and Conciliation Act, 1996.[102]

Interim award

Interim award can be passed by the arbitrator after the commencement of arbitration, after notice is served on the respondent as provided under Section 21, Arbitration and Conciliation Act, 1996.[103]

Enforcement of interim orders [S. 17(2)]

Section 17(2) has been introduced by the 2015 Amendment. Section 17(2) has been added so that the cumbersome procedure of an Arbitral Tribunal having to apply every time to the High Court for contempt of its orders would no longer be necessary. Therefore, now such orders are deemed to be orders of the court for all purposes and shall be enforced under the CPC in the same manner as if they were the orders of the court.[104]

---

102. *Amazon.Com NV Investment Holdings LLC* v. *Future Retail Ltd.*, (2022) 1 SCC 209.
103. *Hedge Finance (P) Ltd.* v. *Bijish Joseph*, 2022 SCC OnLine Ker 11064.
104. *Alka Chandewar* v. *Shamshul Ishrar Khan*, (2017) 16 SCC 119.

Furnishing of security

The Arbitral Tribunal does not have power to order furnishing of security at interlocutory stage, without prima facie determination as to the likelihood of success of the counterclaim even on the principles analogous to those governing the power of court under Section 9 of the Act. Grant of interim relief under Section 17 is required to be preceded by determination that the party seeking interim relief has a prima facie case.[105]

The power to direct furnishing of security in connection with the subject-matter of the arbitral dispute is vested in the Arbitral Tribunal even under the pre-amended Section 17, by virtue of sub-section (2). The law relating to the power to direct furnishing of security, as a measure of interim protection, as enunciated in the pre-amended regime, continues to apply to that extent, even after Section 17 stands amended with effect from 23 October 2015. Post amendment, Section 17(1)(*ii*)(*b*) specifically empowers the Arbitral Tribunal to secure the amount in dispute in the arbitration.[106]

The court though not constrained by similar provision in Order 38 Rule 5, yet it is supposed to keep in mind the broad principles of this provision.[107]

Arbitrator's order to pay stamp duty—Not executable

Order of the arbitrator to pay stamp duty under Section 17 of the Act of 1996 does not fall within the expression "award" under Article 11, Karnataka Stamp Act, 1957, is interim order, and hence, not executable.[108]

Gujarat Public Works Contracts Disputes Arbitration Tribunal Act, 1992 (4 of 1992)

The powers vested in the Arbitral Tribunal in terms of Section 17, Arbitration and Conciliation Act can be exercised by the tribunal constituted under the Gujarat Act because there is no inconsistency in these two Acts as far as the grant of interim relief is concerned. This power is already vested in the tribunal under the Gujarat Act and Section 17, Arbitration and Conciliation Act compliments these powers and, therefore, it cannot be said that the provisions of Section 17, Arbitration and Conciliation Act are inconsistent with the Gujarat Act.[109]

---

105. *Intertoll Ics Cecons O & M Co. (P) Ltd.* v. *NHAI*, 2013 SCC OnLine Del 447: (2013) 135 DRJ 160.
106. *Augmont Gold (P) Ltd.* v. *One97 Communication Ltd.*, (2021) 4 HCC (Del) 642.
107. *Ibid.*
108. *Shaila Mathias* v. *Nitesh Estates Ltd.*, 2019 SCC OnLine Kar 3040: ILR 2019 Kar 887.
109. *State of Gujarat* v. *Amber Builders*, (2020) 2 SCC 540.

Appeal

An appeal lies against an order granting or refusing to grant an interim measure under Section 17. [S. 37(2) cl. (*b*)]. An order passed under Section 17(1) of the Act by the Arbitral Tribunal is appealable under Section 37(2)(*b*) of the Act. Enforcement of an order of the Arbitral Tribunal by the court under Section 17(2) of the Act is subject to any orders passed in an appeal under Section 37 of the Act.[110] The petitioner did not file an appeal under Section 37(2)(*b*) against the order passed by the Arbitral Tribunal; the order being unchallenged became enforceable under Section 17(2) of the Act. Refusal to restore possession of the vehicle to the petitioner was proper.[111]

An application for seeking inspection, interrogation filed by a party does not fall under Section 17 of the Act, and an appeal under Section 37 is not maintainable.[112]

The scope of interference in an appeal, with the exercise of such discretion, is quite limited. The court cannot ordinarily interfere with the order on the ground that, in its estimation, the urgency was not such as would justify the passing of the impugned order. If, no doubt, the Arbitral Tribunal has relied on irrelevant or inadmissible material to return a finding of urgency, or if the Arbitral Tribunal has passed the interlocutory protective order without returning any finding of urgency, the court may interfere as such exercise borders on perversity. Where, however, the Arbitral Tribunal has returned a finding of urgency, supported by factual material, then, if the material is not found to be incorrect or irrelevant, the question of whether the material denotes urgency of a degree sufficient to grant interim protection is, essentially, a matter relating to the subjective satisfaction of the tribunal. The court does not substitute its subjective satisfaction for that of the tribunal.[113]

Interim order—Appeal—Period of limitation

The period of limitation for filing appeal against the interim order passed by the Arbitral Tribunal is 90 days from the date of the order.[114]

---

110. *Manoj C.J.* v. *Shriram Transport Finance Co. Ltd.*, 2020 SCC OnLine Ker 4241: (2020) 5 KLT 775.
111. *Ibid.*
112. *Areeb Rolling Mills (P) Ltd.* v. *NKGSB Coop. Bank Ltd.*, 2013 SCC OnLine Bom 14: (2013) 2 Mah LJ 424.
113. *Sanjay Arora* v. *Rajan Chadha*, (2021) 3 HCC (Del) 654.
114. *Jagat Singh Chopra* v. *Raj Singh Chopra*, 2018 SCC OnLine Cal 5310: (2018) 2 Cal LT 534.

CHAPTER V
Conduct of Arbitral Proceedings

EQUAL TREATMENT OF PARTIES [S. 18]

18. *Equal treatment of parties.*—The parties shall be treated with equality and each party shall be given a full opportunity to present his case.

COMMENTS

Corresponding old law

Section 18 is new and did not exist in the Arbitration Act, 1940. There was no specific provision in the Arbitration Act, 1940 corresponding to Section 18, but such provisions were applicable as principles of natural justice.

UNCITRAL Model Law

Article 18. *Equal treatment of parties*

The parties shall be treated with equality and each party shall be given a full opportunity of presenting his case.

Scope and application

Section 18 provides that the parties to arbitration proceedings shall be treated with equality by the arbitrator/Arbitral Tribunal, and each party shall be given a full opportunity to present its case. This is the basic and fundamental principle of equal trial.

Section 18 by itself is not a ground to challenge the award; challenge to award can be only under Section 34(2).[1]

Merely because a written submission is not served in advance on the other side, it would not be possible to infer that there is denial of equal treatment to the parties. This could hardly be said to be a lapse on the part of the

1. *Godrej Properties & Investments Ltd.* v. *Tripura Construction*, 2003 SCC OnLine Bom 13: (2003) 2 Mah LJ 306.

arbitrator so as to set aside the award under Section 34(2)(*a*)(*v*) of the 1996 Act.[2]

"Full opportunity to present his case" [S. 18(1)]

The expression "full opportunity to present his case" in Section 18(1) means full opportunity to be given to both parties before the arbitrator.[3] Making an application for leading oral evidence cannot be allowed at any stage of the proceedings. Rejection of application for leading oral evidence filed at the stage of conclusion of the final arguments in the case just to delay the proceedings was held proper.[4]

Where the arbitrator directed the parties to file documents but did not give opportunity to the parties to make their respective submissions on those added documents, the award of the arbitrator was set aside for not complying with the principles of natural justice or *ex aequo et bono* or *amiable compositeur.*[5]

Bias on part of arbitrator

The claimant before the arbitrator was unable to produce a document to prove his claim. The arbitrator did not commence the proceedings and waited for the claimant to produce the document. It was held that the arbitrator ought not to have acted as agent of the claimant, and ought to have entered reference and issued notice to both the parties; bias on the part of the arbitrator was established.[6]

Counter claims—Jurisdiction of arbitrator

The arbitrator is required not only to decide counterclaim(s), but is also required to assign reasons for the decision.[7]

2. *Viraj Holdings* v. *Motilal Oswal Securities (P) Ltd.*, 2002 SCC OnLine Bom 558: (2002) 4 Mah LJ 65.
3. *Pradyuman Kumar Sharma* v. *Jays Agar M. Sancheti*, 2013 SCC OnLine Bom 453: (2013) 5 Mah LJ 86.
4. *Ibid.*
5. *Networth Stock Broking Ltd.* v. *Subhasis Panda*, 2009 SCC OnLine Bom 1680: (2010) 1 Mah LJ 646.
6. *Dhandapani Finance Ltd.* v. *B.T. Ravi*, 2013 SCC OnLine Mad 1268: (2013) 3 CTC 410.
7. *Jeypore Sugar Co. Ltd.* v. *Laxmi Organic Industries Ltd.*, 2015 SCC OnLine Mad 13440.

DETERMINATION OF RULES OF PROCEDURE [S. 19]

19. *Determination of rules of procedure.*—(1) The arbitral tribunal shall not be bound by the Code of Civil Procedure, 1908 (5 of 1908) or the Indian Evidence Act, 1872 (1 of 1872).

(2) Subject to this Part, the parties are free to agree on the procedure to be followed by the arbitral tribunal in conducting its proceedings.

(3) Failing any agreement referred to in sub-section (2), the arbitral tribunal may, subject to this Part, conduct the proceedings in the manner it considers appropriate.

(4) The power of the arbitral tribunal under sub-section (3) includes the power to determine the admissibility, relevance, materiality and weight of any evidence.

COMMENTS

Corresponding old law

Section 19 is new and did not find place in the Arbitration Act, 1940.

UNCITRAL Model Law

Article 19. *Determination of rules of procedure*

(1) Subject to the provisions of this Law, the parties are free to agree on the procedure to be followed by the arbitral tribunal in conducting the proceedings.

(2) Failing such agreement, the arbitral tribunal may, subject to the provisions of this Law, conduct the arbitration in such manner as it considers appropriate. The power conferred upon the arbitral tribunal includes the power to determine the admissibility, relevance, materiality and weight of any evidence.

Scope and application

Section 19 provides that the Arbitrator Tribunal shall not be bound by the CPC nor by the Evidence Act, 1872. The parties are free to agree on the procedure to be followed by the Arbitral Tribunal in conducting its proceedings. Where the parties fail to arrive at such agreement, the Arbitral Tribunal shall conduct the proceedings in the manner it considers appropriate. The Arbitral Tribunal shall have the power to determine the admissibility, relevance, materiality and weight of any evidence. The basic purpose of this section is that the arbitration proceedings are decided/conducted expeditiously being unhampered by the technical rules of CPC and the Evidence Act.

Enquiry before the arbitrator suffers from shortcomings and deficiencies. Rules of procedure and evidence are not binding on proceedings before the arbitrator.[8]

An Arbitral Tribunal is not a court; any lacuna in the procedure does not vitiate the award unless it is in breach of the principles of natural justice, equity, fair play by the aggrieved parties. The parties, by consent, may adopt their own procedure for conducting arbitration.[9] Basic parameters of arbitration proceedings being stated, where the parties agree on a particular procedure to be followed by the Arbitral Tribunal, all are bound to follow the same but in its absence, the Arbitral Tribunal is bound to conduct the proceeding in the manner it considers appropriate.[10] The claim must be raised within limitation; by consent of the parties, the issue with regard to limitation cannot be overlooked.[11]

Where the parties before the Arbitral Tribunal had agreed on the procedure to be followed by the Arbitral Tribunal in conducting its proceedings, the Arbitral Tribunal shall not depart from the agreed procedure.[12]

Matters were adjourned for final award and the parties were informed that no fresh notice would be given, the plea that no notice of closure of reference was given was held untenable.[13]

Order 9 Rule 9 CPC

In Section 19, the words "Arbitral Tribunal shall not be bound" are the words of amplitude and not of restriction. These words do not prohibit the Arbitral Tribunal from drawing sustenance from the fundamental principles underlying the CPC or the Evidence Act, but the tribunal is not bound to observe the provisions of the Code with all of its rigour. Thus, principles underlying Order 9 Rule 9 can very well be invoked as there was nothing on record to indicate that the parties have agreed to the contrary.[14]

Just because the Arbitral Tribunal is not bound by CPC, it does not mean that it would have no jurisdiction to exercise power of court as contained in CPC.[15]

---

8. *H.G. Oomor Sait* v. *O. Aslam Sait*, 2001 SCC OnLine Mad 465: (2001) 3 CTC 269.
9. *Sahyadri Earthmovers* v. *L and T Finance Ltd.*, 2011 SCC OnLine Bom 434: (2011) 4 Mah LJ 200.
10. *Ibid.*
11. *Chaudhary Transport* v. *Hindustan Petroleum Corpn. Ltd.*, 2011 SCC OnLine Bom 1511: (2012) 2 Mah LJ 646.
12. *U.P. Samaj Kalyan Nirman Nigam Ltd.* v. *Jamuna Construction Co.*, 2010 SCC OnLine All 795: (2010) 4 All LJ 81.
13. *Atul R. Shah* v. *V. Vrijlal Lalloobhai and Co.*, 1998 SCC OnLine Bom 403: (1999) 1 Mah LJ 629.
14. *Srei Infrastructure Finance Ltd.* v. *Tuff Drilling (P) Ltd.*, (2018) 11 SCC 470.
15. *Palmview Investments Overseas Ltd.* v. *Ravi Arya*, (2023) 1 HCC (Bom) 259.

As per Section 19 of the Act, the tribunal is not bound by the CPC or the Evidence Act; the parties are free to agree on the procedure to be followed by the tribunal in conducting its proceedings. In the absence of any agreement between the parties, the Arbitral Tribunal has to conduct the proceedings in the manner it considers to be appropriate.[16]

Requirement of security in arbitration clause

In a government contract, arbitration clause postulated that the contractor could not invoke arbitration without furnishing security at the rates specified in the contract, though no such restriction was imposed on the government. The court held that the restriction was valid.[17]

Claim petition on behalf of company

The Board of Directors of the company by a resolution approved the power of attorney in favour of the company secretary, also authorised him to delegate this power to another official. The company secretary executed a power of attorney in favour of Assistant Credit Manager. The claim petition filed by the Assistant Credit Manager was held maintainable.[18]

Commencement of arbitration proceeding under the 1940 Act or 1996 Act—Choice of parties

The choice to proceed under the 1940 Act or 1996 Act is of the parties and not of the arbitrator.[19]

"Admissibility, relevance, materiality and weight of evidence" [S. 19(4)]

In terms of sub-section (4) of Section 19, Arbitration and Conciliation Act, 1996, it is the Arbitral Tribunal which has to decide the questions of admissibility, relevance, materiality and the weight of evidence. An award cannot be set aside simply on the ground that the arbitrator excluded certain evidence placed before him; such ground or plea does not come under the expression "misconduct". The award was not set aside.[20]

---

16. *Union of India* v. *L.S.N. Murthy*, 2006 SCC OnLine AP 414: (2006) 2 AP LJ 170.
17. *S.K. Jain* v. *State of Haryana*, (2009) 4 SCC 357.
18. *Bhjrang Cranes* v. *Shriram Transport Finance Co. Ltd.*, 2019 SCC OnLine AP 297.
19. *Radhey Shyam Associates* v. *State of Maharashtra*, 2008 SCC OnLine Bom 161: (2008) 3 Mah LJ 926.
20. *State (NCT of Delhi)* v. *Khem Chand*, 2003 SCC OnLine Del 400: (2003) 68 DRJ 518; *Union of India* v. *L.S.N. Murthy*, 2006 SCC OnLine AP 414: (2006) 2 AP LJ 170.

Framing of issues

The Arbitral Tribunal is not strictly required to frame issues as laid down in the CPC. The procedure before the tribunal is informal in nature.[21] It is not compulsory for the tribunal to record decisions on each and every issue as required by CPC.[22]

Arbitral Tribunal must follow the basic principles of natural justice, fair play and equity

The Arbitral Tribunal must follow the basic principles of natural justice, fair play, equity and principle of law.[23]

A document that is disputed by a party and if not proved cannot be considered by the arbitrator to be on record or as a piece of evidence. Taking into consideration such a document by an arbitrator would be in violation of the principles of natural justice.[24]

Rules of procedure in arbitral proceedings, however informal they may be, cannot be stretched to make room for oral evidence to be received from the respondent after the conclusion of the claimant's agreements.[25] Where the claim is based on a document of which either the original or, in its absence, a certified copy has not been produced, the award passed is not sustainable.[26]

Where the parties fail to arrive at an agreement about the procedure to be followed by the procedure, the arbitrator is free to conduct the proceedings in any manner he thinks appropriate.[27]

Execution of award—Application of CPC and Evidence Act

The provisions under the Arbitration and Conciliation Act, 1996 do not lay down a specific procedure of execution of the award. Though Section 19 of the Act restricts the applicability of the CPC and the Evidence Act insofar as the proceeding before the Arbitral Tribunal is concerned, however the

---

21. *VSNL* v. *Shapoorji Pallonji & Co. Ltd.*, 2007 SCC OnLine Cal 670: (2008) 1 CHN 721.
22. *Gammon India Ltd.* v. *Sankaranarayana Construction (Bangalore) (P) Ltd.*, 2011 SCC OnLine Mad 2266: (2011) 6 CTC 736.
23. *Prakash Kumar Sinha* v. *Konkan Mercantile Coop. Bank Ltd.*, 2012 SCC OnLine Bom 409: (2012) 6 Mah LJ 274; *Shunk Corrugators (P) Ltd.* v. *Bharat Coop. Bank (Mumbai) Ltd.*, 2011 SCC OnLine Bom 19: (2011) 1 Mah LJ 981.
24. *Pradyuman Kumar Sharma* v. *Jays Agar M. Sancheti*, 2013 SCC OnLine Bom 453: (2013) 5 Mah LJ 86.
25. *VSNL* v. *Shapoorji Pallonji & Co. Ltd.*, 2007 SCC OnLine Cal 670: (2008) 1 CHN 721.
26. *Nagasrinivasulu* v. *Galada Finance Ltd.*, 2008 SCC OnLine Mad 831: (2009) 1 CTC 158.
27. *Satgur Sewak Rice and General Mills* v. *Punjab State Civil Supplies Corpn. Ltd.*, 1999 SCC OnLine P&H 1320: PLR (2000) 124 P&H 748.

restriction contained under Section 19 of the Act cannot be extended to the execution proceeding.[28]

PLACE OF ARBITRATION [S. 20]

20. *Place of arbitration.*—(1) The parties are free to agree on the place of arbitration.

(2) Failing any agreement referred to in sub-section (1), the place of arbitration shall be determined by the arbitral tribunal having regard to the circumstances of the case, including the convenience of the parties.

(3) Notwithstanding sub-section (1) or sub-section (2), the arbitral tribunal may, unless otherwise agreed by the parties, meet at any place it considers appropriate for consultation among its members, for hearing witnesses, experts or the parties, or for inspection of documents, goods or other property.

COMMENTS

Corresponding old law

Section 20 is new; no such provision existed in the Arbitration Act, 1940.

UNCITRAL Model Law

Article 20. *Place of arbitration*

(1) The parties are free to agree on the place of arbitration. Failing such agreement, the place of arbitration shall be determined by the arbitral tribunal having regard to the circumstances of the case, including the convenience of the parties.

(2) Notwithstanding the provisions of paragraph (1) of this article, the arbitral tribunal may, unless otherwise agreed by the parties, meet at any place it considers appropriate for consultation among its members, for hearing witnesses, experts or the parties, or for inspection of goods, other property or documents.

Scope and application

Section 20 envisages provisions about the place of arbitration. The parties may agree on the place of arbitration; where the parties fail to arrive at an agreement about the place of arbitration, the place of arbitration shall be determined by the Arbitral Tribunal having regard to the circumstances of the case and the convenience of the parties. However, the Arbitral Tribunal may, unless otherwise agreed by the parties, meet at any place it considers

28. *Indusind Bank Ltd.* v. *Rajesh Dayal*, 2015 SCC OnLine Jhar 3655: (2016) 4 Arb LR 184.

appropriate for consultation amongst its members, for hearing of witnesses, experts or the parties, or for the inspection of the documents, goods or other property.

Section 20 of the Act provides for the place of arbitration. The parties are free to agree on the place of arbitration. Failing any agreement between the parties about the place of arbitration, the Arbitral Tribunal shall determine the place of arbitration having regard to the circumstances of the case and the convenience of the parties.

The arbitration law envisages two jurisdictions; one is the "place" where the arbitration may be conducted keeping the convenience of the parties in mind, and the other is the "seat" which determines the jurisdiction of the courts where the parties may agitate any controversy arising out of the arbitration.[29]

Merely because the arbitrator itself chooses the venue of arbitration, it cannot be said that the arbitrator has exercised jurisdiction not vested in it.[30]

The Arbitral Tribunal may, unless otherwise agreed between the parties, meet at any place it considers appropriate for

1. consultation among its members;
2. for hearing witnesses, experts or the parties;
3. for inspection of documents, goods or other property.

There was express agreement between the parties to get the dispute settled by arbitration in Seoul (Korea). In view of the express agreement between the parties, the jurisdiction of the Indian courts was specifically excluded. The plea that because of the bracketed portion in the relevant contract clause, *viz.* "or such other place as parties may agree in writing the seat could be elsewhere", the seat of arbitration could be anywhere else as per the choice of the parties was not accepted. Bracketed portion cannot be allowed to control the main clause.[31]

The courts at the seat or place of arbitration would have territorial jurisdiction to entertain an application subject to provisions of Section 42 of the 1996 Act, irrespective of the cause of action and residence of the respondent.[32]

The Agreement as to the seat of arbitration is analogous to exclusive jurisdiction clause.[33] Arbitration proceedings conducted were in the nature of

29. *Samsung India Electronics (P) Ltd.* v. *Enn Enn Corpn. Ltd.*, 2023 SCC OnLine Del 3827.
30. *Rajiv Bhatia* v. *Indusind Bank Ltd.*, 2017 SCC OnLine HP 329.
31. *Dozco India (P) Ltd.* v. *Doosan Infracore Co. Ltd.*, (2011) 6 SCC 179.
32. *ION Exchange (India) Ltd.* v. *Panasonic Electric Works Co. Ltd.*, 2014 SCC OnLine Del 7499.
33. *State of W.B.* v. *Chatterjee Petrochem (Mauritius) Co.*, 2020 SCC OnLine Cal 3301: (2020) 2 Cal LT 139.

"international commercial arbitration", as the purchaser company was a body incorporated outside India. As per the clauses of agreement, parties themselves agreed to have a juridical seat of arbitration at Paris, France. Request of the purchaser-company to shift the "venue" from Paris to India cannot be construed as a change in the "seat" of arbitration. The agreement as to the seat of arbitration is analogous to exclusive jurisdiction clause. It was held, the seat of arbitration would be the International Chamber of Commerce at Paris, France.[34]

The courts in Rajasthan were vested with jurisdiction as the seat of arbitration was to be at Jaipur. By mutual agreement, the parties shifted the venue/place of arbitration from Jaipur to Ahmedabad; the jurisdiction was now vested in the courts at Ahmedabad, and the courts at Rajasthan were no longer vested with jurisdiction. The moment the seat is chosen as Ahmedabad, it is akin to an exclusive jurisdiction clause, thereby vesting the courts at Ahmedabad with exclusive jurisdiction to deal with the arbitration. This being the case, the parties may mutually arrive at a seat of arbitration and may change the seat of arbitration by mutual agreement.[35]

In the context of domestic arbitrations once the "seat of arbitration" has been fixed, the courts at the said location alone will have exclusive jurisdiction to exercise the supervisory powers over the arbitration. The courts at other locations would not have jurisdiction, including the courts where the cause of action has arisen. The moment the parties by agreement designate "the seat", it becomes akin to an exclusive jurisdiction clause. It would then vest the courts at "the seat" with exclusive jurisdiction to regulate arbitration proceedings arising out of the agreement between the parties. Once the jurisdictional "seat" of arbitration is fixed in terms of sub-section (2) of Section 20, Arbitration and Conciliation Act, 1996, then, without the express mutual consent of the parties to the arbitration, "the seat" cannot be changed. Therefore, the appointment of a new arbitrator who holds the arbitration proceedings at a different location would not change the jurisdictional "seat" already fixed by the earlier or first arbitrator. The place of arbitration in such an event should be treated as a venue where arbitration proceedings are held.[36]

The moment the seat is designated, it is akin to an exclusive jurisdiction clause.[37] According to the arbitration clause, the seat of arbitration was Kolkata where the contract was issued. An application under Section 9 could

34. *State of W.B.* v. *Chatterjee Petrochem (Mauritius) Co.*, 2020 SCC OnLine Cal 3301: (2020) 2 Cal LT 139.
35. *Renewables Ltd.* v. *Jayesh Electricals Ltd.*, (2023) 3 SCC 733.
36. *BBR (India) (P) Ltd.* v. *S.P. Singla Constructions (P) Ltd.*, (2023) 1 SCC 693.
37. *Indus Mobile Distribution (P) Ltd.* v. *Datawind Innovations (P) Ltd.*, (2017) 7 SCC 678.

be filed before the Calcutta High Court.[38] The specific clause mentioned the venue of arbitration to be at *B*; the Principal Bench of the High Court at *B* would have jurisdiction to hear the matter.[39]

Venue of arbitration cannot be read as the seat of arbitration.[40]

Parties belonged to Hyderabad, loan was granted in relation to the property situated at Hyderabad, the office of the financier was also located at Hyderabad. The court at Hyderabad had jurisdiction to entertain arbitration. The court at New Delhi had no jurisdiction to entertain the application for appointment of arbitrator.[41]

Venue and seat of arbitration

There is a marked difference between the "venue of arbitration" and "seat of arbitration". It is only the seat of arbitration which will give territorial jurisdiction and not the venue of arbitration. "Seat" is the place where the court or arbitration is located, which will have territorial jurisdiction with regard to the case or in the matter, whereas, "venue" is the place where the Arbitral Tribunal sits to hold the arbitration proceedings and this place need not essentially be the place "where the seat of arbitration is located".[42]

Seat of arbitration—Neutral venue

"Neutral venue" can be chosen by the parties, even if no cause of action may have arisen at a neutral venue, not having jurisdiction in a classical sense.[43] In *Indus Mobile Distribution (P) Ltd.* v. *Datawind Innovations (P) Ltd.*[44], the arbitration clause stipulated the seat of arbitration as Mumbai. It was held that once the seat of arbitration was determined at Mumbai, "Mumbai court" was vested with exclusive jurisdiction for the purposes of arbitration proceedings arising out of the agreement.
Seat of arbitration

The arbitration agreement was silent about the seat of arbitration, and the arbitrator fixed the seat of arbitration as Panchkula in Haryana. The newly appointed arbitrator conducted proceedings in Delhi. The seat of arbitration

38. *Golden Edge Engg. (P) Ltd.* v. *BHEL.*, 2020 SCC OnLine Cal 996.
39. *Power Gear Ltd.* v. *Gulbarga Electricity Supply Co. Ltd.*, 2014 SCC OnLine Kar 12566: (2014) 2 Kant LJ 619.
40. *V. Balakrishnan* v. *Capital First Ltd.*, 2019 SCC OnLine TS 1290: (2019) 5 ALD 414.
41. *Ibid.*
42. *Rajiv Bhatia* v. *Indusind Bank Ltd.*, 2017 SCC OnLine HP 329.
43. *Indus Mobile Distribution (P) Ltd.* v. *Datawind Innovations (P) Ltd.*, (2017) 7 SCC 678.
44. (2017) 7 SCC 678; *Samsung India Electronics (P) Ltd.* v. *Enn Enn Corpn. Ltd.*, 2023 SCC OnLine Del 3827.

once fixed by the Arbitral Tribunal under Section 20(2) remains static and fixed. Held, the seat of arbitration would be Panchkula in Haryana.[45]

"The seat" once fixed by the Arbitral Tribunal under Section 20(2) should remain static and fixed, whereas the "venue" of arbitration can change and move from "the seat" to a new location. Venue is not constant and stationary and can move and change in terms of sub-section (3) to Section 20 of the Act. Change of venue does not result in change or relocation of the "seat of arbitration".[46]

Reference to arbitration at place other than agreed upon in the arbitration agreement

Where the arbitration agreement provides "Delhi" as the venue, the prayer of the respondent that matter be referred to arbitration in London or in Singapore, where other arbitrations between the parties were in progress could/was not granted.[47]

International commercial arbitration—Juridical seat of arbitration

Where the agreement provided that the agreement was governed by the laws of the Republic of Korea and all disputes shall be settled by arbitration in Seoul (Korea) (or such other place as the parties may agree in writing), it was held on the facts of the case that Part I stood excluded, and the Supreme Court had no jurisdiction to entertain an application under Section 11(6) for appointment of arbitrator.[48]

As per the clause of the arbitration agreement, the seat of arbitration was Kuala Lumpur, Malaysia. Due to the outbreak of SARS epidemics, an Arbitral Tribunal decided to hold its meeting first at Amsterdam and then at London and the parties did not object to it. This did not amount to shifting of the physical or jurisdictional seat of arbitration from Kuala Lumpur to London. Neither was there any agreement between the parties to shift the juridical seat of arbitration from Kuala Lumpur to London, nor any written instrument was signed for amending the clause of the agreement. It was held, the mere fact that parties to a particular arbitration had agreed to shift the seat of arbitration could not be interpreted as anything except a physical change of venue of arbitration from Kuala Lumpur to London.[49]

---

45. *BBR (India) (P) Ltd.* v. *S.P. Singla Constructions (P) Ltd.*, (2023) 1 SCC 693.
46. *Ibid.*
47. *Shin Satellite Public Co. Ltd.* v. *Jain Studios Ltd.*, (2006) 2 SCC 628.
48. *Dozco India (P) Ltd.* v. *Doosan Infracore Co. Ltd.*, (2011) 6 SCC 179.
49. *Videocon Industries Ltd.* v. *Union of India*, (2011) 6 SCC 161; *Dozco India (P) Ltd.* v. *Doosan Infracore Co. Ltd.*, (2011) 6 SCC 179.

As per the arbitration clause, the juridical seat of arbitration was expressed at a neutral venue, *i.e.* Mumbai. Even though, no part of the cause of action may have arisen at Mumbai, the moment an express designation of venue was made, it would vest Mumbai courts with exclusive jurisdiction for the purpose of regulating the arbitral proceedings arising out of the agreement between the parties.[50]

Venue of arbitration when may be outside juridical seat of arbitration

The juridical seat was India. It was agreed between the parties that the venue of arbitration proceedings would be Singapore. The court directed that the arbitral proceedings subject to mutual consensus to the contrary shall be conducted at Singapore.[51]

Jurisdiction cannot be conferred by consent of parties

Jurisdiction cannot be conferred with the consent of the parties. Where the court(s) in India have no jurisdiction, mere filing of an application in courts in India cannot clothe such courts with jurisdiction, unless the law vests the same in them.[52]

Erroneous decision on question of venue can be assailed under Section 34(2)

Where the erroneous decision on the question of venue is not assailed at the stage of Section 20 which ultimately affected the procedure that has been followed in the arbitral proceedings, it would come within the scope of Section 34(2), and the award can be set aside under Section 34. It cannot be said that the aggrieved party has no remedy.[53]

Appeal

A decision as to the place of arbitration under Section 20 does not have the characteristics of an arbitration award nor an interim award so as to be appealable under Section 34 of the Act.[54]

50. *NIMS University* v. *Valuer HR E-Solutions (P) Ltd.*, 2020 SCC OnLine Raj 2082: (2020) 3 RLW 2118.
51. *ONGC Petro Additions Ltd.* v. *Daelim Industrial Co. Ltd.*, (2015) 13 SCC 176.
52. *Roger Shashoua* v. *Mukesh Sharma*, (2017) 14 SCC 722.
53. *Sanshin Chemicals Industry* v. *Oriental Carbons & Chemicals Ltd.*, (2001) 3 SCC 341.
54. *Ibid.*

A decision under Section 20 regarding the venue is distinct from making of an arbitral award under Sections 28 to 33, Arbitration and Conciliation Act, 1996.[55]

COMMENCEMENT OF ARBITRAL PROCEEDINGS [S. 21]

21. *Commencement of arbitral proceedings.*—Unless otherwise agreed by the parties, the arbitral proceedings in respect of a particular dispute commence on the date on which a request for that dispute to be referred to arbitration is received by the respondent.

COMMENTS

Corresponding old law

Section 21 in material particulars corresponds to Section 37(3), Arbitration Act, 1940. Section 37(3), Arbitration Act, 1940 read as under:

(3) For the purposes of this section and of the Indian Limitation Act, 1908 (9 of 1908), an arbitration shall be deemed to be commenced when one party to the arbitration agreement serves on the other parties thereto a notice requiring the appointment of an arbitrator, or where the arbitration agreement provides that the reference shall be to a person named or designated in the agreement, requiring that the difference be submitted to the person so named or designated.

UNCITRAL Model Law

Article 21. *Commencement of arbitral proceedings*

Unless otherwise agreed by the parties, the arbitral proceedings in respect of a particular dispute commence on the date on which a request for that dispute to be referred to arbitration is received by the respondent.

Scope and application

As laid down by Section 21, unless otherwise agreed by the parties, the arbitration proceedings in respect of a particular dispute commence on the date on which a request for that dispute to be referred to arbitration is received by the opposite party.[56] The constitution of the tribunal has to be interpreted in a purposive way so as to mean the assumption of jurisdiction

---

55. *Ibid.*
56. *Enkay Construction Co.* v. *DDA*, 2002 SCC OnLine Del 33: (2002) 96 DLT 417; *Dey & Co.* v. *Union of India*, 2005 SCC OnLine Gau 216: (2005) 3 Gau LR 404.

by the Arbitral Tribunal after commencement of arbitral proceedings under Section 21 of the Act.[57]

Sections 21 and 43(2), Arbitration and Conciliation Act, 1996 are not inconsistent or repugnant to each other, and must be construed harmoniously.[58]

Considering the provisions of Section 21 of the Act, it is the date of commencement of arbitral proceedings which is an essential criteria and not the date on which the present petitions are filed before the court. Therefore, the date of commencement of arbitral proceedings being prior to coming into force of the Amendment Act on 23 October 2015, it is the 1996 Act which is applicable to the present proceedings and not the Amendment Act, 2015.[59]

Section 21 does not require that requests should be made expressly in writing. There was a request by conduct of the parties and it had to be understood in that manner. Had it been essential that the request should be in writing for the appointment of the arbitrator, then the word "written" should have found place in Section 21 before the word "request".[60]

Whether the notice was a notice under Section 21 and whether the giving of notice under Section 21 is to be construed as a precondition to the exercise of jurisdiction by the Arbitral Tribunal are questions which the tribunal will have to decide.[61]

Notice sine qua non for commencement of proceedings

Unless otherwise agreed to between the parties, issuance of notice under Section 21 is the sine qua non for commencement of proceedings.[62]

Commencement of arbitration proceedings

The purpose of Section 21 is to determine the date of commencement of arbitration proceedings for deciding whether the claims are barred by limitation or not.[63] Section 21 makes it clear that the commencement of the

57. *Quippo Infrastructure Ltd.* v. *A2Z Infraservices Ltd.*, 2021 SCC OnLine Cal 1684: (2021) 3 Arb LR 262.
58. *Prashant Kumar Sahu* v. *Optel Telecommunication Ltd.*, 2008 SCC OnLine MP 39: (2008) 2 MPLJ 481.
59. *Betamax Ltd.* v. *State Trading Corpn.*, 2019 SCC OnLine Kar 2092: ILR 2019 Kar 4877.
60. *ABB ABL Ltd.* v. *Cement Corpn. of India*, 1999 SCC OnLine Del 84: (1999) 49 DRJ 131.
61. *Oval Investment (P) Ltd.* v. *Indiabulls Financial Services Ltd.*, 2009 SCC OnLine Del 3497: (2009) 113 DRJ 504.
62. *Amit Kumar Agarwala* v. *Maa Saarda and Co.*, 2019 SCC OnLine Gau 5068: (2020) 3 Gau LR 351.
63. *State of Goa* v. *Praveen Enterprises*, (2012) 12 SCC 581.

arbitration proceedings is possible only after the respondent received the request for reference to arbitration.[64]

Notice for arbitration amounted to initiation of arbitration proceedings.[65]

Change in the constitution of Arbitral Tribunal is irrelevant for determining when the arbitration proceedings commenced within the meaning of Section 21 of the Act.[66]

The factum of giving notices dated 6 August 2001 and 2002 was admitted by the respondents. Therefore, the application filed under Section 11 on 30 April 2002 was held not barred by the prescribed period of limitation.[67]

By virtue of Section 21, arbitration proceedings can be commenced when notice has been served and received by the party concerned. Receipt of notice by the party concerned is also mandated by Section 21. In *Indus Ind Bank Ltd.* v. *Mulchand B. Jain*[68], when no proper notice was served on Respondent 1, arbitral proceedings could not be said to be commenced with respect to Respondent 1 when no notice was received by Respondent 1; arbitral proceedings would be barred by limitation by application of Section 43.

As per Section 21 of the Act of 1996, commencement of the proceedings is taken from the date when request for reference of the dispute to the arbitrator is received by the respondents. In the present case, request to refer the case to the arbitrator was received prior to Amending Act, 2015; thus, commencement of the proceedings is prior to the amendment in the Act of 1996. Provisions of the Amendment Act were not applicable.[69]

Unilateral appointment of arbitrator

Issuance of a valid notice under Section 21 for referring disputes between parties to arbitration is a condition precedent for commencement of valid arbitral proceedings. There was unilateral appointment of the arbitrator; arbitration proceedings initiated by the arbitrator were held invalid.[70]

---

64. *Mulchand B Jain* v. *Indus Ind Bank Ltd.*, 2010 SCC OnLine Mad 3542: (2010) 4 LW 231.
65. *A.P. Power Coordination Committee* v. *Lanco Kondapalli Power Ltd.*, (2016) 3 SCC 468.
66. *Milkfood Ltd.* v. *GMC Ice Cream (P) Ltd.*, (2004) 7 SCC 288.
67. *Prashant Kumar Sahu* v. *Optel Telecommunication Ltd.*, 2008 SCC OnLine MP 39: (2008) 2 MPLJ 481.
68. 2013 SCC OnLine Mad 555: (2013) 2 CTC 533.
69. *Shilpa Construction* v. *Jaipur Municipal Corpn.*, 2017 SCC OnLine Raj 4312: (2017) 4 WLC 101.
70. *Arun Kumar Bhunia* v. *Badal Midya*, 2019 SCC OnLine Cal 9410: (2019) 4 Cal LT 545.

Application for appointment of arbitrator filed prior to commencement of 1996 Act

In *U.P. State Sugar Corpn. Ltd.* v. *Jain Construction Co.*[71], disputes and differences between the parties arose in the year 1991. The respondent filed an application under Section 20 of the 1940 Act on 1 May 1991. It invoked the arbitration agreement. The arbitral proceeding was, therefore, set in motion within the meaning of Section 21 of the 1996 Act. In respect of the arbitral proceedings commenced before coming into force of the 1996 Act, the provisions of the 1940 Act shall apply. Therefore, in view of Section 85(2)(*a*) of the 1996 Act, the decision of the High Court that remedy under the 1996 Act was available to the applicant was not sustainable, was set aside.

Once the arbitration proceedings commenced under the old Act of 1940, it would be the old Act which would apply in arbitration proceedings and also for enforcing the award.[72] The Act of 1996 was enforced on 25 January 1996. A notice for appointment of arbitrator was served on 3 September 1994. Arbitration proceedings shall be deemed to have commenced on 6 September 1996 when the plaint was filed in court. It was held, the provisions of Section 21 of the 1996 Act would not apply.[73]

Whether a dispute is governed by the provisions of the 1996 Act or the provisions of the Act of 1940 would be governed by the date of the dispute, *i.e.* the cause of arbitration which will ultimately lead to the commencement to the satisfaction of both Sections 37(3) and 21 of both the Acts, respectively.[74] Where the demand for appointment of arbitrator was made when the Act of 1940 was in force, but the appointment of arbitrator was made on 4 July 1996 when the new Act of 1996 came into force, and the old Act of 1940 already stood repealed, the arbitrator conducted the proceedings under the 1996 Act; the new Act of 1996 applied.[75]

Where the petitioner invoked the arbitration clause of the contract before the new Act came into force, the proceedings have to be governed by the Arbitration Act, 1940.[76] Where the arbitration proceedings commenced before the Arbitration and Conciliation Act, 1996, the Act of 1940 would

71. (2004) 7 SCC 332.
72. *Union of India* v. *R.K. Goal and Associates*, 2008 SCC OnLine Bom 316: (2009) 1 Mah LJ 354.
73. *Wimco Ltd.* v. *Vikarm Singh*, 2002 SCC OnLine All 54: (2002) 46 ALR 774.
74. *Food Corporation of India* v. *Dilip Kumar Dutta*, 1998 SCC OnLine Cal 260: (1999) 1 CWN 400.
75. *Rose Advertising* v. *DTC*, 2001 SCC OnLine Del 119: (2001) 58 DRJ 516.
76. *Continental Construction Ltd.* v. *Chief Engineer*, 2003 SCC OnLine Del 977.

continue to apply as there was nothing to show on record that there was any agreement to the contrary.[77]

Claims proposed to be made in the reference need not be stated in the notice under Section 21 invoking the arbitration, unless the arbitration agreement itself requires the invocation in a particular manner.[78]

A dispute arose between the parties because of the non-payment of alleged dues of the respondent in 1990. The stage of making the application for appointment of arbitrator had arisen in 1990. The respondent did not make such an application for appointment of arbitrator within 20 days in terms of the agreement. It was held that the dispute between the parties came to end when the contractor failed to refer the dispute to the arbitrator.[79]

Additional claims—Limitation

In case of additional claims, the date of amendment by which additional claim is sought to be adduced is relevant.[80]

Counterclaims—Limitation

The date on which the counterclaim is made by the respondent before the arbitrator will be the date of its institution. Section 21, Arbitration and Conciliation Act, 1996 is not relevant for counterclaims.[81]

Merely because an arbitral reference may have been lodged before the arbitrator on a particular day would not imply that the period of limitation to file the counterclaim would begin to be counted from such date. The period of limitation in a counterclaim starts to run from when the cause of action arises.[82]

Recovery proceedings under SARFAESI Act, 2002

The proceedings for arbitration operate in a different field and the provisions of the SARFAESI Act are confined to the recovery of dues of financial institutions by enforcement of its security interest by the financial institution/bank. Therefore, the proceedings for arbitration will not come in the way of recovery of the defaulted amount from the petitioners by Respondent 2

77. *Good Value Engineers* v. *M.M.S. Nanda*, 2001 SCC OnLine Del 1177: ILR (2001) 2 Del 563.
78. *Veena* v. *Seth Industries Ltd.*, 2010 SCC OnLine Bom 1707: (2011) 2 Mah LJ 226.
79. *Godawari Marathwada Irrigation Development Corpn.* v. *Pawar and Co.*, 2013 SCC OnLine Bom 225: (2013) 4 Mah LJ 183.
80. *State of Goa* v. *Praveen Enterprises*, (2012) 12 SCC 581.
81. *Ibid.*
82. *Chief Engineer* v. *Roman Tarmat Ltd.*, 2021 SCC OnLine Mad 2467: (2021) 5 CTC 1.

by means of proceedings under Section 13(4), SARFAESI Act.[83] Proceedings under the SARFAESI Act, 2002 are not barred by the pendency of arbitration proceedings.[84]

LANGUAGE [S. 22]

22. *Language.*—(1) The parties are free to agree upon the language or languages to be used in the arbitral proceedings.

(2) Failing any agreement referred to in sub-section (1), the arbitral tribunal shall determine the language or languages to be used in the arbitral proceedings.

(3) The agreement or determination, unless otherwise specified, shall apply to any written statement by a party, any hearing and any arbitral award, decision or other communication by the arbitral tribunal.

(4) The arbitral tribunal may order that any documentary evidence shall be accompanied by a translation into the language or languages agreed upon by the parties or determined by the arbitral tribunal.

COMMENTS

Corresponding old law

Section 22 is new; no such provision existed in the Arbitration Act, 1940.

UNCITRAL Model Law

Article 22. *Language*

(1) The parties are free to agree on the language or languages to be used in the arbitral proceedings. Failing such agreement, the arbitral tribunal shall determine the language or languages to be used in the proceedings. This agreement or determination, unless otherwise specified therein, shall apply to any written statement by a party, any hearing and any award, decision or other communication by the arbitral tribunal.

(2) The arbitral tribunal may order that any documentary evidence shall be accompanied by a translation into the language or languages agreed upon by the parties or determined by the arbitral tribunal.

Scope and application

The parties are free to agree on the language/languages to be used in the arbitral proceedings. Where the parties fail to arrive at any such agreement,

83. *Shiv Shakti Traders* v. *Union of India*, 2017 SCC OnLine All 2933: (2018) 2 All LJ 60.
84. *Nafees Sultana* v. *Rajadhani Coop. Urban Bank Ltd.*, 2016 SCC OnLine Hyd 398: (2016) 6 ALT 500.

the Arbitral Tribunal shall determine the language/languages to be used in the arbitration.

The tribunal has a discretion to determine the language to be used in the proceedings.[85]

STATEMENTS OF CLAIM AND DEFENCE [S. 23]

23. *Statements of claim and defence.*—(1) Within the period of time agreed upon by the parties or determined by the arbitral tribunal, the claimant shall state the facts supporting his claim, the points at issue and the relief or remedy sought, and the respondent shall state his defence in respect of these particulars, unless the parties have otherwise agreed as to the required elements of those statements.

(2) The parties may submit with their statements all documents they consider to be relevant or may add a reference to the documents or other evidence they will submit.

[86][(2-A) The respondent, in support of his case, may also submit a counter claim or plead a set-off, which shall be adjudicated upon by the arbitral tribunal, if such counter claim or set-off falls within the scope of the arbitration agreement.]

(3) Unless otherwise agreed by the parties, either party may amend or supplement his claim or defence during the course of the arbitral proceedings, unless the arbitral tribunal considers it inappropriate to allow the amendment or supplement having regard to the delay in making it.

[87][(4) The statement of claim and defence under this section shall be completed within a period of six months from the date the arbitrator or all the arbitrators, as the case may be, received notice, in writing, of their appointment.]

COMMENTS

Corresponding old law

Section 23 is new; no such provision existed in the Arbitration Act, 1940.

UNCITRAL Model Law

Article 23. *Statements of claim and defence*

(1) Within the period of time agreed by the parties or determined by the arbitral tribunal, the claimant shall state the facts supporting his claim, the points at issue and the relief or remedy sought, and the respondent shall state his defence in respect of these particulars, unless the parties have otherwise

85. *Balmukund Pandey* v. *V.K. Singh*, 2009 SCC OnLine MP 30: (2010) 1 MP LJ 372.
86. *Ins.* by Act 3 of 2016, S. 11 (w.r.e.f. 23-10-2015).
87. *Ins.* by Act 33 of 2019, S. 5 (w.e.f. 30-8-2019).

agreed as to the required elements of such statements. The parties may submit with their statements all documents they consider to be relevant or may add a reference to the documents or other evidence they will submit.

(2) Unless otherwise agreed by the parties, either party may amend or supplement his claim or defence during the course of the arbitral proceedings, unless the arbitral tribunal considers it inappropriate to allow such amendment having regard to the delay in making it.

Legislative changes

Arbitration and Conciliation (Amendment) Act, 2015 (3 of 2016)

In Section 23 of the principal Act, after sub-section (2), the following sub-section shall be *inserted*, namely—

> "(2-A) The respondent, in support of his case, may also submit a counter-claim or plead a set-off, which shall be adjudicated upon by the arbitral tribunal, if such counter-claim or set-off falls within the scope of the arbitration agreement."

OBJECTS AND REASONS

Clause 11 of the Bill seeks to insert a new sub-section (2-A) in Section 23 of the principal Act to provide that the respondent, in support of his case, may also submit a counter claim or a set off, if such counter claim or set off falls within the scope of the arbitration agreement.

Arbitration and Conciliation (Amendment) Act, 2019 (33 of 2019)

In Section 23 of the principal Act, after sub-section (3), the following sub-section shall be inserted, namely:—

"(4) The statement of claim and defence under this section shall be completed within a period of six months from the date the arbitrator or all the arbitrators, as the case may be, received notice, in writing, of their appointment.".

Scope and application

Section 23 lays down the procedure for filing statements of claim and defence. The statement of claim and defence shall be filed within a period of six months from the date the arbitrator/arbitrators received notice of their appointment.

The issue as to whether the invocation of arbitration is within limitation has to be distinguished from the question as to whether a substantive claim is within limitation.[88]

88. *Vijaypat Singhania* v. *Hari Shankar Singhania*, 2013 SCC OnLine Bom 434: (2013) 5 Mah LJ 744.

Filing of documents [S. 23(2)]

Under sub-section (2) of Section 23, the parties are required to submit all the documents they consider relevant along with their statements. Alternatively, they must at least add a reference to the documents that they will submit. Non-disclosure of relevant documents by a party to the arbitration proceedings is erroneous.[89]

Amendment of claim petition [S. 23]

A party can oppose the amendment on various grounds, including the ground of delay. It is significant that Section 23(3) uses the words "having regard to the delay in making it" in contradistinction to the words "having regard only to". Thus, the respondents were entitled to oppose the application for amendment filed by the petitioner on all available grounds.[90]

Termination of arbitration proceedings—Recall of order

On default of a party to file its claim statement when arbitration proceedings are terminated, the claimant can file a claim on sufficient cause being shown under Section 23(1). The Arbitral Tribunal has jurisdiction to recall its earlier order of termination of proceedings. When the Arbitral Tribunal without sufficient cause being shown by the claimant to file the claim statement can terminate the proceedings, if sufficient cause is shown, there is no impediment in the power of the tribunal to accept the show cause and permit the claimant to file the claim. The scheme of Section 25 clearly indicates that on sufficient cause being shown, the statement of claim can be permitted to be filed even after the time as fixed by Section 23(1) has expired. Thus, even after passing the order of terminating the proceedings, if sufficient cause is shown, the claims of the claimant can be accepted by the Arbitral Tribunal by accepting the show cause and there is no lack of jurisdiction in the Arbitral Tribunal to recall the earlier order on sufficient cause being shown, and recommence the proceedings.[91]

HEARINGS AND WRITTEN PROCEEDINGS [S. 24]

24. *Hearings and written proceedings.*—(1) Unless otherwise agreed by the parties, the arbitral tribunal shall decide whether to hold oral hearings for the

89. *R. Narayanan* v. *India Info Line Securities (P) Ltd.*, 2013 SCC OnLine Mad 1744: (2013) 5 LW 89.

90. *Kavis Fashions (P) Ltd.* v. *Dimple Enterprises*, 2023 SCC OnLine Bom 2891; *Lindsay International (P) Ltd.* v. *IFGL Refractors Ltd.*, 2021 SCC OnLine Cal 1979.

91. *Srei Infrastructure Finance Ltd.* v. *Tuff Drilling (P) Ltd.*, (2018) 11 SCC 470.

presentation of evidence or for oral argument, or whether the proceedings shall be conducted on the basis of documents and other materials:

Provided that the arbitral tribunal shall hold oral hearings, at an appropriate stage of the proceedings, on a request by a party, unless the parties have agreed that no oral hearing shall be held.

[92][Provided further that the arbitral tribunal shall, as far as possible, hold oral hearings for the presentation of evidence or for oral argument on day-to-day basis, and not grant any adjournments unless sufficient cause is made out, and may impose costs including exemplary costs on the party seeking adjournment without any sufficient cause.]

(2) The parties shall be given sufficient advance notice of any hearing and of any meeting of the arbitral tribunal for the purposes of inspection of documents, goods or other property.

(3) All statements, documents or other information supplied to, or applications made to the arbitral tribunal by one party shall be communicated to the other party, and any expert report or evidentiary document on which the arbitral tribunal may rely in making its decision shall be communicated to the parties.

COMMENTS

Corresponding old law

Section 24 is new; no such provision existed in the Arbitration Act, 1940.

UNCITRAL Model Law

Article 24. *Hearings and written proceedings*

(1) Subject to any contrary agreement by the parties, the arbitral tribunal shall decide whether to hold oral hearings for the presentation of evidence or for oral argument, or whether the proceedings shall be conducted on the basis of documents and other materials. However, unless the parties have agreed that no hearings shall be held, the arbitral tribunal shall hold such hearings at an appropriate stage of the proceedings, if so requested by a party.

(2) The parties shall be given sufficient advance notice of any hearing and of any meeting of the arbitral tribunal for the purposes of inspection of goods, other property or documents.

(3) All statements, documents or other information supplied to the arbitral tribunal by one party shall be communicated to the other party. Also any expert report or evidentiary document on which the arbitral tribunal may rely in making its decision shall be communicated to the parties.

---

92. *Ins.* by Act 3 of 2016, S. 12 (w.r.e.f. 23-10-2015).

Legislative changes

Arbitration and Conciliation (Amendment) Act, 2015 (3 of 2016)

In Section 24 of the principal Act, after the proviso to sub-section (1), the following proviso shall be *inserted*, namely—

"Provided further that the arbitral tribunal shall, as far as possible, hold oral hearings for the presentation of evidence or for oral argument on day-to-day basis, and not grant any adjournments unless sufficient cause is made out, and may impose costs including exemplary costs on the party seeking adjournment without any sufficient cause."

NOTES ON CLAUSES

Clause 12 of the Bill seeks to insert a proviso in sub-section (1) of Section 24 of the principal Act to provide that the arbitral tribunal shall hold oral hearing for the presentation of the evidence or oral arguments on day to day basis and shall not grant any adjournments without any sufficient cause.

Scope and application

Section 24 makes provisions about the hearing and written proceedings before the Arbitral Tribunal.

Where no documents indicated if any procedure was followed by the arbitrator and the pleadings or documents produced was considered, or the proceedings of the dates of hearing were maintained, the award of the arbitrator was set aside.[93]

Hearing and meeting of Arbitral Tribunal [Sub-s. (2), (3)]

The arbitrator has to give sufficient advance notice of any hearing and of any meeting of the Arbitral Tribunal to the parties. All statements, documents or other information supplied or application made to the Arbitral Tribunal by one party on which the Arbitral Tribunal may rely in making decisions must be communicated to the other party.[94]

It is the duty of an arbitrator to give proper opportunity of hearing to both the parties in accordance with the provisions of the Arbitration and Conciliation Act, 1996.[95]

The date notified for the appearance of the petitioner before the arbitration court was declared holiday by the government. The Arbitral Tribunal

---

93. *Savitri Goenka* v. *Kanti Bhai Damani*, 2009 SCC OnLine Del 177: (2009) 108 DRJ 698.
94. *Naresh Kanayalal Rajwani* v. *Citi Financial Consumer Finance India Ltd.*, 2015 SCC OnLine Bom 6265: (2015) 6 Mah LJ 44.
95. *Alandur Municipal Corpn.* v. *IVRCL Infrastructures & Projects Ltd.*, 2010 SCC OnLine Mad 6048: (2011) 2 CTC 38.

conducted the proceedings and passed an ex parte award. It was held, when the date fixed was declared holiday, the arbitrator should have given another notice to the appellant specifying his intention that he wanted to proceed ex parte or regarding the evidence which was produced against him. The ex parte decree passed in the case was not sustainable.[96]

Where the first notice was received by the petitioners but they had not chosen to appear or to file counter affidavit, and the second notice sent by registered post was returned with an endorsement "addressee has gone out for an indefinite period", the service to the petitioners was good and the award passed in the case was valid.[97]

The arbitrator in all cases is to give notice of hearing for the purpose of inspection of documents, goods or properties. In *R. Narayanan* v. *India Info Line Securities Private Ltd.*[98], the Arbitral Tribunal did not adhere to the procedure laid down by Section 24. Even when the petitioner was collecting evidence to the knowledge of the arbitrator, the arbitrator closed the proceedings and passed the award. The arbitrator did not even put the petitioner on notice that he was closing the proceedings and that no documents could be called for. In such circumstances, presumption by the party that the proceedings were not condoned was valid.

Section 24(3) mandates the arbitrator that any expert report or evidentiary document on which he may rely in giving its decision shall be communicated to the parties. The arbitrator relied upon a circular issued by the Department of Telecommunications Headquarters at New Delhi which did not form part of the pleadings or the evidence. The award passed by the arbitrator was found not sustainable, and was set aside.[99]

Parties are entitled to be represented by a legal practitioner

Parties have a right to be heard by the Arbitral Tribunal. The right of being heard is specifically conferred on the parties under Section 24 of the Act. The Arbitration and Conciliation Act, 1996 contains no provision which bars the representation of the parties by a legal practitioner. In arbitration proceedings, the parties are entitled to be represented by a legal practitioner, if they so desire, unless they have agreed in writing that none of the parties shall be represented by a lawyer.[100]

96. *Shaminder Singh* v. *Motor and General Finance Ltd.*, 2007 SCC OnLine Del 772: (2008) 147 DLT 354.
97. *Harish Chand Gupta* v. *Ashok Leyland Finance (a Division of IndusInd Bank Ltd.)*, 2009 SCC OnLine Mad 1676: (2010) 3 CTC 133.
98. 2013 SCC OnLine Mad 1744: (2013) 5 LW 89.
99. *BSNL* v. *Vindhya Telelinks Ltd.*, 2006 SCC OnLine Del 415: ILR (2006) 1 Del 605.
100. *Faze Three Exports Ltd.* v. *Pankaj Trading Co.*, 2003 SCC OnLine Bom 1024: (2004) 2 Mah LJ 196.

DEFAULT OF A PARTY [S. 25]

25. *Default of a party.*—Unless, otherwise agreed by the parties, where, without showing sufficient cause,—

(*a*) the claimant fails to communicate his statement of claim in accordance with sub-section (1) of Section 23, the arbitral tribunal shall terminate the proceedings;

(*b*) the respondent fails to communicate his statement of defence in accordance with sub-section (1) of Section 23, the arbitral tribunal shall continue the proceedings without treating that failure in itself as an admission of the allegations by the claimant [101][and shall have the discretion to treat the right of the respondent to file such statement of defence as having been forfeited];

(*c*) a party fails to appear at an oral hearing or to produce documentary evidence, the arbitral tribunal may continue the proceedings and make the arbitral award on the evidence before it.

COMMENTS

Corresponding old law

Section 25 is a new provision; such provision did not exist in the Arbitration Act, 1940.

UNCITRAL Model Law

Article 25. *Default of a party*

Unless otherwise agreed by the parties, if, without showing sufficient cause,

(*a*) the claimant fails to communicate his statement of claim in accordance with article 23(1), the arbitral tribunal shall terminate the proceedings;

(*b*) the respondent fails to communicate his statement of defence in accordance with article 23(1), the arbitral tribunal shall continue the proceedings without treating such failure in itself as an admission of the claimant's allegations;

(*c*) any party fails to appear at a hearing or to produce documentary evidence, the arbitral tribunal may continue the proceedings and make the award on the evidence before it.

---

101. *Ins.* by Act 3 of 2016, S. 13 (w.r.e.f. 23-10-2015).

Legislative changes

Arbitration and Conciliation (Amendment) Act, 2015 (3 of 2016)

In Section 25 of the principal Act, in clause (*b*), at the end, after the words "allegations by the claimant", the words "and shall have the discretion to treat the right of the respondent to file such statement of defence as having been forfeited" shall be *inserted*.

OBJECTS AND REASONS

Clause 13 of the Bill seeks to amend Section 25 of the principal Act to treat the right of the respondent to file the statement of defence to have been forfeited, if the respondent fails to communicate such statement in accordance with sub-section (1) of Section 23 without reasonable cause.

Scope and application

When the party deliberately avoids participating in the arbitration proceedings in order to frustrate and delay the admitted claim, the Arbitral Tribunal is empowered to pass the award.[102]

Termination of the arbitration proceedings owing to default of the claimant/failure of the claimant in communicating his statement of claim is not permissible in the absence of notice by the arbitrator indicating that no adjournments would be given.[103]

An arbitrator was appointed for the settlement of a dispute with regard to a partnership deed. Proceedings were closed under Section 25 of the Act. After the closure of proceedings, there is no further power under Section 11 to once again refer the same dispute to the arbitrator. An application for the appointment of a substitute arbitrator is not maintainable.[104]

There was default on the part of ATV in filing the statement of claim, and there was no appearance on the part of ATV; also, there was no explanation for not filing a statement of claim on the date on which the order was passed the Arbitral Tribunal had no option but to terminate the arbitration proceedings.[105] The petitioner did not submit his statement of claim in accordance with Section 23(1) without any sufficient cause. It was held that the Arbitral Tribunal was justified in terminating the arbitral proceedings.[106]

---

102. *Ratan Agarwala* v. *Sulochana Jagdishprasad Agrawal*, 2009 SCC OnLine Bom 992: (2009) 6 Mah LJ 561.
103. *S.P. Singla Constructions (P) Ltd.* v. *State of H.P.*, (2019) 2 SCC 488.
104. *Satya Prakash Singh* v. *Dinesh Prakash Singh*, 2014 SCC OnLine All 16183: (2015) 4 All LJ 441.
105. *Indian Oil Corpn. Ltd.* v. *ATV Projects India Ltd.*, 2004 SCC OnLine Del 483: ILR (2004) 2 Del 26.
106. *Balmukund Pandey* v. *V.K. Singh*, 2009 SCC OnLine MP 30: (2010) 1 MP LJ 372.

Termination of arbitration proceedings—Recall of order (*See*, S. 23 under same heading)

When an arbitrator decides to set anyone ex parte, the parties must be informed about the said decision. An ex parte order passed would be set aside if it results in prejudice to the defaulting party by reason that no opportunity was granted to the defaulting party to defend. When there had been consistent absence by a party, failure to give notice to proceed ex parte would not vitiate the award, and there is no misconduct on the part of the arbitrator.[107]

A party who once appears before the arbitrator and seeks an extension of time for filing a written statement accepts the jurisdiction of the arbitrator, and is entitled to reasonable opportunity. A party who sought an extension of time four times spanned over a period of four months and who failed to appear thereafter cannot complain about the violation of the principles of natural justice.[108]

Where one of the arbitrators appointed by the other party was not qualified to be appointed as arbitrator in terms of the arbitration agreement, termination of the arbitration proceedings on the ground that the claimant had failed to file his statement of claim was ex facie illegal, without jurisdiction, and was liable to be set aside.[109]

Arbitration proceedings—Dismissed in default

Arbitration proceedings cannot be dismissed in default; the arbitrator is required to make an award on the evidence available before it.[110]

Writ petition

An order under Section 25(*a*) cannot be challenged before the High Court in a petition under Article 226 of the Constitution.[111]

107. *Nagasrinivasulu* v. *Galada Finance Ltd.*, 2008 SCC OnLine Mad 831: (2009) 1 CTC 158.
108. *Saraswathi Chemicals* v. *Balmer Lawrie & Co. Ltd.*, 2011 SCC OnLine Mad 442: (2011) 3 CTC 9.
109. *Anuptech Equipments (P) Ltd.* v. *Ganpati Coop. Housing Society Ltd.*, 1999 SCC OnLine Bom 54: (1999) 2 Mah LJ 161.
110. *Satgur Sewak Rice and General Mills* v. *Punjab State Civil Supplies Corpn. Ltd.*, 1999 SCC OnLine P&H 1320: PLR (2000) 124 P&H 748.
111. *NRP Projects (P) Ltd.* v. *Hirak Mukhopadhyay*, 2012 SCC OnLine Cal 10496: (2013) 1 Cal LJ 621.

EXPERT APPOINTED BY ARBITRAL TRIBUNAL [S. 26]

26. *Expert appointed by arbitral tribunal.*—(1) Unless otherwise agreed by the parties, the arbitral tribunal may—

(*a*) appoint one or more experts to report to it on specific issues to be determined by the arbitral tribunal; and

(*b*) require a party to give the expert any relevant information or to produce, or to provide access to, any relevant documents, goods or other property for his inspection.

(2) Unless otherwise agreed by the parties, if a party so requests or if the arbitral tribunal considers it necessary, the expert shall, after delivery of his written or oral report, participate in an oral hearing where the parties have the opportunity to put questions to him and to present expert witnesses in order to testify on the points at issue.

(3) Unless otherwise agreed by the parties, the expert shall, on the request of a party, make available to that party for examination all documents, goods or other property in the possession of the expert with which he was provided in order to prepare his report.

COMMENTS

Corresponding old law

Section 26 is new; no such provision existed in the Arbitration Act, 1940.

UNCITRAL Model Law

Article 26. *Expert appointed by arbitral tribunal*

(1) Unless otherwise agreed by the parties, the arbitral tribunal

(*a*) may appoint one or more experts to report to it on specific issues to be determined by the arbitral tribunal;

(*b*) may require a party to give the expert any relevant information or to produce, or to provide access to, any relevant documents, goods or other property for his inspection.

(2) Unless otherwise agreed by the parties, if a party so requests or if the arbitral tribunal considers it necessary, the expert shall, after delivery of his written or oral report, participate in a hearing where the parties have the opportunity to put questions to him and to present expert witnesses in order to testify on the points at issue.

Scope and application

It is not necessary that an arbitrator should possess a special knowledge in the matter.[112] Appointment of an independent auditor for the purpose of verification of the accounts of the firm by the tribunal consisting of two chartered accountants is a step in aid in determining the issues raised before the tribunal. The directions were of a nature which can be issued by the tribunal under Section 2 of the Act.[113]

COURT ASSISTANCE IN TAKING EVIDENCE [S. 27]

27. *Court assistance in taking evidence.*—(1) The arbitral tribunal, or a party with the approval of the arbitral tribunal, may apply to the Court for assistance in taking evidence.

(2) The application shall specify—

(*a*) the names and addresses of the parties and the arbitrators;

(*b*) the general nature of the claim and the relief sought;

(*c*) the evidence to be obtained, in particular,—

(*i*) the name and address of any person to be heard as witness or expert witness and a statement of the subject-matter of the testimony required;

(*ii*) the description of any document to be produced or property to be inspected.

(3) The Court may, within its competence and according to its rules on taking evidence, execute the request by ordering that the evidence be provided directly to the arbitral tribunal.

(4) The Court may, while making an order under sub-section (3), issue the same processes to witnesses as it may issue in suits tried before it.

(5) Persons failing to attend in accordance with such process, or making any other default, or refusing to give their evidence, or guilty of any contempt to the arbitral tribunal during the conduct of arbitral proceedings, shall be subject to the like disadvantages, penalties and punishments by order of the Court on the representation of the arbitral tribunal as they would incur for the like offences in suits tried before the Court.

(6) In this section the expression "Processes" includes summonses and commissions for the examination of witnesses and summonses to produce documents.

---

112. *Union of India* v. *Vengamamba Engg. Co.*, 2001 SCC OnLine AP 430: (2001) 3 ALD 776.

113. *Mahavirchand* v. *Ashaykumar*, 2011 SCC OnLine Bom 794: (2011) 6 Mah LJ 170.

COMMENTS

Corresponding old law

Sub-sections (3) and (4) of Section 27 correspond to Section 43(1), Arbitration Act, 1940. Sub-section (6) corresponds to Section 43(3), Arbitration Act, 1940. Section 43, Arbitration Act, 1940 states:

(1) The Court shall issue the same processes to the parties and witnesses whom the arbitrator or umpire desires to examine as the Court may issue in suits tried before it.

(2) Persons failing to attend in accordance with such process, or making any other default, or refusing to give their evidence, or guilty of any contempt to the arbitrator or umpire during the investigation of the reference, shall be subject to the like disadvantages, penalties and punishments by order of the Court on the representation of the arbitrator or umpire as they would incur for the like offences in suits tried before the Court.

(3) In this section the expression "process" includes summonses and commissions for the examination of witnesses and summonses to produce documents.

UNCITRAL Model Law

Article 27. *Court assistance in taking evidence*

The arbitral tribunal or a party with the approval of the arbitral tribunal may request from a competent court of this State assistance in taking evidence. The court may execute the request within its competence and according to its rules on taking evidence.

Scope and application

Under Section 27, the Arbitral Tribunal, or a party with the approval of the Arbitral Tribunal, may apply to the court for assistance in taking evidence. Section 27 enables the arbitrator to seek assistance of the court in taking evidence.[114]

Assistance of court for taking evidence can be sought as regards any person who fails to cooperate with the tribunal, be it a witness or a party to proceedings.[115]

Where a party or a witness who has been directed to give evidence or produce a document before the Arbitral Tribunal has refused to do so, either the Arbitral Tribunal itself or a party is entitled to apply to the court for its

114. *H.G. Oomor Sait* v. *O. Aslam Sait*, 2001 SCC OnLine Mad 465: (2001) 3 CTC 269.
115. *Delta Distilleries Ltd.* v. *United Spirits Ltd.*, (2014) 1 SCC 113.

assistance in taking evidence.[116] Court's assistance in taking assistance is restricted only to give direction to the parties to produce the document or issue summons to witnesses.[117]

Section 27 permits the court assistance in taking evidence if the Arbitral Tribunal or a party with the approval of the Arbitral Tribunal applies to the court for assistance in taking evidence. In *Satinder Narayan Singh* v. *Indian Labour Coop. Society Ltd.*[118], the petitioner had not obtained the approval of the Arbitral Tribunal before moving the court seeking its assistance for taking evidence by invocation of Section 27 of the Act. Therefore, the application filed was not maintainable. The arbitrator is under no obligation to give reasons in support of the decision given on application filed under Section 27.[119]

The court has no jurisdiction to adjudicate upon the admissibility of documents sought to be summoned.[120]

An order rejecting an application under Section 27 of the 1996 Act is a decision and/or order, and is definitely not an interim award. It would be open to the party finally aggrieved by an award to challenge the award in which the order rejecting an application under Section 27 has merged under Section 34(2), if in law a challenge would be available under that section.[121] An order of the arbitrator is not open to challenge before the court on merits in the absence of proceedings provided under the Act.[122]

Power of sole arbitrator to take assistance of an expert

It is clearly provided in the Arbitration and Conciliation Act, 1996 that an Arbitral Tribunal can, if necessary, take the help of experts in terms of Section 27 of the said Act. If the sole arbitrator requires the assistance of an expert, it can always take such assistance.[123]

---

116. *United Spirits Ltd.* v. *Delta Distilleries Ltd.*, 2012 SCC OnLine Bom 1008: (2012) 6 Mah LJ 522.
117. *Rasiklal Ratilal* v. *Fancy Corpn. Ltd.*, 2007 SCC OnLine Bom 299: (2007) 4 Mah LJ 876.
118. 2007 SCC OnLine Del 1675: ILR (2008) 1 Del 1084.
119. *Hindustan Petroleum Corpn. Ltd.* v. *Ashok Kumar Garg*, 2006 SCC OnLine Del 1056: (2006) 91 DRJ 591.
120. *BJ-Techno-HAS (JV)* v. *National Hydroelectric Power Corpn. Ltd.*, 2019 SCC OnLine P&H 2118: PLR (2019) 195 P&H 448.
121. *Harinarayan G. Bajaj* v. *Sharedeal Financial Consultants (P) Ltd.*, 2002 SCC OnLine Bom 1186: (2003) 2 Mah LJ 598; *Satinder Narayan Singh* v. *Indian Labour Coop. Society Ltd.*, 2007 SCC OnLine Del 1675: ILR (2008) 1 Del 1084.
122. *Montana Developers (P) Ltd.* v. *Aditya Developers*, 2016 SCC OnLine Bom 5318: (2016) 6 Mah LJ 660.
123. *Sime Darby Engg. SDN. BHD.* v. *Engineers India Ltd.*, (2009) 7 SCC 545.

Sub-section (5)—Scope

Section 27(5) is not confined to a person being guilty of contempt only when he fails to attend the court in accordance with the court process and persons guilty of any contempt to the Arbitral Tribunal during the conduct of the arbitral proceedings are within its ken. Section 27(5) empowers the tribunal to make representation to the court for contempt of its interim orders. In *Alka Chandewar* v. *Shamshul Ishrar Khan*[124], the sole arbitrator appointed by the parties passed an interim order and directed that no further flats were to be disposed of without the leave of the Arbitral Tribunal. In breach of this restraint order, the respondent transferred five flats. The arbitrator referred the matter of its contempt to the High Court for passing necessary orders under Section 27(5). The High Court rejected the reference in limine. The Supreme Court remanded the matter to the High Court to decide the contempt matter on facts of the case.

No power has been conferred on the Arbitral Tribunal to enforce its order, nor does it provide judicial enforcement. Section 27(5) provides the remedy for breach. Any person failing to comply with the order of the Arbitral Tribunal would be deemed to be "making any other default" or "guilty of any contempt to the arbitral tribunal during the conduct of the proceedings". Once such a representation is received by the court from the Arbitral Tribunal, the court would be competent to deal with such party in default or in contempt as if in contempt of the order of court, *i.e.* either under the provisions of the Contempt of Courts Act or under the provisions of Order 39 Rule 2-A CPC.[125]

Arbitral Tribunal is not a court but a creature of contract between the parties; its functions are not judicial functions. Contempt of court is applicable to breach or violation of the orders of the court. Section 27(5) does not empower the tribunal to make representation to the court for contempt of court if the order including an interim order passed by the arbitrator except in respect of taking evidence is violated by the party. A contempt petition is not maintainable.[126]

124. (2017) 16 SCC 119.
125. *Alka Chandewar* v. *Shamshul Ishrar Khan*, (2017) 16 SCC 119; *Krishan* v. *Anand*, 2009 SCC OnLine Del 2472: (2009) 112 DRJ 657.
126. *Alka Chandewar* v. *Shamshul Ishrar Khan*, 2015 SCC OnLine Bom 5618: (2016) 1 Mah LJ 52.

CHAPTER VI

Making of Arbitral Award and Termination of Proceedings

RULES APPLICABLE TO SUBSTANCE OF DISPUTE [S. 28]

28. *Rules applicable to substance of dispute.*—(1) Where the place of arbitration is situated in India,—

(*a*) in an arbitration other than an international commercial arbitration, the arbitral tribunal shall decide the dispute submitted to arbitration in accordance with the substantive law for the time being in force in India;

(*b*) in international commercial arbitration,—

(*i*) the arbitral tribunal shall decide the dispute in accordance with the rules of law designated by the parties as applicable to the substance of the dispute;

(*ii*) any designation by the parties of the law or legal system of a given country shall be construed, unless otherwise expressed, as directly referring to the substantive law of that country and not to its conflict of laws rules;

(*iii*) failing any designation of the law under sub-clause (*ii*) by the parties, the arbitral tribunal shall apply the rules of law it considers to be appropriate given all the circumstances surrounding the dispute.

(2) The arbitral tribunal shall decide *ex aequo et bono* or as *amiable compositeur* only if the parties have expressly authorised it to do so.

[1][(3) While deciding and making an award, the arbitral tribunal shall, in all cases, take into account the terms of the contract and trade usages applicable to the transaction.]

---

1. *Subs.* by Act 3 of 2016, S. 14 (w.r.e.f. 23-10-2015). Prior to substitution it read as:

"(3) In all cases, the arbitral tribunal shall decide in accordance with the terms of the contract and shall take into account the usages of the trade applicable to the transaction."

COMMENTS

Corresponding old law

Section 28 is new, and did not exist in the Arbitration Act, 1940.

UNCITRAL Model Law

Article 28. *Rules applicable to substance of dispute*

(1) The arbitral tribunal shall decide the dispute in accordance with such rules of law as are chosen by the parties as applicable to the substance of the dispute. Any designation of the law or legal system of a given State shall be construed, unless otherwise expressed, as directly referring to the substantive law of that State and not to its conflict of laws rules.

(2) Failing any designation by the parties, the arbitral tribunal shall apply the law determined by the conflict of laws rules which it considers applicable.

(3) The arbitral tribunal shall decide ex aequo et bono or as amiable compositeur only if the parties have expressly authorized it to do so.

(4) In all cases, the arbitral tribunal shall decide in accordance with the terms of the contract and shall take into account the usages of the trade applicable to the transaction.

Legislative changes

Arbitration and Conciliation (Amendment) Act, 2015 (3 of 2016)

In Section 28 of the principal Act, for sub-section (3), the following sub-section shall be *substituted*, namely —

"(3) While deciding and making an award, the arbitral tribunal shall, in all cases, take into account the terms of the contract and trade usages applicable to the transaction."

OBJECTS AND REASONS

Clause 14 of the Bill seeks to insert a new sub-section (3) of the principal Act to provide that the arbitral tribunal, while deciding and making an award, take into account the terms of the contract and trade and usage applicable to the transaction.

Scope and application

Section 28 is imperative in nature. Legislative intent is that Indian nationals should not be permitted to derogate from Indian law. This is part of the public policy of the country.[2]

---

2. *TDM Infrastructure (P) Ltd.* v. *UE Development India (P) Ltd.*, (2008) 14 SCC 271.

Under Section 28(1)(*a*) of the Act, the Arbitral Tribunal has to decide the dispute in accordance with the substantive law for the time being in force. Substantive law would include the Contract Act, 1872 and consequently, it is open to the Arbitral Tribunal to invoke the provisions of Section 70 and to grant compensation even after concluding that the contract was void. A person whose contract is void would be entitled to compensation under Section 70, Contract Act if he had established his claim that the other person had enjoyed the benefit of the thing delivered and that the said thing was never intended to be delivered gratuitously.[3]

Section 28(1)(*a*) and Section 28(1)(*b*)—Applicability of

In respect of "international commercial arbitration", Section 28(1)(*b*) of the 1996 Act would apply, whereas in respect of any other dispute where the place of arbitration is situated in India, Section 28(1)(*a*) shall apply. When both the companies are incorporated in India, clause (*ii*) of Section 2(1)(*f*) and not clause (*iii*) is relevant.[4]

So long as the obligations arising under Agreement I subsist and the American company is not discharged of its obligation under Agreement I, there is a "foreign element" therein and the dispute arising thereon. The autonomy of the parties in such a case to choose the governing law is well recognised in law. Section 28(1)(*b*) expressly recognises such autonomy.[5]

In accordance with the substantive law for the time being in force in India [Sub-s. (1)(*a*)]

The award was to be passed on consideration of the substantive law of India. A contract entered into in contravention of the bye-laws of Bombay Stock Exchange is void. An award passed by the arbitrator on a contract contrary to bye-laws of the Bombay Stock Exchange would be arbitrary and without jurisdiction.[6] The jurisdiction of the Arbitral Tribunal to pass an award would be only in the event the contract entered into was a valid contract. An award without jurisdiction or an award which is arbitrary would be contrary to the public policy of India, covered by Section 34(*b*)(*ii*), Arbitration and Conciliation Act, 1996 and would be set aside.[7]

A contract between the contractor and Railway provided that the rate clause and conditions in the agreement shall continue to be of full effect and binding on respective parties. The award granting sums of money to

3. *Union of India* v. *L.S.N. Murthy*, 2006 SCC OnLine AP 414: (2006) 2 AP LJ 170.
4. *TDM Infrastructure (P) Ltd.* v. *UE Development India (P) Ltd.*, (2008) 14 SCC 271.
5. *Sasan Power Ltd.* v. *North American Coal Corpn. (India) (P) Ltd.*, (2016) 10 SCC 813.
6. *G.R. Didwania* v. *A.C. Choksey*, 2001 SCC OnLine Bom 955: (2002) 2 Mah LJ 604.
7. *Ibid.*

the contractor for overstay of work was beyond specific clauses of terms of agreement and rider agreement. Such grant is liable to be set aside.[8]

Mere erroneous interpretation of the contract by the arbitrator would not justify interference by the court under Section 28(3).[9] Wrong interpretation of law by tribunal is no ground for interference by court unless the result shocks the conscience of the court.[10] If substantive law is disregarded, a challenger would make out a case for interference.[11]

Law applicable to arbitration proceedings does not include rulings of arbitrators

The law applicable to arbitration proceedings does not include rulings of arbitrators. What is relevant is what the arbitrator, who may be appointed, will hold in the present case and not what some other arbitrator held in some other arbitration and some other contract even if it be between the same parties. Moreover, the court cannot be bound by what an arbitrator might have held in an arbitration proceedings unless it be that the said award operates as a bar between the parties barring either of them from raising a plea on that behalf.[12]

Personal knowledge of arbitrator—Use of

An Arbitral Tribunal cannot make use of its personal knowledge of the facts of the dispute, which is not a part of the record, to decide the dispute. But an Arbitral Tribunal can certainly use their expert or technical knowledge or the general knowledge about the particular trade in deciding a matter. In fact, that is why in many arbitrations, persons with technical knowledge are appointed as they will be well-versed with the practices and customs in the respective fields. In *P.R. Shah, Shares & Stock Brokers (P) Ltd.* v. *B.H.H. Securities (P) Ltd.*[13], all that the arbitrators have referred to was the market practice. That cannot be considered as using some personal knowledge of facts of a transaction to decide a dispute.

Waiver of British rules of arbitration

It was a case of international contract for supply of steel products. Parties had agreed to settle their disputes by arbitration in London. The mere fact that

8. *Sree Kamatchi Amman Constructions* v. *Railways*, 2007 SCC OnLine Mad 610: (2007) 4 LW 379.
9. *ONGC Ltd.* v. *Surya Paints and Oil Works*, 2004 SCC OnLine Bom 214: (2004) 3 Mah LJ 391.
10. *VSNL* v. *Shapoorji Pallonji & Co. Ltd.*, 2007 SCC OnLine Cal 670: (2008) 1 CHN 721.
11. *Ibid.*
12. *Adhunik Steels Ltd.* v. *Orissa Manganese and Minerals (P) Ltd.*, (2007) 7 SCC 125.
13. (2012) 1 SCC 594.

the respondent agreed or concurred in principle that too without prejudice to the offer made by the petitioner to be guided by the Arbitration and Conciliation Act, 1996 cannot constitute waiver of the applicability of the British Rules of Arbitration. Parties have stood by the terms of the contract. The procedural law applicable to the arbitration proceedings had to be the British Rules of Arbitration; it was not possible for the court to substitute the British Rules of Arbitration by the procedural law under the Arbitration and Conciliation Act, 1996.[14]

Moulding of relief sought [Sub-s. (2)]

Granting compensation for the alleged lost potential of the land was not permissible by moulding the relief. It was not the case of the appellants in the writ petition, even in the alternative that the land could not be reclaimed and there was no claim for compensation for the alleged lost potential of the land. The relief that was sought was a direction to the second respondent to reclaim the appellant's land; awarding compensation for the alleged lost potential of the land was not moulding the relief that was sought.[15]

Award to be in accordance with the terms of the contract and trade uses applicable to the transaction [S. 28(3)]

An award of the arbitrator has to be in accordance with the terms of the contract, and if not, it shall be set aside. In *ONGC Ltd.* v. *Saw Pipes Ltd.*[16], there was a contract for the supply of goods. Pre-estimated damages were stipulated in the case of breach. Liquidated damages are not penalty. There was a delay in the supply of goods by the contractor. A dispute was raised over the recovery of liquidated damages. The arbitrator held that as the purchaser had failed to prove loss, it was not entitled to damages. In certain contracts, it is impossible to assess the damages or prove the same. Such a situation is taken care of by Sections 73 and 74, Contract Act and in the present case by the specific terms of the contract. In such a case as the present one, it was for the party who contended that the amount was not a reasonable compensation to prove the same. The award was not in accordance with the terms of the contract and, as such, was set aside.

The Arbitral Tribunal has to decide the dispute in accordance with the terms and conditions of the contract. Usage of trade can also be taken into consideration. Granting of price escalation to some firm by another department cannot be considered as an ordinary usage of trade.[17] The

14. *Aurohill Global Commodities Ltd.* v. *Maharashtra STC Ltd.*, (2007) 7 SCC 120.
15. *Rajinder Krishan Khanna* v. *Union of India*, (1998) 7 SCC 129 (para 16).
16. (2003) 5 SCC 705.
17. *Union of India* v. *Freight Carriers*, 2008 SCC OnLine Gau 48: (2008) 5 Gau LR 256.

arbitrator acted beyond its jurisdiction in giving the award on the basis of principles of fair play and equity.[18]

The award of the arbitrator has to be in accordance with the terms of the contract. The award of the arbitrator that the appellant-Board cannot levy pre-estimated damages because extensions were granted to complete the work was contrary to agreement conditions, and hence liable to be set aside.[19]

In case of physical distribution of properties in specie between the parties, an exact division is impossible.[20]

Assessment and adjudication of any claim or counterclaim, especially compensation or damages based upon the terms of the contract, requires evidence and the material to assess the actual loss or damages.[21]

DECISION-MAKING BY PANEL OF ARBITRATORS [S. 29]

29. *Decision-making by panel of arbitrators.*—(1) Unless otherwise agreed by the parties, in arbitral proceedings with more than one arbitrator, any decision of the arbitral tribunal shall be made by a majority of all its members.

(2) Notwithstanding sub-section (1), if authorised by the parties or all the members of the arbitral tribunal, questions of procedure may be decided by the presiding arbitrator.

COMMENTS

Legislative changes

Section 29 is new; a similar provision did not exist in the Arbitration Act, 1940.

UNCITRAL Model Law

Article 29. *Decision-making by panel of arbitrators*

In arbitral proceedings with more than one arbitrator, any decision of the arbitral tribunal shall be made, unless otherwise agreed by the parties, by a majority of all its members. However, questions of procedure may be decided

18. *Ibid.*
19. *Chennai Metropolitan Water Supply and Sewerage Board* v. *Aban Constructions (P) Ltd.*, 2006 SCC OnLine Mad 486: (2006) 3 CTC 794.
20. *Vijaypat Singhania* v. *Hari Shankar Singhania*, 2013 SCC OnLine Bom 434: (2013) 5 Mah LJ 744.
21. *R.M. Cylinders (P) Ltd.* v. *Hindustan Petroleum Corpn. Ltd.*, 2013 SCC OnLine Bom 573: (2013) 4 Mah LJ 67.

by a presiding arbitrator, if so authorized by the parties or all members of the arbitral tribunal.

Scope and application

As laid down by Section 29, in arbitral proceedings where there is more than one arbitrator, the decision of the arbitrators shall be made by a majority of all its arbitrators.

Questions of procedure may be decided by a presiding arbitrator, if so authorised by the parties or all the members of the Arbitral Tribunal.

The Arbitration and Conciliation Act, 1996 places the matter beyond doubt by providing that what is required in law for a valid award is an award of the majority constituting an Arbitral Tribunal. Majority of the Arbitral Tribunal consisting of *K* and *C* made and signed the arbitral award on 18 February 2004. *C* died. Before the death of *C* constituting the majority, there was a valid award which was made and signed by the majority. That was sufficient to constitute a valid award in law.[22]

Decision by majority of arbitrators [Sub-s. (1)]

In arbitration proceedings with more than one arbitrator, the decision by the Arbitral Tribunal shall be made by the majority of all its members.[23]

TIME LIMIT FOR ARBITRAL AWARD [S. 29-A]

[24][**29-A.** *Time limit for arbitral award.*—[25][(1) The award in matters other than international commercial arbitration shall be made by the arbitral tribunal within a period of twelve months from the date of completion of pleadings under sub-section (4) of Section 23:

Provided that the award in the matter of international commercial arbitration may be made as expeditiously as possible and endeavour may be made to dispose of the matter within a period of twelve months from the date of completion of pleadings under sub-section (4) of Section 23.]

---

22. *Moti* v. *Sheroo Jal Vakil*, 2009 SCC OnLine Bom 604: (2009) 6 Mah LJ 535.
23. *Ibid.*
24. *Ins.* by Act 3 of 2016, S. 15 (w.r.e.f. 23-10-2015).
25. *Subs.* by Act 33 of 2019, S. 6(*a*) (w.e.f. 30-8-2019). Prior to substitution it read as:

"(1) The award shall be made within a period of twelve months from the date the arbitral tribunal enters upon the reference.

Explanation.—For the purpose of this sub-section, an arbitral tribunal shall be deemed to have entered upon the reference on the date on which the arbitrator or all the arbitrators, as the case may be, have received notice, in writing, of their appointment."

(2) If the award is made within a period of six months from the date the arbitral tribunal enters upon the reference, the arbitral tribunal shall be entitled to receive such amount of additional fees as the parties may agree.

(3) The parties may, by consent, extend the period specified in sub-section (1) for making award for a further period not exceeding six months.

(4) If the award is not made within the period specified in sub-section (1) or the extended period specified under sub-section (3), the mandate of the arbitrator(s) shall terminate unless the court has, either prior to or after the expiry of the period so specified, extended the period:

Provided that while extending the period under this sub-section, if the court finds that the proceedings have been delayed for the reasons attributable to the arbitral tribunal, then, it may order reduction of fees of arbitrator(s) by not exceeding five per cent for each month of such delay:

[26][Provided further that where an application under sub-section (5) is pending, the mandate of the arbitrator shall continue till the disposal of the said application:

Provided also that the arbitrator shall be given an opportunity of being heard before the fees is reduced.]

(5) The extension of period referred to in sub-section (4) may be on the application of any of the parties and may be granted only for sufficient cause and on such terms and conditions as may be imposed by the court.

(6) While extending the period referred to in sub-section (4), it shall be open to the court to substitute one or all of the arbitrators and if one or all of the arbitrators are substituted, the arbitral proceedings shall continue from the stage already reached and on the basis of the evidence and material already on record, and the arbitrator(s) appointed under this section shall be deemed to have received the said evidence and material.

(7) In the event of arbitrator(s) being appointed under this section, the arbitral tribunal thus reconstituted shall be deemed to be in continuation of the previously appointed arbitral tribunal.

(8) It shall be open to the court to impose actual or exemplary costs upon any of the parties under this section.

(9) An application filed under sub-section (5) shall be disposed of by the court as expeditiously as possible and endeavour shall be made to dispose of the matter within a period of sixty days from the date of service of notice on the opposite party.]

STATE AMENDMENTS

Union Territory of Jammu and Kashmir.—In its application to the Union Territory of Jammu and Kashmir,—

---

26. *Ins.* by Act 33 of 2019, S. 6(*b*) (w.e.f. 30-8-2019).

(*a*) for sub-section (1), the following sub-section shall be *substituted*, namely:—

"(1) The award shall be made within a period of twelve months from the date the arbitral tribunal enters upon the reference.

Explanation.—For the purposes of this sub-section, an arbitral tribunal shall be deemed to have entered upon the reference on the date on which the arbitrator or all the arbitrators, as the case may be, have received notice, in writing, of their appointment.";

(*b*) in sub-section (4), *omit* second and third provisos. [*Vide* S.O. 1123(E), dated 18-3-2020 (w.e.f. 18-3-2020)].

Union Territory of Ladakh.—In its application to the Union Territory of Ladakh,

(*a*) for sub-section (1), *substitute*—

"(1) The award shall be made within a period of twelve months from the date the arbitral tribunal enters upon the reference.

Explanation.—For the purposes of this sub-section, an arbitral tribunal shall be deemed to have entered upon the reference on the date on which the arbitrator or all the arbitrators, as the case may be, have received notice, in writing, of their appointment".

(*b*) in sub-section (4), *omit* second and third provisos. [*Vide* S.O. 3774(E), dated 23-10-2020].

COMMENTS

Corresponding old law

Section 29-A is a new section, added by Amendment Act 3 of 2016. Such provisions did not exist in the Arbitration Act, 1940.

Legislative changes

Arbitration and Conciliation (Amendment) Act, 2015 (3 of 2016)

Section 29-A is new, inserted by the Amendment Act, 2015 (3 of 2016).

OBJECTS AND REASONS

Clause 15 of the Bill seeks to insert new Section 29-A and 29-B in the principal Act to specify the time limit for making arbitral awards. Section 29-A provides that the award is to be made within a period of twelve months from the date the arbitral tribunal enters upon the reference. However, the parties may extend such period for a further period not exceeding six months. If the award is made within a period of six months, the arbitral tribunal shall be entitled to receive additional fees as the parties agree. If the award is not made within the specified period or extended period, the mandate of the arbitrator shall terminate unless the time is extended by the Court in accordance with the provisions of sub-section (4) to (9).

Arbitration and Conciliation (Amendment) Act, 2019 (33 of 2019)

In Section 29-A of the principal Act,—

(*a*) for sub-section (1), the following sub-section shall be substituted, namely:—

"(1) The award in matters other than international commercial arbitration shall be made by the arbitral tribunal within a period of twelve months from the date of completion of pleadings under sub-section (4) of Section 23:

Provided that the award in the matter of international commercial arbitration may be made as expeditiously as possible and endeavour may be made to dispose of the matter within a period of twelve months from the date of completion of pleadings under sub-section (4) of Section 23.";

(*b*) in sub-section (4), after the proviso, the following provisos shall be inserted, namely:—

"Provided further that where an application under sub-section (5) is pending, the mandate of the arbitrator shall continue till the disposal of the said application:

Provided also that the arbitrator shall be given an opportunity of being heard before the fees is reduced."

Since Section 29-A(1), as amended, is remedial in nature, it should be applicable to all pending arbitral proceedings as on the effective date, *i.e.* 30 August 2019.[27]

Scope and application

Section 29-A, a new section, inserted by Amendment Act 3 of 2016 prescribes time limit for making arbitral award by the tribunal.

Section 29-A provides that the award is to be made within a period of 12 months from the date the Arbitral Tribunal enters upon the reference. However, the parties may extend such a period for a further period not exceeding six months. If the award is made within a period of six months, the Arbitral Tribunal shall be entitled to receive additional fees as the parties agree. If the award is not made within the specified period or extended period, the mandate of the arbitrator shall terminate unless the time is extended by the court in accordance with the provisions of sub-section (4) to (9).

---

27. *Tata Sons (P) Ltd.* v. *Siva Industries & Holdings Ltd.*, (2023) 5 SCC 421.

The time for completion of arbitration was mentioned in the arbitration agreement itself. The arbitrator becomes *de jure* and is unable to perform his functions upon expiry of such time.[28]

In the absence of mutual consent, time for making an award by the Arbitral Tribunal cannot be extended.[29] Where the time for making an award stipulated in the agreement has expired, and the arbitrator decides not to further proceed in the arbitration proceedings, the court cannot compel the arbitrator to continue; the passing of such an order would, in fact, amount to modification and/or alteration of the arbitration agreement.[30]

If the agreement specifies the period within which an award has to be passed, the arbitrator is duty bound to comply with the same, and has no power or mandate to extend time suo moto.[31]

Matters were adjourned by the arbitrator on numerous occasions. If in a case mandate of the arbitrator is terminated due to failure to complete the proceedings within time, a great prejudice would be caused to parties fighting for their claim for years together. In view of such facts, the time to conclude arbitration proceedings was extended.[32]

There is no specific provision in the IBC, 2016 which bars the authority of a resolution professional to move the application for the extension of the time limit. The court, while exercising its jurisdiction under Section 29-A, is not supposed to go into controversies in detail; the scope of its consideration is confined to "sufficient cause" for extension of Arbitration Tribunal's mandate. It was known to the Arbitral Tribunal that the corporate insolvency resolution process was pending before the National Company Law Appellate Tribunal and that the applicant was moving court for extension of time. He was a duly appointed resolution professional. The Arbitral Tribunal's mandate was extended leaving the arbitration related issues to be examined by the Arbitral Tribunal.[33]

Retrospective operation

The provision of Section 29-A is retrospective in nature and hence it is applicable to all pending arbitration proceedings which commenced after 23 October 2015. For domestic arbitration, therefore, the clock for the timeline of 12 months envisaged in the substituted provision of Section 29-A(1) for

28. *Ghanshyam Sarda* v. *Govind Kumar Sarda*, 2009 SCC OnLine Cal 1698: (2010) 3 ICC 342.
29. *Ibid.*
30. *Ibid.*
31. *Nitya Nand and Sons* v. *Union of India*, 2019 SCC OnLine P&H 7921.
32. *Puran Singh* v. *LAO*, 2023 SCC OnLine HP 1823.
33. *Reliance Communications Infrastructure Ltd.* v. *BSNL*, (2021) 1 HCC (Del) 416.

passing of the award would start ticking from the date of completion of the proceeding as per Section 23(4) of the Act.[34]

The Amendment Act, 2019 is clearly prospective. The time for making the award was extended.[35]

"Court" [Sub-s. (4)]

The term "Court" contained in Section 29-A(4) has to be interpreted as the "Supreme Court" in the case of international commercial arbitrations and as the "High Court" in the case of domestic arbitrations. Either of the party will be at liberty to file an arbitration petition before the High Court under Section 29-A(5) of the Act, seeking extension of time for continuance of the arbitration proceedings in exercise of the power conferred under Section 29-A(4) of the Act, in the case of any domestic arbitration.[36] The arbitration proceedings were not concluded within the stipulated time as the facts and evidence in the case were elaborative and highly technical in nature; three months' time was granted for passing an arbitral award.[37]

Where appointment of arbitrator under Section 11 of the Act was made by the High Court, an application for extension of time filed under Section 29-A of the Act is maintainable before the said High Court.[38]

The District Judge allowed the application for extension of time; by ex parte order extended the mandate of arbitrator for one year, and the copy of the order was served on the opposite party; the grant of extension of time was proper.[39]

The word "Court" in Section 2(1)(*e*) means the principal civil court of original jurisdiction in the district and includes the High Court if it exercises ordinary original civil jurisdiction. It would apply to the term "Court" appearing in Section 29-A, while making an application for extension of the period of the Arbitral Tribunal. Since Gauhati High Court does not exercise ordinary original civil jurisdiction, an application for extension of the period of the Arbitral Tribunal before the Gauhati High Court was held not maintainable.[40]

---

34. *SARA International (P) Ltd.* v. *South Eastern Railways*, 2020 SCC OnLine Ori 973: AIR OnLine 2020 Bom 210.
35. *G.N. Pandian* v. *S. Vasudevan*, 2019 SCC OnLine Mad 9789.
36. *Lots Shipping Co. Ltd.* v. *Cochin Port Trust*, 2020 SCC OnLine Ker 21443: (2020) 2 KLT 907.
37. *Ibid.*
38. *Indian Farmers Fertilizers Coop. Ltd.* v. *Manish Engg. Enterprises*, 2022 SCC OnLine All 150.
39. *Liladitya Deb* v. *Tara Ranjan Pattanaik*, 2021 SCC OnLine Ori 928.
40. *Aplus Projects and Technology (P) Ltd.* v. *Oil India Ltd.*, 2019 SCC OnLine Gau 5739: (2020) 1 Gau LR 99.

The appointment of the arbitrator was made by the High Court under Section 11, Arbitration and Conciliation Act 1996. An application for extension of time for arbitral award shall lie before the said High Court.[41]

Extension of time only once

A substantial change in arbitration law was brought about by the Act of 1996. The Arbitration Act, 1940 had Section 28 providing for extension of time to conclude the reference, as could be made by the court from "time-to-time". The 1996 Act did not have in it a provision for extension of time to conclude the reference. Interpretation on this can well be that the legislature thought it fit to do away with the procedure of repeated approach to court for extension of time, to leave the tribunal to conclude the reference without limitation of period, in which to do it. Instead, the omission would have to be taken into consideration for the purpose of interpreting Section 29-A, later incorporated by the Amendment of 2015 with further amendment made to it. Such consideration does not lead to the conclusion that approach to court for extension of time can be made only once. The court granted extension of time to conclude the reference.[42]

COVID-19 pandemic—Extension of time for completion of proceedings [Sub-Ss. (4), (5) and (8)]

A dispute arose between the parties out of wagon investment agreement and as such the dispute was referred to arbitration. The Arbitral Tribunal entered upon the reference, and pleadings were completed on 27 August 2019. As per the provisions of Section 29-A(1), the date of passing of the award could be 26 August 2020. Due to COVID-19 pandemic situation, the functioning of the Arbitral Tribunals was delayed due to the lockdown situation. The provisions of Section 29-A applied as it had retrospective effect. The time for completion of the arbitral proceedings was extended by six months.[43]

Covid-19 pandemic—Time extended

In the instant case, pleadings were completed in May 2018 and the matter was fixed for evidence. Movement of the general public was restricted due to COVID-19 pandemic for almost two years and no substantive work could be

41. *Indian Farmers Fertilizers Coop. Ltd.* v. *Manish Engg. Enterprises*, 2022 SCC OnLine All 150.
42. *Senbo Engg. Ltd.* v. *Hooghly River Bridge Commissioners*, 2020 SCC OnLine Cal 2250.
43. *SARA International (P) Ltd.* v. *Railways*, 2020 SCC OnLine Ori 973.

undertaken by the arbitrator. Six months' time was granted to the arbitrator for concluding arbitral proceedings.[44]

COVID-19 pandemic contributed to the delay in the conclusion of the proceedings. The arbitrator had passed his award 14 days beyond the stipulated time. The petitioner's petition seeking extension of the mandate of the arbitrator was allowed; the mandate of the arbitrator was regularised till the passing of the award.[45]

Section 29-A enables the court to enlarge the time, if it is satisfied that the Arbitral Tribunal has not been able to conclude the proceedings on account of circumstances which were completely beyond its control. The arbitrator entered the reference but on account of lock down in the wake of COVID-19 pandemic could not complete the proceedings within the stipulated period of 12 months. Sufficient reason was available to enlarge the time. The High Court granted six months' time to conclude the arbitral proceedings.[46]

Pleadings were completed on 22 August 2019, but thereafter, there were restrictions on movement of the general public due to COVID-19 pandemic. The said restrictions remained in force for almost two years. During that period, no substantive work could be undertaken by the arbitrator. Further six months to conclude the arbitration proceedings/pass award was granted.[47]

Award not passed within one year, time also not extended—Award null and void

According to Section 29-A, the arbitrator has to pass an award within one year of entering appearance. Section 29-A(3) gives power to extend this period for a maximum period of six months. An award was not passed within the stipulated period. The arbitrator became functus officio and was not competent to deal with the dispute. The award passed in the case was null and void was not enforceable.[48]

The arbitrator is obliged to pass an award within the statutory period/or extended period. The award passed after the expiry of an extended period is nullity.[49]

---

44. *Daya Ram* v. *LAO*, 2023 SCC OnLine HP 1826; See also, *Jagdish* v. *LAO*, 2019 SCC OnLine MP 4908.
45. *Harkirat Singh Sodhi* v. *Oram Foods (P) Ltd.*, 2023 SCC OnLine Del 3674.
46. *Ashwani Kumar* v. *LAO*, 2022 SCC OnLine HP 6823.
47. *Sanjeev Kumar* v. *LAO*, 2022 SCC OnLine HP 6204; *Daya Ram* v. *LAO*, 2023 SCC OnLine HP 1826.
48. *Roop Singh Bhatty* v. *Shriram City Union Finance Ltd.*, 2022 SCC OnLine TS 1049.
49. *New Engg. Enterprises* v. *Indian Overseas Bank*, 2019 SCC OnLine Utt 1861.

Extension of time under Article 227 of the Constitution

The relief of extension of time for passing arbitral award cannot be granted under supervisory jurisdiction. However, to avoid multiplicity of proceedings, the said relief was granted.[50]

Additional arbitrator [S. 29-A(6)]

The court can substitute one or all arbitrators. The word "substitute" in Section 29-A(6) cannot be interpreted to mean appointment of additional arbitrators.[51]

Substitution of arbitrator—Allegation of bias [S. 29-A(6)]

When specific provisions are incorporated under Sections 13, 14 and 15 for challenge against an arbitrator and for substitution, allegation of bias cannot be raised as cause to seek substitution of the arbitrator under Section 29-A.[52]

Writ petition for termination of mandate of arbitrator

Section 29-A contains a complete mechanism to deal with situations that may arise after termination of the mandate of the arbitrator on account of delay in passing the award. In event of termination of the mandate of arbitrator, substitution can be attained within the framework of the provisions under the principal Arbitration and Conciliation Act, 1996 and Amending Act. A writ petition for termination of the mandate of arbitrator is not maintainable.[53]

FAST TRACK PROCEDURE [S. 29-B]

[54][**29-B.** *Fast track procedure.*—(1) Notwithstanding anything contained in this Act, the parties to an arbitration agreement, may, at any stage either before or at the time of appointment of the arbitral tribunal, agree in writing to have their dispute resolved by fast track procedure specified in sub-section (3).

(2) The parties to the arbitration agreement, while agreeing for resolution of dispute by fast track procedure, may agree that the arbitral tribunal shall consist of a sole arbitrator who shall be chosen by the parties.

50. *Lots Shipping Co. Ltd.* v. *Cochin Port Trust*, 2020 SCC OnLine Ker 21443: (2020) 2 KLT 907.
51. *Aplus Projects and Technology (P) Ltd.* v. *Oil India Ltd.*, 2019 SCC OnLine Gau 5739: (2020) 1 Gau LR 99.
52. *Flemingo Duty Free Shop (P) Ltd.* v. *Airports Authority of India*, 2022 SCC OnLine Ker 3459: (2022) 4 KLT 783.
53. *P.K. Construction Co.* v. *Shimla Municipal Corpn.*, 2017 SCC OnLine HP 2641.
54. *Ins.* by Act 3 of 2016, S. 15 (w.r.e.f. 23-10-2015).

(3) The arbitral tribunal shall follow the following procedure while conducting arbitration proceedings under sub-section (1):

(*a*) The arbitral tribunal shall decide the dispute on the basis of written pleadings, documents and submissions filed by the parties without any oral hearing;

(*b*) The arbitral tribunal shall have power to call for any further information or clarification from the parties in addition to the pleadings and documents filed by them;

(*c*) An oral hearing may be held only, if, all the parties make a request or if the arbitral tribunal considers it necessary to have oral hearing for clarifying certain issues;

(*d*) The arbitral tribunal may dispense with any technical formalities, if an oral hearing is held, and adopt such procedure as deemed appropriate for expeditious disposal of the case.

(4) The award under this section shall be made within a period of six months from the date the arbitral tribunal enters upon the reference.

(5) If the award is not made within the period specified in sub-section (4), the provisions of sub-sections (3) to (9) of Section 29-A shall apply to the proceedings.

(6) The fees payable to the arbitrator and the manner of payment of the fees shall be such as may be agreed between the arbitrator and the parties.]

COMMENTS

Corresponding old law

Section 29-B is newly added by the Amending Act 3 of 2016. Such a provision did not exist in the Arbitration Act, 1940

Legislative changes

Arbitration and Conciliation (Amendment) Act, 2015 (3 of 2016)

Section 29-B has been added by the Amending Act 3 of 2016. Section 29-B lays down fast track procedure for the resolution of arbitration disputes, where the parties mutually agree for such procedure.

OBJECTS AND REASONS

Clause 15 of the Bill seeks to insert new Section 29-A and 29-B in the principal Act to specify the time limit for making an arbitral award.

Further, Section 29-B provides for fast track procedure for conducting arbitral proceedings, in a case where the parties mutually agree for such procedure. In such cases, the Arbitral Tribunal shall decide the dispute on the basis of written pleadings, documents and written submission and shall not hold oral hearing. The award is to be made within a period of six months from the date the Arbitral Tribunal enters, failing which the provisions of sub-section (3) to (9) of Section 29 shall apply.

Scope and application

New Section 29-B, inserted by Amending Act 3 of 2016, lays down the procedure for fast-track resolution of arbitration disputes where the parties mutually agree to such procedure. In such cases, the Arbitral Tribunal shall decide the dispute on the basis of written pleadings, documents and written submission and shall not hold oral hearing. The award is to be made within a period of six months from the date the Arbitral Tribunal enters, failing which the provisions of sub-sections (3) to (9) of Section 29 shall apply.

Oral hearing [Sub-s. (3)]

The Arbitral Tribunal shall decide the dispute on the basis of written pleadings, documents and submissions filed by the parties without any oral hearing.

The parties may file written arguments/submissions.

No oral hearing(s) shall be held. An oral hearing may be held only if the parties request for the same or where the Arbitral Tribunal considers oral hearing for clarifying certain issues necessary.

Award shall be made within six months [Sub-s. (4)]

The award shall be made within a period of six months from the date the Arbitral Tribunal enters upon the reference. Where the award is not made within a period of six months, the provisions of sub-sections (3) to (9) of Section 29-A shall apply to the proceedings.

Arbitrator's fee

The amount of fee payable to the arbitrator and the manner of payment of fees shall be as per the agreement between the arbitrator and the parties.

SETTLEMENT [S. 30]

30. *Settlement.*—(1) It is not incompatible with an arbitration agreement for an arbitral tribunal to encourage settlement of the dispute and, with the agreement of the parties, the arbitral tribunal may use mediation, conciliation or other procedures at any time during the arbitral proceedings to encourage settlement.

(2) If, during arbitral proceedings, the parties settle the dispute, the arbitral tribunal shall terminate the proceedings and, if requested by the parties and not objected to by the arbitral tribunal, record the settlement in the form of an arbitral award on agreed terms.

(3) An arbitral award on agreed terms shall be made in accordance with Section 31 and shall state that it is an arbitral award.

(4) An arbitral award on agreed terms shall have the same status and effect as any other arbitral award on the substance of the dispute.

COMMENTS

Corresponding old law

Section 30 is a new one; no such provision existed in the Arbitration Act, 1940.

UNCITRAL Model Law

Article 30. *Settlement*

(1) If, during arbitral proceedings, the parties settle the dispute, the arbitral tribunal shall terminate the proceedings and, if requested by the parties and not objected to by the arbitral tribunal, record the settlement in the form of an arbitral award on agreed terms.

(2) An award on agreed terms shall be made in accordance with the provisions of Article 31 and shall state that it is an award. Such an award has the same status and effect as any other award on the merits of the case.

Scope and application

As provided by Section 30, the Arbitral Tribunal shall encourage settlement of disputes between the parties. Where during arbitral proceedings, the parties settle the disputed subject-matter of arbitration proceedings, the arbitral proceedings shall terminate. The Arbitral Tribunal shall record the settlement which shall be in the form of an arbitral award on agreed terms in accordance with the provisions of Section 31, which shall have the status and effect of an arbitral award on the substance of the dispute. The settlement arrived at in pre-litigation mediation under Section 12-A, Commercial Courts Act, 2015, is to be treated as award under Section 30(4), Arbitration and Conciliation Act.[55]

The arbitrator gets the jurisdiction to make an award on agreed terms only if there is a request made by all the parties. In the absence of such

55. *Patil Automation (P) Ltd.* v. *Rakheja Engineers (P) Ltd.*, (2022) 10 SCC 1.

a request, the award passed by the arbitrator is liable to be set aside. In *Taherbhai Abdullabhai* v. *Mohd. Hussain Abdullabhai*[56], no request was made by all the parties to the settlement to make an award in terms of the alleged settlement. For this sole reason, the award passed by the arbitrator was set aside.

Parties to the arbitration agreed to the settlement and reduced in writing the terms of the reference. Terms of the reference were filed before the court with prayer for disposal of the matter in terms of the settlement. The order passed by the High Court in terms of the settlement was not a nullity.[57]

An award passed on the basis of settlement under this section need not state the reasons on which it is based [S. 31(3)].

Status of settlement agreement—Stamp duty [Sub-s. (4)]

A settlement agreement effected as per Section 73, Arbitration and Conciliation Act shall be deemed to be an arbitral award for all purposes as it shall have the same status and effect as any other arbitral award in view of the legal fiction created by Section 74 read with Section 30(4) of the Act and is chargeable with stamp duty as indicated in the schedule to the Stamp Act.[58]

FORM AND CONTENTS OF ARBITRAL AWARD [S. 31]

31. *Form and contents of arbitral award.*—(1) An arbitral award shall be made in writing and shall be signed by the members of the arbitral tribunal.

(2) For the purposes of sub-section (1), in arbitral proceedings with more than one arbitrator, the signatures of the majority of all the members of the arbitral tribunal shall be sufficient so long as the reason for any omitted signature is stated.

(3) The arbitral award shall state the reasons upon which it is based, unless—

(*a*) the parties have agreed that no reasons are to be given; or

(*b*) the award is an arbitral award on agreed terms under Section 30.

(4) The arbitral award shall state its date and the place of arbitration as determined in accordance with Section 20 and the award shall be deemed to have been made at that place.

(5) After the arbitral award is made, a signed copy shall be delivered to each party.

56. 2004 SCC OnLine Bom 783: (2005) 1 Mah LJ 566.
57. *Borgang Tea Co. (P) Ltd.* v. *State of Assam*, 2009 SCC OnLine Gau 581: (2010) 5 Gau LR 219.
58. *N.S. Geetha* v. *B. Raghuveer*, 2008 SCC OnLine Kar 138: ILR 2008 Kar 3850.

(6) The arbitral tribunal may, at any time during the arbitral proceedings, make an interim arbitral award on any matter with respect to which it may make a final arbitral award.

(7)(*a*) Unless otherwise agreed by the parties, where and in so far as an arbitral award is for the payment of money, the arbitral tribunal may include in the sum for which the award is made interest, at such rate as it deems reasonable, on the whole or any part of the money, for the whole or any part of the period between the date on which the cause of action arose and the date on which the award is made.

[59][(*b*) A sum directed to be paid by an arbitral award shall, unless the award otherwise directs, carry interest at the rate of two per cent higher than the current rate of interest prevalent on the date of award, from the date of award to the date of payment.

Explanation.—The expression "current rate of interest" shall have the same meaning as assigned to it under clause (*b*) of Section 2 of the Interest Act, 1978 (14 of 1978).]

[60][(8) The costs of an arbitration shall be fixed by the arbitral tribunal in accordance with Section 31-A.]

COMMENTS

Corresponding old law

Section 31(1) of the present Act corresponds to Section 14(1), Arbitration Act, 1940. Section 31(2) of the present Act corresponds to Section 19(2), Arbitration Act, 1940. Section 31(8) of the present section corresponds to Section 38 and clause 8 of Schedule 1 of the Arbitration Act, 1940.

---

59. *Subs.* by Act 3 of 2016, S. 16(*i*) (w.r.e.f. 23-10-2015). Prior to substitution it read as:
 "(*b*) A sum directed to be paid by an arbitral award shall, unless the award otherwise directs, carry interest at the rate of eighteen per centum per annum from the date of the award to the date of payment."
60. *Subs.* by Act 3 of 2016, S. 16(*ii*) (w.r.e.f. 23-10-2015). Prior to substitution it read as:
 "(8) Unless otherwise agreed by the parties,—
 (*a*) the costs of an arbitration shall be fixed by the arbitral tribunal;
 (*b*) the arbitral tribunal shall specify—
 (*i*) the party entitled to costs,
 (*ii*) the party who shall pay the costs,
 (*iii*) the amount of costs or method of determining that amount, and
 (*iv*) the manner in which the costs shall be paid.
 Explanation.—For the purpose of clause (*a*), "costs" means reasonable costs relating to—
 (*i*) the fees and expenses of the arbitrators and witnesses,
 (*ii*) legal fees and expenses,
 (*iii*) any administration fees of the institution supervising the arbitration, and
 (*iv*) any other expenses incurred in connection with the arbitral proceedings and the arbitral award."

UNCITRAL Model Law

Article 31. *Form and contents of award*

(1) The award shall be made in writing and shall be signed by the arbitrator or arbitrators. In arbitral proceedings with more than one arbitrator, the signatures of the majority of all members of the arbitral tribunal shall suffice, provided that the reason for any omitted signature is stated.

(2) The award shall state the reasons upon which it is based, unless the parties have agreed that no reasons are to be given or the award is an award on agreed terms under article 30.

(3) The award shall state its date and the place of arbitration as determined in accordance with article 20(1). The award shall be deemed to have been made at that place.

(4) After the award is made, a copy signed by the arbitrators in accordance with paragraph (1) of this article shall be delivered to each party.

Legislative changes

Arbitration and Conciliation (Amendment) Act, 2015 (3 of 2016)

In Section 31 of the principal Act,—

(*i*) in sub-section (7), for clause (*b*), the following clause shall be *substituted*, namely—

"(*b*) A sum directed to be paid by an arbitral award shall, unless the award otherwise directs, carry interest at the rate of two per cent higher than the current rate of interest prevalent on the date of award, from the date of award to the date of payment.

Explanation.—The expression 'current rate of interest' shall have the same meaning as assigned to it under clause (*b*) of Section 2 of the Interest Act, 1978 (14 of 1978).";

(*ii*) for sub-section (8), the following sub-section shall be *substituted*, namely—

"(8) The costs of an arbitration shall be fixed by the arbitral tribunal in accordance with Section 31-A.".

OBJECTS AND REASONS

Clause 16 of the Bill seeks to amend Section 31 of the principal Act by substituting clause (*b*) of sub-section (7) to provide that a sum directed to be paid by an arbitral award shall, unless the award otherwise directs, carry interest at the rate of two interest higher than the current rate of interest prevalent on the date of the award, from the date of the award to the date of payment. It further seeks to substitute sub-section (8) of the said section to provide that the costs of an arbitration shall be fixed by the arbitral tribunal in accordance with Section 31-A.

1940 Act and 1996 Act

The scheme of the 1996 Act is absolutely distinct and different from the 1940 Act as also from the 1961 Act. In the 1940 Act, no reason was required to be stated in the award unless otherwise agreed upon. In the 1996 Act, reasons are required to be stated unless agreed to otherwise by the parties. The court's intervention is sought to be minimised under the provisions of the 1996 Act not only having regard to the concerns expressed in the international community as regards delay in the arbitration proceedings but also in view of the fact that an award under the 1996 Act is to be a reasoned one.[61]

Scope and application

Section 31 prescribes the form and contents of an arbitral award.

An award shall be made in writing and shall be signed by the arbitrator or the arbitrators.

The award shall state the reasons upon which it is based unless the parties have agreed that no reasons are to be given. The award shall also state the date and place of arbitration.

After the award is made, a signed copy of the award shall be delivered to each party.

The Arbitral Tribunal at any time during the arbitral proceedings may make an interim award on the subject-matter of the arbitral proceedings.

Unless otherwise agreed where insofar as an arbitral award is for the payment of money, the award may provide for the payment of interest for the period on which the cause of action arose and the date on which the award is made.

An award amount shall carry interest at the rate of two per cent higher than the current rate of interest prevalent on the date of award, from the date of award to the date of payment.

Where the arbitrator allowed interest but omitted to specify the period for which it was payable, it was an obvious error that did not affect the decision/award of the arbitrator; the application for correction was allowed and the date from which interest was payable was specified.[62]

---

61. *Centrotrade Minerals & Metals Inc.* v. *Hindustan Copper Ltd.*, (2006) 11 SCC 245.
62. *United Trade Agency Contractor* v. *District Judge, Mirzapur*, 2014 SCC OnLine All 15986: (2015) 2 All LJ 184.

International commercial arbitration

In the absence of agreement between parties on interest the rate of interest would be governed by the law of the seat of arbitration.[63]

Interim award, additional award, settlement award, final award

Whereas under the 1940 Act only an interim award or final award could be made, four types of awards are contemplated under the 1996 Act, *viz.* interim award, additional award, settlement or agreed award and final award.[64]

"An award shall be in writing" [Sub-s. (1)]

An arbitral award shall be in writing. The word "shall" has been used in sub-section (1), but oral award has not been recognised by the Act.

"Shall be signed by the members of the Arbitral Tribunal"

An award of the Arbitral Tribunal shall be signed by the members of the Arbitral Tribunal. [Sub-s. (1)] Where the Arbitral Tribunal consists of more than one member, the signatures by the majority of the members of the Arbitral Tribunal shall be sufficient, provided the reason for any omitted signatures is stated. [Sub-s. (2)] If the award is not signed by all the members of the Arbitral Tribunal, the reasons for omitted signatures must be stated which must be adequate and germane for the fulfillment of requirement of law. Where no justifiable reason is given, the award will not be valid.[65] In view of the differences of opinion, two of the arbitrators gave the majority award, the dissenting arbitrator gave the minority award, and thereafter, the final operative award was signed by all the three arbitrators. The operative award was not challenged, but only the majority award was challenged. It was held, there was no reason for the Single Judge of the High Court to go into any other aspect of the matter.[66]

If one out of three arbitrators refused to sign an award, that does not mean that the majority would be left high and dry. It is open to the third arbitrator to give a dissenting award.[67]

---

63. *Vedanta Ltd.* v. *Shenzhen Shandong Nuclear Power Construction Co. Ltd.*, (2019) 11 SCC 465.
64. *Centrotrade Minerals & Metals Inc.* v. *Hindustan Copper Ltd.*, (2006) 11 SCC 245.
65. *Maharashtra State Electricity Distribution Co. Ltd.* v. *Deltron Electronics*, 2016 SCC OnLine Bom 9521: (2017) 2 Mah LJ 605.
66. *Bfil Finance Ltd.* v. *G. Tech Stone Ltd.*, 2002 SCC OnLine Bom 734: (2002) 4 Mah LJ 434.
67. *Union of India* v. *Sudhir Engg. Co.*, 2009 SCC OnLine Del 2047: (2009) 112 DRJ 510.

Section 31(1) is couched in mandatory terms, and provides that an arbitral award shall be made in writing and signed by all members of the Arbitral Tribunal. If the Arbitral Tribunal comprises of more than one arbitrator, the award is made when the arbitrators acting together finally express their decision in writing, and are authenticated by their signatures. An award takes legal effect only after it is signed by the arbitrators, which gives it authentication. There can be no finality of the award, except after it is signed since signing of the award gives legal effect and validity to it. The making and delivery of the award are different stages of an arbitration proceeding. An award is made when it is authenticated by the person who makes it. The statute makes it obligatory for each of the members of the tribunal to sign the award, to make it a valid award. The usage of the term "shall" makes it a mandatory requirement. It is not merely a ministerial act or an empty formality which can be dispensed with.[68] The signature of the arbitrator on award is mandatory to make the award of the arbitrator valid.[69]

The majority award can only be set aside on what is stated therein if the challenge is sustained and not on the basis of what is stated in the minority award.[70]

"Arbitral award shall state the reasons upon which it is based" [S. 31(3)]

The arbitral award shall state the reasons upon which it is based. The scheme of the 1996 Act is absolutely distinct and different from the 1940 Act as also from the 1961 Act. In the 1940 Act, no reason was required to be stated in the award unless otherwise agreed upon. In the 1996 Act, reasons are required to be stated unless agreed to otherwise by the parties. The court's intervention is sought to be minimised under the provisions of the 1996 Act not only having regard to the concerns expressed in the international community as regards delay in the arbitration proceedings but also in view of the fact that an award under the 1996 Act is to be a reasoned one. Whereas in relation to an unreasoned award, the court's jurisdiction to interfere with the award was absolutely limited, a greater latitude had been given in relation to a reasoned award.[71] Once the parties to an arbitration agreement have imposed conditions on the arbitrator to give reasons in

68. *Dakshin Haryana Bijli Vitran Nigam Ltd.* v. *Navigant Technologies (P) Ltd.*, (2021) 7 SCC 657.
69. *NHAI* v. *Jogendar Parosottam Shetiya*, 2021 SCC OnLine Guj 3179.
70. *Axios Navigation Co. Ltd.* v. *Indian Oil Corpn. Ltd.*, 2012 SCC OnLine Bom 4: (2012) 3 Mah LJ 701.
71. *Centrotrade Minerals & Metals Inc.* v. *Hindustan Copper Ltd.*, (2006) 11 SCC 245; *McDermott International Inc.* v. *Burn Standard Co. Ltd.*, (2006) 11 SCC 181.

award, the arbitrator is bound by the condition; in such a case, an award passed by the arbitrator without giving reasons cannot be sustained.[72]

The requirement of reasons in support of the award under Section 31(3) is not an empty formality. It guarantees fair and legitimate consideration of the controversy by the Arbitral Tribunal. It is true that the Arbitral Tribunal is not expected to write a judgment like a court nor is it expected to give elaborate and detailed reasons in support of its finding(s), but mere noticing the submissions of the parties or reference to documents is no substitute for reasons which the Arbitral Tribunal is obliged to give. However brief these may be, reasons must be indicated in the award as that would reflect the thought process leading to a particular conclusion. To satisfy the requirement of Section 31(3), the reasons must be stated by the Arbitral Tribunal upon which the award is based; a lack of reasons would make such an award legally flawed. Where the award was non-speaking, the award was set aside and the matter was remitted to the arbitrator for recording reasons.[73] Where the arbitration award contained no reasons in support of the conclusion drawn therein, the award of the arbitrator was set aside, and another arbitrator was appointed for fresh decision in accordance with the law.[74]

Giving of reasons is one of the basic features of an award unless the parties agree for dispensing with reasons or the award is based on settlement between the parties.[75] The arbitral award must state reasons unless the parties to the agreement have agreed otherwise.[76] An arbitral award passed by the arbitrator without giving reasons is not proper. An award sans reasons is liable to be set aside.[77]

When a tribunal constituted under law is bound to give reasons or to follow the substantive law of India, it cannot bypass the said term of the contract. An award not disclosing the reasons would be contrary to the provisions of the Act and contrary to the public policy, and would be rendered arbitrary, liable to be set aside.[78]

---

72. *Shastri Construction Co.* v. *Union of India*, 2007 SCC OnLine P&H 757: PLR (2008) 149 P&H 52.
73. *Som Datt Builders Ltd.* v. *State of Kerala*, (2009) 10 SCC 259.
74. *Saroj Bala* v. *Rajive Stock Brokers Ltd.*, 2005 SCC OnLine Del 339: (2005) 81 DRJ 143.
75. *Mafatlal Securities Ltd.* v. *Birla Sun-Life Securities Ltd.*, 2002 SCC OnLine Bom 304: (2002) 3 Mah LJ 116; *Mutta International* v. *Nandnandan Silk Mills (P) Ltd.*, 2007 SCC OnLine Bom 350: (2007) 4 Mah LJ 503.
76. *G. & T. Beckfield Drilling Services (P) Ltd.* v. *ONGC*, 2019 SCC OnLine Gau 5967: (2019) 4 Arb LR 410.
77. *Swapan Kumar Dutta* v. *Union of India*, 2014 SCC OnLine Cal 17204.
78. *Vashdev Morumal Sawlani* v. *Yogesh Mehta*, 2001 SCC OnLine Bom 977: (2002) 2 Mah LJ 76; *Kamakhya Enterprise* v. *Union of India*, 2013 SCC OnLine Gau 472: (2013) 5 Gau LR 33; *Abhijeet Saraswat* v. *Nalamaty Doraiah*, 2003 SCC OnLine Bom 1117: (2004) 2 Mah LJ 145.

An unreasoned award is valid when the parties have agreed that no reasons are to be given.[79] Giving of reasons cannot be said to be a fundamental policy of Indian law as the statute itself dispenses with the requirement to give reasons if the parties agree that reasons need not be given.[80]

Arbitrators cannot be expected to write a detailed judgment as is done in courts.[81]

Sub-section (3) stipulates that the arbitral award shall state the reasons upon which it is based. Where the High Court found that the arbitrator did not assign reasons, and remanded the matter to the arbitrator for assigning reasons but did not set aside the award, the High Court should not have remanded the matter without setting aside the award; the award of the arbitrator was set aside and the matter was remanded to the arbitrator for assigning reasons.[82]

The arbitrator is required only to indicate his thought process, he is not required to give detailed judgment or detailed reasons.[83]

The arbitrator has to disclose and discuss the evidence on what basis the claim is quantified.[84] The arbitrator on the basis of meticulous appreciation of material evidence on record made an award, assigned reasons for rejection of the claims, and therefore, the award could not be said to have been passed in contravention of Section 31.[85]

The petitioner was allotted a tender and a dispute arose between the parties regarding calculations and the amount to be paid. The arbitrator, simply, without recording any reasons concluded that the calculations done by the respondent were correct. The award as stipulated in Section 31(3) of the Act should contain reasons to support the conclusion arrived at, unless otherwise agreed between the parties. There was nothing on record to show that the parties agreed that no reasons are to be given in the award. The award of the arbitrator was set aside.[86]

---

79. *Mutta International* v. *Laxmi Polytex (P) Ltd.*, 2007 SCC OnLine Bom 351: (2007) 4 Mah LJ 801.
80. *Force Shipping Ltd.* v. *Ashapura Minechem Ltd.*, 2003 SCC OnLine Bom 291: (2003) 4 Mah LJ 329.
81. *Crompton Greaves Ltd.* v. *Dyna*, 2007 SCC OnLine Mad 427: (2007) 3 CTC 417.
82. *Ambica Construction* v. *Union of India*, (2015) 17 SCC 357.
83. *DDA* v. *Harbans Singh*, 2008 SCC OnLine Del 831; *Ircon International Ltd.* v. *Arvind Construction Co. Ltd.*, 1999 SCC OnLine Del 551: ILR (1999) 2 Del 234.
84. *Damodar Valley Corpn.* v. *Central Concrete & Allied Products Ltd.*, 2006 SCC OnLine Cal 660: (2007) 2 CHN 441.
85. *K.T. Construction (I) Ltd.* v. *State of M.P.*, 2016 SCC OnLine MP 8005: (2016) 3 MP LJ 316.
86. *Vinod Kumar* v. *Union of India*, 2023 SCC OnLine P&H 6694.

Dissenting opinion

A dissenting opinion cannot be treated as an award if the majority award is set aside.[87]

Non-speaking award

Where the arbitrator is empowered to pass non-speaking award and has passed non-speaking award, the reasoning of the award cannot be gone into by the court.[88]

"Arbitral award shall state its date and the place of arbitration" [Sub-s. (4)]

The arbitral award shall state its date and the place of arbitration as determined in accordance with Section 20 of the Act, and the award shall be deemed to have been made at that place. Section 20 of the Act stipulates that the parties are free to agree on the place of arbitration, and where the parties fail to agree on the place of arbitration, the place of arbitration shall be determined by the Arbitral Tribunal having regard to the circumstances of the case and the convenience of the parties.

Sub-section (4) of Section 31 provides that the arbitral award shall state its date and place of arbitration. Where the majority did not indicate any date or place of arbitration, the award violated the provisions of Section 31 of the Act, and the award was liable to be set aside.[89]

"A signed copy (of award) shall be delivered to each party" [Sub-s. (5)]

Sub-section (5) of Section 31 stipulates that after the arbitral award is made, a signed copy of the award shall be delivered to each party. Delivery of a signed copy of the award on each party to the arbitral proceedings is the mandatory requirement of the section.

There can be no doubt that the arbitral award would necessarily have to be signed by all the arbitrators or at least by the majority of the members of the Arbitral Tribunal. However, it was not the intention of the legislature that all the copies of the award, dispatched to the respective parties would have to be separately signed by the arbitrators. A certified photocopy of the

87. *Hindustan Construction Co. Ltd.* v. *NHAI*, (2024) 2 SCC 613.
88. *Nemichand Suthar* v. *Mohan Lal Gasgorh*, 2016 SCC OnLine Chh 964.
89. *ONGC Ltd.* v. *SIV Magcobar Lignins Ltd.*, 2019 SCC OnLine Utt 943.

original award along with the signatures of the members of the Arbitral Tribunal would suffice.[90]

Section 34(3) provides that an application under Section 34 for setting aside an award shall not be entertained by the court if it is made after three months have elapsed from the date on which the applicant had received the arbitral award. The delivery of an award under Section 31(5) is not a matter of mere formality; the delivery of the award to the party must be effective, and the copy of the award has to be "received" by the party.[91] Receipt of a signed copy of award by all the parties is not necessary when such parties were represented by the family head/common power of attorney holder who received the copy of the award on their behalf, he being the person directly connected with and in control of the proceedings.[92]

Certified copy of the award [S. 31(5)]

A certified copy of the award can be treated as a signed copy of the award.[93]

Delivery of arbitral award and receipt thereof by the party [Sub-s. (5)]

The delivery of an arbitral award under sub-section (5) of Section 31 is not a matter of mere formality. It is a matter of substance. It is only after the stage under Section 31 has passed that the stage of termination of arbitral proceedings within the meaning of Section 32 of the Act arises. The delivery of an arbitral award to the party, to be effective, has to be "received" by the party. This delivery by the Arbitral Tribunal and receipt by the party of the award sets in motion several periods of limitation. As this delivery of the copy of award has the effect of conferring certain rights on the party as also bringing to an end the right to exercise those rights on expiry of the prescribed period of limitation which would be calculated from that date, the delivery of the copy of award by the tribunal and the receipt thereof by each party constitutes an important stage in the arbitral proceedings. In awarding the award passed by the arbitrator against the Railways, the Chief Engineer had represented the Union of India in arbitral proceedings; the subject-matter of arbitration also related to the department of the Chief Engineer who had direct knowledge of the arbitral proceedings and the question involved before the arbitrator. Service of the arbitral award on the General Manager could not be taken as sufficient notice so as to activate the

---

90. *National Agricultural Coop. Mktg. Federation of Indian Ltd.* v. *R. Piyarelall Import and Export Ltd.*, 2015 SCC OnLine Cal 7198: (2015) 4 Cal LT 100.
91. *Anilkumar Jinabhai Patel* v. *Pravinchandra Jinabhai Patel*, (2018) 15 SCC 178.
92. *Ibid.*
93. *Dayashankar* v. *LAO*, 2019 SCC OnLine Chh 451.

department. Service of the arbitral award on the Chief Engineer would be the starting point of limitation for setting aside the award of the arbitrator.[94]

In an Arbitral Tribunal if one of the members gives a dissenting opinion, it must be delivered contemporaneously on the same date as the final award, and not on a subsequent date, as the tribunal becomes *functus officio* upon the passing of the final award. Further, the period for rendering the award and dissenting opinion must be within the period prescribed by Section 29-A. The dissenting opinion of a minority arbitrator can be relied upon by the party seeking to set aside the award to buttress its submissions in the proceedings under Section 34. At the stage of judicial scrutiny by the court under Section 34, the court is not precluded from considering the findings and conclusions of the dissenting opinion of the minority member of the tribunal.[95]

In the context of a huge organisation, the copy of the award has to be received by the person who has knowledge of the proceedings and who would be the best person to understand and appreciate the arbitral award and also to take a decision in the matter of moving an application under Section 33 or Section 34(1). Delivery of award on the officer concerned of such organisation would be the starting point of limitation.[96] The limitation for setting aside the award on a petition under Section 34 of the Act would not commence to run from the date when a signed copy of the award is served on the advocate representing the party but from the date of its service on the party as contemplated under Section 31(5).[97]

Service of copy of award on the wife of the partner—Held sufficient

Once a postal article addressed to a partner of a firm is received at such appropriate address and acknowledged to be received on behalf of the addressee, by his wife no less, service would be deemed to have been appropriately effected on the addressee. Of course, it is open to the addressee to demonstrate otherwise, but the burden is on the addressee. It is evident that Section 31(5) of the Act was complied with in either case upon the signed copy of the arbitral awards being delivered at the address of the relevant partner.[98]

94. *Union of India* v. *Tecco Trichy Engineers & Contractors*, (2005) 4 SCC 239.
95. *Dakshin Haryana Bijli Vitran Nigam Ltd.* v. *Navigant Technologies (P) Ltd.*, (2021) 7 SCC 657.
96. *Union of India* v. *Wishwa Mittar Bajaj & Sons*, 2007 SCC OnLine Del 363: (2007) 141 DLT 179.
97. *Jolly Bros. (P) Ltd.* v. *Surendra Nath Jolly*, 2016 SCC OnLine Bom 3973: (2016) 5 Mah LJ 250.
98. *Manohar Lal & Co.* v. *Axis Bank Ltd.*, 2018 SCC OnLine Cal 16868: (2019) 1 CHN 18.

Delivery of copy of award by registered post on business address

A copy of the award passed by the arbitrator was sent to the party at the place which was the subject-matter of a dispute between the parties. Postman went to the place twice and on the second visit the party met and refused to accept a copy of the award passed in the case. The postman made the endorsement of refusal on the envelope and returned it to the vendor. It was held that by virtue of Section 3(1)(*a*) read with Section 3(3), there was a presumption that the award had been delivered to the said party.[99]

Date of receipt of award when award delivered on holiday/non-working day

Such a question gains importance where one of the parties to arbitration is a government or a statutory body or a corporation and an award was delivered to it on a holiday. When the award is delivered or deposited or left in the office of a party on a non-working day, the date of such physical delivery is not the date of "receipt" of the award by that party. The fact that the beldar or a watchman was present on a holiday or non-working day and had received the copy of the award cannot be considered as "receipt of the award" by the party concerned, for the purposes of Section 31(5) of the Act. Necessarily the date of receipt will have to be the next working day.[100]

Award not delivered

The awards as well the proceedings were neither sent to the Registrar, nor its certified copies were issued to parties. The arbitrator in his affidavit had stated that after he delivered the awards, he felt uneasiness and he left his office at about 6 pm with intention to get the order sheet prepared on 24 March 2015. The proceedings were thereafter withdrawn from his office and transferred to another arbitrator on account of which he could not make any endorsement regarding delivery of awards in the order sheet. The High Court concluded that the parties were under the belief that the arbitration proceedings still continued as they continued to appear in arbitration proceedings. No award was delivered as contemplated in law. The High Court directed that the proceedings before the arbitrator shall continue.[101]

---

99. *Kailash Rani Dang* v. *Rakesh Bala Aneja*, (2009) 1 SCC 732.
100. *State of H.P.* v. *Himachal Techno Engineers*, (2010) 12 SCC 210.
101. *Yogesh Kumar* v. *State of U.P.*, 2016 SCC OnLine All 2908: (2016) 118 ALR 431.

Certified copy of award can be treated as signed copy of award [Sub-s. (5)]

A certified copy of the award can be treated as a signed copy of the award.[102]

Application for certified copy of award by third party

When the adjudication of the arbitrator is culminated into award and the award is brought before the court, in custody of the public office, any third party is certainly entitled to get certified copies of such award to establish his independent right, which is likely to be affected by such award.[103]

Interim award [Sub-s. (6)]

Sub-section (6) of Section 31 envisages provision for passing of an interim award by the arbitrator. Sub-section (6) provides that the Arbitral Tribunal may, at any time during the arbitration proceedings, make an interim award on any matter with respect to which it may make a final award. The respondent had admitted in affidavit the fact of withholding the payment of 108 bills. The arbitrator passed an interim award. It was held, the interim award did not suffer from any illegality or irregularity. The interim award was upheld.[104] The power conferred by Section 31(6) cannot be restricted to exclude from its purview the power to pass an interim award on admission.[105]

An interim award was made by the tribunal on the basis of alleged admission made in the written statement without considering the entire written statement and the explanation. The order granting unconditional stay on the execution of the award was proper.[106]

An appeal against an interim award is not maintainable.[107]

Deciding the issue of limitation or any other matter is an interim award, can be challenged separately and independently under Section 34.[108]

---

102. *Dayashankar* v. *LAO*, 2019 SCC OnLine Chh 451.
103. *Embassy Property Developments (P) Ltd.* v. *SNP Ventures LLP*, 2019 SCC OnLine Mad 2845.
104. *Graphic Industries Co.* v. *Union of India*, 2010 SCC OnLine Cal 2206: (2011) 1 CHN 792.
105. *Gammon India Ltd.* v. *Sankaranarayana Construction (Bangalore) (P) Ltd.*, 2009 SCC OnLine Mad 2261: (2010) 1 LW 325.
106. *Ecopack India Paper Cup (P) Ltd.* v. *Sphere International*, 2018 SCC OnLine Bom 540.
107. *Ibid*; *Asian Electronics Ltd.* v. *M.P. SEB*, 2007 SCC OnLine MP 179: (2007) 3 MP LJ 203.
108. *IFFCO Ltd.* v. *Bhadra Products*, (2018) 2 SCC 534.

Award of interest by Arbitral Tribunal [Sub-s. (7)]

Sub-section (7) of Section 31 makes provision for award of interest by the Arbitral Tribunal. In case there is express stipulation which debars pendente lite interest, obviously, it cannot be granted by an arbitrator. The award of pendente lite interest inter alia must depend upon the overall intention of the agreement and what is expressly excluded.[109]

The Arbitration Act, 1940 did not contain any specific provision relating to the power of the arbitrator to award interest. That led to considerable confusion about the power of arbitrators in regard to award of interest from the date of cause of action to the date of award, *i.e.* the pre-reference period (from the date of cause of action up to the date of reference) and pendente lite period (from the date of reference to the date of award). Ultimately, the Supreme Court made it clear that the arbitrator had the jurisdiction and authority to award interest for the three periods, *namely*, pre-reference period, pendente lite period and future period (from the date of award) if there was no express bar in the contract regarding the award of interest. The legislature, while enacting the Arbitration and Conciliation Act, 1996, incorporated a specific provision in regard to the award of interest by arbitrators. Having regard to Section 31(7) of the 1996 Act, the difference between the pre-reference period and the pendente lite period has disappeared insofar as the award of interest by the arbitrator is concerned. The section recognises only two periods.[110] The arbitrator has the power to grant interest beyond the terms of agreement, for all three stages: pre-reference period, pendente lite period and future period.[111]

Payment of interest is always subject to the interpretation of the terms of the contract. On the facts of the case, the award of interest was upheld.[112] In the absence of an agreement between the parties to the contrary, Section 31(7) of the Act of 1996 gives wide power to the arbitrator to award interest with regard to pre-reference, pendente lite and future claims of the parties.[113]

The discretion of the arbitrator to award interest must be exercised reasonably. An Arbitral Tribunal while making an award for interest must take into consideration a host of factors, such as: 1) the "loss of use" of the principal sum; 2) the types of sums to which the interest must apply; 3) the time period over which interest should be awarded; 4) the internationally

---

109. *Ibid.*
110. *Sayeed Ahmed & Co.* v. *State of U.P.*, (2009) 12 SCC 26; *State of U.P.* v. *Coromandal Engg. Co. Ltd.*, 2013 SCC OnLine All 13622: (2013) 3 All LJ 746 .
111. *Ibid.*
112. *Tehri Hydro Development Corpn. Ltd.* v. *Mohd. Hassan*, 2022 SCC OnLine Utt 1036.
113. *Union of India* v. *Railtrack Concrete Products (P) Ltd.*, 2019 SCC OnLine Gau 5243: (2020) 4 Gau LR 698; *Dhenkanal Minor Irrigation Division* v. *N.C. Budharaj*, (2001) 2 SCC 721.

prevailing rates of interest; 5) whether simple or compound rate of interest is to be applied; 6) whether the rate of interest awarded is commercially prudent from an economic standpoint; 7) the rates of inflation; 8) proportionality of the count awarded as interest to the principal sums awarded. On the one hand, the rate of interest must be compensatory as it is a form of reparation granted to the award holder, while on the other it must not be punitive, unconscionable or usurious in nature.[114]

The High Court rightly held that the Arbitral Tribunal was justified in following contractual provisions and provisions of Section 31(7) of the Act and rightly did not interfere with the award of interest for the pre-reference period and period during which proceedings were pending before the Arbitral Tribunal. However, the reduction of rate of interest by the High Court was unjustified. The High Court was not exercising any equity jurisdiction so as to resettle the rate of interest as deemed fit by it. The Arbitral Tribunal was justified in granting interest at the rate of 15 per cent per annum post award.[115]

Where a contract between the parties proscribes award of interest, the Arbitral Tribunal does not have the power to award interest under Section 31(7)(*a*), Arbitration and Conciliation Act, 1996, and for the period prior to the date of the award. The expression "unless otherwise agreed by the parties" as used in Section 31(7)(*a*) imply that the arbitrator is bound by the terms of the contract insofar as the award of interest from the date of cause of action to the date of award is concerned.[116] A stipulation in the contract prohibiting grant of interest on amount payable to the contractor under contract debars the arbitrator from granting pendente lite interest.[117]

The grant of interest is discretionary. Where the majority of the arbitrators had granted interest at the rate of 12 per cent pendente lite and at the rate of 18 per cent post pendente lite, the award of interest was held proper and affirmed.[118]

In matters of grant of interest, the Arbitral Tribunal's discretion is considerably wide. On the facts of the case, held interest at the rate of 15 per cent was not so excessive as to warrant court's interference.[119]

The Arbitral Tribunal under Section 31(7)(*a*) has discretion to grant interest and also to determine the rate of such interest. However, this discretion is not unfettered and must be exercised as per the facts and circumstances of

114. *Ibid.*
115. *Reliance Infrastructure Ltd.* v. *State of Goa*, (2024) 1 SCC 479.
116. *KMC Construction Ltd.* v. *NHAI*, (2021) 4 HCC (Del) 464.
117. *Union of India* v. *Venus Engg. Concern (P) Ltd.*, 2017 SCC OnLine Cal 337.
118. *Numaligarh Refinery Ltd.* v. *Daelim Industrial Co. Ltd.*, (2007) 8 SCC 466.
119. *GAIL (India) Ltd.* v. *Triveni Engg. & Industries Ltd.*, (2022) 3 HCC (Del) 324.

each case, within the parameters of statute and in accordance with the rule of law.[120] Where the arbitrator granted 18 per cent interest on the amount to be refunded, the court held that the interest of 18 per cent was exorbitant and was modified to 10 per cent reasonable rate of interest.[121]

Where the parties had agreed that no interest shall be payable, the arbitrator cannot award pendente lite interest ignoring the terms of contract. The award of the arbitrator allowing interest was set aside.[122]

Section 31(7)(*a*), Arbitration and Conciliation Act, 1996 deals with the grant of pre-award interest while Section 31(7)(*b*) deals with the grant of post-award interest. Pre-award interest is at the discretion of the Arbitral Tribunal, while post-award interest on the awarded sum is the mandate of the statute, the only difference being that of rate of interest to be awarded by the Arbitral Tribunal. If the Arbitral Tribunal has awarded post-award interest payable from the date of the award to the date of payment at a particular rate in its discretion, then it will prevail, else the party will be entitled to claim post-award interest on the awarded sum at the statutory rate specified in Section 31(7)(*b*), *i.e.* 18 per cent per annum.[123]

The Arbitral Tribunal has autonomy to award a specific rate of interest; in case of default, the statutory rate would be allowed.[124]

Granting of interest over and above the rate which was specifically agreed upon between the parties can by no stretch of imagination be considered as a mere error of law or fact. It would be a case of misconduct on the part of the arbitrator, interference by the High Court would be justified.[125] Where the arbitrator neither acted arbitrarily nor erroneously directed payment of interest in award, award of the arbitrator was restored.[126]

Where the arbitrator has given reasons for awarding interest, which are reasonable and not perverse, the High Court will not scrutinise the same.[127]

Decisions under Arbitration Act, 1940

The decisions rendered under the Arbitration Act, 1940 may not be of assistance to decide the validity of grant of interest under the new Act.[128]

120. *Hyder Consulting (UK) Ltd.* v. *State of Orissa*, (2015) 2 SCC 189.
121. *Vivek Jain* v. *Union of India*, 2008 SCC OnLine Del 263: (2008) 148 DLT 333.
122. *Union of India* v. *Krafters Engg. & Leasing (P) Ltd.*, (2011) 7 SCC 279 (case under 1940 Act).
123. *Hyder Consulting (UK) Ltd.* v. *State of Orissa*, (2015) 2 SCC 189.
124. *Shakti Nath* v. *Alpha Tiger Cyprus Investment No. 3 Ltd.*, 2017 SCC OnLine Del 8294: (2017) 164 DRJ 563.
125. *Indian Institute of Technology* v. *Creative Construction*, 2007 SCC OnLine Bom 252: (2007) 5 Mah LJ 323.
126. *Union of India* v. *Arctic India*, 2006 SCC OnLine Cal 137: (2006) 2 CHN 707.
127. *Subhash Verma* v. *Darshan Singh*, 2019 SCC OnLine Del 7169.
128. *Sree Kamatchi Amman Constructions* v. *Railways*, (2010) 8 SCC 767.

Grant of pre-award and post-award interest—Purpose of

Interest is imposed to compensate for denial to one party by the other party of money which rightly belongs to the said former party under the relevant agreement governing arbitration proceedings. Pre-award interest is allowed to ensure that arbitral proceedings are concluded without unreasonable delay as the longer the proceedings, the longer would be the period attracting interest. Similarly, post-award interest is to ensure speedy payment in compliance with the arbitral award and to discourage the usual delay which occurs due to the execution of the award as a decree of civil court.[129]

Post-award period interest

There was prohibition on awarding interest on amounts due to the contractor in the agreement for pre-award period; the respondent was entitled to interest only from the date of award till the date of payment, *i.e.* post-award interest. The award of the arbitrator was modified accordingly.[130]

Sub-section (7)—Applies to arbitration award for payment of money

Sub-section (7) of Section 31 applies only to an arbitral award which is for payment of money.[131] The words used in sub-section (7) are "where and insofar as an arbitral award is for the payment of money".

An agreement between the parties provided that no interest is payable upon the earnest money or the security deposit or amounts payable to the contractor under the contract; and further that, where the arbitral award is for the payment of money, no interest shall be payable on whole or any part of the said amount for any period till the date on which the award is made. Evidently, there was an unequivocal agreement between the parties that no interest shall be payable prior to the date of the award, and in such circumstances, the provisions of Section 31(7)(*a*), Arbitration Act, 1996 come into play in all its force. Therefore, the grant of interest in the award of the Arbitral Tribunal for the period up to the date of the award was found not tenable and was set aside.[132]

Award of interest by arbitrator in absence of express bar

In the absence of express bar in contract with regard to interest, the arbitrator can award interest.[133] The contract agreement did not prohibit grant of

129. *Hyder Consulting (UK) Ltd.* v. *State of Orissa*, (2015) 2 SCC 189.
130. *BHEL* v. *Tata Projects Ltd.*, (2015) 5 SCC 682.
131. *Hyder Consulting (UK) Ltd.* v. *State of Orissa*, (2015) 2 SCC 189.
132. *Chief Engineer* v. *P. Rajendran Asari*, 2020 SCC OnLine Ker 967: (2020) 2 KLJ 240.
133. *State of Rajasthan* v. *Ferro Concrete Construction (P) Ltd.*, (2009) 12 SCC 1.

interest. Award of interest at the rate of 15.7 per cent per annum was found not excessive.[134]

General conditions of contract (GCC) debarring interest

A clause in general conditions of contract debarred the claim of the contractor for payment of interest, only if it is made in connection with withholding of earnest money, security deposit or any amount payable to the contractor under the contract. The general conditions of contract did not prohibit the arbitrator to award interest with regard to pre-reference, pendente lite and future claims. The arbitrator had jurisdiction to award interest for loss of production, pendente lite and future claims.[135]

Clause 16(3) of general conditions of contract prohibiting grant of interest cannot be construed as an integral part of the agreement. The award of interest was proper.[136]

Where clause in arbitration bars payment of interest

Where the provision in the contract bars the employer from entertaining any claim for interest or bars the contractor from making any claim for interest, it amounts to a clear prohibition regarding interest. The provision need not contain another bar prohibiting the arbitrator from awarding interest.[137]

The Arbitral Tribunal cannot award interest for pre-reference period and pendente lite period when the agreement prohibits the grant of interest thereon. The expression "unless otherwise agreed by the parties" in Section 31(7)(*a*) clarifies that the arbitrator is bound by the terms of the contract for award of interest.[138]

Railway contract

Where the general conditions of contract of the Railways prohibit grant of interest against the Railways, the award of interest against the Railways for the pre-reference period was erroneous and set aside.[139]

---

134. *South Eastern Coalfields Ltd.* v. *Tirupati Construction Structural Engineers and Building Contractors*, 2017 SCC OnLine Chh 1904.
135. *Union of India* v. *Railtrack Concrete Products (P) Ltd.*, 2019 SCC OnLine Gau 5243: (2020) 4 Gau LR 698.
136. *Raitani Engg. Works (P) Ltd.* v. *Union of India*, 2018 SCC OnLine Gau 1970: (2018) 5 Gau LR 145.
137. *Sayeed Ahmed & Co.* v. *State of U.P.*, (2009) 12 SCC 26; *Sree Kamatchi Amman Constructions* v. *Railways*, (2010) 8 SCC 767.
138. *Sree Kamatchi Amman Constructions* v. *Railways*, (2010) 8 SCC 767.
139. *Union of India* v. *Jasumall & Co.*, 2017 SCC OnLine Cal 312.

Bar against payment of interest is applicable both against the parties concerned and the power of the arbitrator

The bar imposed in agreement against payment of interest operates not only between the parties, but also affects the authority of the arbitrator to grant interest. The arbitration agreement imposed a ban on the award of pre-reference and pendente lite interest; the award of pre-reference and pendente lite interest by the arbitrator was not legally sustainable and was set aside. The view taken by the High Court that the bar did not affect the authority of the arbitrator to award interest was erroneous and was not sustainable.[140]

"Unless otherwise agreed by the parties" [Sub-s. (7)(*a*)]

Section 31(7)(*a*) begins with the words "unless otherwise agreed by the parties". If there is agreement between the parties regarding pre-award interest, the said agreement would prevail over the provisions of Section 31(7)(*a*). Therefore, the power of the Arbitral Tribunal to grant pre-award interest under Section 31(7)(*a*) is subject to an agreement between the parties.[141] In *BHEL* v. *Globe Hi-Fabs Ltd.*[142], a clause in the agreement provided that no interest shall be payable on "earnest money, security deposit or on any money due to contractor by employer". It was held, the said clause barring interest is very widely worded as the words used are "any amount due to contractor by the employer"; the said words cannot be read *ejusdem generis* along with the earlier words "earnest money" or "security deposit". No interest was payable on "any money due to contractor by the employer" for the pre-award period; the claim of the contract or for interest for the pre-award period was found not sustainable. Pre-award and pendente lite interest disallowed. The clause "unless otherwise agreed by the parties" prevails over the entire scheme of power of the arbitrator to grant interest at all stages.[143]

Where the contract did not prohibit the arbitrator from granting interest, an award of interest by the arbitrator to the contractor was not improper.[144]

If clause (*a*) of sub-section (7) of Section 31 of the 1996 Act is given a plain and literal meaning, the legislative intent would be clear that the discretion with regard to grant of interest would be available to the Arbitral Tribunal only when there is no agreement to the contrary between the parties. The phrase "unless otherwise agreed by the parties" clearly emphasises that

140. *Union of India* v. *Saraswat Trading Agency*, (2009) 16 SCC 504.
141. *Hyder Consulting (UK) Ltd.* v. *State of Orissa*, (2015) 2 SCC 189.
142. (2015) 5 SCC 718; see also, *Chittaranjan Maity* v. *Union of India*, (2017) 9 SCC 611.
143. *ONGC Ltd.* v. *Dolphin Offshore Enterprises (I) Ltd.*, 2010 SCC OnLine Bom 1598: (2011) 1 Mah LJ 377.
144. *Madnani Construction Corpn. (P) Ltd.* v. *Union of India*, (2010) 1 SCC 549.

when the parties have agreed with regard to any of the aspects covered under clause (*a*) of sub-section (7) of Section 31 of the 1996 Act, the Arbitral Tribunal would cease to have any discretion with regard to the aspects mentioned in the said provision. Only in the absence of such an agreement, the Arbitral Tribunal would have a discretion to exercise its powers under clause (*a*) of sub-section (7) of Section 31 of the 1996 Act. The discretion is wide enough. It may grant or may not grant interest. It may grant interest for the entire period or any part thereof. It may also grant interest on the whole or any part of the money.[145]

Power of arbitrator to grant interest is regulated by agreement between the parties

Power of the court to grant interest is regulated by the agreement between the parties. The non-obstante clause "unless otherwise agreed by the parties" in Section 31(7)(*a*) prevails over all other provisions of interest in all the stages by the arbitrator. The court needs to consider the agreed clause between the parties while making the award final.[146] The provision leaves the initial choice to the parties to make their own agreement on matters of interest.[147]

Interest cannot be granted in the absence of a claim in that regard.[148]

Arbitrators cannot award interest in respect of antelite and pendente lite period unless agreed by the parties.[149]

When an arbitration agreement contains provision for award of interest, the tribunal should grant interest in accordance with the terms of the agreement. In the absence of any provision for award of interest in the agreement, the tribunal can exercise its discretion. The tribunal awarded interest at 15 per cent per annum which was modified to 10 per cent per annum.[150] The provisions and the power to award interest are not mandatory but discretionary.[151] Section 31(7)(*a*) underlines the discretion of the Arbitral Tribunal to award interest it deems reasonable.[152]

145. *Delhi Airport Metro Express (P) Ltd.* v. *DMRC*, (2022) 9 SCC 286.
146. *ONGC Ltd.* v. *Dolphin Offshore Enterprises (I) Ltd.*, 2010 SCC OnLine Bom 1598: (2011) 1 Mah LJ 377.
147. *Union of India* v. *Arctic India*, 2006 SCC OnLine Cal 137: (2006) 2 CHN 707.
148. *Em and Em Associates* v. *DDA*, 2002 SCC OnLine Del 392: (2003) 2 AP LJ (DNC) 16.
149. *Union of India* v. *Ravi Builders and Rajendra Agrawal and Associates*, 2015 SCC OnLine MP 6706: (2015) 4 MPLJ 100.
150. *Ennore Port Ltd.* v. *HCC Van Oord ACZ Joint Venture*, 2013 SCC OnLine Mad 2910: (2013) 3 MWN (Civil) 727.
151. *ONGC Ltd.* v. *Dolphin Offshore Enterprises (I) Ltd.*, 2010 SCC OnLine Bom 1598: (2011) 1 Mah LJ 377.
152. *Sree Kamatchi Amman Constructions* v. *Railways*, 2007 SCC OnLine Mad 610: (2007) 4 LW 379.

Where the arbitrator allowed interest at the rate of 10 per cent per annum, the rate of interest awarded by the arbitrator was found reasonable and not interfered with.[153]

Pendente lite interest is a matter of discretion of the arbitrators and the court would not interfere with the exercise of such discretion.[154] Order of the District Judge directing payment of interest at the rate of 18 per cent per annum was not interfered with by the High Court in revision.[155] The matter of grant of interest is entirely left to the discretion of the Arbitral Tribunal.[156]

In a commercial contract, a specific clause which debars the arbitrator to grant interest should prevail over the general submission of entitlement of interest.[157]

Where the general conditions governing Railway contracts contain embargo on payment of interest, award of interest by the arbitrator was not sustained and was set aside.[158] Where revised clause in contract prohibited grant of interest, the revised clause was intimated to the respondent after the dispute arose; the award of interest by the arbitrator was held in accordance with law.[159]

If there is no agreement between parties that the party will not be entitled to get interest on the claimed amount, the Arbitral Tribunal can award interest and the interest can be 18 per cent per annum.[160]

Where the arbitrator has granted interest in accordance with terms of the contract between the parties, such award cannot be set aside by invoking the general principles of fairness of equity.[161]

---

153. *MTNL* v. *Asco Engg.*, 2015 SCC OnLine Bom 360: (2015) 4 Mah LJ 883.
154. *Sree Kamatchi Amman Constructions* v. *Southern Railway*, 2007 SCC OnLine Mad 610: (2007) 5 CTC 17.
155. *State of Haryana* v. *Goel Projects (P) Ltd.*, 2006 SCC OnLine P&H 1029: PLR (2007) 145 P&H 137.
156. *Susaka (P) Ltd.* v. *Union of India*, 2005 SCC OnLine Bom 159: (2005) 2 Mah LJ 327.
157. *G.D. Anklesaria and Co.* v. *Airports Authority of India*, 2010 SCC OnLine Bom 250: (2010) 2 Mah LJ 921; *ONGC Ltd.* v. *Dolphin Offshore Enterprises (I) Ltd.*, 2010 SCC OnLine Bom 1598: (2011) 1 Mah LJ 377.
158. *Union of India* v. *Panihati Rubber Ltd.*, 2014 SCC OnLine Cal 5032: (2014) 2 Cal LT 232.
159. *Union of India* v. *Prashant Raj and Co.*, 2007 SCC OnLine Bom 249: (2007) 4 Mah LJ 442.
160. *Vitthalrao Shinde Sahakari Sakhar Karkhana Ltd.* v. *Gangapur Sahakari Sakhar Karkhana Ltd.*, 2017 SCC OnLine Bom 1669: (2017) 5 Mah LJ 390.
161. *BPL Ltd.* v. *Morgan Securities & Credits (P) Ltd.*, 2018 SCC OnLine Del 13109.

Penal rate of interest

An award debtor cannot be subjected to penal rate of interest, either during the period of exercising his statutory right to challenge the award or later.[162]

Uniform rate of interest for INR and EUR

Interest rates differ depending upon the currency. It is necessary for the Arbitral Tribunal to coordinate the choice of currency with the interest rate. A uniform rate of interest for INR and EUR would, therefore, not be justified.[163]

Pre-reference and pendente lite interest

When the agreement between the parties bars interest on amounts from the cause of action to the date of award, the arbitrator is bound by it and cannot award interest. In view of the words "unless otherwise agreed by the parties" in Section 31(7)(*a*), the arbitrator is bound by the terms of the contract so far as the award of interest from the date of cause of action to the date of the award is concerned. In *Union of India* v. *Bright Power Projects (India) (P) Ltd.*[164], clause 13(3) of the contract specifically stipulated that no interest of interest will be payable on the earnest money, security deposit or amounts payable to the contractor under the contract. The arbitrator exceeded his jurisdiction in awarding the pendente lite interest.

Where the arbitrators correctly disallowed pre-reference, pendente lite interest and allowed only post-award interest under clause (*b*) of Section 31(7), the award of the arbitrators was not set aside.[165]

The arbitrator has no power to grant pendente lite interest if the agreement between the parties prohibits the same.[166] In view of the general conditions of contract barring grant of interest which is binding on the parties, the Single Judge rightly set aside the grant of interest for the pendente lite period; the order of the Single Judge was not interfered with.[167] An arbitrator is competent to award interest pendente lite. However, the rate of interest is to be fixed in the circumstances of each case. Substantive law allowed grant

162. *Vedanta Ltd.* v. *Shenzhen Shandong Nuclear Power Construction Co. Ltd.*, (2019) 11 SCC 465.
163. *Ibid.*
164. (2015) 9 SCC 695; *BHEL* v. *Tata Projects Ltd.*, (2015) 5 SCC 682.
165. *Jawaharlal Nehru Port Trust* v. *Seatrans Shipping Ltd.*, 2020 SCC OnLine Bom 641: (2020) 5 Mah LJ 552.
166. *Union of India* v. *Tapan Kumar Roy*, 2020 SCC OnLine Cal 3303.
167. *Prime Habitals (P) Ltd.* v. *Railways*, 2011 SCC OnLine Mad 781: (2011) 5 CTC 775; *Union of India* v. *Ravi Builders and Rajendra Agrawal and Associates*, 2015 SCC OnLine MP 6706: (2015) 4 MPLJ 100; *Raghavendra Construction Co.* v. *Railways*, 2011 SCC OnLine Mad 216: (2011) 2 CTC 194.

of interest not more than 6 per cent. Therefore, grant of 6 per cent interest proper and equitable against interest at the rate of 10 per cent awarded by the Arbitrator.[168]

In the present case, a clause in the contract barred payment of interest. The High Court was justified in rejecting the claim of the appellant seeking pendente lite interest on award amount.[169]

The claim of the contractor for interest related to two periods, *i.e.* one for the period when the agreement between the parties concerned was subsisting and the other for the period beyond the agreement, *i.e.* when the agreement was terminated but the contractor carried the work on the request of the other party to the contract. It was held, in view of the said bar, that no pre-reference or pendente lite interest was payable to the contractor for the period when the agreement was subsisting. Hence, the arbitrator as well as the High Court erred in granting pre-reference and pendente lite interest on amount pertaining to the said period. However, the position with regard to claim for a period when the agreement was terminated but the contractor was carrying on work on request of the other party was different. The above bar did not apply to this latter period, and hence, there was no infirmity in the grant of pre-reference and pendente lite interest on the amount pertaining to that period.[170]

In view of the express bar in the contract regarding grant of pre-reference and pendente lite interest, both the arbitrator and the District Judge erred in granting pre-reference and pendente lite interest.[171]

Pre-reference period—Award of interest

An arbitrator is empowered to allow interest if the contract is silent as to payment of interest in regard to the pre-reference period in terms of the Interest Act, 1978.[172] Where a contract provides for interest, it shall be paid in accordance with the contract and where there is express bar in the contract on the payment of interest, no interest shall be awarded.[173]

There was an unequivocal agreement between the parties that no interest shall be payable prior to the date of the award, and in such circumstances, the provisions of Section 31(7)(*a*), Arbitration Act, 1996, comes into play

168. *MD (J and K Power Development Corpn.)* v. *Trust House Construction Engineers and Builders*, 2021 SCC OnLine J&K 1109.
169. *Garg Builders* v. *BHEL*, (2022) 11 SCC 697.
170. *Union of India* v. *Saraswat Trading Agency*, (2009) 16 SCC 504.
171. *Paradeep Port Trust* v. *Udayanath Rout*, 2019 SCC OnLine Ori 531: (2019) 128 CLT 308.
172. *State of Rajasthan* v. *Ferro Concrete Construction (P) Ltd.*, (2009) 12 SCC 1.
173. *Ibid.*

in all its force. Therefore, the grant of interest in the award of the Arbitral Tribunal for the period up to the date of the award was not tenable. Hence, the award of the arbitrator was set aside.[174]

Discretionary power of the court to award interest

Parties to the contract had agreed that no interest shall be payable prior to the date of award. The arbitrator would be bound by the terms of the contract and cannot award interest by exercising discretion for pre-award period, *i.e.* between the date when the cause of action arose to the date of award. However, he can award interest at the rate of 18 per cent per annum from the date of award till date of payment by exercising his discretion.[175]

Pendente lite and future interest

Award of interest for pendente lite and future period will be governed by the provisions of Section 34 CPC or the law governing arbitration. The provisions of Interest Act, 1978 are not applicable.[176] The arbitrator is entitled to award pendente lite and future interest.[177]

Pendente lite interest—General conditions of contract [S. 31(7)]

As a clause of general conditions of contract put a bar on the Arbitral Tribunal to award interest on delayed payment due to the contractor, the Arbitral Tribunal did not have any jurisdiction to grant interest.[178]

Award of interest proper

Work order was for design, engineering, etc. of water cooler type central air conditioning system. The contract executed and there was no complaint regarding the performance of the air conditioning system. Though there was no agreement as regards interest, grant of interest at the rate of 6 per cent per annum till realisation of its dues was proper.[179]

A bar to award interest on amounts payable under contract in terms of clause 16(3) of General Contract Clause is not sufficient to deny payment of

---

174. *Chief Engineer* v. *P. Rajendran Asari*, 2020 SCC OnLine Ker 967: (2020) 2 KLJ 240.
175. *J.S. Construction (P) Ltd.* v. *Chief Engineer*, 2015 SCC OnLine Ori 28: (2015) 120 CLT 53.
176. *Ibid.*
177. *Bhilai Wires Ltd.* v. *BSNL*, 2010 SCC OnLine Cal 1788: (2010) 3 CHN 329.
178. *Jaiprakash Associates Ltd.* v. *Tehri Hydro Development Corpn. (India) Ltd.*, (2019) 17 SCC 786.
179. *Laxmi Pat Surana* v. *Voltas Ltd.*, 2019 SCC OnLine Cal 1008.

interest pendente lite. The arbitrator has power to award interest pendente lite where it is justified.[180]

"Sum" [Sub-s. (7)(*a*)]

The word "sum" in Section 31(7) refers to the aggregate amounts that may be directed to be paid by the Arbitral Tribunal and not merely the "principal sum" without interest. By Section 31(7)(*a*), Parliament intended that an award for payment of money may be inclusive of interest and the "sum" of principal amount plus interest may be directed to be paid by the Arbitral Tribunal for the pre-award period.[181] Section 31(7) empowers the arbitrator to award interest on the entire sum for which the award is made which may include the amount of interest. Provisions operate unless there is an agreement to the contrary between the parties.[182]

Compound interest

Earlier the Supreme Court held that in the absence of provision in the contract, the Arbitral Tribunal is not empowered to award interest upon interest or compound interest either for pre-award or for post-award period.[183] The said view has been overruled by the Supreme Court in *Hyder Consulting (UK) Ltd.* v. *State of Orissa*[184]; the court has held that under clause (*b*) of Section 31(7), "sum" means a sum arrived at after merging of interest with principal, and it would be inclusive of interest pendente lite. Compound interest can be awarded only if there is a specific contract or authority under a statute for compounding of interest.[185]

A petitioner cannot claim interest on interest pendente lite.[186]

Rate of interest at the rate of 18 per cent on award

Where no award is made for interest, the statutory rate of interest at the rate of 18 per cent per annum is payable from the date of award till the date of payment. However, as the Arbitral Tribunal had already awarded interest at the rate of 10.5 per cent, the rate of interest was not enhanced.[187] Even

180. *Raveechee & Co.* v. *Union of India*, (2018) 7 SCC 664.
181. *Hyder Consulting (UK) Ltd.* v. *State of Orissa*, (2015) 2 SCC 189; *Morgan Securities & Credits (P) Ltd.* v. *Videocon Industries Ltd.*, (2023) 1 SCC 602.
182. *Angel Infin (P) Ltd.* v. *Echjay Industries Ltd.*, 2007 SCC OnLine Bom 50: (2007) 4 Mah LJ 618.
183. *Pournima Suryakant Pawar* v. *State of Maharashtra*, (2013) 3 SCC 690.
184. (2015) 2 SCC 189; *UHL Power Co. Ltd.* v. *State of H.P.*, (2022) 4 SCC 116.
185. *Pt. Munshi Ram & Associates (P) Ltd.* v. *DDA*, 2010 SCC OnLine Del 2444: ILR (2010) 5 Del 449.
186. *Chandi Contractors (P) Ltd.* v. *Executive Engineer*, 2023 SCC OnLine P&H 6688.
187. *BHEL* v. *Tata Projects Ltd.*, (2015) 5 SCC 682.

though prior to amendment of Section 31(7), by Amending Act 3 of 2016, the Act permitted interest at the rate of 18 per cent per annum, there has to be a basis for awarding interest at the rate of 18 per cent per annum.[188]

It is the policy of law insofar as arbitral proceedings are concerned to award 18 per cent per annum interest.[189]

The interest rate of 18 per cent prescribed under Section 31(7)(*b*) is not mandatory. After economic reforms, interest rates have substantially reduced, and therefore, a balance has to be struck between the legal provisions and economic reality of the day. Reducing interest from 18 per cent to 10 per cent per annum was held justified.[190]

Leave and licence agreement, being a contractual agreement, the interest awarded should be reasonable and not exorbitant. Interest awarded was reduced from 18 per cent to 7.5 per cent per annum from the date of the award.[191]

"Carry interest at the rate of two per cent higher" [S. 31(7)(*b*)]

Section 31(7) has been amended by the Amendment Act 3 of 2016. The amended sub-section (7) provides that unless otherwise agreed by the parties, the arbitral award for payment of money may include a direction for payment of interest on the sum awarded at such rate as it deems reasonable on the whole or any part of the money for the whole or any part of the period between the date on which the cause of action arose and the date on which the award is made. The rate of future interest shall be 2 per cent higher than the current rate of interest prevalent from the date of award to the date of payment. Prior to amendment, clause (*b*) of Section 31(7) read as under:

> (*b*) A sum directed to be paid by an arbitral award shall, unless the award otherwise directs, carry interest at the rate of eighteen percent per annum from the date of award to the date of payment.

188. *VSNL* v. *Shapoorji Pallonji & Co. Ltd.*, 2007 SCC OnLine Cal 670: (2008) 1 CHN 721.
189. *Godrej Properties & Investments Ltd.* v. *Tripura Construction*, 2003 SCC OnLine Bom 13: (2003) 2 Mah LJ 306; *Union of India* v. *Arctic India*, 2006 SCC OnLine Cal 137: (2006) 2 CHN 707; *Pt. Munshi Ram & Associates (P) Ltd.* v. *DDA*, 2010 SCC OnLine Del 2444: ILR (2010) 5 Del 449.
190. *MSK Projects (I) (JV) Ltd.* v. *State of Rajasthan*, 2007 SCC OnLine Raj 96: (2008) 2 RLW 1157.
191. *Vinod Batla* v. *Matrimmony.com*, 2019 SCC OnLine Mad 39354.

A higher rate of interest is provided in clause (*b*) with the deliberate intent of discouraging award debtors from adopting dilatory tactics and to persuade them to comply with the award.[192]

If the award grants interest at a specified rate up to the date of payment, or specifies the rate of interest payable from the date of award till the date of payment, or if the award specifically refused interest, Section 31(*b*) will not come into play. But if the award is silent with regard to the interest from the date of award, or does not specify the rate of interest from the date of award, then the party in whose favour an award for money has been made will be entitled to interest at the rate of 2 per cent higher than the current rate of interest prevalent on the date of award from the date of award to the date of payment.[193]

Where no direction was given by the arbitrator for payment of interest, clause (*b*) was attracted and the beneficiary of the award was entitled to interest at the rate of 18 per cent per annum from the date of award.[194]

Award of interest at the rate of 15 per cent was not so excessive as to warrant court's interference.[195]

Pendente lite interest

The parties had agreed that no interest will be payable upon the earnest money or the security deposit or on the amount payable to the contractor under the contract. In view of the specific bar, the Arbitral Tribunal could not award pendente lite interest to the contractor.[196] Pendente lite interest can be granted by the arbitrator only if payment of interest is not expressly barred by the contract.[197] The arbitrator has jurisdiction to award pendente lite interest.[198]

Pendente lite interest can be granted by the arbitrator only if payment of interest is not expressly barred by the contract.[199]

---

192. *State of Haryana* v. *S.L. Arora & Co.*, (2010) 3 SCC 690; *State of Haryana* v. *S.L. Arora & Co.*, (2010) 3 SCC 690.
193. *Ibid.*
194. *Madhu Mehra* v. *Pritpal Singh*, 2010 SCC OnLine Del 2174: (2010) 117 DRJ 462; *Eskay Engineers* v. *BSNL*, 2009 SCC OnLine Bom 893: (2009) 5 Mah LJ 565.
195. *GAIL (India) Ltd.* v. *Triveni Engg. & Industries Ltd.*, (2022) 3 HCC (Del) 324.
196. *Sree Kamatchi Amman Constructions* v. *Railways*, (2010) 8 SCC 767.
197. *Tehri Hydro Development Corpn. Ltd.* v. *Jai Prakash Associates Ltd.*, (2012) 12 SCC 10; *Indian Railway Construction Co. Ltd.* v. *National Buildings Construction Corpn. Ltd.*, (2023) 7 SCC 390.
198. *Union of India* v. *Jai Forging and Stampings (P) Ltd.*, 2004 SCC OnLine MP 100: (2004) 3 MP LJ 263.
199. *Tehri Hydro Development Corpn. Ltd.* v. *Jai Prakash Associates Ltd.*, (2012) 12 SCC 10.

Arbitrator's power to award interest

The arbitrator has the power to award interest at all three stages, *namely*, pre-reference period, pendente lite and post-award period, provided there is no provision to the contrary in an arbitration agreement and the rate of interest is not unreasonable. The arbitrator had granted uniform interest at the rate of 12 per cent per annum all throughout. The award was made under the rule of the court and the trial court did not find illegality therein. The High Court, therefore, should not have interfered with the said order and reduced the rate of interest from the date of award till the date of realisation of the amount.[200]

Looking at the facts and circumstances of the case, the award of interest by the arbitrator at the rate of 12 per cent from the date of award, *i.e.* 4 April 1997, till the date of realisation was found excessive and as such was reduced to 6 per cent per annum.[201]

Section 31(7)(*b*) does not fetter or restrict the discretion that the arbitrator holds in granting post-award interest. The arbitrator has the discretion to award post-award interest on a part of the sum. The arbitrator must exercise the discretionary power to grant post-award interest reasonably and in good faith, taking into account all relevant circumstances.[202] A clause in the agreement which provided that the contractor shall not be entitled to interest in case of non-payment of bills applies to parties to the agreement and not to the arbitrator. The arbitrator has inherent power to award pre-pendente lite and post-pendente lite interest.[203]

Pre-reference and post-reference period

The arbitrator is competent to award interest for period commencing with date of award to date of decree or date of realisation, whichever is earlier. Award of interest for period prior to arbitrator entering upon reference is a matter of substantive law, while grant of interest for post-award period is a matter of procedure.[204]

Grant of interest till date of award

Interest allowed by the arbitrator till the date of award was held proper.[205]

200. *Manalal Prabhudayal* v. *Oriental Insurance Co. Ltd.*, (2009) 17 SCC 296.
201. *Rajasthan SRTC* v. *Indag Rubber Ltd.*, (2006) 7 SCC 700.
202. *Morgan Securities & Credits (P) Ltd.* v. *Videocon Industries Ltd.*, (2023) 1 SCC 602.
203. *Kapil Dev Bansal* v. *H.P. Urban Development Authority*, 2018 SCC OnLine HP 929.
204. *MSK Projects (I) (JV) Ltd.* v. *State of Rajasthan*, (2011) 10 SCC 573.
205. *Fertilizer Corporation of India* v. *Balaji Laminating Works*, 2019 SCC OnLine Jhar 611.

Interest on deferred payment

There was a contract for construction of works. The work was suspended by the contractor for want of funds. Assurance was given by the government-company for payment and forbade foreclosure of the contract by the contractor. The general conditions of contract provided for payment of compensation in case of suspension of work. Claim for interest on deferred payment was in accordance with the terms and conditions of the contract, and the contractor was held entitled to the interest claimed.[206]

Interest on delayed payment

There was a contract for the upgradation of State highways. Specific terms of the agreement provided for payment of interest on delayed payment. Leaving blank space in the "appendix to the bid" for the rate of interest cannot be construed as cancellation of the clause for interest. The agreement did not contain any express exclusion clause for payment of interest—simple interest at the rate of 8 per cent would be just and equitable.[207]

Power of Arbitral Tribunal to award compensation and interest

The Arbitral Tribunal is empowered to award the interest in the form of compensation if such has been agreed by the parties. However, in the event of absence of such agreement, the tribunal can award interest to the extent of delay in payment of money in the form of compensation.[208]

Award of interest on equitable considerations

Interest can also be seen as a measure for compensating in monetary terms for the period during which money has been wrongfully withheld. Hence, on equitable considerations, once the arbitrator found that a certain sum of money had wrongfully been imposed on account of liquidated damages by the respondent on the petitioner, the award of the said sum should have carried an interest component. Where the agreement between the parties does not contain a clear prohibition in relation to grant of interest, it must be presumed that interest is an implied term of such an agreement and the arbitrator has the power to award the same. The ground on which the arbitrator refused to grant interest, *namely*, that the supply orders did not contain any clause to that effect, is contrary to the mandate of the 1996 Act. Claim for interest was allowed.[209]

---

206. *RITES Ltd.* v. *Bhardwaj Construction Co. (P) Ltd.*, 2020 SCC OnLine Jhar 1857.
207. *Oriental Structural Engineers (P) Ltd.* v. *State of Kerala*, (2021) 6 SCC 150.
208. *PWD* v. *East Coast Constructions and Industries Ltd.*, 2023 SCC OnLine Mad 8072.
209. *Batliboi Ltd.* v. *Union of India*, 2020 SCC OnLine Cal 946: (2020) 1 Cal LT 158.

Award of interest by executing court

The executing court cannot pass any order for payment of interest.[210] A Division Bench of the Delhi High Court has taken a contrary view. The Division Bench has held that the court has inherent jurisdiction to award interest in the absence of any legislation, agreement or custom subject to the contrary agreement.

Whether rate of interest awarded by arbitrator can be interfered with by the High Court exercising powers under Section 34 of the Act

When an arbitrator assigns reasons for awarding a particular rate of interest and the same is not unwarranted, no interference is required. Interest awarded by the arbitrator was restored.[211]

Court's power to vary interest

Section 3 of the Interest Act (14 of 1978) empowers the court to award interest at rate prevailing in banking transactions. Impliedly, the court has the power to vary the rate of interest agreed by the parties.[212]

Reduction of interest

Arbitration proceedings were commenced after the 1996 Act had come into force, and were conducted in accordance with the 1996 Act, though the arbitration agreement was prior to the 1996 Act. It was held, Para 7 of Section 24 of U.P. Amendment Act amending First Schedule to the Arbitration Act, 1940 had no application to the case. Since the arbitrator had granted interest at the rate of 18 per cent in accordance with Section 31(7)(*b*) of the Act of 1996, the High Court and District Judge were not justified in reducing it from 18 per cent to 6 per cent by following the U.P. Amendment Act.[213]

JD depositing amount in court pending appeal—Not liable to pay post-award interest

The word "payment" may have different meaning in different contexts; in the context of Section 37(1)(*b*), Arbitration and Conciliation Act, 1996, it means extinguishment of liability arising under the award. It signifies satisfaction of the award. The deposit of the award amount into the court is

210. *M.P. Housing Board* v. *Satish Kumar Raizada*, 2002 SCC OnLine MP 601: (2003) 2 MPLJ 346.
211. *Mekala Traders* v. *T.N. Civil Supplies Corpn. Ltd.*, 2010 SCC OnLine Mad 3486: (2010) 4 CTC 611.
212. *MSK Projects (I) (JV) Ltd.* v. *State of Rajasthan*, (2011) 10 SCC 573.
213. *Shahi & Associates* v. *State of U.P.*, (2019) 8 SCC 329.

nothing but a payment to the credit of the decree-holder. In this view, once the award amount was deposited by the appellants before the court on 24 May 2001, the liability of post-award interest from 24 May 2001 ceased. The High Court was not right in directing the appellants to pay the interest at the rate of 18 per cent per annum beyond 24 May 2001.[214]

Interest for post-award period—Stay period would be excluded

In working out the amount of interest for the post-award period, the period(s) for which the operation of the award was stayed by the court would be excluded.[215]

Interest on damages

Arbitrator is empowered to award interest even on claim for damages from the date of cause of action till the date of the award.[216]

Interest on bank guarantee

Where there is agreement that no interest would be awarded to the contractor, the arbitrator committed grave error in awarding interest to the arbitrator on bank guarantee.[217]

Interest on earnest money/security deposit

There was express provision in general conditions of contract prohibiting payment of interest read with Section 31(7)(*a*), and therefore, the award of interest by the arbitrator was contrary to the terms of contract and Section 31(7)(*a*). The award was in conflict with the public policy of India. The award of interest was set aside.[218]

Insurance claim—Interest

Interest would be payable from the month after the expiry of the window statutorily granted to the insurance company for settling claim. Award of interest at the rate of 12 per cent per annum by the Arbitral Tribunal was proper.[219]

---

214. *H.P. Housing & Urban Development Authority* v. *Ranjit Singh Rana*, (2012) 4 SCC 505.
215. *Union of India* v. *Saraswat Trading Agency*, (2009) 16 SCC 504.
216. *Hindustan Petroleum Corpn. Ltd.* v. *Offshore Infrastructure Ltd.*, 2015 SCC OnLine Bom 4146: (2015) 6 Mah LJ 287.
217. *Godawari Marathawada Irrigation Development Corpn.* v. *Y.R. Reddy Engineers and Builders*, 2017 SCC OnLine Bom 1670: (2017) 5 Mah LJ 660.
218. *Union of India* v. *S.N. Naik and Bros.*, 2013 SCC OnLine Bom 13: (2013) 2 Mah LJ 390.
219. *United India Insurance Co. Ltd.* v. *Suryo Udyog Ltd.*, 2023 SCC OnLine Ori 7009.

Hudson's formula

To apply Hudson's formula, one has to take into account the contract value that is awarded and not the work completed.[220]

Challenge to award of interest—Waiver of

The appellant had not raised the plea that the contract between the parties did not allow the tribunal to award interest in the proceedings before the Single Judge at the time of making a reference to the Arbitral Tribunal or in their reply before the Arbitral Tribunal and the plea was taken for the first time in Section 34 proceedings before the Single Judge, but the same was not pressed at the time of arguments, and even the plea was not raised before the Division Bench, any indulgence to the appellant (Union of India) to raise the plea before the Supreme Court was not allowed. The award of interest by the Arbitral Tribunal was upheld.[221]

Interest—Reasoned/speaking order necessary

Where the court grants, varies or reduces the rate of interest awarded by the arbitrator, reasoned order is necessary.[222] Where the High Court by the impugned order without assigning any reason refused to grant interest to the appellant on a sum of ₹30 lakhs awarded by the arbitrator from the date of the decree till the date of realisation, the order of the High Court was set aside and the matter was remanded to the High Court for consideration.[223] Where the High Court had not assigned any reason for reducing the rate of interest, the impugned order of the High Court was not sustained.[224]

Award of interest at rate higher than agreed by the parties [Sub-s. (7)]

The contract between the parties provided for payment of interest at the rate of 13 per cent per annum. However, the arbitrator awarded interest at the rate of 18 per cent per annum from the date of submission of the final bill. It was held, the grant of interest by the arbitrator at 18 per cent per annum was directly opposed to the specific terms of the contract; it was not permissible for the arbitrator or the court dealing with the validity of the award to award interest at a higher rate than the mutually agreed rate which

220. *Associate Builders* v. *DDA*, (2015) 3 SCC 49.
221. *Union of India* v. *Susaka (P) Ltd.*, (2018) 2 SCC 182.
222. *Mohinder Singh & Co.* v. *Port of Bombay*, (2009) 4 SCC 86; *Sayeed Ahmed & Co.* v. *State of U.P.*, (2009) 12 SCC 26.
223. *Sayeed Ahmed & Co.* v. *State of U.P.*, (2009) 12 SCC 26.
224. *Ibid.*

is binding on the parties. The arbitrator and the court are not within jurisdiction in awarding interest at a rate higher than the one mutually agreed upon between the parties.[225]

Section 31(7) of the 1996 Act and Interest on Delayed Payments to Small Scale and Ancillary Industrial Undertakings Act, 1993

The provisions of Section 7 of the 1993 Act prevail over the provisions of Section 31(7), Arbitration and Conciliation Act, 1996.[226]

Costs of arbitration [Sub-s. (8)]

The costs of arbitration shall be fixed by the Arbitral Tribunal in accordance with Section 31-A. *See*, comments under Section 31-A *infra*.

Award of costs is entirely in the discretion of the court, so also the tribunal, cannot be claimed as a matter of right. Considering the facts and circumstances of the case, the tribunal awarded the cost of ₹5,00,000 in favour of the losing party, and the order of the tribunal was not interfered with.[227]

The award of costs of arbitration was justified as the claimant was forced into arbitration proceedings for the recovery of dues.[228]

If the respondent had approached the arbitral forum, it cannot be said that the petitioner "dragged" (in the words of the arbitrator) the respondent to arbitration by reason of which the respondent would be entitled to costs for the same.[229]

The Arbitral Tribunal while deciding the allocation of costs under Section 31(8) read with Section 31-A or advance of costs under Section 38 cannot issue any binding or enforceable orders regarding their own remuneration.[230]

Section 17, 1940 Act—Judgment in terms of award

The scheme of the 1940 Act would itself reveal that the passing of the judgment and decree under Section 17 is not a mere formality and the

---

225. *Gautam Constructions and Fisheries Ltd.* v. *National Bank for Agriculture & Rural Development*, (2000) 6 SCC 519.
226. *Snehadeep Structures (P) Ltd.* v. *Maharashtra Small-Scale Industries Development Corpn. Ltd.*, (2010) 3 SCC 34.
227. *ONGC Ltd.* v. *Dolphin Offshore Enterprises (I) Ltd.*, 2010 SCC OnLine Bom 1598: (2011) 1 Mah LJ 377.
228. *MTNL* v. *Asco Engg.*, 2015 SCC OnLine Bom 360: (2015) 4 Mah LJ 883.
229. *Union of India* v. *Tapan Kumar Roy*, 2020 SCC OnLine Cal 3303.
230. *ONGC Ltd.* v. *Afcons Gunanusa JV*, (2024) 4 SCC 481.

judgment can be pronounced only when the court is satisfied that no cause is made out for remitting the award or setting aside the award. Further, before making an award "rule of court" by passing a judgment and decree, the court is required to take into consideration various factors, apply its mind and also exercise its discretion judicially. Thus, the power exercised by the court under Section 17 of the 1940 Act is a judicial power.[231]

Stamp duty on arbitration award

The Arbitration Act nowhere specifically deals with the aspect of stamp duty on any award. Section 3 and Schedule I (Article 12) of the Bombay Stamp Act provide that the award is chargeable to stamp duty and must be stamped at the time of its execution and/or making it. Section 31 of the 1996 Act nowhere prescribes any particular format and/or obligation of either of the parties to provide a valid stamp paper.[232]

The award of the arbitrator is not invalid merely because it does not subscribe to any particular format. Unstamped or insufficiently stamped award is a curable irregularity.[233]

REGIME FOR COSTS [S. 31-A]

[234][**31-A.** *Regime for costs.*—(1) In relation to any arbitration proceeding or a proceeding under any of the provisions of this Act pertaining to the arbitration, the court or arbitral tribunal, notwithstanding anything contained in the Code of Civil Procedure, 1908 (5 of 1908), shall have the discretion to determine—

(*a*) whether costs are payable by one party to another;

(*b*) the amount of such costs; and

(*c*) when such costs are to be paid.

Explanation.—For the purpose of this sub-section, "costs" means reasonable costs relating to—

(*i*) the fees and expenses of the arbitrators, courts and witnesses;

(*ii*) legal fees and expenses;

(*iii*) any administration fees of the institution supervising the arbitration; and

(*iv*) any other expenses incurred in connection with the arbitral or court proceedings and the arbitral award.

231. *State of Kerala* v. *James Varghese*, (2022) 9 SCC 593.
232. *Indian Oil Corpn. Ltd.* v. *Megi Control Systems (P) Ltd.*, 2011 SCC OnLine Bom 598: (2011) 5 Mah LJ 892.
233. *Subhas Projects and Mktg. Ltd.* v. *Assam Urban Water Supply and Sewerage Board*, 2003 SCC OnLine Gau 18: (2003) 2 Gau LR 449.
234. *Ins.* by Act 3 of 2016, S. 17 (w.r.e.f. 23-10-2015).

(2) If the court or arbitral tribunal decides to make an order as to payment of costs,—

(*a*) the general rule is that the unsuccessful party will be ordered to pay the costs of the successful party; or

(*b*) the court or arbitral tribunal may make a different order for reasons to be recorded in writing.

(3) In determining the costs, the court or arbitral tribunal shall have regard to all the circumstances, including—

(*a*) the conduct of all the parties;

(*b*) whether a party has succeeded partly in the case;

(*c*) whether the party had made a frivolous counter-claim leading to delay in the disposal of the arbitral proceedings; and

(*d*) whether any reasonable offer to settle the dispute is made by a party and refused by the other party.

(4) The court or arbitral tribunal may make any order under this section including the order that a party shall pay—

(*a*) a proportion of another party's costs;

(*b*) a stated amount in respect of another party's costs;

(*c*) costs from or until a certain date only;

(*d*) costs incurred before proceedings have begun;

(*e*) costs relating to particular steps taken in the proceedings;

(*f*) costs relating only to a distinct part of the proceedings; and

(*g*) interest on costs from or until a certain date.

(5) An agreement which has the effect that a party is to pay the whole or part of the costs of the arbitration in any event shall be only valid if such agreement is made after the dispute in question has arisen.]

COMMENTS

Corresponding old law

Section 31-A about costs was added by the Amending Act 3 of 2016. Earlier the provisions about costs were in sub-section (8) of Section 30. The provisions of Section 31-A correspond to Section 38 and clause 8 of Schedule I of the Arbitration Act, 1940.

NOTES ON CLAUSES

Clause 17 of the Bill seeks to insert a new Section 31-A in the principal Act to provide in detail, provisions related to regime of costs which may be determined and ordered by the court or Arbitral Tribunal in relation to any arbitral proceedings or any proceedings under the Act.

Scope and application

The new Section 31-A provides detailed provisions relating to costs which may be determined and ordered by the court or the Arbitral Tribunal in relation to any arbitral proceedings or any proceedings under the Arbitration and Conciliation Act, 1996.

The provisions about costs in CPC are contained in Sections 35, 35-A and 35-B of the Code.

The general rule universally followed is that costs shall follow the event, *i.e.* the successful party shall be entitled to the costs of the suit/or proceedings. However, looking at the facts and circumstances of the case, the court may direct the parties to bear the costs proportionately or themselves.

TERMINATION OF PROCEEDINGS [S. 32]

32. *Termination of proceedings.*—(1) The arbitral proceedings shall be terminated by the final arbitral award or by an order of the arbitral tribunal under sub-section (2).

(2) The arbitral tribunal shall issue an order for the termination of the arbitral proceedings where—

(*a*) the claimant withdraws his claim, unless the respondent objects to the order and the arbitral tribunal recognises a legitimate interest on his part in obtaining a final settlement of the dispute;

(*b*) the parties agree on the termination of the proceedings; or

(*c*) the arbitral tribunal finds that the continuation of the proceedings has for any other reason become unnecessary or impossible.

(3) Subject to Section 33 and sub-section (4) of Section 34, the mandate of the arbitral tribunal shall terminate with the termination of the arbitral proceedings.

COMMENTS

Corresponding old law

Section 32 is new and no such section existed in the Arbitration Act, 1940.

UNCITRAL Model Law

Article 32. *Termination of proceedings*

(1) The arbitral proceedings are terminated by the final award or by an order of the arbitral tribunal in accordance with paragraph (2) of this article.

(2) The arbitral tribunal shall issue an order for the termination of the arbitral proceedings when:

(*a*) the claimant withdraws his claim, unless the respondent objects thereto and the arbitral tribunal recognizes a legitimate interest on his part in obtaining a final settlement of the dispute;

(*b*) the parties agree on the termination of the proceedings;

(*c*) the arbitral tribunal finds that the continuation of the proceedings has for any other reason become unnecessary or impossible.

(3) The mandate of the arbitral tribunal terminates with the termination of the arbitral proceedings, subject to the provisions of Articles 33 and 34(4).

Scope and application

Section 32 provides for the termination of the arbitration proceedings. Arbitration proceedings are terminated by the passing of the final award or by the order passed by the Arbitral Tribunal.

The Arbitral Tribunal shall pass an order of termination of the arbitration proceedings in the following events:

(*a*) where the claimant withdraws his claim;

(*b*) where the parties agree on the termination of the proceedings;

(*c*) the Arbitral Tribunal finds that the continuation of the arbitration proceedings has for some other reasons become unnecessary or impossible.

Once the arbitrator had passed an award closing the case on account of non-filing of claim, the appellant could not file a suit on the same cause of action.[235]

The tribunal held that in event the parties fail to deposit fees as directed, arbitral proceedings would stand terminated. It was impossible for the Arbitral Tribunal to proceed with the case considering the conduct of one of the parties in not depositing fees directed to be paid by Arbitral Tribunal. Arbitral proceedings stood terminated by virtue of order of the Arbitral Tribunal. Once proceedings stood terminated, it was not permissible for the Arbitral Tribunal to revive arbitral proceedings even though parties participated in subsequent proceedings. Termination of arbitration proceedings was proper.[236]

---

235. *Union of India* v. *Central India Machinery MFRs. Co. Ltd.*, 2007 SCC OnLine Del 46: ILR (2007) 1 Del 350.

236. *Hyderabad Metropolitan Development Authority* v. *Ramky Elsamex Hyderabad Ring Road Ltd.*, 2023 SCC OnLine TS 4416.

As per Section 32(2), Arbitration and Conciliation Act, 1996, arbitral proceedings shall be terminated by the final arbitral award or by an order of the Arbitral Tribunal.[237]

Once the mandate of an arbitrator terminates, the arbitrator is rendered functus officio. He has no jurisdiction thereafter to entertain any application or pass any order. The limited orders which an arbitrator whose mandate stands terminated may pass are restricted to orders under Section 33, Arbitration and Conciliation Act, 1996, which does not apply in the present case. By operation of Section 32(3), the mandate of the sole arbitrator was terminated in this case.[238]

Where in termination of arbitration proceedings no award is passed, it cannot give rise to challenge under Section 34, Arbitration Act. But the party cannot be left without a remedy; it can challenge the order terminating the proceedings by filing a writ petition under Article 226 of the Constitution.[239]

De novo arbitration proceedings

Termination of arbitration proceedings can give rise to de novo arbitration proceedings provided action is within limitation.[240]

CORRECTION AND INTERPRETATION OF AWARD; ADDITIONAL AWARD [S. 33]

33. *Correction and interpretation of award; additional award.*—(1) Within thirty days from the receipt of the arbitral award, unless another period of time has been agreed upon by the parties—

(*a*) a party, with notice to the other party, may request the arbitral tribunal to correct any computation errors, any clerical or typographical errors or any other errors of a similar nature occurring in the award;

(*b*) if so agreed by the parties, a party, with notice to the other party, may request the arbitral tribunal to give an interpretation of a specific point or part of the award.

(2) If the arbitral tribunal considers the request made under sub-section (1) to be justified, it shall make the correction or give the interpretation within thirty days from the receipt of the request and the interpretation shall form part of the arbitral award.

---

237. *Ramjee Power Construction Ltd.* v. *Jharkhand Urja Vikas Nigam Ltd.*, 2019 SCC OnLine Jhar 1524.
238. *MS Vag Educational Services* v. *Aakash Educational Services Ltd.*, (2022) 6 HCC (Del) 249.
239. *S.K. and Associates* v. *Indian Farmer and Fertilizers Coop. Ltd.*, 2010 SCC OnLine All 1884: (2011) 1 All LJ 43.
240. *Ibid.*

(3) The arbitral tribunal may correct any error of the type referred to in clause (*a*) of sub-section (1), on its own initiative, within thirty days from the date of the arbitral award.

(4) Unless otherwise agreed by the parties, a party with notice to the other party, may request, within thirty days from the receipt of the arbitral award, the arbitral tribunal to make an additional arbitral award as to claims presented in the arbitral proceedings but omitted from the arbitral award.

(5) If the arbitral tribunal considers the request made under sub-section (4) to be justified, it shall make the additional arbitral award within sixty days from the receipt of such request.

(6) The arbitral tribunal may extend, if necessary, the period of time within which it shall make a correction, give an interpretation or make an additional arbitral award under sub-section (2) or sub-section (5).

(7) Section 31 shall apply to a correction or interpretation of the arbitral award or to an additional arbitral award made under this section.

COMMENTS

Corresponding old law

Section 31(1)(*a*) contains the provisions of Section 13(*d*), Arbitration Act, 1940. Section 13(*d*), Arbitration Act read as under:

13. *Powers to arbitrator.*—The arbitrators or umpire shall, unless a different intention is expressed in the agreement, have power to—

(*a*) administer oath to the parties and witnesses appearing;

(*b*) state a special case for the opinion of the Court on any question of law involved, or state the award, wholly or in part, in the form of a special case of such question for the opinion of the Court;

(*c*) make the award conditional or in the alternative;

(*d*) correct in an award any clerical mistake or error arising from any accidental slip or omission;

(*e*) administer to any party to arbitration such interrogatories as may, in the opinion of the arbitrators or umpire, be necessary.

UNCITRAL Model Law

Article 33. *Correction and interpretation of award; additional award*

(1) Within thirty days of receipt of the award, unless another period of time has been agreed upon by the parties:

(*a*) a party, with notice to the other party, may request the arbitral tribunal to correct in the award any errors in computation, any clerical or typographical errors or any errors of similar nature;

(*b*) if so agreed by the parties, a party, with notice to the other party, may request the arbitral tribunal to give an interpretation of a specific point or part of the award.

If the arbitral tribunal considers the request to be justified, it shall make the correction or give the interpretation within thirty days of receipt of the request. The interpretation shall form part of the award.

(2) The arbitral tribunal may correct any error of the type referred to in paragraph (1)(*a*) of this article on its own initiative within thirty days of the date of the award.

(3) Unless otherwise agreed by the parties, a party, with notice to the other party, may request, within thirty days of receipt of the award, the arbitral tribunal to make an additional award as to claims presented in the arbitral proceedings but omitted from the award. If the arbitral tribunal considers the request to be justified, it shall make the additional award within sixty days.

(4) The arbitral tribunal may extend, if necessary, the period of time within which it shall make a correction, interpretation or an additional award under paragraph (1) or (3) of this article.

(5) The provisions of Article 31 shall apply to a correction or interpretation of the award or to an additional award.

Scope and application

Section 33 of the 1996 Act clearly postulates that the arbitrator has the jurisdiction to correct and interpret an award in terms whereof he may amend his core award.[241]

An arbitral award after correction, clarification and/or additional award, loses its originality for the purpose of limitation as contemplated under Section 34(3).[242]

The Arbitral Tribunal is not under obligation to award to the petitioner the amounts that the petitioner had not even claimed before it.[243]

Where the finding of the arbitrator was that invocation of the bank guarantee was unjustified, failure of the arbitrator to refund the amount of

241. *Centrotrade Minerals & Metals Inc.* v. *Hindustan Copper Ltd.*, (2006) 11 SCC 245.

242. *Amit Suryakant Lunavat* v. *Kotak Securities*, 2010 SCC OnLine Bom 1434: (2010) 6 Mah LJ 764.

243. *Uttam Co.* v. *S.G. Stock Services Ltd.*, 2008 SCC OnLine Del 234: (2009) 162 DLT 294.

bank guarantee was error on the face of the record; failure of the arbitrator to correct the award under Section 33 was improper.[244]

Amount under the different heads were interchanged and the amount of taxes which was granted in the body of the ground remained to be incorporated in the operative portion of the award, which was included in the correction. None of the changes carried out altered the award in any manner. No fault was found with the arbitrator in carrying out these changes on their own accord.[245]

In the award, the arbitrator had accepted the claim and had also determined the amount payable. However, the arbitrator had omitted to specify the period for which interest was payable. It was an obvious error; the specification of the date would not affect the award. Such modification was permissible. The arbitrator specified the date from which interest was payable, and the order was upheld.[246]

Arbitrator has no power to review award on merits

An application seeking review of an award before the arbitrator is not maintainable. Under Section 33 of the Act, a party can seek certain correction in computation errors, or clerical or typographical errors or any other errors of a similar nature occurring in the award with notice to the other party or if agreed between the parties, a party may request the Arbitral Tribunal to give an interpretation of a specific point or part of the award.[247]

Under Section 33, an award can be modified only to the extent of correcting arithmetical and/or clerical errors without any material changes. The respondent had filed an application under Section 33 for modification of an award by correcting computational/arithmetical/clerical error by substituting ₹20,747 in place of ₹740 per gram as the rate for calculation of the cost of gold. The arbitrator allowed the application and modified the original award accordingly. Held, there was no arithmetical/clerical error in the original award. Hence, the order passed by the arbitrator in the application under Section 33 by modifying the original award was beyond the scope and ambit of his jurisdiction under Section 33.[248]

---

244. *Tal Mfg. Solutions Ltd.* v. *Union of India*, 2013 SCC OnLine Del 429: (2013) 135 DRJ 107.
245. *Metalmeccanica Fracasso India (P) Ltd.* v. *Prakash Industrial Infrastructure (P) Ltd.*, 2014 SCC OnLine Bom 161: (2014) 2 Mah LJ 775.
246. *United Trade Agency Contractor* v. *District Judge, Mirzapur*, 2014 SCC OnLine All 15986: (2015) 2 All LJ 184.
247. *State of Arunachal Pradesh* v. *Damani Construction Co.*, (2007) 10 SCC 742.
248. *Gyan Prakash Arya* v. *Titan Industries Ltd.*, (2023) 1 SCC 153.

It is obligatory on the part of the arbitrator to dispose of the application filed under Section 33(1) within 30 days.[249]

Additional arbitral award

Consent of both the parties is necessary; one party cannot apply for additional award.[250]

Acquiescence

The contractor challenged the award of the arbitrator in respect of the unpaid amount. Additional award was passed by the arbitrator behind the back of the petitioner during pendency of proceedings under Section 34 followed by issuing a certificate of full and final payment by the contractor for an amount lesser than that awarded under additional award. The petitioner immediately raised protest about issuance of the certificate under duress. The principle of acquiescence was not invoked.[251]

Counterclaim

When a counterclaim is filed before the arbitrator, it is the duty of the arbitrator to decide the same also. When an omission to decide counterclaim is brought to the notice of the arbitrator under Section 33(4), it will be the duty of the party applying under Section 33(4) to see that the other side gets an opportunity to contest the same.[252]

Corrections under Sections 151 and 152 CPC

Non-correction of clerical/typographical errors by invoking the remedy under Section 33 within the specified time does not curtail the power of the court to allow the correction of mistakes of the nature provided in Sections 151 and 152 CPC.[253]

---

249. *Ex. Engineer H.S.A.M. Board* v. *Dharam Pal*, 2000 SCC OnLine P&H 1264: PLR (2001) 128 P&H 452.
250. *Amit Suryakant Lunavat* v. *Kotak Securities*, 2010 SCC OnLine Bom 1434: (2010) 6 Mah LJ 764.
251. *Marwah Co.* v. *NTPC*, 2019 SCC OnLine Ori 163: (2019) 128 CLT 33.
252. *Vitthalrao Shinde Sahakari Sakhar Karkhana Ltd.* v. *Gangapur Sahakari Sakhar Karkhana Ltd.*, 2017 SCC OnLine Bom 1669: (2017) 5 Mah LJ 390.
253. *Manmohan Exims (P) Ltd.* v. *Sarju International*, 2005 SCC OnLine Bom 1081: (2005) 4 Mah LJ 721.

Chapter VII
Recourse Against Arbitral Award

APPLICATION FOR SETTING ASIDE ARBITRAL AWARD [S. 34]

34. *Application for setting aside arbitral award.*—(1) Recourse to a Court against an arbitral award may be made only by an application for setting aside such award in accordance with sub-section (2) and sub-section (3).

(2) An arbitral award may be set aside by the Court only if—

(*a*) the party making the application [1][establishes on the basis of the record of the arbitral tribunal that]—

(*i*) a party was under some incapacity; or

(*ii*) the arbitration agreement is not valid under the law to which the parties have subjected it or, failing any indication thereon, under the law for the time being in force; or

(*iii*) the party making the application was not given proper notice of the appointment of an arbitrator or of the arbitral proceedings or was otherwise unable to present his case; or

(*iv*) the arbitral award deals with a dispute not contemplated by or not falling within the terms of the submission to arbitration, or it contains decisions on matters beyond the scope of the submission to arbitration:

Provided that, if the decisions on matters submitted to arbitration can be separated from those not so submitted, only that part of the arbitral award which contains decisions on matters not submitted to arbitration may be set aside; or

(*v*) the composition of the arbitral tribunal or the arbitral procedure was not in accordance with the agreement of the parties, unless such agreement was in conflict with a provision of this Part from which the parties cannot derogate, or, failing such agreement, was not in accordance with this Part; or

(*b*) the Court finds that—

(*i*) the subject-matter of the dispute is not capable of settlement by arbitration under the law for the time being in force, or

---

1. *Subs.* for "furnishes proof that" by Act 33 of 2019, S. 7 (w.e.f. 30-8-2019).

(*ii*) the arbitral award is in conflict with the public policy of India.

[2][*Explanation 1.*—For the avoidance of any doubt, it is clarified that an award is in conflict with the public policy of India, only if,—

(*i*) the making of the award was induced or affected by fraud or corruption or was in violation of Section 75 or Section 81; or

(*ii*) it is in contravention with the fundamental policy of Indian law; or

(*iii*) it is in conflict with the most basic notions of morality or justice.

Explanation 2.—For the avoidance of doubt, the test as to whether there is a contravention with the fundamental policy of Indian law shall not entail a review on the merits of the dispute.]

[3][(2-A) An arbitral award arising out of arbitrations other than international commercial arbitrations, may also be set aside by the court, if the court finds that the award is vitiated by patent illegality appearing on the face of the award:

Provided that an award shall not be set aside merely on the ground of an erroneous application of the law or by reappreciation of evidence.]

(3) An application for setting aside may not be made after three months have elapsed from the date on which the party making that application had received the arbitral award or, if a request had been made under Section 33, from the date on which that request had been disposed of by the arbitral tribunal:

Provided that if the Court is satisfied that the applicant was prevented by sufficient cause from making the application within the said period of three months it may entertain the application within a further period of thirty days, but not thereafter.

(4) On receipt of an application under sub-section (1), the Court may, where it is appropriate and it is so requested by a party, adjourn the proceedings for a period of time determined by it in order to give the arbitral tribunal an opportunity to resume the arbitral proceedings or to take such other action as in the opinion of arbitral tribunal will eliminate the grounds for setting aside the arbitral award.

[4][(5) An application under this section shall be filed by a party only after issuing a prior notice to the other party and such application shall be accompanied by an affidavit by the applicant endorsing compliance with the said requirement.

(6) An application under this section shall be disposed of expeditiously, and in any event, within a period of one year from the date on which the notice referred to in sub-section (5) is served upon the other party.]

---

2. *Subs.* by Act 3 of 2016, S. 18(I) (w.r.e.f. 23-10-2015). Prior to substitution it read as:

"*Explanation.*—Without prejudice to the generality of sub-clause (*ii*), it is hereby declared, for the avoidance of any doubt, that an award is in conflict with the public policy of India if the making of the award was induced or affected by fraud or corruption or was in violation of Section 75 or Section 81."

3. *Ins.* by Act 3 of 2016, S. 18(II) (w.r.e.f. 23-10-2015).

4. *Ins.* by Act 3 of 2016, S. 18(III) (w.r.e.f. 23-10-2015).

STATE AMENDMENTS

Union Territory of Jammu and Kashmir.—In its application to the Union Territory of Jammu and Kashmir,—

(*i*) after sub-section (2), *insert* the following sub-section, namely:—

"(2-A) An arbitral award may also be set aside by the Court, if the Court finds that the award is vitiated by patent illegality appearing on the face of the award:

Provided that an award shall not be set aside merely on the ground of an erroneous application of the law or by re-appreciation of evidence.";

(*ii*) in sub-section (3),—

(*i*) for "three months" *substitute*, "six months";

(*ii*) in proviso thereto, for, "three months" and "thirty days" *substitute* respectively "six months" and "sixty days". [*Vide* S.O. 1123(E), dated 18-3-2020 (w.e.f. 18-3-2020)].

Union Territory of Ladakh.—In its application to the Union Territory of Ladakh,

(*i*) after sub-section (2), *insert*—

"(2-A) An arbitral award may also be set aside by the Court, if the Court finds that the award is vitiated by patent illegality appearing on the face of the award:

Provided that an award shall not be set aside merely on the ground of an erroneous application of the law or by re-appreciation of evidence."

(*ii*) in sub-section (3),—

(*a*) for "three months" *substitute* "six months";

(*b*) in the proviso, for "three months" and "thirty days" *substitute* respectively "six months" and "sixty days". [*Vide* S.O. 3774(E), dated 23-10-2020].

COMMENTS

Corresponding old law

Section 34 corresponds to Section 30, Arbitration Act 1940. Section 30, Arbitration Act, 1940 provided as under:

30. *Grounds for setting aside award.*—An award shall not be set aside except on one or more of the following grounds, namely—

(*a*) that an arbitrator or umpire has misconducted himself or the proceedings;

(*b*) that an award has been made after the issue of an order by the Court superseding the arbitration or after arbitration proceedings have become invalid under Section 35;

(*c*) that an award has been improperly procured or is otherwise invalid.

UNCITRAL Model Law

Article 34. *Application for setting aside as exclusive recourse against arbitral award*

(1) Recourse to a court against an arbitral award may be made only by an application for setting aside in accordance with paragraphs (2) and (3) of this article.

(2) An arbitral award may be set aside by the court specified in Article 6 only if:

(*a*) the party making the application furnishes proof that:

(*i*) a party to the arbitration agreement referred to in Article 7 was under some incapacity; or the said agreement is not valid under the law to which the parties have subjected it or, failing any indication thereon, under the law of this State; or

(*ii*) the party making the application was not given proper notice of the appointment of an arbitrator or of the arbitral proceedings or was otherwise unable to present his case; or

(*iii*) the award deals with a dispute not contemplated by or not falling within the terms of the submission to arbitration, or contains decisions on matters beyond the scope of the submission to arbitration, provided that, if the decisions on matters submitted to arbitration can be separated from those not so submitted, only that part of the award which contains decisions on matters not submitted to arbitration may be set aside; or

(*iv*) the composition of the arbitral tribunal or the arbitral procedure was not in accordance with the agreement of the parties, unless such agreement was in conflict with a provision of this Law from which the parties cannot derogate, or, failing such agreement, was not in accordance with this Law; or

(*b*) the court finds that:

(*i*) the subject-matter of the dispute is not capable of settlement by arbitration under the law of this State; or

(*ii*) the award is in conflict with the public policy of this State.

(3) An application for setting aside may not be made after three months have elapsed from the date on which the party making that application had received the award or, if a request had been made under Article 33, from the date on which that request had been disposed of by the arbitral tribunal.

(4) The court, when asked to set aside an award, may, where appropriate and so requested by a party, suspend the setting aside proceedings for a period of time determined by it in order to give the arbitral tribunal an opportunity to resume the arbitral proceedings or to take such other action as in the arbitral tribunal's opinion will eliminate the grounds for setting aside.

Section 34, Arbitration and Conciliation Act, 1996 is based on Article 34 of the UNCITRAL Model Law.[5]

Legislative changes

Arbitration and Conciliation (Amendment) Act, 2015 (3 of 2016)

In Section 34 of the principal Act,—

(*I*) in sub-section (2), in clause (*b*), for the Explanation, the following Explanations shall be *substituted*, namely—

"*Explanation 1.*— For the avoidance of any doubt, it is clarified that an award is in conflict with the public policy of India, only if,—

(*i*) the making of the award was induced or affected by fraud or corruption or was in violation of Section 75 or Section 81; or

(*ii*) it is in contravention with the fundamental policy of Indian law; or

(*iii*) it is in conflict with the most basic notions of morality or justice.

Explanation 2.— For the avoidance of doubt, the test as to whether there is a contravention with the fundamental policy of Indian law shall not entail a review on the merits of the dispute.";

(*II*) after sub-section (2), the following sub-section shall be *inserted*, namely—

"(2-A) An arbitral award arising out of arbitrations other than international commercial arbitrations, may also be set aside by the Court, if the Court finds that the award is vitiated by patent illegality appearing on the face of the award:

Provided that an award shall not be set aside merely on the ground of an erroneous application of the law or by reappreciation of evidence.";

(*III*) after sub-section (4), the following sub-sections shall be *inserted*, namely—

"(5) An application under this section shall be filed by a party only after issuing a prior notice to the other party and such application shall be accompanied by an affidavit by the applicant endorsing compliance with the said requirement.

(6) An application under this section shall be disposed of expeditiously, and in any event, within a period of one year from the date on which the notice referred to in sub-section (5) is served upon the other party.".

NOTES ON CLAUSES

Clause 18 of the Bill seeks to amend Section 34 of the principal Act to provide for Explanation to the term "public policy of India" in sub-clause (*ii*) of

5. *Olympus Superstructures (P) Ltd.* v. *Meena Vijay Khetan*, (1999) 5 SCC 651.

clause (*b*) of sub-section (2) to the effect that an arbitral award shall be treated as an award in conflict with the public policy of India only where making of award was induced or affected by fraud or corruption or was in violation of Section 75 or Section 81; or is in contravention with the fundamental policy of Indian law; or it is in conflict with the most basic notions of morality or justice. *Explanation* 2 is inserted to explain that the test as to whether there is a contravention with the fundamental policy of Indian law shall not entail a review on the merits of the dispute. A new sub-section (2-A) is inserted to provide an additional ground of patent illegality to challenge the arbitral award arising out of arbitrations other than international commercial arbitrations. Sub-section (5) is inserted to provide that an application for setting aside an award under this section is to be filed after issuing prior notice to the other party. Sub-section (6) is inserted to prescribe a period of one year for disposal of an application for setting aside an arbitral award.

The Amendment Act, 2019 is prospective in nature and will not be applicable to the application for setting aside the arbitral award filed prior to the amendment.[6]

The Amending Act of 2015 would not apply to arbitration proceedings commenced as per Section 21 of the Act of 1996 prior to the amendment. It can apply with the agreement of the parties even if the commencement of proceedings is prior to the Amending Act of 2015.[7]

Arbitration and Conciliation (Amendment) Act, 2019 (33 of 2019)

In sub-section (2), clause (*a*), the words "establishes on the basis of the records of the arbitral tribunal" have been substituted for the words "furnishes proof that" appearing earlier in the section.

Prior to 2019 Amendment

Where arbitration proceedings commenced and concluded prior to the amendment of Section 34(2)(*a*) by Act 33 of 2019, pre-amendment provisions of Section 34(2)(*a*) shall be applicable.[8]

Scope and application

Section 34 is based on Article 34 of UNCITRAL Model Law and the scope of the provisions for setting aside the award is more or less the same as under Section 30 or Section 33, Arbitration Act, 1940.[9]

6. *Macro Marvel Projects Ltd.* v. *J. Vengatesh*, 2022 SCC OnLine Mad 4702.
7. *Shilpa Construction* v. *Jaipur Municipal Corpn.*, 2017 SCC OnLine Raj 4312: (2017) 4 WLC 101.
8. *Alpine Housing Development Corpn. (P) Ltd.* v. *Ashok S. Dhariwal*, 2023 SCC OnLine SC 55.
9. *Olympus Superstructures (P) Ltd.* v. *Meena Vijay Khetan*, (1999) 5 SCC 651.

It is well settled that the scope for setting aside the award is limited to the grounds which have been well defined by the decided cases.[10] The scope of interference is very limited and narrow. Unless the award suffers from any of the infirmities provided in Section 34(2), the award of the arbitrator cannot be set aside.[11] The power under Section 34 for setting aside arbitral awards can be invoked only under two contingencies prescribed under Section 34(2)(*b*)(*i*) and (*ii*).[12] The court will interfere with the award under Section 34 or in appeal under Section 37 only when the award shocks the conscience of the court and the court comes to the conclusion that the finding arrived at by the arbitrator could not have come in normal course.[13] The scope of interference with an arbitral award is extremely limited.[14] The scope of interference with an arbitral award is restricted to the grounds as set out under Section 34, Arbitration and Conciliation Act, 1996. Unless the court finds that the Arbitral Tribunal's view is not possible and such error vitiates the award, the arbitral award cannot be interfered with.[15]

The endeavour of the legislation is to make arbitration more responsive to the contemporary requirement as an alternative dispute redressal mechanism. One of the objectives is to minimise the supervisory role of the courts. A court while dealing with objections under Section 34, Arbitration and Conciliation Act, 1996 does not sit in appeal over the arbitral award. The courts can exercise their jurisdiction to interfere and can travel on the well-settled limited grounds. An award can be set aside only if it is contrary to substantive provisions of the law or the provisions of the Act or against the terms of the contract. Interference can be made only if the award suffers from patent illegality.[16]

The scope of interference under Sections 34 and 37, Arbitration and Conciliation Act, 1996 is limited. The court's interference is called for when an award is in conflict with the public policy of India which includes fraud, breach of fundamental policy of Indian law and breach of public morality or is patently illegal.[17]

---

10. *State of Rajasthan* v. *Nav Bharat Construction Co.*, (2002) 1 SCC 659.
11. *T.P. Akbar* v. *Sundaram Finance Ltd.*, 2020 SCC OnLine Mad 28361.
12. *Pandi Devi Oil (P) Ltd.* v. *Shakti International (P) Ltd.*, 2017 SCC OnLine Bom 5545: (2017) 4 Mah LJ 740; *R.S. Jiwani* v. *Ircon International Ltd.*, 2009 SCC OnLine Bom 2021: (2010) 1 Mah LJ 547; *PPSA SICAL Terminals (P) Ltd.* v. *V.O. Chidambranar Port Trust*, 2021 SCC OnLine SC 508.
13. *PWD* v. *Chandragiri Construction Co.*, 2011 SCC OnLine Mad 343: (2011) 2 CTC 669.
14. *SAIL* v. *Western Bulk Carriers KS*, 2010 SCC OnLine Del 1828: (2010) 118 DRJ 334; *State of Karnataka* v. *Gateway Hotels and Gateway Resorts Ltd.*, 2015 SCC OnLine Kar 9499.
15. *Cement Corpn. of India Ltd.* v. *SAIL*, (2022) 4 HCC (Del) 278.
16. *DDA* v. *Eros Resorts & Hotels Ltd.*, (2022) 2 HCC (Del) 384.
17. *Delhi State Industrial & Infrastructure Development Corpn. Ltd.* v. *HR Builders*, (2022) 4 HCC (Del) 123.

The court may not be justified in interfering with the impugned award by re-appreciation of evidence as the same is not permissible in law. The scope while exercising power under Section 34 of the Act is very limited. The court can interfere if the award is against public policy of India. Violation of public policy would mean contravention of fundamental laws and statutes.[18]

The award can be interfered with only where the finding of the tribunal is either contrary to terms of the contract between the parties or ex facie, perverse. The arbitrator is the final arbiter on facts as well as on law, and even errors, factual or legal, which falls short of perversity do not merit interference under Sections 34 or 37, Arbitration Act. It is not open to the court to interfere with the award merely because in the opinion of the court, another view is possible.[19]

The power of the court under Section 34 to "set aside" award does not include the power to modify such an award.[20]

The courts, while exercising jurisdiction under Section 34 or Section 37 of the Act, are not required to substitute its own decision in place of the decision taken by the arbitrator if there are materials on record for the arbitrator in taking the decision, even if it is not found logical by the court.[21] Factual aspects once decided by the arbitrator, the court of law under Section 34 or under Section 37, in appeal, is not ordinarily required to enter into the factual aspects and re-appreciate the matter.[22] The arbitrator had on appreciation of documentary evidence found the claim of damages of the appellant to be unsustainable as neither was there any delay ascribable to the respondent nor had any damages resulted from the delayed completion of the supplies; these were findings of facts which were not perverse in nature and hence were not interfered with by the court.[23]

The jurisdiction under Section 34 of the Act is exercised only to see if the Arbitral Tribunal's view is perverse or manifestly arbitrary. Accordingly, the question of reinterpreting the contract on an alternative view does not arise.[24]

There was a breach of contract for supply of battens. The dispute was referred to arbitration. The sole arbitrator on the basis of evidence and

18. *H.P. Housing & Urban Development Authority* v. *Ajay Kumar*, 2022 SCC OnLine HP 6492.
19. *Ibid.*
20. *NHAI* v. *M. Hakeem*, (2021) 9 SCC 1.
21. *ONGC Ltd.* v. *Astra Construction (P) Ltd.*, 2012 SCC OnLine Gau 515: (2013) 2 Gau LR 464.
22. *State of Tripura* v. *Ketaki Ranjan Deb*, 2013 SCC OnLine Gau 378: (2013) 2 Gau LR 527.
23. *BSNL* v. *BWL Ltd.*, 2011 SCC OnLine Del 1809: ILR (2011) 3 Del 396.
24. *Konkan Railway Corpn. Ltd.* v. *Chenab Bridge Project*, (2023) 9 SCC 85.

material supplied arrived at findings that the material supplied was defective and forfeiture of security was valid. While considering a petition under Section 34, Arbitration and Conciliation Act, the court does not act as an appellate forum. Rejection of challenge to the award of the arbitrator was proper.[25]

Section 34 in conjunction with Section 5 of the 1996 Act makes it clear that an arbitral award that is governed by Part I of the 1996 Act can only be set aside on grounds mentioned under Section 34(2) and (3) of the said Act and not otherwise. The court, considering an application for setting aside an award under Section 34 of the 1996 Act, cannot look into the merits of the award except when the award is in conflict with the public policy of India as provided in Section 34(2)(*b*)(*ii*) of the 1996 Act.[26]

It is on very limited grounds that the award of the arbitrator can be set aside by the court under Section 34.[27] Interference could be made in the award only if the arbitration award is in conflict with the public policy of India. Post award interest was reduced from 18 per cent per annum to 9 per cent per annum from the date of the award.[28]

Section 34 of the Act provides for setting aside of the award on the grounds enumerated therein and none other. The question as to whether the award is required to be stamped and registered would be relevant only when the parties file the award for its enforcement under Section 36 of the Act. It is at this stage that the parties can raise objections regarding its admissibility on account of non-registration and non-stamping under Section 17, Registration Act. The question whether an award requires stamping and registration is within the ambit of Section 47 CPC and not covered by Section 34, Arbitration and Conciliation Act.[29] Insufficient stamp duty is not a ground on which the award can be set aside.[30]

An award contrary to substantive provisions of law or provisions of the Arbitration and Conciliation Act, 1996 or against the terms of the contract would be patently illegal and opposed to the public policy of India, and if it affects the rights of the parties, would be open to interference by the court under Section 34(2) of the 1996 Act.[31]

---

25. *Punjab State Civil Supplies Corpn. Ltd.* v. *Ramesh Kumar & Co.*, (2021) 16 SCC 138.
26. *Indian Oil Corpn. Ltd.* v. *Shree Ganesh Petroleum*, (2022) 4 SCC 463.
27. *Mahanagar Gas Ltd.* v. *Babulal Uttamchand and Co.*, 2012 SCC OnLine Bom 1254: (2013) 2 Mah LJ 94.
28. *PWD* v. *Chandragiri Construction Co.*, 2011 SCC OnLine Mad 343: (2011) 2 CTC 669.
29. *M. Anasuya Devi* v. *M. Manik Reddy*, (2003) 8 SCC 565.
30. *M.P. Stock Exchange* v. *C.M.C. Ltd.*, 2011 SCC OnLine MP 164: (2011) 3 MP LJ 94.
31. *Hindustan Zinc Ltd.* v. *Friends Coal Carbonisation*, (2006) 4 SCC 445.

Section 34 as amended will apply only to Section 4 applications that have been made to the court on or after 23 October 2015, irrespective of the fact that the arbitration proceedings may have commenced prior to that date.[32]

The legality of the order passed under Section 11(6) of the Act cannot be gone into by the court in application under Section 34 of the Act.[33]

The relief of setting aside awards cannot be granted under Section 15 of the Act. For setting aside part of the award which is not acceptable to the party, the remedy lies only under Section 34 and not under Section 15 of the Act.[34] No petition under Section 34 filed by a person aggrieved by findings is maintainable.[35]

The grounds of challenge in Sections 14 and 15 are not specific grounds for setting aside an award under Section 34 of the Act. It means that the party desiring to challenge the mandate of an arbitrator can move a petition under Section 14 when the cause of action for the same arises. He cannot be expected to raise this as a challenge after the passing of the award.[36]

Where there is no award passed by the arbitrator, the question of filing an application under Section 34 for setting aside an award before the civil court does not arise.[37]

Under Section 34, the court cannot assume the powers of the appellate court and modify the award. Under Section 34, the court can either set aside the award entirely or dismiss the application. The court cannot set aside the award in part.[38]

An award was passed by the arbitrator and accepted by the parties by a joint letter. A party feeling aggrieved has to move an application for setting aside the award but if no such application is made and the award is not challenged, it assumes the status of a decree by a civil court.[39]

A petition under Section 34 can be filed challenging the appellate award.[40]

32. *Ratnam Sudesh Iyer* v. *Jackie Kakubhai Shroff*, (2022) 4 SCC 206.
33. *Central Public Works Deptt.* v. *Shankarrao Kulkarni*, 2000 SCC OnLine Bom 627: (2000) 4 Mah LJ 267.
34. *Universal Insulators & Ceramics Ltd.* v. *U.P. Power Corpn. Ltd.*, 2018 SCC OnLine All 5152: (2019) 1 All LJ 132.
35. *Nirfabrics Ltd.* v. *Nirlon Ltd.*, 1998 SCC OnLine Bom 496: (1999) 1 Mah LJ 512.
36. *Alcove Industries Ltd.* v. *Oriental Structural Engineers Ltd.*, 2007 SCC OnLine Del 1709: ILR (2008) 1 Del 1113.
37. *M.A. Mohd. Amanulla* v. *B.R. Chandrashekar*, 2004 SCC OnLine Kar 401: ILR 2004 Kar 4292.
38. *Anugraha Engineers & Contractors* v. *Union of India*, 2013 SCC OnLine Mad 3440: (2014) 3 CTC 116.
39. *Brij Ratan Mohta* v. *State of Rajasthan*, 2002 SCC OnLine Raj 158: (2003) 2 RLW 955.
40. *Abhijeet Saraswat* v. *Nalamaty Doraiah*, 2003 SCC OnLine Bom 1117: (2004) 2 Mah LJ 145.

Where the application filed under Section 34 for setting aside the award of the arbitrator is not decided finally, the award is not enforceable.[41]

1940 Act/1996 Act

Arbitration proceedings started under the Arbitration Act, 1940, and the award was filed in the court after the commencement of the new Act; the provisions of the Arbitration and Conciliation Act, 1996 would apply.[42]

Parameters for setting aside an award

1. A mere contravention of substantive law is not a ground to set aside an award.
2. The court while exercising the power of judicial review should not re-appreciate evidence.
3. The construction of a contract is essentially a matter for the Arbitral Tribunal to decide.
4. An award can be construed to be perverse only if it is based on no evidence or has ignored vital evidence.
5. The illegality of an award must be of such a nature or character so as to go to the root of the award.
6. Judicial intervention under Section 34 would not be warranted only because an alternative view on facts or the construction of the award is available.[43]

Foreign award—Setting aside of

Courts in India have no jurisdiction to set aside a foreign award.[44] A civil suit filed for declaration that a foreign award cannot be enforced in India is not maintainable.[45]

Parties had agreed to be governed by English law and the venue was to be in England. Therefore, the award can only be challenged before the courts in England. Part I of the Arbitration and Conciliation Act, 1996 stood excluded.[46]

---

41. *Rajendra N. Mehta* v. *Prabhudas Liladhar (P) Ltd.*, 2012 SCC OnLine Bom 1554: (2013) 1 Mah LJ 532.
42. *Bhai Sardar Singh* v. *DDA*, 2001 SCC OnLine Del 793: (2002) 61 DRJ 767.
43. *ONGC Ltd.* v. *Discovery Enterprises (P) Ltd.*, (2022) 8 SCC 42.
44. *State of W.B.* v. *Chatterjee Petrochem (Mauritius) Co.*, 2020 SCC OnLine Cal 3301: (2020) 2 Cal LT 139; *Golderest Exports* v. *Swissgen N.V.*, 2004 SCC OnLine Bom 991: (2005) 2 Mah LJ 105.
45. *Spentex Industries Ltd.* v. *Dunvant S.A.*, 2009 SCC OnLine Del 3451: (2009) 113 DRJ 397; *Alagar Exports* v. *Islamic Republic of Iran, Shipping Lines of Tehran*, 2008 SCC OnLine Mad 751: 2008 Supp (1) Arb LR 228.
46. *Sakuma Exports Ltd.* v. *Louis Drefus Commodities Suisse S.A.*, 2011 SCC OnLine Bom 1469: (2012) 3 Mah LJ 94.

A challenge under Section 34, Arbitration and Conciliation Act is not maintainable where the judicial seat of arbitration is outside India and arbitration is conducted in accordance with the rules of International Chamber of Commerce (ICC).[47]

An arbitration agreement clearly stipulated the venue of arbitration at Paris and the law governing the conduct of arbitration to be in accordance with the ICC Rules. The agreement about the seat of arbitration should be regarded as an exclusive jurisdiction clause. By necessary implication, parties excluded the application of Part I of the 1996 Act. Courts in India would have no jurisdiction to entertain an application to set aside the final award.[48]

The tribunal did not act contrary to contract nor had exceeded its jurisdiction. Foreign award was held proper.[49]

International commercial arbitral award

An award passed in International Commercial Arbitration can be challenged in Indian courts when arbitration proceedings are held in India.[50]

International commercial arbitral award—Jurisdiction of the High Court

Only the High Court has jurisdiction to entertain any challenge to the international commercial arbitral award; the District Court or the Commercial Court constituted under the Commercial Courts Act, 2015 cannot entertain the challenge.[51]

Stay of execution of award

Filing of application under Section 34 for setting aside an award does not make the award unenforceable. The new Section 36 and sub-section (2) thereunder requires the court to grant an order of stay of the operation of the arbitral award in accordance with Section 36(3) on a separate application for stay taken out by the award-debtor. Section 36(2) marks a significant departure from the erstwhile provision in clarifying that filing of an application for setting aside an award under Section 34 shall not by itself make the award unenforceable unless the award is stayed by an order of the court

---

47. *Noy Vallesina Engg. SpA* v. *Jindal Drugs Ltd.*, (2021) 1 SCC 382.
48. *State of W.B.* v. *Chatterjee Petrochem (Mauritius) Co.*, 2020 SCC OnLine Cal 3301: (2020) 2 Cal LT 139.
49. *Sleepwell Industries Co. Ltd.* v. *LMJ International Ltd.*, 2018 SCC OnLine Cal 4676: (2018) 3 Cal LT 312.
50. *ITI Ltd.* v. *Alphion Corpn.*, 2022 SCC OnLine Kar 1631.
51. *Ibid.*

in an application made in the manner provided under Section 36(3) of the Act.[52]

The provisions of Order 41, Rules 1(3) and 5, CPC apply. The court can impose conditions while allowing a stay application.[53]

The seat of arbitration at London was agreed by both the parties. Jurisdiction of Indian courts to entertain an application seeking to set aside the arbitration award is clearly barred. Only courts in London can determine the validity of the arbitral award.[54]

Filing of petition under Section 34 operates as stay on the enforcement of award. Consequently, bank guarantee cannot be enforced for that period. Similarly, interest thereof also not payable for that period.[55]

An award was challenged on the ground of fraud. Several glaring irregularities were found in the conduct of the arbitral proceedings. The award was of over ₹4000 crores. Considering the magnitude of the claim and potential harm to the public exchequer, an unconditional stay was granted on the operation of the arbitral award.[56]

Award passed binding till set aside

Once the award has been delivered by the Arbitration Council regarding which proceedings under Section 34 of the Act are pending, at the present stage, the award passed by the Council has to be taken as a binding award subject of course to the outcome of the proceedings under Section 34 of the Act.[57]

Stay of money decree

An award when challenged under Section 34 does not become unexecutable. The amended Section 36 is clarificatory in nature; it merely clarifies the position that the unamended Section 36 does not stand in the way of the law as to grant of stay of a money decree under the provisions of the CPC.[58]

The second proviso to sub-section 3 of Section 36 makes provision that

---

52. *Sirpur Paper Mills Ltd.* v. *I.K. Merchants (P) Ltd.*, 2021 SCC OnLine Cal 1601: (2022) 1 Cal LT 151; see also, *BCCI* v. *Kochi Cricket (P) Ltd.*, (2018) 6 SCC 287.
53. *Subrat Ranjan Dash* v. *ACC Ltd.*, 2018 SCC OnLine Ori 456.
54. *R.K. Industries* v. *Maximus International General Trading*, 2018 SCC OnLine Raj 2592: (2019) 1 RLW 347.
55. *Bhadani Associates* v. *Kamlini Dharamraj Ashar*, 2017 SCC OnLine Bom 249: (2017) 3 Mah LJ 437.
56. *Union of India* v. *Rashmi Metaliks Ltd.*, 2023 SCC OnLine Cal 2272.
57. *Hindustan Zinc Ltd.* v. *Shree RN Metals (India) (P) Ltd.*, 2019 SCC OnLine Raj 3345.
58. *Hindustan Construction Co. Ltd.* v. *Union of India*, (2020) 17 SCC 324.

where the Court is satisfied that a prima facie case is made out that,—

(*a*) the arbitration agreement or contract which is the basis of the award; or

(*b*) the making of the award, was induced or effected by fraud or corruption, it shall stay the award unconditionally pending disposal of the challenge under Section 34 to the award.

The scope of interference with an arbitral award is much less under the Arbitration and Conciliation Act, 1996 than under Sections 30 and 33, Arbitration Act, 1940. The arbitrator awarded amount towards escalation on the basis of consensus arrived at between the parties through minutes of understanding. The view of the arbitrator was plausible, and the award of the arbitrator was upheld.[59]

An application under Section 34 for setting aside the award can be entertained only if the pre-conditions mentioned in Section 74 are satisfied.[60]

The scope of the court to interfere in arbitral award is limited. The court cannot re-appreciate or re-examine findings of facts.[61] Interpretation of contract is a matter for the arbitrator to determine even if it calls for determination of the question of law.[62]

Prior to the 1996 Act coming into force, the award of the arbitrator was available for judicial review under Section 33, Arbitration Act, 1940 on the grounds mentioned therein. The scope of challenge was much wider than what is now restricted in Section 34 of the Act of 1996. With the 1996 Act coming into force, the courts of law were searching in vain to find their power to examine an award under Section 34 on merits. The legislature in their wisdom restricted the grounds of challenge.[63]

Award under the 1996 Act and 1940 Act—Distinction

An award under the 1996 Act stands on a different footing vis-à-vis an award made under the Arbitration Act, 1940. Whereas under the 1940 Act, an award was required to be made by the rule of the court to make it enforceable, the 1996 Act, however, raises a legal fiction. Once an application challenging an award is filed, the award remains under suspension in the sense that it will not be enforceable. Only on the expiry of the period specified in Section 34 of the 1996 Act to challenge an award or when the objection/challenge is refused, it would be enforceable. Section 36 merely specifies as to how such an award can be enforced by laying down that it can

59. *NTPC* v. *R.S. Avtar Singh & Co.*, 2002 SCC OnLine Del 490: ILR (2002) 2 Del 1.
60. *Sri Chand* v. *Satyavati Devi*, 2007 SCC OnLine Del 757: ILR (2007) 2 Del 1177.
61. *S.K Mahajan* v. *B. Subhash Chandra Shetty*, 2008 SCC OnLine Del 633.
62. *Pure Pharma Ltd.* v. *Union of India*, 2008 SCC OnLine Del 739: ILR (2009) 1 Del 272.
63. *Union of India* v. *Ajabul Biswas*, 2007 SCC OnLine Cal 617: (2008) 1 CHN 16.

be enforced as if it were a decree. The legal fiction created under Section 36 has, therefore, a limited application. An award is to be treated to be a decree even without the intervention of the court only for the limited purpose of its enforceability.[64]

An award which is patently against the statutory provisions or is passed without giving an opportunity of hearing or without giving reasons is liable to be set aside.[65]

In an application under Section 11, the Chief Justice recorded finding that there was a concluded contract between the parties. The finding recorded by the Chief Justice was binding on the arbitrator.[66]

Setting aside award—Rule of court

In terms of the 1996 Act, a departure was made so far as the jurisdiction of the court to set aside an arbitral award is concerned vis-à-vis the earlier Act. Whereas under Sections 30 and 33 of the 1940 Act, the power of the court was wide, Section 34 of the 1996 Act brings about certain changes envisaged thereunder. Section 30, Arbitration Act, 1940 did not contain the expression "error of law". The same was added by judicial interpretation. The arbitral award can be set aside if it is contrary to 1) the fundamental policy of Indian law; 2) the interests of India; 3) justice or morality; or 4) if it is patently illegal or arbitrary. Such patent illegality, however, must go to the root of the matter. The public policy violation, indisputably, should be so unfair and unreasonable as to shock the conscience of the court. Lastly, where the arbitrator, however, has gone contrary to or beyond the expressed law of the contract or granted relief in the matter not in dispute would come within the purview of Section 34 of the Act. What would constitute public policy is a matter dependent upon the nature of transaction and nature of statute.[67]

Part 1 of the Act applies only to arbitrations having their seat/place in India.[68]

The power to modify, vary or remit the award does not exist under Section 34 of the Act.[69]

---

64. *Morgan Securities & Credit (P) Ltd.* v. *Modi Rubber Ltd.*, (2006) 12 SCC 642.
65. *Pritpal Singh* v. *Delhi Metro Rail Corpn. Ltd.*, 2007 SCC OnLine Del 248: (2007) 95 DRJ 21.
66. *SAIL* v. *Gulf (Oil) Corpn. Ltd.*, 2009 SCC OnLine Cal 2258: (2010) 1 CHN 357.
67. *McDermott International Inc.* v. *Burn Standard Co. Ltd.*, (2006) 11 SCC 181.
68. *Noy Vallesina Engg. SpA* v. *Jindal Drugs Ltd.*, (2021) 1 SCC 382.
69. *P.N. Garg, Engineers & Contractors* v. *Chief Engineer, Bhopal Zone*, 2021 SCC OnLine All 1064: (2022) 150 ALR 78.

Jurisdiction of the court

In the arbitration agreement between the parties, the seat stipulated in the agreement was Madras. There were arbitration centres at Mumbai, Calcutta, Delhi and Madras. A new arbitration centre was created at Hyderabad formed after the formation of a new State. The arbitration centre at Madras could only be construed as "venue" and it would no longer be called as "seat" for the purpose of jurisdictional point of view after formation of the new centre. The entire cause of action had arisen at Hyderabad. The court at Hyderabad alone would have jurisdiction to decide the petition filed under Section 34, Arbitration and Conciliation Act, 1996.[70]

Parties had decided that arbitration proceedings would be held at Chandigarh, and as a matter of fact were held at Chandigarh. Only the Principal Civil Judge at Chandigarh will have jurisdiction to entertain disputes arising out of arbitration proceedings including objections raised against the arbitral award.[71]

A substantial part of the contract had arisen in Mumbai. The High Court at Mumbai had territorial jurisdiction to decide petitions under Section 34.[72]

Notwithstanding the fact that the City Civil Court at Calcutta may have jurisdiction to adjudicate upon the subject-matter of a civil suit to the extent of its pecuniary jurisdiction, it cannot come within the definition of a "principal Civil Court of original jurisdiction" as provided under Section 2(1)(*e*), Arbitration and Conciliation Act, 1996, being a "Civil Court of a grade inferior", and this court shall have exclusive jurisdiction for the purpose of entertaining, trying and determining applications under Section 34, Arbitration and Conciliation Act, 1996, provided, of course, the cause of action arises within this court's "ordinary original civil jurisdiction". The High Court alone has jurisdiction to decide the petition under Section 34 for setting aside the award of the arbitrator.[73]

Jurisdiction of Civil Judge (Senior Division)

Neither Santhal Parganas Justice Regulation, 1893 nor the CPC bars the jurisdiction of a Civil Judge (Senior Division) in a district to entertain applications under Section 34, Arbitration and Conciliation Act, 1996. Under the

70. *India Infoline Ltd.* v. *Rami Reddy Gayam*, 2019 SCC OnLine Mad 9180.
71. *Madhava Brahamputra Consortium Ltd.* v. *State of Punjab*, 2021 SCC OnLine P&H 4661.
72. *Delton Electricals* v. *Maharashtra State Electricity Distribution Co. Ltd.*, 2017 SCC OnLine Bom 9000.
73. *Md. Nasim Akhtar* v. *Union of India*, 2015 SCC OnLine Cal 10443: (2015) 1 Cal LJ 629.

Bengal, Agra and Assam Civil Courts Act, 1887, the Court of Civil Judge (Senior Division) is the principal civil court of original jurisdiction in the district.[74]

Jurisdiction of civil court examining validity of award—Nature of

The jurisdiction of the civil court examining the validity of the award is supervisory and not appellate jurisdiction. The court can set aside an award only if any of the grounds mentioned in Section 34(2)(*a*)(*i*) to (*v*) or Section 34(2)(*b*)(*i*) and (*ii*), or Section 28(1)(*a*) or Section 28(3), read with Section 34(2)(*b*)(*ii*) of the Act is made out.[75]

Unless an award suffers from any infirmity provided in Section 34(2), the award cannot be set aside.[76]

Section 34 provides for a supervisory jurisdiction to correct manifest errors and to ensure that there is no grave miscarriage of justice.[77]

The court rightly refused to set aside the arbitral award on the point of claim being barred by time.[78]

An order or decision is an interim award if it finally decides an issue or matter between the parties on which the tribunal can make final award, including an order determining whether the claimant is authorised to file claim.[79]

Deciding an issue of limitations or any other matter is an interim award, can be challenged separately and independently under Section 34 of the Act.[80]

Territorial jurisdiction of court

When parties had not agreed on the place of arbitration and the arbitrator fixed the "seat" or "place" of arbitration at Ernakulam, then the District Court, Ernakulam alone would have jurisdiction to entertain the application.[81]

---

74. *Mira Sinha* v. *State of Jharkhand*, 2015 SCC OnLine Jhar 4377.
75. *J.G. Engineers (P) Ltd.* v. *Union of India*, (2011) 5 SCC 758; *Gopal Das Gaur* v. *Suman Sharma*, 2009 SCC OnLine All 438: (2009) 75 ALR 752.
76. *T.P. Akbar* v. *Sundaram Finance Ltd.*, 2020 SCC OnLine Mad 28361.
77. *Hindustan Petroleum Corpn. Ltd.* v. *Banu Constructions*, 2021 SCC OnLine Mad 724: (2021) 1 LW 657.
78. *Gopal Das Gaur* v. *Suman Sharma*, 2009 SCC OnLine All 438: (2009) 75 ALR 752.
79. *Palmview Investments Overseas Ltd.* v. *Ravi Arya*, (2023) 1 HCC (Bom) 259.
80. *IFFCO Ltd.* v. *Bhadra Products*, (2018) 2 SCC 534.
81. *Railways* v. *M.R. Ramakrishnan*, 2023 SCC OnLine Ker 843: (2023) 2 KLT 8.

The courts of Delhi where award was passed as well the courts in Jhansi where the workshop of North Central Railway was to be modernised would have jurisdiction to entertain the application filed under Section 34, Arbitration Act.[82]

Pecuniary jurisdiction

In any application filed under Part I of the 1996 Act after the statement of claim has been filed in the arbitral reference, the pecuniary jurisdiction of the court is assessed on the basis of the quantum of claim carried to the arbitral reference. The amount awarded by the Arbitral Tribunal at the end of the reference is not the basis on which the pecuniary jurisdiction of a court to which a challenge to the award has been carried, has to be assessed. The assessment has to be based on the statement of claim and the quantum of claim evident therefrom. The quantum of claim in the arbitral reference was in excess of ₹10 lakhs, and the Calcutta High Court had territorial jurisdiction to entertain the application under Section 34 of the Act.[83]

The mere fact that rules of procedure are not followed does not make the award nugatory. The court shall not interfere unless the award is perverse.[84]

Proceedings under Section 34 are summary proceedings

The proceedings under Section 34 are not full-fledged regular suits under the CPC. Applications under Section 34 of the Act are summary proceedings with a provision for objection by the respondent-defendant, followed by an opportunity to the applicant to "prove" the existence of any ground under Section 34(2). The applicant is permitted to file affidavits of his witnesses in proof. A corresponding opportunity is given to the respondent-defendant to place his evidence by affidavit. Where the case warrants, the court permits cross-examination of the persons swearing to the affidavit. Thereafter, the court hears arguments and/or receives written submissions and decides the matter. This is of course the routing procedure. The court may vary the said procedure depending upon the facts of any particular case or the local rules.[85]

Relief that may be granted

The 1996 Act makes provision for the supervisory role of courts for the review of the arbitral award only to ensure fairness. The intervention of the

82. *Union of India* v. *Larsen & Tubro Ltd.*, 2023 SCC OnLine All 1117: (2023) 4 All LJ 490.
83. *Narayan Prasad Saraff* v. *Ashok Kr. Saraff*, 2020 SCC OnLine Cal 3289.
84. *Videsh Sanchar Nigam Ltd.* v. *Shapoorji Pallonji & Co. Ltd.*, 2007 SCC OnLine Cal 670: (2008) 1 CHN 721.
85. *Fiza Developers & Inter-Trade (P) Ltd.* v. *Amci (I) (P) Ltd.*, (2009) 17 SCC 796.

court is envisaged in a few circumstances only, like in case of fraud or bias by the arbitrators, violation of natural justice, etc. The court cannot correct errors of the arbitrators. It can only quash the award, leaving the parties free to begin the arbitration again if desired. So, the scheme of the provision aims at keeping the supervisory role of the court at a minimum level, and this can be justified as the parties to the agreement make a conscious decision to exclude the court's jurisdiction by opting for arbitration as they prefer the expediency and finality offered by it.[86]

Relief after setting aside award by court

After setting aside the award of the arbitrator, the court cannot grant further relief by modifying the award.[87]

Imposition of condition

The court which admits the application under Section 34 challenging the award cannot impose any condition for admission of such application as the court has no discretion to do so.[88]

The finding of the arbitrator need not be interfered with unless perversity is writ large on the face of the record.[89] The court is not sitting in appeal over the arbitral award and the scope of its power is very limited.[90] The courts are not required to be indulged in fault-finding exercise.[91] The court does not sit in appeal over the award of the arbitrator or to re-examine the evidence.[92]

It is a well-settled principle of law that an award made and published by an arbitrator cannot be set aside unless an error is apparent on the face of the record. It can also be interfered with on the ground that the arbitrator has misconducted himself or the proceedings or that he has not applied his mind to the material on record.[93]

The court must not exercise appellate power, but the proposition cannot provide an umbrella to awards where the justice is a casualty.[94]

---

86. *McDermott International Inc.* v. *Burn Standard Co. Ltd.*, (2006) 11 SCC 181.
87. *Indian Oil Corpn. Ltd.* v. *Sathyanarayana Service Station*, 2023 SCC OnLine SC 597.
88. *Superintending Engineer (Highways and Rural Works)* v. *D.G. Deivasigamani*, 2004 SCC OnLine Mad 492: (2004) 4 CTC 1.
89. *India Tourism & Development Corpn. Ltd.* v. *T.P. Sharma*, 2002 SCC OnLine Del 634: (2002) 64 DRJ 423.
90. *Paramjit Singh* v. *Satyawati*, 2002 SCC OnLine Del 704: (2002) 64 DRJ 798.
91. *Tribal Coop. Mktg. Development Federation of India Ltd.* v. *Auro Industries Ltd.*, 2002 SCC OnLine Del 418: (2002) 98 DLT 654.
92. *DDA* v. *Manohar Lal*, 2006 SCC OnLine Del 46: (2006) 86 DRJ 751.
93. *Union of India* v. *Arctic India*, 2006 SCC OnLine Cal 137: (2006) 2 CHN 707.
94. *Glaxo Smith Kline Consumer Health Care Ltd.* v. *Heinz India (P) Ltd.*, 2006 SCC OnLine Cal 574: (2007) 2 CHN 44.

The arbitration court cannot interfere with the award on the ground that the decision is erroneous if the award is otherwise proper. The award of the arbitrator is ordinarily final and conclusive. Right or wrong, the decision of the arbitrator is final and binding if it is reached fairly after giving adequate opportunities to the parties to place their grievances during the arbitral proceedings.[95]

Acceptance of money due under award without protest—Award not set aside

Where the decree holder has accepted the money due under award without protest, an application under Section 34 for setting aside the award is not maintainable.[96]

Powers of court

The court does not sit as one in appeal over the award. Where the view taken by the arbitrator is permissible, then no interference is called for on the premises that a different view was also possible.[97] In *Associated Construction* v. *Pawanhans Helicopters Ltd.*[98], a deed of works contract required the work to be completed within the stipulated period and prohibited the contractor from claiming any extra amount for escalation of cost of work. The deed further provided without prejudice to other remedies for indemnity in case the delay in the completion of work was attributable to another party. In such circumstances, when the completion of the work was delayed due to reasons attributable to the other party and the arbitrator allowed the contractor's claim for escalation of cost of work, it was held that the award was not so unconscionable as to warrant judicial interference.

The civil court can either set aside or affirm the award; it cannot alter or modify the award of the arbitrator in a petition filed under Section 34, Arbitration and Conciliation Act.[99]

A challenge to an arbitral award is not treated as an appeal and the limited scope of interference does not permit the court to correct an error within the bounds of the arbitrator's authority, unless the error is apparent on the face of the award and results in manifest miscarriage of justice.[100]

95. *Union of India* v. *Pam Developments (P) Ltd.*, 2003 SCC OnLine Cal 491: (2004) 1 CHN 407.
96. *Sunil Kanotra* v. *Indian Oil Corpn.*, 2016 SCC OnLine HP 2697.
97. *Associated Construction* v. *Pawanhans Helicopters Ltd.*, (2008) 16 SCC 128; *New Delhi Apartment Group Housing Society* v. *Jyoti Swaroop Mittal*, 2007 SCC OnLine Del 1591: (2008) 100 DRJ 439.
98. (2008) 16 SCC 128.
99. *Raqya Bee* v. *P.S.R. Constructions*, 2022 SCC OnLine TS 3386: (2022) 3 ALD 151.
100. *Tonganagaon Tea Co. (P) Ltd.* v. *Associated Tea Industries*, 2015 SCC OnLine Cal 1432.

The court under Section 34 has only limited power to set aside the award of the arbitrator but has no authority to grant any further relief. It has no power to grant original relief claimed before the arbitrator.[101] The court can only set aside the award leaving the parties free to begin the arbitration, if so they desired.[102] A well-reasoned award made/passed by the arbitrator will not be interfered with by the court in its jurisdiction under Section 34.[103]

Setting aside award—Powers of the court

An award passed by the arbitrator can be set aside only in case of fraud or violation of the principles of natural justice or if it is against public policy of India. Parties during proceedings stated that they were given full opportunity to present their case and requested the arbitrator to pass final award. The award was not set aside.[104]

An application under Section 34 is neither an appeal nor revision and not even a full-fledged review. It is a limited judicial review within the slots adumbrated in Section 34(2).[105]

The power of the court to set aside the award of the arbitrator is restricted to Section 30 of the Act of 1940 and Section 34 of the 1996 Act.[106]

Under Section 34 of the Act, the court does not sit as an appellate court to go into the correctness or otherwise go over the amount of evidence led by the parties.[107] While exercising the powers granted under this provision by the arbitrators, the basic principles must be followed. The High Court cannot re-appreciate the evidence which was produced before the Arbitral Tribunal and arrive at a different finding than the one which was given by the tribunal. The High Court cannot sit in appeal over the findings recorded by the tribunal and decide whether the quantum of compensation determined by the tribunal is proper or not.[108] Where the findings recorded by the tribunal are not perverse, are based on documentary evidence on record and on oral evidence adduced by both the parties, no interference is called

101. *U.P. State Handloom Corpn. Ltd.* v. *Asha Lata Talwar*, 2009 SCC OnLine All 624: (2009) 76 ALR 233.
102. *U.P. Jal Nigam* v. *Driplex Water Engg. Ltd.*, 2007 SCC OnLine All 2540; *McDermott International Inc.* v. *Burn Standard Co. Ltd.*, (2006) 11 SCC 181.
103. *Larsen and Toubro Ltd.* v. *Sunfield Resources (P) Ltd.*, 2005 SCC OnLine Bom 726: (2005) 4 Mah LJ 607.
104. *State of H.P.* v. *Harbinder Singh*, 2018 SCC OnLine HP 3052.
105. *Nadippisai Pulavar K.P. Ramasamy Coop., Sugar Mill'* v. *Binny Engg. Ltd.*, 2021 SCC OnLine Mad 5679.
106. *Indian Rare Earths Ltd.* v. *Unique Builders Ltd.*, (2016) 1 SCC 700.
107. *Vijayakumar Raju* v. *Indus Ind Bank Ltd.*, 2009 SCC OnLine Mad 885: (2009) 4 LW 86; *Satinderpal Singh Anand* v. *Sharanpal Balmukund Chopra*, 2008 SCC OnLine Bom 473: (2008) 6 Mah LJ 86.
108. *United India Insurance Co. Ltd.* v. *Crescent International*, 2008 SCC OnLine Bom 850: (2009) 1 Mah LJ 704.

for.[109] While considering the application under Section 34 for setting aside the award, the High Court is not required to consider the matter as if it is hearing the regular appeal against the order of the arbitrator.[110]

The Arbitral Tribunal had considered the documentary evidence before it as well as the provisions of the contract, and recorded finding that a fixed rate which was not to be multiplied as per the provisions of the Power Purchase Agreement was agreed between the parties. The award also gave reasons for such a finding. The High Court substituted its own view and reinterpreted the documentary evidence for setting aside the award. Such a substitution of view is/was not permissible for the court under Section 34 of the Act.[111]

Under Section 34 of the Act, the court does not sit as an appellate court to go into the correctness or otherwise of the amount of evidence led by the parties.[112]

While exercising jurisdiction under Section 34, the court does not act as a court of appeal, and hence, interference would be permissible only when findings of the arbitrator are arbitrary, capricious or perverse or when conscience of the court is shocked but not otherwise.[113]

It will thus appear to be a more than settled legal position that in an application under Section 34, the court is not expected to act as an appellate court and reappreciate the evidence. The scope of interference would be limited to grounds provided under Section 34, Arbitration Act. The interference would be so warranted when the award is in violation of the "public policy of India", which has been held to mean "the fundamental policy of Indian law". A judicial intervention on account of interfering on the merits of the award would not be permissible. However, the principles of natural justice as contained in Sections 18 and 34(2)(*a*)(*iii*), Arbitration Act would continue to be the grounds of challenge of an award. The ground for interference on the basis that the award is in conflict with justice or morality is now to be understood as a conflict with the "most basic notions of morality or justice". It is only such arbitral awards that shock the conscience of the court that can be set aside on the said ground. An award would be set aside on the ground of patent illegality appearing on the face of the award and as such, which goes to the roots of the matter. However, an illegality with regard to a mere erroneous application of law would not be a ground for interference.

---

109. *Ibid.*
110. *Sarvajanik Shikshan Sanstha* v. *Alfred Ashtamkar*, 2012 SCC OnLine Bom 583: (2012) 3 Mah LJ 776.
111. *Ibid.*
112. *Vijayakumar Raju* v. *Indus Ind Bank Ltd.*, 2009 SCC OnLine Mad 885: (2009) 4 LW 86.
113. *G. & T. Beckfield Drilling Services (P) Ltd.* v. *ONGC*, 2019 SCC OnLine Gau 5967: (2019) 4 Arb LR 410.

Equally, re-appreciation of evidence would not be permissible on the ground of patent illegality appearing on the face of the award. A decision which is perverse, though it would not be a ground for challenge under "public policy of India", would certainly amount to a patent illegality appearing on the face of the award. However, a finding based on no evidence at all or an award which ignores vital evidence in arriving at its decision would be perverse and liable to be set aside on the ground of patent illegality.[114]

It is also settled law that interference under Section 34 of the Act does not mean a review of the merits of the dispute. The interference is warranted only when the findings are arbitrary, capricious or perverse, or when the conscience of the court is shocked, or when the illegality goes to the root of the matter. The court under Section 34 of the Act does not act as a court of appeal. The errors of facts cannot be lightly rectified. If a view taken by the arbitrator is a possible view based on fact, it should not be interfered with.[115]

Power of civil court to set aside award

In a suit for declaration of title, an arbitrator was appointed by the civil court to resolve the dispute in suit. With the appointment of the arbitrator, the suit stood disposed of. The civil court thereafter would become *functus officio*, unable to entertain proceedings for setting aside the arbitral award. The remedy is to file an application under Section 34 of the Act.[116]

Partial/interim, final awards may be challenged

Both partial/interim and final awards can be subject-matter of challenge under Section 34.[117] In view of the definition given in Section 2(1)(*c*), an interim award is also an "arbitral award" which can be challenged by making an application in accordance with Section 34, Arbitration and Conciliation Act, 1996.[118] Pendency of proceedings before the court under Section 34 challenging the interim award cannot stall the Arbitral Tribunal from passing the final award.[119]

In the absence of a challenge to a partial final award, the challenge to the final award cannot succeed.[120]

---

114. *PSA SICAL Terminals (P) Ltd.* v. *V.O. Chidambranar Port Trust*, 2021 SCC OnLine SC 508.
115. *State of Uttarakhand* v. *Madhav Nayan*, 2021 SCC OnLine Utt 1848.
116. *Radha Devi* v. *Punay Pratap Mandal*, 2015 SCC OnLine Pat 4191: (2015) 4 PLJR 17.
117. *McDermott International Inc.* v. *Burn Standard Co. Ltd.*, (2006) 11 SCC 181.
118. *Union of India* v. *High Court of Allahabad*, 2001 SCC OnLine All 371: 2001 All LJ 1896.
119. *V. Raghavan* v. *R. Venkitapathy*, 2015 SCC OnLine Mad 8514: (2015) 4 LW 909.
120. *Aero Club* v. *Solar Creations (P) Ltd.*, 2020 SCC OnLine Bom 472: (2021) 2 Mah LJ 186.

Rejection of objection by the arbitrator as to admissibility of a document is not an interim award, and cannot be challenged under Section 34.[121]

An interim award can be challenged separately and independently under Section 34.[122]

Deciding the issue of limitation prior to rendering of award on other issues is an interim award, can be challenged separately and independently under Section 34, Arbitration and Conciliation Act, 1996.[123]

Interim award and final award can be challenged under Section 34(3) of the Act within three months. The interim award finally decided the matter between the parties by breaking an amendment of the Constitution on the basis of which subsequent elections were held. No challenge was made within three months. The principle of merger was not attracted. The final award was made. Elections having been permitted cannot be allowed to be turned down and challenged. No illegality was committed while refusing to set aside an interim award under Section 34 of the Act.[124]

Foreign award may be challenged under Section 34

Following *Bhatia International* v. *Bulk Trading S.A.*[125], the Supreme Court held that the provisions of Part I are equally applicable to international commercial arbitration held outside India, unless any or all such provisions have been excluded by agreement between the parties, expressly or by implication. Unless the applicability of Section 34 has been excluded, parties may challenge the award before an Indian court as defined in Section 2(1)(*e*). A judgment-debtor cannot be deprived of his right under Section 34 to invoke the public policy of India, nor can the decree-holder seek to evade compliance with the legal and regulatory scrutiny that might be necessary in India in case of enforcement of the award concerned in India. Sections 45, 48, 54 or any other provision of Part II do not exclude the applicability of Part I to foreign awards.[126] A foreign award can be challenged under Section 34 of the Act.[127]

The arbitrator held a meeting at Kuala Lumpur and signed the award. It was held that it did not amount to determination. There was neither any agreement nor determination. Kuala Lumpur was not the seat nor the place

121. *Ranjiv Kumar* v. *Sanjiv Kumar*, 2018 SCC OnLine Cal 1933: (2018) 3 CHN 378.
122. *Ibid.*
123. *IFFCO Ltd.* v. *Bhadra Products*, (2018) 2 SCC 534.
124. *Ram Saran Chaudhary* v. *Bankey Lal Ghunghruwale*, 2002 SCC OnLine All 285: (2002) 48 ALR 113.
125. (2002) 4 SCC 105.
126. *Venture Global Engg.* v. *Satyam Computer Services Ltd.*, (2008) 4 SCC 190.
127. *Venture Global Engg.* v. *Satyam Computer Services Ltd.*, (2010) 8 SCC 660.

of arbitration. Courts in India have jurisdiction to entertain an application under Section 34 for setting aside the award.[128]

Party

The plain reading of Section 34 shows that only a party to the arbitration agreement and a party to the arbitration award can file an application to set aside the award and that too only on the grounds provided under Section 34(2) of the Act.[129] Non-party to arbitration agreement does not have *locus standi* to challenge the arbitral award.[130] However, if a person is wrongly impleaded as party to arbitration proceedings and is aggrieved by the arbitral award, he can invoke Section 34 of the Act.[131]

Escrow agent not necessary party

The escrow agent was neither a party to the arbitration agreement nor a party to the transaction under the MOU. He was not a necessary party. His non-joinder did not affect the award. The award of the arbitrator was not set aside.[132]

Challenge to award by shareholders of company

A challenge to the award by the shareholders of the company, espousing personal cause of action or on the ground of intense dispute regarding the management of the company and not as derivative action is not maintainable.[133]

"Court" [Sub-s. (1)]

The court before which an award passed by the arbitrator can be challenged is the court as defined in Section 2(1), clause (*e*), and not the court to which an application under Section 8 of the Act is made. An application before a court under Section 8 merely brings to the court's notice that the subject-matter of the action before it is the subject of an arbitration agreement. This would not be such an application as contemplated under Section 42 of the Act as the court trying the action may or may not have the jurisdiction to

128. *Union of India* v. *Hardy Exploration & Production (India) Inc.*, (2019) 13 SCC 472.
129. *Chennai Container Terminal (P) Ltd.* v. *Union of India*, 2007 SCC OnLine Mad 506: (2007) 4 CTC 284; *Mukesh Nanji Gala* v. *Heritage Enterprises*, 2014 SCC OnLine Bom 1817: (2015) 5 Mah LJ 620.
130. *Union of India* v. *Des Raj Nagpal*, 2022 SCC OnLine J&K 1080.
131. *Ibid.*
132. *Emerald Woollen Mills (P) Ltd.* v. *Hanuman Developers*, 2020 SCC OnLine Bom 1.
133. *Starlight Real Estate (Ascot) Mauritius Ltd.* v. *Jagrati Trade Serevices (P) Ltd.*, 2015 SCC OnLine Cal 6583: (2016) 195 Comp Cas 434.

try the suit to start with or be the competent court within the meaning of Section 2(1)(*e*) of the 1996 Act.[134]

In view of the clear definition of the word "Court" in Section 2(1)(*e*) of the 1996 Act read with Section 20 CPC, Section 34 application by any party dissatisfied with the arbitral award had to be instituted and filed only in such court within the local limits of whose jurisdiction the cause of action or part thereof had arisen or accrued. The agreement in question was executed at Lucknow, but the work in question was executed at Uttarkashi. The court held, the entire cause of action arose at Uttarkashi, and hence, the Uttarkashi court alone had jurisdiction to entertain and decide applications filed under Section 34. Merely because the office of the General Manager of the petitioner was at Dehradun and certain decisions were to be taken there would not confer jurisdiction on courts at Dehradun.[135]

The order of the court appointing the arbitrator containing provisions therefor is determinative. In *Mcdermott International Inc.* v. *Burn Standard Co. Ltd.*[136], an arbitrator was appointed by the Supreme Court; the order provided that any application which might become necessary to be filed during or after the conclusion of the proceedings would be filed only in the Supreme Court. It was held, an application under Section 34 for setting aside an arbitral award could be filed only in the Supreme Court. Subsequently, it has been held by a Constitution Bench of the court that the definition of court in Section 2(1)(*e*) of the Act of 1996 is materially different from its predecessor. The Supreme Court cannot be considered to be "Court" within the meaning of Section 2(1)(*e*) even if it retains seisen over the arbitration proceedings.[137] The Allahabad High Court does not exercise original civil jurisdiction, and is not a court as defined under Section 2(1)(*e*). An application for setting aside the award and an appeal from the order setting aside or refusing to set aside the order would not be entertained by the High Court.[138] A petition for setting aside arbitral award is not maintainable before the High Court. The proper remedy available to the party is to file a proper application under Section 34 of the Act to the principal civil court of original jurisdiction of the district concerned.[139]

---

134. *P. Anand Gajapathi Raju* v. *P.V.G. Raju*, (2000) 4 SCC 539.
135. *Uttarakhand Jal Vidyut Nigam* v. *Rapti Contractors*, 2008 SCC OnLine Utt 145: (2009) 1 All LJ 350.
136. (2005) 10 SCC 353.
137. *State of Jharkhand* v. *Hindustan Construction Co. Ltd.*, (2018) 2 SCC 602; *State of W.B.* v. *Associated Contractors*, (2015) 1 SCC 32.
138. *Ashish Kumar Sadh* v. *Putul Chaubey*, 2015 SCC OnLine All 9371: (2016) 115 ALR 587.
139. *India Waste Energy Development Ltd.* v. *Greater Noida Industrial Development Authority*, 2013 SCC OnLine All 13525: (2013) 98 ALR 348; *Ashish Kumar Sadh* v. *Putul Chaubey*, 2015 SCC OnLine All 9371: (2016) 115 ALR 587.

The court of Additional District Judge is not the principal civil court of original jurisdiction for the purpose of Section 2(1)(*e*) of the Act, and has no jurisdiction to dispose of objections under Section 34 of the Act.[140] The order of the District Judge transferring the case to the court of the Additional District Judge was improper.[141]

Disposal of petition under Sections 34 and 36 by Additional District Judge

An application for execution of award or setting aside of award can be heard and decided not only by the District Judge but also by the Court of Additional District Judge.[142]

Section 4(2) of the Kerala Civil Courts Act empowers the Additional District Judge with powers to discharge functions of a District Judge. There is no jurisdictional error in the Additional District Judge hearing petitions under the Act of 1996.[143]

The Supreme Court earlier, by consent of parties, had appointed the arbitrator in the case. A plea was raised that since earlier the Supreme Court had appointed the arbitrator in the case, an application under Section 34 for setting aside the arbitrator's award should also be filed before the Supreme Court. The plea was rejected; the application lies before the District Judge. The Supreme Court held thus:

> If the plea of the respondent is accepted that the matter should be decided by the Supreme Court that would mean that in every case where the Supreme Court passes an order, be it in appeal from the order passed by the High Court under Section 11(6) of the Arbitration and Conciliation Act, 1996, the Supreme Court will become a Principal Civil Court of Original Jurisdiction. If the argument is taken to its local conclusion that would mean that the parties will have to approach the Supreme Court by making an application under Section 34 *i.e.* for setting aside the award. The expression 'Court' used in Section 34 of the Act will also have to be understood ignoring the definition of 'Court' in the Act. Similarly, if the High Court exercises jurisdiction under Section 11(6), the High Court would become Principal Civil Court of Original Jurisdiction. In such a situation, right to appeal under Section 37(1)(*b*) will also be circumvented. Such a plea cannot be accepted.[144]

---

140. *Northern Coalfields Ltd.* v. *Aluminium Industries Ltd.*, 2013 SCC OnLine All 13492: (2013) 99 ALR 89.
141. *Ashish Kumar Sadh* v. *Putul Chaubey*, 2015 SCC OnLine All 9371: (2016) 115 ALR 587.
142. *A Suo Moto Taken* v. *State of Chhattisgarh*, 2018 SCC OnLine Chh 617.
143. *Kasim V.K.* v. *M. Ashraf*, (2021) 1 HCC (Ker) 379.
144. *Garhwal Mandal Vikas Nigam Ltd.* v. *Krishna Travel Agency*, (2008) 6 SCC 741.

An application under Section 34 for setting aside the award of the arbitrator shall be filed before the court which dealt with the application under Section 11(6) for the appointment of the arbitrator.[145]

The State Government issued a notification on the recommendation of the High Court whereby the Additional District Judge at Khetri was appointed as District Judge. As such the Additional District Judge has the jurisdiction to discharge the functions as District Judge. As per the provisions of Khasi Siemships (Administration of Justice) Order, 1950, the Additional District Judge is fully empowered to exercise the powers as the District Judge had. There was no error in filing the application under Section 34 before the District Judge at Khetri. The cause of action arose within the jurisdiction of the Deputy Commissioner/Additional Deputy Commissioner, East Khasi Hills District, Meghalaya. The Deputy Commissioner/Additional Deputy Commissioner is the principal civil court of original jurisdiction invested with the original civil jurisdiction, and can entertain applications under Section 34 of the Act.[146]

It is well settled that territorial jurisdiction of the court shall be where the contract was entered into and the same was executed. Irrespective of the place where the arbitration was concluded and the award was passed, the court having territorial jurisdiction shall be the competent court. Besides the above, an award can be filed only in that court in which the suit would lie with regard to the subject-matter of reference. Hence, filing of award or challenging the award under Section 34 of the 1996 Act shall be only in a court having territorial jurisdiction. Therefore, the District Judge has rightly held that merely because the arbitration took place at Chennai, the courts at Chennai shall not have jurisdiction to entertain the petition for setting aside the award.[147] Both the parties had their offices at Pune. Though a clause in the contract provided that the High Court at Mumbai alone would have jurisdiction to decide the dispute between the parties, it could not be said that the jurisdiction of the court at Pune was completely ousted.[148]

Neither the judgment-debtors nor their properties were within the jurisdiction of court. An arbitral award might be executed either by the court which passed it or by the court to which it was sent for execution in view of Section 38 CPC. The High Court can execute arbitral awards beyond its

145. *Ranjita Apartment Owners' Assn.* v. *Prabir Kumar Chakraborty*, 2011 SCC OnLine Cal 369: (2011) 4 CHN 88.

146. *North Eastern Electric Power Corpn. Ltd.* v. *S. Marbaniang*, 2006 SCC OnLine Gau 436: (2007) 2 Gau LR 311.

147. *Nortan Intee Rubbers (P) Ltd.* v. *Neyveli Lignite Corpn.*, 2012 SCC OnLine Mad 1314: (2012) 3 CTC 1.

148. *Maharashtra State Road Development Corpn. Ltd.* v. *Larsen and Toubro Ltd.*, 2004 SCC OnLine Bom 141: (2004) 3 Mah LJ 285.

territorial jurisdiction only in exceptional cases. In this case, no exceptional ground for summoning the judgment-debtor in the court had been made out. The decree-holder was directed to apply for transferring of arbitral award to appropriate executing forum.[149]

A contract was concluded at Mohali, tender was accepted at Chennai the venue of arbitration was fixed at Chennai. Exclusive jurisdiction clause signed by the parties conferred jurisdiction upon courts at Chennai. It was held, the courts at Chennai would have exclusive jurisdiction to entertain objections under Section 34 of the Act.[150]

The petitioner, a public sector undertaking, carried business in Cuddalore District. As a dispute arose, arbitration took place at Chennai because of the provisions contained in the Micro, Small and Medium Enterprises Development Act, 2006. In view of Section 2(1)(*e*), only the court at Cuddalore had jurisdiction to entertain a petition under Section 34 for setting aside the award. The court at Cuddalore having territorial jurisdiction to entertain the petition merely because arbitration took place at Chennai, the courts at Chennai had no jurisdiction to entertain the petition under Section 34 for setting aside the award.[151]

In a case of compulsory acquisition for widening of national highway, there was no arbitration agreement between the parties. The Central Government had appointed the Commissioner of Jabalpur as arbitrator for determining compensation. Both the parties participated in the arbitration proceedings before the Commissioner. The seat as well as the venue of arbitration proceedings were at Jabalpur. The application for setting aside the award of the arbitrator would lie before the principal civil court of original jurisdiction in Jabalpur and not at Mandala; the District Judge Mandala rightly returned the application for presentation before the proper court.[152]

Parties had not fixed the seat of arbitration. Award of the arbitrator was passed at Hyderabad. Subject-matter of the dispute was situated at Guntur. In case of an arbitration other than international commercial arbitration, the principal civil court of original jurisdiction in a district will have jurisdiction to decide the issues forming the subject-matter of arbitration if the same had been the subject-matter of suit. The District Court at Guntur would have

149. *Srei Equipment Finance (P) Ltd.* v. *Khyoda Apik*, 2011 SCC OnLine Cal 1400: (2011) 5 CHN 698.

150. *Shivalik Fastners (P) Ltd.* v. *Union of India*, 2019 SCC OnLine P&H 7255: PLR (2019) 196 P&H 800.

151. *Nortan Intee Rubbers (P) Ltd.* v. *Neyveli Lignite Corpn.*, 2012 SCC OnLine Mad 1314: (2012) 3 CTC 1.

152. *M.P. Road Development Corpn.* v. *Baisakhu*, 2021 SCC OnLine MP 6040.

jurisdiction to entertain an application under Section 34 for setting aside the award of the arbitrator.[153]

The moment the seat of arbitration is designated, it is akin to an exclusive jurisdiction clause. In the present case, the arbitration clause indicated the seat of arbitration at Udupi only; the arbitrator conducted whole arbitration proceedings at Udupi. It was held, the District Court, Thiruvananthapuram would not have jurisdiction to entertain applications under Section 34(1).[154]

"Court" means where the cause of action arose and/or the subject-matter of arbitration is situated. When admittedly the construction work was at Ratnagiri, the "Court" at Ratnagiri has jurisdiction to entertain the petition filed under Section 34.[155]

A competent court of civil jurisdiction can decide the petition filed under Section 34. Jurisdiction cannot be conferred on a court within whose jurisdiction no part of the cause of action regarding dispute has ever arisen. The original contract was entered and all transactions took place only in Bangalore. No part of the cause of action had arisen in Chennai, and the court in Chennai did not have jurisdiction over the subject-matter of the dispute; the petition filed under Section 34 before the court in Chennai was dismissed.[156] Part of the cause of action arose at Lucknow, and part of the cause of action arose at Gorakhpur as work had been executed at Gorakhpur. Courts at Lucknow also had territorial jurisdiction to entertain a petition under Section 34 challenging the award, and hence, the order of District Judge, Lucknow rejecting the petition under Section 34 was set aside.[157]

The District Court is the principal court of original jurisdiction for the purpose of Section 34 of the Act; it does not include any other court inferior to the District Court.[158] Principal District Judge and District Judges are within the scope of the term "Principal Civil Court of original jurisdiction in a district".[159]

The place where arbitration proceedings took place normally determine jurisdiction of the court. In the instant case, arbitration proceedings took

153. *Nandini Cold Storage (P) Ltd.* v. *National Insurance Co. Ltd.*, 2020 SCC OnLine AP 5041.
154. *S. Balu* v. *ICDS Ltd.*, 2019 SCC OnLine Ker 502.
155. *Premlaxmi and Co.* v. *Konkan Railway Corpn. Ltd.*, 2012 SCC OnLine Bom 1619: (2013) 1 Mah LJ 360.
156. *Motila Oswal Securities Ltd.* v. *D. Renuka*, 2010 SCC OnLine Mad 5231: (2011) 1 CTC 303.
157. *U.P. Coop. Sugar Factories Federation Ltd.* v. *P.S. Misra*, 2002 SCC OnLine All 1095: 2003 All LJ 1038.
158. *Fountain Head Developers* v. *Maria Arcangela Sequeira*, 2007 SCC OnLine Bom 340.
159. *Union of India* v. *Arun Kumar Deedwania*, 2017 SCC OnLine Bom 1717: (2017) 4 Mah LJ 130.

place at Mumbai. It was held, the court at Mumbai would have jurisdiction to annul the arbitration award.[160]

Where the cause of action arose at Chennai, as agreed the Chennai city court has exclusive jurisdiction to entertain the petition under Section 34 of the Act. Merely because the place of arbitration was in Mumbai and as Mumbai court has appointed the arbitrator, that itself gives no jurisdiction to Mumbai court to entertain a petition under Section 34, in view of the specific clause agreed between the parties.[161]

A court has territorial jurisdiction to set aside an award of the arbitrator where the subject-matter is situated when there is no clause about jurisdiction. In this case, the property in dispute was situated at Varanasi. The first application under Section 9 for interim measure was filed before the District Judge, Varanasi. An application for setting aside the arbitral award was maintainable only before the District Judge in view of the provisions of Section 42. The District Judge, Varanasi being the principal civil court of original jurisdiction was held competent to entertain the application under Section 34.[162]

Maintainability of application under Section 34 challenging arbitral award before the Supreme Court

The Supreme Court had appointed the arbitrator with the consent of the parties. Since the Supreme Court in the order appointing the arbitrator had not retained any power or control over the arbitration proceedings, in view of the provisions of Section 34 read with Section 2(*e*) of the 1996 Act, it was not the Supreme Court which had jurisdiction to entertain an application for setting aside/modification of the award; it was only the principal civil court of original jurisdiction which could entertain such an application as contemplated under Section 2(*e*) of the Act.[163]

"Establishes on the basis of the record of the arbitral tribunal" [Sub-s. (2)(*a*)]

By Amendment Act 33 of 2019 in sub-section (2), clause (*a*) for the words "furnishes proof that", the words "establishes on the basis of the record of the Arbitral Tribunal" have been substituted.

---

160. *Sunil Kumar Srivastava* v. *Mahindra & Mahindra Services Ltd.*, 2018 SCC OnLine All 6425: (2018) 5 All LJ 89.
161. *Vachaspati Sharma* v. *India Cements-Capital and Finance Ltd.*, 2013 SCC OnLine Bom 1296: (2013) 6 Mah LJ 342.
162. *Manjusha Premi* v. *Prakash Gupta*, 2016 SCC OnLine All 2796: (2016) 116 ALR 657.
163. *National Aluminium Co. Ltd.* v. *Pressteel & Fabrications (P) Ltd.*, (2004) 1 SCC 540.

An application for setting aside an arbitral award will not ordinarily require anything beyond the record that was before the arbitrator. If there are matters not contained in such a record and are relevant to the determination of issues arising under Section 34(2)(*a*), they may be brought on record by way of affidavits filed by both the parties. Cross-examination of the persons swearing to the affidavits should not be allowed unless absolutely necessary as the truth will emerge on the reading of the affidavits filed by both the parties.[164]

The provisions of sub-section (2) of Section 34 contemplate a higher decree of deliberation than a mere statement of fact when the award is challenged.[165]

Principles for interference

The principles for interference with an arbitral award under Section 34(2) of the 1996 Act are follows:

(*a*) An award which is:
  (*i*) contrary to substantive provisions of law; or
  (*ii*) the provisions of the Arbitration and Conciliation Act, 1996; or
  (*iii*) against the terms of the respective contract; or
  (*iv*) patently illegal; or
  (*v*) prejudicial to the rights of the parties;
  is open to interference by the court under Section 34(2) of the Act.

(*b*) The award could be set aside if it is contrary to:
  (*i*) fundamental policy of Indian law; or
  (*ii*) the interest of India; or
  (*iii*) justice or morality.

(*c*) The award could also be set aside if it is so unfair and unreasonable that it shocks the conscience of the court.

(*d*) It is open to the court to consider whether the award is against the specific terms of contract and if so, interfere with it on the ground that it is patently illegal and opposed to the public policy of India.[166]

The court can set aside an arbitral award under Section 34(2):

(1) for the reasons mentioned in Section 34(2)(*a*)(*i*) to (*v*);
(2) for the reasons stated in Section 28(1)(*a*);
(3) for the reasons stated in Section 34(2)(*b*)(*ii*) on the ground of conflict with the public policy of India, that is to say, if it is contrary to:
  (*a*) fundamental policy of Indian law; or
  (*b*) the interest of India; or

---

164. *Emkay Global Financial Services Ltd.* v. *Girdhar Sondhi*, (2018) 9 SCC 49.
165. *R.S. Jiwani* v. *Ircon International Ltd.*, 2009 SCC OnLine Bom 2021: (2010) 1 Mah LJ 547.
166. *DDA* v. *R.S. Sharma and Co.*, (2008) 13 SCC 80.

(*c*) justice or morality; or
(*d*) if it is patently illegal; or

(4) for the reasons stated in Section 13(5) and 16(6).[167]

An Award can be set aside it it is contrary to:

(*a*) fundamental policy of India; or
(*b*) the interest of India; or
(*c*) justice or morality; or
(*d*) if it is so unfair and unreasonable that it shocks the conscience of the court.[168]

The scope of interference by the court with a reasoned award is very limited. The well-reasoned award passed by the arbitrator was restored.[169] The parties had filed their claims, counterclaims, rejoinder, documents, evidence as well as other documents and written arguments, etc. before the arbitrator and the arbitrator also recorded that he had carefully gone through various documents, etc. while passing the award. Therefore, it cannot be said that the award was based on no evidence.[170]

When the court is called upon to decide the objections raised by a party against the arbitral award, the jurisdiction of the court is limited as expressly indicated in Section 34 of the Act and it has no jurisdiction to sit in appeal and to examine the correctness of the award on merits with reference to the material produced before the Arbitral Tribunal.[171]

Where the conclusions of the arbitrators are perverse, the very basis of the arbitrator's award is wrong, and the court's interference is warranted. In this case, the norms prescribed by the arbitrator for computing repairs and maintenance expenses for the purpose of determining floor day rate in respect of the vessels chartered to ONGC by shipowners were found perverse, and the arbitrator's award was set aside.[172]

Where the arbitrator was appointed without any consent obtained from the petitioners to appoint and/or nominate the arbitrator, an award made in the case was in breach of the principles of natural justice and was set aside.[173]

---

167. *ONGC Ltd.* v. *Saw Pipes Ltd.*, (2003) 5 SCC 705.
168. *MCD* v. *Modern Food Industries (India) Ltd.*, 2009 SCC OnLine Del 3151: (2009) 113 DRJ 290.
169. *Bharat Drilling & Foundation Treatment (P) Ltd.* v. *State of Jharkhand*, (2009) 16 SCC 705; *Ispat Engg. & Foundry Works* v. *SAIL*, (2001) 6 SCC 347.
170. *Fertilizer Corporation of India* v. *Balaji Laminating Works*, 2019 SCC OnLine Jhar 611.
171. *Laxmi Mathur* v. *MTNL*, 2000 SCC OnLine Bom 243: (2000) 3 Mah LJ 841.
172. *ONGC Ltd.* v. *Garware Shipping Corpn. Ltd.*, (2007) 13 SCC 434.
173. *Madhur Pandey* v. *Larsen and Toubro Infotech Ltd.*, 2013 SCC OnLine Bom 567: (2013) 3 Mah LJ 654.

Grounds for setting aside award

An application to a court for setting aside an award may be made to a court in accordance with sub-section (2) and sub-section (3) *vide* Section 34(1). An application to set aside the arbitration award can be filed only on the grounds provided in Section 34(2) of the Act.[174] The grounds for setting aside the award have been enumerated in sub-sections (2) and (3) of Section 34 of the Act. The sub-section (2-A) added by Amendment Act 3 of 2016 provides an additional ground for setting aside an arbitral award arising out of arbitrations other than international commercial arbitration, *viz.* where the award is vitiated by patent illegality appearing on the face of the award.

The objection as to the existence of the arbitration agreement cannot be entertained for the first time by way of amendment and that too after the expiry of the prescribed period under Section 34(3).[175]

Irregularities in cross-examination of witnesses do not fall within the ambit of objections under Section 34.[176]

Patent illegality

The seller appointed an arbitrator unilaterally and no notice was sent to the petitioners. When a person is ineligible to be appointed as arbitrator, he is also ineligible to nominate any arbitrator. The seller appointed the arbitrator unilaterally without the consent of the petitioners. The arbitrator did send any notice about the hearing to the petitioners and the seller also failed to furnish a claim statement to the petitioners. The petitioners also did not get any opportunity to file counter and contest matter. There was a clear violation of the provisions of Section 12(5). The award was set aside.[177]

"A party was under some incapacity" [Sub-s. (2)(*a*)(*i*)]

An award may be set aside by the court if the party filing Section 34 application establishes that a party to the arbitration agreement was under *some incapacity*. An agreement with a party who is under some incapacity like a person of unsound mind or being a minor is void. Incapacity in Section 34(2)(*a*)(*i*) refers to mental incapacity, minority, etc.[178]

---

174. *Chennai Container Terminal (P) Ltd.* v. *Union of India*, 2007 SCC OnLine Mad 506: (2007) 4 CTC 284.
175. *Chaddha and Co.* v. *U.P. Jal Nigam*, 2015 SCC OnLine All 9478: (2016) 2 All LJ 204.
176. *Thyssen Krupp Werkstoffe Gmbh* v. *SAIL*, 2011 SCC OnLine Del 1747: (2011) 123 DRJ 724.
177. *Hina Suneet Sharma* v. *Nissan Renault Financial Services India (P) Ltd.*, 2023 SCC OnLine Mad 758.
178. *Delhi Jal Board* v. *Reliable Diesel Engg. (P) Ltd.*, 2005 SCC OnLine Del 1360: (2006) 86 DRJ 153.

"Arbitration agreement is not valid under the law to which the parties have subjected it" [Sub-s. (2)(*a*)(*ii*)]

An award passed by the Arbitral Tribunal shall be set aside if the applicant establishes that the arbitration agreement is not valid under the law to which the parties have subjected it or under the law for the time being in force. Even if the arbitrator decides that an arbitration agreement is valid, the award can be successfully challenged under Section 34 on the ground that there exists no valid arbitration agreement and if the award of the arbitrator is found invalid, the award would be set aside.[179]

An award can be set aside if a party applying for its setting aside was under some incapacity or the arbitration agreement was not valid.[180]

The ground for setting aside the award was that the directors who acted on behalf of the company and filed reference were disqualified under Section 164(2)(*a*), Companies Act. The office of the Directors had not fallen vacant on their disqualifications incurred under Section 164(2)(*a*), and they could represent the company. The award of the arbitrator could not be set aside on this ground.[181]

Stamp and registration

An award cannot be set aside under Section 34 for want of stamping and registration. The question as to whether the award is required to be stamped and registered would be relevant only when the parties would file the award for the purpose of enforcement under Section 36 of the Act.[182]

"The party making the application was not given proper notice of the appointment of an arbitrator or of the arbitral proceedings" [Sub-s. (2)(*a*)(*iii*)]

The party making the Section 34 application can challenge the award if he was not given proper notice of:

1. the appointment of an arbitrator; or
2. the arbitration proceedings.

Where a party was not given proper notice of the appointment of the arbitrator or of the arbitration proceedings, he can successfully challenge

179. *Sydney Apparels* v. *Alagan & Co.*, 1999 SCC OnLine Mad 646.
180. *Union of India* v. *Hakam Chand & Co.*, 2002 SCC OnLine Del 945: (2002) 65 DRJ 400.
181. *Kaynet Finance Ltd.* v. *Verona Capital Ltd.*, 2019 SCC OnLine Bom 1203: (2020) 1 Mah LJ 430.
182. *M. Anasuya Devi* v. *M. Manik Reddy*, (2003) 8 SCC 565.

the award on a petition filed under Section 34, Arbitration and Conciliation Act, 1996.

An ex parte award passed without giving notice of the change of arbitrator was liable to be set aside, and set aside.[183]

Where the defendant-respondent had adequate notice, the arbitrator was not expected to continue issuing notices to an entity which voluntarily chose to not appear before it. The impugned award was not set aside.[184]

Where claims not notified

Where the claims are not notified, the arbitrator has no jurisdiction to make an award on such claims.[185]

"Or was otherwise unable to present his case" [Sub-s. (2)(*a*)(*iii*)]

A party can successfully challenge an award of the arbitrator when it proves that it was unable to present its case before the arbitrator. The petitioner was under some incapacity to make a proper representation due to the non-receipt of documents and particulars summoned by him before the conclusion of the arbitration proceedings. When the petitioner was collecting evidence to the knowledge of the arbitrator, the arbitrator closed the proceedings and the passed the award. The petitioner was disabled from presenting his case properly, and the award was liable to be set aside.[186]

Arbitral award beyond the terms of the contract—Permissibility of

The Arbitral Tribunal commits misconduct if by its award it decides the matters excluded by the agreement. A deliberate departure from the contract amounts to not only manifest disregard of its authority or misconduct on its part but it may tantamount to a malafide act and the award passed by the arbitrator is illegal and not binding.[187]

---

183. *Muthoot Vehcile & Asset Finance Ltd.* v. *Omana Mohandas*, 2019 SCC OnLine Ker 10848.
184. *Tommorrowland Ltd.* v. *Ensource Finance Ltd.*, (2022) 3 HCC (Del) 147.
185. *Indian Oil Corpn. Ltd.* v. *Artson Engg. Ltd.*, 2006 SCC OnLine Bom 1106: (2007) 1 Mah LJ 825.
186. *R. Narayanan* v. *India Info Line Securities (P) Ltd.*, 2013 SCC OnLine Mad 1744: (2013) 5 LW 89; *Narinder Singh* v. *Union of India*, 2021 SCC OnLine SC 1082 (the respondent was "unable to present his case", award was set aside).
187. *BHEL* v. *Tata Projects Ltd.*, 2010 SCC OnLine Cal 397: (2010) 1 CHN 747.

"Arbitral award deals with a dispute not contemplated by or not falling within the terms of the submission to arbitration" [Sub-s. (2)(*a*)(*iv*)]

An award of the arbitrator shall be set aside where the party challenging the award proves that the award deals with a dispute not falling within the submission to the arbitrator. Without any pleading, claim or evidence, the arbitrator granted compensation/a huge amount. When the award deals with dispute not contemplated by or not falling within the terms of submissions to arbitration, such award can be interfered with under Section 34(2)(*a*)(*iv*), Arbitration and Conciliation Act.[188]

An award can be said to be beyond the scope of submission to arbitration where the tribunal decides matters either beyond the scope of arbitration agreement or beyond disputes referred to Arbitral Tribunal.[189]

There is a difference between a non-arbitrable claim and non-arbitrable subject-matter. The former may arise on account of the scope of an arbitration agreement and also when the claim is not capable of being resolved through arbitration. Generally, non-arbitrability of the subject-matter relates to non-arbitrability in law. Exclusion or non-arbitrability, when clearly expressed, would have no difficulty. However, exclusion or non-arbitrability of subjects or disputes from the purview of a private forum like arbitration by necessary implication requires setting out of the principles that should be applied.[190]

"Arbitral award contains decisions on matters beyond the scope of the submission to arbitration" [Sub-s. (2)(*a*)(*iv*)]

The arbitration agreement between the parties stated that the disputes and differences arising between the parties shall be referred to arbitration. The claim was for damages for the destruction of the houses, crops and orchards, and a direction to the respondents to reclaim agricultural land rendered unfit by the activity of the respondents. The arbitrator awarded a sum for "loss of potential of land" and interest thereon. It was held that the award was outside the scope of reference to arbitration.[191]

All the claims for money by way of compensation made by the respondent before the arbitrator were beyond the scope of clause 9 of the construction agreement. The claim of money by the respondent related to damages, loss of salary, court expenses and advocate fee. These items were not contemplated

188. *Indian Oil Corpn. Ltd.* v. *S.N. Sridharan*, 2021 SCC OnLine Mad 16584.
189. *Ibid.*
190. *Delhi State Industrial & Infrastructure Development Corpn. Ltd.* v. *HR Builders*, (2022) 4 HCC (Del) 123.
191. *Rajinder Krishan Khanna* v. *Union of India*, (1998) 7 SCC 129.

in the arbitration clause. By considering and awarding these amounts to the respondent, the arbitrator had not properly appreciated clause 9 of the construction agreement and, thereby, misconducted himself by exceeding his jurisdiction and acted arbitrarily.[192]

The arbitrator had awarded compensation under the heading "Off site expenses" although not claimed by the contractor. An arbitrator has only jurisdiction to decide what is referred to him and does not have jurisdiction to decide what is not referred to him. If a claim is not made, there is no dispute with regard to that matter before the arbitrator. It cannot and does not form part of the terms of "the submission to arbitration". Therefore, if an arbitral award is made in respect of that matter, it can be considered as a decision "on matters beyond the scope of the submission to arbitration". It was held that the arbitrator transgressed his jurisdiction by deciding issues not referred to him. The award was patently illegal, and was set aside.[193]

The expression "submission to arbitration" consists of three facets, *i.e.* 1) dealing with the dispute not contemplated by terms of submission to arbitration; 2) dealing with the dispute not falling within the terms of submission to arbitration; and 3) containing decision on matters beyond the scope of submission. There is a presumption that the Arbitral Tribunal has acted within its mandate and the onus of establishing otherwise rests on the party seeking to set aside the award on the said ground.[194]

The arbitration agreement specified that all disputes arising between the parties save and except those in respect of which the decision of the Commander Works Engineer (CWE) or any other person is expressed to be final and binding are arbitrable. It was not the contention that the dispute was not arbitrable on the ground that there was a decision of CWE, nor any other ground was attracted.[195]

The award of the arbitrator was challenged on the ground of existence of an arbitral dispute. The consignment agent in terms of the agreement entered into between him and the manufacturing company released goods to the purchaser without raising any objection, and thereafter, engaged in correspondence of transaction. There was gross negligence of the consignment agent as he did not make any effort to ensure that the letter of credit was honoured. The dispute was governed by the arbitration clause in the agreement. The majority award was not entered on the ground that the subject-matter of the award was not arbitrable.[196]

192. *R. Natesan* v. *R. Padmanaban*, 2016 SCC OnLine Mad 3449: (2016) 3 LW 814.
193. *Pam Developments (P) Ltd.* v. *State of W.B.*, 2021 SCC OnLine Cal 1668.
194. *NCC Ltd.* v. *Indian Institute of Technology*, 2020 SCC OnLine Mad 5857.
195. *Union of India* v. *Moti Enterprises*, 2002 SCC OnLine Bom 806: (2003) 1 Mah LJ 930.
196. *MMTC Ltd.* v. *Vedanta Ltd.*, (2019) 4 SCC 163.

(*a*) *Arbitral Tribunal cannot travel beyond terms of reference*

It is a settled legal proposition that special tribunals like Arbitral Tribunals and labour courts get jurisdiction to proceed with the case only from the reference made to them. Thus, it is not permissible for such tribunals/authorities to travel beyond the terms of reference. Powers cannot be exercised by the tribunal so as to enlarge materially the scope of reference itself. If the award goes beyond the reference or there is an error apparent on the face of the award, it would certainly be open to the court to interfere with such an award. Thus, an arbitrator cannot be allowed to assume jurisdiction over a question which has not been referred to him, and similarly, he cannot widen his jurisdiction by holding contrary to the fact that the matter which he wants to decide is within the submission of the parties. The Arbitral Tribunal cannot travel beyond the terms of the contract and statutory provisions. In the absence of proper pleadings and objections, such a course may not be permissible.[197] If the arbitrator gives an award ignoring the terms and conditions of the contract and has travelled beyond the terms and conditions of the contract, the award of the arbitrator is liable to be set aside; the conduct of the arbitrator amounts to misconduct.[198]

Section 34(2)(*iv*) envisages that an arbitral award may be set aside if the arbitral award deals with a dispute not contemplated or not falling within the terms of the submission to the arbitrator. When a specific exclusion is there in the contract, obviously the Arbitral Tribunal cannot travel beyond the contract and give an award.[199]

(*b*) *Excepted matters—Section 34(2)(a)(iv) and 34(2)(b)—Whether contractor or department responsible for the delay/breach of contract*

An award adjudicating claims which are "excepted matters" excluded from the scope of arbitration would violate Sections 34(2)(*b*), Arbitration and Conciliation Act, 1996.[200] It was not open to the arbitrator to decide the issues which were not arbitrable and the award, so far as it relates to disputes regarding non-arbitrable disputes is concerned, is bad in law. It was not open to the arbitrator to decide on the "excepted matter". The award of the arbitrator was set aside.[201]

The work contract in the present case contained an arbitration clause. Questions whether it was the contractor or the department who was

197. *MSK Projects (I) (JV) Ltd.* v. *State of Rajasthan*, (2011) 10 SCC 573.
198. *Vivek Jain* v. *Union of India*, 2008 SCC OnLine Del 263: (2008) 148 DLT 333.
199. *Crompton Greaves Ltd.* v. *Dyna*, 2007 SCC OnLine Mad 427: (2007) 3 CTC 417.
200. *J.G. Engineers (P) Ltd.* v. *Union of India*, (2011) 5 SCC 758.
201. *Harsha Constructions* v. *Union of India*, (2014) 9 SCC 246.

responsible for the delay or was in breach or the issue of validity of termination of contract cannot be excluded from the arbitrator's jurisdiction.[202] The award of the arbitrator was upheld, and rejection of the counterclaims of the respondent was also held proper.[203]

(c) *"Force majeure" and "change in law"*

The appellant-contractor was awarded a contract for the purpose of well drilling and other auxiliary operation. During the subsistence of the contract, the price of high speed diesel, an essential material required for the operation, increased. The arbitrator interpreted the change in law clause of the agreement in wide terms and awarded additional reimbursement. Clauses in the agreement specifically provided that the contract was based on a fixed rate and the contractor shall bear the expenses of the fuel. It was held, the arbitrator had failed to interpret the contract in view of all the clauses of the agreement. The High Court rightly interpreted the change in law clause as similar to the *force majeure* clause and set aside the award. The judgment of the High Court was upheld.[204] The *force majeure* clause in the contract would apply only if the act could not be performed due to some event beyond the control of the person.[205]

The contract was for the supply of gunny bags. The Corporation deducted liquidated damages and GTA without providing an extension of time to the contractor for the supply of bags. The contractor invoked force majeure clause in the arbitration agreement on account of fire in its unit. The contractor established fire in its unit on the basis of documents like the fire brigade service report and other certificates. The arbitrator accepted the claim of the contractor. The award was not set aside.[206]

The issue whether in the circumstances of the case in which the appellant was placed entitled him to plead force majeure or not is a question of fact.[207]

(d) *"Not falling within the terms of the submission to arbitration" Section 34(2)(a)(iv)—Acquiescence*

The objector in its reply to the statement of claim contended that the claim fell beyond the scope of reference. It was held, the objector could not be

202. *Ibid.*
203. *Ibid.*
204. *South East Asia Marine Engg. & Constructions Ltd.* v. *Oil India Ltd.*, (2020) 5 SCC 164.
205. *Interore Fertichem Resources Sa* v. *Mmtc of India Ltd.*, 2007 SCC OnLine Del 1400: (2008) 146 DLT 61.
206. *T.N. Civil Supplies Corpn.* v. *AI Champdany Industries Ltd.*, 2019 SCC OnLine Mad 39348.
207. *World Window Infrastructure (P) Ltd.* v. *Central Warehousing Corpn.*, (2021) 3 HCC (Del) 731.

said to have acquiesced in the determination of such claim. The award of the arbitrator referred only to the points for determination and did not deal with any question regarding the scope of the reference. Mere mention in the award of the points for determination does not automatically mean that the points are within the scope of reference.[208]

Where an arbitrator entertains claims and disputes not referred to by the court, he misconducts himself. The award was modified.[209]

Severable award [Sub-s. (2)(*a*)(*iv*), proviso]

The proviso to Section 34(2)(*a*), clause (*iv*), provides that if the decisions on matters submitted to arbitration can be separated from those not so submitted, only that part of the award which contains decisions on matters not submitted to arbitration may be set aside.

(*a*) *Severable award—Setting aside entire award erroneous [S. 37(1)(b)]*

If an award deals with and decides several claims separately and distinctly, even if the court finds that the award in regard to some items is bad, the court will segregate the award on items which did not suffer from any infirmity and uphold the award to that extent. In the present case as the award on Items 2, 4, 6, 7, 8 and 9 was upheld by the civil court and as the High Court in appeal did not find any infirmity in regard to the award on those claims, the judgment of the High Court setting aside the award in regard to Claims 2, 4, 6, 7, 8 and 9 of the appellant was not sustained.[210]

The doctrine of severability can be applied to awards which are severable. The judicial discretion vested in the court in terms of the provisions of Section 34 takes within its ambit the power to set aside an award partly or wholly depending on the facts and circumstances of the given case.[211]

Modification of award

The power to set aside an arbitral award under Section 34 would not include the power to modify the award. A two-judge Bench of the Supreme Court in a very recent case has held as under:

---

208. *Rajinder Krishan Khanna* v. *Union of India*, (1998) 7 SCC 129.
209. *South Eastern Coalfields Ltd.* v. *Sarvatra Road Runners (P) Ltd.*, 2016 SCC OnLine Chh 2137: (2017) 2 CGLJ 381.
210. *J.G. Engineers (P) Ltd.* v. *Union of India*, (2011) 5 SCC 758.
211. *R.S. Jiwani* v. *Ircon International Ltd.*, 2009 SCC OnLine Bom 2021: (2010) 1 Mah LJ 547.

> What is important to note is that, far from Section 34 being in the nature of an appellate provision, it provides only for setting aside awards on very limited grounds, such grounds being contained in sub-sections (2) and (3) of Section 34. Secondly, as the marginal note of Section 34 indicates, 'recourse' to a court against an arbitral award may be made *only* by an application for *setting aside* such award in accordance with sub-sections (2) and (3). 'Recourse' is defined by P. Ramanatha Aiyar's *Advanced Law Lexicon (3rd Edn.)* as the enforcement or method of enforcing a right. Where the right is itself truncated, enforcement of such truncated right can also be only limited in nature. What is clear from a reading of the said provisions is that, given the limited grounds of challenge under sub-sections (2) and (3), an application can only be made to set aside an award. This becomes even clearer when we see sub-section (4) under which, on receipt of an application under sub-section (1) of Section 34, the court may adjourn the Section 34 proceedings and give the Arbitral Tribunal an opportunity to resume the arbitral proceedings or take such action as will eliminate the grounds for setting aside the arbitral award. Here again, it is important to note that it is the opinion of the Arbitral Tribunal which counts in order to eliminate the grounds for setting aside the award, which may be indicated by the court hearing the Section 34 application.[212]

The same view has been taken by the Supreme Court in the undermentioned case.[213] The Supreme Court held thus:

> The limited and extremely circumscribed jurisdiction of the court under Section 34 of the Act, permits the court to interfere with an award, *sans* the grounds of patent illegality, i.e. that '*illegality must go to the root of the matter and cannot be of a trivial nature*'; and that the tribunal '*must decide in accordance with the terms of the contract, but if an arbitrator construes a term of the contract in a reasonable manner, it will not mean that the award can be set aside on this ground*'.[214] The other ground would be denial of natural justice. In appeal, Section 37 of the Act grants narrower scope to the appellate court to review the findings in an award, if it has been upheld, or substantially upheld under Section 34. It is important to notice that the old Act contained a provision[215], which enabled the court to modify an award. However, that power has been consciously omitted by Parliament, while enacting the Act of 1996. This means that the Parliamentary intent was to exclude power to modify an award, in any manner, to the court.

---

212. *Project Director, N.H. No. 45 E and 220 NHAI* v. *M. Hakeem*, (2021) 9 SCC 1.
213. *Larsen Air Conditioning & Refrigration Co.* v. *Union of India*, 2023 SCC OnLine SC 982.
214. *Associate Builders* v. *DDA*, (2015) 3 SCC 49.
215. **15.** *Power of court to modify award.*—The court may by order modify or correct an award—(*a*) where it appears that a part of the award is upon a matter not referred to arbitration and such part can be separated from the other part and does not affect the decision on the matter referred; or (*b*) where the award is imperfect in form, or contains any obvious error which can be amended without affecting such decision; or (*c*) where the award contains a clerical mistake or an error arising from an accidental slip or omission.

> This position has been iterated decisively by this court in *Project Director, National Highways No. 45E and 220 National Highways Authority of India* v. *M. Hakeem*[216].

The interference of variance or modification of the award and grant of any new/additional/modified reliefs are totally out of the question while considering the application under Section 34, Arbitration Act.[217]

It is not permissible for the court to re-appreciate the evidence to calculate the damages as established by the respondent and modify the award of damages. It is not open to the court in this proceeding to modify the arbitral award. The impugned award to the extent that it wrongly determines the damages was set aside.[218]

The court has the power to modify the offending part of the award in case it is severable from the rest.[219]

The court can go into the quantum of claim as granted and quantum of claim rejected, and can modify the award.[220] An arbitral award can be modified or the award can be challenged partly.[221]

Where the appointment of a particular officer as an arbitrator by the Chief Engineer is coterminous with his tenure in that particular office held by him at the time of appointment, once he ceases to hold that particular office for the reason of his being transferred, resignation or his incapacity on any account, he cannot continue with office in the Arbitral Tribunal.[222] The point of jurisdiction and authority of judicial or quasi-judicial functionaries are the fundamental ones and need to be examined, and the same can be done under Section 34, Arbitration and Conciliation Act.[223]

The extension granted to the arbitrator cannot travel beyond the date of retirement.[224]

Where, in objection, the appellant did not assail the composition of the Arbitral Tribunal, but later assailed the composition of the tribunal, and

---

216. *NHAI* v. *M. Hakeem*, (2021) 9 SCC 1.
217. *Macro Marvel Projects Ltd.* v. *J. Vengatesh*, 2022 SCC OnLine Mad 4702; *S.V. Samudram* v. *State of Karnataka*, (2024) 3 SCC 623.
218. *Aneja Constructions (India) Ltd.* v. *Grim-Tech Projects (I) (P) Ltd.*, (2022) 1 HCC (Del) 523.
219. *M.P. Power Generation Co. Ltd.* v. *ANSALDO Energia SpA*, (2018) 16 SCC 661.
220. *Union of India* v. *Arctic India*, 2007 SCC OnLine Bom 409: (2007) 5 Mah LJ 174.
221. *G.D. Anklesaria and Co.* v. *Airports Authority of India*, 2010 SCC OnLine Bom 250: (2010) 2 Mah LJ 921; *Axios Navigation Co. Ltd.* v. *Indian Oil Corpn. Ltd.*, 2012 SCC OnLine Bom 4: (2012) 3 Mah LJ 701.
222. *Union of India* v. *Surendranath Kanungo*, 2004 SCC OnLine Cal 353: (2005) 1 Cal LT 457.
223. *Ibid.*
224. *Ibid.*

participated in the arbitral proceedings, the appellant shall be deemed to have waived the objection about the composition of the Arbitral Tribunal. The principle of acquiescence by long participation was awarded in the case.[225]

"Composition of the Arbitral Tribunal or the arbitral procedure" [S. 34(2)(*a*)(*v*)]

Section 34(2)(*a*)(*v*) only applies if "the composition of the Arbitral Tribunal or the arbitral procedure was not in accordance with the agreement of the parties"; if the composition of the Arbitral Tribunal or the arbitral procedure was in accordance with the agreement of the parties, then there can be no challenge under this provision. The question of unless such agreement was in conflict with a provision of this Act would only arise if the composition of the Arbitral Tribunal or the arbitral procedure is not in accordance with the agreement of the parties. When the composition or the procedure is not in accordance with the agreement of the parties, then the parties get a right to challenge the award. But even in such a case the right to challenge the award is restricted. The challenge can only be made provided the agreement of the parties is in conflict with a provision of Part I from which the parties cannot derogate. In other words, even if the composition of the Arbitral Tribunal or the arbitral procedure is not in accordance with the agreement of the parties but if such composition or procedure is in accordance with the provisions of the said Act, then the party cannot challenge the award. The words "falling such agreement" have reference to an agreement providing for the composition of the Arbitral Tribunal or the arbitral procedure. They would come into play only if there is no agreement providing for the composition of the Arbitral Tribunal or the arbitral procedure. If there is no agreement providing for the composition of the Arbitral Tribunal or the arbitral procedure and the composition of the Arbitral Tribunal or the arbitral procedure is not in accordance with Part I of the said Act, then also a challenge to the award would be available. Therefore, so long as the composition of the Arbitral Tribunal or the arbitral procedure is in accordance with the agreement of the parties, Section 34 does not permit challenge to an award merely on the ground that the composition of the Arbitral Tribunal was in conflict with the provisions of Part I of the said Act.[226]

In Section 34(2)(*a*)(*v*) of the Act, the composition of the Arbitral Tribunal should be in accordance with the agreement. Similarly, the procedure that is required to be followed by the arbitrators should also be in accordance with

---

225. *Union of India* v. *Pam Development (P) Ltd.*, 2005 SCC OnLine Cal 299: (2005) 4 CHN 279; *Union of India* v. *Pam Development (P) Ltd.*, (2014) 11 SCC 366.

226. *Narayan Prasad Lohia* v. *Nikunj Kumar Lohia*, (2002) 3 SCC 572.

the agreement of the parties. If there is no such agreement, then it should be in accordance with the procedure prescribed to be followed by the Arbitral Tribunal coupled with its powers. Power and procedure are synonymous in the present case. By prescribing the procedure, the Arbitral Tribunal is empowered and required to decide the dispute in accordance with the provisions of the Act, that is to say, the jurisdiction of the tribunal to decide the dispute is prescribed. In these sections, there is no distinction between the jurisdiction/power and the procedure. Therefore, if the award dehors the said provisions, it would be, on the face of it, illegal. The decision of the tribunal must be within the bounds of its jurisdiction conferred under the Act or the contract. In exercising jurisdiction, the Arbitral Tribunal cannot act in breach of some provision of substantive law or the provisions of the Act.[227] The designate of the Chief Justice under Section 11 appointed two arbitrators with a direction that they would appoint the third presiding arbitrator, but without appointing the presiding officer the two arbitrators proceeded with the arbitration ex parte. It was held, the composition of the tribunal was not in accordance with the direction of the designate of the Chief Justice, and the award was set aside.[228]

If the award is contrary to the substantive provisions of law or the provisions of the Act or against the terms of the contract, it would be patently illegal, which could be interfered with under Section 34. However, such failure of procedure should be patently affecting the rights of the parties.[229]

In view of the office order, the CMD of the respondent was empowered to exercise all the powers of the Project Director including the power to appoint an arbitrator. The appointment of the arbitrator by the CMD was not defective in any manner.[230]

As per the agreement between the parties, a sole arbitrator was to be appointed/nominated jointly by the parties. The respondent appointed an arbitrator unilaterally and consent of the petitioners was not obtained. Even notices of the appointment of arbitration proceedings were not issued to the petitioners. It was held, arbitration proceedings were illegal and the award was set aside.[231]

227. *ONGC Ltd.* v. *Saw Pipes Ltd.*, (2003) 5 SCC 705.

228. *Haresh Chinnubhai Shah* v. *Rajesh Prabhakar Jhaveri*, 2003 SCC OnLine Bom 1009: (2004) 1 Mah LJ 1109.

229. *ONGC Ltd.* v. *Saw Pipes Ltd.*, (2003) 5 SCC 705.

230. *Reunion Engg. Co. (P) Ltd.* v. *NBCC Ltd.*, 2012 SCC OnLine Del 2860: (2013) 135 DRJ 530.

231. *Sheeba Jose* v. *Subramanian S. Iyer*, 2012 SCC OnLine Bom 168: (2012) 4 Mah LJ 887; *Zenith Fire Services (India) (P) Ltd.* v. *Charmi Sales*, 2013 SCC OnLine Bom 23: (2013) 2 Mah LJ 623.

The respondent appointed its own chartered accountant as arbitrator and did not approach the court for the appointment of independent arbitrator. The arbitrator was appointed without obtaining the consent of the petitioner. The award was set aside as being void ab initio as the arbitrator had no authority to enter into the reference.[232]

Plea of jurisdiction

Where a party has second notice and he does not raise a plea of lack of jurisdiction before the Arbitral Tribunal, he must make out a strong case why he did not do so if he choose to move a petition for setting aside the award under Section 34(2)(*v*) on the ground that the composition of the Arbitral Tribunal was not in accordance with the agreement of the parties. If the plea of jurisdiction is not taken before the arbitrator as provided in Section 16 of the Act, such a plea cannot be permitted to be raised in proceedings under Section 34 of the Act for setting aside the award, unless good reasons are shown.[233]

There is no bar to the plea of jurisdiction under Section 34 of the Act, even if no such objection was raised under Section 16.[234] Where the plea of lack of jurisdiction was not taken before the arbitrator as provided in Section 16, it cannot be permitted to be raised in proceedings under Section 34 for setting aside the award.[235] Questions relating to inherent lack of jurisdiction may be raised before the arbitrator, and if not raised, may be raised in a petition under Section 34.[236]

Merely filing of objections in wrong court would not confer jurisdiction on the court.[237] The issue regarding jurisdiction of the Arbitral Tribunal raised after the expiry of period provided in Section 34(3) of the Act cannot be entertained in a petition under Section 34.[238]

In an application for setting aside the award of the Arbitral Tribunal, the petitioner raised an objection as to territorial jurisdiction in the petition

---

232. *Dhcmbla Enterprises* v. *Chelsea Products*, 2001 SCC OnLine Del 1253.
233. *GAIL* v. *Keti Construction (I) Ltd.*, (2007) 5 SCC 38; *S. Harinder Singh* v. *S. Nirmal Singh*, 2012 SCC OnLine Del 4675: (2012) 132 DRJ 218; *ONGC Ltd.* v. *International Certification Services (P) Ltd.*, 2016 SCC OnLine Bom 3966: (2016) 4 Mah LJ 727; *Kasim V.K.* v. *M. Ashraf*, (2021) 1 HCC (Ker) 379.
234. *Lion Engg. Consultants* v. *State of M.P.*, (2018) 16 SCC 758.
235. *Saraswati Ojha* v. *Birendra Prasad Singh*, 2021 SCC OnLine Cal 441.
236. *Veena* v. *Seth Industries Ltd.*, 2010 SCC OnLine Bom 1707: (2011) 2 Mah LJ 226; *Hindustan Petroleum Corpn. Ltd.* v. *Barun Sankar Chatterjee*, 2012 SCC OnLine Cal 509: (2012) 3 CHN 160.
237. *Apparel Export Promotion Council* v. *Prabhati Patni, Proprietor Comfort Furnishers*, 2005 SCC OnLine Del 1287: (2006) 86 DRJ 48.
238. *Vastu Invest & Holdings (P) Ltd.* v. *Gujarat Lease Financing Ltd.*, 2000 SCC OnLine Bom 729: (2001) 2 Mah LJ 565.

under Section 34 of the Act, and had not raised any such objection before the Arbitral Tribunal. The petitioner had fully participated in the proceedings before the arbitrator and had not raised any objection within the time-limit specified under Section 16(2). It was held, the petitioner cannot be allowed to raise any such objection directly under Section 34.[239]

Waiver of objection as to jurisdiction of the arbitrator

Considering the facts that the respondent failed to participate in the proceedings before the arbitrator and did not raise any submission that the arbitrator did not have jurisdiction or that he was exceeding the scope of his authority, the respondent must be deemed to have waived all such objections.[240]

Independence/impartiality of the arbitrator

An advocate was representing the arbitrator in his personal case, and this fact was within the exclusive knowledge of the advocate. He was duty-bound to disclose this fact to both the parties to the dispute referred to the Arbitral Tribunal, which he did not. The award passed by the arbitrator was set aside.[241]

Arbitrator having other arbitration cases of one party before him

The arbitrator appointed was already having 80 arbitrations of one party to arbitration proceedings, which was permitting him to derive significant financial income from arbitration from that party. The said fact created justifiable doubt about impartiality and independence of the arbitrator. Arbitration proceedings were hit by Section 12 read with Items 1, 14, 22 of Fifth Schedule. The appointment of the arbitrator itself being illegal, the award passed by him was liable to be set aside.[242]

Impartiality of the arbitrator—Arbitrator had acted as counsel for the party in another case—Award set aside

The record showed that the arbitrator had acted as counsel in another case for one of the parties to the dispute in the instant case. Despite objection taken with regard to his appointment, the arbitrator proceeded with the

239. *Engg. Projects India Ltd.* v. *Balaji Projects*, 2021 SCC OnLine Mad 409.
240. *Quippo Construction Equipment Ltd.* v. *Janardan Nirman (P) Ltd.*, (2020) 18 SCC 277.
241. *Murlidhar Roongta* v. *S. Jagannath Tibrewala*, 2004 SCC OnLine Bom 727: (2005) 2 Mah LJ 285.
242. *Raghani Tradelink (P) Ltd.* v. *HDB Financial Services Ltd.*, 2019 SCC OnLine Bom 13379.

matter without disclosing facts within his knowledge as per Section 12. The award passed by the arbitrator was found unsustainable, and was set aside.[243]

Allegation of bias against arbitrator

No bias can be imputed against the arbitrator, if he has allowed the claim of the respondent on merits.[244]

Perceived bias, fraud and corruption

In the disclosure letter filed by the sole arbitrator appointed, the arbitrator clearly mentioned that he is serving on the Board of some companies associated with the respondent. The plea was raised by the petitioner when the arbitrator had not accepted the claim of the petitioner wholly. No material/evidence was produced to prove fraud and corruption, and hence, the award of the arbitrator was not set aside.[245]

"Subject-matter of the dispute is not capable of settlement by arbitration under the law" [Sub-s. (2)(*b*)(*i*)]

The court shall set aside an award of the arbitrator if it finds that the subject-matter of the dispute is not capable of settlement by arbitration under the law for the time being in force.

If the claim itself is not arbitrable, it does not become arbitrable only because of its inclusion in the notice invoking the arbitration clause.[246]

Public policy

An award can be set aside if it is contrary to fundamental policy and Indian law or to the interest of India or justice or morality or in addition if patently illegal.

Illegality must go to the root of the matter; if the illegality is of trivial nature, the award cannot be said against public policy.[247]

The petitioner has to show that the award is in conflict with public policy of India. In the instant case, the arbitrator had divided the property amongst

---

243. *Vinod Bhaiyalal Jain* v. *Wadhwani Parmeshwari Cold Storage (P) Ltd.*, (2020) 15 SCC 726.
244. *Pradyuman Kumar Sharma* v. *Jays Agar M. Sancheti*, 2013 SCC OnLine Bom 453: (2013) 5 Mah LJ 86.
245. *R. Gowrishanker* v. *Krishnamurty Chandra*, 2019 SCC OnLine Mad 10631.
246. *Indian Oil Corpn. Ltd.* v. *Artson Engg. Ltd.*, 2006 SCC OnLine Bom 1106: (2007) 1 Mah LJ 825.
247. *Raghubir Singh* v. *Delhi Metro Rail Corpn. Ltd.*, 2007 SCC OnLine Del 253: ILR (2007) 1 Del 965.

its co-owners by specifying their respective shares. Tenancy was not even the subject-matter of reference. Nothing was shown that the partition of the tenanted premises between its co-owner was against the public policy of India. The petition under Section 34 was dismissed.[248]

Arbitration involved various works under the contract. Assessment of compensation on different heads was based on the material available on record. Held, the award was not in conflict with the public policy of India.[249]

Objection to jurisdiction of arbitrator that the subject-matter cannot be dealt with by arbitrator

There is nothing to warrant the inference that all objections to the jurisdiction of the Arbitral Tribunal cannot be raised under Section 16 and that the tribunal does not have the power to do so on its own jurisdiction. The words used in Section 34(2)(*b*) are "subject-matter of the dispute is not capable of settlement by arbitration". This phraseology does not necessarily refer to an objection to jurisdiction as the term is well known. In fact, it refers to a situation where the dispute referred to arbitration by reason of its subject-matter is not capable of settlement at all. The scheme of the Act is clear. All objections to jurisdiction of whatever nature must be taken at the stage of the submission of the statement of defence and must be dealt with under Section 16, Arbitration and Conciliation Act, 1996. However, if one of the parties seeks to contend that the subject-matter of the dispute is such that it cannot be dealt with by arbitration, it may be dealt with under Section 34.[250]

The High Court held that the claim raised by the contractor fell within the "expected matters" under contract, hence are not arbitrable. The High Court had ignored the arbitrator's clear finding that the procedure to be followed for bringing the claim within the excepted matters was not followed. The finding of the arbitrator was not perverse, and the order of the High Court holding the claim as non-arbitrable was set aside.[251]

"Award is in conflict with the public policy of India" [S. 34(2)(*b*)(*ii*)]

The defence that the arbitral award is in conflict with the public policy of India itself can be a ground to set aside the award in view of Section 34(2)(*b*) of the Act.[252]

---

248. *Paramjit Singh* v. *Satyawati*, 2002 SCC OnLine Del 704: (2002) 64 DRJ 798.
249. *Integrated Tribal Development Agency* v. *Odyssey Advanced Telematics Systems*, 2019 SCC OnLine Ori 37.
250. *MSP Infrastructure Ltd.* v. *M.P. Road Development Corpn. Ltd.*, (2015) 13 SCC 713.
251. *Madnani Construction Corpn. (P) Ltd.* v. *Union of India*, (2010) 1 SCC 549.
252. *Ibid.*

An arbitral award shall be set aside if the court finds that the award is in conflict with the public policy of India.

Explanation I in Section 34(2)(*b*)(*ii*) has been amended by Amending Act 3 of 2016. Under the amended provision, it has been clarified that an award is in conflict with the public policy of India, only if

(*i*) the making of the award was induced or affected by fraud or corruption or was in violation of Section 75 or Section 81; or
(*ii*) is in contravention with the fundamental policy of Indian law; or
(*iii*) it is in conflict with the most basic notions of morality or justice.

The phrase "public policy of India" used in Section 34 in context is required to be given a wider meaning. The concept of public policy connotes some matter which concerns public good and the public interest. What is for public good or in public interest or what would be injurious or harmful to the public good or public interest has varied from time to time. However, the award which is, on the face of it, patently in violation of statutory provisions cannot be said to be in public interest. Such award/judgment/decision is likely to adversely affect the administration of justice. Hence, in addition to the narrower meaning given to the term "public policy" in the *Renusagar case*[253], it was held that the award could be set aside if it is patently illegal. The result would be that an award could be set aside if it is contrary to:

1. the fundamental policy of Indian law; or
2. the interest of India; or
3. justice or morality; or
4. in addition, if it is patently illegal.

Illegality must go to the root of the matter and if the illegality is of trivial nature, it cannot be held that the award is against public policy. An award could also be set aside if it is so unfair and unreasonable that it shocks the conscience of the court. Such an award is opposed to public policy and is required to be adjudged void.[254]

A court can set aside an award under Section 34(2)(*b*)(*ii*) of the Act as being in conflict with the public policy of India, if it is 1) contrary to the fundamental policy of Indian law; or 2) contrary to the interests of India; or 3) contrary to justice or morality; or 4) patently illegal. To hold an award to be opposed to public policy, the patent illegality should go to the very root of the matter and not a trivial illegality. An award can be set aside if it is so unfair and unreasonable that it shocks the conscience of the court, as then it would be opposed to the public policy. It is well settled that where the contract, in clear and in ambiguous terms, bars or prohibits a particular

253. *Renusagar Power Co. Ltd.* v. *General Electric Co.*, 1994 Supp (1) SCC 644.
254. *ONGC Ltd.* v. *Saw Pipes Ltd.*, (2003) 5 SCC 705.

claim, any award made in violation of the terms of the contract would violate Section 28(3) of the Act, and would be considered to be patently illegal, and therefore, liable to be set aside under Section 34(2)(*b*) of the Act.[255]

The expression "public policy of India", whether contained in Section 34 or in Section 48, would now mean the "fundamental policy of India law".[256]

The Plea that the words "public policy" are completely explained in the Explanation to Section 34(2)(*b*) is a very narrow construction of the provision.[257]

Apart from the grounds available to a party to challenge the award on incapacity, lack of notice or the composition of the Arbitral Tribunal under Section 34(2)(*a*), Section 34(2)(*b*) lays down broader grounds such as the award being in conflict with the public policy of India. The expression "public policy of India" has been clarified further under the three subheads to mean an award induced or affected by fraud, is in contravention with the fundamental policy of India law, or is in conflict with the most basic notions of morality or justice.[258] "Public policy" would mean law in India.[259]

A land was acquired by the National Highways Authority of India. Compensation granted was re-determined by the arbitrator. While re-determining the compensation, the arbitrator had not followed the procedure, and had also not considered the parameters as given in Section 3-G(7) of the National Highways Act (48 of 1956). It was held that the award was against public policy.[260]

The law of limitation is based on public policy, infraction of the same clearly vitiates the arbitral award as being in conflict with the public policy of India.[261]

Where the arbitrator had rendered the award, though there was no arbitration agreement between the parties, the arbitrator had exceeded jurisdiction; the award was in contravention of the substantial law of India, and was set aside.[262]

---

255. *J.G. Engineers (P) Ltd.* v. *Union of India*, (2011) 5 SCC 758.
256. *Ibid.*
257. *Dominant Offset (P) Ltd.* v. *Adamovske Strojirny A.S.*, 2000 SCC OnLine Del 38: ILR (2000) 1 Del 378.
258. *Board of Trustees* v. *ABG Kolkata Container Terminal (P) Ltd.*, 2020 SCC OnLine Cal 2273.
259. *State of Tripura* v. *Himangshu Bikash Saha*, 2011 SCC OnLine Gau 248: (2011) 6 Gau LR 200.
260. *Navin Tyagi* v. *Union of India*, 2013 SCC OnLine All 10549: (2014) 3 All LJ 13; *Sharda Prasad* v. *Union of India*, 2013 SCC OnLine All 13740: (2013) 6 All LJ 405.
261. *OPG Power Generation (P) Ltd.* v. *Enexio Power Cooling Solutions India (P) Ltd.*, 2020 SCC OnLine Mad 27362; *Nirav Securities (P) Ltd.* v. *Prabhuta Motiram Adhvaryu*, 2002 SCC OnLine Bom 685: (2002) 4 Mah LJ 478.
262. *Gill and Co. (P) Ltd.* v. *Patodia Ginning Factory*, 2016 SCC OnLine Bom 2184: (2016) 3 Mah LJ 890.

Lack of judicial approach, violation of the principles of natural justice, perversity and patent illegality have been identified as grounds for interference with an award of the arbitrator.[263] Invocation of the arbitration clause after having received the entire amount in full and final settlement was clearly an abuse of the process of law. The dispute was finally settled upon. The award of the arbitrator was against the public policy of India, and was set aside.[264]

The consensus of opinion amongst judges is that the concept of public policy is incapable of precise definition. The Supreme Court has held that an award is considered contrary to public policy if it is opposed to: 1) the fundamental policy of Indian law; 2) interests of India; and 3) justice or morality. This concept of public policy, in the realm of arbitration law, is a rather vexed concept, in the sense that different countries have different concepts of public policy. In view of such varying standards of public policy in different countries, an attempt is made to arrive at a somewhat acceptable standard by construing that something is opposed to public policy where there is an excess of jurisdiction and a lack of due process. The concept of public policy in the Arbitration and Conciliation Act, 1996 as given in Section 34(2) Explanation has virtually adopted the aforesaid international standard, *namely*, if anything is found in excess of jurisdiction and depicts a lack of due process, it will be opposed to public policy of India. When an award is induced or affected by fraud or corruption, the same will fall within the aforesaid grounds of excess of jurisdiction and a lack of due process.[265] An award induced by fraud or corruption is against the public policy of India.[266]

In a case where validity of an award is challenged, there is no necessity of giving a narrow meaning to the term "public policy of India", on the contrary a wider meaning is required to be given so that the "patently" illegal award passed by the Arbitral Tribunal would be set aside.[267] When during the acquisition of land for the construction of national highway, the arbitrator determined compensation without complying with the provisions of the 1996 Act, it resulted in patent illegality. The award of the Arbitral Tribunal was liable to be set aside.[268]

---

263. *M.P. Power Generation Co. Ltd.* v. *ANSALDO Energia SpA*, (2018) 16 SCC 661.
264. *Goyal MG Gases Ltd.* v. *Double Dot Finance Ltd.*, 2009 SCC OnLine Del 1478: (2009) 111 DRJ 217.
265. *Venture Global Engg.* v. *Satyam Computer Services Ltd.*, (2010) 8 SCC 660.
266. *Ibid.*
267. *Kaushal Kishore Mishra* v. *State of U.P.*, 2017 SCC OnLine All 4299: (2018) 2 All LJ 717.
268. *Ibid.*

The appellant-landlord had executed a business service agreement in favour of the respondent. A dispute arose between the two. The dispute was referred to the Arbitral Tribunal which held the appellant liable to pay a certain amount alongwith interest to the respondent. The award was challenged on the ground that the award was in conflict with the public policy and public interest, and the agreement executed was in fact of leave and licence. There was no evidence to show that the agreement was a leave and licence agreement. It was held, the award was not against public policy. Challenge to the award was rejected.[269]

In a case relating to international commercial arbitration arising out of a charter party contract, the court found that the Arbitral Tribunal (by majority) interpreted the terms and conditions of the contract consistent with common law settled by the Reid test formulated in the UK and accepted in India. Held, the award could not be termed as in conflict with the public policy of India. It did not warrant court's interference.[270]

A mere error of law would not amount to a breach of public policy within the meaning of Section 34(2)(*b*)(*ii*). It would be impermissible for the court to interfere in the absence of the party having demonstrably established that the award is, in any manner, in conflict with public policy.[271]

The majority of the arbitrator had arrived at a conclusion which was not acceptable to the appellant. It was held, it could not be said that the award was opposed to the public policy of India. The award of the arbitrator was not set aside.[272]

Explanation I reveals that an arbitral award being in contravention of the "fundamental policy of India law" is still a ground to hold that it is in conflict with the public policy of India, but this is clearly controlled by Explanation 2, which says that while testing an arbitral award on this ground, it shall not give a passport and it shall not entail a review of the merits of the dispute. As contravention of the "fundamental policy of Indian law" is still a part of the expression "conflict with public policy of India" occurring in Section 34, Arbitration and Conciliation Act, one can look into the elucidation qua fundamental policy of Indian law, but while testing an arbitral award that will be circumscribed by Explanation 2, which says that the test as to whether there is a contravention of the fundamental policy of Indian law shall not entail a review on merits of the dispute.[273]

---

269. *Vastu Invest & Holdings (P) Ltd.* v. *Gujarat Lease Financing Ltd.*, 2000 SCC OnLine Bom 729: (2001) 2 Mah LJ 565.
270. *Bridge Marine Ltd.* v. *Indian Oil Corpn. Ltd.*, (2021) 4 HCC (Del) 478.
271. *Union of India* v. *Moti Enterprises*, 2002 SCC OnLine Bom 806: (2003) 1 Mah LJ 930.
272. *Sulochana Modi* v. *Pawan Kumar Modi*, 2021 SCC OnLine Ori 711.
273. *Suryadev Alloys and Power (P) Ltd.* v. *East Coast Construction and Industries Ltd.*, 2020 SCC OnLine Mad 15438.

Whenever a conclusion reached in the arbitral award is patently illegal or perverse or is the result of non-application of mind to the material aspects of the case, it would be violating the fundamental policy of the Indian law, a ground available for interference under Section 34(2)(*b*)(*ii*) of the 1996 Act. The arbitrator had taken for granted that the contracted work was completed by EEI, although no evidence in this regard was adduced by the parties. The award contravened the fundamental policy of India, and was set aside.[274]

The words "Public Policy of India" refer to the public policy of the Union of India and not of one State. A plea that jurisdiction lay with the tribunal constituted under the State Act and not with the tribunal under the Central Act is not a plea raising the question of public policy of India which can be a ground to set aside the award.[275]

In a suit for specific performance of contract, the aspect of readiness and willingness was not adhered to. However, the award was passed without considering the requirement of Section 16, Specific Relief Act, 1963. The arbitral award was rightly set aside under Section 34(2)(*b*)(*ii*), Arbitration and Conciliation Act, 1996.[276]

The arbitrator had awarded compensation under the heading "Off site expenses" although not claimed by the contractor. An arbitrator has only jurisdiction to decide what is referred to him and does not have jurisdiction to decide what is not referred to him. If a claim is not made, there is no dispute with regard to that matter before the arbitrator. It cannot and does not form part of the terms of "the submission to arbitration". Therefore, if an arbitral award is made in respect of that matter, it can be considered as a decision "on matters beyond the scope of the submission to arbitration". It was held, the arbitrator transgressed his jurisdiction by deciding issues not referred to him. The award was patently illegal, and was set aside.[277]

The expression "submission to arbitration" consists of three facets, *i.e.* 1) dealing with dispute not contemplated by terms of submission to arbitration; 2) dealing with dispute not falling within terms of submission to arbitration; and 3) containing decision on matters beyond the scope of submission. There is a presumption that the Arbitral Tribunal has acted within its mandate and the onus of establishing otherwise rests on the party seeking to set aside the award on the said ground.[278]

---

274. *Raipur Alloys and Steel Ltd.* v. *Environmental Engineers Inc.*, 2017 SCC OnLine Bom 35: (2017) 2 Mah LJ 615.
275. *MSP Infrastructure Ltd.* v. *M.P. Road Development Corpn. Ltd.*, (2015) 13 SCC 713.
276. *State of Maharashtra* v. *Ram*, 2018 SCC OnLine Bom 1220: (2018) 4 Bom CR (Cri) 840.
277. *Pam Developments (P) Ltd.* v. *State of W.B.*, 2021 SCC OnLine Cal 1668.
278. *NCC Ltd.* v. *Indian Institute of Technology*, 2020 SCC OnLine Mad 5857.

An award which seeks to overreach a binding judicial decision conflicts with the fundamental public policy of India as contemplated by Section 34(2)(*b*), and be set aside.[279]

Failure of the arbitrator to decide matters in accordance with the terms of contract governing parties would attract patent illegality grounds as it amounts to gross contravention of Section 28(3). The award of the arbitrator would be set aside.[280]

Where the award was primarily based on interpretation of the terms and conditions of the contract consistently with the settled law, additional documents were seen for the limited purpose of ascertaining the practice prevailing, rather than influencing the outcome of the award. It was held that the award could not be interfered with on the ground that additional documents were wrongly taken on record.[281]

Failure of arbitrator to correctly apply law of limitation

An arbitral award can be set aside if that award is in conflict with the public policy of India. The issue, whether an arbitral award is time barred or not and hit by the law of limitation may come within the purview of the expression "public policy of India". If the decision of the Arbitral Tribunal is contrary to the law of arbitration as applicable in India, it can be said that the arbitrator while deciding the law of limitation has not correctly applied the law of limitation; the award of the arbitrator not in conformity with the public policy of India can be set aside under Section 34, Arbitration and Conciliation Act, 1996.[282]

Extraordinary delay in pronouncement of award

It cannot be laid down as an inviolable law that irrespective of the facts and circumstances of a case, if there is delay in pronouncing an award, then it should be set aside. Where a party continued to participate in the arbitration proceedings beyond a period of two years without objecting to delay beyond two years and the majority award deals with each issue, it cannot be said that the delay in pronouncement of the award rendered it patently illegal or opposed to public policy of India.[283] In written submission, the respondent did not contend that the mandate of the arbitrator had come to end as the award was passed after the period provided for in the agreement was over.

279. *Unibros* v. *All India Radio*, 2023 SCC OnLine SC 1366.
280. *State of Chhattisgarh* v. *SAL Udyog (P) Ltd.*, (2022) 2 SCC 275.
281. *Bridge Marine Ltd.* v. *Indian Oil Corpn. Ltd.*, (2021) 4 HCC (Del) 478.
282. *State of Manipur* v. *Th. Haridas Singh*, 2016 SCC OnLine Mani 11: (2021) 4 GLT 720.
283. *Oil India Ltd.* v. *Essar Oil Ltd.*, 2012 SCC OnLine Del 4279: (2012) 192 DLT 417.

It was held, the conduct of the respondent was such that it had waived the time-limit stipulated in the agreement and the objection regarding the jurisdiction of the arbitrator. The order setting aside the award was set aside.[284]

The award of the arbitrator was passed after three years of last effective hearing. Order sheet of the case showed that the arbitrator proceeded to make pronouncement without finally concluding the proceedings. The arbitrator should make/publish the award within reasonable time. The award was passed in hurry as the arbitrator had resigned and had to take new assignment. The award was contrary to the principles of fair play and natural justice, and was set aside.[285]

Delayed award goes against the very essence of the legislative policy, namely, expeditious resolution of conflict. Such an award is bad under Section 34(2)(*b*)(*ii*). A sole arbitrator was appointed on 29 September 2014. The first hearing took place on 6 April 2015 and the last on 23 December 2017, *i.e.* after more than two years. The award was rendered on 31 May 2019, *i.e.* after about one-and-a-half years. Held, so much of delay was against the policy of law. On facts, it was further found that the award overlooked several relevant aspects. Such an award was unsustainable.[286]

Extension of time for making/passing the award by arbitrator

The arbitrator cannot on its own, without consent, even within a stipulated period, extend the time for making/passing the award. In this case, the arbitration clause provided that the arbitrator should make the award within 12 months of entering into reference. The period of 12 months expired in May 2006. The arbitrator in the absence of the petitioner suo motu extended the time for passing the award. The arbitrator lost jurisdiction to pass the award, and the impugned award was set aside.[287]

Extension of time by mutual consent of parties

Where the time for passing an award is extended by the mutual consent of the parties, the award not passed within the stipulated time is not illegal.[288]

284. *Snehdeep Auto Centre* v. *Hindustan Petroleum Corpn. Ltd.*, 2012 SCC OnLine Bom 580: (2012) 6 Mah LJ 344.
285. *Harji Engg. Works (P) Ltd.* v. *BHEL*, 2008 SCC OnLine Del 1080: (2009) 107 DRJ 213.
286. *CRPF* v. *Fibroplast Marine (P) Ltd.*, (2022) 3 HCC (Del) 304.
287. *B.K. Gopakumar* v. *National Film Development Corpn. Ltd.*, 2010 SCC OnLine Bom 1474: (2010) 6 Mah LJ 807.
288. *Northern Coalfields Ltd.* v. *Saluja Construction Co.*, 2018 SCC OnLine MP 1625.

Counterclaim not decided by arbitrator

Where the counterclaim made by the respondent is not decided by the arbitrator, the award made by the arbitrator is, on the face of it, illegal and in conflict with the public policy. The award of the arbitrator was set aside.[289] Where the counterclaim was not considered, the award passed in the case was contrary to law; the award was set aside and the matter was remanded.[290] Where the arbitrator does not adjudicate upon the counterclaims, the award is illegal.[291] Where the appellant failed to produce any proof in support of the counterclaim, the arbitrator rightly rejected the counter claim made by the appellant.[292]

Where counterclaim was rejected by the arbitrator and the reason was perverse the award of the arbitrator was set aside.[293]

Arbitral Tribunal of three members—One arbitrator remained absent for the entire period

Where, for the entire period of arbitration, one member was absent, in such circumstances, the award made by the arbitrator cannot be sustained, and was set aside.[294]

In a case where validity of an award is challenged, there is no necessity of giving a narrow meaning to the term "public policy of India"; on the contrary, a wider meaning is required to be given so that the "patently" illegal award passed by the Arbitral Tribunal would be set aside.[295]

"Making of the award was induced or affected by fraud" [S. 34(2)(*b*)(*ii*) Expl. 1(*i*)]

It is well known that fraud cannot be put in a straitjacket and it has a very wide connotation in legal parlance. "Fraud in the making of the award" cannot be narrowly construed. Fraud being of "infinite variety" may take

289. *Anand Umashankar Gupta* v. *Jayant Maniklal Lunawat*, 2012 SCC OnLine Bom 1531: (2013) 1 Mah LJ 65; *Rajendra A. Shah* v. *Angel Capital and Debt Market Ltd.*, 2012 SCC OnLine Bom 1380: (2013) 1 Mah LJ 385.

290. *Rajendra A. Shah* v. *Angel Capital and Debt Market Ltd.*, 2012 SCC OnLine Bom 1380: (2013) 1 Mah LJ 385.

291. *Central Mine Planning and Designing Institute Ltd.* v. *Telekrik Electricals (Nagpur) (P) Ltd.*, 2017 SCC OnLine Chh 1592: (2017) 4 CGLJ 84.

292. *Pankaj Dyes and Chemicals Ltd.* v. *Taco Hendrickson Suspensions (P) Ltd.*, 2016 SCC OnLine Bom 2604: (2016) 5 Mah LJ 726.

293. *Union of India* v. *Pawan Construction Co. Engineers and Civil Contractors*, 2023 SCC OnLine Cal 1141.

294. *Faze Three Exports Ltd.* v. *Pankaj Trading Co.*, 2003 SCC OnLine Bom 1024: (2004) 2 Mah LJ 196.

295. *Kaushal Kishore Mishra* v. *State of U.P.*, 2017 SCC OnLine All 4299: (2018) 2 All LJ 717.

many forms, and *secondly*, the expression "the making of the award" will have to be read in conjunction with whether the award "was induced or affected by fraud". Concealment of relevant and material facts, which should have been disclosed before the arbitrator, is an act of fraud. If a narrow construction is to be placed on the above said expression, then the party who has suffered an award against another party who has concealed facts and obtained an award cannot rely on facts which have surfaced subsequently even if those facts have a bearing on the facts constituting the award. Concealed facts in every nature of things surface subsequently. Such a construction would defeat the principle of due process and would be opposed to the concept of public policy incorporated in Section 34(2)(*b*), Explanation 1.[296] Furthermore, the facts concealed must have a causative link. If the concealed facts, disclosed after the passing of the award, have a causative link with the facts constituting or inducing the award, such facts are relevant in a setting-aside proceeding and the award may be set aside as affected or induced by fraud.[297]

A contract was entered into between the parties for energy generation by Wind Farm Project. The respondent had made misleading and highly exaggerated estimate about average energy generation. The revenue generated from the sale of energy was very low. It was held the claimant was entitled to compensation from the respondent till the date of the award as the agreement was vitiated by fraud and misrepresentation.[298]

Events subsequently to making of award, which have nexus with facts constituting the award, cannot be left out of consideration.[299]

Award contrary to provisions of law, terms of contract or public policy—Patently illegal

An arbitral award contrary to the provisions of law, terms of contract or public policy would be patently illegal. In such a case, the court would interfere with the award exercising powers under Section 34 of the Act.[300] Where the award was contrary to the contract between the parties, the arbitrator had misconducted.[301] An award of an Arbitral Tribunal cannot be contrary to law and that which is not permissible cannot be granted in such proceedings or cannot be approved by the court because it was granted

296. *Venture Global Engg.* v. *Satyam Computer Services Ltd.*, (2010) 8 SCC 660.
297. *Ibid.*
298. *Vestas Wind Technology India (P) Ltd.* v. *Inox Renewables Ltd.*, 2019 SCC OnLine Bom 554.
299. *Ibid.*
300. *MSK Projects (I) (JV) Ltd.* v. *State of Rajasthan*, (2011) 10 SCC 573.
301. *MSTC Ltd.* v. *Jain Traders*, 2011 SCC OnLine Del 3304: (2011) 125 DRJ 435.

by arbitrators.[302] Where the arbitration agreement prohibited the tribunal to proceed and/or deal with claims having valuation of 20 per cent more than the contract, and the total claim was more than 20 per cent of the contract, grant of award by the Arbitral Tribunal was illegal and in breach of the agreed terms and conditions between the parties.[303]

Re-appreciation of evidence is not permissible while testing the award for patent illegality. Mere erroneous application of law cannot by itself constitute patent illegality.[304]

Tribunal has erred in law

The scope of interfering with an arbitral award is restricted. It is permissible only on the grounds as set out under Section 34, Arbitration and Conciliation Act, 1996. The view of an Arbitral Tribunal is final and binding unless it is found that the impugned award is vitiated by patent illegality or falls foul of the public policy of India. Even in those cases, where it is found that the Arbitral Tribunal has erred in law, interference with the arbitral award is not permissible unless it is found that the patent illegality goes to the root of the matter and which vitiates the award. The impugned award was not vitiated by patent illegality or in conflict with public policy of India.[305]

Decision of the umpire on issue of law contrary to the decision of the Supreme Court

Where the decision of the umpire on the issue of law was directly contrary to the decision of the Supreme Court, the interference with the award was justified.[306]

Where the question of law stands determined by an authoritative decision of a superior court, ignoring such a binding precedent may be a good ground to challenge an arbitral award.[307]

302. *Prabhubhai Jadhavji Rathod* v. *Union of India*, 2008 SCC OnLine Bom 239: (2008) 4 Mah LJ 238.
303. *Union of India* v. *Suraj Construction Co.*, 2010 SCC OnLine Bom 177: (2010) 4 Mah LJ 241.
304. *14 Reels Entertainment (P) Ltd.* v. *Eros International Media Ltd.*, 2020 SCC OnLine Mad 18730.
305. *Indian Highways Management Co. Ltd.* v. *Sowil Ltd.*, (2021) 3 HCC (Del) 615.
306. *Tata Hydro-Electric Power Supply Co. Ltd.* v. *Union of India*, 2000 SCC OnLine Bom 677.
307. *Glitter Overseas* v. *MMTC Ltd.*, (2022) 4 HCC (Del) 400.

Finding in subsequent award—Effect of

A finding in a subsequent award would not render the previous award illegal or contrary to law. The award would have to be tested as on the date when it was pronounced, on its own merits, and not on the basis of subsequent findings which may have been rendered by a later Arbitral Tribunal. In *Vijay Karia* v. *Prysmian Cavi E Sistemi SRL*[308], the Supreme Court rejected the argument that since the award under challenge is irreconcilable and inconsistent with another award, it deserved to be set aside.[309]

Subsequent events

Subsequent events need not be taken into consideration.[310]

Issues relating to specific performance—Reference to arbitration [S. 34(2)(*b*)(*i*) and (*ii*)]

The right to specific performance of an agreement for sale deals with the contractual rights and so it is open to the parties to agree to refer the issues relating to specific performance to arbitration.[311] The arbitrator can grant specific performance of a contract.[312] As the points raised in respect of the issues between the parties on merits of the award related to default, time as being of the essence, and readiness and willingness to perform, it was held they did not fell within the mischief of Section 34(2)(*b*)(*ii*), and therefore, could not be questioned thereunder also.[313]

Public policy of India

The award should not be in conflict with the public policy of India, is referable to the public policy of India as a whole, *i.e.* the policy of the Union of India and not merely the policy of individual State. Where the question arises out of a conflict between an action under a State law and an action under a Central law, the term "public policy of India" must necessarily be understood as being referable to the policy of the Union.[314] The expression "public policy" cannot mean contravention of law.[315]

---

308. (2020) 11 SCC 1.
309. *Gammon India Ltd.* v. *National Highways Authority*, 2020 SCC OnLine Del 659.
310. *Delhi Airport Metro Express (P) Ltd.* v. *DMRC*, (2022) 1 SCC 131.
311. *Olympus Superstructures (P) Ltd.* v. *Meena Vijay Khetan*, (1999) 5 SCC 651.
312. *Satinderpal Singh Anand* v. *Sharanpal Balmukund Chopra*, 2008 SCC OnLine Bom 473: (2008) 6 Mah LJ 86.
313. *Olympus Superstructures (P) Ltd.* v. *Meena Vijay Khetan*, (1999) 5 SCC 651.
314. *MSP Infrastructure Ltd.* v. *M.P. Road Development Corpn. Ltd.*, (2015) 13 SCC 713.
315. *Bfil Finance Ltd.* v. *G. Tech Stone Ltd.*, 2002 SCC OnLine Bom 734: (2002) 4 Mah LJ 434.

The expression "public policy of India" referred to in Section 34(2)(*b*)(*ii*), Arbitration and Conciliation Act, 1996 means fundamental policy of Indian law.[316]

In terms of Section 34(2)(*b*)(*ii*), Arbitration and Conciliation Act, 1996, an award of the Arbitral Tribunal can be challenged if it is in conflict with the public policy of India. By the Amendment Act, 2015, Explanation 1 was inserted and it was clarified that an award is in conflict with the public policy of India, only if 1) making of the award was induced or affected by fraud or corruption or was in violation of Section 75 or Section 81; or 2) it is in contravention with the fundamental policy of Indian law; or 3) it is in conflict with the most basic notions of morality and justice. Explanation 2 clarifies that the test as to whether there is contravention of the fundamental policy of Indian law does not entail a review on merits of the dispute.[317]

Mere illegality in the arbitration award cannot be a ground to construe that the award is against the public policy of India.[318]

The evidence did not show that the award was affected by fraud or corruption or was against public policy. The award was not interfered with, and was not set aside.[319]

The Arbitral Tribunal considered the case which was not pleaded by the party, failed to take note of SEBI Regulations which were binding on the parties, and relied on hearsay evidence. The award was clearly contrary to public policy of India, and was set aside.[320] Something which is so unconscionable so as to be contrary to fundamental notions of justice or morality may well be regarded as breach of public policy.[321]

If an arbitral award is based on what had transpired in the conciliation proceedings which ultimately failed and not on adjudication by the Arbitral Tribunal, it would be deemed to be in conflict with the public policy of India.[322]

An award ignoring the terms of the contract would not be in public interest. In the instant case, an award in respect of the lease rent and the

316. *Bridge Marine Ltd.* v. *Indian Oil Corpn. Ltd.*, (2021) 4 HCC (Del) 478.
317. *Ibid.*
318. *Nathu Ram Sahu* v. *Collector*, 2018 SCC OnLine All 6772: (2018) 5 All LJ 224.
319. *NHAI* v. *Ashish Panwar*, 2017 SCC OnLine Utt 1934.
320. *Bharat M. Nagori* v. *Satish Ashok Sabnis*, 2003 SCC OnLine Bom 348: (2003) 4 Mah LJ 259.
321. *Municipal Corpn. of Greater Mumbai* v. *Jyoti Construction Co.*, 2002 SCC OnLine Bom 1067: (2003) 4 Mah LJ 25.
322. *NHAI* v. *Oriental Structural Engineers (P) Ltd.*, 2015 SCC OnLine Del 6524: (2015) 217 DLT 678.

lease term in discard of the terms and conditions of the lease agreement was held against the public policy.[323]

Insufficiency of evidence, if any, cannot nullify the award.[324]

An arbitral award cannot be set aside on the ground that it is erroneous. In order to interfere with an arbitral award, the court has to conclude that the award is vitiated by patent illegality on the face of the award. The tribunal allowed the respondent's claim and merely because the price as claimed by the respondent was higher than what according to the petitioner was payable, it does not render the award contrary to public policy of India. The petitioner cannot fault the impugned award by contending that inclusion of customs duty in the price is contrary to the public policy of Indian law.[325]

Not contrary to public policy of India [S. 34(2)(*b*)]

A dispute arose from allegations of granting a high number of fake LPG connections. No material was produced by the petitioner to refute the allegations. The award of the arbitrator rejecting the petitioner's claim and upholding the imposition of penalty was not contrary to public policy of India. The award was upheld.[326]

Time-barred claim allowed

The Arbitral Tribunal allowed a time-barred claim. Such an award is in conflict with the public policy of India, and liable to be set aside.[327]

Central as well as State law

"Public policy of India" refers to laws in force in India, *i.e.* both Central as well as State law.[328]

The court does not possess power to condone the delay in filing objections beyond 120 days from the date on which the award was delivered to the objectors; it is essential that the delivery/service of the award must be meticulously and properly effected. In the case of a company, a copy of the award must be served to the Secretary or Director or principal officer or delivered at the registered office.[329]

---

323. *Indian Oil Corpn. Ltd.* v. *Shree Ganesh Petroleum*, (2022) 4 SCC 463.
324. *Sarkar Enterprise* v. *Garden Reach Shipbuilders and Engineers Ltd.*, 2001 SCC OnLine Cal 256: (2002) 2 RAJ 252.
325. *BSNL* v. *Vindhya Telelinks (P) Ltd.*, (2021) 4 HCC (Del) 547.
326. *Ibid.*
327. *CMC Ltd.* v. *Unit Trust of India*, 2015 SCC OnLine Bom 318.
328. *Lion Engg. Consultants* v. *State of M.P.*, (2018) 16 SCC 758.
329. *National Projects Constructions Corpn. Ltd.* v. *Bundela Bandhu Constructions Co.*, 2007 SCC OnLine Del 574: ILR (2007) 2 Del 59.

Public policy of India—Compliance with statutes, judicial precedents

Violation of Indian statutes, *i.e.* the award which is on the face of it patently in violation of the statutory provisions cannot be said to be in public interest. Such award/judgment/decision is likely to adversely affect the administration of justice and would be regarded as being contrary to the fundamental policy of Indian law.[330]

Binding effect of the judgments of a superior court when disregarded would be equally violative of the fundamental policy of India.[331]

The relevant date for filing proceeding under Section 34 of the Act is when the arbitrator delivers the award.[332]

Public policy—Justice

The expression "justice" when it comes to setting aside awards under the public policy ground can only mean that an award shocks the conscience of the court. It cannot possibly include what the court thinks is unjust on the facts of the case for which it then seeks to substitute its view for the arbitrator's view and does what it considers to be "justice".[333]

Award against public policy has to be set aside

There may be allegations of corruption against the arbitrator or he may have conducted the proceedings arbitrarily or unfairly. He may not have given a party an adequate opportunity of presenting his case. He may have been biased in favour of one party. The evidence proposed to be adduced by a party may have been shut out or while considering the evidence, the arbitrator considered some evidence and ignored the material part or he may have acted on no evidence or ignored the terms of the contract. He may have adjudicated on a subject-matter not referred to him or not capable of being decided by him. In all these cases, the award is liable to be set aside. In cases where the basic foundation on which the Indian legal system is built is disregarded or jurisprudence of the country has been ignored, awards could be said to be against public policy and liable to be set aside.[334]

---

330. *Associate Builders* v. *DDA*, (2015) 3 SCC 49.
331. *Ibid.*
332. *Vitthalrao Shinde Sahakari Sakhar Karkhana Ltd.* v. *Gangapur Sahakari Sakhar Karkhana Ltd.*, 2017 SCC OnLine Bom 1669: (2017) 5 Mah LJ 390.
333. *Ibid*; *Sutlej Construction Ltd.* v. *State (UT of Chandigarh)*, (2018) 1 SCC 718.
334. *S.B.I.W. Steels (P) Ltd.* v. *SAIL*, 2022 SCC OnLine Cal 3842.

"Fundamental Policy of Indian Law" [Sub-s. (2), Cl. (*ii*), Expl. I]

An arbitral award may be set aside by the court only if the court finds the arbitral award is in conflict with the public policy of India. Explanation I clarifies that an arbitral award is in conflict with the public policy of India when it is in contravention of the fundamental policy of Indian law.[335]

The fundamental policy of Indian law includes all such fundamental principles as providing a basis for administration of justice and enforcement of law in the country. The requirement that adjudicatory authority must apply its mind can be described as a fundamental policy of Indian law. Arbitrators committed error resulting in miscarriage of justice. They also failed to appreciate and draw logical inference from proven facts. The arbitral award was interfered with.[336]

Entertainment of time-barred claims

Where the arbitrator has allowed time-barred claims, the award is in conflict with the public policy and in contravention of the fundamental policy of India, and would be set aside.[337]

The question of limitation is a mixed question of law and fact. The arbitrator found that the claim was not barred by limitation. The finding was not erroneous, and the award was not set aside.[338]

Death of one of the arbitrators—Award null and void, set aside

The award was passed by only two arbitrators after the death of the third arbitrator. The Arbitral Tribunal became functus officio after the death of the third arbitrator; the award passed was null and void, and liable to be set aside.[339]

Procedure under the Arbitration Act not followed

A sole arbitrator was appointed by family members to resolve the dispute between the parties. He was requested to follow the procedure laid down by the Arbitration Act. The arbitrator decided the claim on the basis of documents filed by the parties without statement of claims, replies, counter-claim, supporting documents and oral evidence. The arbitrator did not follow the procedure laid down by the Arbitration Act, which was not proper. The award was set aside.[340]

---

335. *Associate Builders* v. *DDA*, (2015) 3 SCC 49.
336. *ONGC* v. *Western Geco International Ltd.*, (2014) 9 SCC 263.
337. *K.M. Suresh Babu* v. *Sundaram Finance Ltd.*, 2020 SCC OnLine Mad 27501.
338. *DLF Home Developers Ltd.* v. *Mahanthi Rangarajan*, 2019 SCC OnLine Mad 26403.
339. *S.A. Fasludeen* v. *Siyauddin*, 2017 SCC OnLine Mad 11917: (2018) 1 LW 233.
340. *Nitin Harjivandas Rajyagor* v. *Rajesh Pravinchand Rajyagor*, 2016 SCC OnLine Bom 5316: (2016) 6 Mah LJ 634.

Award passed by sole retired arbitrator

In the arbitration clause involved in the case there was no provision that the arbitrator will not be entitled to proceed further upon the cessation of his office. Moreover, the appellant-objector throughout participated in the proceedings even after the retirement of the sole arbitrator from his office. The arbitrator was also appointed by his name, as such there was no question of his discontinuing with the arbitration proceedings even after cessation of office. The award passed by the arbitrator was not invalid.[341]

Officer of the department was appointed as sole arbitrator in view of the arbitration clause. His mandate to continue arbitration proceedings would not come to end on his retirement. He continues to be the sole arbitrator till arbitration proceedings are concluded unless he incurs disqualification under the Arbitration Act.[342]

Award passed by a designated arbitrator and not by named arbitrator

By the agreement between the parties, the Managing Director of the appellant-Corporation was appointed as arbitrator, who delegated his authority to one RK, a retired officer. The award given by the designated arbitrator and not named arbitrator is without jurisdiction and non-est in the eye of law. The right to object was not waived.[343]

"If the court finds that the award is vitiated by patent illegality appearing on the face of the record" [S. 34(2-A)]

Sub-section (2-A) is newly inserted by the Amendment Act 3 of 2016. As laid down by sub-section (2-A) in case of arbitrations other than international commercial arbitrations, an Arbitral award may also be set aside if the award is vitiated by patent illegality appearing on the face of record.

The proviso to sub-section (2-A) lays down that the award shall not be set aside merely on the ground of

1. an erroneous application of law; or
2. by re-appreciation of evidence.

The plea of patent illegality shall be tested without going into the realm of erroneous application of law or re-appreciation of evidence. Where on the

341. *Fertilizer Corporation of India* v. *Balaji Laminating Works*, 2019 SCC OnLine Jhar 611.
342. *Laxmi Continental Construction Co.* v. *State of U.P.*, (2021) 13 SCC 142.
343. *M.P. State Agro Industries Development Corpn. Ltd.* v. *Suresh Gupta*, 2015 SCC OnLine MP 2836: (2015) 2 MP LJ 702.

appreciation of oral and documentary evidence the Arbitral Tribunal held that out of seven heads of deductions made by the trust, two heads were untenable and not valid and five heads of deductions were upheld, this by itself showed the appreciation of evidence. There was no scope for re-appreciation of evidence. The award of the arbitrator did not suffer from patent illegality and was proper.[344]

The award can be said to be suffering from "patent illegality" only if it is an illegality apparent on the face of the award. The High Court had travelled beyond its jurisdiction under Section 37 and rather than remaining within the confines of consideration under Section 34, entered into an arena which was exclusively within the domain of the Arbitral Tribunal.[345]

The scope of examination under Section 34(2-A), Arbitration and Conciliation Act, 1996 is limited. The court is not supposed to revaluate and re-appreciate the evidence and supplant its opinion over that of the Arbitral Tribunal. Unless the decision is found to be patently illegal, no interference with the arbitral award is called for. Even an erroneous view does not vitiate the arbitral award unless the error is manifest and one that strikes at the root of the matter. An Arbitral Tribunal is a final adjudicator of the evidence and its conclusion cannot be interfered with except where it is found to be patently illegal or in conflict with the public policy of India. The courts do not interfere merely because an alternative view on facts exists. A possible view by the arbitrator on facts has necessarily to pass muster as the arbitrator is the ultimate master of the quantity and quality of evidence to be relied upon when he delivers his arbitral award.[346]

The ground of patent illegality is available for setting aside domestic award.[347]

The domestic awards can be challenged on the ground of patent illegality only if it is one which appears on the face of the award, and is such which goes to the root of the matter. Mere erroneous application of the law, or appreciation of evidence, does not call for interference of the award on the ground of patent illegality. The court cannot set aside the award by re-appreciating the evidence, which is taken into consideration by the Arbitral Tribunal.[348]

The new clause specifically uses the expression "arbitrations other than international commercial arbitrations". It implies that patent illegality is a

344. *Qualtech Engineers (P) Ltd.* v. *Ommayal Achi*, 2021 SCC OnLine Mad 16564.
345. *Reliance Infrastructure Ltd.* v. *State of Goa*, (2024) 1 SCC 479.
346. *Delhi State Industrial & Infrastructure Development Corpn. Ltd.* v. *Well Protect Manpower Services (P) Ltd.*, (2022) 2 HCC (Del) 118.
347. *Patel Engg. Ltd.* v. *North Eastern Electric Power Corpn. Ltd.*, (2020) 7 SCC 167.
348. *Oriental Insurance Co. Ltd.* v. *Diamond Product Ltd.*, (2021) 3 HCC (Del) 281.

ground not available in international commercial arbitration. Such arbitration award has to be considered on the touchstone of Section 43(2)(*b*)(*ii*), *i.e.* public policy of India as clarified through two explanations incorporated *vide* the 2015 Amendment.[349]

An award passed contrary to the provisions of law or the provisions of the Arbitration and Conciliation Act, 1996 or against the terms of the contract would be patently illegal and would be subject to interference under Section 34(2)(*a*)(*v*).[350]

Where the Arbitral Tribunal's finding allows a party to take advantage of its own wrong, it would be a case of patent illegality.[351]

The omission in the arbitral award to record a finding on the contentious issue of interest is a patent illegality.[352]

Patent illegality [S. 34(2-A)]

The ground of patent illegality is a ground available under the statute for setting aside a domestic award if the decision of the arbitrator is found to be perverse or so irrational that no reasonable person would have arrived at the same, or the construction of the contract is such that no fair or reasonable person would take, or that the view of the arbitrator is not even a possible view. The present case arose from a domestic award between two Indian entities. The award of the arbitrator was perverse and irrational and was rightly set aside.[353]

A decision which is perverse, though would not be a ground for challenge under "public policy of India", would certainly amount to a patent illegality appearing on the face of the award. However, a finding based on no evidence at all or an award which ignores vital evidence in arriving at its decision would be perverse and liable to be set aside on the ground of patent illegality.[354]

Rewriting a contract for parties would be a breach of fundamental principles of justice. Arbitral awards substituting "royalty payment module" for "revenue sharing module" come within the realm of patent illegality. Setting aside the arbitral award was proper.[355]

---

349. *Bridge Marine Ltd.* v. *Indian Oil Corpn. Ltd.*, (2021) 4 HCC (Del) 478.
350. *ONGC Ltd.* v. *Saw Pipes Ltd.*, (2003) 5 SCC 705; *State of Chhattisgarh* v. *SAL Udyog (P) Ltd.*, (2022) 2 SCC 275.
351. *GMR Pochanpalli Expressways Ltd.* v. *NHAI*, (2022) 2 HCC (Del) 612.
352. *Canara Bank* v. *State Trading Corpn. of India Ltd.*, (2022) 5 HCC (Del) 638 (DB).
353. *Patel Engg. Ltd.* v. *North Eastern Electric Power Corpn. Ltd.*, (2020) 7 SCC 167.
354. *PSA SICAL Terminals (P) Ltd.* v. *V.O. Chidambranar Port Trust*, 2021 SCC OnLine SC 508.
355. *Ibid.*

The respondent-contractor entered into a contract with the appellant-ONGC for supply of pipes of specified description by the specified date. Terms of the contract entitled the ONGC to recover damages at the stipulated rate for the delay, if any, in the supply of goods and further stated the same to be agreed and genuine pre-estimate of damages and not as penalty. The terms of the contract further authorised the ONGC to deduct the amount of damages from the contractor's bill. Moreover, the terms specifically stated that no interest would be paid on the disputed claims. At a subsequent stage at the contractor's request, the ONGC extended the time for the supply of the goods subject to the condition that ONGC would recover the agreed stipulated damages. ONGC deducted the amount of damages. The contractor disputed such deduction before the Arbitral Tribunal. The Arbitral Tribunal held the deduction to be wrongful on the ground that the ONGC had failed to establish that it had suffered any monetary loss and directed the same to be refunded with costs. Held, such award was in violation of the provisions of Section 28(2) and (3) and totally unjustified. Further, held that in respect of situations where it was impossible to assess or prove damages, the specified terms of the contract itself had made a provision in consonance with the provisions of Sections 73 and 74, Contract Act. The award directing the ONGC to refund the deducted amount was set aside.[356]

The award of loss of profit and loss of reputation and goodwill was without any basis and inconsistent with the findings of the Arbitral Tribunal. This was patent illegality, and the award was set aside.[357]

Principles of natural justice

The appellant in spite of due service of notice about arbitration proceedings deliberately did not participate in arbitration proceedings before the arbitrator though served with claim as well as supporting documents. The award of the arbitrator was not against provisions of law and/or even against settled principles of natural justice. The award of the arbitrator was not set aside.[358] The appellants did not file any written settlement nor appeared before the arbitrator. In the absence of a written statement, monetary claims made by the respondent were deemed to have been admitted. The award passed by the arbitrator was not set aside.[359] First

356. *ONGC Ltd.* v. *Saw Pipes Ltd.*, (2003) 5 SCC 705.

357. *ITDC Ltd.* v. *Bougainvillea Multipex & Entertainment Centre (P) Ltd.*, (2022) 2 HCC (Del) 127.

358. *Shree Sati Travels (P) Ltd.* v. *Amadeus India (P) Ltd.*, 2016 SCC OnLine Bom 2641: (2016) 3 Mah LJ 412; *State of Maharashtra* v. *Ram*, 2018 SCC OnLine Bom 1220: (2018) 4 Bom CR (Cri) 840.

359. *Birla International (P) Ltd.* v. *Karvy Financial Services Ltd.*, 2016 SCC OnLine Bom 27: (2016) 3 Mah LJ 819.

notice was issued to the petitioners but they had not chosen to appear or to file the counter. Second notice sent by registered post was returned with an endorsement "addressee has gone out for an indefinite period". It was held, the principles of natural justice were observed and Section 34(2)(*a*)(*ii*) was not violated.[360]

Where the parties had not waived right of hearing in respect of their claim, the arbitrator is required to give hearing and opportunity to the parties. In spite of the request by the petitioner, the arbitrator did not give opportunity to lead evidence. It was held that the award passed was in breach of the principles of natural justice, and was set aside.[361] Where one of the parties requests for oral hearing, it is the duty of the arbitrator to conduct the same.[362]

Affidavit evidence was considered by the arbitrator without effecting its service on the other side. The arbitrator could not have proceeded with the matter without effecting service of notice of hearing on the other side. The arbitrator has to give sufficient advance notice of the hearing or meeting of the Arbitral Tribunal to both the parties. The award was vitiated being violative of the principles of natural justice, and was set aside.[363]

Principles of natural justice are violated when a party is unable to present its case but when the party fails to avail of the opportunity available, it cannot later complain of the violation of its right to present its case.[364]

Opportunity of hearing

An award was passed by the arbitrator without giving an opportunity of hearing to the landowner. The award was violative of the principles of natural justice and was set aside.[365] Parties were not given notice of the commencement of arbitration proceedings. The award was passed in the case without giving any opportunity to lead evidence to both parties. The award was set aside, and the matter was remanded for fresh consideration.[366]

360. *Harish Chand Gupta* v. *Ashok Leyland Finance (a Division of IndusInd Bank Ltd.)*, 2009 SCC OnLine Mad 1676: (2010) 3 CTC 133.
361. *Milaan C. Jhaveri* v. *Venture Securities Ltd.*, 2013 SCC OnLine Bom 595: (2013) 4 Mah LJ 450.
362. *ADV Consultant* v. *Pioneer Equity Trade (India) (P) Ltd.*, 2009 SCC OnLine Mad 1072: (2009) 4 LW 573.
363. *Rajnikant B. Vora* v. *Fincruise Credit Services (P) Ltd.*, 2015 SCC OnLine Bom 4179: (2015) 6 Mah LJ 515.
364. *Bridge Marine Ltd.* v. *Indian Oil Corpn. Ltd.*, (2021) 4 HCC (Del) 478.
365. *Hisar Water Services Division* v. *Manish Kumar*, 2019 SCC OnLine P&H 8044.
366. *DSC Ltd.* v. *MSEFC, M.P.*, 2021 SCC OnLine MP 6081.

Principles of equity

The arbitrator, by invoking the principles of equity, directed the insurer to pay a discretionary amount of 20 per cent towards customs duty. Unless parties have agreed, the award cannot be on the basis of equitable principles. Such award is against substantial law of India and it is nothing but perversity. The award passed by the arbitrator in respect of customs duty was set aside.[367]

Personal hearing denial of—Award set aside

In the arbitration proceedings, the petitioner sought permission and requested for personal hearing. The arbitrator, however, rejected the said application and proceeded with the matter without giving personal hearing to the petitioner. It was held, the procedure adopted was against the principles of natural justice; the award of the arbitrator was against the principles of natural justice, and was set aside.[368]

Ex parte hearing [S. 34(2)(*a*)(*iii*)]

Arbitral records indicated that the arbitrator has sent notice to parties. Notice dated 11 March 2017 duly served on 24 March 2017 through registered post. Though there was delay in dispatch of notices by the Arbitral Tribunal and parties received notice very close to the date of hearing, the petitioners did not make any effort even to write to the arbitrator seeking for adjournment/rescheduling. The petitioners did not do anything till ex parte arbitral award was ultimately served. Grounds for judicial intervention under Section 34 were not made out. The award was not set aside.[369]

Award of interest by arbitrator

Where an arbitrator assigns reasons for awarding a particular rate of interest and the same is not unwarranted, no interference is required.[370] Rate of interest is normally decided on the appraisal of the circumstances of a given case. The arbitrator awarded interest at the rate of 12 per cent per annum on the amount spent by the contractor on the purchase of cement bags from the open market, held proper.[371]

---

367. *United Insurance Co. Ltd.* v. *Continental Warehousing Corpn. (Nhava Seva) Ltd.*, 2021 SCC OnLine Mad 16588.
368. *Rajesh Tiwari* v. *Motilal Oswal Financial Services Ltd.*, 2013 SCC OnLine Bom 2: (2013) 3 Mah LJ 523.
369. *Ekaa Engineers and Infrastructure (P) Ltd.* v. *Daimler Financial Services India (P) Ltd.*, 2019 SCC OnLine Mad 39351.
370. *Mekala Traders* v. *T.N. Civil Supplies Corpn. Ltd.*, 2010 SCC OnLine Mad 3486: (2010) 4 CTC 611.
371. *State of Goa* v. *Manohar D. Harmalkar*, 2007 SCC OnLine Bom 272: (2007) 6 Mah LJ 103.

Interest allowed by the arbitrator till the date of award was held proper.[372]

Award was made in accordance with Swiss law. Capitalisation of interest according to Swiss law was upheld. The award was not opposed to public policy of India.[373]

Six months period was fixed in the agreement as "observation period" so that the department could see whether the work was done satisfactorily or not. The said clause could not be construed as total prohibition on the award of interest but operated for a limited period of six months from the date of completion of the work.[374]

The time taken for discussion between the parties could not be to the advantage of the respondent or a disadvantage to the petitioner. It did not absolve the respondent to pay interest which the Arbitral Tribunal held was payable under the agreement.[375]

Compound interest

The Arbitral Tribunal could not have awarded any compound interest. The Arbitral Tribunal had awarded 12 per cent simple interest. However, it further held that if the amount is not paid within the period of 30 days of the award, interest shall be compounded at the rate of 12 per cent till the date of realisation. No such claim for compound interest was made by the respondent. The award for compound interest on failure on the part of the petitioner to pay the awarded amount is start. It was not sustainable.[376]

Ex facie illegal, perverse award

An award passed without due consideration of evidence or has been arrived at by excluding relevant material or by taking in to account some irrelevant material is perverse and liable to be set aside.[377]

Normally, the courts are very slow in interfering with the finding and interpretation given by the arbitrator. However, the courts are not powerless to interfere with award(s) which are ex facie illegal or perverse award(s). The arbitrator gave overriding effect to the terms and conditions of tender

---

372. *Fertilizer Corporation of India* v. *Balaji Laminating Works*, 2019 SCC OnLine Jhar 611.
373. *JK Industries Ltd.* v. *DS Stratagem Trade A.G.*, 2012 SCC OnLine Del 141: (2012) 129 DRJ 210.
374. *T.N. Small Industries Development Corpn. Ltd.* v. *Sathya Constructions*, 2007 SCC OnLine Mad 974: (2008) 2 LW 1115.
375. *KMC Construction Ltd.* v. *NHAI*, (2021) 4 HCC (Del) 464.
376. *Aneja Constructions (India) Ltd.* v. *Grim-Tech Projects (I) (P) Ltd.*, (2022) 1 HCC (Del) 523.
377. *Ibid.*

rather than the terms contained in the subsequent supply order placed by the appellant corporation and accepted by the respondent-corporation. The appellant-corporation was also entitled to MODVAT credit, the subject-matter of dispute under the law denied by the arbitrator. The award of the arbitrator was found not sustainable, and was set aside.[378]

When the finding of fact recorded by the arbitrator is not perverse, it cannot be interfered with by court under Section 34 of the Act.[379]

An award would be perverse or illegal when no reasonable man would have arrived at such a finding, findings are not based on evidence, or the Arbitral Tribunal has taken into account irrelevant considerations, or has ignored vital evidence in arriving at its decision.[380]

Delayed payment

There is no illegality in granting award of interest to the contractor on delayed payment.[381]

Subject-matter of dispute is not capable of settlement by arbitration

It is not necessary for the party making the application to furnish proof that the subject-matter of the dispute is capable of settlement by parties. Even if the court itself finds that the subject-matter of the dispute is not capable of settlement by arbitration, the award may be set aside.[382]

Where a litigant approaches a wrong court on a bona fide mistake, the pronouncements of Section 14, Limitation Act, 1963 would apply.[383]

Interest of India [S. 34(2)(*b*)(*ii*)]

The "interest of India" must be considered taking India as a member of the world community in its relations with foreign powers.[384]

---

378. *ONGC Ltd.* v. *Saw Pipes Ltd.*, (2003) 5 SCC 705.
379. *ONGC Ltd.* v. *International Certification Services (P) Ltd.*, 2016 SCC OnLine Bom 3966: (2016) 4 Mah LJ 727; *Kamal Constructions* v. *Union of India*, 2016 SCC OnLine Bom 5315: (2016) 5 Mah LJ 161; *Anjana Singh* v. *Metropolis Healthcare Ltd.*, 2016 SCC OnLine Bom 5320: (2016) 5 Mah LJ 185.
380. *Associate Builders* v. *DDA*, (2015) 3 SCC 49; *Mitesh Mehta* v. *Saregama India Ltd.*, 2021 SCC OnLine Cal 453; *Union of India* v. *Recon*, 2020 SCC OnLine Bom 2278: (2020) 6 Mah LJ 509.
381. *Union of India* v. *Pradeep Vinod Construction Co.*, (2021) 20 SCC 650.
382. *Veena* v. *Seth Industries Ltd.*, 2010 SCC OnLine Bom 1707: (2011) 2 Mah LJ 226.
383. *SAIL* v. *Indian Cements Ltd.*, 2012 SCC OnLine Cal 9467: (2013) 1 CHN 194.
384. *Associate Builders* v. *DDA*, (2015) 3 SCC 49.

Merits of arbitral award

None of the grounds contained in Section 34(2), Arbitration and Conciliation Act, 1996 deals with the merits of the decision rendered by an arbitral award. It is only when the award is in conflict with the public policy of India as prescribed in Section 34(2)(*b*)(*ii*), Arbitration and Conciliation Act, 1996 that the merits of an arbitral award are to be looked into under certain specified circumstances.[385]

Explanation 2 to Section 34(2)(*b*) substituted by Act 3 of 2016 clarifies that the test as to whether there is contravention of the fundamental policy of Indian law shall not entail a review on the merits of the dispute.[386]

Award based on appreciation of documentary and oral evidence

The award of the arbitrator based on appreciation of documentary and oral evidence cannot be interfered with under Section 34 of the Act.[387]

Insufficiency of evidence

Insufficiency of evidence cannot be a ground for interference by the court. Re-examination of the facts to find out whether a different decision can be arrived at is impermissible.[388]

Pleadings not supported by affidavit—Award set aside

The dispute was about a custom milling agreement. The arbitrator went beyond the terms and conditions and concluded that time was the essence of the contract, and held that the mill was entitled even to expenses not specifically mentioned in the terms and conditions. The arbitrator accepted the pleadings not supported by an affidavit. The award was set aside.[389]

Arbitral award based on little evidence/no evidence

A possible view by the arbitrator on facts has necessarily to pass muster as the arbitrator is the ultimate master of the quantity and quality of evidence to be relied upon when he delivers his arbitral award. An award based on little evidence or on evidence which does not measure up in quality to a trained legal mind would not be held to be invalid on this score.[390]

---

385. *Ibid.*
386. *Ibid.*
387. *Ibid*
388. *M.P. Power Generation Co. Ltd.* v. *ANSALDO Energia SpA*, (2018) 16 SCC 661.
389. *Kalwanoo Rice Mills* v. *Punjab Warehousing Corpn. Ltd.*, 2023 SCC OnLine P&H 6693.
390. *Parsa Kente Collieries Ltd.* v. *Rajasthan Rajya Vidyut Utpadan Nigam Ltd.*, (2019) 7 SCC 236.

Claim contrary to evidence—Award set aside

In the relevant year, the quantity of coal lifted by the respondent was found to be much above the fixed quantity. Claim was found to be contrary to evidence on record, and therefore, was rightly set aside by the High Court.[391]

Well-reasoned award

Where the award made by the arbitrator is well-reasoned and within the framework of law and record, the court under Section 34 would not like to interfere by appreciating and/or re-assessing the evidence and material placed on record.[392]

Section 34 has a different methodology and it cannot be considered as a typical appellate jurisdiction. The award, being supported by reasons, does not call for any interference. The court is not permitted to independently evaluate the merits of the award, but must confine its authority to the parameters permitted under the statute.[393]

"Application for setting aside may not be made after three months" [Sub-s. (3)]—Limitation period

An application for setting aside an award may not be made after three months have elapsed from the date:

1. on which the party making that application had received the arbitral award; or
2. where a request had been made under Section 33, from the date on which that request had been disposed of by the Arbitral Tribunal.

However, if the court is satisfied that the applicant was prevented by *sufficient cause* from making the application within the said period of three months, the court may entertain the application within a further period of 30 days, but not thereafter. Thus, only a period of 30 days can be condoned by the court on being satisfied of the sufficient cause. The court has no jurisdiction to condone the delay after the expiry of 3 months and 30 days.[394] The court has no power to condone the delay beyond 30 days and that too unless sufficient cause is shown. The petitions were not filed within three

391. *Ibid.*
392. *Sahyadri Earthmovers* v. *L and T Finance Ltd.*, 2012 SCC OnLine Bom 1861: (2013) 2 Mah LJ 302.
393. *BHEL* v. *Zillion Infraprojects (P) Ltd.*, (2023) 1 HCC (Del) 635.
394. *Vastu Invest & Holdings (P) Ltd.* v. *Gujarat Lease Financing Ltd.*, 2000 SCC OnLine Bom 729: (2001) 2 Mah LJ 565; *Pushpa P. Mulchandani* v. *Admiral Radhakrishin Tahilani (Retd.)*, 2000 SCC OnLine Bom 620: (2000) 4 Mah LJ 819.

months from the date of getting the copy of the award, and were barred by limitation prescribed under Section 34(3).[395]

Once an arbitral award sought to be challenged is put through request under Section 33 for correction of award, then limitation as provided in Section 34(3) will apply and the limitation will commence from the date of disposal of application under Section 33. Where an application under Section 34(1) for setting aside the award of the arbitrator is filed beyond the period of 3 months and 30 days prescribed under Section 34(3), the delay cannot be considered. In the present case, an application under Section 33 for correction of the award dated 3 March 2017 came to be decided on 28 July 2017. Thereafter, an application for condonation of delay was filed on 2 December 2017, *i.e.* beyond the period of 3 months and 30 days, the court did not have power to consider the delay, and the delay was not condoned.[396] Section 34(3) makes an exception to the rule only in case of an application being carried out for correction of an error of computation or clerical or typographical error or error of a similar nature.[397]

The additional award was not passed to correct the typographical errors, and it is a case where the arbitrator has, in fact, changed the findings of the award on an application moved under Section 33, Arbitration and Conciliation Act, 1996. The limitation commences from the date of passing of the additional award.[398]

By virtue of Section 43 of the 1996 Act, the Limitation Act, 1963 applies to the 1996 Act, but by virtue of sub-section (2) of Section 29, Limitation Act, if any other period has been prescribed under the special enactment for moving the application or otherwise, then that period of limitation will govern the proceedings under that Act and not the provisions of the Limitation Act. Under the 1996 Act, for setting aside an award on any of the grounds mentioned in sub-section (2) of Section 34, the period of limitation has been prescribed. Period of condonation of delay, *i.e.* 30 days has been provided in the proviso to the section.[399]

An application under Section 34 for setting aside the award of the arbitrator has to be filed within 90 days from the date on which the copy

395. *P.C.V. Traders* v. *Kapol Coop. Bank Ltd.*, 2012 SCC OnLine Bom 1627: (2013) 1 Mah LJ 364; *Mahindra & Mahindra Financial Services Ltd.* v. *Maheshbhai Tinabhai Rathod*, (2022) 4 SCC 162.

396. *National Authority of India* v. *Ram Niranjan*, 2021 SCC OnLine All 1095: (2021) 4 All LJ 124.

397. *State of W.B.* v. *B.B.J. Construction Co. Ltd.*, 2012 SCC OnLine Cal 12918: (2013) 1 Cal LT 607.

398. *DDA* v. *Ajab Singh & Co.*, (2022) 5 HCC (Del) 48.

399. *State of Goa* v. *Western Builders*, (2006) 6 SCC 239.

of the award was received by the party and not from the date on which the award was stamped.[400]

The relevant date for filing proceeding under Section 34 of the Act is when the arbitrator delivers the award.[401]

Limitation for application under Section 34 for setting aside the award starts running from the date when a signed copy of the award is made available to the parties. A certified copy of the award can be treated as a signed copy of the award.[402]

The petitioners were served with a copy of award in the year 2012, and they lodged a petition under Section 34 on 22 April 2014. The petition filed beyond three months from the date of service of the impugned award was ex facie barred by limitation and was dismissed.[403] No objection could be filed after the expiry of a four-month period.[404]

An award was delivered by the arbitrator on 15 July 1997. Notice by the court to the party was sent on 4 October 1997. The application for setting aside the award was filed on 1 November 1997, *i.e.* well within 30 days from the date of service of notice upon the party. The application for setting aside the award was not barred by limitation.[405] An application under Section 33 submitted by the respondent for correction of computational error in the award before the arbitrator was rejected on 4 July 2009. The limitation for filing an application under Section 34 would commence on 4 July 2009; the application under Section 34 for setting aside the award filed on 22 September 2009 was within 90 days from the date of disposal of the petition under Section 33 and was well within the limitation period.[406] The relevant date for the purpose of application for setting aside the award of the arbitrator is the date of the receipt of the arbitral award by the party and not the date on which the application under Section 33 has been dismissed as barred by limitation.[407]

---

400. *D.M. Jawahar Merican* v. *Engineer India Ltd.*, 2008 SCC OnLine Del 980: (2008) 153 DLT 642.
401. *Vitthalrao Shinde Sahakari Sakhar Karkhana Ltd.* v. *Gangapur Sahakari Sakhar Karkhana Ltd.*, 2017 SCC OnLine Bom 1669: (2017) 5 Mah LJ 390.
402. *Dayashankar* v. *LAO*, 2019 SCC OnLine Chh 451.
403. *Francisco A. D'souza* v. *L and T Finance Ltd.*, 2015 SCC OnLine Bom 6864: (2015) 5 Mah LJ 390; *Vitthalrao Shinde Sahakari Sakhar Karkhana Ltd.* v. *Gangapur Sahakari Sakhar Karkhana Ltd.*, 2017 SCC OnLine Bom 1669: (2017) 5 Mah LJ 390.
404. *Union of India* v. *Radha Krishna Seth*, 2005 SCC OnLine All 840: (2006) 63 ALR 92.
405. *U.P. State Sugar Corpn.* v. *Lal and Kumar Humayunpur*, 2014 SCC OnLine All 16104: (2015) 2 All LJ 384.
406. *M.P. SEB* v. *Rama Steels Tubes Ltd.*, 2011 SCC OnLine MP 260: (2011) 2 MP LJ 678.
407. *Union of India* v. *Todarmull Infrastructures (P) Ltd.*, 2019 SCC OnLine Chh 169: (2020) 3 CGLJ 21.

Section 34(3) merely talks of receipt of the "arbitral award" and the expression "arbitral award" does not necessarily mean the stamp embossed on stamped paper. Merely because the application styled as one under Section 33 was filed, it would not entitle the objector to extension of limitation under Section 34(3) till the disposal of such an application if such an application was not a request for correction of computational error, clerical or typographical error.[408]

If the application under Section 33 had been filed within time, the appellant would have been entitled to exclusion of time taken in pursuing the said application. In the instant case as the application under Section 33 was barred by time, the appellant was not entitled to the advantage of Section 34(3), and the objection under Section 34 was dismissed as time barred.[409]

Condonation of delay where application under Section 33 filed

Once an arbitral award sought to be challenged is put through request under Section 33, in that case the limitation as provided in Section 34(3) will apply and the limitation would commence from the date of the disposal of the application under Section 33. In the instant case, the application under Section 34(1) for setting aside the award was filed beyond the period of 3 months and 30 days prescribed under Section 34(3), and the delay could not be condoned.[410]

Bar of limitation [S. 34(3)]

When a special statute provides the period of limitation with the outer cap, it impliedly and necessarily excludes the operation of Sections 4 to 28 of the Limitation Act. The application for condonation of delay beyond the outer cap provided in the proviso to sub-section (3) of Section 34 of the Act is impliedly excluded and the application under Section 34 of the Act is not maintainable.[411]

Limitation period—Interim award—When time begins to run

The interim award passed in the case clearly and unambiguously showed that it was final in respect of the claims adjudicated therein. In such a case

408. *D.M. Jawahar Merican* v. *Engineer India Ltd.*, 2008 SCC OnLine Del 980: (2008) 153 DLT 642.

409. *Union of India* v. *Saboo Minerals (P) Ltd.*, 2003 SCC OnLine Del 618: (2003) 71 DRJ 166.

410. *National Authority of India* v. *Ram Niranjan*, 2021 SCC OnLine All 1095: (2021) 4 All LJ 124.

411. *Executive Engineer* v. *Manickam Enterprises*, 2021 SCC OnLine Cal 4318.

the date from which time would begin to run for challenging the award in respect of such claims would be the date on which the interim award was passed. A later clarificatory award by the arbitrator passed on clarification being sought in this regard stated that the "interim award" was final when the same was evident from the interim award itself, would not provide a fresh cause of action to challenge the award so as to permit the counting of time from the date of the clarificatory award.[412]

"Party making that application had received the arbitral award" [Sub-s. (3)]

The expression "party making that application had received the arbitral award" cannot be read in isolation and it must be understood in light of what is said earlier in Section 31(5) that requires a signed copy of the award to be delivered to each party. Reading the two provisions together, it is quite clear that the limitation prescribed under Section 34(3) would commence only from the date a signed copy of the award is delivered to the party making the application for setting it aside.[413] In *Union of India* v. *Tecco Trichy Engineers & Contractors*[414], the Supreme Court held as under:

> The delivery of an arbitral award under sub-section (5) of Section 31 is not a matter of mere formality. It is a matter of substance. It is only after the stage under Section 31 has passed that the stage of termination of arbitral proceedings within the meaning of Section 32 of the Act arises. The delivery of arbitral award to the party, to be effective, has to be 'received' by the party. This delivery by the Arbitral Tribunal and receipt by the party of the award sets in motion several periods of limitation such as an application for correction and interpretation of an award within 30 days under Section 33(1), an application for making an additional award under Section 33(4) and an application for making an additional award under Section 33(4) and and an application for setting aside an award under Section 34(3) and so on. As this delivery of the copy of award has the effect of conferring certain rights on the party as also bringing to an end the right to exercise those rights on expiry of the prescribed period of limitation which would be calculated from that date, the delivery of the copy of award by the Tribunal and the receipt thereof by each party constitutes an important stage in the arbitral proceedings.

The period of limitation prescribed under Section 34(3) of the Act would start running only from the date a signed copy of the award is delivered to be received by the party making the application for setting it aside under Section 34(1) of the Act. If the law prescribes that a copy of the order/award

412. *State of Arunachal Pradesh* v. *Damani Construction Co.*, (2007) 10 SCC 742.
413. *State of Maharashtra* v. *ARK Builders (P) Ltd.*, (2011) 4 SCC 616; *Union of India* v. *Tecco Trichy Engineers & Contractors*, (2005) 4 SCC 239; *Prem Lata Tewari* v. *Sushil Kumar*, 2017 SCC OnLine All 4472: (2017) 5 All LJ 29.
414. (2005) 4 SCC 239.

is to be communicated, delivered, dispatched, forwarded, rendered or sent to the parties concerned in a particular way and in case the law also sets a period of limitation for challenging the order/award in question by the aggrieved party, then the period of limitation can only commence from the date on which the order/award was received by the party concerned in the manner prescribed by the law. The limitation period for setting aside an arbitral award is to be reckoned not from the date the copy of the award is received by the objector from any other source but from the date the copy of the award duly signed by the arbitrator is delivered to/received by the objector.[415]

Party in Section 34(3) in the context of the State or a department of a large government organisation like Railways means the departmental head concerned who is directly connected with and is in control of the arbitral proceedings and not the GM. A copy of the award has to be received by the departmental head. Where the Chief Engineer of the Southern Railways had on behalf of the Union of India represented the Union of India in the arbitral proceedings and notices were served on him during the arbitral proceedings, the date of service of the copy of award on him, instead of on GM, by way of receipt in his inward office would be the starting point of limitation. On the facts and circumstances of the case, a delay of 27 days in filing an application under Section 34 filed by the Chief Engineer of the Railways was condoned.[416]

The limitation for a petition under Section 34 for setting aside an award would not commence from the date when a signed copy of the award is served on the advocate representing the party but from the date of its service on the party as contemplated under Section 31(5).[417] The date of dispatch of arbitral award engrossed on stamp paper is not of any relevance for the purposes of limitation under Section 34(3), Arbitration Act.[418]

Even though the award was pronounced on 27 April 2018, a signed copy of the award was provided to the parties only on 19 May 2018. On 27 April 2018 only a copy of the award was provided to the parties to point out any computation error, any clerical or typographical error which may have occurred in the award on the next date. It was held, the period of limitation for filing objections would have to be reckoned from the date on which a signed copy of the award was made available to the parties, *i.e.* 19 May 2018.

---

415. *State of Maharashtra* v. *ARK Builders (P) Ltd.*, (2011) 4 SCC 616; *Union of India* v. *Tecco Trichy Engineers & Contractors*, (2005) 4 SCC 239.
416. *Union of India* v. *Tecco Trichy Engineers & Contractors*, (2005) 4 SCC 239.
417. *Jolly Bros. (P) Ltd.* v. *Surendra Nath Jolly*, 2016 SCC OnLine Bom 3973: (2016) 5 Mah LJ 250.
418. *D.M. Jawhar Merican* v. *Engineers India Ltd.*, 2009 SCC OnLine Del 578: ILR (2009) 4 Del 571.

Admittedly, objections were filed within the period of limitation prescribed by Section 34(3) of the Act, reckoned from 19 May 2018. The order of the District Judge dismissing the objections filed under Section 34 as time barred was set aside, and the objections were restored.[419]

The limitation for setting aside awards begins to run from the date the signed copy of the award is delivered to the party filing application under Section 34. In the instant case, the copy of the award was duly served and received by one member of the family of the petitioner. Other members of the petitioner's family could not contend the non-service of the copy of the award. An application under Section 34 filed eight years after the receipt of the copy of the award was found barred by limitation and as such was dismissed.[420]

Section 34(3) provides a limitation of three months from the date of the award. No objection was raised by the applicant as to the receipt of the award. An application under Section 34 filed after two years from the date of the award was barred by limitation.[421]

The limitation for application for setting aside an award commences from the date of receipt of the signed copy of the award. Rejection of the application filed under Section 34 by the District Judge without deciding the question whether the applicant had received the copy of the award or not was erroneous, and the order of rejection was set aside.[422] The time-limit as set out in Section 34(3) starts where the award is amended from the date when the award was amended and copy served.[423]

The limitation under Section 34(3) of the Act runs from the date when a party receives the copy of the award. Where the trial court has condoned the delay without recording finding as to when the respondent had received the copy of the award, the order of the trial court condoning delay suffered from non-application of mind, and was set aside.[424]

The limitation for setting aside awards starts running from the date on which the party making the application received a copy of the award.[425] In the instant case, the award was pronounced in the presence of the parties and the copy thereof was given to both of them on 29 March 2000 itself by

---

419. *Dakshin Haryana Bijli Vitran Nigam Ltd.* v. *Navigant Technologies (P) Ltd.*, (2021) 7 SCC 657.
420. *Anilkumar Jinabhai Patel* v. *Pravinchandra Jinabhai Patel*, (2018) 15 SCC 178.
421. *Kapiruddin Mondal* v. *Magma Fincorp Ltd.*, 2018 SCC OnLine Cal 153.
422. *Siya Ram Nag* v. *Magma Fincorp Ltd.*, 2018 SCC OnLine Chh 1046.
423. *HMP Engineers Ltd.* v. *Rallis India Ltd.*, 2003 SCC OnLine Bom 203: (2003) 3 Mah LJ 853.
424. *Prakash Acharya* v. *Sairabanu*, 2018 SCC OnLine Kar 3919.
425. *Executive Engineer* v. *Satya Prakash & Bros. (P) Ltd.*, 2017 SCC OnLine All 4572: (2017) 4 All LJ 695 (DB).

the arbitrator, and the award in fact was given effect to when two cheques were handed over by the judgment-debtor to the respondent. There remained nothing to be done further and the limitation commenced from that date itself. A petition under Section 34 for setting aside the award filed in 2005 was barred by time. The order of the District Judge dismissing the petition as time barred was upheld.[426]

As the signed copy of the award was not delivered by the Arbitral Tribunal to the appellant, the limitation for filing an application under Section 34(3) for challenging the award did not commence. Merely because a copy of the award was subsequently delivered by the respondents to the appellants would not commence the period of limitation.[427]

The limitation starts running from the date of receipt of a signed copy of the award from the Arbitral Tribunal by the applicant party. The said copy need not necessarily be signed in original by the arbitrator/majority of arbitrators. Authentic photocopy along with signatures would suffice.[428]

Copies of award were served on a person who was not a party to arbitration. In the absence of service of a copy of award on proper party, it cannot be said that limitation had started running. An application even if filed beyond the period of 3 months and 30 days is not barred by limitation.[429]

Delivery of the arbitral award under Section 31(5) must be on the party to the arbitration agreement who is in control of the proceedings before the arbitrator; delivery to any other person including the counsel appearing for the parties to arbitration does not satisfy compliance of the provisions of Section 31(5) of the Act. In the absence of any other material on record, the date claimed by the petitioner of the receipt of award by him will have to be accepted as the correct date. The petition filed under Section 34 would be within the period of limitation prescribed under Section 34(3) of the Act.[430]

An application under Section 34 for setting aside the award of the arbitrator has to be filed within the time prescribed under Section 34(3). The time to file such an application commences from the date of such party receiving a copy of the arbitral award from the arbitrator.[431] The limitation period of three months has to be counted from the date of delivery of "signed copy" of the award to the applicant.[432] If a signed copy of the award is not

---

426. *Prem Lata Tewari* v. *Sushil Kumar*, 2017 SCC OnLine All 4472: (2017) 5 All LJ 29.
427. *E-Square Leisure (P) Ltd.* v. *K.K. Dani Consultants and Engineers (P) Ltd.*, 2013 SCC OnLine Bom 183: (2013) 3 Mah LJ 24.
428. *State of W.B.* v. *Motilal Agarwala*, 2016 SCC OnLine Cal 482: (2016) 4 Civ LT 132.
429. *Ibid.*
430. *Gaurang* v. *Vinay A. Choksi*, 2014 SCC OnLine Bom 1139: (2014) 6 Mah LJ 570.
431. *Mukesh Nanji Gala* v. *Heritage Enterprises*, 2014 SCC OnLine Bom 1817: (2015) 5 Mah LJ 620.
432. *Ramesh Pratap Singh* v. *Vimala Singh*, 2003 SCC OnLine MP 587: (2004) 2 MP LJ 135.

received, the question of expiry of time-limit for setting aside the award does not arise.[433]

The endorsement "not claimed" on the registered envelope through which award was sent tantamount to good service, and the award was held served on the petitioner by registered post.[434]

The period of limitation for filing objections for setting aside arbitral award commences after signing of award. In the present case, the signed copy of the arbitral award was supplied to the Assistant Executive Engineer. The appellant could not feign ignorance regarding passing of award. The prescribed period of three months expired before the court was closed for winter vacations, and the appellant was not entitled to the benefit of extended period of limitation. The delay in filing objection for setting aside the arbitral award was not condoned.[435]

Application under Section 34(1) filed beyond limitation period

Section 34(1) itself provides that recourse to a court against an arbitral award may be made only by an application for setting aside such award "in accordance with" sub-section (2) and sub-section (3). But an application filed beyond the period mentioned in Section 34, sub-section (3) would not be an application "in accordance with" that sub-section. Consequently, by virtue of Section 34(1), recourse to the court against an arbitral award cannot be made beyond the period prescribed.[436]

The notice dated 10 December 1996 of the award was received by the postal clerk in the office of the Superintending Engineer, Irrigation from the process-server of the court. The State had knowledge of the award dated 10 December 1996 on 10 December 1996, and the limitation period started on 10 December 1996. The period of limitation under Section 14(2), Arbitration Act, 1940 expired on 9 January 1997. The application for setting aside the award filed on 29 January 1997 was barred by limitation.[437]

The arbitral award was passed in the year 2009, and respondents were in possession of the award in the year 2012 when the suit for cancellation of the award was filed. The respondents had full knowledge and consequences

433. *Assam State Weaving & Mfg. Co. Ltd.* v. *Vinny Engg. Enterprises (P) Ltd.*, 2009 SCC OnLine Cal 2464: (2010) 1 CHN 363.
434. *New Globe Transport Corpn.* v. *Magma Shrachi Finance Ltd.*, 2011 SCC OnLine Cal 425: (2011) 2 CHN 287.
435. *H.P. Electricity Board Ltd.* v. *Shyam Indus Power Solution (P) Ltd.*, 2021 SCC OnLine HP 8534.
436. *Union of India* v. *Popular Construction Co.*, (2001) 8 SCC 470; *Executive Engineer* v. *Satya Prakash & Bros. (P) Ltd.*, 2017 SCC OnLine All 4572: (2017) 4 All LJ 695 (DB).
437. *State of U.P.* v. *Coromandal Engg. Co. Ltd.*, 2013 SCC OnLine All 13622: (2013) 3 All LJ 746.

of the award which was passed in the year 2009. The application under Section 34, Arbitration Act was rejected as time barred.[438]

Condonation of delay (proviso)

The proviso to Section 34(3) provides that if the court is satisfied that the applicant was prevented by sufficient cause from making the application within the limitation period of three months, it may entertain the application within a further period of 30 days but not thereafter. The question whether the time for making an application for setting aside an award can be extended will have to be decided as and when an application for that purpose is made.[439]

Section 5, Limitation Act, 1963 is not applicable to petitions under Section 34 of the Act. Hence, the court can condone delay under the proviso to Section 34(3) up to a maximum period of 30 days on showing sufficient cause.[440] The applicability of Section 5, Limitation Act in the matter of making an application under Section 34, Arbitration and Conciliation Act, is expressly excluded.[441] A delay beyond 3 months and 30 days in filing an application under Section 34 for setting aside the award of the arbitrator cannot be condoned.[442] Discretion of the court to condone delay cannot be exercised beyond the period of 30 days.[443] The competent authority has no jurisdiction to condone delay caused by an applicant in making an application beyond a maximum period of four months.[444] The court has no discretion to condone delay beyond 3 months plus 30 days.[445] The limitation period prescribed for making an application for setting aside an arbitral award is 3 months and not 3 months plus 30 days. Where an arbitration

---

438. *Narendra Kumar* v. *State of M.P.*, 2021 SCC OnLine MP 6080.

439. *Delhi Transport Corpn. Ltd.* v. *Rose Advertising*, (2003) 6 SCC 36; *State of Maharashtra* v. *Ramdas Construction Co.*, (2021) 4 SCC 629.

440. *State of H.P.* v. *Himachal Techno Engineers*, (2010) 12 SCC 210.

441. *Darbari Industries* v. *President of India*, 2008 SCC OnLine Cal 781; *State of W.B.* v. *Afcons Infrastructure Ltd.*, 2007 SCC OnLine Cal 566: (2008) 2 CHN 68; *S.K. Dey and Bros.* v. *Union of India*, 1999 SCC OnLine Cal 610: (1999) 1 ICC 1; *Union of India* v. *Nav Bharat Construction*, 2001 SCC OnLine Cal 531: (2002) 1 CHN 226; *Hindustan Construction Co.* v. *North Eastern Electrical Power Corpn. Ltd.*, 2004 SCC OnLine Gau 71: (2005) 1 Gau LR 102.

442. *Haryana State Coop. L&C Federation Ltd.* v. *Unique Coop. L&C Coop. Society Ltd.*, (2018) 14 SCC 248; *Bageshwari Sahakari Sakhar Karkhana Ltd.* v. *Shivajirao*, 2004 SCC OnLine Bom 158: (2004) 4 Mah LJ 28.

443. *Esteem Mercantile (P) Ltd.* v. *K.H. Parekh*, 2001 SCC OnLine Bom 419: (2002) 2 Mah LJ 216.

444. *Mahindra and Mahindra Financial Services Ltd.* v. *Manik Vitthal Kawle*, 2014 SCC OnLine Bom 4652: (2015) 4 Mah LJ 844.

445. *Union of India* v. *Mukherjee & Mukherjee (P) Ltd.*, 2006 SCC OnLine Cal 541; *Union of India* v. *Wishwa Mittar Bajaj & Sons*, 2007 SCC OnLine Del 363: (2007) 141 DLT 179.

petition is filed beyond a period of three months and not within the period of three months, the court cannot condone the delay of more than 30 days, even if sufficient cause is shown by the applicant. The petition filed under Section 34 is liable to be dismissed.[446] There was no scope for extending the time and/or condoning the delay of 108 days, thereby allowing the petitioner to question the award passed by the sole arbitrator.[447]

The expression "three months" in Section 34(3) has to be construed as three calendar months from the date on which the signed award by the arbitrator was delivered to the party.[448]

Where objections under Section 34 of the Act are filed beyond the period of 30 days after the expiry of three months of receiving the arbitral award, the District Judge has no power to condone delay of more than 30 days, and the application under Section 34 for setting aside the award would thus be time barred. Rejection of the application under Section 34 as time barred was proper.[449] In the present case, the appellant after availing five remedies to assail the award before different forums filed an application under Section 34 for setting aside the award of the arbitrator with a delay of five years and eight months. Held, it was a case of abuse of the process of court, and hence, the delay condonation application was dismissed with an exemplary costs ₹5 lakhs.[450] A delay of 5½ months cannot be condoned.[451] The reason assigned for the delay was that the wife of one of the petitioners was unwell. There were six petitioners who could have pursued the petition in time. The delay was not condoned, and the petition under Section 34 was dismissed as time barred.[452]

The proviso attached to Section 34(3) empowers the court to condone the delay of 30 days beyond the stipulated period. The term "month" is not defined under the Act. The date on which the award was received has to be excluded. Three months expired on 16 October 2003. Objections were filed

---

446. *Tirumala Roadways* v. *Indian Oil Corpn. Ltd.*, 2016 SCC OnLine Bom 3974: (2016) 5 Mah LJ 679; *Rafik* v. *Magma Leasing Ltd.*, 2009 SCC OnLine Cal 2372: (2010) 1 CHN 143.
447. *Union of India* v. *Shree Durga Iron Stores*, 2011 SCC OnLine Cal 498: (2011) 2 CHN 78.
448. *Union of India* v. *Wishwa Mittar Bajaj & Sons*, 2007 SCC OnLine Del 363: (2007) 141 DLT 179.
449. *Krishi Utpadan Mandi Samiti* v. *U.P. Industrial Facilitation Council*, 2011 SCC OnLine All 409: (2011) 5 All LJ 50.
450. *Haryana State Coop. L&C Federation Ltd.* v. *Unique Coop. L&C Coop. Society Ltd.*, (2018) 14 SCC 248.
451. *Executive Engineer* v. *Satya Prakash & Bros. (P) Ltd.*, 2017 SCC OnLine All 4572: (2017) 4 All LJ 695 (DB).
452. *Maruppiah Mahalingam* v. *Kotak Mahindra Bank Ltd.*, 2017 SCC OnLine Bom 3953: (2017) 5 Mah LJ 333.

on 15 November 2003; the objections were delayed by 30 days, and were found within condonable limits.[453]

There was delay in filing petition under Section 34. The petition was filed after a delay of 164 days of the receipt of the award under Section 34(3); the court is empowered to condone delay of 30 days. The delay was not condoned. The petition under Section 34 was dismissed as time barred.[454]

An application under Section 34 of the 1996 Act can be filed within three months from the date when the aggrieved party has received the arbitration award. As per the proviso to Section 34 of the 1996 Act, such application can be entertained if the same is filed within a further period of 30 days if the court is satisfied that the applicant was prevented by sufficient cause from making the application within the prescribed period of three months. In the present case, the first application for setting aside the award was filed after seven months from the date of passing of award and that too before the wrong forum. Thereafter, the applicant took nearly three months to file a second application. No application for condonation of delay either under Section 34(3) of the 1996 Act or Section 14, Limitation Act, 1963 was filed. Both applications were filed clearly beyond the prescribed period of limitation. The application was rightly dismissed as time barred.[455]

In the language of Section 34 of the 1996 Act, the crucial words are "but not thereafter" used in the proviso to sub-section (3). This phrase would amount to an express exclusion within the meaning of Section 29(2), Limitation Act, and would, therefore, bar the application of Section 5 of that Act. An application filed beyond the period mentioned in Section 34, sub-section (3) would not be an application "in accordance with" that sub-section. The time-limit prescribed under Section 34 is absolute and cannot be extended. Section 5, Limitation Act does not apply.[456] The bar imposed by the proviso to sub-section (3) of Section 34 cannot be removed by invoking recourse to Article 227 of the Constitution of India.[457]

An objection under Section 34(3), Arbitration and Conciliation Act, 1996 was filed after the expiry of 137 days, *i.e.* opening of the court after winter vacation. Grace period of 30 days over and above the period of three months as prescribed under Section 34(3) of the Act already had lapsed. The delay in filing application for setting aside the arbitral award was not condoned.[458]

---

453. *MCD* v. *G.D. Builders*, 2005 SCC OnLine Del 340: (2005) 81 DRJ 310.
454. *Union of India* v. *K.P. Chandradasan*, 2018 SCC OnLine Mad 14050.
455. *Punjab State Civil Supplies Corpn. Ltd.* v. *Raman Rice Mills*, 2020 SCC OnLine P&H 5168: PLR (2020) 199 P&H 538.
456. *Union of India* v. *Popular Construction Co.*, (2001) 8 SCC 470.
457. *North Eastern Electrical Power Corpn. Ltd.* v. *Hindustan Const. Co.*, 2004 SCC OnLine Gau 293: (2005) 1 Gau LR 95.
458. *State of H.P.* v. *Sanjay Chauhan*, 2021 SCC OnLine HP 9284.

"Sufficient cause" [Sub-s. (3) (proviso)]

Where the time consumed in prosecution of the proceedings under Section 34 was due to prosecution of the application in the wrong forum, the delay in filing application under Section 34 of the Act was condoned.[459] The time during which the applicant was prosecuting matters bona fide and with due diligence before wrong court may be excluded.[460] In *Consolidated Engg. Enterprises* v. *Irrigation Deptt.*[461], record of the case indicated that the applicant had honest doubt about the court competent to entertain the application for setting aside the award made by the arbitrator. The applicant believed bona fide that the court in which it had instituted proceedings had jurisdiction in the matter. It was held, the applicant can be said to have prosecuted matters in other courts with due diligence and in good faith, and was entitled to claim exclusion of time under Section 14, Limitation Act.

Delivery of signed copy of award to each party is *sine qua non* to run the period of limitation. The arbitrator gave a copy of the award to the defendant which allegedly was dispatched to the plaintiff. There was no material on the record to show that a copy of the award was delivered to the plaintiff. The delay of 30 days in filing an application under Section 34 for setting aside the award of the arbitrator was condoned.[462]

Adequate details were given how the delay of 23 days occurred against a permissible period of 30 days. The delay was inter alia due to misunderstanding of territorial jurisdiction and panel counsel's fault. Held, it was a bona fide delay which deserved to be condoned. The appellate court condoned the delay.[463]

Where delay occurred due to departmental/official process on account of functioning of local body, and no unfair advantage occurred to the petitioner, the delay in filing Section 34 application was condoned.[464]

The explanation given by the appellant that he was not in the country and on his return, he was quarantined and thereafter, a nationwide lockdown was imposed, sufficiently explains the delay for not filing the objections within the prescribed period of three months. The objections filed under Section 34, Arbitration and Conciliation Act were held to be within time in terms of the proviso to Section 34(3), Arbitration and Conciliation Act, 1996.[465]

---

459. *National Aluminium Co. Ltd.* v. *Pressteel & Fabrications (P) Ltd.*, (2004) 1 SCC 540.
460. *Coal India Ltd.* v. *Ujjal Transport Agency*, (2011) 1 SCC 117.
461. (2008) 7 SCC 169.
462. *Parsvnath Developers Ltd.* v. *Wisecan Engg. (P) Ltd.*, 2021 SCC OnLine P&H 4608.
463. *DDA* v. *Ajab Singh & Co.*, (2022) 5 HCC (Del) 48.
464. *MCD* v. *G.D. Builders*, 2005 SCC OnLine Del 340: (2005) 81 DRJ 310.
465. *Sharma & Associates* v. *NDMC*, (2022) 3 HCC (Del) 207.

A copy of the award was sent to the correct address and to a competent person. The appellant cannot be allowed to take benefit of inter-departmental delay in putting up the matter before the Director. Limitation would not commence from the date, the matter was put up before the Director; the delay was not condoned.[466]

The petitioner filed an application under Section 34(2) for setting aside the award of the arbitrator alleging that the authorities did not communicate the award to him and only on his application did the District Collector communicate the award to him and as such the petition was being filed within three months of the date of communication of the order. The court dismissed the petition at the threshold without directing the same to be numbered. It was held, rejection of the application was unjust and not proper. The impugned order of rejection was set aside, and the matter was remanded for decision afresh.[467]

Copy of documents not given, delay condoned

Where the delay of 25 days occurred as MSME Facilitation Council had not given certified copies of entire papers and proceedings including Roznama, the delay was condoned.[468]

Period during which court closed

As 30 days' period extendable by the court is not the prescribed period of limitation, Section 4, Limitation Act, 1963 is not applicable. Hence, the benefit of exclusion of the period during which the court is closed is not available.[469] As per Section 34(3), the limitation period is of three months with further extension of 30 days if the applicant is prevented by sufficient cause from making an application. The said mandate of law is imperative and admits no exception. In the facts of the case, the period of three months as prescribed under sub-section (3) of Section 34, Arbitration and Conciliation Act expired on 4 October 2022. Even the period of 30 days for which the applicant could have been permitted by virtue of the proviso expired on 4 November 2022. Admittedly, during this period no application was filed

466. *Deptt. of Food, Civil Supplies and Consumer Affairs* v. *Virgo Softech Ltd.*, 2019 SCC OnLine P&H 5630.

467. *M. Santhiramudu* v. *Competent Authority*, 2020 SCC OnLine AP 1759: (2021) 1 ALD 668.

468. *Forefront (P) Ltd.* v. *S.D. Infra and MEP Services (P) Ltd.*, 2023 SCC OnLine Bom 2882.

469. *Assam Urban Water Supply & Sewerage Board* v. *Subash Projects & Mktg. Ltd.*, (2012) 2 SCC 624; *Assam Urban Water Supply and Sewerage Board* v. *Subhash Project and Mktg. Ltd.*, 2005 SCC OnLine Gau 3: (2005) 3 Gau LR 439.

seeking extension of time. In these circumstances, the prayer made in the application could not be allowed.[470]

The period of 90 days prescribed under Section 34(3) for filing an application for setting aside the arbitral award had expired on 24 November 2016. An extended period of 30 days was granted from 23 November 2016 to 24 December 2016. However, courts were closed due to winter vacation during the period from 19 December 2016 to 1 January 2017. Immediately on reopening of the court, *i.e.* after the lapse of extended period, the application for setting aside the arbitral award was filed. The benefit of exclusion of the period during which the court was closed is available only when the application for setting aside the award is filed within the "prescribed period of limitation", and it is not available in respect of the period extended by the court in exercise of its discretion. The delay was not condoned.[471]

The court is not bound to award compensation when no legal injury has resulted. A party claiming liquidated damages is required to prove loss suffered by it.[472]

Benefit of exclusion of period of court vacations

The prescribed period for limitation under Section 34 is 90 days and 30 days are extended period which can be condoned by the court after three months. However, the benefit of exclusion of the period of vacation/holidays of court would not be available where three months have expired prior to closure of court and 30 days expired during closure of court.[473]

"Three months" [Sub-s. (3), proviso]

A "month" does not refer to a period of 30 days, but refers to the actual period of a calendar month. The legislature did not intend that the period of three months used in Section 34(3) be equated to 90 days, nor intended that the period of 30 days in the proviso be taken as one month.[474] Sub-section (3) uses the words "three months" while prescribing the period of limitation and the proviso uses the words "thirty days" while referring to the outside limit of condonable delay. The legislature had the choice of describing periods of time in the same units, that is to describe the periods as "three months" and

470. *H.P. Tourism Development Board* v. *AKS Engineer and Contractors Co.*, 2023 SCC OnLine HP 1824.
471. *Bhimashankar Sahakari Sakkare Karkhane Niyamita* v. *Walchandnagar Industries Ltd.*, (2023) 8 SCC 453.
472. *Haryana Telecom Ltd.* v. *Union of India*, 2006 SCC OnLine Del 575: (2006) 90 DRJ 211.
473. *State of H.P.* v. *Sanjay Chauhan*, 2021 SCC OnLine HP 9283.
474. *State of H.P.* v. *Himachal Techno Engineers*, (2010) 12 SCC 210.

"one month" respectively or by describing the periods as "ninety days" and "thirty days" respectively, but it did not do so. In the instant case, the award was received by the Executive Engineer on 12 November 2007. For the purpose of calculating the three months' period, the said date shall have to be excluded having regard to Section 12(1), Limitation Act, 1963 and Section 9, General Clauses Act, 1897. Consequently, the three months should be calculated from 13 November 2007 and expire on 12 February 2008. Thirty days from 12 February 2008 under the proviso should be calculated from 13 February 2008 and, having regard to the number of days in February, would expire on 13 March 2008. Therefore, the petition filed on 11 March 2008 was well in time and was not barred by limitation.[475]

In *Coal India Ltd.* v. *Ujjal Transport Agency*[476], the award was passed on 2 February 2009, and the appeal before the wrong forum was filed on 6 May 2009 and was withdrawn on 30 October 2009. The petition under Section 34 was filed on 19 October 2009. Appellants were under the impression that proceedings under Section 34 were in the nature of appeal against the award, but realising their mistake immediately on re-opening of court, without waiting for a formal order of withdrawal of appeal under Section 34 before the wrong forum, filed an application under Section 34 on 19 October 2009 itself, which demonstrated their diligence and bona fides. It was held, appellants were entitled to exclusion of time from 6 May 2009 to 30 October 2009 (or till 19 October 2009 when they filed the application before proper forum) which was within the period of limitation, even without the benefit of extension of time under the proviso to Section 34(3).

Delay condoned on the basis of the order of 10 January 2022 passed by the Supreme Court in *Suo Motu Writ Petition No. 3 of 2020*[477]. As per the decision of the Supreme Court passed in the writ petition, the period between 15 March 2020 and 28 February 2022 will not be included while computing the limitation period. As the award of the arbitrator was published on 18 June 2021, it was covered by the order of the Supreme Court. The period of three months for filing a challenge under Section 34 of the Act would only start running from 1 March 2022 in accordance with the order of the Supreme Court. The same will end on 31 May 2022. The application to challenge the award of the arbitrator was filed by the award-debtor on 30 June 2022, *i.e.* after a lapse of 30 days. The proviso to Section 34(3) bestows the High Court with power to condone delay of up to 30 days beyond the statutory mandated limit of three months. The delay was condoned.[478]

---

475. *Ibid.*
476. (2011) 1 SCC 117.
477. *Cognizance for Extension of Limitation, re*, (2022) 3 SCC 117.
478. *Union of India* v. *PREMCO-GPT JV.*, 2023 SCC OnLine Cal 6511.

Delay of six months in filing application

There was a delay of six months in filing an application under Section 34. Report of the Ministerial Officer of the court showing the application within time is not final. The application was rejected as time barred.[479]

Application for setting aside arbitral award—Sections 3 and 5, Limitation Act not applicable

Section 34(3) of the 1996 Act excludes the applicability of Section 5, Limitation Act, 1963.[480] Section 5, Limitation Act, 1963 has no application to an application challenging an arbitral award under Section 34 of the 1996 Act.[481]

In view of Section 34(3) of the 1996 Act, a delay beyond 3 months and 30 days in filing an application under Section 34 of the 1996 Act for setting aside an award cannot be condoned under Section 5, Limitation Act, 1963.[482]

Sections 5 and 3, Limitation Act are not applicable to the application under Section 34, Arbitration and Conciliation Act, 1996.[483] Section 34, Arbitration and Conciliation Act, 1996 expressly excludes the application of Section 5, Limitation Act, 1963.[484] On the lapse of specified prescribed period, the court cannot exercise the power of condonation of delay even on having sufficient cause as specified in Section 5, Limitation Act.[485]

The application under Section 34, Arbitration and Conciliation Act, 1996 for setting aside the arbitral award is governed by Section 34, Arbitration and Conciliation Act, 1996; hence, the Limitation Act, 1963 is not applicable. The delay in filing the application cannot be condoned by applying Section 5 of the Limitation Act. The application filed after the period prescribed in the Arbitration Act is barred by limitation.[486]

---

479. *Ibid.*
480. *State of U.P.* v. *Coromandal Engg. Co. Ltd.*, 2013 SCC OnLine All 13622: (2013) 3 All LJ 746; *U.P. Instruments Ltd.* v. *Delhi Jal Board*, 2008 SCC OnLine Del 102: ILR (2008) 2 Del 361.
481. *Simplex Infrastructure Ltd.* v. *Union of India*, (2019) 2 SCC 455; *Union of India* v. *Popular Construction Co.*, (2001) 8 SCC 470. The time-limit prescribed under Section 34 to challenge an award is absolute and unextendible by the court under Section 5, Limitation Act.
482. *Ibid.*
483. *State of Goa* v. *Western Builders*, (2006) 6 SCC 239; *Union of India* v. *Radha Krishna Seth*, 2005 SCC OnLine All 840: (2006) 63 ALR 92; *Turnkey Constructions (P) Ltd.* v. *V.R. Bijur*, 2001 SCC OnLine Kar 330: ILR 2001 Kar 4666; *Mahindra & Mahindra Financial Services Ltd.* v. *Maheshbhai Tinabhai Rathod*, (2022) 4 SCC 162.
484. *Turnkey Constructions (P) Ltd.* v. *V.R. Bijur*, 2001 SCC OnLine Kar 330: ILR 2001 Kar 4666.
485. *Union of India* v. *Naveen Kumar Contractors and Suppliers*, 2012 SCC OnLine MP 10971: (2013) 1 MP LJ 487.
486. *State of U.P.* v. *Harnam Singh*, 2015 SCC OnLine All 9062: (2015) 111 ALR 16.

The appellant had mentioned that Directors of the appellant were engaged in the marriage of their daughter and were busy in completing formalities for sending their daughter to the US after marriage. As sufficient cause was shown, the delay of 19 days in filing the petition under Section 34 was condoned.[487]

Application for setting aside arbitral award—Section 14, Limitation Act applicable

Section 14, Limitation Act, is applicable to the application under Section 34, Arbitration and Conciliation Act, 1996 for setting aside arbitral award.[488] Section 14, Limitation Act would apply to proceedings under Section 34(2), Arbitration and Conciliation Act, 1996. The time spent in presenting application under Section 34(2) before the court having no jurisdiction would be excluded while computing the period of limitation for filing application under Section 34(2) before a competent court.[489] The time spent in prosecuting a remedy before a wrong forum bona fide is liable to be excluded.[490]

Section 14, Limitation Act, 1963 is not excluded while considering claims under Section 34, Arbitration and Conciliation Act, 1996.[491]

Section 14, Limitation Act, 1963 applies to Section 34(3) of the 1996 Act.[492] The benefit of Section 14 cannot be given to a party which has filed a proceeding before a wrong forum beyond limitation.[493] The period when the matter was pending before the wrong forum shall be excluded in computing the limitation period.[494] Section 14, Limitation Act covers civil proceedings before the arbitrator who had no jurisdiction to enter upon reference for resolution of dispute between the parties. The period spent in prosecuting petition before the Jharkhand High Court was excluded for counting the

487. *S.R. Themocole (EPS) Packaging (P) Ltd.* v. *Bajaj Allianz General Insurance Co. Ltd.*, 2015 SCC OnLine Bom 4891: (2015) 5 Mah LJ 417.
488. *State of Goa* v. *Western Builders*, (2006) 6 SCC 239; *Union of India* v. *Shring Construction Co. (P) Ltd.*, (2006) 8 SCC 18; *United India Insurance Co. Ltd.* v. *J.A. Infra Structure (P) Ltd.*, (2006) 8 SCC 21; *Union of India* v. *Bhavna Engg. Co.*, (2008) 13 SCC 546; *Gulbarga University* v. *Mallikarjun S. Kodagali*, (2008) 13 SCC 539.
489. *Dayashankar* v. *LAO*, 2019 SCC OnLine Chh 451; *Meerut Development Authority* v. *Chaddha Construction Co.*, 1998 SCC OnLine All 502: (1999) 37 ALR 318; *Defence Estate Officer* v. *Damodhar*, 2013 SCC OnLine Bom 1079: (2013) 6 Mah LJ 404.
490. *M.P. Housing Board* v. *Mohanlal and Co.*, 2013 SCC OnLine MP 6215: (2014) 1 MP LJ 121; *PWD* v. *Er. Sundharam Contractor*, 2010 SCC OnLine Mad 2667: (2010) 3 CTC 360.
491. *HMP Engineers Ltd.* v. *Rallis India Ltd.*, 2003 SCC OnLine Bom 203: (2003) 3 Mah LJ 853.
492. *M.P. Housing Board* v. *Mohanlal & Co.*, (2016) 14 SCC 199.
493. *K.M. Palve* v. *State of Maharashtra*, 2007 SCC OnLine Bom 659: (2007) 6 Mah LJ 583.
494. *Union of India* v. *Abdul Hakim*, 2010 SCC OnLine Cal 253: (2010) 2 CHN 794.

period of limitation of three years from the date of the termination of the contract.[495]

Section 14, Limitation Act, 1963 Act would apply in proceeding under Section 34(2), Arbitration and Conciliation Act. The time spent in prosecuting application under Section 34(2) in court which has no jurisdiction would be excluded while computing the period of limitation for filing application under Section 34(2) before the court of competent jurisdiction.[496]

Where the applicant prosecuted its remedy before the High Court which is a wrong forum, caused delay in filing application before the proper court, and was equipped with all legal expertise, it could not be said to have acted in good faith; the applicant was held not entitled to the benefit of Section 14, Limitation Act, and the delay was not condoned.[497] The plaint was directed to be returned on 25 November 2008, but the plaint was taken back on 2 February 2009, and was represented on 17 June 2009. It was held, the proceedings were barred by statute, and the respondent was not entitled to the benefit of time spent by him before filing a suit before the Bombay High Court.[498]

Filing of objection before wrong forum—Delay shall be condoned

Where an objection under Section 34 for setting aside an award has been filed in the wrong forum, under erroneous legal advice, the time spent in the wrong forum is liable to be excluded while computing the period of limitation.[499]

Section 17 of the Limitation Act

Once a party has received an arbitral award, the limitation period under Section 34(3), Limitation Act commences; Section 17, Limitation Act cannot be invoked to challenge the award. Words "but not thereafter" in the proviso to Section 34(3) are mandatory in nature and amount to "express exclusion" of Section 17, Limitation Act.[500]

---

495. *Ibid.*
496. *Dayashankar* v. *LAO*, 2019 SCC OnLine Chh 451. Limitation commences from the date of the receipt of the signed copy of the award. *Siya Ram Nag* v. *Magma Fincorp Ltd.*, 2018 SCC OnLine Chh 1046.
497. *Union of India* v. *Sankalp Associates*, 2015 SCC OnLine All 691.
498. *Chethan Bhandary* v. *Kotak Securities Ltd.*, 2010 SCC OnLine Kar 80: ILR 2010 Kar 2454.
499. *Hindustan Copper Ltd.* v. *Paramount Ltd.*, 2018 SCC OnLine Raj 3032: (2019) 2 RLW 1320; *Consolidated Engg. Enterprises* v. *Irrigation Deptt.*, (2008) 7 SCC 169 followed.
500. *P. Radha Bai* v. *P. Ashok Kumar*, (2019) 13 SCC 445.

Section 34(3) not applicable to refiling of applications

Section 34(3), Arbitration and Conciliation Act, 1996 is not applicable to refiling of applications under Section 34(3) after removal of defects. An application under Section 34 challenging award was filed within the limitation period. As the application had certain defects, the Deputy Registrar of the High Court granted time for re-submission of the application after removal of defects. The High Court refused to condone 65 days' delay in refiling the application. Since Section 34(3) is not applicable to refiling of applications, the delay was condoned as there was sufficient cause for condonation of delay. The application was restored.[501]

The delay caused due to withdrawal of earlier bona fide application for setting aside the award of the Arbitral Tribunal deserves to be condoned.[502]

Delay of more than 120 days—Delay not condoned

The last date for filing of petitions under Section 34 by NHAI to challenge awards was 29 April 2019. The application was filed on 17 June 2019. In view of Section 34(3), it is not possible for any challenge to be entertained beyond the outer limit of 120 days. Dismissal of application was proper.[503]

Inter-departmental delay—Delay not condoned

A copy of the award was received in the office of Director, Food and Supplies by registered post. The award was sent to the correct address and to a competent person. The appellant cannot be allowed to take benefit on account of inter-departmental delay in putting up the matter before the Director. Limitation would not commence from the date when the matter was put before the Director. The delay was not condoned.[504]

Order condoning delay—No appeal lies

The remedy of appeal has been provided only against an order setting aside or refusing to set aside an arbitral award as per Section 37(1)(*c*), but no appeal is provided against the order passed by the court of competent jurisdiction condoning the delay in filing the appeal under Section 34.[505]

---

501. *Railways* v. *Pioneer Publicity Corpn. (P) Ltd.*, (2017) 11 SCC 234; see also, *Union of India* v. *Sunrise Enterprises*, 2012 SCC OnLine Del 654: ILR (2012) 2 Del 763.
502. *Tripura State Electricity Corpn. Ltd.* v. *Horizon Hi-Tech Engicon Ltd.*, 2018 SCC OnLine Tri 206.
503. *NHAI* v. *Dillip Kumar Pati*, 2021 SCC OnLine Ori 2428.
504. *Deptt. of Food, Civil Supplies and Consumer Affairs* v. *Virgo Softech Ltd.*, 2019 SCC OnLine P&H 5630.
505. *Union of India* v. *Simplex Infrastructures Ltd.*, (2017) 14 SCC 225.

The arbitrator is not bound by technical rules of evidence and can waive formal proof of letters and drawings. Objection in regard to such procedure adopted by the arbitrator is not maintainable.[506]

Order refusing to condone delay—Appeal lies

An appeal under Section 37(1)(*c*), Arbitration and Conciliation Act, 1996 would be maintainable against an order refusing to condone delay in filing an application under Section 34, Arbitration and Conciliation Act, 1996 to set aside an award.[507]

Order condoning delay in filing Section 34 petition—Letters Patent Appeal

The 1996 Act is self-contained and a Letters Aatent Appeal is excluded. Whether a Single Judge of the High Court has rightly exercised the discretion or otherwise in condoning the delay in filing Section 34 petition, the only remedy is by way of a special leave petition before the Supreme Court and not by way of a Letters Patent Appeal before the Division Bench of the High Court.[508]

Personal knowledge of arbitrator—Use of

An Arbitral Tribunal cannot make use of its personal knowledge of the facts of the dispute, which is not a part of the record, to decide the dispute. But an Arbitral Tribunal can certainly use their expert or technical knowledge or the general knowledge about the particular trade in deciding a matter. In fact, that is why in many arbitrations, persons with technical knowledge are appointed as they will be well-versed with the practices and customs in the respective fields. In *State (NCT of Delhi)* v. *Khem Chand*[509], all that the arbitrators have referred to was the market practice. That cannot be considered as using some personal knowledge of facts of a transaction to decide a dispute.[510]

The power of re-appraisal or re-appreciation of evidence in an award has not been conferred upon the court.[511]

506. *NPCC Ltd.* v. *Jyoti Sarup Mittal Engineers, Contractors and Builders*, 2006 SCC OnLine Del 1496: (2007) 93 DRJ 397.
507. *Chintels (India) Ltd.* v. *Bhayana Builders (P) Ltd.*, (2021) 4 SCC 602.
508. *Union of India* v. *Simplex Infrastructures Ltd.*, (2017) 14 SCC 225.
509. 2003 SCC OnLine Del 400: (2003) 68 DRJ 518
510. *P.R. Shah, Shares & Stock Brokers (P) Ltd.* v. *B.H.H. Securities (P) Ltd.*, (2012) 1 SCC 594.
511. *Union of India* v. *Surendranath Kanungo*, 2004 SCC OnLine Cal 353: (2005) 1 Cal LT 457.

Misconduct of arbitrator

The plea of objector that the arbitrator ignored the evidence placed by it before him did not amount to misconduct on the part of the arbitrator. The award was not set aside.[512] The arbitrator passed an award with the consent of both the parties and also obtained their signatures. It could not be said that the arbitrator had misconducted himself by not giving an opportunity of hearing to the parties. This was a case under the 1940 Act.[513]

Impartiality of arbitrator—Award set aside

The petitioner had taken a loan from the company. The arbitration clause specifically provided that the arbitrator shall be appointed by the company. The borrower intimated the company that the arbitrator appointed by the company was not impartial. There was substantial possibility of bias on the part of the arbitrator. The award was set aside.[514]

Legal misconduct is not one of the grounds provided by Section 34 for setting aside the award of the arbitrator.[515]

Extra cartage—Award of

An agreement between DDA and the contractor was entered into for carrying out work for development of land at a particular place in Delhi according to the terms and conditions mentioned in the contract. The contract deed provided that the rates quoted by the contractor would hold good irrespective of the source from which the materials were brought so long as they conformed to the specifications. There was no specific clause in the contract for bringing stones from elsewhere. The contractor brought stone aggregate from Nooh quarries of Haryana State to Delhi and claimed extra rate of cartage over and above the contractual rate. There was nothing on the record to show that the DDA had insisted upon aggregate stone only from Nooh. In such circumstances, and in view of the fact that the terms and conditions of the contract were binding on the parties, the award of extra cartage in favour of the contractor by the arbitrator was an error on the face of the record as well as contrary to the terms of the agreement. The award of the arbitrator was set aside.[516]

---

512. *State (NCT of Delhi)* v. *Khem Chand*, 2003 SCC OnLine Del 400: (2003) 68 DRJ 518.
513. *Nemichand Suthar* v. *Mohan Lal Gasgorh*, 2016 SCC OnLine Chh 964.
514. *P.V. Jojo* v. *India Cements Capital & Finance Ltd.*, 2019 SCC OnLine Ker 317.
515. *Indian Commercial Co. Ltd.* v. *Amrish Kilachand*, 2002 SCC OnLine Bom 307: (2002) 5 Mah LJ 650.
516. *DDA* v. *R.S. Sharma and Co.*, (2008) 13 SCC 80.

In appreciation of evidence and fact made by an arbitrator as a general rule, the court will not interfere. But where the arbitrator has ignored the conclusive evidence and has proceeded on the basis of assumption, the court can interfere.[517]

Crane-hire charges

There was a specific bar in the contract for any claim being made on account of cost-overrun charges. The award of the Arbitral Tribunal for ₹15 lakhs under such need is in derogation of the agreement. The award for overrun charges was set aside.[518]

Extra/additional work

Though no written orders for execution of extra item works were issued by the department, they were executed on oral instruction issued by the department. The claimant was entitled to payment for extra work done. The award was not against public policy.[519]

The petitioner was entitled to be recompensed for carrying out the overlay work by renewal of the highway coat using bituminous concrete as under the contract, this was not required to be done. It qualified as extra work for which the petitioner was entitled to extra payment. The petitioner was also entitled to the costs of recycling of the mild material.[520]

The petitioner had undertaken a project of construction in a multi-storeyed building. The contractor had put up a claim for additional work done without prior permission. The award of amount by the arbitrator, former Chief Engineer, by referring tender documents, annexures to claim, statement of fact, pour cards, by recording evidence of parties and by giving detailed arithmetical calculations, was proper and upheld.[521]

The work assigned under the contract and extra work was duly completed by the contractor. The undertaking to receive lesser payment than agreed as per the contract given by the contractor owing to dire need of money was unenforceable. The arbitral award holding the Corporation liable to make full payment for work as per the contract was proper.[522]

---

517. *Michigan Engineers (P) Ltd.* v. *Senbo Engg. Ltd.*, 2011 SCC OnLine Cal 5442: (2012) 4 CHN 92.
518. *BHEL* v. *Tata Projects Ltd.*, 2010 SCC OnLine Cal 397: (2010) 1 CHN 747.
519. *Bundelkhand University Jhansi* v. *Woodfun A Registered Partnership Firm*, 2022 SCC OnLine All 994: (2022) 5 All LJ 26.
520. *GMR Pochanpalli Expressways Ltd.* v. *NHAI*, (2022) 2 HCC (Del) 612.
521. *W.B. Housing Board* v. *Civcon Construction (P) Ltd.*, 2020 SCC OnLine Cal 659.
522. *W.B. Tourism Development Corpn. Ltd.* v. *Supratik Banerjee*, (2022) 1 HCC (Cal) 241.

The appellant had not led any evidence to prove his claim for payment of extra work alleged to be done; the appellant's claim for extra work done was dismissed.[523] Although no written work orders were issued for execution of extra work items, they were executed on oral instructions which was duly acknowledged by the appellant. The contract stood modified by the conduct of the parties, and it was held that the claimant was entitled to payment for such extra work executed.[524]

There is an implied contract between the parties to do additional work. The employer corporation was held bound to pay for the additional work. The award of the arbitrator was not set aside.[525]

Extra payment for extended period

Once the contractor sought and obtained an extension irrespective of the fact that such extension was on account of delay attributable solely to the employer, the contractor could not seek extra payment for the extended period.[526]

Contract for construction of bridge—Claim for increased quantity of steel

A work was required to be completed within 24 calendar months as per the terms and conditions of the contract. However, the work was completed beyond the stipulated period. The contract was awarded on turnkey basis. Therefore, it cannot be heard saying from the mouth of the contractor that it was unable to make plans about seven bridges and it was unable to prepare structural design. The award of claim towards increase in quantity of steel used in superstructure was not set aside.[527]

Extra royalty

No specific clause in the contract barred award of claim for extra royalty. It would not fall within any of the predicates under Section 34 of the Act. The challenge to the award of extra royalty by the arbitrator was not sustainable, and was rejected.[528]

---

523. *Shirdi Country Inns (P) Ltd.* v. *Suvidha Engineers India (P) Ltd.*, 2016 SCC OnLine Bom 5314: (2016) 5 Mah LJ 152.
524. *Bundelkhand University Jhansi* v. *Woodfun A Registered Partnership Firm*, 2022 SCC OnLine All 994: (2022) 5 All LJ 26.
525. *ESI Corpn.* v. *Shaji V.K.*, 2022 SCC OnLine Ker 1040.
526. *Port of Calcutta* v. *Batliboi & Co. Ltd.*, 2007 SCC OnLine Cal 686: (2008) 3 CHN 799.
527. *UT of J&K* v. *S.P. Singla Constructions (P) Ltd.*, 2023 SCC OnLine J&K 1343.
528. *Union of India* v. *Chawla Interbild Construction Co. (P) Ltd.*, 2002 SCC OnLine Bom 1158: (2003) 3 Mah LJ 889.

Refund of amount

The vendee required land for construction of the hotel. The vendor made misrepresentation about the contiguous nature of land. Boundries were not correctly described in the agreement. The Arbitral Tribunal directed refund of the amount with interest at 7.5 per cent per annum. The award was held proper.[529]

Remand

Matter can be remitted back to the arbitrator to decide matters afresh if the court considers just and proper.[530]

Discretion of court to pass interlocutory orders once award is challenged

From the mandatory language of Section 34 of the 1996 Act it is clear that an award, when challenged under Section 34 within the time stipulated therein, becomes unexecutable. There is no discretion left with the court to pass any interlocutory order in regard to the said award except to adjudicate on the correctness of the claim made by the applicant therein. The automatic suspension of the execution of the award the moment an application challenging the award is filed under Section 34 of the Act, leaving no discretion in the court to put the parties on terms, defeats the very objective of the alternate dispute resolution system to which the arbitration belongs.[531]

Interpretation/construction of contract

The interpretation of the contract is the matter of the arbitrator who is the judge chosen by the parties to determine and decide the dispute. The findings of facts recorded by the arbitrator cannot be interfered with on the ground that the terms of the contract were not interpreted by him.[532] Section 28 of the Act mandates that the arbitrator has to decide the dispute in terms of the contract.[533]

Construction of the terms of a contract is within the exclusive domain of the arbitrator and the construction given to such terms can only be interfered with if found that no reasonable man would have arrived at such

529. *Antram* v. *Graviss Hotels & Resorts Ltd.*, 2019 SCC OnLine P&H 6241.
530. *Bhasin Associates* v. *NBCC*, 2005 SCC OnLine Del 689: ILR (2005) 2 Del 88.
531. *National Aluminium Co. Ltd.* v. *Pressteel & Fabrications (P) Ltd.*, (2004) 1 SCC 540.
532. *Swan Gold Mining Ltd.* v. *Hindustan Copper Ltd.*, (2015) 5 SCC 739; *Satinderpal Singh Anand* v. *Sharanpal Balmukund Chopra*, 2008 SCC OnLine Bom 473: (2008) 6 Mah LJ 86.
533. *Unitech Ltd.* v. *Housing and Urban Development Corpn.*, 2012 SCC OnLine Del 5109: (2012) 194 DLT 481.

construction.[534] If the interpretation of the contract made by the arbitrator is utterly unreasonable and totally implausible, the view taken is not even possible, a challenge lies.[535] Interpretation of the clause in the agreement between the parties is an exclusive domain of the arbitrator and the court in its jurisdiction under Section 34 cannot interfere with such an interpretation even if two views are possible.[536]

It has consistently been laid down by the Supreme Court that construction of the terms of a contract is primarily for an arbitrator or Arbitral Tribunal to decide and unless the arbitrator or Arbitral Tribunal construes the contract in such a way that no fair-minded or reasonable person could do, no interference by the court is called for. The view that the increase in rates of service tax in respect of the bank guarantee and insurance premium is directly relatable to terms of the contract and performance under the contract was certainly a possible view.[537]

The scope of examination in these proceedings is limited to ascertaining whether the impugned award is vitiated by patent illegality or that the impugned award is in conflict with the public policy of India. It is well settled that an Arbitral Tribunal is also the final authority for interpreting the contract and the impugned award cannot be interfered with merely because a different interpretation is possible.[538]

The construction of the terms of a contract is primarily the domain of the arbitrator, unless the arbitrator construes the contract in a manner that no fair-minded or reasonable person would, *i.e.* the view of the arbitrator is not even a possible view to take.[539]

In *Swan Gold Mining Ltd.* v. *Hindustan Copper Ltd.*[540], the parties have entered into a concluded contract and agreed upon the terms and conditions of the said contract, which was finally acted upon. In such a case, the parties to the said contract cannot back out and challenge the award on the ground that the same is against public policy.

The interpretation of a contract is a matter for the arbitrator to determine even if it gives rise to determination of a question of law. The court, while considering a challenge to an arbitral award, does not sit in appeal over the

534. *Mitesh Mehta* v. *Saregama India Ltd.*, 2021 SCC OnLine Cal 453.
535. *Union of India* v. *Recon*, 2020 SCC OnLine Bom 2278: (2020) 6 Mah LJ 509.
536. *ONGC Ltd.* v. *Garware Shipping Corpn. Ltd.*, 2004 SCC OnLine Bom 1009: (2005) 1 Mah LJ 838; *Indian Lead Ltd.* v. *R.L. Dalal & Co. (P) Ltd.*, 2004 SCC OnLine Bom 1061: (2006) 2 Mah LJ 260.
537. *NHAI* v. *JSC Centrodorstroy*, (2016) 12 SCC 592.
538. *SMS Water Grace Bmw (P) Ltd.* v. *State (NCT of Delhi)*, (2021) 3 HCC (Del) 601.
539. *Bridge Marine Ltd.* v. *Indian Oil Corpn. Ltd.*, (2021) 4 HCC (Del) 478.
540. (2015) 5 SCC 739.

findings and decision of the arbitrator.[541] Findings of the Arbitral Tribunal on requisition as well the interpretation of the agreement are within the domain of the Arbitral Tribunal and cannot be disturbed in Section 34 proceedings.[542]

An Arbitral Tribunal must decide in accordance with the terms of the contract, but if an arbitrator construes the terms of the contract in a reasonable manner, it will not mean that the award can be set aside on this ground. Construction of the terms of a contract is primarily for an arbitrator to decide unless the arbitrator construes the contract in such a way that it could be said to be something that no fair-minded or reasonable person could do. The arbitrator is entitled to take the view which he holds to be the correct one after considering the material before him and after interpreting the provisions of the Act.[543]

If there are two possible interpretations of the terms of a contract, the arbitrator's interpretation has to be accepted and the court under Section 34 cannot substitute its opinion over the arbitrator's view.[544]

Where the clause in a contract is capable of two interpretations, the view taken by the arbitrator is clearly a possible if not a plausible one; it cannot be said that the arbitrator had travelled outside his jurisdiction, or that the view taken by him is against the terms of the contract. The High Court had no reason to interfere with the award and substitute its view in place of the interpretation accepted by the arbitrator.[545] Courts shall not ordinarily substitute their interpretation for that of the arbitrator. If the parties with their eyes wide open have consented to refer the matter to arbitration, then normally the finding of the arbitrator should be accepted without demur. But in a case where it is found that the arbitrator has acted without jurisdiction and has put an interpretation on the clause of the agreement which is wholly contrary to law, then, in that case, there is no prohibition for the courts to set things right.[546]

The general consensus of the view of the Supreme Court is that the court should not sit in appeal and normally should not interfere with the views of

---

541. *NHAI* v. *ITD Cementation India Ltd.*, (2015) 14 SCC 21; *M.P. Power Generation Co. Ltd.* v. *ANSALDO Energia SpA*, (2018) 16 SCC 661.
542. *Metalmeccanica Fracasso India (P) Ltd.* v. *Prakash Industrial Infrastructure (P) Ltd.*, 2014 SCC OnLine Bom 161: (2014) 2 Mah LJ 775.
543. *NHAI* v. *ITD Cementation India Ltd.*, (2015) 14 SCC 21; *M.P. Power Generation Co. Ltd.* v. *ANSALDO Energia SpA*, (2018) 16 SCC 661.
544. *M.P. Power Generation Co. Ltd.* v. *ANSALDO Energia SpA*, (2018) 16 SCC 661; *NHAI* v. *JSC Centrodorstroy*, (2016) 12 SCC 592.
545. *Rashtriya Ispat Nigam Ltd.* v. *Dewan Chand Ram Saran*, (2012) 5 SCC 306.
546. *Numaligarh Refinery Ltd.* v. *Daelim Industrial Co. Ltd.*, (2007) 8 SCC 466.

the arbitrator in interpretation of the terms of the agreement interpreted by the arbitrator when the arbitrator is appointed with consent of parties.[547]

In *Numaligarh Refinery Ltd.* v. *Daelim Industrial Co. Ltd.*[548], two arbitrators had taken one view of the matter, and the third arbitrator had taken another view of the matter. The District Judge had also set aside the award on some issues, and the High Court had also accepted some items of the majority award and some items of the minority award. In view of the conflicting views on the subject, the Supreme Court had to enter into merit to put an end to the controversy by adjudicating upon the conflicting views of various forums.

Interpretation of contract falls within the realm of the arbitrator. If two views are possible, the court will refrain itself from interfering.[549] There was a dispute regarding installation of the VSAT system. Interpretation of the contract is a matter for the arbitrator. Arbitrator's interpretation was certainly a possible view. The court would not set aside the award on the ground that another view is possible.[550]

Arbitrator is the creation of the contract; he gets jurisdiction under the terms of the contract. He is expected to interpret and apply the provisions of the contract and pass awards accordingly. In *Hindustan Petroleum Corpn. Ltd.* v. *Batliboi Environmental Engineers Ltd.*[551], the contractor sought extension of time twice. In none of the letters seeking extension of time, the contractor indicated that he would seek compensation for the delay as required by Section 55, Contract Act. In view of the terms of the contract, the contractor could not claim any compensation on account of the delay. The award of compensation by the arbitrator on account of the delay in the extension of time for completion of the work against the terms of the contract was arbitrary and was set aside.

The arbitration award passed without examining the correct provisions of the contract is erroneous, and would be set aside.[552]

A challenge to an arbitral award takes up considerable court time; routine challenges to arbitral awards destroy the very fundamental ethos of alternative dispute resolution mechanism.[553]

---

547. *Ibid.*
548. (2007) 8 SCC 466.
549. *G. Ramachandra Reddy* v. *Union of India*, (2009) 6 SCC 414.
550. *VFC Securities (P) Ltd.* v. *Rashesh N. Shah, Shares and Brokers (P) Ltd.*, 2005 SCC OnLine Bom 99: (2005) 2 Mah LJ 386.
551. 2007 SCC OnLine Bom 1016: (2008) 2 Mah LJ 542.
552. *Athletic Sangh* v. *State of M.P.*, 2016 SCC OnLine MP 12010.
553. *State of W.B.* v. *K. Banerjee & Bros.*, 2012 SCC OnLine Cal 11417: (2012) 4 Cal LT 692.

Work order

The arbitrator imposed liability to pay service tax on the port authority on the basis of the clause work order. The arbitrator failed to notice that the work order was issued long after the letter of acceptance which crystallized contractual terms between the parties. A work order cannot change the contractual terms between the parties. The award of the arbitrator imposing liability on the port authority was set aside.[554] Where the work contract contains a specific prohibition, the general principle would have to give way to specific prohibition contained in the contract. The clause in the contract provided that notwithstanding the grant of an extension, the appellant would not be entitled to claim damages or compensation. Held, the award made by the arbitrator was rightly not interfered with by the Single Judge in view of the specific prohibition clause contained in the works contract.[555]

In works contract between the parties as per the agreement clause, any claim whatsoever would not be entertained except where any quarry was changed for circumstances beyond the control of the contract or under a written order of the Superintending Engineer in charge of the work. The employer (Superintending Engineer) had permitted the contractor to bring sand from different quarries to complete the work. It was held, variation in the method of quarrying was sanctioned by the employer in the interest of work to facilitate the contractor to complete the work. The award of the arbitrator was not set aside.[556]

Work was undertaken by the respondent of conduit pipes that had been improperly done by the previous contractor. Since the work was done by the respondent to the benefit of the petitioner, the respondent was required to be compensated.[557]

Where the authority of the arbitrator is never challenged, the appellant is precluded from raising the question of jurisdiction of the arbitrator to adjudicate the dispute.[558]

Where objection as to the jurisdiction of the arbitrator as required by Section 16 of the Act is not raised before the arbitrator by the respondent,

---

554. *Board of Trustees* v. *ABG Kolkata Container Terminal (P) Ltd.*, 2020 SCC OnLine Cal 2273.
555. *Bombay Railways Engg. Co.* v. *Railways*, 2013 SCC OnLine Bom 783: (2014) 4 Mah LJ 103.
556. *State of M.P.* v. *Sew Construction Ltd.*, 2019 SCC OnLine MP 3340: (2019) 3 MP LJ 714.
557. *Punjab National Bank* v. *Bijlee Construction*, 2012 SCC OnLine Del 2067: (2012) 130 DRJ 579.
558. *Union of India* v. *Budhlani Engg. (P) Ltd.*, 2008 SCC OnLine Cal 334: (2008) 3 CHN 661.

the respondent had waived his right to make objection to the jurisdiction of the Arbitral Tribunal, and the award of the arbitrator was upheld.[559]

Construction of contract—Possible view

Construction of the terms of the contract is primarily for the arbitrator/Arbitral Tribunal to decide. The appellant, NHAI, had awarded a contract to the respondent for the execution of laning works. The view taken by the Arbitral Tribunal that increase in rates of service tax with respect to bank guarantee and insurance premium was directly relatable to the terms of the contract and performance under the contract was a possible view and was not interfered with by the court.[560]

The Courts should not interfere with the award merely because an alternative view on facts and interpretation of contract exists.[561]

The arbitrator is not expected to write a detailed judgment. It is sufficient if he records his findings and how he reached the conclusion.[562]

Breach of contract—Measure of damages

Whilst the measure of damages adopted is unconventional, the court is unable to accept that it falls within the parameters of Section 34(2-A) or Section 34(2)(*b*)(*ii*), Arbitration and Conciliation Act, 1996. The Arbitral Tribunal's view is not one that no reasonable person could possibly accept. The measure of damages is not always precise and in the given circumstances, there may be multiple methods for computing the measure of damages. The methodology adopted by the Arbitral Tribunal is a novel one but is a possible view. The award was not vitiated, and was not set aside.[563]

Fire insurance claim

Depreciation amount was assessed by the surveyor. The arbitrator had no expertise, and the reduction of rate by the arbitrator without giving reasons was not proper. The award of the arbitrator was set aside.[564]

---

559. *S.N. Malhotra* v. *Airport Authority of India*, 2008 SCC OnLine Del 442: (2008) 103 DRJ 196; see also, *S.K. Contractor & Engineers* v. *Hindustan Petroleum Corpn. Ltd.*, 2008 SCC OnLine Del 527: (2008) 103 DRJ 61.
560. *NHAI* v. *JSC Centrodorstroy*, (2016) 12 SCC 592; *Satinderpal Singh Anand* v. *Sharanpal Balmukund Chopra*, 2008 SCC OnLine Bom 473: (2008) 6 Mah LJ 86.
561. *Dheeraj Rastogi* v. *Dnata International (P) Ltd.*, (2024) 1 HCC (Del) 51.
562. *Ircon International Ltd.* v. *Arvind Construction Co. Ltd.*, 1999 SCC OnLine Del 551: ILR (1999) 2 Del 234.
563. *HSIIDC* v. *IDBI Bank Ltd.*, (2022) 1 HCC (Del) 714.
564. *Oriental Insurance Co. Ltd.* v. *AI Champdany Industries Ltd.*, 2014 SCC OnLine Cal 21029: (2015) 3 CHN 737.

Two views possible—Plausible view taken

Where a plausible view has been taken by the arbitrator or when two views are possible, such view should not be interfered with in a proceeding under Section 34 of the 1996 Act.[565] Where an arbitrator takes a view on provision of an agreement and which is a possible view, the court under Section 34 will not interfere.[566] Where the view taken by the arbitrator is a plausible view, the award of the arbitrator cannot be set aside.[567] The only issue was relatable to the interpretation of the clauses dealing with the aspect of the payment of ground rent. The view taken by the arbitrator was plausible and was not interfered with.[568] The Arbitral Tribunal held that the claim made by the respondent was within time and not barred by limitation. The view taken by the arbitrator was a possible view and was not interfered with in the petition filed under Section 34.[569]

Merely because the arbitrator has taken a view that is plausible and there may be another view also, the award cannot be interfered with. The award can be interfered with only if the view taken by the arbitrator is patently illegal or against the fundamental policy of India.[570]

Whether a particular amount was liable to be paid is a decision within the competence of the arbitrator. If a view taken on the contract, the decision of the arbitrator on certain amounts awarded is a possible view though perhaps not only the correct view, the award cannot be examined by the court. When the reasons have been given by the arbitrator in making the award, the court cannot examine the reasonableness of the reasons. Objection filed under Section 34 was dismissed.[571] If a possible view has been taken by the tribunal, the High Court would not disturb the award exercising its limited jurisdiction under Section 34.[572]

---

565. *State of Jharkhand* v. *HSS Integrated Sdn*, (2019) 9 SCC 798; *Union of India* v. *Moti Enterprises*, 2002 SCC OnLine Bom 806: (2003) 1 Mah LJ 930.
566. *Vijaypat Singhania* v. *Hari Shankar Singhania*, 2013 SCC OnLine Bom 434: (2013) 5 Mah LJ 744.
567. *Turner Morrison Ltd.* v. *Rani Parvati Devi*, 2009 SCC OnLine Del 3257; *Indian Oil Corpn. Ltd.* v. *Sathyanarayana Service Station*, 2023 SCC OnLine SC 597.
568. *Ansal Properties & Infrastructure Ltd.* v. *Housing & Urban Development Corpn. Ltd.*, 2013 SCC OnLine Del 328: (2013) 134 DRJ 120; *UHL Power Co. Ltd.* v. *State of H.P.*, (2022) 4 SCC 116.
569. *Zee Sports Ltd.* v. *Nimbus Media Pte. Ltd.*, 2017 SCC OnLine Bom 426: (2018) 1 Mah LJ 349; *Maganlal Dalichand Santokchand* v. *Narpatraj Besarmal Mehta*, 2006 SCC OnLine Bom 537: (2006) 6 Mah LJ 71; *Union of India* v. *Annavaram Concrete (P) Ltd.*, (2021) 3 HCC (Del) 440.
570. *DDA* v. *Eros Resorts & Hotels Ltd.*, (2022) 2 HCC (Del) 384.
571. *Reunion Engg. Co. (P) Ltd.* v. *NBCC Ltd.*, 2010 SCC OnLine Del 2570: (2010) 120 DRJ 96.
572. *Madhu Kacharam Achra* v. *Gul Kachharam Achra*, 2005 SCC OnLine Bom 510: (2005) 3 Mah LJ 713.

The view taken by the Arbitral Tribunal on the question of loss suffered by the petitioner on account of delay in the execution of works was a plausible view, if not the correct view, and cannot be interfered with by the court.[573]

It is well settled that if the interpretation of a contract is involved, then the interpretation of the arbitrator must be accepted unless it is one which could not be reasonably possible. The court cannot substitute its own interpretation to avoid arbitrariness so long as the interpretation of the arbitrator is a possible one.[574] The court would be transgressing its own boundaries and interloping upon those of the arbitrator in substituting the view preferred by it for that of the latter.[575]

Where the view taken by the arbitrator is plausible and not based upon any erroneous proposition of law, attempting to challenge the award on merit cannot be permitted.[576]

There are limited grounds under Section 34 to lay challenge to an arbitral award. Plausible view of the arbitrator cannot be substituted by court. No interference in the award is warranted.[577]

The third arbitrator, while passing the award, gave plausible interpretation to the clause of agreement, and did not substitute any new term to the agreement. There was no perversity in the award, and the award was not liable to be interfered with.[578]

Merely because the impugned award is contrary to the arbitral awards rendered in other cases does not render it amenable to challenge under Section 34, Arbitration and Conciliation Act, 1996. An arbitral award can be set aside only if an Arbitral Tribunal's view is not a possible view and no reasonable person could possibly accept the same. If an Arbitral Tribunal's decision is found to be a possible one, it does not warrant interference. In certain contentious cases, where there are two plausible views, the decision of the Arbitral Tribunal accepting either one of them would not render the award vulnerable under Section 34, Arbitration and Conciliation Act.[579]

---

573. *Haryana Vidyut Prasaran Nigam Ltd.* v. *Cobra Instalaciones Y. Services*, (2022) 3 HCC (Del) 128.
574. *State of M.P.* v. *Shukla Construction Co.*, 2009 SCC OnLine MP 105: (2009) 3 MP LJ 197; *Indian Oil Corpn. Ltd.* v. *Langkawi Shipping Ltd.*, 2004 SCC OnLine Bom 460: (2004) 4 Mah LJ 969.
575. *Em and Em Associates* v. *DDA*, 2002 SCC OnLine Del 392: (2003) 2 AP LJ (DNC) 16.
576. *Goel Associates* v. *SAIL Coop. Group Housing Society Ltd.*, 2001 SCC OnLine Del 621: ILR (2001) 1 Del 649; *Vijaypat Singhania* v. *Hari Shankar Singhania*, 2013 SCC OnLine Bom 434: (2013) 5 Mah LJ 744.
577. *State of Jharkhand* v. *Prem Kumar*, 2023 SCC OnLine Jhar 556.
578. *Chettinad International Coal Terminal (P) Ltd.* v. *Kamarajar Port Ltd.*, 2018 SCC OnLine Mad 638: (2018) 3 LW 695.
579. *Glitter Overseas* v. *MMTC Ltd.*, (2022) 4 HCC (Del) 400.

Another view possible

While looking into the question of the legality or validity of the award under Section 34, the court, even if it has another view of the matter, cannot substitute its own view over that of the arbitrators as that will be clearly outside its jurisdiction.[580]

The courts do not interfere merely because an alternative view on facts exists. A possible view by the arbitrator on facts has necessarily to pass muster as the arbitrator is the ultimate master of the quantity and quality of evidence to be relied upon when he delivers his arbitral award.[581]

Computation of damages/compensation—Modes permissible when method not specified in contract, Emden, Hudson, Eichleay formulae

Sections 55 and 73, Contract Act, 1872 do not lay down the mode and manner as to how and in what manner the computation of damages or compensation has to be made. The method used for computation of damages will depend upon the facts and circumstances of each case. In the assessment of damages, the court must consider only strict legal obligations, and not the expectations, however reasonable, of one contractor that the other will do something that he has assumed no legal obligation to do.[582]

Although the Hudson formula has received judicial support in many cases, it has been criticised principally because it adopts the head office overhead percentage from the contract as the factor for calculating the costs, and this may bear little or no relation to the actual head office costs of the contractor.

Using the Emden formula, the head office overhead percentage is arrived at by dividing the total overhead cost and profit of the contractor's organisation as a whole by the total turnover. This formula has the advantage of using the contractor's actual head office overhead and profit percentage rather than those contained in the contract. This formula has been widely applied and has received judicial support in a number of cases.

The Eichleay formula is used where it is not possible to prove loss of opportunity and the claim is based on actual cost. The total head office overhead during the contract period is first determined by comparing the value of work carried out in the contract period for the project with the value of work carried out by the contractor as a whole for the contract period. A share of head office overheads for the contractor is allocated in the same ratio and expressed as a lump sum to the particular contract. The amount of

580. *Bfil Finance Ltd.* v. *G. Tech Stone Ltd.*, 2002 SCC OnLine Bom 734: (2002) 4 Mah LJ 434.
581. *DSIIDC* v. *Well Protect Manpower Services (P) Ltd.*, (2022) 2 HCC (Del) 118.
582. *McDermott International Inc.* v. *Burn Standard Co. Ltd.*, (2006) 11 SCC 181.

head office overhead allocated to the particular contract is then expressed as a weekly amount by dividing it by the contract period. The period of delay is then multiplied by the weekly amount to give the total sum claimed. The Eichleay formula is regarded by the Federal Circuit Courts of America as the exclusive means for compensating a contractor for overhead expenses.[583]

In *McDermott International Inc.* v. *Burn Standard Co. Ltd.*[584], the arbitrator quantified the claim by taking recourse to Emden formula. It was held, the arbitrator had not committed any error warranting interference.

Loss—Recovery of

Unless loss suffered is pleaded and proved, it cannot be recovered.[585]

Breach of contract—Loss of profit awarded

In works contract if the party entrusting work commits breach of contract, the contractor is entitled to claim damages for loss of profit which he expected to earn by undertaking the works contract. As the petitioner had illegally terminated the contract, he was legally bound to compensate the other party to the contract.[586] A contract was given for construction of 12 single JCOs accommodation for ASC School. The initial plan given to the contractor was changed by the department thrice. It was held, there was a fundamental breach of contract and unilateral termination of the original contract by the department. The award of ₹1,39,400 by the arbitrator as 10 per cent of the contract amount towards loss of profit was held proper.[587]

Claim of the respondent on account of loss of opportunity was not granted by the arbitrator, but he granted relief on account of loss of profit. There was no question of granting the claim of the respondent on both the counts. On principle, it was one and the same thing.[588]

Doctrine of frustration

The appellant employer unilaterally terminated the works contract on the ground of poor bearing capacity of the proposed site. No notice in terms

---

583. *Ibid.*
584. *Ibid.*
585. *MTNL* v. *SRV Telecom (P) Ltd.*, 2016 SCC OnLine Bom 3964: (2016) 5 Mah LJ 29.
586. *Rites Ltd.* v. *Subrata Kumar Ghose*, 2023 SCC OnLine Cal 165; See, *Unibros* v. *All India Radio*, 2023 SCC OnLine SC 1366.
587. *Union of India* v. *R.K. Traders*, 2013 SCC OnLine All 4916: (2013) 100 ALR 435; *A.T. Brij Paul Singh* v. *State of Gujarat*, (1984) 4 SCC 59; *Dwaraka Das* v. *State of M.P.*, (1999) 3 SCC 500.
588. *Mahanagar Gas Ltd.* v. *Babulal Uttamchand and Co.*, 2012 SCC OnLine Bom 377: (2012) 4 Mah LJ 344.

of the agreement was issued to the contractor. Possibilities to improve the site by taking measures suggested by the Geo technical Investigation Report were not explored, and the proposal of the contractor providing an alternative site was also not considered. It was held, the doctrine of frustration was not applicable. The award of damages by the arbitrator to the contractor was upheld.[589]

Interest on deferred payment

There was a contract for construction of work. The work was suspended by the contractor for want of funds. Assurance was given by the government company for payment and forbade foreclosure of the contract by the contractor. The general conditions of contract provided for payment of compensation in case of suspension of work. The claim for interest on deferred payment was in accordance with the terms and conditions of the contract, and the contractor was held entitled to the interest claimed.[590]

Where the respondent's claim for interest on deferred payment was accepted by the arbitrator without any basis, the award of interest was set aside.[591]

Award of interest [S. 31(7)]

Where the arbitrator has granted interest in accordance with the terms of the contract between the parties, such award cannot be set aside by invoking the general principles of fairness of equity.[592]

Pendente lite interest

The arbitrator has power to award interest pendente lite even if the agreement does not provide for the grant of such interest nor prohibit awarding such interests.[593]

Claim for future interest

No direction was given by the High Court for payment of future interest on the amount payable by the High Court. In the absence of direction it shall be deemed that the court has refused interest. The contractor cannot claim interest on the amount payable beyond the date of judgment.[594]

---

589. *State of Tripura* v. *N.G. Bhattacharjee Construction Co.*, 2021 SCC OnLine Tri 43.
590. *RITES Ltd.* v. *Bhardwaj Construction Co. (P) Ltd.*, 2020 SCC OnLine Jhar 1857.
591. *Glitter Overseas* v. *MMTC Ltd.*, (2022) 4 HCC (Del) 400.
592. *Ibid.*
593. *Union of India* v. *R.C. Singhal*, 2006 SCC OnLine Del 361: ILR (2006) 1 Del 438.
594. *Ibid.*

High rate of interest

The rate of interest at the rate of 24 per cent per annum is high. The export agreement contained no clause, whereby the petitioner had agreed to pay interest at the rate of 1 per cent above the SBI rate. There was no basis for awarding interest at the rate of 24 per cent per annum considering that even according to the respondent the rate of interest charged by SBI was increased to 19 per cent in the year 1992. Interest at the rate of 12 per cent per annum was awarded.[595]

Breach of contract—Award of damages

The basic principles of awarding damages as provided under the Contract Act, 1872 cannot be ignored by the arbitrator. Hence, awarding damages without any material evidence and supporting documents is not sustainable.[596]

In case of breach of contract, award of damages without ascertaining the actual loss suffered by the party and without assigning reasons was improper, and set aside.[597]

Reasonable opportunity of hearing

Where the arbitrator failed to provide reasonable opportunity of hearing to the claimant and passed the award, and thus had misconducted himself and the proceedings, the arbitral award was set aside.[598]

The award of damages (maintenance cost without any evidence) is manifestly erroneous. It cannot be sustained.[599]

The Arbitral Tribunal is the master of evidence; findings arrived at by the tribunal on the basis of evidence on record are not to be scrutinised as if the court was sitting in appeal. The respondent was awarded a contract for the installation of Low Tension Load Management System (LTLMS) at various locations by the appellant. The respondent terminated the contract and claimed damages on the premise that the appellant did not supply the list of locations where the contract objects were to be installed. The Arbitral Tribunal recorded categorical findings that Respondent 2 was prevented by the appellant from performance of contractual obligations as the appellant

---

595. *Glitter Overseas* v. *MMTC Ltd.*, (2022) 4 HCC (Del) 400.
596. *Indian Oil Corpn. Ltd.* v. *Kadbrotee Engg. Industries*, 2011 SCC OnLine Bom 61: (2011) 2 Mah LJ 659.
597. *Union of India* v. *Jasumall & Co.*, 2017 SCC OnLine Cal 312.
598. *Union of India* v. *Roshni Devi*, 2021 SCC OnLine J&K 289.
599. *CRPF* v. *Fibroplast Marine (P) Ltd.*, (2022) 3 HCC (Del) 304.

had not given the lists of locations to the respondent. Findings of the Arbitral Tribunal were not interfered with.[600]

Illegal termination of control

The petitioner had undertaken a project of construction in a multi-storeyed building. The contractor had put up a claim for additional work done without prior permission. The award of amount by the arbitrator, former Chief Engineer, by referring tender documents, annexures to claim, statement of fact, pour cards, by recording evidence of parties and by giving detailed arithmetical calculations, was proper and upheld.[601]

Claim on account of delay in discharge of vessel

There was a delay in action due to non-berthing of vessels. The majority award granting the claim of damages was legal and valid, and no ground was made out for setting aside the award of the arbitrator.[602]

Unless weather would actually prevent discharge of vessels, no exception can be taken. There was admission by the petitioner that discharge of the vessel was possible on a particular day, and the award called for no interference.[603]

Liquidated damages

Where it is stipulated in the agreement that on extension of time for completion of work, liquidated damages would be levied, even though no loss is suffered due to delay, still liquidated damages would be levied.[604] Levy of liquidated damages is interconnected and interlinked damages as it arose out of the same contract and work in question.[605]

In the absence of proof of loss, liquidated damages cannot be claimed/granted.[606]

The Arbitral Tribunal cannot reduce the liquidated damages on guess work if it finds that it is a genuine pre-estimate of damages and it is not possible to prove the quantum.[607]

---

600. *Maharashtra State Electricity Distribution Co. Ltd.* v. *Datar Switchgear Ltd.*, (2018) 3 SCC 133.
601. *W.B. Housing Board* v. *Civcon Construction (P) Ltd.*, 2020 SCC OnLine Cal 659.
602. *SAIL* v. *Fednav Asia Ltd.*, 2004 SCC OnLine Del 629: (2004) 76 DRJ 389.
603. *SAIL* v. *Western Bulk Carriers KS*, 2010 SCC OnLine Del 1828: (2010) 118 DRJ 334.
604. *Chimmco Birla Ltd.* v. *Cochin Port Trust*, 2019 SCC OnLine Ker 7896.
605. *MTNL* v. *Ultramatx Computer Support Systems (P) Ltd.*, 2012 SCC OnLine Bom 178: (2012) 5 Mah LJ 762.
606. *S.B.I.W. Steels (P) Ltd.* v. *SAIL*, 2022 SCC OnLine Cal 3842.
607. *Haryana Vidyut Prasaran Nigam Ltd.* v. *Cobra Instalaciones Y. Services*, (2022) 3 HCC (Del) 128.

Award for damages set aside

The claimant prayed for damages only in event the prayer for specific performance, perpetual injunction and mandatory injunction was not granted. The arbitrator travelled beyond the scope of prayers made by the claimant and granted prayer for damages without any acceptable reason or justification even after granting prayers for specific performance, perpetual injunction and mandatory injunction. The award of the arbitrator was set aside.[608]

The petitioner was running his business over premises of the respondent on commission basis. The petitioner challenged imposition of damages, rent during closure of business and its quantum. The petitioner had not handed over possession of vacant premises after a dispute between them, and therefore, imposition of damages and rent was proper.[609]

Delay in execution of work beyond scheduled period was on account of lapse or negligence on part of the company and not the contractor. The claim for liquidated damages on part of the company was not tenable.[610]

Escalation of cost of work

Where the completion of the work was delayed due to reasons attributable to other parties, the award of the arbitrator allowing the contractor's claim for escalation of costs of work was held proper, and was upheld.[611] Allowing claims for escalation and interest *per se* are not perverse.[612]

The State itself prevented the contractor from performing his promise. The order awarding compensation for losses suffered and escalation prices to the contractor was proper.[613]

A works contract was extended beyond the period of completion. A clause in the contract granting fixed price during the original period of the contract will not prevent authorities from granting escalation if the contract is extended beyond the stipulated period. The award of the arbitrator granting escalation cost was not improper.[614] The applications/requests made by the respondent contractors for payment of escalation costs deserve to be examined in accordance with the principal Act of 1996 without taking

608. *Sikkim Power Development Corpn. Ltd.* v. *Amalgamated Transpower (India) Ltd.*, 2023 SCC OnLine Sikk 117.
609. *Arun Kumar Kamal Kumar* v. *Selected Marble Home*, 2020 SCC OnLine SC 797.
610. *Ibid.*
611. *Associated Construction* v. *Pawanhans Helicopters Ltd.*, (2008) 16 SCC 128.
612. *Port of Calcutta* v. *Mahalakshmi Constructions*, 2001 SCC OnLine Cal 268: (2002) 1 CHN 288.
613. *Vijai Constructions* v. *State of U.P.*, 2017 SCC OnLine All 2732: (2018) 2 All LJ 499.
614. *State of M.P.* v. *Tirupati Buildcon (P) Ltd*, 2015 SCC OnLine MP 7502.

resort to the Amendment Act, 2015, which came into force from 23 October 2015.[615]

Escalation clause absent in arbitration agreement. Mere absence of an escalation clause is not sufficient to refuse escalation because escalation is a normal incident.[616]

A tenderer had accepted work undertaken by the bidder beyond the period of contract without objections. The arbitrator assessed the period of delay attributable to the tenderer and awarded escalation to the bidder only for the same. The award of escalation charges for work done beyond the scheduled period was not interfered with.[617]

Where a major part of the delay in the execution of the work contract was attributable to the appellant beneficiary, the contractor was entitled to escalation costs. The award of the arbitrator was proper.[618]

The claim regarding price adjustment/escalation was a pure and simple case of interpretation of relevant clauses of the agreement which does not involve any public policy. The judgment of the High Court quashing/setting aside the award of the arbitrator was not sustainable, and was set aside.[619]

To determine the escalation, the base price is required to be determined and in the absence of determination of the base price, the escalation of price cannot be even calculated. No error was committed by the arbitrators in arriving at the conclusion with reference to clauses. The court below exceeded its jurisdiction in setting aside the award passed by the arbitrator.[620]

The contractor had failed to complete the work within the stipulated time. No specific condition was enumerated in the contract between parties entitling the claimant-contractor to claim higher/revised/escalated rates of work in respect of the work done beyond the normal schedule of work. The claimant was not entitled to an escalated rate.[621]

The contract of transportation of some goods was awarded to the respondent on a fixed rate and that was the reason for not having any price revision clause in the contract agreement. The arbitrator acceded to the claim of the contractor to grant price escalation of petrol and diesel. It was

615. *Union of India* v. *Parmar Construction Co.*, (2019) 15 SCC 682.
616. *Tarapore & Co.* v. *State of M.P.*, (1994) 3 SCC 521.
617. *NTPC Ltd.* v. *Deconar Services (P) Ltd.*, (2021) 19 SCC 694.
618. *DSIIDC* v. *HR Builders*, (2022) 4 HCC (Del) 123.
619. *Parsa Kente Collieries Ltd.* v. *Rajasthan Rajya Vidyut Utpadan Nigam Ltd.*, (2019) 7 SCC 236.
620. *Friends Coal Carbonisation* v. *Hindustan Zinc Ltd.*, 2001 SCC OnLine Raj 137: (2002) 4 RLW 2013.
621. *Bharat Aluminium Co. Ltd.* v. *Lark Constructions (P) Ltd.*, 2018 SCC OnLine Chh 1045.

held, the arbitrator acted beyond his jurisdiction in giving the award on the basis of principles of fair play and equity. The award of the arbitrator was set aside.[622]

The claimant's case was that the total cost escalation due to failure of the opposite party was ₹120 crores. But the arbitrator granted ₹265.10 crores to the claimant for cost escalation. The claimant had not even laid a single brick or stone for any of the projects. The award of damages of ₹265.10 crores when the claimant had sought a specific sum of ₹120 crores was set aside as being against the most basic notions of justice which shocked the conscience of the court.[623]

Reimbursement of wages in case of escalation

A clause in the contract between the parties provided that no escalation or reimbursement whatsoever shall be made to the contractor for an increase in wages of labour. Another clause of special conditions of the contract provided that the contractor shall have no claim whatsoever if, on account of local factors/or regulations, he is required to pay wages in excess of minimum wages during the execution of work. It was held, parties are free to decide their own terms and conditions in case of a contract. Once the respondent-contractor voluntarily agreed that no escalation would be reimbursed even in case of regulation before accepting the contract, the respondent could not claim reimbursement of excess of minimum wages on account of a hike due to notification of the government. The award of the arbitrator on this issue was set aside.[624]

Idling of machinery—Claim for loss

The general conditions of contract provided that the contractor would be entitled to compensation when work was suspended by the Engineer-in-Chief and the suspension of work exceeded 14 days. However, there was also a negative clause in the contract on claim for compensation during the period of suspension including when it related to idling of machinery. It was held, in view of the negative clause, the claim for compensation on account of idling of machinery was ex facie illegal, and was rejected.[625]

Although, the Arbitral Tribunal itself observed that there was no cogent and convincing evidence for calculating compensation for the loss suffered by the complainant to demobilise their machinery due to non-issue of exit gate

622. *Union of India* v. *Freight Carriers*, 2008 SCC OnLine Gau 48: (2008) 5 Gau LR 256.
623. *Sikkim Power Development Corpn. Ltd.* v. *Amalgamated Transpower (India) Ltd.*, 2023 SCC OnLine Sikk 117.
624. *Union of India* v. *Varindera Constructions Ltd.*, (2018) 7 SCC 794.
625. *RITES Ltd.* v. *Bhardwaj Construction Co. (P) Ltd.*, 2020 SCC OnLine Jhar 1857.

pass on account of dispute ensued, yet it considered reasonable to calculate the loss at an average of the amount shown in running account bills. There was no real basis for quantifying the damages. The award of damages was set aside.[626]

Compensation for delayed work

Clause 16 of the additional conditions of arbitration agreement provided:

> No delay in completion of works is anticipated. If there is any delay in completion of civil works, the contractor shall execute the work on same rates/conditions up to a maximum period of 16 months from the date of the award of the contract which is inclusive of four months as stated against Sl. No. 2 of this order.

It was held, the aforesaid clause does not make an absolute prohibition in regard to the payment of compensation for delayed work. On the other hand, it provides for payment of compensation for delayed work, provided the work is delayed beyond 16 months from the date of the award of the contract. In the present case, the period of work during which the arbitrator executed the contract exceeded 16 months, hence the prohibition in clause 16 against grant of compensation disappeared. The arbitrator did not exceed jurisdiction in awarding compensation for delayed work. Appeals were dismissed.[627]

Where the delay in the completion of the contract could not be attributed to the contractor alone, and the State was equally liable, the arbitrator rightly concluded that the liability to pay penalty for delay in execution of contract could not be imposed upon the contractor. Applications were filed by the contractor for extension of time on the ground that requisite facilities as agreed by the appellant State were not provided to the contractor and, therefore, there was no question of the penalty being imposed on the contractor for not completing the work in time. The petition under Section 34, Arbitration and Conciliation Act, 1996 was rightly rejected.[628]

The contract was for construction of a post office building and staff quarters. As a large old tree fell on the construction site, construction work was stopped and clearance for removal of the tree was given by the authority after three years. The delay was beyond the control of the contractor, grant of damages/compensation to the contractor towards loss of overheads during

626. *Aneja Constructions (India) Ltd.* v. *Grim-Tech Projects (I) (P) Ltd.*, (2022) 1 HCC (Del) 523.
627. *U.P. SEB* v. *Om Metals & Minerals (P) Ltd.*, (2002) 9 SCC 512.
628. *State of Rajasthan* v. *Ashok Kumar Contractor*, 2021 SCC OnLine Raj 4272: (2021) 4 RLW 2709.

prolongation of work beyond stipulated time was proper. The award was not set aside.[629]

An agreement entered into between the State and contractor was for completing contract work within six months. The agreement was executed when no fund was available for execution of work. Breach of contract was thus committed by the State. The contractor was entitled to payment of compensation. The award for payment of compensation passed by the arbitrator by recording elaborate reasons in support of each of its findings was proper.[630]

Compensation for additional costs

The arbitrator has not assigned reasons and evaluated evidence and material on record for awarding compensation for additional costs on account of depreciation of tools and plant. The award of the arbitrator was set aside.[631]

Compensation for termination of contract

The contract expressly stated that no compensation is payable if the contract is prematurely terminated by the Principal, namely, DCM. In face of such express prohibition, the Arbitral Tribunal committed error by directing payment of compensation even without disclosing the basis for arriving at such a conclusion. The law is well settled that an arbitrator cannot travel beyond the contract to award compensation.[632] The respondents did not lead any evidence to prove the factum of any loss on account of termination of contract on the basis of unsatisfactory work. No damages as consequence for non-performance of contract could be granted in the absence of such evidence.[633] Where termination of contract is held valid, the question of awarding compensation for termination of contract does not arise.[634]

Compensation—Valuation of

Both the parties submitted before the arbitrator that the arbitrator can decide valuation of compensation according to what was just and proper. The method of valuation was adopted by the arbitrator with the consent of both the parties. The award of the arbitrator was not set aside.[635]

629. *Union of India* v. *Recon*, 2020 SCC OnLine Bom 2278: (2020) 6 Mah LJ 509.
630. *State of Orissa* v. *Bhagyadhar Dash*, 2016 SCC OnLine Ori 1039: (2016) 122 CLT 570; *Steel Fabs* v. *State of Uttarakhand*, 2015 SCC OnLine Utt 2736: (2015) 5 Arb LR 586.
631. *Digha Shankarpur Development Authority* v. *A.K. Enterprises*, 2022 SCC OnLine Cal 1926.
632. *Crompton Greaves Ltd.* v. *Dyna*, 2007 SCC OnLine Mad 427: (2007) 3 CTC 417.
633. *BSNL* v. *Media Mktg. Services*, 2015 SCC OnLine Bom 735: (2015) 2 Mah LJ 281.
634. *Ibid.*
635. *Ibid.*

Refund of security deposit to contractor proper

There was a recession of contract. The reasons for non-completion of contract work were attributable to both the parties. Grant of refund of security to the contractor by the arbitrator was proper.[636]

Expenditure on watch and ward staff

The contractor claimed expenditure alleged to be incurred on watch and ward staff. No material was referred to in the award and, in fact, no material existed in the record of the arbitrator showing that watch and ward staff was, in fact, employed. Finding of the arbitrator allowing the claim was based on no evidence. The award of the arbitrator was set aside.[637]

Goodwill and loss of business

Where the arbitrator awarded a sum of ₹1 crore for loss of goodwill without any evidence, the award for compensation relating to loss of goodwill and business was set aside.[638]

Award made contrary to terms of contract—Modified

Under the tender document there was a clear stipulation for recovery of hire charges for the use of crane from the contractor's bill/security deposit in one instalment. The arbitrator was not justified in disallowing the respondent's claim for recovery of crane hire charges. Further, there was prohibition of award of interest on amounts due to the contractor in the agreement for pre-award period; the respondent was entitled to interest only from the date of award till the date of payment, *i.e.* post-award interest. The award of the arbitrator was modified accordingly.[639]

Award against terms of contract

Award passed by the arbitrator against the terms of the contract would be set aside.[640]

---

636. *State of Bihar* v. *Ram Pravesh Rai Estate (P) Ltd.*, 2017 SCC OnLine Pat 851: (2017) 6 Arb LR 150.
637. *MCD* v. *Rakesh Bros.*, 2005 SCC OnLine Del 484: (2005) 82 DRJ 147.
638. *Tata Steel Ltd.* v. *Lindsay International (P) Ltd.*, 2016 SCC OnLine Cal 6521: (2017) 3 CHN 301.
639. *BHEL* v. *Tata Projects Ltd.*, (2015) 5 SCC 682.
640. *BSNL* v. *Optel Telecommunication Ltd.*, 2018 SCC OnLine MP 202: (2018) 4 MP LJ 393.

Partial final award not challenged

In the absence of a challenge to partial final award, challenge to final award cannot succeed.[641]

Error of law apparent on the face of record (Electricity Act, 1910)

An agreement was reached between the appellant licensees under the Electricity Act and Railways for supply of electric power to certain Railway electrified track routes by the licensees. A dispute arose between the parties with respect to the liability of Railways to pay for the supplementary bill submitted by the licensees for the electrical energy supplied by them, which was not recorded. The fact that the current transformer (CT), which was an "apparatus" within the meaning of Section 26(7), Electricity Act, was defective was not in dispute between the parties. It was held, the dispute did not fall under Section 26(6), Electricity Act so as to be resolved by the Electrical Inspector, and hence, arbitrable by private arbitration. There was no error on the face of record by awarding a lump sum amount in favour of the licensees which was made on the basis of materials available, particularly total energy consumed by Railways. Interest at the rate of 12 per cent per annum was awarded from the date of award, *viz.* 30 March 1998 instead of August 1993.[642]

Land acquisition cases—Compensation

The award was passed by the arbitrator under the provisions of the National Highways Act. The arbitrator had awarded compensation on a completely perverse basis by taking into consideration guideline values which are relevant for stamp duty purposes and not sale deeds which would have reflected proper market value of land. It was held, the awards passed in all such cases were perverse.[643] Where the arbitrator applied two different notifications in determining the market value, it would be a case of patent illegality.[644]

The arbitrator had not made his objective assessment as to the market value of land by considering parameters prescribed under Sections 26 to 28 of the 2013 Act. The award being patently illegal was set aside.[645]

---

641. *Aero Club* v. *Solar Creations (P) Ltd.*, 2020 SCC OnLine Bom 472: (2021) 2 Mah LJ 186.
642. *Tata Hydro-Electric Power Supply Co. Ltd.* v. *Union of India*, (2003) 4 SCC 172.
643. *NHAI* v. *M. Hakeem*, (2021) 9 SCC 1.
644. *NHAI* v. *P. Nagaraju*, (2022) 15 SCC 1.
645. *Ram Lal* v. *NHAI*, 2023 SCC OnLine HP 1822.

An arbitral award which determined the compensation amount for land to be paid under the agreement for sale cannot be directed to be executed as a suit for specific performance of the agreement when reference to the arbitrator was only for fixation of price of land in question and the award was also only with regard to the same.[646]

Stock exchange

Dispute between the parties was related to a transaction which was subject to the bye-laws, rules and regulations of the Bombay Stock Exchange. Though the respondent ceased to be a member during the pendency of the dispute, the dispute between the member and the non-member continued to be arbitrable. The Arbitral Tribunal does not lose its jurisdiction to continue to decide the reference.[647]

Two-tier arbitration

As shown by Sections 34 and 35, an arbitral award would be final and binding on the parties unless it is set aside by a competent court, but it does not exclude the autonomy of the parties to an arbitral award to mutually agree to a procedure whereby the arbitral award might be reconsidered by another arbitrator or panel of arbitrators by way of an appeal and the result of that appeal is accepted by the parties to be final and binding, subject to a challenge provided by the 1996 Act. The fact that recourse to a court is available to a party for challenging an award does not *ipso facto* prohibit the parties from mutually agreeing to a second look at an award with the intention of an early settlement of disputes and differences.[648] The arbitration clause in the agreement which provides for such a two-tier arbitration between the parties does not violate the fundamental policy or public policy of India.[649]

Award against a person not party to the arbitration agreement/ proceedings

Since ONGC company was not a party to any contract or arbitration agreement with the appellant-company EOL, ONGC could not have been represented before the Arbitral Tribunal in arbitration proceedings initiated by EOL on the basis of the arbitration agreement existing between the EOL and respondent-company HSL. Majority view of the Arbitral Tribunal that

---

646. *Rajasthan Udyog* v. *Hindustan Engg. & Industries Ltd.*, (2020) 6 SCC 660.
647. *Murlidhar Roongta* v. *S. Jagannath Tibrewala*, 2004 SCC OnLine Bom 727: (2005) 2 Mah LJ 285.
648. *Centrotrade Minerals & Metal Inc.* v. *Hindustan Copper Ltd.*, (2017) 2 SCC 228.
649. *Ibid.*

in the absence of ONGC as a party before the Arbitral Tribunal, ONGC could not have been made liable to make any payment to EOL was upheld.[650]

The appellant was not a party to the arbitration agreement. The award made by the arbitrator against the appellant was without jurisdiction, and was set aside.[651]

Award of the appellate Bench

The award of the appellate Bench completely replaces the award made by the arbitrators. Once there is an award passed by the appellant Bench, the party aggrieved by the award made by the appellate court cannot challenge the original award by filing application under Section 34 of the Act.[652]

Setting aside of arbitral award—Practice and Procedure

(*a*) *Framing of issues*

Arbitral Tribunal is not required to frame issue.[653]

In an application for setting aside the award of the arbitrator, framing of issues is not necessary. Framing of issues as contemplated under Order 14 Rule 1 CPC is not an integral part of the process of proceedings under Section 34, Arbitration and Conciliation Act, 1996. Speedy resolution of arbitral disputes has been the reason for enacting the 1996 Act and continues to be the reason for adding amendments to the said Act. If issues are framed and oral evidence taken in a summary proceeding under Section 34, this object would be defeated.[654]

(*b*) *Provisions of CPC and Evidence Act*

Though the provisions of the CPC or Evidence Act need not be strictly proved, yet on aspects of principles of natural justice, an opportunity must be given to the party to agitate and/or raise defence or at least put his case. The award which reflects such breaches is unsustainable.[655] The Arbitral Tribunal is not bound by the provisions of the CPC or the provisions of the Evidence Act.[656]

---

650. *Essar Oil Ltd.* v. *Hindustan Shipyard Ltd.*, (2015) 10 SCC 642.
651. *Manoj Kumar Goswami* v. *P.V. Sanghavi*, 2007 SCC OnLine Bom 321: (2007) 4 Mah LJ 569.
652. *Dhansukh K. Sethia* v. *Rajendra Capital Services Ltd.*, 2007 SCC OnLine Bom 792: (2008) 1 Mah LJ 114.
653. *BHEL* v. *Aarti Steel Ltd.*, 2017 SCC OnLine Del 7483.
654. *Emkay Global Financial Services Ltd.* v. *Girdhar Sondhi*, (2018) 9 SCC 49.
655. *Rajesh P. Thakkar* v. *Kotak Mahindra Bank Ltd.*, 2011 SCC OnLine Bom 1284: (2012) 1 Mah LJ 119.
656. *Agarwal Rasayan* v. *National Aluminium Co. Ltd.*, 2019 SCC OnLine Ori 431: (2019) 128 CLT 410.

An arbitral award cannot be faulted on the ground that it is non-compliant with the Evidence Act, 1872 or the CPC. There may however be instances where an arbitral award may be faulted as being in conflict with the public policy of India or on the ground of patent illegality, including that it falls foul of the most basic principles underlying the Evidence Act, 1872. But that does not mean that in all cases where the material relied upon by the Arbitral Tribunal does not measure up to the standards under the Evidence Act, 1872, the arbitral award is liable to be set aside. An arbitral award which is based on no material or evidence at all may be vitiated by patent illegality. However, insufficiency of evidence or material is not a ground for setting aside an arbitral award. In the present case, there is material available on record to substantiate the claim made by the lessor.[657]

Issues as contemplated under Order 14 Rule 1 CPC are not obligatory to be framed in applications under Section 34, Arbitration and Conciliation Act, 1996. Framing of issues is not an integral part of a proceedings under Section 34 of the Act.[658]

(c) *Reasonable opportunity of hearing*

No notice for invocation of the arbitration clause was given to the petitioner. The sole arbitrator nominated by the respondent reserved matter for passing of award. Thereafter, a new arbitrator was appointed without stating any reasons as to why the earlier arbitrator could not pass the award. The award passed by the new arbitrator was silent about service of notice. The said award was passed on the basis of materials already filed before the first arbitrator. No opportunity of hearing was given to the petitioner. It was held, the arbitrator had not conducted a fair hearing. The award of the arbitrator was unsustainable and was set aside.[659]

(d) *Opportunity to parties to lead evidence*

An applicant who approaches the civil court under Section 34 will have to plead the facts and the grounds of challenge and prove the same. The burden of proof is on the applicant, and the court cannot deny opportunity to the applicant to prove allegations.[660]

---

657. *Scholastic India (P) Ltd.* v. *Kanta Batra*, (2022) 5 HCC (Del) 122.
658. *Fiza Developers & Inter-Trade (P) Ltd.* v. *Amci (I)(P) Ltd.*, (2009) 17 SCC 796.
659. *Magesh Kumar S.* v. *Cholamandalam Investment & Finance Co. Ltd.*, 2021 SCC OnLine Mad 16578.
660. *Mahesh Kumar Agarwal* v. *Suresh Chand Agarwal*, 2015 SCC OnLine All 6246: (2016) 2 All LJ 175.

(e) *Oral evidence*

There is no requirement under the provision of Section 34 for the parties to lead evidence. The record of the arbitrator is sufficient in order to furnish proof of whether the grounds under Section 34 have been made out.[661]

(f) *Production of additional evidence*

Where an exceptional case is made out and if it is brought to the court on the matters not containing the record of the arbitrator that certain things are relevant to the determination of the issues arising under Section 34(2)(*a*), then the party who has assailed the award on the grounds set out in Section 34(2)(*a*) can be permitted to file affidavit in the form of evidence. However, the same shall be allowed when absolutely necessary.[662]

The claim of the petitioner was rejected by the arbitrator due to non-production of invoices, as such it cannot be said that they were not relevant. Rejection of the application was not proper. A direction was issued to admit additional evidence.[663]

In the application filed by the respondents seeking permission to adduce evidence, no ground was made out as to the necessity of adducing evidence and what was the nature of the evidence sought to be led by the respondents. The proceedings under Section 34 of the Act are summary proceedings and are not in the nature of a regular suit. By adding sub-sections (5) and (6) to Section 34 of the Act, the Act has specified the time period of one year for disposal of the application under Section 34 of the Act. The object of sub-sections (5) and (6) to Section 34 fixing time frame to dispose of the matter filed under Section 34, Arbitration Act, 1996 is to avoid delay and to dispose of the application expeditiously and in any event within a period of one year from the date on which the notice referred to in Section 34(5) of the Act is served upon the other party. In the arbitration proceedings, the parties had sufficient opportunity to adduce oral and documentary evidence. The order of the High Court permitting the parties to adduce additional evidence was erroneous, and was set aside.[664]

(g) *Additional evidence by way of affidavit*

An application for setting aside an arbitral award will not ordinarily require anything beyond the record that was before the arbitrator. However, if there

661. *Emkay Global Financial Services Ltd.* v. *Girdhar Sondhi*, (2018) 9 SCC 49; *Sandeep Kumar* v. *Ashok Hans*, 2004 SCC OnLine Del 106.
662. *Alpine Housing Development Corpn. (P) Ltd.* v. *Ashok S. Dhariwal*, 2023 SCC OnLine SC 55.
663. *Bhadra Products* v. *Indian Farmers Fertilizer Coop. Ltd.*, 2022 SCC OnLine Ori 3549.
664. *Canara Nidhi Ltd.* v. *M. Shashikala*, (2019) 9 SCC 462.

are matters not contained in such a record, and are relevant to the determination of issues arising under Section 34(2)(*a*), they may be brought to the notice of the court by way of affidavits filed by both the parties.[665] The petition under Section 34 has to be decided on affidavit.[666]

Applications under Section 34 of the Act are proceedings before the civil court within the meaning of Section 141 CPC. Parties are permitted to give evidence on affidavit, and if the parties want to cross-examine the witnesses, the court may permit cross-examination of the persons swearing to the affidavit.[667]

Where an exceptional case is made out and if it is brought to the court on the matters not containing the record of the arbitrator that certain things are relevant to the determination of the issues arising under Section 34(2)(*a*), then the party who has assailed the award on the grounds set out in Section 34(2)(*a*) can be permitted to file affidavit in the form of evidence. However, the same shall be allowed when absolutely necessary.[668]

(*h*) *Rejoinder affidavit*

Ordinarily, in an application under Section 34, Arbitration and Conciliation Act, the court does not require anything beyond the record that was before the arbitrator. The statute does not envisage filing of additional statements, documents/facts at the stage of Section 34 proceeding. Such recourse can be taken only in exceptional circumstances. Additional facts/documents should not be accepted by the Additional District Judge without giving reasons.[669]

(*i*) *Cross-examination of the witnesses swearing affidavits*

Cross-examination of persons swearing to the affidavits should not be allowed unless absolutely necessary, as truth will emerge on the reading of the affidavits filed by both the parties.[670]

---

665. *Emkay Global Financial Services Ltd.* v. *Girdhar Sondhi*, (2018) 9 SCC 49; *Alpine Housing Development Corpn. (P) Ltd.* v. *Ashok S. Dhariwal*, 2023 SCC OnLine SC 55.
666. *S.S.M. Soundappan* v. *K.G. Balakrishnan*, 1997 SCC OnLine Mad 503: (1997) 2 CTC 385.
667. *Amit Mohan Mittal* v. *Atul Kumar Gupta*, 2013 SCC OnLine All 13434: (2013) 99 ALR 387.
668. *Alpine Housing Development Corpn. (P) Ltd.* v. *Ashok S. Dhariwal*, 2023 SCC OnLine SC 55.
669. *S.K. Dynamics (P) Ltd.* v. *Center of Excellence in Disaster M. & M.*, 2022 SCC OnLine Utt 1853.
670. *Emkay Global Financial Services Ltd.* v. *Girdhar Sondhi*, (2018) 9 SCC 49.

(*j*) *Inspection of record by arbitrator*

It is open to the arbitrator to carry out inspection of any record after due notice to both the parties. The contention that the arbitrator carried out inspection of records behind the back of a party was rejected when he had given notice to both the parties.[671]

Amendment in Section 34 petition

An amendment in a petition under Section 34 of the Act of 1996 was sought after eight years of filing of the petition, and the appeal was pending for more than last three years. Rejection of amendment was held proper.[672] Where no sufficient cause was shown by the petitioner for bringing an amendment at a belated stage, the application for setting aside the award was filed on 11 July 2005, and the application for amendment was filed on 24 March 2008, the application for amendment was rightly rejected by the trial court barred by limitation.[673] An amendment to application filed under Section 34 of the Act for setting aside an award after the expiry of limitation as prescribed under Section 34(2) seeking additional grounds is not permissible.[674] The petitioners by way of an amendment sought to furnish material particulars. No reasons were assigned by the petitioners for not incorporating pleas under Section 34. Grounds which were not initially raised in the petition to challenge an award cannot be permitted to be raised by way of an amendment. The amendment sought beyond the period of limitation of 120 days as prescribed in the proviso to Section 34(3) was barred by limitation.[675]

The test for allowing or rejecting an amendment to existing grounds in an arbitration petition is whether the proposed grounds would necessitate filing of a fresh application for setting aside the award. As several of the new grounds also do not have a foundational basis in the existing petition, the petitioner cannot enter through the "amplification" route as has been contended and if the amplification recourse fails, the petitioner has no other statutory cushion to fall back on under the existing law; hence, the amendment was not allowed.[676]

---

671. *Environmental Engineer Inc.* v. *Maharashtra Pollution Control Board*, 2004 SCC OnLine Bom 227: (2004) 3 Mah LJ 37.
672. *Maharashtra State Electricity Distribution Co. Ltd.* v. *Datar Switchgear Ltd.*, (2018) 3 SCC 133.
673. *Union of India* v. *B.C. Biyani*, 2009 SCC OnLine Bom 1554: (2010) 1 Mah LJ 615.
674. *Pushpa P. Mulchandani* v. *Admiral Radhakrishin Tahilani (Retd.)*, 2000 SCC OnLine Bom 620: (2000) 4 Mah LJ 819.
675. *Kanthamma Chandrashekar* v. *Rohan Housing (P) Ltd.*, 2019 SCC OnLine Kar 3522: (2019) 5 KCCR 1371.
676. *Prakash Industries Ltd.* v. *Bengal Energy Ltd.*, 2020 SCC OnLine Cal 971.

Where the amendment sought is for amplification and does not change in any way the nature of the pleadings, and is amplifying the grounds for setting aside the award, the amendment of the petition filed under Section 34 shall be allowed.[677]

Leave to amend grounds in Section 34

Where an application under Section 34 has been made within the prescribed time, leave to amend grounds in such an application, if the peculiar circumstances of the case and the interest of justice so warrant can be granted. While dealing with a prayer for amendment, the courts normally prefer substance to form and techniques, and the interest of justice is one of the most relevant considerations. Therefore, if a party is entitled to amend its pleadings, having regard to the justice of the case, the right of the party to amend cannot be defeated just because a wrong section or a wrong provision has been quoted in the amendment petition. The approach of the High Court in this case in rejecting the appellant's prayer for amendment, inter alia, on the ground that a wrong provision has been quoted in the amendment petition was obviously a very hyper-technical one.[678]

An amendment which gave further details of bias of the arbitrator was allowed.[679]

Parties to proceedings under Section 34—Arbitrator not necessary party

In proceedings under Section 34, the arbitrator cannot be made party thereto or in consequential proceedings thereafter.[680] It is completely unnecessary for arbitrators to be arrayed as a party unless personal allegations are made and the arbitrator is required to answer such allegations.[681]

Unless direct allegations of misconduct or like are made against arbitrators, it is quite unnecessary to implead arbitrators as party in proceedings under Section 34 for setting aside the award.[682]

---

677. *Maharashtra Krishna Valley Development Corpn.* v. *B.T. Patil & Son Belgaum (Consti.) (P) Ltd.*, 2020 SCC OnLine Bom 2810.
678. *Venture Global Engg.* v. *Satyam Computer Services Ltd.*, (2010) 8 SCC 660.
679. *Inox Leisure Ltd.* v. *Goa State Infrastructure Development Corpn. Ltd.*, 2014 SCC OnLine Bom 1535: (2015) 2 Mah LJ 38.
680. *Ircon International Ltd.* v. *Vinay Heavy Equipments*, (2015) 13 SCC 680.
681. *NAPC Ltd.* v. *National Highways*, 2021 SCC OnLine Mad 5427.
682. *3i Infotech Ltd.* v. *P. Balasubramanian*, 2021 SCC OnLine Mad 2641: (2021) 4 LW 300.

Re-appreciation of evidence

Appreciation of evidence is the sole and exclusive domain of the arbitrator. The court in exercise of its power under Section 34 of the Act cannot re-appreciate the evidence so as to arrive at its own conclusion. The said exercise would be completely outside the scope of its jurisdiction under Section 34 of the Act.[683]

The appellant was awarded a contract by the respondent for execution of earth excavation work and loading. The respondent alleged that the appellant did not fulfil its obligation; the appellant on the contrary alleged that the respondent was required to facilitate the execution of work which was not done by the respondent. The arbitrator on appreciation of evidence on record held that the respondent had failed to fulfil its required obligation and partly allowed the appellant's claim. A Single Judge of the High Court appreciated the evidence on record and came to a different conclusion. It was held, the arbitrator had taken a plausible view. The rights and obligations of the parties were interdependent. The Single Judge of the High Court ought not to have re-appreciated the evidence and acted like a second appellate court. The order of the Single Judge was set aside and enforcement of the award was upheld.[684]

Intervention of the court with an arbitral award is envisaged only in the supervisory role of the courts. Therefore, the courts while exercising its powers under Section 34 cannot reappreciate the evidence or examine the correctness of the conclusions arrived at by the arbitrator. The proviso to sub-section (2-A) to Section 34 puts a specific restriction on the powers of the court inasmuch as a wrong decision of the arbitrator shall not be a ground to interfere with the arbitral award.[685]

The decision of the Arbitral Tribunal as to the evidentiary value of the independent engineer's certificate is final. The court is not required to reappreciate and consider each and every piece of evidence or material that is placed before the Arbitral Tribunal. The impugned award cannot be interfered with on the ground that one of the documents may be inadmissible in evidence or is of little evidentiary value.[686]

Reappraising material on record by the court and substitution of its own view in place of arbitrator's view is not permissible in the absence of

---

683. *Ircon International Ltd.* v. *Patil Rail Infrastructure (P) Ltd.*, 2018 SCC OnLine Del 9384.
684. *Sutlej Construction Ltd.* v. *State (UT of Chandigarh)*, (2018) 1 SCC 718; *Maharashtra State Electricity Distribution Co. Ltd.* v. *Datar Switchgear Ltd.*, (2018) 3 SCC 133.
685. *Union of India* v. *Anup & Co.*, 2023 SCC OnLine Jhar 3880: (2023) 3 JLJR 452.
686. *ITDC Ltd.* v. *Bougainvillea Multipex & Entertainment Centre (P) Ltd.*, (2022) 2 HCC (Del) 127.

perversity merely because two views are permissible. Once the arbitrator has applied his mind to the matter before him, the court would not re-appreciate the said matter as if it were an appeal. Even if two views are possible, the view taken by the arbitrator would prevail.[687] An agreement was arrived at between the parties to procure, install and operate an amusement ride by the first respondent, to be maintained by the appellant. Collections from the ride were to be shared at the rate of 60:40 by the first respondent and the appellant in the first year and at the rate of 50:50 thereafter. The appellant failed to make payments from 2000 to 2001 despite repeated demands. The dispute was referred to the arbitrator. The arbitrator allowed claim to the tune of ₹ 13,94,240, and the agreement also stipulated guaranteed minimum gross collection of ₹ 10 lakhs in the first year and ₹ 8.53 lakhs thereafter. The award was affirmed by the Division Bench of the High Court. The arbitrator had applied his mind to the facts of the case. The award was not perverse, and was not set aside.[688]

The basic principle that the courts have to follow is that the re-appraisal of evidence is not permissible and the arbitrator is the sole judge of the quality and quantity of the evidence. This would be subject to the condition of clause (*b*)(*ii*) of sub-section (2) of Section 34 of the Act.[689]

The court cannot sit, in appeal, over the award by reassessing or re-appreciating evidence to find out whether different decisions could be arrived at against findings of an Arbitral Tribunal in absence of grounds under Section 34.[690]

The court does not sit as the first appellate court and cannot re-appreciate the evidence and supplant its opinion over that of the Arbitral Tribunal. An arbitral award, which is contrary to the terms of the contract, is amenable to challenge under Section 34, Arbitration and Conciliation Act, 1996.[691]

The proviso to new sub-section (2-A), added by Amendment Act 3 of 2016 also stipulates that an award of the arbitrator shall not be set aside on the ground of erroneous application of law or by appreciation of evidence.

The arbitrator is the final arbiter for the dispute between the parties and it is not open to challenge the award on the ground that the arbitrator has drawn his own conclusion or has failed to appreciate the facts.[692] The

687. *Navodaya Mass Entertainment Ltd.* v. *J.M. Combines*, (2015) 5 SCC 698.
688. *Ibid.*
689. *Shree Ambika Construction Co., Nagpur* v. *Union of India*, 2007 SCC OnLine Bom 1126: (2008) 3 Mah LJ 214.
690. *P.R. Shah, Shares & Stock Brokers (P) Ltd.* v. *B.H.H. Securities (P) Ltd.*, (2012) 1 SCC 594; *McDermott International Inc.* v. *Burn Standard Co. Ltd.*, (2006) 11 SCC 181.
691. *GAIL (India) Ltd.* v. *Triveni Engg. & Industries Ltd.*, (2022) 3 HCC (Del) 324.
692. *State of Rajasthan* v. *Puri Construction Co. Ltd.*, (1994) 6 SCC 485.

court cannot substitute its own evaluation of the conclusion of law or fact to come to the conclusion that the arbitrator had acted contrary to the bargain between the parties.[693] In *Ravindra Kumar Gupta & Co.* v. *Union of India*[694], the contractor's claim for loss caused due to delay and hold-ups attributed to the employer Union of India was allowed by the arbitrator. The arbitrator had duly appreciated the evidence adduced before it. The conclusion of the arbitrator was erroneously substituted by the High Court with its own opinion on appreciation of evidence. The Supreme Court held that such a course was not permissible to the High Court while examining objections to the award under Section 30, Arbitration Act, 1940 (Section 34 of the 1996 Act). Reappraisal of material on record of Arbitral Tribunal is not permissible in action under Section 34.[695]

Where there is no perversity in the award, but the appellant had not produced the record though the respondent had asked for the same. The appellant took the plea that the documents/records were destroyed in fire, re-appreciation of evidence by the court was not required.[696]

Findings of facts of arbitrator—Re-appreciation of evidence

Arbitrator's decision is generally considered binding between the parties; the power of the court to set aside the award would be exercised only in cases where the court finds that the arbitral award is erroneous or patently illegal or in contravention of the provisions of the Act. The court shall not ordinarily substitute its interpretation for that of the arbitrator. The findings of facts recorded by the arbitrator cannot be interfered with on the ground that the terms of the contract were not correctly interpreted by him.[697] Factual determination by the arbitrator cannot again be re-appreciated.[698] The court would not be entitled to re-appreciate the material before the arbitrator with a view to substitute its own findings for those of the arbitrator.[699]

The arbitrator is the final adjudicator of questions of fact. His findings on questions of fact are not amenable to judicial review unless it is established that it is virtually impossible to arrive at such findings on the basis of the

---

693. *Sudarsan Trading Co.* v. *State of Kerala*, (1989) 2 SCC 38.
694. (2010) 1 SCC 409.
695. *Shree Vinayak Cement Clearing Agency* v. *Cement Corpn. of India*, 2007 SCC OnLine Del 1012: ILR (2008) 1 Del 347.
696. *Royal Palms (India) (P) Ltd.* v. *Neeta Jignesh Parikh*, 2016 SCC OnLine Bom 6785: (2016) 6 Mah LJ 214.
697. *Swan Gold Mining Ltd.* v. *Hindustan Copper Ltd.*, (2015) 5 SCC 739.
698. *Municipal Corpn. of Greater Mumbai* v. *Jyoti Construction Co.*, 2002 SCC OnLine Bom 1067: (2003) 4 Mah LJ 25.
699. *Ibid.*

material-on-record; such findings strike at the root of the disputes and vitiate the arbitral award on the ground of patent illegality.[700]

It is not open to the court to re-appreciate the reasonableness of the reasons for the reasons in the arbitral award even if it were to have another view of the matter.[701]

Where finding of fact recorded by the Arbitral Tribunal in its award is not perverse, interference in exercise of jurisdiction under Section 34 is not permissible.[702] Where material is available on record on the basis of which the Appellate Tribunal recorded finding, there is no scope for interference with the findings recorded on the basis of documentary evidence available on record.[703] Where finding of fact was arrived at by the arbitrator after considering evidence, the challenge to the award was found not sustainable.[704] Finding of fact recorded by the arbitrator cannot be disturbed by the High Court exercising jurisdiction under Section 34 unless there is an error apparent on the face of the record or the finding suffers from violation of the principles of natural justice.[705] The court shall not interfere with the possible interpretation of the arbitrator, and cannot substitute its own views in place of interpretation accepted by the arbitrator.[706]

The High Court in jurisdiction under Section 34 cannot re-determine the work actually carried out and the amount computed thereon is payable or not.[707]

Factual determination of the arbitrator cannot be re-appreciated unless the award is capricious or arbitrary. It is not open to the arbitration court to re-appreciate reasonableness of reasons in the arbitral award.[708]

A possible view by the arbitrator on facts has necessarily to pass muster as the arbitrator is the ultimate master of the quantity and quality of evidence to be relied upon when he delivers his award. An award based on little evidence

---

700. *Eastern Coalfields Ltd.* v. *India Power Corpn. Ltd.*, (2022) 4 HCC (Del) 294.
701. *Municipal Corpn. of Greater Mumbai* v. *Jyoti Construction Co.*, 2002 SCC OnLine Bom 1067: (2003) 4 Mah LJ 25.
702. *Syntrex Corpn.* v. *Rajkumar Keshardev*, 2007 SCC OnLine Bom 620: (2007) 6 Mah LJ 34; *Pradyuman Kumar Sharma* v. *Jays Agar M. Sancheti*, 2013 SCC OnLine Bom 453: (2013) 5 Mah LJ 86.
703. *Dhansukh K. Sethia* v. *Rajendra Capital Services Ltd.*, 2007 SCC OnLine Bom 792: (2008) 1 Mah LJ 114.
704. *Union of India* v. *Moti Enterprises*, 2005 SCC OnLine Bom 196: (2005) 2 Mah LJ 791.
705. *Larsen and Toubro Ltd.* v. *Sunfield Resources (P) Ltd.*, 2005 SCC OnLine Bom 726: (2005) 4 Mah LJ 607.
706. *Ropa Plastics (P) Ltd.* v. *IPN Packaging (P) Ltd.*, 2013 SCC OnLine Bom 716: (2014) 3 Mah LJ 150.
707. *Indian Lead Ltd.* v. *R.L. Dalal & Co. (P) Ltd.*, 2004 SCC OnLine Bom 1061: (2006) 2 Mah LJ 260.
708. *Union of India* v. *Pam Developments (P) Ltd.*, 2003 SCC OnLine Cal 491: (2004) 1 CHN 407.

or on evidence which does not measure in quality to a trained legal mind would not be held invalid on this score. Once it is found that the arbitrator's approach is not arbitrary or capricious, then he is the last word on facts.[709]

Finding of the arbitrator relating to escalation in price being finding of fact was not interfered with.[710]

Finding of the arbitrator based on material-on-record cannot be interfered with by court.[711]

The Supreme Court cannot sit over the finding of fact arrived at by the majority of arbitrators and affirmed by the High Court. The view taken by the Division Bench of the High Court in accepting the view of the majority of the arbitrators in granting damages to the respondent on this ground was accepted.[712]

The fact that a certain piece of evidence is not advertised to or ignored by the arbitrator while relying on other evidence would not furnish an aggrieved party with a ground for challenging the arbitral award under Section 28 or 34 of the 1996 Act.[713]

An award passed by the Arbitral Tribunal after consideration of all the facts would not be set aside.[714]

Validity of appointment of arbitrator

In an application filed under Section 34 of the Act, the validity or otherwise of an appointment of the arbitrator made under Section 11(6) of the Act could not have been gone into. The District Judge was only required to see whether the award passed by the arbitrator is hit by the vice of Section 34(2) of the Act. The District Judge has completely misdirected itself in going into the question of appointment of the arbitrator and setting aside the award on that score.[715]

Interference on facts impermissible

Interference with the possible view of the arbitrator on facts is not permissible.[716]

---

709. *Associate Builders* v. *DDA*, (2015) 3 SCC 49.
710. *Ravindra & Associates* v. *Union of India*, (2010) 1 SCC 80.
711. *ITDC Ltd.* v. *Bougainvillea Multipex & Entertainment Centre (P) Ltd.*, (2022) 2 HCC (Del) 127.
712. *Numaligarh Refinery Ltd.* v. *Daelim Industrial Co. Ltd.*, (2007) 8 SCC 466.
713. *Viraj Holdings* v. *Motilal Oswal Securities (P) Ltd.*, 2002 SCC OnLine Bom 558: (2002) 4 Mah LJ 65.
714. *Union of India* v. *Maheswari Builders*, 2023 SCC OnLine Mad 16.
715. *Udayanath Rout v. Paradip Port Trust*, 2016 SCC OnLine Ori 131.
716. *Associate Builders* v. *DDA*, (2015) 3 SCC 49.

Finality of the arbitral award—When award not enforced

An award is not a waste paper merely because it has not been enforced. After an award is pronounced, no action can be started on the original claim which had been the subject-matter of the reference. An award possesses all the elements of vitality, even though it has not been formally enforced, and it may be relied upon in a litigation between the parties relating to the same subject-matter.[717]

Remand [Sub-s. (4)]

The power of the court to remand the matter to the Arbitral Tribunal is only to adjourn the proceedings for the limited purpose mentioned in Section 34(4), *i.e.* to give the Arbitral Tribunal an opportunity to resume the arbitral proceedings or to take such other action as in the opinion of the Arbitral Tribunal will eliminate the grounds for setting aside the award. The conditions required to be satisfied for such remand are:

1. there is a written request made by a party to the arbitral proceedings;
2. the arbitral award has not already been set aside;
3. the challenge to the award has been set up under Section 34 about the deficiencies in the award which may be curable by allowing the Arbitral Tribunal to take such measures, which can eliminate the grounds for setting aside.

The scope of enquiry under Section 34(4) is left to the discretion of the Arbitral Tribunal and is not to be dictated by the court which considers the application under Section 34(1).[718] The power under Section 34(4) can be exercised by the court only at the request of the parties.[719]

In *Kinnari Mullick* v. *Ghanshyam Das Damani*[720], the High Court set aside the award of the arbitrator as the award did not contain reasons and remanded the matter to the arbitrator to assign reasons in support of its award. It was held, the impugned direction of the High Court suffered from the vice of jurisdictional error and could not be sustained and, hence, was set aside.

717. *Centrotrade Minerals & Metal Inc.* v. *Hindustan Copper Ltd.*, (2017) 2 SCC 228.

718. *M.M.T.C.* v. *Vicnivass Agency*, 2008 SCC OnLine Mad 584: (2008) 3 LW 1063; *Kinnari Mullick* v. *Ghanshyam Das Damani*, (2018) 11 SCC 328.

719. *Indian Oil Corpn. Ltd.* v. *Artson Engg. Ltd.*, 2006 SCC OnLine Bom 1106: (2007) 1 Mah LJ 825; *Chandrashekar* v. *Yogi Construction*, 2018 SCC OnLine Bom 12200: (2019) 1 Mah LJ 628. (Only if a written request is made by a party before passing of award.).

720. (2018) 11 SCC 328; *M.M.T.C.* v. *Vicnivass Agency*, 2008 SCC OnLine Mad 584: (2008) 3 LW 1063.

The object of sub-section (4) of Section 34 is to give opportunity to the Arbitral Tribunal to resume the arbitral proceedings or to enable it to take such other action which will eliminate the grounds for setting aside the arbitral award. The court cannot exercise the limited power of deferring the proceedings before it suo motu.[721] There was no illegality or any jurisdictional error committed by the trial court in allowing the application under Section 34(4) and resume the arbitral proceedings.[722] There is no provision for an order of remand.[723] The power of the court under Section 34 of the Act is not to remand the matter to the Arbitral Tribunal after setting aside the arbitral award .[724] The commercial court, after considering all decisions cited and pleadings put forth by parties, held that the arbitral award suffered from patent illegality as it failed to consider counterclaim of the respondent, and set aside the award. Once a decision is made in Section 34 application, the court has no power to remit arbitration matter to the arbitrator. The only course available is to set aside or to uphold the award. The order of commercial court setting aside the award and giving liberty to both parties to resolve the dispute initiating fresh arbitral proceedings was held proper.[725]

The respondent sought adjournment of court proceedings so as to go back to the tribunal on lump sum damages. The court found that damages as awarded were without any basis and the award was liable to be set aside. There was also no necessity to seek any clarification on the point whether the awarded amount was inclusive of bank guarantees. The request for adjournment of court proceedings and reference back to the tribunal under Section 34(4) was declined.[726]

Remission of matter to an arbitrator under Section 34(4) for the elimination of grounds for setting aside the award cannot be permitted in the absence of findings on the contentious issues.[727]

The court can remand the matter in part and/or whole to the Arbitral Tribunal. It depends on the issue involved. If all the issues are connected

---

721. *McDermott International Inc.* v. *Burn Standard Co. Ltd.*, (2006) 11 SCC 181; *M.M.T.C.* v. *Vicnivass Agency*, 2008 SCC OnLine Mad 584: (2008) 3 LW 1063.
722. *Midex Overseas Ltd.* v. *Dewas Soya Ltd.*, 2001 SCC OnLine MP 79: (2001) 2 MP LJ 391.
723. *R. Narayanan* v. *India Info Line Securities (P) Ltd.*, 2013 SCC OnLine Mad 1744: (2013) 5 LW 89.
724. *Bhaskar Industrial Development Ltd.* v. *Railways*, 2016 SCC OnLine Kar 8330: (2016) 3 KCCR 2285 (DB).
725. *Sri Rama Constructions* v. *Max Infra (I) Ltd.*, 2023 SCC OnLine TS 644.
726. *Kanti Bijlee Utpadan Nigam Ltd.* v. *Paltech Cooling Towers & Equipments Ltd.*, (2022) 4 HCC (Del) 233.
727. *I-Pay Clearing Services (P) Ltd.* v. *ICICI Bank Ltd.*, (2022) 3 SCC 121

or interlinked, there is no question of remanding the matter on a particular issue.[728]

"Prior notice to the other party" [Sub-s. (5)]

Sub-section (5), added by Amendment Act 3 of 2016, envisages a provision that an application under Section 34 shall be filed by a party only after issuing a prior notice to the other party, and such application shall be accompanied by an affidavit by the applicant endorsing compliance with the said requirement. Sub-section (5) is not a condition precedent but a procedural provision, is directory and not mandatory, and does not provide for the penal consequence in the event of non-compliance with the provision. Order of the Division Bench of the Patna High Court which held the provisions of sub-section (5) mandatory and dismissed the petition filed under Section 34 for failure to issue required notice was set aside.[729] Section 34(5) is directory and in contrast to the provision of Section 80 CPC and Section 29-A, Arbitration and Conciliation Act, 1996.[730]

There is restriction under the Act to issue notice limited to some or one of the grounds laid out to challenge the award. The court should pass a reasoned order indicating reasons for issuance of notice on limited grounds.[731]

Notice not issued to respondent—Award set aside

As no notice was issued to the respondent by the arbitrator, award of the arbitrator was set aside.[732]

Ex parte award set aside

The award suffered from very basic infirmities. There was absence of evidence in support of issuance/service of notice on the appellant. The appellant was not given sufficient opportunity for filing written statement and adducing his evidence. The award of the arbitrator was set aside.[733]

---

728. *Rajesh Tiwari* v. *Motilal Oswal Financial Services Ltd.*, 2013 SCC OnLine Bom 2: (2013) 3 Mah LJ 523.
729. *State of Bihar* v. *Bihar Rajya Bhumi Vikas Bank Samiti*, (2018) 9 SCC 472.
730. *Ibid.*
731. *NHAI* v. *Oriental Structure Engineers Ltd.-Gammon India Ltd. (JV)*, 2012 SCC OnLine Del 4787: (2012) 132 DRJ 769.
732. *Sachin Gupta* v. *K.S. Forge Metal (P) Ltd.*, (2013) 10 SCC 540.
733. *Eastern Coalfields Ltd.* v. *Satish Constructions*, 2022 SCC OnLine Jhar 1571: (2023) 1 JBCJ 154.

Appointment of another arbitrator

The arbitrator had made an award without notice to the objectors. Service of notice on the objectors was found manipulated, and, hence, the court set aside the arbitrator's award and appointed another arbitrator in the case.[734]

Expeditious disposal of Section 34 application within one year [Sub-s. (6)]

Sub-section (6), inserted by Amendment Act 3 of 2016, stipulates that an application under Section 34 shall be disposed of expeditiously and in any event within a period of one year from the date on which the notice referred to in sub-section (5) is served upon the other party. It shall be the endeavour of every court in which a Section 34 application is filed to stick to the time-limit of one year from the date of service of the notice to the opposite party by the applicant, or by the court, as the case may be. In case the court issues notice after the period mentioned in Section 34(3) has elapsed, every court shall endeavour to dispose of the Section 34 application within a period of one year from the date of filing of the said application similar to what has been provided in Section 14, Commercial Courts Act, 2015.

Sub-section (6) refers to the date on which the notice referred to in sub-section (6) is served upon the other party. This is for the reason that an anterior date to that of filing the application is to be the starting point of the period of one year referred to in Section 34(6).[735]

Fees to be taken as a composite amount and not to be paid separately and individually to each arbitrator.[736]

Plea of limitation

Where the plea of limitation has not been raised in the pleadings, the petitioner cannot be allowed to raise the plea of limitation in a petition under Section 34, the Arbitration and Conciliation Act, 1995.[737]

Setting aside award on the ground of non-existence of arbitration agreement

An arbitration agreement was contained only in invoices raised by the respondent on the petitioner. The said invoices were not disputed. Since the petitioner did not dispute the existence of the arbitration agreement in its

---

734. *Taruna Vaid* v. *Rakesh Kumar*, (2005) 12 SCC 235.
735. *State of Bihar* v. *Bihar Rajya Bhumi Vikas Bank Samiti*, (2018) 9 SCC 472.
736. *State of U.P.* v. *Shyam Lal*, 2021 SCC OnLine All 514: (2021) 148 ALR 344.
737. *Jai Gurudev Textile Agencies* v. *Surya Processors (P) Ltd.*, 2022 SCC OnLine Del 984.

reply to the respondent, he cannot be heard to deny the existence of the arbitration agreement later.[738]

Non-speaking award

The scope of interference by the court under Section 34 in non-speaking award is extremely limited. The court should endeavour to support a non-speaking arbitration award, provided it has adhered to the parties' agreement and was not invalidated due to arbitrator's misconduct.[739] The court shall make endeavour to support the award when no misconduct on the part of the arbitrator is alleged or found.[740] Where the arbitrator allowed claims without assigning reasons and also awarded interest though the claimant was himself guilty of latches in submitting claims before the arbitrator, it was held that the arbitrator had misconduct jurisdiction, and the award passed by him was set aside.[741] Where the arbitrator had rejected certain items of counterclaim but had not given any reason, the award being in breach of principles of natural justice was set aside and proceedings were remitted for reconsideration of the items of the counterclaim.[742]

The absence of adducing reasons in the award is not one of the grounds found in Section 34 of the Act for setting aside an award, but it is the statutory requirement under Section 31 of the Act. However, mere non-mentioning of the reasons would not make the award illegal.[743] Recording of reasons is to facilitate scrutiny by the court in an application under Section 34 for setting aside the award.[744]

In *Board of Trustees* v. *ABG Kolkata Container Terminal (P) Ltd.*[745], the arbitrator had awarded the amount without adjudication of quantum; the award was vitiated for lack of reasons and was set aside.

It is imperative that reasons be furnished in support of an award unless the parties dispense therewith by agreement. Where the reasoning given by

738. *Ibid.*
739. *Markfed Vanaspati & Allied Industries* v. *Union of India*, (2007) 7 SCC 679.
740. *Ram Engg. Constructions* v. *Pondicherry Municipality*, 2009 SCC OnLine Mad 620: (2009) 2 LW 937.
741. *Allahabad Development Authority* v. *Vidyawati Construction Co.*, 2001 SCC OnLine All 625: (2002) 46 ALR 73.
742. *Kishore Textiles Mills* v. *Union of India*, 2000 SCC OnLine Bom 280: (2000) 3 Mah LJ 395.
743. *Ram Engg. Constructions* v. *Pondicherry Municipality*, 2009 SCC OnLine Mad 620: (2009) 2 LW 937; *Mafatlal Securities Ltd.* v. *Birla Sun-Life Securities Ltd.*, 2002 SCC OnLine Bom 304: (2002) 3 Mah LJ 116.
744. *Ram Engg. Constructions* v. *Pondicherry Municipality*, 2009 SCC OnLine Mad 620: (2009) 2 LW 937.
745. 2020 SCC OnLine Cal 2273.

the arbitrator did not indicate how the money claimed was due, the award of the arbitrator would be set aside.[746]

Where the document styled award does not contain reasons, it cannot be an award, nor can be set aside.[747] In the absence of any contrary agreement, it is the primary duty of the arbitrator to give reasons for the award. In the absence of records, the award was not sustained and was set aside; the matter was remanded to the arbitrator for fresh determination in view of the mandate of Section 31(3) of the Act.[748]

Where an application under Section 34 for setting aside an award was dismissed by a cryptic order without reasons, the impugned order of dismissal was set aside.[749]

An arbitrator is expected to give at least a brief summary of reasons in his award. Failure of the arbitrator constituted misconduct. The award was set aside.[750]

Relevant records were not produced by the petitioner before the arbitrator. Despite affidavits filed by the claimant-deponents, they were not cross-examined by the petitioner-State. As such the arbitrator was not in a position to give detailed reasons. It was held, lack of detailed reasons was no ground to set aside the arbitral award. As award was supported by reasons, it was not set aside.[751]

An award in favour of the contractor allowed certain claims. The arbitrator assigned proper reasons while allowing certain claims and rejecting other claims. The award could not be held to be non-speaking award, and refusal to set aside award was proper.[752] The arbitrator had considered individual claims and had given reasons for the award of the specific amount in relation to that particular claim, but had not given reason for awarding pendente lite interest at the rate of 12 per cent per annum instead of 18 per cent claimed. In the total absence of reasons either by way of adjudication or the quantum of interest, the award cannot be upheld. The award in respect of all the claims except in relation to the grant of interest was upheld.[753] In a

746. *Hindustan Petroleum Corpn. Ltd.* v. *Banu Constructions*, 2021 SCC OnLine Mad 724: (2021) 1 LW 657.
747. *Mafatlal Securities Ltd.* v. *Birla Sun-Life Securities Ltd.*, 2002 SCC OnLine Bom 304: (2002) 3 Mah LJ 116.
748. *Janki Ram* v. *State of H.P.*, 2007 SCC OnLine HP 119.
749. *Union of India* v. *D.D. Sharma*, 2016 SCC OnLine Gau 721: (2016) 4 Gau LR 370.
750. *AVI Coach Builders* v. *Union of India*, 2009 SCC OnLine Del 100: (2009) 108 DRJ 297.
751. *Union of India* v. *Harbans Singh Tuli & Sons Building (P) Ltd.*, (2010) 13 SCC 252; *Union of India* v. *Mukul Builders (P) Ltd.*, 2015 SCC OnLine All 2623: (2015) 112 ALR 583.
752. *Union of India* v. *Chadha & Co.*, 2020 SCC OnLine HP 958.
753. *Ircon International Ltd.* v. *Meumal Athwani*, 2020 SCC OnLine Cal 1045.

claim, particularly relating to works contracts, every head of claim has to be dealt with in principle and the quantum awarded or declined has next to be justified. It will not do for merely head of claim to be explained and the quantum awarded in respect thereof not to be. Both must have reasons in support of the conclusion and, in the absence of either, the award becomes vulnerable. In *Hindustan Petroleum Corpn. Ltd.* v. *Banu Constructions*[754], the arbitrator without assigning any reason awarded amount under two heads of claim. In respect of the third head, the arbitrator stated that considerable delay on the part of the claimant would not defeat his claim but no justification was recorded for such findings. The reasons recorded by the arbitrator did not show how any money was due on account of the claim raised. The award of the arbitrator was set aside.

An award in order to be so must contain reasons upon which it is based, otherwise it cannot be termed as an award. If a document does not contain reasons, it is not an award, though signed by the arbitrators, and cannot be set aside under Section 34.[755]

Reasonableness of reasons

The arbitrator is the final arbiter for the dispute between the parties in proceeding. The court cannot take upon itself the task of being a judge to examine the reasonableness of reasons. The court would not interfere with a well-reasoned award.[756]

Award of majority

Where the parties are aggrieved by the reasoned award, though for the purpose of finality and/or decision, the majority assenting opinion shall be treated as an award. Yet the dissenting arbitrator's reasoned opinion cannot be overlooked while deciding the objection/contention raised by the losing party/petitioner who has challenged the majority opinion.[757]

Non-challenge to later award—Effect on earlier award

An earlier award must be presupposed to be valid when the validity of the later award has not been disapproved or rebutted.[758]

754. 2021 SCC OnLine Mad 724: (2021) 1 LW 657.
755. *Mafatlal Securities Ltd.* v. *Birla Sun-Life Securities Ltd.*, 2002 SCC OnLine Bom 304: (2002) 3 Mah LJ 116.
756. *Union of India* v. *Ashok Katyal*, 2007 SCC OnLine Del 933: ILR (2008) 1 Del 105.
757. *Axios Navigation Co. Ltd.* v. *Indian Oil Corpn. Ltd.*, 2012 SCC OnLine Bom 4: (2012) 3 Mah LJ 701.
758. *Ircon International Ltd.* v. *Vinay Heavy Equipments*, (2015) 13 SCC 680.

Issue estoppel

The principle of issue estoppel would apply only to those cases where the matters have attained finality and no judicial proceedings are pending.[759]

New plea/defence not raised before the arbitrator cannot be raised before the court

A plea/claim/defence not raised before the arbitrator during arbitration proceedings cannot be allowed to be raised before the court in a petition under Section 34 for setting aside the arbitral award.[760]

Claims not pressed before arbitrator

Where certain claims are not pressed before the arbitrator and the arbitrator recorded the factual statement to that effect and passed the award, the award cannot be reopened or set aside to pass the claims for the first time.[761]

Plea not considered

Where a plea raised by a party was not considered by the arbitrator, the court interferes where it is convinced that this plea, if considered, could affect the impugned award or order, and that the arbitrator's omission to consider the contention has resulted in prejudice to either party. Omission to consider, or deal with, an argument canvassed is not invariably fatal to the arbitrator's decision.[762]

Failure to exercise jurisdiction

Where the arbitrator fails to address correct questions and real dispute between the parties, it is a case of failure to exercise jurisdiction and the award shall be set aside.[763]

Issue estoppel applies to criminal proceedings only

The principle of "issue estoppel" applies to criminal proceedings only and not to other proceedings. An application filed by the appellant under

---

759. *NHAI* v. *Progressive-MVR (JV)*, (2018) 14 SCC 688.
760. *MSK Projects (I) (JV) Ltd.* v. *State of Rajasthan*, (2011) 10 SCC 573; *Indian Oil Corpn. Ltd.* v. *Artson Engg. Ltd.*, 2006 SCC OnLine Bom 1106: (2007) 1 Mah LJ 825; *Indian Institute of Technology* v. *Creative Construction*, 2007 SCC OnLine Bom 252: (2007) 5 Mah LJ 323.
761. *Ambika Construction Co.* v. *Union of India*, 2011 SCC OnLine Bom 1361: (2012) 1 Mah LJ 455.
762. *World Window Infrastructure (P) Ltd.* v. *Central Warehousing Corpn.*, (2021) 3 HCC (Del) 731.
763. *Ibid*

Section 34, Arbitration and Conciliation Act, 1996 could not be dismissed by applying the principle of "issue estoppel" which has no application to the civil proceedings.[764]

Whether person not party to arbitration agreement and award can file appeal

A conjoint reading of Sections 2(1)(*b*) and (*h*), 7, 8 and 34 makes it clear that only a party to the arbitration agreement and party to the award can file an application to set aside the arbitration award on the grounds set out in Section 34.[765]

Section 9 CPC—Not applicable to Section 34 proceedings

The Arbitration and Conciliation Act, 1996 is a self-contained Code. There is no provision in the Act which indicates that provisions of Section 9-A CPC applies to petitions filed under Section 34, Arbitration and Conciliation Act, 1996.[766]

Sick Industrial Companies (Special Provisions) Act 1986 [S. 22]

Proceedings in arbitration are neither suit under Section 22(1), SICA nor proceedings mentioned in Section 22(1) and would, therefore, not constitute a prohibition of Section 22 of the Act. The proceedings covered under Section 22, SICA are proceedings of a coercive nature and would not prohibit arbitration proceedings.[767]

Award under Multi-State Cooperative Societies Act, 2002

An award passed by the arbitrator on reference made under Section 84, Multi-State Cooperative Societies Act was without jurisdiction and illegal. The court under Section 4, Arbitration and Conciliation Act, 1996 is entitled to set aside the same.[768]

---

764. *Venture Global Engg. LLC* v. *Tech Mahindra Ltd.*, (2018) 1 SCC 656.
765. *Chennai Container Terminal (P) Ltd.* v. *Union of India*, 2007 SCC OnLine Mad 506: (2007) 4 CTC 284.
766. *Hariprasad Mohanlal Soni* v. *Malegaon Municipal Corpn.*, 2015 SCC OnLine Bom 3639: (2015) 4 Mah LJ 406.
767. *San-A Tradubg Co. Ltd.* v. *I.C. Textiles Ltd.*, (2012) 7 SCC 192; *Marmagoa Steels Ltd.* v. *MSTC Ltd.*, 2021 SCC OnLine Cal 531.
768. *Prakash Kumar Sinha* v. *Konkan Mercantile Coop. Bank Ltd.*, 2012 SCC OnLine Bom 409: (2012) 6 Mah LJ 274.

Appeal against condonation of delay

An appeal against an order allowing an application for condonation of delay accompanying an application filed under Section 34 is not maintainable. The Act does not provide any appeal or revision against an order allowing an application for condonation of delay.[769]

Writ petition

If the award of the arbitrator goes against the petitioner, it can challenge the award on the grounds available to it under Section 34 of the Act. The mere fact that this may cause the inconvenience of having to await the conclusions of the arbitral proceedings is no ground to entertain a writ at an intermediate stage. Attempts to expand the scope for interference would defeat the object and purposes of the Act.[770] A writ petition for setting aside the award of the arbitrator was dismissed as not maintainable.[771]

Against an award of the arbitrator, alternative remedy is available under Section 34 of the Act. A writ petition cannot be entertained. The petitioner challenged an arbitral award regarding compensation in respect of the land acquired under the Land Acquisition Act. The writ petition was dismissed as not maintainable, more so when disputed questions of facts were unsolved in the case.[772] Orders passed by the Arbitral Tribunal are not open to challenge under Articles 226 and 227 of the Constitution.[773]

An award was given by the Electricity Ombudsman. A writ petition challenging the award is not maintainable.[774]

A petition for setting aside the award of the arbitrator can be filed before the District Court. A writ petition for setting aside the award of the arbitrator does not lie before the High Court.[775]

A writ petition against an interlocutory order passed during arbitration proceedings is not maintainable unless some extraordinary circumstances exist or grave injustice is being done. The aggrieved party has an avenue

769. *Ibid.*

770. *Cadre Estate (P) Ltd.* v. *Salochna Goyal*, 2010 SCC OnLine Del 3520: (2010) 119 DRJ 457.

771. *State of Tripura* v. *Himangshu Bikash Saha*, 2011 SCC OnLine Gau 248: (2011) 6 Gau LR 200.

772. *Mahandra Kumar* v. *Union of India*, 2020 SCC OnLine All 2016: (2020) 6 All LJ 443.

773. *Satya Prakash Singh* v. *Dinesh Prakash Singh*, 2014 SCC OnLine All 16183: (2015) 4 All LJ 441; *Navin Tyagi* v. *Union of India*, 2013 SCC OnLine All 10549: (2014) 3 All LJ 13; *Sharda Prasad* v. *Union of India*, 2013 SCC OnLine All 13740: (2013) 6 All LJ 405.

774. *Electricity Urban Distribution Division IInd* v. *Electricity Ombudsman*, 2010 SCC OnLine All 2611: (2010) 6 All LJ 446.

775. *Shilpa Construction* v. *Jaipur Municipal Corpn.*, 2017 SCC OnLine Raj 4312: (2017) 4 WLC 101.

under Section 34 of the Act for ventilating his grievance against the award including any in-between orders that might have been passed by the Arbitral Tribunal.[776]

Letters Patent Appeal

The Arbitration Act is a complete Code in itself and provides remedy to file an appeal under Section 37. Letters Patent Appeal against an order setting aside an award or refusal to set aside an award is not maintainable.[777]

Requirement of pre-deposit under Section 7—Interest on Delayed Payments to Small Scale and Ancillary Industrial Undertakings Act, 1993

In an application under Section 34, Arbitration and Conciliation Act, 1996 for setting aside the arbitral award, the requirement of pre-deposit under Section 7, Interest on Delayed payments to Small Scale and Ancillary Undertakings Act, 1993 has to be fulfilled. The respondent-corporation was directed to pre-deposit 75 per cent of the award amount as a condition precedent for hearing of its application under Section 34, Arbitration and Conciliation Act, 1996.[778] An appeal or an application for setting aside the award made by the Industry Facilitation Council can only be entertained if the applicant deposits 75 per cent of the amount awarded. This condition of deposit is in addition to the conditions or procedure laid down under Section 34 of the 1996 Act.[779] The deposit of 75 per cent must be computed on the basis of all the amounts awarded under an award.[780]

The requirement of pre-deposit of 75 per cent of the award amount under Section 7, Interest on Delayed Payments to Small Scale and Ancillary Industrial Undertakings Act, 1993 is applicable for hearing of a Section 34 application under the Arbitration and Conciliation Act.[781]

---

776. *U.P. Samaj Kalyan Nirman Nigam Ltd.* v. *Jamuna Construction Co.*, 2010 SCC OnLine All 795: (2010) 4 All LJ 81.
777. *Landmark Housing Projects (P) Ltd.* v. *Savithri Naidu*, 2021 SCC OnLine Mad 723.
778. *Snehadeep Structures (P) Ltd.* v. *Maharashtra Small-Scale Industries Development Corpn. Ltd.*, (2010) 3 SCC 34.
779. *U.P. Rajya Karmchari Kalyan Nigam* v. *District Judge, Kanpur Nagar*, 2013 SCC OnLine All 13624: (2013) 3 All LJ 52.
780. *Maharashtra Small Scale Industries Development Corpn. Ltd.* v. *Snehadeep Structures (P) Ltd.*, 2010 SCC OnLine Bom 1636: (2011) 1 Mah LJ 397.
781. *Sri Paravathi Parmeshwar Cables* v. *A.P. Transmission Corpn. Ltd.*, (2013) 10 SCC 693; *Snehadeep Structures (P) Ltd.* v. *Maharashtra Small-Scale Industries Development Corpn. Ltd.*, (2010) 3 SCC 34.

Micro, Small and Medium Enterprises Development Act, 2006

The award of the Facilitation Council can be questioned in proceedings under Section 34, Arbitration and Conciliation Act, 1996.[782]

An award under Section 18 of the Act is akin to the award passed under the Arbitration and Conciliation Act, 1996 and can be challenged under Section 34, Arbitration and Conciliation Act, 1996.[783]

Under Section 19 of the 2006 Act, deposit of 75 per cent of the awarded amount is a condition for acceptance or registration of an application under Section 34 of the 1996 Act when the entire 100 per cent of the decretal amount is secured with the bank, and a further direction to deposit 75 per cent of the awarded amount is not required. Section 19, MSMED Act, 2006 is a special provision and mandates that while challenging an award, a deposit of 75 per cent of the awarded amount shall be made. Where 75 per cent of the awarded amount was not made, rejection of the application under Section 34 for setting aside the award was proper.[784]

The requirement of a deposit of 75 per cent of the amount in terms of the award as a pre-deposit as per Section 19, MSMED Act is mandatory.[785] The District Judge has no discretion to grant exemption from the statutory condition of pre-deposit.[786]

An application under Section 34, Arbitration and Conciliation Act, 1996 was filed for setting aside the award of the arbitrator. Section 19, MSMED Act is special in nature and mandates that while challenging an award, a deposit of 75 per cent of the awarded amount has to be made. It was obligatory on part of the applicant, to deposit 75 per cent of the awarded amount. Though the award was well within the knowledge of the applicant, despite that he failed to comply with the mandatory provision. Rejection of the application under Section 34, Arbitration and Conciliation Act, 1996 for setting aside the award of the arbitrator was proper.[787] The requirement of pre-deposit of 75 per cent of the amount cannot be waived.[788]

---

782. *Best Towers (P) Ltd.* v. *Reliance Communications Ltd.*, 2019 SCC OnLine Pat 3357: (2019) 3 PLJR 486.
783. *Sanghi Industries Ltd.* v. *MSEFC, Rajasthan*, 2018 SCC OnLine Raj 3589.
784. *Salzgitter Hydrolics (P) Ltd.* v. *Eastern Coalfields Ltd.*, 2021 SCC OnLine Cal 4276; *Commr. Health* v. *Nitapol Industries*, 2017 SCC OnLine Cal 15714: (2018) 5 CHN 552.
785. *Tirupati Steels* v. *Shubh Industrial Component*, (2022) 7 SCC 429; *Saryu Plastics (P) Ltd.* v. *Gujarat Water Supply and Sewerage Board*, 2017 SCC OnLine Guj 2483.
786. *Jai Prakash Associates Ltd.* v. *High Tech Tyre Retreaders (P) Ltd.*, 2022 SCC OnLine All 979: (2022) 3 All LJ 352.
787. *Haryana Pradesh Congress Committee* v. *First Newsmedia (P) Ltd.*, 2020 SCC OnLine HP 103.
788. *Saryu Plastics (P) Ltd.* v. *Gujarat Water Supply and Sewerage Board*, 2017 SCC OnLine Guj 2483.

Arbitral proceedings under the MSMED Act, 2006 are governed by the provisions of the Arbitration and Conciliation Act, 1996. There is no separate provision for limitation in filing an application for challenging the award rendered by the Facilitation Council under the provisions of the 2006 Act. Limitation would be governed by Section 34(3) of the 1996 Act. The appellant is not required to deposit 75 per cent of the awarded amount along with the application filed under Section 34 of the Act. Such an amount of deposit could be made when the said application is ultimately entertained.[789]

Maintainability of application for setting aside the award itself was challenged on ground of failure to deposit 75 per cent of the awarded amount. It was held, the intervener has no locus to seek intervention. Rejection of application for intervention was proper.[790]

The petition for challenging the award of the Facilitation Council has to be filed within 90 days or within a further 30 days from the date of award or date of receipt of the same, to be mandatorily accompanied by 75 per cent of the amount stipulated in the impugned award.[791]

Where the State Government applies for setting aside the award, whether the prior deposit of 75 per cent security under the Act of 2006 is mandatory? The application to set aside the award cannot be moved without a deposit of 75 per cent of the awarded amount. If an application is filed by the State for obtaining a stay of award under Section 34 of the Act of 1996, furnishing of security is not required in view of the exemption under Order 27, Rule 8-A.[792]

National Highways Act, 1956—Compensation award

Section 3-G(7), National Highways Act provides that the competent authority/arbitrator would determine the compensation amount after considering the provisions of Section 3-G(7) and the evidence adduced by the complainant. Where the competent authority fails to do so, the claimant can file a petition under Section 34(1), Arbitration and Conciliation Act, 1996. The court may interfere on any of the grounds of Section 34(2) after consideration of the provisions of Section 3-G(7), National Highways Act.[793] When the remedy

---

789. *Ravindranath Ge Medicate Associate (P) Ltd.* v. *Clean Coats (P) Ltd.*, 2016 SCC OnLine Bom 5068: (2016) 6 Mah LJ 49; *E-Square Leisure (P) Ltd.* v. *K.K. Dani Consultants and Engineers (P) Ltd.*, 2013 SCC OnLine Bom 183: (2013) 3 Mah LJ 24.
790. *Luxury Lifeline* v. *Sun Petpack Jabalpur (P) Ltd.*, 2019 SCC OnLine Bom 625: (2019) 6 Mah LJ 527.
791. *Goodyear India Ltd.* v. *Nortan Intec Rubber (P) Ltd.*, 2013 SCC OnLine Mad 1047: (2013) 5 CTC 25.
792. *Commr. Health* v. *Nitapol Industries*, 2017 SCC OnLine Cal 15714: (2018) 5 CHN 552.
793. *Paul Mani* v. *LAO*, 2019 SCC OnLine Ker 2700: (2019) 3 KLT 1058.

under Section 34, Arbitration and Conciliation Act, 1996 is available, a writ petition is not maintainable.[794]

Land was acquired under the National Highways Act for construction of a four lane road and compensation was granted to land owners. The arbitrator awarded enhanced compensation by comparing compensation paid to another Revenue Circle. The award was set aside by the District Judge on the ground that the date of notification under Section 3 published for the said Revenue Circle was not mentioned. Held, the dispute between parties was only in regard to the amount of compensation and compensation was assessed as directed by the Central Government from the date of the publication of the notification under Section 3-A by the arbitrator. The arbitration award could not be said to be illegal or without any authority.[795]

Security money—Refund of

The respondent had completed the contract as awarded by the petitioner. The petitioner was liable to return the security deposit. The arbitrator was justified in directing the refund of security deposit.[796]

Claim for amount lying in escrow account

The escrow account was required to be opened as per the guidelines issued by the Ministry of Coal, Government of India for the preparation of mine closure plant. The guidelines required, inter alia, the mining company to open an escrow account with any scheduled bank. Accordingly, the respondent opened an escrow account and executed an escrow agreement. From the correspondence between the parties, it appeared that even the appellant consented for opening the escrow account. The appellant also agreed that the amount to be deposited in the escrow account will be recovered by the respondent from immediate next payment of the coal bills of the joint venture company—PKCL—raised toward dispatches of coal from the appellant's coal blocks. Thus, thereafter, it was not open for the appellant to claim the amount lying in the escrow account. If the amount lying in the escrow account is returned to the appellant, the purpose and object of opening the escrow account which was as per the guidelines of the Ministry of Coal would be frustrated. The object and purpose of opening the escrow account was to see that the appellant company fulfils the contract as per the agreement and till the closure of the coal blocks. Therefore, the High Court

794. *State of Rajasthan* v. *Sigma Engg.*, 2017 SCC OnLine Raj 2939: (2017) 3 RLW 1846.

795. *Rajib Kumar Bora* v. *NHAI*, 2023 SCC OnLine Gau 2327: (2023) 5 GLT 252.

796. *Union of India* v. *Airwide Express Cargo*, 2015 SCC OnLine Bom 4917: (2015) 5 Mah LJ 57; *Pankaj Dyes and Chemicals Ltd.* v. *Taco Hendrickson Suspensions (P) Ltd.*, 2016 SCC OnLine Bom 2604: (2016) 5 Mah LJ 726.

has rightly interfered with the award passed by the arbitrator with respect to Claim 3—escrow account—by observing that the reasoning is perverse or so irrational that no reasonable person could have arrived at the material/evidence on record. The court expressed agreement with the view taken by the learned Division Bench of the High Court. The award of the arbitrator with respect to the escrow account was held perverse and was set aside.[797]

Arbitration fee

What Section 11(6-A) of the 1996 Act contemplates is a contract and it is not an agreement which cannot be treated as a contract. The contract must conform to Section 7 of the Act and must also fulfil the requirement of the Contract Act for the purported arbitration clause or arbitration agreement to be valid.[798]

An award was passed by the tribunal which consisted of three arbitrators. Fee was charged by them according to the Fourth Schedule of the Act. The objection against the award was dismissed.[799]

Court fee

On an application under Section 34 for setting aside an arbitral award, court fee as prescribed under Article 18 of Schedule II of the Court Fees Act would be payable.[800] When a petition under Section 34 challenging an award is filed before any principal civil court of original jurisdiction which is not a High Court, no court fees under the Bombay Court Fees Act is payable.[801]

Registration of award

Registration of awards is not required.[802]

Effect of filing civil suit—Challenging the award of the arbitrator

When a civil suit challenging the award of the arbitrator is filed in time, and is pending without attaining finality, the award loses its efficacy and during the said period cannot be relied on in any collateral or other proceedings regarding the rights declared by the arbitrator.[803]

797. *Ibid.*
798. *N.N. Global Mercantile (P) Ltd.* v. *Indo Unique Flame Ltd.*, (2023) 7 SCC 1.
799. *NHAI* v. *Gayatri-ECI (Joint Venture)*, 2019 SCC OnLine Del 8083.
800. *U.P. Jal Nigam* v. *Driplex Water Engg. Ltd.*, 2007 SCC OnLine All 2540.
801. *Puneet Malhotra* v. *R.S. Gai*, 2008 SCC OnLine Bom 1043: (2008) 6 Mah LJ 867; *TISCO Ltd.* v. *Durgapur Project Ltd.*, 2005 SCC OnLine Cal 422: (2005) 4 CHN 501.
802. *Subal Chandra Giri* v. *Panchanan Jana*, 2011 SCC OnLine Cal 2715: (2011) 3 Cal LJ 471.
803. *Afza Teachers Training Institute* v. *Regional Director*, 2003 SCC OnLine Kar 304: (2003) 3 KCCR 2128.

Costs of arbitration proceedings

Petitioners sought costs on account of illegal initiation of arbitration proceedings. Though initiation of the arbitration proceedings was not as per scheme of the Arbitration Act, but non-participation of the petitioners and non-initiation of the proceedings within reasonable time disentitled them to claim the cost of the proceedings under Section 34.[804]

Exorbitant fee demanded by Arbitral Tribunal

Party applicant participated in arbitration proceedings but did not object to such fees. A party that challenged fees after the award is passed against the party cannot raise the issue of fee for the first time.[805]

Award was set aside

1. An award was passed without considering the objection of the party about the jurisdiction of the Arbitral Tribunal and accepting documents without deciding the issue of interpolation in the said document; the award was set aside.[806]

2. Award made beyond prescribed period—The first arbitrator was not able to give the award within reasonable time and had resigned; a second arbitrator was appointed and directed by the court to submit the award within a period of four months. The second arbitrator did not pass an award within the stipulated period, and extension of time was neither sought by the arbitrator nor consented to by the parties. The arbitrator had become *functus officio*, and the award rendered by him was non-est and was set aside.[807]

A mere failure on the part of the arbitrator to pass an award after the expiry of the extended period was held only an irregularity and not an illegality sufficient to question the award.[808] A party to an arbitration agreement who voluntarily takes part in the arbitration proceedings after the expiry of the period prescribed in the agreement and periodically extending the time for the arbitrator to pass an award will be deemed to have waived the implied condition as to time.[809]

---

804. *Prajakta Mahesh Joshi* v. *Rekha Uday Prabhu*, 2012 SCC OnLine Bom 1800: (2013) 2 Mah LJ 603.
805. *Vestas Wind Technology India (P) Ltd.* v. *Inox Renewables Ltd.*, 2019 SCC OnLine Bom 554.
806. *Raghani Tradelink (P) Ltd.* v. *HDB Financial Services Ltd.*, 2019 SCC OnLine Bom 13379.
807. *Nitya Nand and Sons* v. *Union of India*, 2019 SCC OnLine P&H 7921.
808. *Indian Oil Corpn. Ltd.* v. *Devi Constructions*, 2009 SCC OnLine Mad 685: (2009) 2 CTC 791.
809. *Ibid.*

3. Claim time barred—award set aside—A contract was for the construction of the bridge. Cause of action arose in the year 1978 when the work was completed. A dispute was raised by the contractor in 1994. The claim was time-barred. The award passed by the arbitrator was set aside.[810]

4. Award not based on evidence set aside—Where the arbitrator passed/decreed the claim of the contractor without going through the final bill, recorded rates and measurement books, the award was set aside.[811]

5. When an earlier Arbitral Tribunal was in existence, appointment of a fresh arbitrator under Section 11 of the Act was erroneous, and the award of the arbitrator was set aside.[812]

6. Ex parte award—Where the ex parte award passed was vitiated for being in conflict with the public policy of India, and in contravention with the fundamental policy of Indian law, was patently illegal, did not state the reasons on which it was based, the ex parte award was liable to be set aside.[813] Where the notice was sent to the petitioner at the address mentioned in the document, but she was not residing at that place, and she could not appear before the tribunal, the impugned award was set aside.[814] Against an ex parte order, the proper remedy is an application under Section 34 and not a writ petition under Article 226 or 227 for setting aside the ex parte award.[815]

7. The appellant-contractor was awarded work for providing and fixing vitrified tile flooring under the contract. It was obligatory to supply and use agreed-upon branded tiles, but the contractor used an equivalent product which was contrary to the contract, and there was no shortage of vitrified tiles. The order setting aside the award made by the court below was held proper.[816]

8. A dispute application was filed by the petitioner before the arbitrator against the cancellation of his membership of the respondent-bank and forfeiture of his share amount. The termination of membership of the petitioner was itself in breach of the principles of natural justice and contrary

---

810. *State of Rajasthan* v. *Barmer Golden Transport Co.*, 2019 SCC OnLine Raj 5975.
811. *Ibid.*
812. *Vidyawati Construction Co.* v. *Union of India*, 2020 SCC OnLine All 1371: (2021) 2 All LJ 114.
813. *Kopparthi Ramakumar Reddy* v. *Hinduja Leyland Finance Ltd.*, 2020 SCC OnLine Mad 5858.
814. *Bindiya Ajay Chawla* v. *Citifinancial Consumer Finance India Ltd.*, 2012 SCC OnLine Bom 208: (2012) 4 Mah LJ 271.
815. *Narmada Valley Development Authority* v. *Vasudev R. Mendiratta*, 2006 SCC OnLine MP 64: (2006) 3 MP LJ 75.
816. *Sarathi Enterprises* v. *Union of India*, 2016 SCC OnLine Bom 5312: (2016) 6 Mah LJ 598.

to the provisions of laws and by-laws. The arbitrator also overlooked the provisions of the laws and by-laws and dismissed the dispute application of the petitioner. The impugned award was quashed and set aside.[817]

9. The court under Section 34 cannot overlook the issue of law and jurisdiction. The decision to proceed with the matter in spite of objections was wrong. The award was set aside as being without jurisdiction.[818]

10. An award was passed without considering whether the counterclaim was time-barred or not. The award was found not sustainable, and was set aside.[819]

11. Claim time barred—Award set aside—A claim petition filed by the respondent before the Facilitation Council was barred by limitation. The arbitral award was set aside.[820]

12. The arbitrator did not consider the submission made by the petitioner and totally overlooked evidence produced by him. Findings recorded by the arbitrator were perverse. The award of the arbitrator was set aside.[821]

13. Unreasoned ex parte award set aside—The ex parte award made by the arbitrator did not state the reasons upon which it was based, and the award was set aside.[822]

14. Contract work—Final bill was prepared and signed by the contractor, who without any protest accepted the bill. The limitation period started after completion of 180 days from the date when the final bill was signed by the contractor without protest. The contractor did not take steps for five years and ought to have taken steps within three years. Claims being time-barred could not be sustained in law.[823]

15. Conflicting findings in case of different contractors—When the Arbitral Tribunal had given conflicting findings in case of different contractors, the award of the arbitrator was set aside.[824]

---

817. *Yusufkhan Fakhrookhan Tadvi* v. *Konkan Mercantile Coop. Bank Ltd.*, 2013 SCC OnLine Bom 644: (2013) 4 Mah LJ 431.

818. *Home Care Retail Marts (P) Ltd.* v. *Harsh Kaushal Developers*, 2013 SCC OnLine Bom 675: (2013) 5 Mah LJ 652.

819. *Rolta India Ltd.* v. *Voltas Ltd.*, 2013 SCC OnLine Bom 1050: (2014) 3 Mah LJ 765; *Kanti Bijlee Utpadan Nigam Ltd.* v. *Paltech Cooling Towers & Equipments Ltd.*, (2022) 4 HCC (Del) 233.

820. *Gammon Engineers & Contractors (P) Ltd.* v. *Sahay Industries*, 2023 SCC OnLine Bom 750: (2023) 4 Bom CR 566.

821. *Hindustan Petroleum Corpn. Ltd.* v. *Offshore Infrastructure Ltd.*, 2015 SCC OnLine Bom 4146: (2015) 6 Mah LJ 287.

822. *Kopparthi Ramakumar Reddy* v. *Hinduja Leyland Finance Ltd.*, 2020 SCC OnLine Mad 5858.

823. *Godawari Marathawada Irrigation Development Corpn.* v. *Y.R. Reddy Engineers and Builders*, 2017 SCC OnLine Bom 1670: (2017) 5 Mah LJ 660.

824. *NHAI* v. *Progressive-MVR (JV)*, (2018) 14 SCC 688.

16. Award contrary to terms of contract, law laid down by the Supreme Court and High Court—The entire award showed patent illegality on the face of it. It was contrary to the terms of the contract, contrary to the law laid down by the Supreme Court and High Court, and contrary to provisions of the Limitation Act, 1963. It was passed by overlooking pleading and evidence of parties. Such an award is liable to be set aside.[825]

17. Non-consideration of material on record—The document, if considered, would have shown that the claim was within limitation. Rejection of the claim as being barred by limitation was not proper. The impugned award was set aside.[826]

18. The Arbitral Tribunal's award of a lump sum amount of ₹5,50,00,000 was without any basis for the quantification. The tribunal awarded the amount solely for the reason that in its view the same would meet the ends of justice. The award of an arbitrary amount against specified claims, without adjudication of the claims, is unsustainable. There was no determination of the amount as payable on account of supply of goods or damages allegedly incurred by it. The award of an arbitrary amount without any discernible basis could not be sustained.[827]

19. Award against the terms of the agreement—award set aside—There was an agreement for construction of flat between the builder and the buyer. A dispute arose which was referred to the arbitrator. The award of the arbitrator directing the builder to hand over possession without payment of entire consideration and to pay compensation to the buyer for delay on the part of the builder in delivering and handing over possession of flat was against the terms of the agreement. The award was set aside.[828]

20. Hire purchase agreement—award set aside—Neither the financier had issued a notice calling upon the hirer to agree with the appointment of the arbitrator, nor did the hirer ever communicate his consent on the choice of arbitrator. No notice was issued by the financier communicating to the hirer about the commencement of arbitration proceedings. The appointment of the arbitrator being in violation of Sections 11 and 16 was not valid. The arbitral award was set aside.[829]

825. *Ibid.*

826. *Praveen Gupta* v. *Star Share & Stock Brokers Ltd.*, 2008 SCC OnLine Del 444: (2008) 102 DRJ 633.

827. *Kanti Bijlee Utpadan Nigam Ltd.* v. *Paltech Cooling Towers & Equipments Ltd.*, (2022) 4 HCC (Del) 233.

828. *Oyester Homes Chennai (P) Ltd.* v. *G. Cholan*, 2023 SCC OnLine Mad 8071.

829. *Amit Kumar Agarwala* v. *Maa Saarda and Co.*, 2019 SCC OnLine Gau 5068: (2020) 3 Gau LR 351.

Where award was not set aside

1. An appeal lies against an order setting aside or refusing to set aside the award of the arbitrator [S. 37(1)(*c*)]. Appeal against the order rejecting the application under Section 34 is maintainable under Section 37 of the Act.[830]

2. The arbitrator awarded compensation treating the land as agricultural land. The plea of the land owner was that the land in question was residential or commercial land. Since no declaration was made under Section 143, U.P. Zamindari Abolition and Land Reforms Act (1 of 1951) to alter the nature of the land to residential or commercial land, the award of the arbitrator was not erroneous. The petition under Section 34, Arbitration and Conciliation Act, 1996 was rejected.[831]

3. Works contract—An undertaking was given by the contractor for minus price adjustment. The arbitrator had cancelled that undertaking given by the contractor as it was the outcome of dilatory tactics adopted by the State, and in the interest of completion of work, the contractor due to commercial expectancy was induced to sign the undertaking. The conclusion of the arbitrator was supported by the material on record and the technical and departmental knowledge of the arbitrator. The High Court refused to interfere with the award.[832]

4. Where every ground taken by the party for setting aside the award was duly considered by the arbitrator, the arbitrator had not travelled beyond. When the arbitrator had given finding on each individual item of dispute, the arbitrator had not misconducted himself and the order of rejecting the application for setting aside the award was proper.[833]

5. Non-joinder of necessary party—escrow agent—The escrow agent was neither a party to the arbitration agreement nor a party to the transaction under the MOU. He was not a necessary party in the petition under Section 34, and his non-joinder did not affect the award. The award of the arbitrator was not set aside.[834]

6. Where an award is passed after considering all relevant material, the award need not be set aside.[835]

---

830. *U.P. Coop. Sugar Factories Federation Ltd.* v. *P.S. Misra*, 2002 SCC OnLine All 1095: 2003 All LJ 1038.
831. *Nathu Ram Sahu* v. *Collector*, 2018 SCC OnLine All 6772: (2018) 5 All LJ 224.
832. *Union of India* v. *Mukul Builders (P) Ltd.*, 2015 SCC OnLine All 2623: (2015) 112 ALR 583.
833. *U.P. State Sugar Corpn.* v. *Lal and Kumar Humayunpur*, 2014 SCC OnLine All 16104: (2015) 2 All LJ 384.
834. *Emerald Woollen Mills (P) Ltd.* v. *Hanuman Developers*, 2020 SCC OnLine Bom 1.
835. *Ibid.*

7. A finding of fact was recorded by the arbitrator after considering all the documents and after giving full opportunities to both the parties. Findings were not perverse, and the High Court did not interfere in proceedings under Section 34.[836]

8. Dispute regarding payment of retainer's fee—An award was passed in terms of the agreement. There was no decision to reduce the retainer fee. The arbitrator was justified in awarding the same.[837]

9. Where the respondent was responsible for the termination of the contract, and the arbitrator had awarded compensation in favour of the respondent during the prolongation period, a petition filed under Section 34 was rightly dismissed.[838]

10. Where an award was passed by an Arbitral Tribunal consisting of three technical members, the award passed by the tribunal was not set aside.[839]

11. Composite reference [S. 34(2)(*iii*)]—There were two different contracts but a composite reference was made to arbitration. No prejudice was shown to have been caused by petitioners owing to such reference. The award was not set aside.[840]

12. Award corporated by reasons—The award was replete with reasons supported by documents. For each finding extensive reasons were given by the arbitrator. There was no ground for interfering with the conclusions of the arbitrator. The award of the arbitrator was not set aside.[841]

13. Reasoned award—not contrary to substantive law or in conflict with public policy of India (S. 34)—Arbitrators had passed a well-reasoned award and had satisfied the requirement of Sections 29(1) and 31(3). There was nothing to show that the award was in any manner perverse, contrary to substantive law or in conflict with the public policy of India. The award was not set aside.[842]

---

836. *Pradyuman Kumar Sharma* v. *Jays Agar M. Sancheti*, 2013 SCC OnLine Bom 453: (2013) 5 Mah LJ 86.
837. *Maxx Moblink (P) Ltd.* v. *Pickle Advertisement (P) Ltd.*, 2014 SCC OnLine Bom 82: (2014) 3 Mah LJ 616.
838. *Union of India* v. *Bright Power Project (I) (P) Ltd.*, 2015 SCC OnLine Bom 4920: (2015) 4 Mah LJ 668.
839. *Satluj Jal Vidyut Nigam Ltd.* v. *R.J. Shah & Co. Ltd.*, 2007 SCC OnLine Del 1542: (2007) 99 DRJ 685.
840. *Ekaa Engineers and Infrastructure (P) Ltd.* v. *Daimler Financial Services India (P) Ltd.*, 2019 SCC OnLine Mad 39351.
841. *Union of India* v. *Radha Chemicals*, 2020 SCC OnLine Cal 3287.
842. *G. & T. Beckfield Drilling Services (P) Ltd.* v. *ONGC*, 2019 SCC OnLine Gau 5967: (2019) 4 Arb LR 410.

Revision

Where a petition under Section 34, Arbitration and Conciliation Act challenging an ex parte arbitral award is rejected as was filed belatedly, the revision petition being an extraordinary remedy is maintainable.[843]

An award was challenged on the ground that a time-barred claim had been granted. Evidence showed that acknowledgement of liability under Section 18, Limitation Act 1963 was made within the period of limitation, which had extended the period of limitation. The award could not be set aside.[844]

Where a petition under Section 34 for setting aside an ex parte award is rejected on the ground of delay, the remedy of revision is not maintainable.[845]

843. *4G Identity Solutions (P) Ltd.* v. *Bloom Solutions (P) Ltd.*, 2018 SCC OnLine Hyd 22: (2018) 3 ALD 334.

844. *Kaynet Finance Ltd.* v. *Verona Capital Ltd.*, 2019 SCC OnLine Bom 1203: (2020) 1 Mah LJ 430.

845. *4G Identity Solutions (P) Ltd.* v. *Bloom Solutions (P) Ltd.*, 2018 SCC OnLine Hyd 22: (2018) 3 ALD 334.

Chapter VIII
Finality and Enforcement of Arbitral Awards

FINALITY OF ARBITRAL AWARDS [S. 35]

35. *Finality of arbitral awards.*—Subject to this Part an arbitral award shall be final and binding on the parties and persons claiming under them respectively.

COMMENTS

Corresponding old law

Section 35 corresponds to clause 7 of the First Schedule to the Arbitration Act, 1940. The said clause 7 read as under:

7. The award shall be final and binding on the parties and persons claiming under them respectively.

Scope and application

Section 35 provides that an award passed by the arbitrator unless set aside under Section 34 shall be final and binding on the parties and the persons claiming under them respectively.

An award possesses all the elements of validity even though it has not been formally enforced and it may be relied upon in a litigation between the parties relating to the same subject-matter.[1]

In *Cherian Properties Ltd.* v. *Kasturi and Sons Ltd.*[2], the arbitral award required the shares to be transmitted to the claimants. The award had attained finality. The transmission of shares as mandated by the award could be fully effectuated by obtaining a rectification of the register under Section 111, Companies Act, 1956. The National Company Law Tribunal (NCLT) had the jurisdiction to pass an appropriate order directing rectification of the register. The remedy sought was competent.

1. *Cheran Properties Ltd.* v. *Kasturi & Sons Ltd.*, (2018) 16 SCC 413.
2. *Ibid.*

Appellate arbitration

Finality of the arbitral award does not exclude autonomy of parties to the award from adopting other acceptable methods of redressal such as appellate arbitration.[3]

"Shall be final and binding"

As shown by Sections 34 and 35, an arbitral award would be final and binding on the parties unless it is set aside by a competent court, but it does not exclude the autonomy of the parties to an arbitral award to mutually agree to a procedure whereby the arbitral award might be reconsidered by another arbitrator or panel of arbitrators by way of an appeal and result of that appeal is accepted by the parties to be final and binding subject to a challenge provided by the 1996 Act. The fact that recourse to a court is available to a party for challenging an award does not *ipso facto* prohibit the parties from mutually agreeing to a second look at an award with the intention of an early settlement of disputes and differences.[4] Arbitration clause in the agreement which provides for such a two-tier arbitration between the parties does not violate the fundamental policy or public policy of India.[5]

Plea that the award of the arbitrator is subject to another round adjudication under Section 19, Recovery of Debts Due to Banks and Financial Institutions Act, 1993 was rejected.[6]

Emergency award

A party cannot be heard to say, after it participates in an emergency award proceeding, having agreed to institutional rules made in that regard, that thereafter it will not be bound by an emergency arbitrator's ruling. Having agreed to para 12 of First Schedule to the Arbitration Rules of the Singapore International Arbitration Centre, it cannot lie in the mouth of a party to ignore an emergency arbitrator's award by stating that it is a nullity when such party expressly agrees to the binding nature of such award from the date it is made and further undertakes to carry out the said interim order immediately and without delay.[7]

---

3. *Centrotrade Minerals & Metal Inc.* v. *Hindustan Copper Ltd.*, (2017) 2 SCC 228.
4. *Ibid.*
5. *Ibid.*
6. *HDFC Bank Ltd.* v. *Sima Mondal*, 2009 SCC OnLine Cal 2714: (2010) 1 CHN 573.
7. *Amazon.Com NV Investment Holdings LLC* v. *Future Retail Ltd.*, (2022) 1 SCC 209.

"Persons claiming under them"—Enforcement of award against non-signatory to arbitration agreement

Section 35 postulates that an arbitral award "shall be final and binding on the parties and persons claiming them respectively". The expression "claiming under" includes cases of devolution and assignment of interest. The expression "persons claiming under them" in Section 35 widens the net of those whom the arbitral award binds and it does so by reaching out not only to the parties but to those who claim under them as well. The expression "persons claiming under them" is a legislative recognition of the doctrine that besides the parties, an arbitral award binds every person whose capacity or position is derived from and is the same as a party to the arbitration proceedings.[8]

Finality of the arbitral award—When award not enforced

An award is not a waste paper merely because it has not been enforced. After an award is pronounced, no action can be started on the original claim which had been the subject-matter of the reference. An award possesses all the elements of vitality, even though it has not been formally enforced, and it may be relied upon in a litigation between the parties relating to the same subject-matter.[9]

ENFORCEMENT [S. 36]

[10][**36.** *Enforcement.*—(1) Where the time for making an application to set aside the arbitral award under Section 34 has expired, then, subject to the provisions of sub-section (2), such award shall be enforced in accordance with the provisions of the Code of Civil Procedure, 1908 (5 of 1908), in the same manner as if it were a decree of the court.

(2) Where an application to set aside the arbitral award has been filed in the court under Section 34, the filing of such an application shall not by itself render that award unenforceable, unless the court grants an order of stay of the operation of the said arbitral award in accordance with the provisions of sub-section (3), on a separate application made for that purpose.

---

8. *Cheran Properties Ltd.* v. *Kasturi & Sons Ltd.*, (2018) 16 SCC 413.
9. *Centrotrade Minerals & Metal Inc.* v. *Hindustan Copper Ltd.*, (2017) 2 SCC 228.
10. *Subs.* by Act 3 of 2016, S. 19 (w.r.e.f. 23-10-2015). Prior to substitution it read as:
"**36.** *Enforcement.*—Where the time for making an application to set aside the arbitral award under Section 34 has expired, or such application having been made, it has been refused, the award shall be enforced under the Code of Civil Procedure, 1908 (5 of 1908) in the same manner as if it were a decree of the Court."

(3) Upon filing of an application under sub-section (2) for stay of the operation of the arbitral award, the court may, subject to such conditions as it may deem fit, grant stay of the operation of such award for reasons to be recorded in writing:

Provided that the court shall, while considering the application for grant of stay in the case of an arbitral award for payment of money, have due regard to the provisions for grant of stay of a money decree under the provisions of the Code of Civil Procedure, 1908 (5 of 1908):]

[11][Provided further that where the Court is satisfied that a prima facie case is made out that,—

(*a*) the arbitration agreement or contract which is the basis of the award; or

(*b*) the making of the award,

was induced or effected by fraud or corruption, it shall stay the award unconditionally pending disposal of the challenge under Section 34 to the award.

Explanation.—For the removal of doubts, it is hereby clarified that the above proviso shall apply to all court cases arising out of or in relation to arbitral proceedings, irrespective of whether the arbitral or court proceedings were commenced prior to or after the commencement of the Arbitration and Conciliation (Amendment) Act, 2015.]

COMMENTS

Corresponding old law

Section 36 is new, and did not exist in the Arbitration Act, 1940.

UNCITRAL Model Law

Article 35. *Recognition and enforcement*

(1) An arbitral award, irrespective of the country in which it was made, shall be recognized as binding and, upon application in writing to the competent court, shall be enforced subject to the provisions of this article and of Article 36.

(2) The party relying on an award or applying for its enforcement shall supply the original award or a copy thereof. If the award is not made in an official language of this State, the court may request the party to supply a translation thereof into such language.

Legislative changes

Arbitration and Conciliation (Amendment) Act, 2015 (3 of 2016)

For Section 36 of the principal Act, the following section shall be *substituted*, namely —

11. *Ins.* by Act 3 of 2021, S. 2 (w.r.e.f. 23-10-2015).

"36. *Enforcement.*—(1) Where the time for making an application to set aside the arbitral award under Section 34 has expired, then, subject to the provisions of sub-section (2), such award shall be enforced in accordance with the provisions of the Code of Civil Procedure, 1908 (5 of 1908), in the same manner as if it were a decree of the court.

(2) Where an application to set aside the arbitral award has been filed in the Court under Section 34, the filing of such an application shall not by itself render that award unenforceable, unless the Court grants an order of stay of the operation of the said arbitral award in accordance with the provisions of sub-section (3), on a separate application made for that purpose.

(3) Upon filing of an application under sub-section (2) for stay of the operation of the arbitral award, the Court may, subject to such conditions as it may deem fit, grant stay of the operation of such award for reasons to be recorded in writing:

Provided that the Court shall, while considering the application for grant of stay in the case of an arbitral award for payment of money, have due regard to the provisions for grant of stay of a money decree under the provisions of the Code of Civil Procedure, 1908 (5 of 1908).".

NOTES ON CLAUSES

Clause 19 of the Bill seeks to amend Section 36 of the principal Act relating to enforcement of award to the effect that mere filing of application under Section 34 for setting aside arbitral award would not render that award enforceable unless the court grants an order of stay on the operation of the said award on a separate application made for that purpose.

Section 36 is applicable even to pending applications for setting aside arbitral award on the date of commencement of Amendment Act, 2015.[12]

The requirement of filing separate application for stay on furnishing security by the award debtor imposed by substituted Section 36 does not have retrospective effect. It does not affect the vested right of the award debtor to challenge the award without security.[13]

Arbitration and Conciliation (Amendment) Act, 2021 (3 of 2021)

A new proviso has been added by Amendment Act 3 of 2021 with effect from 23 October 2015. The new proviso provides that where the court is satisfied that a prima facie case is made out that the arbitration award or the contract which is the basis of the award or the making of the award was induced or effected by fraud or corruption, it shall stay the award unconditionally pending disposal of the challenge under Section 34 to the award.

---

12. *BCCI* v. *Kochi Cricket (P) Ltd.*, (2018) 6 SCC 287.
13. *Braithwaite Burn & Jessop Construction Co. Ltd.* v. *Indo Wagon Engg. Ltd.*, 2017 SCC OnLine Cal 8283; *W.B. Power Development Corpn. Ltd.* v. *Dongfang Electric Corpn.*, 2017 SCC OnLine Cal 9388.

Scope and application

Section 36 relates to the enforcement of an award passed by the Arbitral Tribunal.

Provisions of Section 36 are a significant departure from those of Arbitration Act, 1940 because they provide that award becomes immediately enforceable upon expiry of the limitation period under Section 34.[14] Under the old Arbitration Act, 1940, award cannot be enforced unless made under the rule of the court. Under the 1996 Act, award of the arbitrator becomes enforceable as decree. Award under the 1996 Act is impressed with the character of decree and is enforceable as decree under CPC.[15]

In the 1996 Act, for the purpose of enforcement, an arbitral award is deemed to be a decree. It is deemed to be a decree only for the limited purpose of enforcement, for which the procedural provisions of CPC are applicable. The award remains an award and does not become a decree as defined in CPC. This is evident from the use of the expression "in the same manner as if it were a decree of the court".[16]

Where arbitral award was decided all the way up to the Supreme Court, has attained finality and all challenges thereto have been rejected, award becomes enforceable as if it were decree of the court under Section 36.[17] Provisions of an automatic decree are not applicable.[18]

The part of the award which is not challenged is enforceable under Section 36 of the Act.[19]

Under the provisions of Section 36, the award can be enforced in the same manner as if it were a decree of the court. After the award has become final, it can be executed anywhere in the country where the decree can be executed.[20]

Power of the executing court

Where the award passed is not challenged under Section 34, Arbitration and Conciliation Act, 1996, only option left with the executing court is to execute the award.[21]

---

14. *Union of India* v. *Popular Construction Co.*, (2001) 8 SCC 470.
15. *N. Poongodi* v. *Tata Finance Ltd.*, 2005 SCC OnLine Mad 311: (2005) 4 CTC 577.
16. *Srei Equipment and Finance (P) Ltd.* v. *Khyoda Apik*, 2016 SCC OnLine Cal 12132.
17. *Eskay Engineers* v. *BSNL*, 2009 SCC OnLine Bom 893: (2009) 5 Mah LJ 565.
18. *A.K. Group* v. *N.K. Group*, 1996 SCC OnLine Del 837: (1997) 40 DRJ 581.
19. *National Buildings Construction Corpn. Ltd.* v. *Lloyd Insulations India Ltd.*, 2004 SCC OnLine Del 98: (2004) 73 DRJ 142.
20. *Cheran Properties Ltd.* v. *Kasturi & Sons Ltd.*, (2018) 16 SCC 413.
21. *Cholamandlam Investment & Finance Co. Ltd.* v. *Narmada Chandrakar*, 2016 SCC OnLine Chh 2236: (2017) 2 CGLJ 241.

Award of the arbitrator is unexecutable once application under Section 34 for setting aside award is filed and is pending.[22] Execution of award cannot take place till the decision of application under Section 34.[23]

Execution application cannot be filed until three months have expired which is given for filing application under Section 34 for setting aside award; execution application being premature was dismissed.[24]

Before execution of a deemed decree, the award-holder has to satisfy the court that no application for setting aside the award has been moved within the period as mentioned in Section 34(3), or such application has been moved and dismissed.[25] If application under Section 34 for setting aside award has been made in time and until it has been refused, the application for enforcement of the award under Section 36 would not be maintainable and the enforcement would remain stayed automatically.[26] If an application under Section 34 for setting aside an award is filed within the period of limitation, enforcement of the award cannot be continued.[27]

An arbitration award which determined compensation amount payable under the agreement for sale cannot be executed as a suit for specific performance of agreement when the reference was only for the fixation of the price of land in question and the award was also in respect of the same.[28]

Award can be enforced even if an appeal against an order refusing to set aside an award is pending.[29]

Language of Section 36 makes it very clear that an arbitral award has to be enforced under CPC in the same manner as if it were a decree of the court.[30] An award made under Part I of the Arbitration and Conciliation Act, 1996 can be executed not only by the court as defined by Section 2(1)(*e*)(*i*) but also by the court to which it is sent for execution under Sections 38 and 39 CPC.[31]

---

22. *Superintending Engineer (Highways and Rural Works)* v. *D.G. Deivasigamani*, 2004 SCC OnLine Mad 492: (2004) 4 CTC 1.
23. *M.M.P. SEB* v. *Rama Steels Tubes Ltd.*, 2011 SCC OnLine MP 260: (2011) 2 MP LJ 678.
24. *Vindhya Telelinks Ltd.* v. *BSNL*, 2003 SCC OnLine Del 100: (2003) 68 DRJ 50.
25. *Srei Equipment Finance (P) Ltd.* v. *Shridhar Jaykrishna Pandey*, 2011 SCC OnLine Cal 1512: (2011) 4 CHN 694.
26. *Vishnu Prasad Gontiya* v. *Ashok Lelyland Finance Ltd.*, 2001 SCC OnLine MP 353: (2002) 1 MP LJ 500.
27. *Banco Construction Co.* v. *Union of India*, 2011 SCC OnLine MP 824: (2012) 2 MP LJ 579.
28. *Rajasthan Udyog* v. *Hindustan Engg. & Industries Ltd.*, (2020) 6 SCC 660.
29. *Vipul Agarwal* v. *Atul Kanodia & Co.*, 2003 SCC OnLine All 1461: 2004 All LJ 2062.
30. *Leela Hotels Ltd.* v. *Housing & Urban Development Corpn. Ltd.*, (2012) 1 SCC 302.
31. *Gemini Bay Transcription (P) Ltd.* v. *Integrated Sales Service Ltd.*, 2018 SCC OnLine Bom 216: (2018) 2 Mah LJ 329.

The expression "as if it were a decree of the court" in Section 36(1) merely creates a fiction in relation to the award or order for the purpose of its enforcement as if it were a decree and that by itself does not transfer it into a decree.[32]

It is the original award which is treated as a decree, certified copy of award cannot be treated as a decree.[33] Only a copy of the award needs to be produced before the executing court for execution, the executing court cannot insist on payment of additional stamp duty.[34]

The award passed by the arbitrator in arbitration proceedings arising out of reference under Section 84, Multi-State Co-operative Societies Act, 2002 has no authority and/or power to appoint a receiver to execute the award so passed without waiting for the finality to be attained as contemplated under 1996 Act.[35]

If the court is satisfied that accord and satisfaction had been arrived at by execution of a full and final receipt and/or final bill, in the absence of any fraud, duress, coercion or the like, the arbitration clause would have come to its logical end and no proceedings under the Act would be maintainable.[36]

In case of enforcement of an arbitral award beyond the territorial jurisdiction of the court, a formal transfer of the award would be necessary under Section 39 read with Order 21 Rules 5 to 7 CPC.[37]

If an award is passed, an application for enforcement of the award by way of execution need not always be filed under Section 36 before the District Judge. Award can be executed by competent civil court having territorial and pecuniary jurisdiction to entertain the matter.[38] Additional District Judge is not strictly considered. Principal civil court is barred from enforcing arbitral awards.[39]

---

32. *Maharashtra Industries Development Corpn.* v. *Govardhani Constructions Co.*, 2007 SCC OnLine Bom 204: (2007) 3 Mah LJ 514.
33. *Srei International Finance Ltd.* v. *Marshal Corpn.*, 2002 SCC OnLine Cal 712.
34. *Maharashtra Apex Corpn. Ltd.* v. *Balaji G*, 2011 SCC OnLine Ker 4039: (2011) 4 KLJ 408.
35. *Ratansi R. Gada* v. *Abhyudaya Coop. Bank Ltd.*, 2011 SCC OnLine Bom 7: (2011) 3 Mah LJ 117.
36. *Sarvesh Chopra* v. *Ircon International Ltd.*, 2010 SCC OnLine Del 889: ILR (2010) 4 Del 138.
37. *Alema Khatun* v. *Tata Motors Finance Ltd.*, 2016 SCC OnLine Gau 691: (2016) 2 Gau LR 536.
38. *Bhoomatha Para Boiled Rice and Oil Mill* v. *Maheshwari Trading Co.*, 2009 SCC OnLine AP 808: (2010) 1 ALD 522.
39. *Lakhamraju Sujatha* v. *Yuvaraj Finance (P) Ltd.*, 2009 SCC OnLine AP 718.

Arbitral award shall be deemed to be decree of civil court, if time for setting aside the award under Section 34 has expired.[40] Where the alleged petition under Section 34 has already been dismissed for want of jurisdiction and returned for presentation before proper court, there is no legal impediment in the execution of the award.[41]

Legality/invalidity of award cannot be challenged in execution proceedings.[42]

Court

The word "court" occurring in Section 36 must be held to be a Court of District Judge for the purpose of enforcement of the award.[43] The expression "court" cannot for the purpose of Section 36 be read at variance within the meaning of the expression under Section 34.[44] Award was made by the sole arbitrator appointed by the High Court at Ranchi. Award was published and objections against the award were pending in the principal city civil court, Ranchi; petition under Section 36 filed at Delhi was not maintainable.[45]

The "court" referred to in Sections 34 and 36 of the Act is the "court" as defined under Section 2(1)(*e*) of the Act and refers to a District Court, but not the character of a grade inferior to the principal civil court of original jurisdiction. Application for enforcement of award is to be filed in the District Court.[46]

Application for execution of award or setting aside of award can be heard and decided not only by District Judge but also by court of additional district judge.[47]

Commercial dispute—Execution of arbitral award

The commercial court constituted under Section 3(*i*), Commercial Courts, Commercial Division and Commercial Appellate Division of High Courts Act, 2015, as defined in Section 2(*b*) of that Act, would be the only competent

40. *Assam State Weaving & Mfg. Co. Ltd.* v. *Vinny Engg. Enterprises (P) Ltd.*, 2009 SCC OnLine Cal 2464: (2010) 1 CHN 363.
41. *State of Orissa* v. *Durga Charan Routray*, 2009 SCC OnLine Ori 84.
42. *Fingertips Solutions (P) Ltd.* v. *Dhanashree Electronics Ltd.*, 2011 SCC OnLine Cal 4974.
43. *Akola Janata Commercial Coop. Bank Ltd.* v. *Raju Natthujibadhe*, 2010 SCC OnLine Bom 1949: (2011) 2 Mah LJ 427.
44. *Shree Harivansh Securities (P) Ltd.* v. *Nikko Stock Broker (P) Ltd.*, 2017 SCC OnLine Bom 4124: (2018) 1 Mah LJ 374.
45. *Engg. Project (India) Ltd.* v. *Indiana Engg. Works (P) Ltd.*, 2004 SCC OnLine Del 517: (2004) 76 DRJ 119.
46. *Potlabathuni Srikanth* v. *Shriram City Union Finance Ltd.*, 2015 SCC OnLine Hyd 555: (2016) 2 ALD 10.
47. *Ibid.*

court to execute an arbitral award on a "commercial dispute" passed under the Arbitration and Conciliation Act, 1996 and not the principal civil court having the original jurisdiction in the district, *i.e.* the Court of District and Sessions Judge as defined under Section 2(1)(*e*), Arbitration and Conciliation Act, 1996.[48]

Section 36 (As amended by Act 3 of 2016)—No automatic stay of award

Amendment Act 3 of 2016 is prospective in nature and will apply to those arbitral proceedings that are commenced as understood by Section 21 of the principal Act, on or after the Amendment Act, and to court proceedings which have commenced on or after the Amendment Act came into force. Section 36, as amended in 2015, applies to pending Section 34 applications even in arbitrations commenced prior to 23 October 2015, *i.e.* date of coming into force of the Amendment Act, 2015, as Section 36 is a procedural provision.[49] Unless a stay of the award decree is granted by the court under Order 41 Rule 5 CPC, there shall no longer be any automatic stay of the award decree as was the case under the unamended Section 36. Rule of automatic stay of operation of award on filing of Section 34 application, even in absence of an order of stay/imposition of conditions by court as per unamended Section 36 is no longer applicable.[50]

Stay of execution of award [Sub-s. (2) and (3)]

Sub-section (2) provides that the filing of an application for setting aside an award under Section 34 shall not by itself render the award enforceable, (automatic stay of the execution of award) unless the court grants an order of stay of the operation of the said arbitral award on separate application for reasons to be recorded in writing.

The provisions of Order 41 Rules 1(3) and 5 CPC apply. The court can impose conditions while allowing a stay application.[51]

First proviso to Section 36(3) substituted by Amendment Act 3 of 2016 provides that the court shall, while considering application for grant of stay in the case of an award for the payment of money, have due regard to the provisions for grant of stay of a money decree under the provisions of CPC. Second proviso to Section 36(3), added by Amendment Act 3 of 2021 provides that where the court is satisfied that a prima facie case is made out

48. *Ess Kay Fincorp Ltd.* v. *Suresh Choudhary*, 2019 SCC OnLine Raj 7770: (2020) 1 RLW 93.
49. *BCCI* v. *Kochi Cricket (P) Ltd.*, (2018) 6 SCC 287.
50. *Ibid.*
51. *Subrat Ranjan Dash* v. *ACC Ltd.*, 2018 SCC OnLine Ori 456.

that the arbitration agreement or the contract which is the basis of the award or that the making of the award was affected by fraud or corruption, it shall stay the award unconditionally pending the disposal of the application under Section 34 for setting aside the award.

There is no automatic stay during the pendency of appeal.[52]

The court has sufficient power to grant unconditional stay on arbitral award, even of its own accord, when there is prima facie observation that such award is influenced or affected by fraud or corruption. Parliament has entrusted the court with discretion to impose stay in cases where arbitral award is tainted by fraudulent or corrupt practices.[53]

Enforcement of arbitral award—Money decree—Exemption to government from furnishing security

The High Court had granted unconditional stay to the arbitration award. Section 36, Arbitration and Conciliation Act does not provide special treatment to the government while dealing with stay applications under proceedings of Section 34. Order 27, Rule 8-A CPC only provides exemption from furnishing security, which would not restrict the court from directing deposit of the awarded amount and part thereof. Stay order granted by the High Court was not sustainable.[54]

Ex parte stay of award without recording reasons—Unsustainable

Arbitral award is in the nature of a money decree and the court, while passing an ex parte order of stay, has to record its reasons for passing such an order. The court, while exercising its power under Section 36 of the Act, can direct the applicant to deposit the amount awarded by award. In *Balajee Education (P) Ltd.* v. *Rajani Kant Pandey*[55], the impugned order granting stay of operation of the arbitral award was passed ex parte without recording any reasons. Order of stay was unsustainable, and was set aside.

Transfer of decree to executing court not necessary

The enforcement of an award through its execution can be filed anywhere in the country where such a decree can be executed and there is no requirement

52. *Decor India (P) Ltd.* v. *National Building Const. Corpn. L.*, 2007 SCC OnLine Del 930: (2007) 97 DRJ 428.
53. *Union of India* v. *Rashmi Metaliks Ltd.*, 2023 SCC OnLine Cal 2272.
54. *Pam Developments (P) Ltd.* v. *State of W.B.*, (2019) 8 SCC 112.
55. 2020 SCC OnLine Cal 3285.

of obtaining a transfer of the decree from the court which would have jurisdiction over the arbitral proceedings.[56]

Arbitral award can be executed in courts where assets of judgment-debtor are located

Section 36 would show that an award is to be enforced in accordance with the provisions of CPC in the same manner as if it were a decree.[57]

The decree of a civil court is liable to be executed primarily by the court which passes the decree where the execution application has to be filed at the first instance. An award under Section 36 of the 1996 Act is equated to a decree of the court for the purposes of execution and only for that purpose. Thus, while an award passed by the Arbitral Tribunal is deemed to be a decree under Section 36 of the 1996 Act, there is no deeming fiction anywhere to hold that the court within whose jurisdiction the arbitral award is passed should be taken to be the court which passed the decree. The 1996 Act actually transcends all territorial barriers.[58]

Execution of non-existent award

On objections to the award filed under Section 34, the award of the arbitrator was set aside by a Single Judge of the High Court. In appeal, the Division Bench of the High Court set aside the order of the Single Judge. In appeal, the Supreme Court set aside the order of the Division Bench of the High Court upholding the award and remanded the matter for fresh disposal. During pendency of appeal on remand, the parties settled the disputes and the appeal was dismissed as infructuous. The order of the Single Judge of the High Court setting aside the award stood revived. There was no award in existence which could be executed. Application for execution was not tenable.[59]

Where the award cannot be regarded or termed arbitral award as defined under 1996 Act and does not contain the essential ingredients in order to give it the status of arbitral award, it is not executable under Section 36 of the 1996 Act.[60]

---

56. *Sundaram Finance Ltd.* v. *Abdul Samad*, (2018) 3 SCC 622.
57. *Ibid.*
58. *Ibid.*
59. *Narayan Prasad Lohia* v. *Nikunj Kumar Lohia*, (2009) 17 SCC 359.
60. *Charan Sharan Khemka* v. *Achint Chemicals*, 2004 SCC OnLine Raj 166: (2005) 1 RLW 734.

Arbitral award—Decretal amount deposited in court—Appropriation first towards interest or towards principal

Award amount was deposited in the court during pendency of Section 34 petition against award, with unilateral stipulation by the debtor to appropriate towards principal amount and not towards interest amount. The amount was accepted under protest by the appellant-creditor. It was held, the appellant-creditor was not bound by appropriation proposed by the debtor as acceptance on protest did not amount to acceptance of the offer. In such a case, the creditor is entitled to appropriate such amount firstly against interest.[61]

Execution of arbitral award—Territorial jurisdiction

The court, where the judgment-debtor resides or carries on business, has territorial jurisdiction to entertain execution proceedings. The decree-holder cannot be compelled to approach the court which passed the decree.[62]

Examination of the judgment debtor as to his assets

Decree holder has right to examine the judgment debtor for ascertainment of judgment debtor's property. Execution will lie before court at Calcutta subject to said examination of judgment debtor.[63]

Enforcement of award—Jurisdiction of court

In *Khaleel Ahmed Dakhani* v. *Hatti Gold Mines Co. Ltd.*[64], a contract was awarded by the respondent-government to the appellant for the construction of a building in Raichur. Arbitration clause stipulated that only courts at Bangalore would have jurisdiction to entertain any claim for the enforcement of the award. As dispute arose between parties, matter was referred to arbitration and award was passed by the arbitrator, arbitrator allowed the claims of the appellant. The respondent filed an application under Section 34 in the Court of Principal City Civil Judge, Bangalore for setting aside the award. While the application under Section 34 of the 1996 Act was pending, appellant decree-holder filed application under Section 36 before the Court of Principal District Judge, Raichur for execution of the award without referring to the pendency of application under Section 34 in the Bangalore

---

61. *Leela Hotels Ltd.* v. *Housing & Urban Development Corpn. Ltd.*, (2012) 1 SCC 302.
62. *Bharat Harmonium Works* v. *State of U.P.*, 2016 SCC OnLine All 2793: (2016) 116 ALR 632.
63. *Mechon Services* v. *Predominant Engineers & Contractors (P) Ltd.*, 2017 SCC OnLine Cal 19196.
64. (2000) 3 SCC 755.

court. The Principal District Judge, Raichur issued order for attachment of the property of the respondent. The respondent filed an application for lifting of attachment on the ground of pendency of application under Section 34. The District Judge dismissed the application holding that the Principal City Civil Judge, Bangalore had no jurisdiction to entertain application under Section 34. The Supreme Court held that the Principal District Judge, Raichur did not take notice of clause 35 of the contract which constituted arbitration agreement between the parties, and specifically provided that only the courts at Bangalore would have jurisdiction to entertain any claim for enforcement of the award. It cannot always be said in view of Section 20 CPC that only one court will have jurisdiction to try the suit. It is not that the principal city civil court, Bangalore is not a court within the meaning of Section 2(*e*) of the Act. The Principal District Judge, Raichur should not have entertained the application for execution and ordered attachment of the movable properties of the respondents. The Principal District Judge, Raichur should have stayed his hands and should not have entertained the execution application filed by the appellant.

The arbitrator had fixed the place of arbitration at Kolkata; the award was made and signed at Kolkata. The subject-matter of arbitration was a sum of money with interest and not immovable property situated within the local limits of Hazaribagh Court. The application for execution can be filed only in the court of competent jurisdiction at Kolkata and not at Hazaribagh.[65]

Enforcement of award—Sale of the mortgaged property

Order 34, Rule 14 CPC is clear that the enforcement of a mortgage debt by way of sale of the mortgaged property can only be by filing a separate suit, and not by means of execution proceedings of the earlier decree. By virtue of Section 36, Arbitration Act, the arbitral award has the force of a decree. Consequently, the property can only be brought to sale by filing a civil suit, and not in execution proceedings.[66]

Execution of award by arrest and detention of judgment debtors

The coercive process of arrest and detention of a judgment debtor ought not to be resorted to by an executing court in the very first instance even before ascertaining whether the decree can be satisfied by the judgment debtor. Such an order would be inherently unfair, unreasonable and contrary to the law explained in *Jolly George Varghese* v. *Bank of Cochin*[67]. In any

65. *Indusind Bank Ltd.* v. *Rajesh Dayal*, 2015 SCC OnLine Jhar 3655: (2016) 4 Arb LR 184.
66. *Punjab and Sind Bank* v. *MMTC Ltd.*, 2015 SCC OnLine Del 13638: (2015) 153 DRJ 435.
67. (1980) 2 SCC 360.

event, such an order can, if at all, be passed only by a court that otherwise has jurisdiction to entertain the execution petition in respect of any of the properties of the judgment debtors located within its jurisdiction or against the judgment debtors if any of them is ordinarily resident there. Neither of the above requirements were satisfied. The mere fact that the judgment debtors are likely to appear before the court of the Metropolitan Magistrates in New Delhi at a future date, although none of them is ordinarily resident within its jurisdiction, would not confer jurisdiction on the court to straightaway order their arrest and detention in these proceedings.[68]

Notice under Order 21 Rule 22(1) CPC

The respondent entered appearance in execution proceedings and also filed an affidavit in reply to two chamber summons taken out by the applicant. The respondent had been given an opportunity to show cause why execution shall not proceed, therefore, no notice under Order 21 Rule 22(1) CPC was required to be given.[69]

Execution/enforcement of award—Limitation period

Under Section 136 of the Limitation Act, the limitation period for the execution of decree is 12 years from the date when the decree becomes enforceable. The award would become enforceable after expiry of time for making an application to set aside the award. Execution proceedings initiated after dismissal of application filed under Section 34 of the Act of 1996 was not barred by limitation.[70]

Objection of facts in execution proceedings

The executing court cannot hold any kind of factual inquiry which might have the effect of nullifying the decree itself but it can undertake limited inquiry regarding jurisdictional issues which goes to the root of the decree and has the effect of rendering the decree nullity. In *Punjab State Civil Supplies Corpn. Ltd.* v. *Atwal Rice and General Mills*[71], none of the objections raised by the judgment debtor were in relation to the jurisdiction of the court affecting the root of very passing of the decree. An inquiry into facts, which ought to have been done in a suit or in an appeal arising out of

68. *State Trading Corpn. of India Ltd.* v. *Global Steel Holdings Ltd.*, 2015 SCC OnLine Del 7968: (2015) 149 DRJ 289.
69. *Shree Harivansh Securities (P) Ltd.* v. *Nikko Stock Broker (P) Ltd.*, 2017 SCC OnLine Bom 4124: (2018) 1 Mah LJ 374.
70. *Ushadevi* v. *Cotton Corpn. of India Ltd.*, 2019 SCC OnLine MP 6113: (2020) 1 MP LJ 200.
71. (2017) 8 SCC 116.

the suit or in proceedings under Section 34 could not be held in execution proceedings in relation to such award/decree. Objections which could be raised by the judgment debtor before the arbitrator or before the trial court at the time of application under Section 34 for setting aside the award of the arbitrator cannot be allowed to be raised in execution proceedings.[72]

Objection under Section 47 CPC not maintainable

The petitioner against whom the arbitral awards were made did not prefer any application under Section 34 of the Act. After the time prescribed for filing such an application expired, the respondent award holder approached the court by filing a petition under Section 36 for enforcement of the arbitral award. Only then, the petitioner State against whom the arbitral awards were passed raised objection under Section 47 CPC. Section 5, Arbitration and Conciliation Act clearly provides that "Notwithstanding anything contained in any other law for the time being in force, in matters governed by this Part, no judicial authority shall intervene except where so provided in this Part", which implies that the only remedy available to the aggrieved party against whom an arbitral award is passed, is Section 34, Arbitration and Conciliation Act. The petitioner State did not avail such remedy to resist the execution within the time prescribed under the law. The petitioner raised an objection to resist the execution only by filing an application under Section 47 CPC despite the specific remedy available under Section 34, Arbitration and Conciliation Act. In view of the prohibition imposed under Section 5 of the Act, objection except under Section 34 of the Act is not entertainable. Objection under Section 47 CPC cannot be entertained.[73]

Enforcement of award—Provisions of Order 21 CPC applicable

Once an application is filed for the enforcement of the award before the "court", execution proceeding takes the colour of regular civil proceeding and comes within the domain of CPC. All trappings of CPC ought to apply to such an execution proceeding, including provisions of Rules 97 to 101 of Order 21 of the Code.[74]

Power of enforcing/executing court to go behind the award

There is no power in a court to direct execution of an award when an application under Section 34 challenging the award is pending. For the purposes

---

72. *Ibid.*
73. *State of Tripura* v. *Ashes Deb*, 2022 SCC OnLine Tri 760; *State of Tripura* v. *Ashes Deb*, 2022 SCC OnLine Tri 760.
74. *Benazir Samad* v. *Feroze Ahmed*, 2018 SCC OnLine Cal 3485.

of Section 36, the court cannot be called upon to go behind the awarded amount and deal with the processes by which the amount was arrived at. Hence, challenge to a process by which award was worked out under Section 34 of the 1996 Act, would render the award as a whole, unenforceable.[75] Plea that there was no arbitration agreement cannot be entertained in execution proceedings.[76]

By virtue of Section 36, award of the arbitrator is enforceable as decree of the court, the executing court cannot go behind the decree, so stipulations by way of interest cannot be gone into. Issue of stamping and registration of award can be raised at the execution stage.[77] The court cannot assume the power and jurisdiction to interpret the award or correct the mistake or error therein.[78]

Judicial intervention—Enforcement of award—Provisions of Section 47, Order 21, Rule 97 CPC have no application

A proceeding before the civil court under Section 36 of the 1996 Act for the enforcement of an arbitral award is a proceeding under the said Act and not a proceeding under CPC. As a necessary corollary, the resort to the provisions of CPC for raising objections having the propensity to annihilate the award, which has been brought before the civil court only for the purpose of enforcement, is clearly excluded. The provisions of Section 47 CPC or Order 21 Rules 97 to 101 CPC have no application to a proceeding under Section 36 of the 1996 Act instituted for enforcement of an arbitral award.[79]

Award of interest by executing court

The executing court cannot pass any order for payment of interest.[80] A Division Bench of the Delhi High Court has taken a contrary view. The Division Bench has held that the court has inherent jurisdiction to award interest in the absence of any legislation, agreement or custom subject to the contrary agreement.

75. *National Buildings Construction Corpn. Ltd.* v. *Lloyds Insulation India Ltd.*, (2005) 2 SCC 367.
76. *R.K. Textiles* v. *Sulabh Textiles (P) Ltd.*, 2002 SCC OnLine Bom 279: (2002) 4 Mah LJ 678.
77. *Jitender Mohan Malik* v. *Ravi Bhushan Malik*, 2008 SCC OnLine Del 748: ILR (2009) 1 Del 282; *Housing & Urban Development Corpn. Ltd.* v. *Leela Hotels Ltd.*, 2013 SCC OnLine Del 979: (2013) 135 DRJ 598.
78. *Global Co. Decree-holder* v. *National Fertilizers Ltd.*, 1999 SCC OnLine Del 356: (1999) 49 DRJ 660.
79. *Between Rajendra Kamal* v. *A.B.M. Developers (P) Ltd.*, 2015 SCC OnLine Pat 10427.
80. *M.P. Housing Board* v. *Satish Kumar Raizada*, 2002 SCC OnLine MP 601: (2003) 2 MPLJ 346.

Award amount—Payment outside court—Non-certification by court—Not recognised

The award amount was alleged to be paid by the judgment debtor to the appellant. The alleged payment was never certified by the court as contemplated under Order 21 Rule 2 CPC at the instance of the appellant or the respondent. It was held, no amount was paid by the respondent to the appellant pursuant to the decree/award so as to enable the executing court to record its full satisfaction in accordance with the provisions of Order 21 Rules 1 and 2 CPC.[81]

Interim award—Execution of

An interim award passed in a case is independently enforceable and it is a full fledged award. The question whether the interim award is final to the extent it goes or has effect till the final award is delivered will depend upon the form of award. If the interim award is intended to have effect only so long as the final award is not delivered, it will have the force of the interim award and it will cease to have effect after the final award is made. If on the other hand, the interim award is intended to finally determine the rights of the parties, it will have the force of a complete award and will have effect even after the final award is delivered. In *Union of India* v. *Best Cast Construction (P) Ltd.*[82], the interim award passed against the Railways had the character of full fledged award, did not merge in the final award, was enforceable in law, *namely*, under the 1996 Act.

Award in US dollars—Enforcement of

The agreement between the parties does not contain any provision regarding conversion of the foreign currency component in Indian rupees. The arbitral award must be enforced on its own terms. However, the arbitral award does not indicate the conversion rate for computing the Indian currency equivalent to the amounts awarded in US dollars. It is not necessary that the commercial transactions between Indian parties be confined to Indian territories alone. There may be transactions which may entail exposure in foreign currency. The exchange rate to be applied for computing the amount due and payable under the awarded amount is the exchange rate as prevailing on the date on which respondent's special leave petition was dismissed by the Supreme Court and the arbitral award attained finality.[83]

81. *Punjab State Civil Supplies Corpn. Ltd.* v. *Atwal Rice and General Mills*, (2017) 8 SCC 116.
82. 2014 SCC OnLine Kar 12021: ILR 2014 Kar 6002.
83. *Karam Chand Thapar & Bros. (Coal Sales) Ltd.* v. *MMTC Ltd.*, (2022) 2 HCC (Del) 368: 2022 SCC OnLine Del 949; see also, *National Projects Construction Corpn. Ltd.* v. *Royal Construction Co. (P) Ltd.*, 2023 SCC OnLine SC 1296.

Enforcement of interim award and final award—Order 21 Rules 18 and 19 CPC

The respondent filed an application for execution of final award, whereas the appellant filed application for execution of interim award. The court held, the provisions of Order 21 Rules 18 and 19 CPC cannot be invoked. Rule 18 is applicable in the case where the applications are made to the court for execution of the cross-decrees in separate suits for payment of two sums of money passed between the same parties and Rule 19 is applicable in the case where the application is made to the court for the execution of a decree under which two parties are entitled to recover sums of money.[84]

Partnership Act, 1932 [S. 69]

Section 69, Partnership Act, 1969 has no application to the proceedings of the arbitrator as arbitral proceedings will not come under the expression "other proceedings" of Section 69(3), Partnership Act, the ban imposed under the said section can have no application to arbitration proceedings as well as arbitration award.[85]

Transfer of proceedings

The language of Section 24(3)(*b*) CPC is clear and explicit, an application for the enforcement of the award filed under Section 36, Arbitration and Conciliation Act, 1996 would come under the category of the word "proceeding" under Section 24 CPC. The District Judge would have the power and jurisdiction to transfer the application filed by judgment debtor under Section 36 of the Act from the court which had no jurisdiction to decide a case in first instance to the court of competent jurisdiction. Proceedings filed under Section 36 of the Act before the civil judge were transferred to the Court of District Judge.[86]

Recovery of award amount as arrears of land revenue

Rule 5 of Madhya Pradesh Micro and Small Enterprises Facilitation Council Rules, 2006, which provides for recovery of amount as arrears of land revenue than the one provided under Section 36, Arbitration and Conciliation Act, 1996 is not ultra vires.[87]

---

84. *N.R. Constructions (P) Ltd.* v. *Ram Badan Singh*, (2007) 11 SCC 19.
85. *Umesh Goel* v. *H.P. Coop. Group Housing Society Ltd.*, (2016) 11 SCC 313.
86. *Shahab Uddin* v. *District Judge, Muzaffarnagar*, 2008 SCC OnLine All 1124: (2009) 74 ALR 12.
87. *Power Machines India Ltd.* v. *State of M.P.*, (2017) 7 SCC 323.

Revision

Where on the execution of the decree, the executing court finally disposed of the execution case, remedy to challenge the order of the executing court is in revision under Section 115 CPC and not writ petition under Article 227 of the Constitution.[88]

Writ petition

Where the award in question has been passed by the arbitrator, the time for setting aside the award has expired, the petitioner intends that the award in question should be enforced, the appropriate remedy is to invoke remedy under Section 36, Arbitration and Conciliation Act, writ petition for enforcement of the award is not maintainable.[89]

88. *M.S. Bajwa & Co.* v. *State of Chhattisgarh*, 2008 SCC OnLine Chh 14: (2009) 1 Arb LR 163.
89. *Jagdish Singh* v. *Union of India*, 2016 SCC OnLine All 3467: (2016) 6 All LJ 264.

Chapter IX
Appeals

APPEALABLE ORDERS [S. 37]

37. *Appealable orders.*—(1) [1][Notwithstanding anything contained in any other law for the time being in force, an appeal] shall lie from the following orders (and from no others) to the court authorised by law to hear appeals from original decrees of the Court passing the order, namely:—

[2][(*a*) refusing to refer the parties to arbitration under Section 8;

(*b*) granting or refusing to grant any measure under Section 9;

(*c*) setting aside or refusing to set aside an arbitral award under Section 34.]

(2) An appeal shall also lie to a court from an order of the arbitral tribunal—

(*a*) accepting the plea referred to in sub-section (2) or sub-section (3) of Section 16; or

(*b*) granting or refusing to grant an interim measure under Section 17.

(3) No second appeal shall lie from an order passed in appeal under this section, but nothing in this section shall affect or take away any right to appeal to the Supreme Court.

COMMENTS

Corresponding old law

Section 37 corresponds to Section 39, Arbitration Act, 1940. Section 39, Arbitration Act, 1940 provided as under:

39. *Appealable orders.*—(1) An appeal shall lie from the following orders passed under this Act (and from no others) to the Court authorised by law to hear appeals from original decrees of the Court passing the order:

---

1. *Subs.* for "An appeal" by Act 33 of 2019, S. 8 (w.e.f. 30-8-2019).
2. *Subs.* for clauses (*a*) and (*b*) by Act 3 of 2016, S. 20 (w.r.e.f. 23-10-2015). Prior to substitution clauses (*a*) and (*b*) read as:

   "(*a*) granting or refusing to grant any measure under Section 9;

   (*b*) setting aside or refusing to set aside an arbitral award under Section 34."

An order—

(*i*) superseding an arbitration;

(*ii*) on an award stated in the form of a special case;

(*iii*) modifying or correcting an award;

(*iv*) filing or refusing to file an arbitration agreement;

(*v*) staying or refusing to stay legal proceedings where there is an arbitration agreement;

(*vi*) setting aside or refusing to set aside an award:

Provided that the provisions of this section shall not apply to any order passed by a Small Cause Court.

(2) No second appeal shall lie from an order passed in appeal under this section, but nothing in this section shall affect or take away any right to appeal to the Supreme Court.

Legislative changes

Arbitration and Conciliation (Amendment) Act, 2015 (3 of 2016)

In Section 37 of the principal Act, in sub-section (1), for clauses (*a*) and (*b*), the following clauses shall be *substituted*, namely—

"(*a*) refusing to refer the parties to arbitration under Section 8;

(*b*) granting or refusing to grant any measure under Section 9;

(*c*) setting aside or refusing to set aside an arbitral award under Section 34.".

As a result of the amendment an order refusing to refer the parties to arbitration under Section 8 has also been made appealable in new clause (*a*).

NOTES ON CLAUSES

Clause 20 of the Bill seeks to amend Section 37 of the principal Act so as to include the order refusing to refer the parties to arbitration under Section 8 also appealable.

Arbitration and Conciliation (Amendment) Act, 2019 (33 of 2019)

In Section 37 of the principal Act, in sub-section (1), for the words "An appeal", the words "Notwithstanding anything contained in any other law for the time being in force, an appeal" shall be substituted.

Scope and application

Section 37 enumerates the orders which are appealable. Appeal to the High Court is available only if the order falls within the ambit of clauses of Section 37 and not otherwise.[3] The words "from no others" used in Section 37(1) of the Act is indicative of the legislative intention which clearly bars the appeal from any other order except those mentioned in Section 37(1) and 37(2) of the Act.[4] The orders from which appeal lies are:

1. An order refusing to refer the parties to arbitration under Section 8. An appeal would lie from an order making or refusing to make a reference. An appeal would lie where the court decides not to make a reference or passes an order making reference.[5]
2. An order granting or refusing to grant any measure under Section 9. An order of injunction passed under Section 9 of the Act is an appealable order under Section 37(1)(*a*) of the Act irrespective of the fact as to whether such an order is passed ex parte or upon hearing of the parties concerned.[6] An order granting or refusing to grant any measure under Section 9, Arbitration and Conciliation Act is appealable.[7] The scope of interference is very limited.[8]

   On an application filed under Section 17 of the Act by the respondent, the Arbitral Tribunal directed the appellant to release an amount of ₹ 1 crore to the respondent; there was dispute regarding the property and assets of a partnership firm, as the tribunal had taken a fair, reasonable and equitable view taking into account the capital investment and assets of the firm, the High Court did not interfere, appeal was rejected.[9] An order dismissing proceedings under Section 9, Arbitration and Conciliation Act, 1996 is not appealable under Section 37(1)(*a*).[10] The Arbitral Tribunal possess power to pass orders of interim measures, the order passed by the arbitrator would not be interfered if the discretion has been exercised in good faith.[11]
3. An order setting aside or refusing to set aside an award under Section 34.[12] Every order setting aside or refusing to set aside an arbitral

3. *Raghuvir Cotton Ginning and Pressing (P) Ltd.* v. *Vijay Cotton and Fibre Co.*, 2017 SCC OnLine Bom 76: (2017) 5 Mah LJ 352.
4. *Krishna Devi* v. *SAIL*, 2013 SCC OnLine Chh 281.
5. *Chief Engineer (Madhya Ganga) U.P. Irrigation Deptt.* v. *Jain Construction Co. Engineers & Contractor*, 2010 SCC OnLine All 2734: (2011) 3 All LJ 567 overruled.
6. *Sati Oil Udyog Ltd.* v. *Avanti Projects and Infrastructure Ltd.*, 2009 SCC OnLine Gau 85: (2010) 2 Gau LR 512.
7. *Sundaram Finance Ltd.* v. *Radhamma*, 2003 SCC OnLine Ker 338: (2003) 3 KLT 289.
8. *Sterling Tree Magnum India Ltd.* v. *G.A.M. Thandapani*, 2011 SCC OnLine Mad 423: (2011) 4 LW 91.
9. *Sudarshan Vyapar (P) Ltd.* v. *Madhusudan Guha*, 2012 SCC OnLine Cal 13125: (2013) 5 CHN 394.
10. *Ambika Enterprises* v. *Trishna Bose*, 2003 SCC OnLine Cal 85: (2003) 2 CHN 335.
11. *Anand Agrawal* v. *Balram Das*, 2001 SCC OnLine All 165: (2001) 43 ALR 853.
12. *U.P. Coop. Sugar Factories Federation Ltd.* v. *P.S. Misra*, 2002 SCC OnLine All 1095: 2003 All LJ 1038.

award under Section 34 is appealable.[13] An order passed on the application filed under Section 34 setting aside the award and dismissing the execution application is in the nature of an order setting aside the award under Section 34, appeal against the order is maintainable.[14]

4. An order accepting the plea referred to in sub-section (2) or sub-section (3) of Section 16. Appeal lies under Section 37(2), against the order of the Arbitral Tribunal passed under Section 16 of the Act.[15]
5. An order granting or refusing to grant an interim measure under Section 17.

An appeal under Section 37(1)(*c*) would be maintainable against an order refusing to condone the delay in filing an application under Section 34 of the Act to set aside an award.[16]

Where issuance of notice is restricted to some or one of the grounds on which award of the arbitrator is challenged, it would not bar more than one appeal being maintained by the aggrieved party.[17]

If the contract is capable of being assigned and is actually assigned, then the arbitration clause in the initial agreement would also bind the assignee. The appellant never raised this issue before the arbitrator and willingly participated in the arbitration proceedings. Appeal was dismissed.[18]

Appealability of an order has to be gauged by not only its immediate effect but also its ripple effect.[19]

Where the Principal District Judge on petition under Section 9 for interim relief has held that the court had no territorial jurisdiction to entertain the application and returned the application for presentation before a proper forum, held the ripple effect of the order brings it within the circumference of Section 9, hence the order would be appealable under Section 37(1)(*b*) of the Act.[20]

In a petition filed under Section 34 for setting aside the award, if the court issues notice on some of the grounds, there is complete autonomy

---

13. *Bisleri International (P) Ltd.* v. *Sun Petpack Jabalpur (P) Ltd.*, 2009 SCC OnLine MP 562: (2009) 4 MP LJ 514.
14. *Pursottam Das Chokhani* v. *Sarita Devi Nathani*, 2005 SCC OnLine Gau 33: (2006) 2 Gau LR 16.
15. *NHAI* v. *PNC Constructions Co. Ltd.*, 2005 SCC OnLine Del 749: (2005) 82 DRJ 489.
16. *Chintels (India) Ltd.* v. *Bhayana Builders (P) Ltd.*, (2021) 4 SCC 602.
17. *NHAI* v. *Oriental Structure Engineers Ltd.-Gammon India Ltd. (JV)*, 2012 SCC OnLine Del 4787: (2012) 132 DRJ 769.
18. *Punjab State Industrial Development Corpn. Ltd.* v. *Triveni Engg. Industries Ltd.*, 2008 SCC OnLine Del 709: (2008) 106 DRJ 207.
19. *Nivaran Solutions* v. *Aura Thia Spa Services (P) Ltd.*, 2016 SCC OnLine Bom 5062: (2016) 5 Mah LJ 234.
20. *Ibid.*

conferred under the Act to prefer appeal against grounds on which the court rejects the petition either at that stage or at the stage when the petition under Section 34 is finally disposed of. Aggrieved parties can maintain more than one appeal.[21]

In an appeal filed under Section 37 against the order of civil court refusing to set aside an award, the court would consider whether the award of the arbitrator was vitiated on account of excess of jurisdiction, incompleteness or misconduct. The appellate court would interfere only when the civil court had acted unreasonably in exercise of its discretion or it had ignored the relevant facts.[22] The court, in appeal, would interfere only when there is patent illegality, the award shocks the conscience of the court, the finding arrived at by the arbitrator could not have come in normal course.[23]

First appellate court can examine whether the interpretation given by the arbitrator of a clause is correct or not.[24] The High Court cannot exercise its jurisdiction under Section 37 as a first appellate court in a civil suit. The High Court under Section 37 cannot award claims that had been rejected by the District Judge under Section 34 of the Act.[25]

It is on very limited grounds that the award of the arbitrator can be set aside. The scope of an appeal from the order passed under Section 34 of the Act would be governed by the same limitations imposed on the exercise of the power under Section 34, if not more stringent.[26] While exercising jurisdiction under Section 37 of the Act, the court is concerned about the jurisdiction that Section 34 court exercised while considering the challenge to the arbitral award. The jurisdiction under Section 34 of the Act is exercised only to see if the Arbitral Tribunal's view is perverse or manifestly arbitrary. Accordingly, the question of reinterpreting the contract on an alternative view does not arise. If this is the principle applicable to the exercise of jurisdiction under Section 34 of the Act, a Division Bench exercising jurisdiction under Section 37 of the Act cannot reverse an award, much less the decision of a Single Judge on the ground that they have not given effect and voice to all clauses of the contract.[27]

---

21. *NHAI* v. *Oriental Structure Engineers Ltd. - Gammon India Ltd. (JV)*, 2012 SCC OnLine Del 4787: (2012) 132 DRJ 769.
22. *Union of India* v. *L.S.N. Murthy*, 2006 SCC OnLine AP 414: (2006) 2 AP LJ 170.
23. *PWD* v. *Chandragiri Construction Co.*, 2011 SCC OnLine Mad 343: (2011) 2 CTC 669.
24. *Sarkar & Sarkar* v. *State of W.B.*, 2006 SCC OnLine Cal 265: (2007) 1 Cal LT 157.
25. *Punjab State Civil Supplies Corpn. Ltd.* v. *Ramesh Kumar & Co.*, (2021) 16 SCC 138.
26. *Mahanagar Gas Ltd.* v. *Babulal Uttamchand and Co.*, 2012 SCC OnLine Bom 1254: (2013) 2 Mah LJ 94; *World Window Infrastructure (P) Ltd.* v. *Central Warehousing Corpn.*, (2021) 3 HCC (Del) 731.
27. *Konkan Railway Corpn. Ltd.* v. *Chenab Bridge Project*, (2023) 9 SCC 85.

Every attempt is required to be made to promote the arbitral process, and every attempt at seeking to retard it, is required to be eschewed. This philosophy is required to pervade the exercise of jurisdiction as much under Section 37(2), as under Section 34 of the Act.[28]

Interference under Section 37, Arbitration and Conciliation Act, 1996 by the appellate court also cannot travel beyond the restrictions under Section 34. The scope of the jurisdiction of the appellate court under Section 37 is very limited. The court has to see whether, within this limited jurisdiction, the case of the appellant is sufficient to exercise that jurisdiction.[29]

While exercising jurisdiction under Section 37 of the Act, the court is concerned about the jurisdiction that the Section 34 court exercised while considering the challenge to the arbitral award. The jurisdiction under Section 34 of the Act is exercised only to see if the Arbitral Tribunal's view is perverse or manifestly arbitrary. Accordingly, the question of reinterpreting the contract on an alternative view does not arise. If this is the principle applicable to exercise of jurisdiction under Section 34 of the Act, a Division Bench exercising jurisdiction under Section 37 of the Act cannot reverse an award, much less the decision of a Single Judge, on the ground that they have not given effect and voice to all clauses of the contract.[30]

Order passed by the Single Judge under Section 8 of the Act is neither an order granting or refusing to grant any measure under Section 9 of the Act nor an order setting aside or refusing to set aside an arbitral award under Section 34. Sub-section (2) of Section 37 has no application.[31] Finding of the Arbitral Tribunal that it has jurisdiction to pass orders against some of the respondents who were not signatories to the arbitration agreement cannot be challenged by filing appeal under Section 37, can be challenged while challenging award under Section 34 of the Act.[32]

Where the issue whether counterclaim was outside the scope of arbitration proceedings is adjudged simultaneously by the arbitrator while passing the award, it cannot be challenged by way of appeal under Section 37. Remedy is an application for setting aside award under Section 34 of the Act.[33] The arbitrator adjudicated the counterclaims and finally decided the same on

28. *Augmont Gold (P) Ltd.* v. *One97 Communication Ltd.*, (2021) 4 HCC (Del) 642.
29. *DDA* v. *Eros Resorts & Hotels Ltd.*, (2022) 2 HCC (Del) 384: 2022 SCC OnLine Del 978 (DB).
30. *Konkan Railway Corpn. Ltd.* v. *Chenab Bridge Project*, (2023) 9 SCC 85.
31. *Tandav Film Entertainment (P) Ltd.* v. *Four Frame Pictures*, 2009 SCC OnLine Del 3930: (2010) 114 DRJ 219.
32. *Shailendra Bhadauria* v. *Matrix Partners India Investment*, 2019 SCC OnLine Bom 1.
33. *B.H.P. Engineers (P) Ltd.* v. *MSEFC, U.P.*, 2009 SCC OnLine All 565: (2009) 5 All LJ 345.

merits and held that some claims were not admissible in the form while the others being subject to prior binding settlement are not admissible. It was held that the order of the Arbitral Tribunal titled "partial final award" did not fall within the scope of appealable orders.[34] Where the arbitrator had no power to pass order under the old Arbitration Act, 1940 or under new 1996 Act, the order passed is non-est in the eye of law, the order would be set aside.[35]

Though an award can be set aside in appeal filed under Section 37, however, the grounds shall be the same as enumerated in Section 34(2) of the Act.[36]

Though the appellate power under Section 37, Arbitration and Conciliation Act, 1996 is limited yet where the illegality in the arbitral proceedings goes to the very root of the matter, court's interference is warranted. Such interference is justified when the arbitrators conduct and impartiality is in doubt.[37]

Section 37(1)(*a*) was incorporated in the principal Act of 1996 with effect from 25 October 2015. Before 25 October 2015, no right existed to file an appeal against order refusing to refer parties to arbitration under Section 8 of the Act of 1996. The date of commencement of court proceedings was 10 July 2015, when application under Section 8 of the Act of 1996 was filed. The appellant had no right to file an appeal at time of commencement of court proceedings on 10 July 2015. Appeal against refusal to refer parties to arbitration, was not maintainable.[38]

Appeal under Section 37, Arbitration and Conciliation Act, 1996 and Section 100 CPC

An appeal under Section 37, Arbitration and Conciliation Act, 1996 cannot be construed as an appeal under Section 100 CPC as the scope of interference in an appeal under the two statutes is distinct and different.[39]

Sections 37 and 50—Relative scope of

Sections 37 and 50 are not comparable because they belong to two different statutory schemes. Section 37 containing the provision of appeal is part of

34. *NTPC Ltd.* v. *Siemens Atiengesellschaft (SAG)*, 2005 SCC OnLine Del 631: (2005) 83 DRJ 46.
35. *BSES Rajdhani Power Ltd.* v. *R.C. Gupta & Bros.*, 2009 SCC OnLine Del 1757: (2009) 162 DLT 356.
36. *State of Uttarakhand* v. *Hill Ways Engg. Co.*, 2016 SCC OnLine Utt 560.
37. *Shriram Transport Finance Co. Ltd.* v. *Narender Singh*, (2022) 6 HCC (Del) 275).
38. *Graviss Foods (P) Ltd.* v. *Ice Cream Garden*, 2023 SCC OnLine HP 1032.
39. *Anheuser Busch Inbev India Ltd.* v. *Scarpe Mktg. (P) Ltd.*, 2021 SCC OnLine Kar 15933: (2022) 2 Kant LJ 196.

a much larger framework and has provisions for the complete range of law concerning domestic arbitration and international commercial arbitration. Section 50 on the other hand contains the provision of appeal in a much limited framework, concerned only with the enforcement of the New York Convention Awards. In one sense, the two sections, though each containing the appellate provision belong to different statutes.[40]

An Interim award—No appeal lies

No appeal lies against an interim arbitral award.[41]

In a partnership dispute the arbitrator passed an order/interim award appointing Receiver-cum-Commissioner and directed the petitioner to hand over possession of the shop and accounts books to the receiver. It was held, the order passed by the arbitrator is an interim order and not an interim award, hence is subject to appeal under Section 37 of the Act.[42]

Appealable orders—What are

Ex parte order of injunction passed under Section 9 of the Act is an appealable order.[43]

Power to grant temporary injunction includes power to pass interim order. Order granting interim injunction would fall under Section 37, appeal against the said order would be maintainable.[44]

Dismissal of counterclaim by the arbitrator is appealable under Section 37.[45]

If an interim order is of a nature which may partake the character of a final order rendering adverse inference, such interim order is appealable under Section 37(1)(*a*) of the Act.[46]

Decision of the Arbitral Tribunal that it lacks jurisdiction to entertain claim against principal company is subject to appellate remedy under Section 37(2)(*a*).[47]

---

40. *Fuerst Day Lawson Ltd.* v. *Jindal Exports Ltd.*, (2011) 8 SCC 333.
41. *Gammon India Ltd.* v. *Sankaranarayana Construction (Bangalore) (P) Ltd.*, 2009 SCC OnLine Mad 2261: (2010) 1 LW 325; *Asian Electronics Ltd.* v. *M.P. SEB*, 2007 SCC OnLine MP 179: (2007) 3 MP LJ 203.
42. *Mohan Das* v. *ADJ No. 3*, 2010 SCC OnLine Raj 768: (2010) 3 RLW 2394.
43. *ICICI Bank Ltd.* v. *IVRCL Ltd.*, 2015 SCC OnLine Hyd 311: (2015) 6 ALD 486.
44. *Road Infrastructure Development Co. of Rajasthan Ltd.* v. *IVRCL Ltd.*, 2014 SCC OnLine Raj 6524: (2014) 4 RLW 3660.
45. *BSNL* v. *Kavveri Telecom Products Ltd.*, 2009 SCC OnLine Del 2337.
46. *Muthukoya Thoopiyakal* v. *UT of Lakshadweep*, 2011 SCC OnLine Ker 3794: (2012) 1 KLJ 109.
47. *ONGC Ltd.* v. *Discovery Enterprises (P) Ltd.*, (2022) 8 SCC 42.

Appeal lies only when the Arbitral Tribunal upholds that it has no jurisdiction.[48]

Non-appealable orders

Order of appointment of substitute arbitrator by the court is not appealable under Section 37.[49]

Appeal against order rejecting application for appointment of arbitrator is not maintainable.[50] Any order passed under Section 8 of the 1996 Act is not appealable under clause 15 of the Letters Patent.[51]

Order of dismissal of the application for the condonation of delay cannot itself amount to an appealable order under Section 34(1) for the purpose of appeal under Section 37(1). Where the appeal is filed under Section 37 against the order rejecting the application filed by the appellants in terms of Section 34(3) of the Act, it is dismissed in limine as being not maintainable under Section 37(1)(*b*) of the Act.[52]

Appeal against non-extension of time for filing an award passed under Section 29-A(4) does not lie under Section 37.[53]

Section 37 does not prescribe any scope for calling any records from the opposite party. Appeal against the order of rejection is not maintainable.[54]

During pendency of the application filed under Section 34 for setting aside the award, the order dismissing the interim application challenging the award on the ground of inadequacy of paid stamp duty on agreement and constitution of the Arbitral Tribunal, is not an appealable order as the main application under Section 34 is pending adjudication.[55]

An appeal against the order issuing notice to the respondent on the application for grant of injunction is not maintainable.[56]

---

48. *Ashalata S. Lohati* v. *Hiralal Liladhar Sharers and Stock Broker*, 1998 SCC OnLine Bom 511: (1999) Mah LJ 352.
49. *Inland Vikas Ltd.* v. *Central Inland Water Transport Corpn. Ltd.* (CIWTC), 2014 SCC OnLine Cal 22894.
50. *Krishna Devi* v. *SAIL*, 2013 SCC OnLine Chh 281.
51. *Kotak Mahindra Investment Ltd.* v. *Kitply Industries Ltd.*, 2011 SCC OnLine Cal 2736: (2012) 5 CHN 489.
52. *State of Maharashtra* v. *Ramdas Construction Co.*, 2006 SCC OnLine Bom 690: (2006) 6 Mah LJ 678.
53. *Indu - ZMJ-Zhengzhou Design-Xinfeng Consortium* v. *Bharat Coking Coal Ltd.*, 2022 SCC OnLine Jhar 842.
54. *Ibid.*
55. *SAV Steels (P) Ltd.* v. *Ekta Ispat and Power Ltd.*, 2015 SCC OnLine Chh 204.
56. *Felguera Gruas India (P) Ltd.* v. *R.V.R. Projects (P) Ltd.*, 2015 SCC OnLine Hyd 376: (2016) 2 ALD 518.

Whenever an order is passed by the Arbitral Tribunal holding that it has got jurisdiction to proceed with the arbitration proceedings, the said order passed by the arbitrator merges with the award that may be passed under sub-section (5) of Section 16 of the Act. The same order on jurisdiction can also be challenged before the competent court under Section 34 of the Act. Where the Arbitral Tribunal passes an order holding that it has got jurisdiction, it cannot be challenged under Section 37(2)(*a*) of the Act, nevertheless that the order of the arbitrator can also be challenged while challenging the award under Section 34 of the Act.[57]

Whenever an order is passed by the Arbitral Tribunal holding that it has got jurisdiction to proceed with the arbitration proceedings, the said order passed by the arbitrator merges with the award that may be passed under sub-section (5) of Section 16 of the Act. The same order on jurisdiction can also be challenged before the competent court under Section 34 of the Act. Where the Arbitral Tribunal passes an order holding that, it has got jurisdiction cannot be challenged under Section 37(2)(*a*) of the Act, nevertheless that the order of the arbitrator can also be challenged while challenging the award under Section 34 of the Act.[58]

No appeal lies under Section 37, Arbitration and Conciliation Act, 1996 against an order of enforcement of an emergency arbitrator's order made under Section 17(2), Arbitration and Conciliation Act, 1996.[59]

Dismissal of application under Section 34 for setting aside award on ground of non-deposit of 75 per cent of the amount as envisaged under Section 19, Micro, Small and Medium Enterprises Development Act, 2006 does not fall within the mischief of Section 34, appeal does not lie.[60]

An appeal under Section 37, Arbitration and Conciliation Act, 1996 is not maintainable against the order dismissing a Section 34(4) application.[61]

Order passed by the arbitrator rejecting application for calling documents after the closure of evidence is not appealable.[62]

Order of appointment of substitute arbitrator is not appealable under Section 37.[63]

---

57. *K. Ravindra Nayak* v. *K. Raghavendra Nayak*, 2018 SCC OnLine Kar 3920: (2019) 1 KCCR 363.
58. *Ibid.*
59. *Amazon.Com NV Investment Holdings LLC* v. *Future Retail Ltd.*, (2022) 1 SCC 209.
60. *Crompton Greaves Ltd.* v. *Annapurna Electronics*, 2015 SCC OnLine Kar 5906: ILR 2015 Kar 4199.
61. *Canara Bank* v. *State Trading Corpn. of India Ltd.*, (2022) 5 HCC (Del) 638 (DB).
62. *Pennar Aluminium Co. Ltd.* v. *National Aluminium Co. Ltd.*, 2019 SCC OnLine Ori 370.
63. *Inland Vikas Ltd.* v. *Central Inland Water Transport Corpn. Ltd.* (CIWTC), 2014 SCC OnLine Cal 22894.

Appeal against order allowing application for condonation of delay accompanying application filed under Section 34 is not maintainable. The Act does not provide any appeal or revision against order allowing application for condonation of delay.[64]

Award of the arbitrator cannot be interfered with on the ground that the arbitrator interpreted the terms of the agreement incorrectly.[65]

SLP before Supreme Court against appellate order [Sub-s. (3)]

Special leave petition against the appellate order before the Supreme Court is not maintainable in view of an efficacious alternative remedy of revision available before the High Court under Section 115 CPC. Bar to second appeal under Section 37(3) is inconsequential.[66]

Section 37(3) places no restriction on filing of second appeal before the Supreme Court. Jurisdiction to entertain such appeal is conferred upon the Supreme Court under Article 136 of the Constitution of India. However, extraordinary constitutional remedy should not be allowed to be resorted to in regular course under normal situations as a substitute for second appeal.[67]

Forum of appeal

The forum of the appellate court must be determined with reference to the definition of "court" in Section 2(1)(*e*). A High Court not exercising original civil jurisdiction is not a "court" within the meaning of Section 2(1)(*e*).[68]

The Allahabad High Court does not exercise original civil jurisdiction and is not a "court" as defined under Section 2(1)(*e*). Appeal from the order setting aside/refusing to set aside the award would not be entertainable directly by the High Court.[69] The city civil court is not the principal court as defined in Section 2(1)(*e*). An application under Section 34 filed before the city civil court is not maintainable, appeal filed by the appellant in the High Court under Section 37 against the rejection of his petition by the city civil court is also not maintainable.[70]

64. *Mahant Subash Shah* v. *Kulbir Singh*, 2023 SCC OnLine J&K 772.
65. *Vinod Bhatla* v. *Matrimony.com*, 2019 SCC OnLine Mad 38964.
66. *Nirma Ltd.* v. *Lurgi Lentjes Energietechnik Gmbh*, (2002) 5 SCC 520.
67. *J. Qumairjee and Co.* v. *ADJ, Dehradun*, 2000 SCC OnLine All 102: (2000) 39 ALR 53.
68. *Pandey & Co. Builders (P) Ltd.* v. *State of Bihar*, (2007) 1 SCC 467.
69. *Ashish Kumar Sadh* v. *Putul Chaubey*, 2015 SCC OnLine All 9371: (2016) 115 ALR 587.
70. *Devendra Shantilal Kothari* v. *Mother India Securities (P) Ltd.*, 2012 SCC OnLine Bom 332: (2013) 2 Mah LJ 897.

Scope of appellate power

The scope of interference, in an appeal, with the exercise of such discretion, is quite limited. The court cannot ordinarily interfere with the order on the ground that, in its estimation, the urgency was not such as would justify passing of the impugned order. If, no doubt, the Arbitral Tribunal has relied on irrelevant or inadmissible material to return a finding of urgency, or if the Arbitral Tribunal has passed the interlocutory protective order without returning any finding of urgency, then, the court may interfere, as such exercise borders on perversity. Where, however, the Arbitral Tribunal has returned a finding of urgency, supported by factual material, then, if the material is not found to be incorrect or irrelevant, the question of whether the material denotes urgency of a degree sufficient to grant interim protection is, essentially, a matter relating to the subjective satisfaction of the tribunal. The court does not substitute its subjective satisfaction for that of the tribunal.[71]

The appellant had not filed statement of defence, dispute, opportunities given, and the arbitrator passed a speaking award. Scope of interference under Section 37 is narrow. If the court is allowed to review the decision of the Arbitral Tribunal on law or on merit, speed and above all, the efficacy of the arbitral process is lost. Appeal was dismissed.[72]

In cases where the agreement expressly provides for payment of interest, unless the terms of the contract in regard to interest are found to be invalid or inapplicable, the Arbitral Tribunal is required to render an arbitral award in conformity with the terms of the contract. In cases where the agreement prescribes award of interest, the Arbitral Tribunal cannot award interest. In cases where the contract is silent as to payment of interest, the Arbitral Tribunal has the discretion to award interest as Section 31(7)(*a*) empowers the Arbitral Tribunal to do so.[73]

The considerations guiding exercise of appellate jurisdiction under Section 37(2)(*b*), Arbitration and Conciliation Act, 1996 are, fundamentally, not really different from those which govern exercise of jurisdiction under Section 34. It is only where the order suffers from patent illegality or perversity that the court would interfere with the Arbitral Tribunal's order, under Section 37(2)(*b*). This is because, unlike appeals under other statutes or under the CPC, appeals against orders of Arbitral Tribunal are subject to the overarching limitations contained in Section 5 of the 1996 Act read with the preamble which proscribes interference, by courts, with the arbitral

71. *Sanjay Arora* v. *Rajan Chadha*, (2021) 3 HCC (Del) 654.
72. *Agra Development Authority* v. *Baba Construction (P) Ltd.*, 2023 SCC OnLine All 2950: (2023) 4 All LJ 154.
73. *KMC Construction Ltd.* v. *NHAI*, (2021) 4 HCC (Del) 464.

process, or with orders passed by Arbitral Tribunal, save and except on the limited grounds envisaged in the Act itself.[74]

The restraints which operate on the court while exercising jurisdiction under Section 34, Arbitration and Conciliation Act, 1996 also apply while exercising jurisdiction under Section 37(2)(*b*). This is because, while Section 34 jurisdiction is exercised against the final award, the court, acting under Section 37(2)(*b*), examines an interlocutory order. The interlocutory orders are, by their very nature, discretionary. The scope of interference, in judicial review, with discretionary orders is limited. Where the discretion exercised is towards direction for a deposit, the court has to be additionally circumspect, as the issue whether a deposit ought or ought not to be directed, so as to secure the sanctity of the arbitral proceedings and ensure that they proceed to fruition, is essentially a matter to be assessed by the Arbitral Tribunal. Unless such assessment is perverse or suffers from manifest illegality, the approach of the court, ordinarily, should be one of restraint.[75]

As there was guarded and sparing use of the powers under Section 37(2)(*b*), Arbitration and Conciliation Act, 1996 in only exceptional circumstances and even more so when the exercise of discretion by the arbitrator is not seen to be arbitrary, capricious, irrational or perverse, there was no reason for the court to interfere in the arbitrator's order in this case.[76]

Re-appreciation of evidence by appellate court

The High Court, in appeal, cannot re-appreciate evidence to record a contrary finding.[77]

The award of the arbitrator was based on evidence and material on record. In an appeal against the order of the trial court refusing to set aside the award, the High Court re-appreciated evidence and reached at a contrary opinion, which was erroneous. The award of the arbitrator and order of the trial court were restored.[78]

In an appeal under Section 37, the court cannot enter into the merits of claim. As per settled position of law, an award can be set aside under Sections 34/37 only if the award is found to be contrary to: (*a*) fundamental

74. *Sanjay Arora* v. *Rajan Chadha*, (2021) 3 HCC (Del) 654.
75. *Dinesh Gupta* v. *Bechu Singh*, (2021) 3 HCC (Del) 763.
76. *Manish Aggarwal* v. *RCI Industries & Technologies Ltd.*, (2022) 3 HCC (Del) 289: 2022 SCC Online Del 1285.
77. *Moona Abousher* v. *Cholamandalam DBS Finance Ltd.*, 2019 SCC OnLine Mad 8898; *World Window Infrastructure (P) Ltd.* v. *Central Warehousing Corpn.*, (2021) 3 HCC (Del) 731.
78. *K. Sugumar* v. *Hindustan Petroleum Corpn. Ltd.*, (2020) 12 SCC 539.

policy of Indian law; or (*b*) the interest of India; or (*c*) justice or morality; or (*d*) if it is patently illegal.[79] An award was passed by the arbitrator after duly considering correspondence between the parties. The arbitrator had dealt with all points and the view taken by him was a possible view. The appellate court cannot re-appreciate or re-examine evidence.[80] Once a possible view is taken by an arbitrator on the totality of consideration of all documents, it is difficult for the court to overturn such a view taken in award.[81]

Where the decision of the Arbitral Tribunal as confirmed by the High Court fell foul of the fundamental policy of Indian law and could not be countenanced, the orders of the Arbitral Tribunal and Single Judge of the High Court were set aside.[82]

While considering an application under Section 37 of the Act of 1996, the District Court has only supervisory jurisdiction. The jurisdiction of the High Court under Section 37 is narrow. Once it is found that the view of the arbitrator is plausible, the court will refrain from interfering in the matter. The court cannot undertake an independent assessment of the merits of the award and must only ascertain that the exercise of power under Section 34 has not exceeded the scope of the provisions; in case an arbitral award has been confirmed by the court under Section 34, in an appeal under Section 37 the appellate court must be extremely cautious and slow in disturbing such concurrent findings.[83]

Amendment in memo of appeal

Amendment in memo of appeal is not absolutely barred after expiry of limitation fixed under Section 34(2). In the interest of justice, the court may allow amendment in memo of appeal.[84] Amendment raising absolutely new ground in memo of appeal was rejected.[85]

Stay and suspension of interim award

The appellate court is empowered to stay and/or suspend an interim award passed by the Arbitral Tribunal pending final decision of the matter.[86]

79. *Haryana Tourism Ltd.* v. *Kandhari Beverages Ltd.*, (2022) 3 SCC 237.
80. *K. Sugumar v. Hindustan Petroleum Corpn. Ltd.*, (2020) 12 SCC 539.
81. *Anand Citi Centre Holdings (P) Ltd.* v. *Consolidated Construction Consortium Ltd.*, 2021 SCC OnLine Mad 5222.
82. *NHAI* v. *Gwalior-Jhansi Expressway Ltd.*, (2018) 8 SCC 243.
83. *Kasim V.K.* v. *M. Ashraf*, (2021) 1 HCC (Ker) 379.
84. *State of Maharashtra* v. *Hindustan Construction Co. Ltd.*, (2010) 4 SCC 518.
85. *Ibid.*
86. *Leslie David Isaac* v. *Bahadur Bapuji Sanjana*, 2012 SCC OnLine Bom 536: (2012) 6 Mah LJ 133.

Interim award set aside

The arbitrator had passed an interim order only on the basis of an oral application and prayer without a claim petition. The appellant was also not given any opportunity to contest the interim protection/order, the interim order was set aside.[87]

Duty of appellate court

All grounds on which award has been set aside, should be examined by appellate court when considering appeal against setting aside of the award. In further appeal, the superior court would have benefit of its views on all the grounds.[88]

Cross-objection in appeal

The 1996 Act is a complete code and Section 5 in categorical terms lead to a definite conclusion that no other provision can be attracted. In appeal, cross-objection cannot be entertained.[89]

Revision

Section 37(3), Arbitration and Conciliation Act only takes away the right of second appeal to the High Court. The remedy of revision under Section 115 CPC is neither expressly nor impliedly taken away by the said Act. The supervisory jurisdiction to be exercised by the High Court under Section 115 CPC is for the purpose of correcting jurisdictional error, if any, committed by a subordinate court in exercise of power in appeal under Section 37(2) of the Act. The approach made to the revisional court under Section 115 of the Code is not a resort to remedy of appeal. In appeal, interference can be made both on facts and law whereas in revision only errors relating to jurisdiction can be corrected. Such revisional remedy is not expressly barred by the provisions of the Act.[90]

Revision petition challenging the order of the arbitrator rejecting application under Section 16 for termination of the arbitration proceedings directly filed before the High Court under Section 115 CPC is not maintainable. Revision petition under Section 115 lies before the High Court only against the order in appeal under Section 37 of the Act and not against

---

87. *BPL Ltd.* v. *Morgan Securities & Credits (P) Ltd.*, 2007 SCC OnLine Del 1643: (2008) 101 DRJ 188.
88. *Narayan Prasad Lohia* v. *Nikunj Kumar Lohia*, (2003) 2 SCC 251.
89. *MTNL* v. *Applied Electronics Ltd.*, (2017) 2 SCC 37.
90. *ITI Ltd.* v. *Siemens Public Communications Network Ltd.*, (2002) 5 SCC 510.

the arbitrator's order.[91] An order denying reference to arbitration is not an order violating the principles of natural justice. Efficacious remedy of appeal before the National Commission is available under the Act, revision petition is not maintainable.[92]

If the tribunal declines jurisdiction or declines to pass an award and dismisses the arbitral proceedings, the party aggrieved is not without a remedy. Section 37(2) deals with such a situation. Thus, what is made directly appealable by Section 37(2)(*a*) of the Act is only an acceptance of a plea of absence of jurisdiction, or of excessive exercise of jurisdiction and the refusal to proceed further either wholly or partly.[93]

Where the appellate court has not awarded interest on the final amount, as second appeal is not available to assail such order, revision petition under CPC is maintainable.[94]

No second appeal against appellate order [Sub-s. (3)]

Section 37(3) bars second appeal against an appellate order under sub-sections (1) and (2) of Section 37.[95] Section 37(3) expressly prohibits a "second appeal" from an order passed under Sections 37(1) and 38(2) except an appeal to the Supreme Court. However, the expression "second appeal" used in Section 37(3) does not mean a second appeal under Section 100 CPC.[96] Order passed by the trial court construing the application filed under Section 34 of this Act, treating it as an appeal under sub-section (2) of Section 37 and adjudicating the same on merits would bar second appeal under sub-section (3) of Section 37. It was held that second appeal was not maintainable.[97]

Order refusing to refer the parties to arbitration under Section 8, appealable

By Amendment Act 3 of 2016, an order of the court refusing to refer the parties to arbitration has also been made appealable.

---

91. *Bedabyas Barik* v. *Sukanti Barik*, 2019 SCC OnLine Ori 380.
92. *Super Diamond Nirman (P) Ltd.* v. *Deepak Agarwal*, 2017 SCC OnLine Cal 99: (2017) 1 ICC 834.
93. *NTPC Ltd.* v. *Siemens Atkeingesellschaft*, (2007) 4 SCC 451.
94. *C.M. Chawla* v. *State of H.P.*, 2016 SCC OnLine HP 4297.
95. *Pandey & Co. Builders (P) Ltd.* v. *State of Bihar*, (2007) 1 SCC 467; *Snehadeep Structures (P) Ltd.* v. *Maharashtra Small-Scale Industries Development Corpn. Ltd.*, (2010) 3 SCC 34.
96. *Fountain Head Developers* v. *Maria Arcangela Sequeira*, 2007 SCC OnLine Bom 340.
97. *A.P. Thomas* v. *Union of India*, 2013 SCC OnLine Kar 9950: (2014) 1 KCCR 554; *Cref Finance Ltd.* v. *Puri Construction Ltd.*, 2001 SCC OnLine Del 413: ILR (2001) 1 Del 360.

Appeal against order passed under Section 34

In appeal under Section 37 against an order passed under Section 34, the High Court cannot act as a court of appeal over the award of the arbitrator.[98] The appellant is not entitled to raise any plea with regard to the merits of the case in order to assail the findings of the arbitrator as the arbitrator is the sole judge of the quantity and quality of the evidence. Appeal was dismissed, award was affirmed.[99]

Limitation period for filing appeal

While providing an appeal under Section 37 the legislature has chosen not to prescribe any period of limitation, the plea of the respondent that the appeal was barred by limitation was rejected.[100] Section 43(1), Arbitration and Conciliation Act provides that the Limitation Act, 1963 does not provide for any period of limitation for filing an appeal under Section 37, Arbitration and Conciliation Act, 1996. No period of limitation is prescribed in Section 37 of the 1966 Act for filing an appeal to set aside an arbitral award. The limitation period prescribed under the general law of the Act of 1963 is applicable when a special statute governing the matter prescribes no limitation period. An appeal filed against the order of a Single Judge setting aside the arbitral award is to be governed by Article 116(*a*) of the Limitation Act, 1963. The period of limitation for appeal against the order setting aside an arbitral award would be 90 days as provided under Article 116(*a*) of the 1963 Act.[101]

Arbitral award was passed on 2 May 2018, appeal against the award was filed on 1 September 2018 after the expiry of limitation period for filing appeal. The appellant failed to explain the reasons for the delay in a satisfactory manner. Appeal challenging the award was dismissed as time barred.[102]

Delay of 703 days in filing appeal against the order passed under Section 34 of the Act refusing to set aside the award was not satisfactorily explained.

---

98. *Ravindra & Associates* v. *Union of India*, (2010) 1 SCC 80; *G. Ramachandra Reddy* v. *Union of India*, (2009) 6 SCC 414; *BOC India Ltd.* v. *Bhagwati Oxygen Ltd.*, (2007) 9 SCC 503; *State of Rajasthan* v. *Puri Construction Co. Ltd.*, (1994) 6 SCC 485; *Port of Madras* v. *Engg. Constructions Corpn. Ltd.*, (1995) 5 SCC 531.
99. *Union of India/National Gallery of Modern Art* v. *K. Bikram Singh*, 2009 SCC OnLine Del 3142: (2009) 113 DRJ 37.
100. *ONGC Ltd.* v. *Jagson International Ltd.*, 2005 SCC OnLine Bom 814: (2005) 3 Mah LJ 1141; see also, *Rameswara Homes & Apartments (P) Ltd.* v. *Manojlal Seal*, 2007 SCC OnLine Cal 619: (2008) 3 CHN 349.
101. *North Eastern Electric Power Corpn. Ltd.* v. *Patel Unity Joint Venture*, 2017 SCC OnLine Megh 386: (2017) 3 Civ LT 107 (DB).
102. *Union of India* v. *Tenzing Construction*, 2022 SCC OnLine Gau 2036: (2022) 3 Gau LR 143.

Mere reference of time taken in correspondence between the officers of the department was found not sufficient explanation. Appeal was rejected as time barred.[103]

Cross appeal—Limitation

For filing cross-appeal against order setting aside/refusing to set aside arbitral award on petition under Section 34 of the Act, limitation starts running from the date the party filing cross-appeal receives notice of the date fixed for hearing of the appeal, and not from the date of the order passed on petition under Section 34.[104]

Condonation of delay in filing appeal

The Limitation Act, 1963 applies to appeals filed under the Arbitration Act. Where sufficient cause is shown, the delay in filing appeal shall be condoned.[105] There was a delay of 206 days in filing appeal. After excluding the copying period, holidays and 90 days period available for filing appeal, there was a delay of 103 days in filing appeal. Since the delay was not properly explained, delay was not condoned.[106]

An arbitral award was passed on 2 May 2018 and the appeal against the award was filed on 1 September 2018 after the expiry of the limitation period for filing appeal. The appellant failed to explain the reasons for the delay in a satisfactory manner. The appeal challenging the award was dismissed as time-barred.[107]

A delay of 703 days in filing the appeal against the order passed under Section 34 of the Act refusing to set aside the award was not satisfactorily explained. Mere reference to time taken in correspondence between the officers of the department was found to be not sufficient explanation. The appeal was rejected as time-barred.[108]

Where there is delay in filing appeal, Section 5, Limitation Act can be applied to condone the delay.[109] In the instant case, judgment was passed in 2021 and certified copy was obtained in the year 2023. No material was placed on record to show on what date earlier certified copy was sent to the

---

103. *U.P. Awas & Vikas Parishad* v. *O.P. Kalra Bros.*, 2022 SCC OnLine Utt 1854.
104. *MTNL* v. *Applied Electronics Ltd.*, 2014 SCC OnLine Del 3829: (2014) 213 DLT 434.
105. *Union of India* v. *Associated Construction Co.*, 2019 SCC OnLine Del 10797: (2019) 264 DLT 523.
106. *Jagdish Shanti Hotels (P) Ltd.* v. *State of M.P.*, 2012 SCC OnLine MP 10746.
107. *Union of India* v. *Tenzing Construction*, 2022 SCC OnLine Gau 2036: (2022) 3 Gau LR 143.
108. *U.P. Awas & Vikas Parishad* v. *O.P. Kalra Bros.*, 2022 SCC OnLine Utt 1854.
109. *NHAI* v. *Meerashivalingaiah*, 2023 SCC OnLine Kar 173: (2023) 6 Kant LJ 51.

department for opinion. A bald affidavit was filed which stated that file was sent for opinion, after receipt of opinion it was decided to file an appeal. It was held, no sufficient cause was shown, delay was not condoned.[110]

Petitioner applied for the certified copy of the award on 3 January 2009, got the copy on 6 January 2009, and filed a petition in February 2009. No reason/sufficient cause was made out to condone the delay. Section 14, Limitation Act was held not applicable in the facts and circumstances of the case.[111]

Appeal was filed on 15 December 2012, application for condonation of delay was filed on 19 July 2013. Merely because the application for condonation of delay came to be filed subsequent to filing for appeal is no ground to hold that the entire period from filing of appeal till the application for condonation of delay was required to be satisfactorily explained. Delay in filing appeal was condoned.[112] Delay of 32 days allegedly occurred due to time spent in official processing of matters and collection of opinions by the party. Delay was not deliberate, it was condoned.[113]

There was a huge delay of 227 days in filing the appeal, there was no sufficient cause to condone the delay, appeal was dismissed as time barred.[114] There was a delay of 551 days in filing appeal against the order passed under Section 34 of the Act. The order impugned in this appeal was passed on 14 September 2018. Lockdown was imposed in the third week of March 2020 and there is no explanation regarding the steps taken by appellants, between 14 September 2018 till imposition of lockdown. Steps taken after lifting of lockdown have also not been indicated. What appellants did after 27 October 2021, when certified copies were delivered to them is also not indicated. For filing appeal after expiry of limitation period, appellants are required to give day-to-day explanation for the delay caused in the matter and only then delay in filing appeal can be condoned. The delay in filing the appeal was not explained. Delay was not condoned. Appeal was dismissed as time barred.[115]

---

110. *Ibid.*
111. *Ashwinneema* v. *Mangalam Clothes (P) Ltd.*, 2009 SCC OnLine Bom 603: (2009) 4 Mah LJ 991.
112. *Jayantrao* v. *Sumatidevi*, 2015 SCC OnLine Bom 3185: (2015) 4 Mah LJ 217.
113. *North Eastern Electric Power Corpn. Ltd.* v. *Patel Unity Joint Venture*, 2017 SCC OnLine Megh 386: (2017) 3 Civ LT 107 (DB).
114. *State of Maharashtra* v. *Borse Bros. Engineers & Contractors (P) Ltd.*, (2021) 6 SCC 460.
115. *Jishan Ali* v. *NHAI (Arbitrator)*, 2022 SCC OnLine Utt 1855.

Order refusing condonation of delay—Appeal lies

Appeal against order refusing to condone delay is maintainable.[116] Rejection of application under Section 5, Limitation Act for condonation of delay in filing application under Section 34 of the Act can be challenged only in revision, no appeal lies under Section 37 of the Act.[117] An order refusing to condone the delay in filing an application for setting aside the award is appealable under Section 37(1)(*b*).[118]

An appeal under Section 37(1)(*c*), Arbitration and Conciliation Act, 1996 would be maintainable against an order refusing to condone delay in filing an application under Section 34, Arbitration and Conciliation Act, 1996 to set aside an award.[119]

Limitation Act, 1963

Appeal against an order allowing a petition under Section 34 of the Act and setting aside the award would be governed by Article 117 of the Schedule to the Limitation Act, 1963.[120]

The period of limitation for filing an appeal against the order passed under Section 17 is 90 days; hence, the appeal filed within 43 days was within the limitation period.[121] The appeal against the order setting aside the arbitral award is governed by Article 116(*a*) of the Limitation Act, 1963. The period of limitation for appeal against the order setting aside the arbitral award would be 90 days as provided under Article 116(*a*) of the Limitation Act.[122]

Order condoning delay—No appeal lies

Remedy of appeal has been provided only against an order setting aside or refusing to set aside an arbitral award as per Section 37(1)(*c*), but no appeal is provided against the order passed by the court of competent jurisdiction condoning the delay in filing the appeal under Section 34.[123]

---

116. *Chintels (India) Ltd.* v. *Bhayana Builders (P) Ltd.*, (2021) 4 SCC 602; *BPDP/REO* v. *Scoot Wilson Kirpatrick India (P) Ltd.*, (2006) 13 SCC 622 followed.
117. *Union of India* v. *Radha Krishna Seth*, 2005 SCC OnLine All 840: (2006) 63 ALR 92.
118. *E-Square Leisure (P) Ltd.* v. *K.K. Dani Consultants and Engineers (P) Ltd.*, 2013 SCC OnLine Bom 183: (2013) 3 Mah LJ 24.
119. *Chintels (India) Ltd.* v. *Bhayana Builders (P) Ltd.*, (2021) 4 SCC 602.
120. *ONGC Ltd.* v. *Dinamic Corpn.*, 2012 SCC OnLine Bom 1540: (2013) 1 Mah LJ 94.
121. *Jagat Singh Chopra* v. *Raj Singh Chopra*, 2018 SCC OnLine Cal 5310: (2018) 2 Cal LT 534.
122. *North Eastern Electric Corpn. Ltd.* v. *Patel Unity Joint Venture*, 2017 SCC OnLine Megh 386.
123. *Union of India* v. *Simplex Infrastructures Ltd.*, (2017) 14 SCC 225.

Unreasoned order

Where the High Court dismissing the appeal did not set out the factual controversy properly, did not deal with any of the grounds taken by the parties in their pleadings and in appeal in support of their respective contentions, matter/appeal was remanded to the High Court for deciding the appeal afresh on merits in accordance with law.[124]

Plausible view

Once a possible view is taken by an arbitrator on totality of consideration of all documents, it is difficult for the court to overturn such a view taken in award.[125]

Appellants-guarantors to a loan agreement were restrained from disposing immovable properties, selling, transferring or creating any third party interest in the property. Scope of hearing of appeal against the ex parte order is extremely limited. The appellate court need not exercise its jurisdiction and discretion merely because it feels that it may take a different view, although the arbitrator had taken the other plausible view. Appeal was dismissed.[126]

Where the reasons mentioned for granting interim protection by the court under Section 9 are unacceptable and perverse, the order of interim protection would be set aside.[127]

Scope of interference

The scope of interference under Section 37 of the 1996 Act is extremely limited. Sections 34 and 37 demand respect to the finality of the arbitral ruling and the party autonomy in having chosen to get their issues resolved through alternate forum of arbitration which would be thwarted if the courts were to accept the challenge to the arbitral rulings on factual issues in a regular manner.[128]

No method of measurement with regard to damages/compensation is mentioned in the contract, the manner in which the quantum thereof should

124. *Navnirman Development Consultants (I) (P) Ltd.* v. *District Sports Complex Executive Committee*, (2017) 8 SCC 603.
125. *Anand Citi Centre Holdings (P) Ltd.* v. *Consolidated Construction Consortium Ltd.*, 2021 SCC OnLine Mad 5222.
126. *Chirawa Investment Ltd.* v. *Indiabulls Financial Services Ltd.*, 2009 SCC OnLine Del 3126: (2009) 113 DRJ 109.
127. *Techmo Car SPA* v. *Madras Aluminium Co. Ltd.*, 2004 SCC OnLine Mad 246: (2004) 3 CTC 754.
128. *BHEL* v. *Zillion Infraprojects (P) Ltd.*, (2023) 1 HCC (Del) 635; *NHAI* v. *M. Hakeem*, (2021) 9 SCC 1.

be determined is a matter which falls for the decision of the arbitrator. In appeal, the High Court cannot enter into the calculation made and the method used.[129]

Pleas open/not open in appeal

The appellant cannot contend before the appellate court that the Arbitration Tribunal had no jurisdiction to decide the dispute between the parties.[130]

New pleas in appeal

Objection with regard to grant of interest, being a pure question of law which arises for consideration on admitted facts, can be raised by the appellants in appeal. The appellants were not precluded from raising objections with regard to grant of interest before the High Court.[131]

Respondent neither filed appeal nor raised issues before the District Judge. It is not open to the respondent to raise new issues at the appellate stage.[132]

Impleadment of arbitrator by name as party in proceedings

It is completely unnecessary for arbitrators to be arrayed as a party unless personal allegations are made and the arbitrator is required to answer such allegations.[133]

Impleadment as party in appeal

The applicant sought to be impleaded as party in appeal. The applicant was not party to the second agreement and, therefore, not party to the arbitration proceedings as well. The arbitrator had examined and rejected the plea of impleading the applicant as a necessary party. The issue was re-examined by the Commercial Court as well, which upheld the view of the arbitrator. The applicant did not seek to implead itself in both the proceedings before the arbitrator as well as the Commercial Court. The impleadment application moved by a third party was rejected.[134]

---

129. *Dhanoa Builders* v. *Union of India*, 2017 SCC OnLine Gau 866: (2017) 4 Gau LR 141.
130. *Mysore Minerals Ltd.* v. *Tam-Tam Pedda Guruva Reddy*, 2013 SCC OnLine Kar 9929: ILR 2014 Kar 1152.
131. *Union of India* v. *Ravi Builders and Rajendra Agrawal and Associates*, 2015 SCC OnLine MP 6706: (2015) 4 MPLJ 100.
132. *Kapil Dev Bansal* v. *H.P. Urban Development Authority*, 2018 SCC OnLine HP 929.
133. *Sankat Pratap Singh* v. *Bhopal Motors*, 2011 SCC OnLine MP 2269.
134. *Sikkim Power Development Corpn.* v. *Amalgamated Transpower (India) Ltd.*, 2022 SCC OnLine Sikk 79: (2022) 237 AIC 360.

Appeal, court fee

Court fee, payable in an appeal against an order passed by the court below is payable under Article 3 and not under Article 4 of Second Schedule of the Court Fees Act, 1959.[135] When a memorandum of appeal is filed under Section 37 challenging an order passed in a petition filed under Section 34, Arbitration and Conciliation Act, 1996, court fee is to be paid under Article 13 of Second Schedule of the Bombay Court Fees Act.[136]

In an appeal against an order passed under Section 34, the appellant is liable to pay court fee in terms of Article 3 of First Schedule of the Bombay Court Fees Act, 1959 (36 of 1959).[137]

Legislature, while enacting Amendment Act 2 of 2003, could have amended Article 4 by substituting 1940 Act with 1996 Act. But the legislature was very conscious to avoid incorporating the 1996 Act to Article 4, thereby virtually permitting appeals be filed with the court fee payable taking into account the unamended provision.[138]

Interest on Delayed Payments to Small Scale and Ancillary Undertakings Act, 1993

A second appeal is prohibited from an order that is passed under Section 37. This bar operates with respect to the period post such appeal, and not prior to it. The section prohibits a second appeal only from an order passed in appeal under that very section. An award may be challenged by an application under Section 34, which may be treated as an appeal for the purposes of the Interest Act, and an order can be made either setting aside/remitting/ or affirming the said award. Only when from that order when an appeal is filed under Section 37, the bar of second appeal under Section 37 applies which is clearly evinced by the use of the words: "from an order passed in appeal under this section".[139]

---

135. *Jaisu Shipping Co. (P) Ltd.* v. *Oilcorp Oil Mktg. Corpn.*, 2001 SCC OnLine Ker 218: (2001) 2 KLT 772.
136. *Puneet Malhotra* v. *R.S. Gai*, 2008 SCC OnLine Bom 1043: (2008) 6 Mah LJ 867; *Harjinder Singh* v. *Paramjeet Singh*, 2008 SCC OnLine Bom 1047: (2008) 6 Mah LJ 884.
137. *Maharashtra Industries Development Corpn.* v. *Govardhani Constructions Co.*, 2007 SCC OnLine Bom 204: (2007) 3 Mah LJ 514.
138. *Alex M. George* v. *Special Deputy Collector*, 2018 SCC OnLine Ker 924: (2018) 2 KLT 127.
139. *Snehadeep Structures (P) Ltd.* v. *Maharashtra Small-Scale Industries Development Corpn. Ltd.*, (2010) 3 SCC 34.

Deposit of award amount/security [Or. 41 R. 1(3) CPC]

Order rejecting application under Section 34 shall not amount to money decree, Order 41 Rule 1(3) CPC would have no application, in event of filing appeal under Section 37, the appellant would not be required to deposit the amount of award or deposit security.[140]

Insolvency and Bankruptcy Code, 2016, Section 14—Imposition of moratorium—Effect

Where a moratorium is imposed under Section 14, Insolvency and Bankruptcy Code, subsequent initiation of arbitration proceedings and filing of appeal under Section 37, Arbitration and Conciliation Act, 1996 is non-est in law.[141]

Letters Patent Appeal

Arbitration and Conciliation Act is a complete code in itself and provides remedy to file appeal under Section 37. Letters Patent Appeal against an order setting aside an award or refusal to set aside an award is not maintainable.[142] No Letters Patent Appeal lies from an order in an appeal filed under Section 37 of the Act.[143] Embargo on appeals in Section 37 is absolute.

Appeal does not lie against an administrative decision of the judge, but it does not exclude an appeal under the Letters Patent.[144] Unless the powers conferred upon the High Court is specifically excluded by a statute, the power of the High Court does not get excluded by a general provision barring an appeal.[145]

Letters Patent Appeal against the order passed by the Single Judge of the High Court in application under Section 8, Arbitration and Conciliation Act seeking reference to arbitration is not maintainable under clause 15 of the Letters Patent being barred by Section 37, Arbitration and Conciliation Act, 1996.[146]

The expression "second appeal" in Section 37(3) includes Letters Patent Appeal. As such Letters Patent Appeal against the judgment of the Single

140. *Uttarakhand Rural Road Development Agency* v. *DM*, 2015 SCC OnLine Utt 518.
141. *Alchemist Asset Reconstrution Co. Ltd.* v. *Hotel Gaudavan (P) Ltd.*, (2018) 16 SCC 94.
142. *Landmark Housing Projects (P) Ltd.* v. *Savithri Naidu*, 2021 SCC OnLine Mad 723.
143. *Fountain Head Developers* v. *Maria Arcangela Sequeira*, 2007 SCC OnLine Bom 340; *Canbank Financial Services Ltd.* v. *Haryana Petrochemicals Ltd.*, 2008 SCC OnLine Del 632: (2008) 104 DRJ 59.
144. *Great Eastern Shipping Co. Ltd.* v. *Port of Calcutta*, 2003 SCC OnLine Cal 442: (2004) 3 CHN 37.
145. *TISCO Ltd.* v. *Standard Chrome*, 2005 SCC OnLine Cal 396: (2006) 2 CHN 378.
146. *Conros Steels (P) Ltd.* v. *Lu Qin (Hong Kong) Co. Ltd.*, 2014 SCC OnLine Bom 2305: (2015) 1 Mah LJ 434; *Kotak Mahindra Investment Ltd.* v. *Kitply Industries Ltd.*, 2011 SCC OnLine Cal 2736: (2012) 5 CHN 489.

Judge in first appeal arising out of the proceedings under the Arbitration and Conciliation Act is not maintainable.[147]

Letters Patent Appeal against the order of the Single Judge refusing to terminate the mandate of the arbitrator named in the arbitration agreement and refusing to appoint another arbitrator is not maintainable in view of the bar of Section 37, Arbitration and Conciliation Act, 1996.[148]

Restoration of appeal dismissed for default

Where appellate court dismissed the objection in default for non-prosecution as counsel pleads no instructions, appellate court has committed palpable error while dismissing the application filed for restoration. Whenever, counsel appearing on behalf of the party pleads no instructions, the court should serve actual date notice upon the party concerned who had engaged that advocate. Award was stayed and appeal was allowed.[149]

The appellate court vested with the jurisdiction to entertain an appeal under Section 37 of the Act of 1996 has the power to dismiss such appeal for default in case the appellant fails to appear when an appeal is called out for hearing by applying the principle akin to Order 41 Rule 17 CPC. Where the appellant satisfies the court with sufficient cause for not appearing in the court at the time when the appeal was called out for hearing, then the court which dismissed the appeal for default also has jurisdiction to readmit the same in appropriate cases. In the absence of any specific bar in the Act of 1996 for applying the provision of CPC, the procedure laid down for appeals under Order 41 Rules 17 and 19 can be applied to appeals filed under Section 37 of the Act of 1996. In the instant case, the name of the counsel for the appellant was not appearing in the cause list and the court was functioning in virtual mode because of the COVID-19 pandemic when the appeal was dismissed for default. Sufficient cause for restoration was made out, and the appeal was restored.[150]

Recall of order

Where the High Court has allowed the appeal without hearing the party causing prejudice to his interests, application for recalling the order dismissing the appeal was allowed.[151]

---

147. *Vishal Retail Ltd.* v. *Kataria Automobiles Ltd.*, 2010 SCC OnLine Guj 3776.
148. *Niranjan Lal Todi* v. *Nandalal Todi*, 2015 SCC OnLine Cal 6425: (2016) 5 CHN 482.
149. *AA Enterprises* v. *Er. J.S. Sekhon*, 2009 SCC OnLine P&H 1.
150. *State of Jharkhand* v. *Webel Technology Ltd.*, 2022 SCC OnLine Jhar 1690.
151. *Supdt. Engineer* v. *Maa Bhairabi Traders*, 2023 SCC OnLine Ori 7019.

Review

The Arbitration and Conciliation Act, 1996 does not provide any remedy of review. Review petition is, therefore, not maintainable.[152]

Writ petition

Orders passed by the Arbitral Tribunal are not open to challenge under Articles 226 and 227 of the Constitution.[153] Order passed by the arbitrator can be challenged under Section 37, writ petition is not maintainable.[154]

With the object of minimising judicial intervention pending arbitral proceedings, such intervention under Article 226 or Article 227 of the Constitution of India would frustrate the very object of the 1996 Act. The petitioner is not entitled to invoke the supervisory jurisdiction of the High Court under Article 227 of the Constitution of India against any order passed by the arbitrator pending arbitration proceedings.[155]

The Arbitration and Conciliation Act, 1996 does not provide for any remedy against an order declining recall of an earlier order, either under Section 34 or Section 36 or any other provision. No alternate remedy being available to the petitioner to challenge the impugned order which was passed under Section 25(*a*) of the Act; the present petitions under Article 227 of the Constitution of India were held ex facie, maintainable.[156]

Pending arbitration proceedings, a party aggrieved by an order of Arbitral Tribunal unless has right of appeal under Section 37 has to wait until award is passed by the tribunal. The party is not entitled to invoke supervisory jurisdiction of the High Court under Article 227 of the Constitution. Intervention by the High Court is not permissible, as the same would frustrate the very object of the Arbitration and Conciliation Act.[157]

Dismissal of application under Section 34 for setting aside award on the ground of non-deposit of 75 per cent of the amount as envisaged under Section 19, Micro, Small and Medium Enterprises Development

---

152. *Madhav Structural Engg. Ltd.* v. *Maharashtra State Road Development Corpn. Ltd.*, 2013 SCC OnLine Bom 134: (2013) 2 Mah LJ 372.
153. *Satya Prakash Singh* v. *Dinesh Prakash Singh*, 2014 SCC OnLine All 16183: (2015) 4 All LJ 441.
154. *Rajasthan State Ganganagar Sugar Mills Ltd.* v. *Global Canesugar Services (P) Ltd.*, 2018 SCC OnLine Raj 3600.
155. *Mohd. Hussain Khan* v. *Mohd. Imtiyaz Ahmed*, 2016 SCC OnLine Hyd 181.
156. *Union of India* v. *Indian Agro Mktg. Coop. Ltd.*, (2022) 3 HCC (Del) 279: 2022 SCC OnLine Del 1291.
157. *Mohd. Hussain Khan* v. *Mohd. Imtiyaz Ahmed*, 2016 SCC OnLine Hyd 181.

Act, 2006 does not fall within the mischief of Section 34, writ petition is maintainable.[158]

This section and Order 44 Rule 11 CPC

An appeal from an order under Section 37(1)(*a*) of 1996 Act cannot be exempted from the hearing under Order 41 Rule 11 CPC.[159]

International arbitration

By the alleged agreement, the parties had agreed to refer their dispute to Singapore International Arbitration Centre at Singapore. Under such circumstances, the parties must be deemed to have agreed that their arbitration should be carried and administered in accordance with such rules. In case of interim ruling of the arbitrator, the parties must resort to their remedy under the international arbitration law and not under Section 37(2)(*b*) of the 1996 Act.[160]

---

158. *Crompton Greaves Ltd.* v. *Annapurna Electronics*, 2015 SCC OnLine Kar 5906: ILR 2015 Kar 4199.
159. *Anup Kumar Biswas* v. *Babul Kumar Biswas*, 2003 SCC OnLine Cal 91: (2003) 4 CHN 275.
160. *Yograj Infrastructure Ltd.* v. *Ssangyong Engg. and Construction Co. Ltd.*, 2010 SCC OnLine MP 329: (2011) 1 MP LJ 86.

Chapter X
Miscellaneous

DEPOSITS [S. 38]

38. *Deposits.*—(1) The arbitral tribunal may fix the amount of the deposit or supplementary deposit, as the case may be, as an advance for the costs referred to in sub-section (8) of Section 31, which it expects will be incurred in respect of the claim submitted to it:

Provided that where, apart from the claim, a counter-claim has been submitted to the arbitral tribunal, it may fix separate amount of deposit for the claim and counter-claim.

(2) The deposit referred to in sub-section (1) shall be payable in equal shares by the parties:

Provided that where one party fails to pay his share of the deposit, the other party may pay that share:

Provided further that where the other party also does not pay the aforesaid share in respect of the claim or the counter-claim, the arbitral tribunal may suspend or terminate the arbitral proceedings in respect of such claim or counter-claim, as the case may be.

(3) Upon termination of the arbitral proceedings, the arbitral tribunal shall render an accounting to the parties of the deposits received and shall return any unexpended balance to the party or parties, as the case may be.

COMMENTS

Corresponding old law

Section 38 is new, no such provision existed in the Arbitration Act, 1940.

Scope and application

Section 38 empowers the Arbitral Tribunal to fix the amount of the deposit or supplementary deposit, as the case may be, as advance for the costs referred to in Section 31-A in respect of the claim submitted to it. Earlier provision of costs appeared in sub-section (8) of Section 31, which by Amending Act of 3 of 2016 have been incorporated in new Section 31-A of the Act. In cases where a counterclaim has been submitted to the Arbitral Tribunal, the Arbitral Tribunal may fix a separate amount of deposit for the claim and counterclaim.

The amount of deposit fixed by the Arbitral Tribunal shall be payable in equal shares by the parties. Where one party fails to pay his share of the deposit, the other party may pay that share. Where the other party also does not pay the aforesaid share in respect of the claim or counterclaim, the Arbitral Tribunal may suspend or terminate the arbitral proceedings in respect of such claim or counterclaim.

When the arbitration proceedings are terminated, the Arbitral Tribunal shall render an accounting to the parties of the deposits received and shall return any unexpended balance to the party or the parties, as case may be.

The arbitrator while adjudicating disputes between the parties can determine his fees.[1]

Where the arbitrator had not fixed any amount of supplementary deposit after remand, the question of payment of the same by the respondent did not arise, non-deposit of the amount could not be a reason for terminating the proceedings, order of termination of the proceedings passed by the arbitrator was set aside.[2]

Not permitting the claimant to pay arbitration fee in installments and passing of the award on preliminary issue does not amount to misconduct. In fact, Section 38 of the Act enables the arbitrator to suspend the proceedings where a party does not pay his share of the cost.[3]

Counterclaim

Neither the Arbitral Tribunal nor the court can compel a party to deposit a contribution of fees and expenses of both parties. The Arbitral Tribunal is justified in terminating the arbitral proceedings in respect of counterclaim in view of the petitioner and respondent refusing to deposit any amount of fees and expenses for hearing counterclaim of the petitioner. The Arbitral Tribunal is entitled to fix a separate amount of deposit for claim and counterclaim.[4]

1. *R.N. Agarwal* v. *Laxmi Sugar Mills Co. (P) Ltd.*, 2010 SCC OnLine All 769.
2. *State of M.P.* v. *Associated Computers Services*, 2016 SCC OnLine MP 9791: (2016) 4 MP LJ 174.
3. *A.P. Thomas* v. *Union of India*, 2013 SCC OnLine Kar 9950: (2014) 1 KCCR 554.
4. *Gammon India Ltd.* v. *Trenchless Engg. Services (P) Ltd.*, 2013 SCC OnLine Bom 1720: (2014) 3 Mah LJ 946.

LIEN ON ARBITRAL AWARD AND DEPOSITS AS TO COSTS [S. 39]

39. *Lien on arbitral award and deposits as to costs.*—(1) Subject to the provisions of sub-section (2) and to any provision to the contrary in the arbitration agreement, the arbitral tribunal shall have a lien on the arbitral award for any unpaid costs of the arbitration.

(2) If in any case an arbitral tribunal refuses to deliver its award except on payment of the costs demanded by it, the Court may, on an application in this behalf, order that the arbitral tribunal shall deliver the arbitral award to the applicant on payment into Court by the applicant of the costs demanded, and shall, after such inquiry, if any, as it thinks fit, further order that out of the money so paid into court there shall be paid to the arbitral tribunal by way of costs such sum as the court may consider reasonable and that the balance of the money, if any, shall be refunded to the applicant.

(3) An application under sub-section (2) may be made by any party unless the fees demanded have been fixed by written agreement between him and the arbitral tribunal, and the arbitral tribunal shall be entitled to appear and be heard on any such application.

(4) The Court may make such orders as it thinks fit respecting the costs of the arbitration where any question arises respecting such costs and the arbitral award contains no sufficient provision concerning them.

COMMENTS

Corresponding old law

Section 39(1) corresponds to sub-sections (1) and (2) of Section 14, Arbitration Act, 1940. Section 39(2) corresponds to Section 38(1), Arbitration Act, 1940. Section 39(3) corresponds to Section 38(2), Arbitration Act, 1940. Section 39(4) corresponds to Section 38(3), Arbitration Act, 1940.

Sub-sections (1) and (2) of Section 14 and Section 38, Arbitration Act, 1940 read as under:

14. *Award to be signed and filed.*—(1) When the arbitrators or umpire have made their award, they shall sign it and shall give notice in writing to the parties of the making and signing thereof and of the amount of fees and charges payable in respect of the arbitration and award.

(2) The arbitrators or umpire shall, at the request of any party to the arbitration agreement or any person claiming under such party or if so directed by the Court and upon payment of the fees and charges due in respect of the arbitration and award and of the costs and charges of filing the award, cause the award or a signed copy of it, together with any depositions and documents which may

have been taken and proved before them, to be filed in Court, and the Court shall thereupon give notice to the parties of the filling of the award.

38. *Disputes as to arbitrator's remuneration or costs.*—(1) If in any case an arbitrator or umpire refuses to deliver his award except on payment of the fees demanded by him, the Court may, on an application in this behalf, order that the arbitrator or umpire shall deliver the award to the applicant on payment into Court by the applicant of the fees demanded and shall after such inquiry, if any, as it thinks fit, further order that out of the money so paid into Court there shall be paid to the arbitrator or umpire by way of fees such sum as the Court may consider reasonable and that the balance of the money, if any, shall be refunded to the applicant.

(2) An application under sub-section (1) may be made by any party to the reference unless the fees demanded have been fixed by written agreement between him and the arbitrator or umpire, and the arbitrator or umpire shall be entitled to appear and be heard on any such application.

(3) The Court may make such orders as it thinks fit respecting the costs of an arbitration where any question arises respecting such costs and the award contains no sufficient provision concerning them.

Scope and application

Section 39 provides that subject to the provisions of sub-section (2) of the section and any provision to the contrary in the arbitration agreement, the Arbitral Tribunal shall have a lien on the arbitral award for any unpaid costs of the arbitration proceedings.

Fees of the arbitrator as determined as per provisions of Section 11(14) read with Fourth Schedule cannot be said to be unpaid costs of arbitration which should have any lien on the arbitral award.[5]

ARBITRATION AGREEMENT NOT TO BE DISCHARGED BY DEATH OF PARTY THERETO [S. 40]

40. *Arbitration agreement not to be discharged by death of party thereto.*—(1) An arbitration agreement shall not be discharged by the death of any party thereto either as respects the deceased or as respects any other party, but shall in such event be enforceable by or against the legal representative of the deceased.

(2) The mandate of an arbitrator shall not be terminated by the death of any party by whom he was appointed.

5. *State of Rajasthan* v. *Electrosteel Casting Ltd.*, 2021 SCC OnLine Raj 4066: (2021) 2 RLW 1465.

(3) Nothing in this section shall affect the operation of any law by virtue of which any right of action is extinguished by the death of a person.

COMMENTS

Corresponding old law

Section 40 corresponds to Section 6, Arbitration Act, 1940. Section 6 of the 1940 Act read as under:

6. *Arbitration agreement not to be discharged by death of party thereto.*—(1) An arbitration agreement shall not be discharged by the death of any party thereto, either as respects the deceased or any other party, but shall in such event be enforceable by or against the legal representative of the deceased.

(2) The authority of an arbitrator shall not be revoked by the death of any party by whom he was appointed.

(3) Nothing in this section shall affect the operation of any law by virtue of which any right of action is extinguished by the death of a person.

Scope and application

Section 40 provides that an arbitration agreement shall not be discharged by the death of any party thereto either as respects the deceased or as respects any other party, but shall in such event be enforceable by or against the legal representative of the deceased.

The mandate of an arbitrator shall not be terminated by the death of any party by whom he was appointed.

Nothing in Section 40 shall affect the operation of any law by virtue of which any right of action is extinguished by the death of a person.

Application for appointment of arbitrator by the LRs of the deceased partner—Maintainable

See, Section 11, under the same heading.

Legal representative of a deceased partner can initiate arbitration proceedings [Sub-s. (2)]

On the dissolution of the firm, the arbitration clause does not come to an end and so if a dispute had arisen during the lifetime of the deceased partner, his legal representatives would be entitled to take proceedings under Section 40, Arbitration and Conciliation Act, 1996. The word "party" as used in the partnership deed did not exclude inclusion of legal heirs, legal representatives, etc. In view of the provisions of Sections 40 and 46, Partnership

Act read with Section 40, Arbitration and Conciliation Act, the appellant had a legal right to commence arbitration by moving an application under Section 11 of the Arbitration and Conciliation Act as the right to sue survived on him as a legal representatives of deceased and he was entitled to invoke the arbitration clause of the partnership deed.[6]

On the death of the deceased partner who was signatory to the partnership agreement, his son being his legal heir and legal representative was held legally competent to enforce the arbitration agreement and to raise dispute for reference to arbitration.[7] Arbitration agreement is not discharged by the death of any party and can be enforced by or against his legal representative.[8]

Execution proceedings against the legal representatives (LRs) of proprietorship firm

During the pendency of Section 34 petition for setting aside the ex parte decree, owner of proprietorship firm died and LRs of proprietor were brought on record. LRs did not challenge order and continued with proceeding without any objection. Order 30 Rule 10 CPC provides that a person carrying on business in a name other than his name or in the name of Hindu undivided family (HUF) and the firm may be sued in such name. Execution proceedings were held maintainable against LRs of proprietor.[9]

PROVISIONS IN CASE OF INSOLVENCY [S. 41]

41. *Provisions in case of insolvency.*—(1) Where it is provided by a term in a contract to which an insolvent is a party that any dispute arising thereout or in connection therewith shall be submitted to arbitration, the said term shall, if the receiver adopts the contract, be enforceable by or against him so far as it relates to any such dispute.

(2) Where a person who has been adjudged an insolvent had, before the commencement of the insolvency proceedings, become a party to an arbitration agreement, and any matter to which the agreement applies is required to be determined in connection with, or for the purposes of, the insolvency proceedings, then, if the case is one to which sub-section (1) does not apply, any other party or the receiver may apply to the judicial authority having jurisdiction in the insolvency proceedings for an order directing that the matter in question shall be submitted to arbitration in accordance with the arbitration agreement,

6. *Ravi Prakash Goel* v. *Chandra Prakash Goel*, (2008) 13 SCC 667; *Sushil Kumar Ojha* v. *Shesh Narayan Tripathi*, 2014 SCC OnLine All 15226: (2014) 4 All LJ 734.
7. *Sushil Kumar Ojha* v. *Shesh Narayan Tripathi*, 2014 SCC OnLine All 15226: (2014) 4 All LJ 734.
8. *Parwati Devi* v. *Kesarwani & Co.*, 2011 SCC OnLine All 786: (2011) 4 All LJ 463.
9. *Ushadevi* v. *Cotton Corpn. of India Ltd.*, 2019 SCC OnLine MP 6113: (2020) 1 MP LJ 200.

and the judicial authority may, if it is of opinion that, having regard to all the circumstances of the case, the matter ought to be determined by arbitration, make an order accordingly.

(3) In this section, the expression "receiver" includes an Official Assignee.

COMMENTS

Corresponding old law

Section 41 corresponds to Section 7, Arbitration Act, 1940. Section 7 of the 1940 Act provides as under:

7. *Provisions in case of insolvency.*—(1) Where it is provided by a term in a contract to which an insolvent is a party that any differences arising thereout or in connection therewith shall be referred to arbitration, the said term shall, if the receiver adopts the contract, be enforceable by or against him so far as it relates to any such differences.

(2) Where a person who has been adjudged an insolvent had, before the commencement of the insolvency proceedings, become a party to an arbitration agreement, and any matter to which the agreement applies is required to be determined in connection with, or for the purposes of the insolvency proceedings, then, if the case is one to which sub-section (1) does not apply, any other party to the agreement or the receiver may apply to the Court having jurisdiction in the insolvency proceedings for an order directing that the matter in question shall be referred to arbitration in accordance with the agreement, and the Court may, if it is of opinion that, having regard to all the circumstances of the case, the matter ought to be determined by arbitration, make an order accordingly.

(3) In this section the expression "receiver" includes an Official Assignee.

JURISDICTION [S. 42]

42. *Jurisdiction.*—Notwithstanding anything contained elsewhere in this Part or in any other law for the time being in force, where with respect to an arbitration agreement any application under this Part has been made in a Court, that Court alone shall have jurisdiction over the arbitral proceedings and all subsequent applications arising out of that agreement and the arbitral proceedings shall be made in that Court and in no other Court.

COMMENTS

Corresponding old law

Section 42 corresponds to Section 31(4), Arbitration Act, 1940. Section 31(4) of the 1940 Act provides as under:

(4) Notwithstanding anything contained elsewhere in this Act or in any other law for the time being in force where in any reference any application under this Act has been made in a Court competent to entertain it, that Court alone shall have jurisdiction over the arbitration proceedings and all subsequent applications arising out of that reference and the arbitration proceedings shall be made in that Court and in no other Court.

Scope and application

Section 42 starts with a non-obstante clause which does away with anything which may be inconsistent with the section either in Part I of the Arbitration and Conciliation Act, 1996 or in any other law for the time being in force. The expression "with respect to an arbitration agreement" widens the scope of Section 42 to include all matters which directly or indirectly pertain to an arbitration agreement. The expression makes it clear that Section 42 will apply to all applications made whether before or during arbitral proceedings or after an award is pronounced under Part I of the 1996 Act. Thus, Section 42 applies even after the arbitral proceedings come to an end. But an essential ingredient of Section 42 is that an application under Part I must be made in a "court".[10] Application under Section 34 for setting aside the arbitral award is to be filed before the same court, which passed the interim orders in the case. Order was passed by the Chief Justice of the court which is not a "court" as defined in Section 2(1)(*e*). Application for setting aside the arbitral award was filed before the lower court at place *A*, application was not maintainable by virtue of the section.[11] Application for enforcement of the award is to be filed in the District Court in view of the relevant rules.[12]

Section 42 has an overriding effect and would prevail notwithstanding any other law including Section 39(4) CPC. An application for execution of

10. *State of W.B.* v. *Associated Contractors*, (2015) 1 SCC 32; *Sundaram Finance Ltd.* v. *Abdul Samad*, (2018) 3 SCC 622; *East Coast Railway Rail Sadan* v. *Hindustan Construction Co. Ltd.*, 2022 SCC OnLine SC 907.
11. *Lafarge India (P) Ltd.* v. *Kishore Kumar Sahoo*, 2017 SCC OnLine Cal 41: (2017) 1 Cal LJ 546 relied on.
12. *Potlabathuni Srikanth* v. *Shriram City Union Finance Ltd.*, 2015 SCC OnLine Hyd 555: (2016) 2 ALD 10.

the award would be filed before the court which had entertained an earlier application with respect to the arbitration agreement.[13]

In the absence of any stipulation in the arbitration clause as to which law would apply to arbitral proceedings, the law governing contract (proper law) would be the law applicable to Arbitral Tribunal. The seat of arbitration in a foreign country does not automatically exclude all foreign arbitration proceedings or awards from purview of the 1996 Act, unless parties have specifically agreed to exclude the same.[14] In *Yograj Infrastructure Ltd.* v. *Ssang Yong Engg. & Construction Co. Ltd.*[15], an agreement between an Indian company and a foreign company stipulated that the seat of arbitration shall be Singapore and Singapore International Arbitration Centre (SIAC) Rules shall be applicable to arbitration proceedings. It was held, SIAC Rules would be curial law of arbitration proceedings and proper law of contract was excluded to that extent. Rule 32 of the SIAC Rules, 2007 provided that if the seat of arbitration is Singapore, law applicable to arbitration proceedings would be Singapore International Arbitration Act, 2002. It was held, once an arbitrator was appointed and arbitral proceedings commenced, the SIAC Rules became applicable shutting out the applicability of Section 42 including right of appeal under Section 37 and Part I of the 1996 Act. Hence, curial and proper law of arbitration were Singapore law and proper law of contract was Indian law. Appeal filed before the Indian court against the interim order passed by the Arbitral Tribunal with its seat in Singapore was not maintainable.

Section 42 is applicable at pre-arbitral stage, when an arbitrator has not been appointed. Where curial law other than 1996 Act is applicable, once arbitrator is appointed and arbitration proceedings have commenced, said curial law would be applicable shutting out the applicability of Sections 42, 37 and Part I of the 1996 Act.[16]

Rendering decision on the first application one way or the other so as to guide the parties to file future applications is not necessary.[17]

Rule of forum conveniens is expressly excluded by Section 42 of the 1996 Act which mandates that all future actions be filed only in the court where

13. *Srei Equipment and Finance (P) Ltd.* v. *Khyoda Apik*, 2016 SCC OnLine Cal 12132.
14. *Yograj Infrastructure Ltd.* v. *Ssang Yong Engg. & Construction Co. Ltd.*, (2011) 9 SCC 735.
15. *Ibid.*
16. *Ibid*; *Sundaram Finance Ltd.* v. *Abdul Samad*, (2018) 3 SCC 622.
17. *Hindustan Petroleum Corpn. Ltd.* v. *Barun Sankar Chatterjee*, 2012 SCC OnLine Cal 509: (2012) 3 CHN 160.

the first application with regard to arbitration was filed.[18] Exclusion of jurisdiction must be strictly construed.[19]

Bar of jurisdiction under Section 42 is intended to apply to a "court" as defined in Section 2(1)(*e*). On an application filed in the Delhi High Court, the court exercised its jurisdiction and appointed an arbitrator to adjudicate the dispute between the parties. Such order is a judicial order passed by a court, creating a bar on the jurisdiction of the Calcutta High Court to entertain an application under Section 34 of the Act.[20]

Matter was referred to an arbitrator by the Rajpura court, hence, objections could only be decided by that very court in view of the provisions of Section 42, Arbitration and Conciliation Act. All proceedings for enforcing award are also supposed to be dealt with by the same court and not by any other court.[21]

If an application is made in a court, it is only that court which has the jurisdiction in relation to any subsequent applications. But the first application which is made in order that bar of Section 42 is attracted must be a competent application and not just any application. Where the respondent had filed application under Section 9 of the Act before the Delhi High Court, conceded the position that the Delhi High Court did not have jurisdiction, and the Delhi High Court permitted the respondent to withdraw the application, the provisions of Section 42 were not attracted in the case.[22] As the execution petition was filed in the Bombay High Court prior to filing of petition under Section 34 for setting aside award in Delhi court, Section 42 would not come into play. The Bombay High Court would have jurisdiction to decide the execution petition.[23]

Where the respondent did not press the proceedings under Section 9 filed before the Madras High Court, the appellant filed proceedings under Section 11 for the appointment of arbitrator before the Bombay High Court which were entertained, the proceedings under Section 9 before the Madras High Court, having not been pressed, Section 42 would not oust the jurisdiction of

18. *Jindal Vijayanagar Steel (JSW Steel Ltd.)* v. *Jindal Praxair Oxygen Co. Ltd.*, (2006) 11 SCC 521.
19. *Vachaspati Sharma* v. *India Cements-Capital and Finance Ltd.*, 2013 SCC OnLine Bom 1296: (2013) 6 Mah LJ 342.
20. *Steel (Singapore) Trading (P) Ltd.* v. *Bhushan Power & Steel Ltd.*, 2011 SCC OnLine Cal 212: (2011) 4 CHN 17.
21. *Punjab Land Development and Reclamation Corpn.* v. *Jai Shankar Transport Co.*, 2000 SCC OnLine P&H 730.
22. *ONGC Ltd.* v. *Jagson International Ltd.*, 2005 SCC OnLine Bom 814: (2005) 3 Mah LJ 1141.
23. *Abhishek Talwar* v. *L&T Finance Ltd.*, 2015 SCC OnLine Bom 3503.

the Bombay High Court to entertain petition under Section 34 challenging the award of the arbitrator.[24]

Where, on an application under Section 11, the Delhi High Court appointed the arbitrator, under Section 42 of the Act, only the Delhi High Court had jurisdiction to entertain the petitions filed under Section 34 challenging the award of the arbitrator.[25]

In order to activate the provisions of Section 42, it has to be shown that an application in respect of an arbitration agreement has been made in the court. The term "court" defined in Section 2(1)(*e*) means "the principal civil court of original jurisdiction in a district".[26]

Section 42 places an embargo upon any other court entertaining any petition once a particular court is approached with respect to arbitration agreement.[27]

Mere filing of petition under Section 34 in a wrong court does not clothe court with jurisdiction.[28]

Jurisdiction referred to in Section 42 would only mean that the court which entertains the first application must have jurisdiction. Section 42 cannot be invoked unless the party who raises the plea of jurisdiction demonstrates that the court which entertained the first application has got the jurisdiction. Arbitration clause in the hire purchase agreement between the parties clearly stipulated that the courts in Chennai only had jurisdiction. Dispute arose between the parties, appellant filed application before the District Court, Chandigarh, while respondent filed application before the Madras High Court. It was held, Section 42 would apply only when it is proved that the court in which the application was filed first, had jurisdiction. Mere filing of application in the court would not bar the jurisdiction conferred on another court by agreement between the parties. Chennai courts only had jurisdiction as per the agreement.[29]

All subsequent applications shall be filed in the court where the first application in respect of the arbitral dispute was filed. However, where the

---

24. *Vachaspati Sharma* v. *India Cements-Capital and Finance Ltd.*, 2013 SCC OnLine Bom 1296: (2013) 6 Mah LJ 342.
25. *Steel (Singapore) Trading (P) Ltd.* v. *Bhushan Power & Steel Ltd.*, 2011 SCC OnLine Cal 212: (2011) 4 CHN 17.
26. *Garden Finance Ltd.* v. *Prakash Industries Ltd.*, 2001 SCC OnLine Bom 351: (2001) 4 Mah LJ 425.
27. *Gammon India Ltd.* v. *Sankaranarayana Construction (Bangalore) (P) Ltd.*, 2008 SCC OnLine Mad 662: (2008) 5 CTC 166.
28. *Apparel Export Promotion Council* v. *Prabhati Patni, Proprietor Comfort Furnishers*, 2005 SCC OnLine Del 1287: (2006) 86 DRJ 48.
29. *Surya Pharmaceuticals Ltd.* v. *First Leasing Co. of India Ltd.*, 2013 SCC OnLine Mad 3384: (2014) 2 CTC 545.

jurisdiction of the court was erroneously invoked, future applications in respect of the arbitration agreement would not lie in the court where the first application was filed. Once the jurisdiction of the court under Section 9 was duly invoked, the mandate of Section 42 required that all subsequent applications shall be filed before the same court. Decision on the first application is not relevant, what is relevant is the date on which the application is duly made to the court having jurisdiction.[30]

Once the court entertains an application filed under Part I of the Act in respect of arbitration agreement and the question of jurisdiction is decided in that application, the said question cannot be raised in subsequent application in view of Section 42.[31]

Where an application under Part I has been made in a court with respect to an arbitration agreement, that court alone shall have jurisdiction over the arbitral proceedings and all subsequent applications arising out of that agreement, no other court would have jurisdiction. The expression "all subsequent applications arising out of arbitral proceedings" has been used in a comprehensive sense by the legislature and must be given full width in interpretation. The judgment-debtor sought a recourse to its remedies before the Bombay High Court in order to challenge the arbitral award. Once that was done, the Bombay High Court alone would have jurisdiction to entertain all subsequent applications arising out of the arbitral proceedings *including applications in execution of the award* as a decree of the court to the exclusion of any other court.[32]

Cause of action did arise at Thane and applications under Part I were made before the court at Thane prior to arbitration petitions. District Court at Thane had curial jurisdiction over the award within the meaning of Sections 42 and 2(1)(*e*) of the Act. It is the only court to exercise jurisdiction in any challenge to an arbitration award.[33] The purpose of Section 42 is to avoid institution of simultaneous proceedings at two places or in two different courts and to have all matters arising out of a particular arbitration agreement decided by one court.[34]

If an arbitration proceeding takes place at the instance of a court, then such arbitral proceeding and all applications that may be made by the parties

30. *Hindustan Petroleum Corpn. Ltd.* v. *Barun Sankar Chatterjee*, 2012 SCC OnLine Cal 509: (2012) 3 CHN 160.
31. *United Spirits Ltd.* v. *Paras Collins Distilleries (P) Ltd.*, 2010 SCC OnLine Bom 1345: (2010) 7 Mah LJ 760.
32. *Eskay Engineers* v. *BSNL*, 2009 SCC OnLine Bom 893: (2009) 5 Mah LJ 565.
33. *Municipal Corpn. for the City of Kalyan and Dombivli* v. *Rudranee Infrastructure Ltd.*, 2017 SCC OnLine Bom 5504: (2017) 6 Mah LJ 753.
34. *N.K.C. Projects (P) Ltd.* v. *Utility Energytech & Engineers (P) Ltd.*, 2009 SCC OnLine All 296: (2009) 75 ALR 397.

pending such arbitration proceeding should remain under the jurisdiction of that court alone for effective resolution of the dispute.[35]

The petitioner challenged termination of proceedings by the arbitrator for non-payment of his fees in the courts at Gurugram, Punjab and Haryana. The parties had agreed on a venue for arbitration proceedings in Delhi at the time of appointment of the arbitrator. The courts at Gurugram would not have jurisdiction.[36]

In respect of arbitration agreement, if any application under Part I is filed in court, that court alone shall have jurisdiction over the arbitral proceedings including any subsequent applications. Application filed under Section 11 of the 1996 Act in the Allahabad High Court is application under Part I of the 1996 Act. Section 42 of the 1996 Act will be attracted, award passed at New Delhi can be executed in the court at Gautam Buddh Nagar.[37]

Applications filed under Sections 8 and 11—Section 42 not attracted

Applications made under Section 11 of the Act are not moved before the "court" as defined under the Act, but before the Chief Justice of the High Court or of the Supreme Court, as the case may be, or their delegates. Section 42 would not apply to applications made before the Chief Justice or his delegate as the Chief Justice or his delegate is not "court" as defined by Section 2(1)(*e*).[38]

It is inconceivable that when a request is made to a High Court of a State where such High Court does not exercise original jurisdiction, that by virtue of Section 42, the future petitions and applications pertaining to the arbitration agreement have per force to be carried to such High Court. Appointment of arbitrator cannot be governed by Section 42.[39]

Arbitration proceedings were conducted within the jurisdiction of the court subordinate to the High Court where application under Section 11 for appointment of arbitrator was filed. Award cannot be challenged before the court subordinate to another High Court as it would be against the provisions of Section 42.[40]

35. *Macrotech India* v. *Uma Roy*, 2002 SCC OnLine Cal 643: (2003) 2 CHN 35.
36. *BWI Educon Venture (P) Ltd.* v. *Auto Serve Equipment (P) Ltd.*, 2019 SCC OnLine P&H 8045.
37. *Hasmukh Prajapati* v. *Jai Prakash Associates Ltd.*, 2022 SCC OnLine All 96: (2022) 3 All LJ 166.
38. *Transparent Energy Systems (P) Ltd.* v. *Chettinad Cement Corpn. Ltd.*, 2017 SCC OnLine Kar 4461: ILR 2017 Kar 4229; *Anand Bhatiya Contractor* v. *Union of India*, 2014 SCC OnLine Raj 691.
39. *Tapas Kumar Bhunia* v. *Jagadish Patra*, 2018 SCC OnLine Cal 15013: (2018) 5 CHN 85.
40. *Bhandari Udyog Ltd.* v. *Industrial Facilitation Council*, (2015) 14 SCC 515 reversed.

Jurisdiction of the court

The enforcement of an award through its execution can be filed anywhere in the country where such decree can be executed and there is no requirement for obtaining a transfer of the decree from the court, which would have jurisdiction over the arbitral proceedings.[41]

Section 34 applications with Section 42

Section 34 applications to set aside arbitral awards are also applications within Section 42.[42]

Once the High Court exercised jurisdiction under Section 11(6), an application under Section 34 could only be made to the judge taking arbitration matters in High Court in its ordinary original civil jurisdiction in view of Section 42. The order of the District Judge that the High Court had jurisdiction in the matter was held proper/upheld.[43]

"Any application under this part has been made in a court"

Section 42 only applies to applications made under Part I if they are made to a "court" as defined in Section 2(1)(*e*) of the Act. Since applications made under Section 8 are made to judicial authorities and since applications made under Section 11 are made to the Chief Justice or his designate, the judicial authority and the Chief Justice or his designate not being "court" as defined such application would be outside Section 42.[44]

Applications under Section 9 are filed in "court"—Section 42 applies

In contrast to applications moved under Sections 8 and 11 of the Act, applications moved under Section 9 are to the "court" as defined for the passing of interim orders before or during arbitration proceedings or at any time after the making of an arbitral award but before its enforcement. In a case an application under Section 9 is made before a particular court, Section 42 will apply to preclude the making of all subsequent applications under Part I to any court, except the court to which an application under Section 9 has been made.[45]

A court has territorial jurisdiction to set aside an award of the arbitrator where subject-matter is situated when there is a clause about jurisdiction. In

---

41. *Mahindra and Mahindra Financial Services Ltd.* v. *Kana Singh*, 2018 SCC OnLine HP 3398.
42. *State of W.B.* v. *Associated Contractors*, (2015) 1 SCC 32.
43. *Union of India* v. *Mohan Lal Jain*, 2013 SCC OnLine Cal 7702: (2013) 3 ICC 163.
44. *State of W.B.* v. *Associated Contractors*, (2015) 1 SCC 32.
45. *Ibid.*

Manjusha Premi v. *Prakash Gupta*[46], the property situated at Varanasi, was in dispute. First application under Section 9 for interim measure was filed before the District Judge, Varanasi. Application for setting aside arbitral award was maintainable only before the District Judge, Varanasi in view of the provisions of Section 42. District Judge, Varanasi being principal civil court of original jurisdiction was held competent to entertain application under Section 34.

Novation of contract

Section 42 states that if an application under Part I had been made in a court with respect to "an arbitration agreement", then it is that court alone which will have jurisdiction over the arbitral proceedings as well as of subsequent applications arising out of "that agreement". The expression "that agreement" connotes the agreement out of which the earliest application arose. Therefore, if the original arbitration agreement had really undergone a complete change leading to novation, Section 42 will have application only to the proceedings that take place after such novation. For instance, in a case where an application under Section 9 is filed in a court and arbitral proceedings are initiated, a settlement is reached during the course of the arbitral proceedings and the parties enter into a fresh contract which contains an arbitration agreement. If such a fresh contract containing an arbitration agreement leads to a fresh dispute, Section 42 will have no application to the first application filed in relation to a fresh dispute. If and when a novation actually takes place, Section 42 cannot be invoked.[47]

Appointment of arbitrator

Agreement provided for reference to named arbitrator for resolution of dispute outside India. Arbitrator at Singapore passed the award. Award was set aside by the court at Singapore with liberty to apply for fresh arbitration. Appellant did not file a fresh application for appointment of arbitrator at Singapore, but filed an application before the Supreme Court in India for appointment of arbitrator. It was held, award of the arbitrator was passed at Singapore, it was set aside by the High Court of Singapore, and therefore, the court at Singapore, which alone shall have jurisdiction over the arbitral proceedings and all applications arising out of that agreement shall be made in that court and no other court. Having mutually agreed to have the dispute referred to an arbitrator in Singapore, the applicant is not permitted to turn around and say that the Supreme Court of India should appoint an

46. 2016 SCC OnLine All 2796: (2016) 116 ALR 657.
47. *VO Chidambaranar Port Trust* v. *PSA Sical Terminals Ltd.*, 2015 SCC OnLine Mad 2905: (2015) 3 LW 541.

arbitrator. Application for appointment of arbitrator filed before Supreme Court in India was rejected.[48]

Transfer of execution proceedings

Petitioner sought transfer of execution proceedings to the court of competent jurisdiction at Bathinda on ground that acquired land was situated in Bathinda and parties were also residents of Bathinda. Arbitrator had fixed the seat of arbitration at Faridkot. Execution proceedings were maintainable before court at Faridkot, execution proceedings could not be transferred from Faridkot court to Bathinda court.[49]

Appeal

Appeal filed before the Indian court against the interim order passed by the Arbitral Tribunal with its seat in Singapore was not maintainable.[50]

CONFIDENTIALITY OF INFORMATION [S. 42-A]

[51][**42-A.** *Confidentiality of information.*—Notwithstanding anything contained in any other law for the time being in force, the arbitrator, the arbitral institution and the parties to the arbitration agreement shall maintain confidentiality of all arbitral proceedings except award where its disclosure is necessary for the purpose of implementation and enforcement of award.]

COMMENTS

Corresponding old law

Section 42-A is newly added by the Amendment Act 33 of 2019.

Scope and applicability

New Section 42-A, provides for confidentiality of all the arbitral proceedings. As mandated by Section 42-A, the arbitrator, the arbitral institution and parties to the arbitration agreement shall maintain confidentiality of all arbitral proceedings except where its disclosure is necessary for the purpose of implementation and enforcement of the award.

48. *Shivnath Rai Harnarain (India) Ltd.* v. *Abdul Ghaffar Abdul Rehman*, (2008) 5 SCC 135.
49. *NHAI* v. *Yashpreet Singh*, 2022 SCC OnLine P&H 4272.
50. *Yograj Infrastructure Ltd.* v. *Ssang Yong Engg. & Construction Co. Ltd.*, (2011) 9 SCC 735.
51. *Ins.* by Act 33 of 2019, S. 9 (w.e.f. 30-8-2019).

PROTECTION OF ACTION TAKEN IN GOOD FAITH [S. 42-B]

[52][**42-B.** *Protection of action taken in good faith.*—No suit or other legal proceedings shall lie against the arbitrator for anything which is in good faith done or intended to be done under this Act or the rules or regulations made thereunder.]

COMMENTS

Corresponding old law

Section 42-B is new, added by the Amendment Act 33 of 2019, no such provision existed in the Arbitration Act, 1940.

Scope and application

As provided by Section 42-B, no suit or other legal proceedings shall lie against the arbitrator for anything done or *intended to be done* in good faith under the Arbitration and Conciliation Act, 1996 or the rules or regulations made under the Act.

LIMITATIONS [S. 43]

43. *Limitations.*—(1) The Limitation Act, 1963 (36 of 1963), shall apply to arbitrations as it applies to proceedings in court.

(2) For the purposes of this section and the Limitation Act, 1963 (36 of 1963), an arbitration shall be deemed to have commenced on the date referred in Section 21.

(3) Where an arbitration agreement to submit future disputes to arbitration provides that any claim to which the agreement applies shall be barred unless some step to commence arbitral proceedings is taken within a time fixed by the agreement, and a dispute arises to which the agreement applies, the Court, if it is of opinion that in the circumstances of the case undue hardship would otherwise be caused, and notwithstanding that the time so fixed has expired, may on such terms, if any, as the justice of the case may require, extend the time for such period as it thinks proper.

(4) Where the Court orders that an arbitral award be set aside, the period between the commencement of the arbitration and the date of the order of the Court shall be excluded in computing the time prescribed by the Limitation Act, 1963 (36 of 1963), for the commencement of the proceedings (including arbitration) with respect to the dispute so submitted.

---

52. *Ins.* by Act 33 of 2019, S. 9 (w.e.f. 30-8-2019).

STATE AMENDMENTS

Bihar.—In its application to the State of Bihar, sub-section (3) of Section 43 shall be *omitted.* [*Vide* Bihar Act 20 of 2002, S. 2 (w.e.f. 9-12-2002)].

COMMENTS

Corresponding old law

Section 43 corresponds to Section 37, Arbitration Act, 1940. Section 37, Arbitration Act, 1940 read as under:

37. *Limitations.*—(1) All the provisions of the Indian Limitation Act, 1908 (9 of 1908)[53] shall apply to arbitrations as they apply to proceedings in Court.

(2) Notwithstanding any term in an arbitration agreement to the effect that no cause of action shall accrue in respect of any matter required by the agreement to be referred until an award is made under the agreement, a cause of action shall, for the purpose of limitation, be deemed to have accrued in respect of any such matter at the time when it would have accrued but for that term in the agreement.

(3) For the purposes of this section and of the Indian Limitation Act, 1908 (9 of 1908), an arbitration shall be deemed to be commenced when one party to the arbitration agreement serves on the other parties thereto a notice requiring the appointment of an arbitrator, or where the arbitration agreement provides that the reference shall be to a person named or designated in the agreement, requiring that the difference be submitted to the person so named or designated.

(4) Where the terms of an agreement to refer future differences, to arbitration provide that any claims to which the agreement applies shall be barred unless notice to appoint an arbitrator is given or an arbitrator is appointed or some other step to commence arbitration proceedings is taken within a time fixed by the agreement, and a difference arises to which the agreement applies, the Court, if it is of opinion that in the circumstances of the case undue hardship would otherwise be caused, and notwithstanding that the time so fixed has expired, may on such terms, if any, as the justice of the case may require, extend the time for such period as it thinks proper.

(5) Where the Court orders that an award be set aside or orders, after the commencement of an arbitration, that the arbitration agreement shall cease to have effect with respect to the difference referred, the period between commencement of the arbitration and the date of the order of the Court shall be excluded in computing the time prescribed by the Indian Limitation Act, 1908 (9 of 1908), for the commencement of the proceedings (including arbitration) with respect to the difference referred.

---

53. Now *see* Limitation Act, 1963 (Act 36 of 1963).

Scope and application

As provided by Section 43, the provisions of the Limitation Act, 1963 shall apply to arbitrations as it applies to the proceedings in the court. Section 43(1), Arbitration and Conciliation Act specifically provides that Limitation Act, 1963 shall apply to arbitrations as it applies to proceeding in the court.[54]

The Limitation Act, 1963 is applicable to arbitration matters covered under the 1996 Act except as expressly provided for under Section 34(3) of the 1996 Act.[55] The provisions of the Limitation Act, 1963 are applicable to the arbitration proceedings under the 1996 Act.[56]

In the case of arbitration, limitation for the claim is to be calculated on the date on which the arbitration is deemed to have commenced.[57]

The provisions of the Limitation Act, 1963 would not apply to arbitration under the bye-laws of the Bombay Stock Exchange; the limitation provided by the bye-laws of the Bombay Stock Exchange would apply.[58]

Section 43 applies to arbitrations and not to proceedings before the court under Section 34, Arbitration and Conciliation Act, 1996. The proceedings before the arbitrator and the proceedings before the court under Section 34 cannot be equated, and therefore, Section 43 cannot be of any help in construing Section 34(3) of the Act.[59]

The applicant had earlier appointed arbitrator, the award passed by the arbitrator in the year 2003 was set aside in the year 2010. Thereafter, an application for appointment of arbitrator was filed. It could not be said that the claim of the arbitrator was dead. Arbitrator was appointed, issue relating to limitation would be adjudicated by the arbitrator on the basis of the evidence to be adduced by the parties.[60]

It is the duty of the arbitrator to go into the question of limitation and decide the same, even if the parties did not raise the question of limitation. Arbitrator is not expected to adjudicate stale claims.[61]

54. *Bhimashankar Sahakari Sakkare Karkhane Niyamita* v. *Walchandnagar Industries Ltd.*, (2023) 8 SCC 453.
55. *Assam Urban Water Supply & Sewerage Board* v. *Subash Projects & Mktg. Ltd.*, (2012) 2 SCC 624.
56. *G.C. Kanungo* v. *Rourkela Steel Plant*, 2011 SCC OnLine Ori 234: (2012) 113 CLT 853.
57. *J.C. Budhraja* v. *Orissa Mining Corpn. Ltd.*, (2008) 2 SCC 444.
58. *R.C. Goenka* v. *Chase Trading Co.*, 2001 SCC OnLine Bom 879: (2002) 1 Mah LJ 774.
59. *Bageshwari Sahakari Sakhar Karkhana Ltd.* v. *Shivajirao*, 2004 SCC OnLine Bom 158: (2004) 4 Mah LJ 28.
60. *Primus Chemicals Ltd.* v. *Guha Industries*, 2014 SCC OnLine MP 6584: (2014) 4 MP LJ 560.
61. *Chennai Metropolitan Water Supply and Sewerage Board* v. *Aban Constructions (P) Ltd.*, 2006 SCC OnLine Mad 486: (2006) 3 CTC 794.

Contract was given for construction of residential complex, maximum period given was two years and six months including grace period. Application for appointment of arbitrator filed after lapse of 17 years beyond prescribed period of limitation of three years was rejected being time barred.[62]

Question whether claim of the party is within limitation or not, is to be decided by the arbitrator

The provisions of Limitation Act, 1963 by virtue of Section 43(1), Limitation Act, 1963 shall apply to arbitrators as it applies to proceedings in court. The question whether the claim of the applicant is within limitation or not, is to be decided by the arbitrator as per the provisions of Section 43(1) of the Act.[63]

Recovery of money

On termination of contract after one year, ₹2,50,000 was forfeited as security amount. Contractor raised a claim for a sum of ₹4,29,208 for hiring vehicle from the open market after seven years, when the matter was referred before an arbitrator. Claim for recovery of money and limitation to make such claim would be three years. Suit for recovery of money filed by contractor beyond prescribed period of limitation was barred by limitation. Award of the arbitrator was set aside.[64]

Additional claims—Limitation

In case of additional claims, the date of amendment by which additional claim is sought to be adduced is relevant.[65]

Counterclaim—Limitation

The date on which counterclaim is made by the respondent before the arbitrator will be the date of its institution. Section 21, Arbitration and Conciliation Act, 1996 is not relevant for counterclaims.[66]

---

62. *Braj Kishore Pandey* v. *Hem Developers (P) Ltd.*, 2016 SCC OnLine Pat 3155: (2016) 3 PLJR 891.
63. *National Dairy Development Board* v. *Suraj Singh*, 2001 SCC OnLine MP 379: (2002) 2 MP LJ 72.
64. *BSNL* v. *K.K. Kakkar*, 2019 SCC OnLine P&H 6246.
65. *State of Goa* v. *Praveen Enterprises*, (2012) 12 SCC 581.
66. *Ibid.*

Extension of period of limitation for arbitration by court [Sub-s. (3)]

The court may exercise power under Section 43(3), and extend the period of limitation if the court is satisfied that if the limitation is not extended undue hardship is likely to be caused to the party concerned, the party would suffer harsh consequences for no fault of his even after he had taken all possible measures within his power. In the present case, merely because the respondent had failed to put up proper pleadings, it cannot be said that the power of the court under Section 43(3) of the Act can be exercised.[67]

The dispute has to be referred to the arbitrator within reasonable time. No time-limit was prescribed in the "agreement of sale" within which the dispute was to be referred to an arbitrator. Reference application was filed by the petitioner immediately after appearance in suit. It was held, provisions of Section 43(3) were not applicable in the case.[68]

Application for extension of time has to be made before commencement of arbitration proceedings and not thereafter. An application for extension of time after the passing of the award is not maintainable.[69]

The period of bona fide negotiations between parties towards amicable settlement may be excluded for computing the period of limitation, subject to specific pleadings of entire negotiations between the parties. Delay of 14 years alleged to be covered by negotiations between the parties was not condoned. Cause of action arose on 8 February 1983, notice served for appointment of arbitrator in 2002 was held barred by limitation.[70]

Agreement was entered into between the parties pertaining to supply of vehicles. On termination of contract, security amount was forfeited. The contractor raised a claim for ₹4,29,208 for hiring vehicles from the open market after seven years, and the matter was referred to an arbitrator. In claim for recovery of money, as the limitation period is three years, the contractor's claim for the recovery of money filed after seven years was held barred by limitation.[71]

---

67. *Pravin Ratilal Share and Stock Brokers Ltd.* v. *Sagar Drugs and Pharmaceuticals Ltd.*, 2006 SCC OnLine Bom 975: (2007) 3 Mah LJ 134.
68. *Suman Baburao Thapa* v. *Jigar K. Mehta*, 2018 SCC OnLine Bom 377: (2018) 5 Mah LJ 260.
69. *E. Muralidharan* v. *Venkataraman and Co.*, 2006 SCC OnLine Mad 473: (2006) 3 Arb LR 477; *E. Muralidharan* v. *Venkataraman*, 2008 SCC OnLine Mad 698.
70. *Geo Miller & Co. (P) Ltd.* v. *Rajasthan Vidyut Utpadan Nigam Ltd.*, (2020) 14 SCC 643.
71. *BSNL* v. *K.K. Kakkar*, 2019 SCC OnLine P&H 6246.

[1][PART I-A

ARBITRATION COUNCIL OF INDIA]

1. *Ins.* by Act 33 of 2019, S. 10 (w.e.f. 12-10-2023).

Chapter I
Arbitration Council of India

DEFINITIONS [S. 43-A]

43-A. *Definitions.*—In this Part, unless the context otherwise requires,—

(*a*) "Chairperson" means the Chairperson of the Arbitration Council of India appointed under clause (*a*) of sub-section (1) of Section 43-C;

(*b*) "Council" means the Arbitration Council of India established under Section 43-B;

(*c*) "Member" means a Member of the Council and includes the Chairperson.

COMMENTS

New Sections 43-A to 43-M added by the Amendment Act 33 of 2019 make provision for establishment and incorporation of an independent body, *namely*, the Arbitration Council of India for the purpose of grading of arbitral institutions, accreditation of arbitrators, etc.

ESTABLISHMENT AND INCORPORATION OF ARBITRATION COUNCIL OF INDIA [S. 43-B]

43-B. *Establishment and incorporation of Arbitration Council of India.*—(1) The Central Government shall, by notification in the Official Gazette, establish, for the purposes of this Act, a Council to be known as the Arbitration Council of India to perform the duties and discharge the functions under this Act.

(2) The Council shall be a body corporate by the name aforesaid, having perpetual succession and a common seal, with power, subject to the provisions of this Act, to acquire, hold and dispose of property, both movable and immovable, and to enter into contract, and shall, by the said name, sue or be sued.

(3) The head office of the Council shall be at Delhi.

(4) The Council may, with the prior approval of the Central Government, establish offices at other places in India.

COMPOSITION OF COUNCIL [S. 43-C]

43-C. *Composition of Council.*—(1) The Council shall consist of the following Members, namely:—

(*a*) a person, who has been, a Judge of the Supreme Court or, Chief Justice of a High Court or, a Judge of a High Court or an eminent person, having special knowledge and experience in the conduct or administration of arbitration, to be appointed by the Central Government in consultation with the Chief Justice of India—Chairperson;

(*b*) an eminent arbitration practitioner having substantial knowledge and experience in institutional arbitration, both domestic and international, to be nominated by the Central Government—Member;

(*c*) an eminent academician having experience in research and teaching in the field of arbitration and alternative dispute resolution laws, to be appointed by the Central Government in consultation with the Chairperson—Member;

(*d*) Secretary to the Government of India in the Department of Legal Affairs, Ministry of Law and Justice or his representative not below the rank of Joint Secretary—Member, ex officio;

(*e*) Secretary to the Government of India in the Department of Expenditure, Ministry of Finance or his representative not below the rank of Joint Secretary—Member, ex officio;

(*f*) one representative of a recognised body of commerce and industry, chosen on rotational basis by the Central Government—Part-time Member; and

(*g*) Chief Executive Officer—Member-Secretary, ex officio.

(2) The Chairperson and Members of the Council, other than ex officio Members, shall hold office as such, for a term of three years from the date on which they enter upon their office:

Provided that no Chairperson or Member, other than ex officio Member, shall hold office as such after he has attained the age of seventy years in the case of Chairperson and sixty-seven years in the case of Member.

(3) The salaries, allowances and other terms and conditions of the Chairperson and Members referred to in clauses (*b*) and (*c*) of sub-section (1) shall be such as may be prescribed by the Central Government.

(4) The Part-time Member shall be entitled to such travelling and other allowances as may be prescribed by the Central Government.

DUTIES AND FUNCTIONS OF COUNCIL [S. 43-D]

43-D. *Duties and functions of Council.*—(1) It shall be the duty of the Council to take all such measures as may be necessary to promote and encourage arbitration, [1][* * *] or other alternative dispute resolution mechanism and for that purpose to frame policy and guidelines for the establishment, operation and maintenance of uniform professional standards in respect of all matters relating to arbitration.

(2) For the purposes of performing the duties and discharging the functions under this Act, the Council may—

(*a*) frame policies governing the grading of arbitral institutions;

(*b*) recognise professional institutes providing accreditation of arbitrators;

(*c*) review the grading of arbitral institutions and arbitrators;

(*d*) hold training, workshops and courses in the area of arbitration in collaboration of law firms, law universities and arbitral institutes;

(*e*) frame, review and update norms to ensure satisfactory level of arbitration [2][* * *];

(*f*) act as a forum for exchange of views and techniques to be adopted for creating a platform to make India a robust centre for domestic and international arbitration [3][* * *];

(*g*) make recommendations to the Central Government on various measures to be adopted to make provision for easy resolution of commercial disputes;

(*h*) promote institutional arbitration by strengthening arbitral institutions;

(*i*) conduct examination and training on various subjects relating to arbitration [4][* * *] and award certificates thereof;

(*j*) establish and maintain depository of arbitral awards made in India;

(*k*) make recommendations regarding personnel, training and infrastructure of arbitral institutions; and

(*l*) such other functions as may be decided by the Central Government.

VACANCIES, ETC., NOT TO INVALIDATE PROCEEDINGS OF COUNCIL [S. 43-E]

43-E. *Vacancies, etc., not to invalidate proceedings of Council.*—No act or proceeding of the Council shall be invalid merely by reason of—

(*a*) any vacancy or any defect, in the constitution of the Council;

(*b*) any defect in the appointment of a person acting as a Member of the Council; or

---

1. The words "mediation, conciliation" *omitted* by Act 32 of 2023, S. 61 and Sch. VI(*a*)(*i*) (w.e.f. the date to be notified).
2. The words "and conciliation" *omitted* by Act 32 of 2023, S. 61 and Sch. VI(*a*)(*ii*) (w.e.f. the date to be notified).
3. *Ibid.*
4. *Ibid.*

(*c*) any irregularity in the procedure of the Council not affecting the merits of the case.

RESIGNATION OF MEMBERS [S. 43-F]

43-F. *Resignation of Members.*—The Chairperson or the Full-time or Part-time Member may, by notice in writing, under his hand addressed to the Central Government, resign his office:

Provided that the Chairperson or the Full-time Member shall, unless he is permitted by the Central Government to relinquish his office sooner, continue to hold office until the expiry of three months from the date of receipt of such notice or until a person duly appointed as his successor enters upon his office or until the expiry of his term of office, whichever is earlier.

REMOVAL OF MEMBER [S. 43-G]

43-G. *Removal of Member.*—(1) The Central Government may, remove a Member from his office if he—

(*a*) is an undischarged insolvent; or

(*b*) has engaged at any time (except Part-time Member), during his term of office, in any paid employment; or

(*c*) has been convicted of an offence which, in the opinion of the Central Government, involves moral turpitude; or

(*d*) has acquired such financial or other interest as is likely to affect prejudicially his functions as a Member; or

(*e*) has so abused his position as to render his continuance in office prejudicial to the public interest; or

(*f*) has become physically or mentally incapable of acting as a Member.

(2) Notwithstanding anything contained in sub-section (1), no Member shall be removed from his office on the grounds specified in clauses (*d*) and (*e*) of that sub-section unless the Supreme Court, on a reference being made to it in this behalf by the Central Government, has, on an inquiry, held by it in accordance with such procedure as may be prescribed in this behalf by the Supreme Court, reported that the Member, ought on such ground or grounds to be removed.

APPOINTMENT OF EXPERTS AND CONSTITUTION OF COMMITTEES THEREOF [S. 43-H]

43-H. *Appointment of experts and constitution of Committees thereof.*—The Council may, appoint such experts and constitute such Committees of experts as it may consider necessary to discharge its functions on such terms and conditions as may be specified by the regulations.

GENERAL NORMS FOR GRADING OF ARBITRAL INSTITUTIONS [S. 43-I]

43-I. *General norms for grading of arbitral institutions.*—The Council shall make grading of arbitral institutions on the basis of criteria relating to infrastructure, quality and calibre of arbitrators, performance and compliance of time limits for disposal of domestic or international commercial arbitrations, in such manner as may be specified by the regulations.

NORMS FOR ACCREDITATION OF ARBITRATORS [S. 43-J]

[5][**43-J.** *Norms for accreditation of arbitrators.*—The qualifications, experience and norms for accreditation of arbitrators shall be such as may be specified by the regulations.]

DEPOSITORY OF AWARDS [S. 43-K]

43-K. *Depository of awards.*—The Council shall maintain an electronic depository of arbitral awards made in India and such other records related thereto in such manner as may be specified by the regulations.

POWER TO MAKE REGULATIONS BY COUNCIL [S. 43-L]

43-L. *Power to make regulations by Council.*—The Council may, in consultation with the Central Government, make regulations, consistent with the provisions of this Act and the rules made thereunder, for the discharge of its functions and perform its duties under this Act.

CHIEF EXECUTIVE OFFICER [S. 43-M]

43-M. *Chief Executive Officer.*—(1) There shall be a Chief Executive Officer of the Council, who shall be responsible for day-to-day administration of the Council.

(2) The qualifications, appointment and other terms and conditions of the service of the Chief Executive Officer shall be such as may be prescribed by the Central Government.

(3) The Chief Executive Officer shall discharge such functions and perform such duties as may be specified by the regulations.

---

5. *Subs.* by Act 3 of 2021, S. 3 (w.r.e.f. 4-11-2020). Prior to substitution it read as:

"43-J. *Norms for accreditation.*—The qualifications, experience and norms for accreditation of arbitrators shall be such as specified in the Eighth Schedule:

Provided that the Central Government may, after consultation with the Council, by notification in the Official Gazette, amend the Eighth Schedule and thereupon, the Eighth Schedule shall be deemed to have been amended accordingly."

(4) There shall be a Secretariat to the Council consisting of such number of officers and employees as may be prescribed by the Central Government.

(5) The qualifications, appointment and other terms and conditions of the service of the employees and other officers of the Council shall be such as may be prescribed by the Central Government.]

Part II

ENFORCEMENT OF CERTAIN FOREIGN AWARDS

CHAPTER I
New York Convention Awards

DEFINITION [S. 44]

44. *Definition.*—In this Chapter, unless the context otherwise requires, "foreign award" means an arbitral award on differences between persons arising out of legal relationships, whether contractual or not, considered as commercial under the law in force in India, made on or after the 11th day of October, 1960—

(*a*) in pursuance of an agreement in writing for arbitration to which the Convention set forth in the First Schedule applies, and

(*b*) in one of such territories as the Central Government, being satisfied that reciprocal provisions have been made may, by notification in the Official Gazette, declare to be territories to which the said Convention applies.

COMMENTS

Corresponding old law

Section 44 is verbatim reproduction of Section 2, Foreign Awards (Recognition and Enforcement) Act, 1961 (now repealed) with marginal changes. The said Section 2 provided as under:

2. *Definition.*—In this Act, unless the context otherwise requires, "foreign award" means an award on differences between persons arising out of legal relationships, whether contractual or not, considered as commercial under the law in force in India, made on or after the 11th day of October, 1960—

(*a*) in pursuance of an agreement in writing for arbitration to which the Convention set forth in the Schedule applies; and

(*b*) in one of such territories as the Central Government being satisfied that reciprocal provisions have been made, may, by notification in the official Gazette, declare to be territories to which the said Convention applies.

Scope and application

Section 44 of the 1996 Act defines a foreign award. The definition given in this section would not apply where the "unless the contract otherwise requires" clause is attached. A definition clause, therefore, does not necessarily apply in all possible contexts in which the award may be found.[1]

The context of Section 44 is that of an international commercial arbitration and cannot, therefore, apply to a foreign award between two Indian parties without the involvement of a foreign element. The Arbitration and Conciliation Act, 1996 is a self-contained code, and that when there is no foreign element involved in an award made in Zurich between two Indian companies, such award cannot be the subject-matter of challenge or enforcement either under Part I or Part II of the Arbitration and Conciliation Act, 1996.[2]

In order to come to a conclusion that a particular award is a foreign award, the following conditions have to be satisfied:

1. The legal relationship between the parties must be commercial.
2. The award must be made in pursuance of an agreement in writing.
3. The award must be made in a New York Convention country.

Section 44 of the 1996 Act makes an award foreign, if the above mentioned criteria are fulfilled, "unless the context otherwise requires".[3]

Section 44, Arbitration and Conciliation Act, 1996 recognises the fact that tort claims may be decided by an arbitrator provided they are disputes that arise in connection with the agreement. Claims in tort may be so intimately connected with a contract that a clause of appropriate width designed primarily to make contractual disputes arbitrable will nevertheless render such claims in tort arbitrable as well.[4]

In case of international arbitration, proper law of arbitral agreement is the substantive law governing the contract itself.[5]

Part I deals with arbitrations where the seat is in India and has no application to a foreign-seated arbitration. Part I applies only if the place of arbitration is in India. Part II is not concerned with arbitral proceedings at all. It concerns only with the enforcement of a foreign award. Part II does

1. *Centrotrade Minerals & Metals Inc.* v. *Hindustan Copper Ltd.*, (2006) 11 SCC 245.
2. *PASL Wind Solutions (P) Ltd.* v. *GE Power Conversion (India) (P) Ltd.*, (2021) 7 SCC 1.
3. Ibid; *Integrated Sales Services Ltd.* v. *DMC Management Consultants Ltd.*, 2016 SCC OnLine Bom 4445: (2016) 6 Mah LJ 195; *PASL Wind Solutions (P) Ltd.* v. *GE Power Conversion (India) (P) Ltd.*, (2021) 7 SCC 1; *Gemini Bay Transcription (P) Ltd.* v. *Integrated Sales Service Ltd.*, (2022) 1 SCC 753.
4. *Gemini Bay Transcription (P) Ltd.* v. *Integrated Sales Service Ltd.*, (2022) 1 SCC 753.
5. *Shin-Etsu Chemical Co. Ltd.* v. *Aksh Optifibre Ltd.*, (2005) 7 SCC 234.

not apply to arbitration proceedings once it commenced in a country outside India.[6]

When Chapter II is applicable, then any application filed by the party under the provisions of Chapter I and the order passed by the court on the aforesaid application is without jurisdiction, is nullity.[7]

"Foreign award" meaning of

One of the conditions to constitute a foreign award within the meaning of Section 44 is that it should be made in one of such territories as the Central Government, by notification in the Official Gazette, declaring it to be a territory in which the New York Convention applies. There is no such requirement qua an agreement for arbitration in Section 44(*a*) and correspondingly in Section 45.[8]

Existence of a defined legal relationship in writing, undertaking to submit to arbitration all or any differences concerning a subject-matter capable of settlement by arbitration is *sine qua non* to constitute a foreign award.[9]

Unless the two conditions (*a*) and (*b*) of Section 44 of the 1996 Act are satisfied, an award cannot be considered to be a foreign award in India, but even if these two conditions are satisfied, there remains a category of awards which are not foreign awards; the opening words of Section 44 are a pointer to this category. The opening words state that the definition of a foreign award according to location will hold unless the context otherwise requires.[10]

"Persons"

"Persons" mentioned in Section 44 has no reference to nationality, residence or domicile.[11]

6. *PASL Wind Solutions (P) Ltd.* v. *GE Power Conversion (India) (P) Ltd.*, (2021) 7 SCC 1.
7. *M.P. Oil Extraction Ltd.* v. *State Trading Corpn. of India*, 2015 SCC OnLine MP 5002: (2015) 3 MPLJ 197.
8. *Rashmi Mehra* v. *EAC Trading Ltd.*, 2006 SCC OnLine Bom 1105: (2007) 2 Mah LJ 737.
9. *Integrated Sales Services Ltd.* v. *DMC Management Consultants Ltd.*, 2016 SCC OnLine Bom 4445: (2016) 6 Mah LJ 195.
10. *Hindustan Copper Ltd.* v. *Centrotrade Minerals & Metals Inc.*, 2004 SCC OnLine Cal 446: (2005) 1 CHN 448.
11. *Dakshin Haryana Bijli Vitran Nigam Ltd.* v. *Navigant Technologies (P) Ltd.*, (2021) 7 SCC 657.

POWER OF JUDICIAL AUTHORITY TO REFER PARTIES TO ARBITRATION [S. 45]

45. *Power of judicial authority to refer parties to arbitration.*—Notwithstanding anything contained in Part I or in the Code of Civil Procedure, 1908 (5 of 1908), a judicial authority, when seized of an action in a matter in respect of which the parties have made an agreement referred to in Section 44, shall, at the request of one of the parties or any person claiming through or under him, refer the parties to arbitration, [12][unless it prima facie finds] that the said agreement is null and void, inoperative or incapable of being performed.

COMMENTS

Corresponding old law

Section 45 corresponds to Section 3, Foreign Awards (Recognition and Enforcement) Act, 1961. The change made in the present section is that under the present Section 45, the court will refer the parties to arbitration unless it prima facie finds that the agreement referred to in Section 44 is null and void, inoperative or incapable of being performed. Section 3, Foreign Awards (Recognition and Enforcement) Act, 1961 provides as under:

> [13][**3.** *Stay of proceedings in respect of matters to be referred to arbitration.*—Notwithstanding anything contained in the Arbitration Act, 1940, or in the Code of Civil Procedure, 1908, if any party to an agreement to which Article II of the Convention set forth in the Schedule applies, or any person claiming through or under him commences any legal proceedings in any court against any other party to the agreement or any person claiming through or under him in respect of any matter agreed to be referred to arbitration in such agreement, any party to such legal proceedings may, at any time after appearance and before filling a written statement or taking any other step in the proceedings, apply to the Court to stay the proceedings and the Court, unless satisfied that the agreement is null and void, inoperative or incapable of being performed or that there is not, in fact, any dispute between the parties with regard to the matter agreed to be referred, shall make an order staying the proceedings].

Legislative changes

Arbitration and Conciliation (Amendment) Act, 2019 (33 of 2019)

The words "unless it prima facie finds" in Section 45 have been unless it finds by the Amendment Act 33 of 2019.

---

12. *Subs.* for "unless it finds" by Act 33 of 2019, S. 11 (w.e.f. 30-8-2019).
13. *Subs.* by Act 47 of 1973.

Analogous provisions

Sections 45 and 50 in Part II of the Act correspond to Sections 8 and 37 of Part I of the Act.[14]

Scope and application

Under Section 45, the court will refer the parties to arbitration, unless it prima facie finds that the agreement referred to in Section 44 is null and void, inoperative or incapable of being performed.

The words "shall" and "unless" appearing in Section 45 mandate that before referring the parties to arbitration, the judicial authority should be satisfied that the arbitration agreement is not null and void, inoperative or incapable of being performed. Under Section 45 of the Act, the judicial authority has to mandatorily refer the parties to arbitration, if conditions specified in the section are fulfilled and the agreement is not found to be null and void, inoperative or incapable of being performed. In *Shin-Etsu Chemical Co. Ltd.* v. *Aksh Optifibre Ltd.*[15], it was evident that there had been no adjudication of the application by the trial court in terms of Section 45 of the Act. The trial court had not gone into the question, prima facie or finally, as to the agreement being null and void, inoperative or incapable of being performed, which was the objection raised by the first respondent in reply to the application of the appellant. Thus, on the ingredients of Section 45, there was no adjudication. Therefore, the direction of the High Court for fresh adjudication of application of the appellant having regard to the provisions of Section 45 of the Act could not be faulted.

When Chapter II is applicable, then any application filed by the party under the provisions of Chapter I and the order passed by the court on the aforesaid application is without jurisdiction, is nullity.[16]

Reference to arbitration is not an indefeasible right. One can claim reference only upon satisfaction of prerequisites stated under Sections 44 and 45 read with First Schedule of the Act.[17] If the judicial authority decides that the arbitration agreement produced before it is null and void, or inoperative or incapable of being performed, it has to refuse to refer the parties to arbitration.[18]

---

14. *Shin-Etsu Chemical Co. Ltd. (2)* v. *Vindhya Telelinks Ltd.*, (2009) 14 SCC 16.
15. *Ibid.*
16. *M.P. Oil Extraction Ltd.* v. *State Trading Corpn. of India*, 2015 SCC OnLine MP 5002: (2015) 3 MPLJ 197.
17. *Integrated Sales Services Ltd.* v. *DMC Management Consultants Ltd.*, 2016 SCC OnLine Bom 4445: (2016) 6 Mah LJ 195.
18. *Ibid.*

Only a prima facie view is required to be taken while dealing with application under Section 45 of the Act with regard to factors mentioned in Section 45.[19]

Neither Section 8 nor Section 45 of the Act restricts the inherent power of a court to entertain any action in a matter relating to arbitration agreements including any action challenging the validity, existence or scope thereof.[20]

Jurisdiction of the judicial authority which takes up petition under Section 45 is not ousted at threshold and such authority can refuse to refer the parties to arbitration if the agreement is null and void, inoperative or incapable of being performed and the validity of the agreement is open to scrutiny by the judicial authority.[21]

Where the reference to arbitration is rejected on the grounds available under Section 45, the court must afford full opportunity to parties to lead documentary or oral evidence they want to lead.[22]

Where there is a valid agreement, the judicial forum shall refer the dispute to tribunal. When there is no valid arbitration agreement, Section 45 is not applicable.[23]

Suit was filed for declaration that no valid arbitration agreement existed between the parties. There was an arbitration clause in the agreement, the dispute could not be said to be totally outside the purview of the arbitration clause, dispute was referred to arbitration.[24]

The court, while dealing with application under Section 45, is entitled to reject request to refer parties to arbitration only if it finds that the agreement is null and void, inoperative or incapable of being performed.[25] One of the circumstances when an arbitration agreement may become inoperative is when the dispute arising out of the underlying contract is solved.[26]

Where the settlement between the parties did not contain arbitration clause, the arbitration clause under the original agreement survived

19. *Shin-Etsu Chemical Co. Ltd.* v. *Vindhya Telelinks Ltd.*, 2011 SCC OnLine MP 446: (2012) 1 MP LJ 649.
20. *Chatterjee Petrochem (Mauritius) Co.* v. *Haldia Petrochemical Ltd.*, 2013 SCC OnLine Cal 9618: (2013) 3 Cal LT 1.
21. *J.S. Ocean Liner LLC* v. *M.V. Golden Progress*, 2007 SCC OnLine Bom 69: (2007) 2 Mah LJ 410.
22. *Caribjet Inc.* v. *AIR India Ltd.*, 2007 SCC OnLine Bom 175: (2007) 3 Mah LJ 166.
23. *Korp. Gems (India) (P) Ltd.* v. *Precious Diamond Ltd.*, 2006 SCC OnLine Cal 317: (2007) 2 CHN 544; see also, *Shivnath Rai Har Narain* v. *Italgrani SPA*, 2001 SCC OnLine Del 747: (2002) 63 DRJ 174.
24. *ITE India (P) Ltd.* v. *Mukesh Sharma*, 2005 SCC OnLine Del 1398: (2006) 87 DRJ 83.
25. *Andritz Oy.* v. *Enmas Engg. (P) Ltd.*, 2007 SCC OnLine Mad 461: (2007) 4 CTC 186; *Ramasamy Athappan* v. *International Chamber of Commerce*, 2008 SCC OnLine Mad 789: (2009) 3 LW 580.
26. *Ibid.*

settlement, the respondent was held bound by the award and could not challenge the same in India by filing a suit.[27]

The judicial remedy under Section 45 pertains to the pre-arbitral stage. A party to an international arbitration if legally aggrieved can approach the court of his natural jurisdiction to avoid the arbitration on the grounds that the agreement is null and void, inoperative and incapable of being performed. Under Section 45, in the case of international arbitration original jurisdiction to the civil court is given to test the legality of the arbitration agreement before the parties are directed to be subjected to arbitration.[28]

The expression "claiming through or under" in Section 45 of the Act cannot be construed so narrowly as to exclude the agents of the defendants.[29]

Referring the parties to arbitration—Necessary conditions

Section 45, Arbitration and Conciliation Act stipulates the requirements to a judicial authority when seized of an action to refer the parties to arbitration. The action must be in a matter in respect of which the parties have made an agreement referred to in Section 44. Further, the reference should be made at the request of one of the parties. Section 45 does not require the existence of the conditions referred to in Section 44(*b*). It naturally cannot, for Section 44(*b*) deals with a situation after the award is made whereas Section 45 deals with the position prior to even the reference being made.[30]

Nationality of the parties

Section 44(*a*) and correspondingly Section 45 of the Act do not limit the recognition of enforcement of the arbitration agreement qua the nationality of the parties. Indeed the New York Convention First Schedule to the Act does not contemplate such a limitation qua arbitration agreements.[31]

"Incapable of being performed"

Under Section 45 of the Act, if a court comes to the conclusion that matter in a suit is the subject-matter of an agreement under Section 44 of the Act, it shall refer the parties to arbitration on a request being made. Request, however, can be declined when the agreement is null and void, inoperative or incapable of being performed. The expression "incapable of being

27. *Interbulk Trading SA* v. *Adam and Coal Resources (P) Ltd.*, 2014 SCC OnLine Mad 8807: (2014) 5 CTC 689.
28. *Vikrant Tyres Ltd.* v. *Techno Export Foreign Trade Co. Ltd.*, 2005 SCC OnLine Kar 258.
29. *Virender Yadav* v. *Aerosvit Airlines*, 2008 SCC OnLine Del 968: (2008) 153 DLT 250.
30. *Rashmi Mehra* v. *EAC Trading Ltd.*, 2006 SCC OnLine Bom 1105: (2007) 2 Mah LJ 737.
31. *Ibid.*

performed" will include cases where the parties have waived or abandoned the arbitration clause by invoking jurisdiction of a civil court. In such a case where a party has decided to give go-by and novated the arbitration clause, they cannot later on be permitted to turn around and invoke the arbitration clause when civil proceedings are initiated by the other side.[32]

Section 45 applies to international commercial arbitration confined to contracting States under New York Convention and it empowers judicial authority to refuse to refer parties to arbitration, if it finds that the agreement is null and void, inoperative or incapable of being performed. Scope of Sections 45 and 54 is not limited to test existence and validity of the arbitration clause or arbitration agreement but also to something more, *viz.* whether such agreement is null and void, inoperative or incapable of being performed. Scope of enquiry under Section 45 by judicial authority is much wider than the one under Section 8.[33]

Even if Section 45 is invoked, the civil court would continue to have jurisdiction until it decides whether the arbitration agreement is void, inoperative or unlawful.[34]

Filing of original arbitration agreement not necessary

The appellant contended that under Section 8, Arbitration and Conciliation Act, 1996 it is necessary for the party making an application to refer the matter to arbitration, to provide the original agreement or a duly certified copy of the same. Section 45 of the Act deals with matters relating to international commercial arbitrations and Section 8 of the same does not have any relevance in the present appeal. Section 45 of the Act does not require the respondent to file the original of the charter party agreement.[35] Where duly authenticated copies of award and charter party are put in court, requirement of proof of award and agreement is satisfied. Award being a decree of court becomes enforceable as per Section 49.[36]

32. *Ministry of Sound International Ltd.* v. *Indus Renaissance Partners Entertainment (P) Ltd.*, 2009 SCC OnLine Del 11: (2009) 156 DLT 406.
33. *Andritz Oy.* v. *Enmas Engg. (P) Ltd.*, 2007 SCC OnLine Mad 461: (2007) 4 CTC 186.
34. *Global Mktg. Direct Ltd.* v. *GTL Ltd.*, 2004 SCC OnLine Bom 247: (2004) 3 Mah LJ 420.
35. *Shakti Bhog Foods Ltd.* v. *Kola Shipping Ltd.*, (2009) 2 SCC 134.
36. *Alagar Exports* v. *Islamic Republic of Iran, Shipping Lines of Tehran*, 2008 SCC OnLine Mad 751: 2008 Supp (1) Arb LR 228.

Determination of validity of arbitration agreement—Affidavits, oral evidence

Ordinarily applications under Section 45 shall be decided on the basis of affidavits and other relevant documents and without oral evidence. There may, however, be few exceptional cases where it may become necessary to grant opportunity to the parties to lead oral evidence. In both eventualities, the judicial authority is required to decide the issue expeditiously within a fixed time frame and not to treat such matters like regular civil suits.[37]

Appeal

An order refusing to refer the parties to arbitration under Section 45 is appealable while an order making a reference is not appealable.[38]

WHEN FOREIGN AWARD BINDING [S. 46]

46. *When foreign award binding.*—Any foreign award which would be enforceable under this Chapter shall be treated as binding for all purposes on the persons as between whom it was made, and may accordingly be relied on by any of those persons by way of defence, set-off or otherwise in any legal proceedings in India and any references in this Chapter to enforcing a foreign award shall be construed as including references to relying on an award.

COMMENTS

Corresponding old law

Section 46 reproduces in verbatim Section 4(2), Foreign Awards (Recognition and Enforcement) Act, 1961. The said Section 4, Foreign Awards (Recognition and Enforcement) Act, 1961 read as under:

4. *Effect of foreign awards.*—(1) A foreign award shall, subject to the provisions of this Act, be enforceable in India as if it were an award made on a matter referred to arbitration in India.

(2) Any foreign award which would be enforceable under this Act shall be treated as binding for all purposes on the persons as between whom it was made, and may accordingly be relied on by any of those persons by way of defence, set off or otherwise in any legal proceedings in India and any references in this Act to enforcing a foreign award shall be construed as including references to relying on an award.

37. *Shin-Etsu Chemical Co. Ltd.* v. *Aksh Optifibre Ltd.*, (2005) 7 SCC 234.
38. *Ibid.*

Scope and application

As provided by Section 46, any foreign award which would be enforceable under Chapter I of Part II of the Act shall be treated as binding for all purposes on the persons as between whom it was made and may be relied on by any of those persons by way of set off or defence and can be defined.

The Arbitration and Conciliation Act, 1996 provides for a single proceeding for deciding enforceability and execution of a foreign award. Two separate proceedings, one for deciding enforceability to make the foreign award rule of court or decree and the other to take up execution thereafter, are not contemplated.[39]

Foreign awards continue to remain an award in the country. It is deemed to be a decree only when the court to which the application is made for the enforcement of the foreign award is satisfied that the foreign award is enforceable. If after hearing the objections, the court rejects the application and is satisfied that the foreign award is enforceable, only then it becomes a deemed decree of the court. As such these will not be proceedings in execution or distress as contemplated by Section 22, Sick Industrial Companies (Special Provisions) Act, 1985.[40]

Foreign award—Meaning of

See, comments under Section 44 ante.

Petition for enforcement of foreign award—Disputes with third parties cannot be decided

In petition under Sections 46 to 49 for enforcement of foreign award(s), the enforcement had necessarily to be between the parties to the award. In such proceedings, serious disputes regarding the liability of third persons to pay up could not be decided. Provisions contained in Part II of the 1996 Act do not permit courts to decide such disputes with third parties in such proceedings.[41]

EVIDENCE [S. 47]

47. *Evidence.*—(1) The party applying for the enforcement of a foreign award shall, at the time of the application, produce before the Court—

39. *Fuerst Day Lawson Ltd.* v. *Jindal Exports Ltd.*, (2001) 6 SCC 356.
40. *Tropic Shipping Co. Ltd.* v. *Kothari Global Ltd.*, 2001 SCC OnLine Bom 889: (2002) 2 Mah LJ 585.
41. *Fargo Freight Ltd.* v. *Commodities Exchange Corpn.*, (2004) 7 SCC 203.

(*a*) the original award or a copy thereof, duly authenticated in the manner required by the law of the country in which it was made;

(*b*) the original agreement for arbitration or a duly certified copy thereof; and

(*c*) such evidence as may be necessary to prove that the award is a foreign award.

(2) If the award or agreement to be produced under sub-section (1) is in a foreign language, the party seeking to enforce the award shall produce a translation into English certified as correct by a diplomatic or consular agent of the country to which that party belongs or certified as correct in such other manner as may be sufficient according to the law in force in India.

[42][*Explanation*.—In this section and in the sections following in this Chapter, "Court" means the High Court having original jurisdiction to decide the questions forming the subject-matter of the arbitral award if the same had been the subject-matter of a suit on its original civil jurisdiction and in other cases, in the High Court having jurisdiction to hear appeals from decrees of courts subordinate to such High Court.]

COMMENTS

Corresponding old law

Section 47 corresponds to and reproduces in verbatim sub-sections (1) and (2) of Section 8, Foreign Awards (Recognition and Enforcement) Act, 1961. The said Section 8, Foreign Awards (Recognition and Enforcement) Act, 1961 provided as under:

8. *Evidence*.—(1) The party applying for the enforcement of a foreign award shall, at the time of the application, produce—

(*a*) the original award or a copy thereof, duly authenticated in the manner required by the law of the country in which it was made;

(*b*) the original agreement for arbitration or a duly certified copy thereof; and

(*c*) such evidence as may be necessary to prove that the award is a foreign award.

42. *Subs.* by Act 3 of 2016, S. 21 (w.r.e.f. 23-10-2015). Prior to substitution it read as:

"*Explanation*.—In this section and all the following sections of this Chapter, "Court" means the Principal Civil Court of Original Jurisdiction in a district, and includes the High Court in exercise of its ordinary original civil jurisdiction, having jurisdiction over the subject-matter of the award if the same had been the subject-matter of a suit, but does not include any civil court of a grade inferior to such Principal Civil Court, or any Court of Small Causes."

(2) If the award or agreement requiring to be produced under sub-section (1) is in a foreign language, the party seeking to enforce the award shall produce a translation into English certified as correct by a diplomatic or consular agent of the country to which that party belongs or certified as correct in such other manner as may be sufficient according to the law in force in India.

Legislative changes

Arbitration and Conciliation (Amendment) Act, 2015 (3 of 2016)

The present new Explanation has been substituted for the old Explanation by the Amendment Act 3 of 2016. The amendment has been made in Section 47 to provide that the court referred to in the section means the High Court.

OBJECTS AND REASONS

Clause 21 of the Bill seeks to substitute the *Explanation* in Section 47 of the principal Act to provide that the Court referred to in that section to mean the High Court.

Scope and application

Enforcement of a foreign award can be upon three requirements, *viz.* filing of the original award, the certified copy of the original agreement and the evidence showing that it is a foreign award under Section 47. Enforcement of the foreign award can be refused if the enforcement was contrary to the public policy of India.[43]

Party seeking enforcement of a foreign award has to give evidence that the award was a foreign award while a party resisting enforcement of foreign award has to give proof in support of the grounds for the same. A party resisting enforcement of a foreign award is expected to furnish proof of a somewhat higher degree and thus to step in accordance with Sections 47–49. There was no question of making the award as a rule of the court/decree again.[44]

This section casts a greater burden on such party than the burden on the party who seeks enforcement of a foreign award who is only expected to produce necessary evidence.[45]

Winding up proceeding on the basis of a foreign award will lead to protracted litigation. So the winding up petition was dismissed, petitioner

43. *Wireless Developers Inc.* v. *Indiagames Ltd.*, 2012 SCC OnLine Bom 115: (2012) 3 Mah LJ 449.
44. *Narayan Trading Co.* v. *Abcom Trading (P) Ltd.*, 2012 SCC OnLine MP 8645: (2013) 2 MP LJ 252.
45. *Integrated Sales Services Ltd.* v. *Arun Dev*, 2017 SCC OnLine Bom 1: (2017) 1 Mah LJ 681.

was given liberty in accordance with the provisions of Part II Chapter I of the 1996 Act.[46]

To maintain a petition under Section 47 to enforce a foreign award, leave under clause 12 of the Letters Patent is required.[47]

The holder of a foreign award need not take out two proceedings; one for directing the enforceability of the award and the other for its execution. Such an award can be directly put in execution and the executing court will be entitled to execute it upon considering whether the award complies with the provisions of Part II, Chapter I in relation to New York Convention Awards and Chapter II in relation to Geneva Convention Awards as may be applicable. Where foreign awards are put in execution under Section 44-A CPC, also the procedure does not contemplate two separate proceedings, one for deciding the enforceability of the foreign decree/award and the other for its execution.[48]

Where assets and properties of the judgment-debtor are situated within the territorial jurisdiction of the court, the provisions of Order 21 Rule 30 CPC are applicable, the court has territorial jurisdiction to proceed with the petition.[49]

The respondent, despite service of notices, had chosen not to appear. The terms of the contracts were very simple, and had been interpreted rightly by the arbitrator. The award satisfied the requirements of Sections 47 and 48. Foreign award shall be deemed to be decree of the court, shall be executed in India.[50]

The rights of the judgment-debtor under Sections 34 and 48(2)(*b*) are similar. He would be heard on merits of his claim that the foreign award is against the public policy of India.[51]

Excess of jurisdiction

Arbitration agreement was governed by "the laws of England" as provided by Article 34.12 of the Production Sharing Contract (PSC). As the seat of arbitration was in Kuala Lumpur, Malaysia, curial law would be Malaysian

46. *Vinayak Oil & Fats (P) Ltd.* v. *Andre (Cayman Islands) Trading Co. Ltd.*, 2004 SCC OnLine Cal 438: (2005) 2 CHN 29.
47. *Tata International Ltd.* v. *Trisuns Chemical Industry Ltd.*, 2001 SCC OnLine Bom 905: (2002) 2 Mah LJ 242.
48. *Euro-Asia Chartering Corpn. (PTE) Ltd.* v. *Fortune International Ltd.*, 2002 SCC OnLine Bom 519: (2002) 4 Mah LJ 179.
49. *Motorola INC* v. *Modi Wellvest*, 2004 SCC OnLine Del 1094: (2005) 79 DRJ 173.
50. *APL Co. (P) Ltd.* v. *Varadariya Exporters*, 2014 SCC OnLine Mad 807: (2014) 3 MWN (Civ) 475.
51. *Wireless Developers Inc.* v. *Indiagames Ltd.*, 2012 SCC OnLine Bom 115: (2012) 3 Mah LJ 449.

law. Article 34.12 of the PSC provides that the arbitration agreement contained in Article 34 shall be governed by the laws of England. Even though the substantive law of contract was Indian law, it would not be applicable for deciding the challenge to the issue of excess of jurisdiction.[52]

"May"

The word "shall" in Section 47 relating to production of evidence at the time of application has to be read as "may". At the initial stage of filing of application for enforcement of award, non-compliance of production of documents should not entail dismissal of application.[53]

Execution of foreign award

After the commencement of the 2015 Amendment Act, execution proceedings pending before the District Court shall be decided by the High Court concerned.[54]

International commercial arbitration

In international commercial arbitration, an award passed will be enforceable in High Court under Section 10, Commercial Courts Act, 2015 and not in District Court under Section 10(2) or Section 10(3).[55]

Production of original award or copy thereof

The party applying for enforcement of a foreign award must, at the time of filing application, produce before the court the original award or copy thereof.[56]

Limitation

The period of limitation for filing a petition for enforcement of a foreign award under Sections 47 and 49 would be governed by Article 137 of the Limitation Act, 1963 which prescribes a period of three years from when right to apply accrues.[57]

52. *Union of India* v. *Vedanta Ltd.*, (2020) 10 SCC 1.
53. *PEC Ltd.* v. *Austbulk Shipping Sdn. Bhd.*, (2019) 11 SCC 620.
54. *OCI Corpn.* v. *Kandla Export Corpn.*, 2016 SCC OnLine Guj 5981.
55. *Dakshin Haryana Bijli Vitran Nigam Ltd.* v. *Navigant Technologies (P) Ltd.*, (2021) 7 SCC 657.
56. *Hugo Neu Corpn.* v. *Lloyds Steel Industries Ltd.*, 2009 SCC OnLine Bom 785: (2009) 5 Mah LJ 902.
57. *Union of India* v. *Vedanta Ltd.*, (2020) 10 SCC 1.

Notice to opposite party

Rules and principles of natural justice are embodied in Section 48, and therefore, when a party applies seeking enforcement of a foreign award, notice has to be given to the opposite party intimating that such an application has been filed in the court seeking enforcement of the award. On service of notice the court shall hear the parties in order to determine and record its satisfaction and at that stage, the court would examine the existence or otherwise of the two conditions as found in Section 48(2) as also the objection if filed by the party under Section 48(1) of the Act is disposed of by recording satisfaction as envisaged in Section 49 of the Act.[58]

Letters Patent Appeal

In case of dismissal of petition seeking execution, appeal against the decision is not maintainable under the provision of Act but the impugned decision affecting valuable rights of the parties is therefore a judgement subject to Letter Patent Appeal. Appeal directed to be registered as Letter Patent Appeal.[59]

CONDITIONS FOR ENFORCEMENT OF FOREIGN AWARDS [S. 48]

48. *Conditions for enforcement of foreign awards.*—(1) Enforcement of a foreign award may be refused, at the request of the party against whom it is invoked, only if that party furnishes to the Court proof that—

(*a*) the parties to the agreement referred to in Section 44 were, under the law applicable to them, under some incapacity, or the said agreement is not valid under the law to which the parties have subjected it or, failing any indication thereon, under the law of the country where the award was made; or

(*b*) the party against whom the award is invoked was not given proper notice of the appointment of the arbitrator or of the arbitral proceedings or was otherwise unable to present his case; or

(*c*) the award deals with a difference not contemplated by or not falling within the terms of the submission to arbitration, or it contains decisions on matters beyond the scope of the submission to arbitration:

Provided that, if the decisions on matters submitted to arbitration can be separated from those not so submitted, that part of the award which

58. *Fuerst Day Lawson Ltd.* v. *Jindal Exports Ltd.*, 1999 SCC OnLine Del 128: (1999) 50 DRJ 374.

59. *Jindal Exports Ltd.* v. *Fuerst Day Lawson Ltd.*, 1999 SCC OnLine Del 675: (1999) 51 DRJ 170.

contains decisions on matters submitted to arbitration may be enforced; or

(*d*) the composition of the arbitral authority or the arbitral procedure was not in accordance with the agreement of the parties, or, failing such agreement, was not in accordance with the law of the country where the arbitration took place; or

(*e*) the award has not yet become binding on the parties, or has been set aside or suspended by a competent authority of the country in which, or under the law of which, that award was made.

(2) Enforcement of an arbitral award may also be refused if the Court finds that—

(*a*) the subject-matter of the difference is not capable of settlement by arbitration under the law of India; or

(*b*) the enforcement of the award would be contrary to the public policy of India.

[60][*Explanation 1.*—For the avoidance of any doubt, it is clarified that an award is in conflict with the public policy of India, only if,—

(*i*) the making of the award was induced or affected by fraud or corruption or was in violation of Section 75 or Section 81; or

(*ii*) it is in contravention with the fundamental policy of Indian law; or

(*iii*) it is in conflict with the most basic notions of morality or justice.

Explanation 2.—For the avoidance of doubt, the test as to whether there is a contravention with the fundamental policy of Indian law shall not entail a review on the merits of the dispute.]

(3) If an application for the setting aside or suspension of the award has been made to a competent authority referred to in clause (*e*) of sub-section (1) the Court may, if it considers it proper, adjourn the decision on the enforcement of the award and may also, on the application of the party claiming enforcement of the award, order the other party to give suitable security.

COMMENTS

Corresponding old law

Section 48 of the Act reproduces the provisions of Section 7, Foreign Awards (Recognition and Enforcement) Act 1961. The said section provided as under:

---

60. *Subs.* by Act 3 of 2016, S. 22 (w.r.e.f. 23-10-2015). Prior to substitution it read as:

"*Explanation.*—Without prejudice to the generality of clause (*b*) of this section, it is hereby declared, for the avoidance of any doubt, that an award is in conflict with the public policy of India if the making of the award was induced or affected by fraud or corruption."

7. *Conditions for enforcement of foreign awards.*—(1) A foreign award may not be enforced under this Act—

(*a*) if the party against whom it is sought to enforce the award proves to the court dealing with the case that—

(*i*) the parties to the agreement were under the law applicable to them, under some incapacity, or the said agreement is not valid under the law to which the parties have subjected it, or failing any indication thereon, under the law of the country where the award was made; or

(*ii*) the party was not given proper notice of the appointment of the arbitrator or of the arbitration proceedings or was otherwise unable to present his case; or

(*iii*) the award deals with questions not referred or contains decisions on matters beyond the scope of the agreement:

Provided that if the decisions on matters submitted to arbitration can be separated from those not submitted, that part of the award which contains decisions on matters submitted to arbitration may be enforced; or

(*iv*) the composition of the arbitral authority or the arbitral procedure was not in accordance with the agreement of the parties or, failing such agreement was not in accordance with the law of the country where the arbitration took place; or

(*v*) the award has not yet become binding on the parties or has been set aside or suspended by a competent authority of the country in which, or under the law of which, that award was made; or

(*b*) if the Court dealing with the case is satisfied that—

(*i*) the subject-matter of the difference is not capable of settlement by arbitration under the law of India; or

(*ii*) the enforcement of the award will be contrary to the public policy.

(2) If the Court before which a foreign award is sought to be relied upon is satisfied that an application for the setting aside or suspension of the award has been made to a competent authority referred to in sub-clause (*v*) of clause (*a*) of sub-section (1), the court may, if it deems proper, adjourn the decision on the enforcement of the award and may also, on the application of the party claiming enforcement of the award, order the other party to furnish suitable security.

Legislative changes

Arbitration and Conciliation (Amendment) Act, 2015 (3 of 2016)

Explanation under sub-section (2) has been substituted by two Explanations 1 and 2. Amended Explanation 1 provides that an award is in conflict with the public policy of India only if the making of the award was induced or affected by fraud or corruption or was in violation of Section 75 or Section 81 or is in contravention with the fundamental policy of Indian law or is in conflict with the most basic notions of morality or justice. New Explanation 2 explains that the test as to whether there is contravention with the fundamental policy of India shall not entail a review on the merits of the dispute.

OBJECTS AND REASONS

Clause 24 of the Bill seeks to amend Section 57 of the principal Act to provide for *Explanation* to the term "public policy of India" in clause (*e*) of sub-section (1) by amending the existing *Explanation* to the effect that an arbitral award is in conflict with the public policy of India only if the making of award was induced or affected by fraud or corruption or was in violation of Section 75 or Section 81; or is in contravention with the fundamental policy of Indian law; or it is in conflict with the most basic notions of morality or justice. *Explanation* 2 is inserted to explain that the test as to whether there is a contravention with the fundamental policy of Indian law shall not entail a review on the merits of the dispute.

Scope and application

The real purpose of Section 48 is to ensure that at some stage, whether pre-award, post-award or both, a judicial authority must decide the validity, operation and capability of performance of the arbitration agreement. In various cases the parties may not resort to Section 45 in the first place, and to overcome such eventuality, the legislature has enacted Section 48(1)(*a*). If the court is not asked to satisfy itself as to the validity of the agreement at a pre-award stage (Section 45), then by virtue of Section 48, it is given another opportunity to do so. Apart from this, under Section 48, the court may refuse to enforce the foreign award on the ground other than the invalidity of the arbitration agreement.[61] Existence of arbitration agreement is *sine qua non* to constitute foreign award.[62] The court has to record its satisfaction that such foreign award is binding upon the parties before it and is enforceable in India.[63]

The enforcement court may "refuse" enforcement of a foreign award, but cannot correct errors or set aside awards even if the conditions under Section 48 are fulfilled.[64] Enforcement of a foreign award cannot be denied

61. *Shin-Etsu Chemical Co. Ltd.* v. *Aksh Optifibre Ltd.*, (2005) 7 SCC 234.
62. *Ibid.*
63. *Integrated Sales Services Ltd.* v. *DMC Management Consultants Ltd.*, 2016 SCC OnLine Bom 4445: (2016) 6 Mah LJ 195.
64. *Union of India* v. *Vedanta Ltd.*, (2020) 10 SCC 1.

when all essential terms of agreement are agreed between the parties and proved.[65]

Remanding the matter to the ICC arbitrator to pass a fresh award is clearly outside the jurisdiction of an enforcing court under Section 48 of the 1996 Act.[66]

Section 48 envisages certain conditions for enforcement of foreign awards. Award is deemed to be a decree of the court and must be executed when conditions for enforcement are fulfilled and the court is satisfied about the enforceability of foreign award.[67] A foreign award cannot be recognised or enforced if it is contrary to:

1. fundamental policy of India;
2. interests of India; or
3. justice or morality.

In *Force Shipping Ltd.* v. *Ashapura Minechem Ltd.*[68], the term of the contract itself provided the manner in which the awards was to be enforced. None of the parties gave notice to the tribunal that reasons be given. Award made in London was enforceable in India.

Mere pleadings without any proof is not sufficient to refuse enforcement. Errors that can be corrected in proceedings challenging foreign award on merits by themselves would not constitute grounds to assail execution of such award.[69]

A foreign award cannot be challenged in India. Section 48 of the 1996 Act gives a right to the award-holder to enforce the award coupled with a right to the losing party to resist such action on the grounds that may be available to him. The losing party has no right to challenge the award in India. Indian law would have no role to play when the parties expressly agreed that they would have sitting of arbitration abroad where Indian law would have no force.[70] Award passed by Arbitral Tribunal in Singapore cannot be set aside under Section 48 by Indian courts.[71]

---

65. *Falcon Progress Ltd.* v. *Sara International Ltd.*, 2017 SCC OnLine Del 6989: (2017) 238 DLT 565.
66. *Centrotrade Minerals & Metals Inc.* v. *Hindustan Copper Ltd.*, (2020) 19 SCC 197.
67. *Videocon Power Ltd.* v. *T.N. Electricity Board*, 2004 SCC OnLine Mad 807: (2004) 5 CTC 668.
68. 2003 SCC OnLine Bom 291: (2003) 4 Mah LJ 329.
69. *Integrated Sales Services Ltd.* v. *Arun Dev*, 2017 SCC OnLine Bom 1: (2017) 1 Mah LJ 681.
70. *Coal India Ltd.* v. *Canadian Commercial Corpn.*, 2013 SCC OnLine Cal 778: (2013) 2 CHN 494.
71. *Interbulk Trading SA* v. *Adam and Coal Resources (P) Ltd.*, 2014 SCC OnLine Mad 8807: (2014) 5 CTC 689; *Videocon Power Ltd.* v. *T.N. Electricity Board*, 2004 SCC OnLine Mad 807: (2004) 5 CTC 668.

Application for leading oral evidence to furnish proof of the foreign award was filed in court. It was held, the whole object of the Act would be defeated if the application was allowed. Application was dismissed.[72]

Person against whom an award is published has the right to contest by pointing out that the conditions enumerated in Section 48 have not been fulfilled.[73]

The tribunal did not act contrary to contract nor had exceeded its jurisdiction. Foreign award was held proper.[74]

Once the requirements of Section 47 are complied with by the petitioner, it is for the respondent to prove that the award is unenforceable as per Section 48 of the Act.[75]

Where international arbitration has taken place outside India and foreign award is sought to be enforced in India, there cannot be presumption that the jurisdiction of the International Arbitral Tribunal to rule on its own jurisdiction stands excluded.[76]

Section 48 does not contain any ground for resisting enforcement of a foreign award based upon the foreign award being contrary to the substantive law agreed to by the parties and which it is to apply in reaching its conclusion.[77]

Perversity as a ground to set aside an award in an international commercial arbitration held in India no longer obtains after the 2015 Amendment to the Arbitration and Conciliation Act, 1996. Section 48, Arbitration and Conciliation Act, 1996 has also been amended in the same manner as Section 34 of the Act. The ground of "patent illegality appearing on the face of the award" is an independent ground of challenge which applies only to awards made under Part I which do not involve international commercial arbitrations. Thus, the "public policy of India" ground after the 2015 Amendment does not take within its scope, "perversity of an award" as a ground to set aside an award in an international commercial arbitration under Section 34, Arbitration and Conciliation Act, 1996; and concomitantly as a ground to refuse enforcement of a foreign award under

72. *Emkay Global Financial Services Ltd.* v. *Girdhar Sondhi*, (2018) 9 SCC 49; *Sial Bioenergie* v. *SBEC Systems*, 2004 SCC OnLine Del 863: (2005) 79 DRJ 156.
73. *Vinayak Oil & Fats (P) Ltd.* v. *Andre (Cayman Islands) Trading Co. Ltd.*, 2004 SCC OnLine Cal 438: (2005) 2 CHN 29.
74. *Sleepwell Industries Co. Ltd.* v. *LMJ International Ltd.*, 2018 SCC OnLine Cal 4676 : (2018) 3 Cal LT 312.
75. *SIMS Metal Management Ltd.* v. *Sabari Exim (P) Ltd.*, 2014 SCC OnLine Mad 9883: (2014) 4 LW 747.
76. *Integrated Sales Services Ltd.* v. *Arun Dev*, 2017 SCC OnLine Bom 1: (2017) 1 Mah LJ 681.
77. *Gemini Bay Transcription (P) Ltd.* v. *Integrated Sales Service Ltd.*, (2022) 1 SCC 753.

Section 48, being a pari materia provision which appears in Part II of the Arbitration and Conciliation Act.[78]

Parties to the agreement [S. 48(1)(*a*) and (*b*)]

While provisions of Section 48(1)(*a*) refer to parties to agreement referred to in Section 44, provisions of Section 48(1)(*b*) refer to a party against whom award is invoked. Section 48(1)(*b*) would, therefore, take within its compass non-signatories to arbitration agreement. In other words, a non-signatory to the agreement could also be a party against whom an award is sought to be invoked. Thus, enforcement of a foreign award against a party who is a non-signatory but a party to the award is also satisfactorily recognised.[79]

A foreign award can be enforced against non-signatories to an arbitration agreement.[80]

"Contrary to the public policy of India" [Sub-s. (2), Cl. (*b*)]

Enforcement of foreign award may be refused if the award is contrary to the public policy of India.[81] The expression "public policy of India" used in Section 48(2)(*b*) has to be given a wider meaning and the award can be set aside, "if it is patently illegal".[82]

Enforcement of foreign awards would be refused under Section 48(2)(*b*) only if such enforcement would be contrary to fundamental policy of Indian law or the interests of India or justice or morality. Appellants neither made out a case of violation of procedural due process in conduct of arbitral proceedings nor made out as to how award is in conflict with basic notions of justice, or in violation of substantive public policy of India. Disputes raised by respondents-claimants emanated from the rights and obligations of parties under PSC. Award was not contrary to fundamental policy of Indian law, or in conflict with notions of justice. Award was not set out.[83]

An award of the arbitrator is contrary to the public policy of India, when the award is in contravention with the fundamental policy of Indian law.[84]

78. *Ibid.*
79. *Integrated Sales Services Ltd.* v. *Arun Dev*, 2017 SCC OnLine Bom 1: (2017) 1 Mah LJ 681; *Gemini Bay Transcription (P) Ltd.* v. *Integrated Sales Service Ltd.*, (2022) 1 SCC 753.
80. *Gemini Bay Transcription (P) Ltd.* v. *Integrated Sales Service Ltd.*, (2022) 1 SCC 753.
81. *Marco Shipping Agency* v. *R. Piyarelal International*, 2008 SCC OnLine Cal 602: (2008) 4 CHN 520; *Force Shipping Ltd.* v. *Ashapura Minechem Ltd.*, 2003 SCC OnLine Bom 291: (2003) 4 Mah LJ 329.
82. *Phulchand Exports Ltd.* v. *O.O.O. Patriot*, (2011) 10 SCC 300; *ONGC Ltd.* v. *Saw Pipes Ltd.*, (2003) 5 SCC 705.
83. *Ibid.*
84. *Ibid.*

Non-applicants 2 and 3 had neither submitted themselves to the arbitration nor to the composition of the International Arbitration Tribunal, award cannot be enforced in India against them by making a decree of court.[85]

"Proof"—Requirement of

The expression "proof" cannot possibly mean the taking of oral evidence as it will otherwise defeat the object of speedy disposal of Section 34 petitions. Given that foreign awards in New York Convention countries need to be enforced as speedily as possible, the same logic would apply to Section 48, as a result of which the expression "proof" in Section 48 would only mean "established on the basis of the record of the Arbitral Tribunal" and such other matters as are relevant to the grounds contained in Section 48.[86]

Absence of hearing [Sub-s. (1)]

Absence of hearing is one of the potent grounds of attack for non-enforceability of a foreign award. When the award itself is in question, recitals in the award about service of notice cannot be accepted. Fax transmissions having been received were denied by the judgment-debtor. Primary evidence was not produced, no explanation for production of only secondary evidence was given. It was held, the award of the arbitrator for want of hearing was vitiated.[87]

Absence of reasons

Section 48(1)(*b*) does not speak of absence of reasons in an arbitral award at all. The only grounds on which a foreign award cannot be enforced under Section 48(1)(*b*) are natural justice grounds relatable to notice of appointment of the arbitrator or of the arbitral proceedings, or that a party was otherwise unable to present its case before the Arbitral Tribunal, all of which are events anterior to the making of the award.[88]

"Was otherwise unable to present his case"

Expression "was otherwise unable to present his case" occurring in Section 48(1)(*b*) would apply at hearing stage and not after the award has

85. *Integrated Sales Services Ltd.* v. *DMC Management Consultants Ltd.*, 2016 SCC OnLine Bom 4445: (2016) 6 Mah LJ 195.
86. *Gemini Bay Transcription (P) Ltd.* v. *Integrated Sales Service Ltd.*, (2022) 1 SCC 753.
87. *Alagar Exports* v. *Islamic Republic of Iran, Shipping Lines of Tehran*, 2008 SCC OnLine Mad 751: 2008 Supp (1) Arb LR 228.
88. *Gemini Bay Transcription (P) Ltd.* v. *Integrated Sales Service Ltd.*, (2022) 1 SCC 753.

been delivered. Failure to consider material issue would not fall within the rubric of Section 48(1)(*b*).[89]

Foreign award—Resistance to enforcement

Transactions which violate Foreign Exchange Management Act, 1999 are not void, nor violative of the fundamental policy of Indian law. Since the award is not void on the ground of violation of FEMA Regulations or Rules, the question of non-enforcement of award on that ground did not arise.[90]

Foreign Award—Enforcement of

Enforcement of a foreign award can be refused only if it is found to be contrary to 1) the fundamental policy of Indian law; 2) interests of India; and 3) justice or morality.[91]

Enforcement of foreign award in foreign court—Injunction granted by Indian court

Respondent 1 could not have pursued the enforcement proceedings in the District Court in Michigan, US in the teeth of the injunction granted by the courts in India which also, on the basis of the comity of courts, should have been respected by the District Courts in Michigan, US. Even though the High Court had only restrained the respondent from effecting transfer of the shares pending further orders by the city civil court, Secunderabad, after the restraint orders of the trial court as well as limited order of the High Court, the first respondent ought not to have proceeded with the issue before the District Court, Michigan without getting the interim orders/direction of in Indian courts/vacated.[92]

Review on the merits of dispute (Expl. 2)

In view of *Explanation* 2 of Section 48, review of award on the ground that it is in contravention with the fundamental policy of India is prohibited.[93]

---

89. *Vijay Karia* v. *Prysmian Cavi E Sistemi SRL*, (2020) 11 SCC 1.
90. *Ibid.*
91. *Daiichi Sankyo Co. Ltd.* v. *Malvinder Mohan Singh*, 2018 SCC OnLine Del 6869 : (2018) 247 DLT 405.
92. *Venture Global Engg.* v. *Satyam Computer Services Ltd.*, (2008) 4 SCC 190.
93. *Integrated Sales Services Ltd.* v. *Arun Dev*, 2017 SCC OnLine Bom 1: (2017) 1 Mah LJ 681.

Indian courts have no jurisdiction to set aside a foreign award by taking recourse to Section 48

Indian courts have no jurisdiction to set aside a foreign award by taking recourse to Section 48.[94]

Enforcement court cannot set aside/correct errors in foreign award

Enforcement court may "refuse" enforcement of a foreign award but cannot set aside or correct errors in the award even if conditions under Section 48 are made out.[95]

Jurisdiction of the Supreme Court

In case(s) of foreign award, the Supreme Court should not interfere unless and until some new or unique point is raised and remains answered and in very exceptional cases of blatant disregard of Section 48 of the Act. In a very recent case the Supreme Court held thus:

> [I]t is important to emphasise that, unlike Section 37 of the Arbitration Act, which is contained in Part I of the said Act, and which provides an appeal against either *setting aside* or *refusing to set aside* a 'domestic' arbitration award, the legislative policy so far as recognition and enforcement of foreign awards is that an appeal is provided against a judgment refusing to recognise and enforce a foreign award but *not* the other way around (*i.e.* an order recognising and enforcing an award). This is because the policy of the legislature is that there ought to be only one bite at the cherry in a case where objections are made to the foreign award on the extremely narrow grounds contained in Section 48 of the Act and which have been rejected. This is in consonance with the fact that India is a signatory to the Convention on the Recognition and Enforcement of Foreign Arbitral Awards, 1958 and intends—through this legislation—to ensure that a person who belongs to a Convention country, and who, in most cases, has gone through a challenge procedure to the said award in the country of its origin, must then be able to get such award recognised and enforced in India as soon as possible. This is so that such person may enjoy the fruits of an award which has been challenged and which challenge has been turned down in the country of its origin, subject to grounds to resist enforcement being made out under Section 48 of the Arbitration Act. Bearing this in mind, it is important to remember that the Supreme Court's jurisdiction under Article 136 should not be used to circumvent the legislative policy so contained. We are saying this because this matter has been argued for several days before us as if it was a first appeal from a judgment recognising and enforcing a foreign award. Given the restricted parameters of Article 136, it is important to note that in cases

94. *Adam & Coal Resources (P) Ltd.* v. *Interbulk Trading*, 2014 SCC OnLine Mad 8808: (2014) 4 LW 833.
95. *Ibid.*

like the present—where no appeal is granted against a judgment which recognises and enforces a foreign award—this Court should be very slow in interfering with such judgments, and should entertain an appeal only with a view to settle the law if some new or unique point is raised which has not been answered by the Supreme Court before, so that the Supreme Court judgment may then be used to guide the course of future litigation in this regard. Also, it would only be in a very exceptional case of a blatant disregard of Section 48 of the Arbitration Act that the Supreme Court would interfere with a judgment which recognises and enforces a foreign award however inelegantly drafted the judgment may be.[96]

ENFORCEMENT OF FOREIGN AWARDS [S. 49]

49. *Enforcement of foreign awards.*—Where the Court is satisfied that the foreign award is enforceable under this Chapter, the award shall be deemed to be a decree of that Court.

COMMENTS

Corresponding old law

Section 49 is the verbatim reproduction of Section 6(1), Foreign Awards (Recognition and Enforcement) Act, 1961 with marginal changes. The said section provided as under:

6. *Enforcement of foreign award.*—(1) Where the Court is satisfied that the foreign award is enforceable under this Act, the Court shall order the award to be filed and shall proceed to pronounce judgment according to the award.

Scope and application

Section 49 provides that when the court in India is satisfied that the foreign award is enforceable under Part II, Chapter I of the 1996 Act, the foreign award shall be deemed to be a decree of that court. In case of a foreign award before the court decides to enforce the award, the executing court must be satisfied that the foreign award is enforceable.[97] Section 49, Arbitration and Conciliation Act, 1996 merely empowers the court to declare that the foreign award is enforceable under the provisions of Chapter II of the Arbitration and Conciliation Act, 1996. The moment such a declaration is granted, an award shall be deemed to be decree of the court. Once it is deemed to be a decree

96. *Vijay Karia* v. *Prysmian Cavi E Sistemi SRL*, (2020) 11 SCC 1.
97. *International Investor KCSC (Kuwait)* v. *Sanghi Polyesters Ltd.*, 2001 SCC OnLine AP 1527.

of the court, it is open to the parties to seek its execution in accordance with the provisions of CPC.[98]

Where the judgment-debtor had means to pay the decree-amount, the order for arrest and detention of the judgment-debtor was proper.[99]

Foreign award—Grant of interest

In the case of foreign award(s), the interest has to be restricted for the purpose of enforcement in India to the interest contained in the award.[100]

Recovery of costs

At the time when enforcement of the award was applied for, the award in respect of the costs was not filed. It was held that would not stand in the way of recovery of costs.[101]

Enforcement of foreign award—Limitation

The period of limitation for filing a petition for enforcement of a foreign award under Sections 47 and 49, would be governed by Article 137 of the Limitation Act, 1963 which prescribes a period of three years from when the right to apply accrues.[102]

Petition for winding up of a company

A decree-holder would not cease to be a creditor. The liability is only crystallised in the form of a decree or award. A creditor has the right to invoke the provisions of the Companies Act, 2015. He will have a right to either execute a decree or file an application under Section 433, Companies Act for winding up of a company.[103]

Commercial Courts Act, 2015

In arbitration cases of enforcement of foreign awards, no appeal lies under Section 50. Hence, appeal under Section 13, Commercial Courts Act is not maintainable.[104]

---

98. *Toepfer International Asia (P) Ltd.* v. *Thapar Ispat Ltd.*, 1999 SCC OnLine Bom 271: (2000) 2 Mah LJ 331.
99. *Peniel Cashew Co.* v. *Ahcom Sarl*, 2023 SCC OnLine Ker 720 : (2023) 2 KLT 168.
100. *Tropic Shipping Co. Ltd.* v. *Kothari Global Ltd.*, 2001 SCC OnLine Bom 889: (2002) 2 Mah LJ 585.
101. *Ibid.*
102. *Union of India* v. *Vedanta Ltd.*, (2020) 10 SCC 1.
103. *SIMS Metal Management Ltd.* v. *Sabari Exim (P) Ltd.*, 2015 SCC OnLine Mad 8847: (2015) 3 LW 563.
104. *Kandla Export Corpn.* v. *OCI Corpn.*, (2018) 14 SCC 715.

Letters Patent Appeal

Letters Patent Appeal against judgment of a Single Judge in an international arbitration matter is maintainable before the Division Bench.[105]

APPEALABLE ORDERS [S. 50]

50. *Appealable orders.*—(1) [106][Notwithstanding anything contained in any other law for the time being in force, an appeal] shall lie from the order refusing to—

(*a*) refer the parties to arbitration under Section 45;

(*b*) enforce a foreign award under Section 48;

to the Court authorised by law to hear appeals from such order.

(2) No second appeal shall lie from an order passed in appeal under this section, but nothing in this section shall affect or take away any right to appeal to the Supreme Court.

COMMENTS

Corresponding old law

Section 50 is new, and did not find place in the Arbitration Act, 1940.

Legislative changes

Arbitration and Conciliation (Amendment) Act, 2019 (33 of 2019)

In Section 50 of the principal Act, in sub-section (1), for the words "An appeal", the words "Notwithstanding anything contained in any other law for the time being in force, an appeal" shall be substituted.

Analogous provisions

Sections 45 and 50 in Part II of the Act correspond to Sections 8 and 37 of Part I of the Act.[107]

Scope and application

The appellate court can examine whether the enforcement of a foreign award deserved to be refused on the touchstone of Section 48 or not.[108]

---

105. *Arun Dev Upadhyaya* v. *Integrated Sales Service Ltd.*, (2016) 9 SCC 524.
106. *Subs.* for "An appeal" by Act 33 of 2019, S. 12 (w.e.f. 30-8-2019).
107. *Shin-Etsu Chemical Co. Ltd. (2)* v. *Vindhya Telelinks Ltd.*, (2009) 14 SCC 16.
108. *Integrated Sales Services Ltd.* v. *Arun Dev*, 2017 SCC OnLine Bom 1: (2017) 1 Mah LJ 681.

"Court authorised by law to hear appeals" [Sub-s. (1)(*b*)]

Unlike *Explanation* to Section 47, Section 50, Arbitration and Conciliation Act, 1996 uses the expression "court" not simpliciter but qualified by the wording "authorised by law to hear appeals from such order". It is not the court having jurisdiction if subject-matter is a suit where jurisdiction is determined in accordance with the provisions of Sections 16–20 CPC. On the other hand, Section 50, Arbitration and Conciliation Act specifically uses the expression "authorised by law" and not the "Civil Procedure Code" or "suit".[109] The question involved in this case was whether the Delhi High Court can entertain appeal against an order passed by the Company Law Board, Principal Bench, New Delhi. Authorisation in the case of an order passed by the Principal Bench is to be determined with reference to Companies Act, 1956, Sections 10(1)(*a*) and 10-F. Section 10(1)(*a*) refers to the place where the company's registered office is situated. Hence, territorial jurisdiction of the High Court under Section 50(1)(*a*) is to be determined with reference to the place of registered office. The company concerned in the present case did not have its registered office in Delhi. Held, Delhi High Court did not have territorial jurisdiction to entertain the appeal, rejection of appeal by the Delhi High Court for want of territorial jurisdiction was proper.[110]

"Any right to appeal to the Supreme Court" [Sub-s. (2)]

The right to appeal to the Supreme Court referred to and excluded from the bar contained in Section 50(2) of the Act, refers to appeals under Article 132 or 133(1) of the Constitution. The words "right to appeal" refer to a right conferred either under the Constitution or under a statute to file an appeal to a higher court against the judgment, decree or order of lower court, without having to first obtain any permission or leave. In the absence of a constitutional or statutory provision for an appeal as of right, the appellant cannot contend that it has a "right to appeal" to the Supreme Court. An appeal by special leave to the Supreme Court cannot, therefore, be considered as an appeal as of right or as an appeal in pursuance of a right to appeal to the Supreme Court.[111]

Though the existence of an alternative remedy by itself will not take away the jurisdiction of the Supreme Court under Article 136, the Supreme Court would not grant leave and entertain appeals against orders/judgment/decrees

---

109. *Sumitomo Corpn.* v. *CDC Financial Services (Mauritius) Ltd.*, (2008) 4 SCC 91.
110. *Ibid.*
111. *Shin-Etsu Chemical Co. Ltd. (2)* v. *Vindhya Telelinks Ltd.*, (2009) 14 SCC 16.

of the District Court or courts subordinate thereto, if remedy by way of appeal or revision to the High Court or other court or forum is available.[112]

Appeal

Appeal lies against an order refusing to execute a foreign award. There is no right of appeal under this section when such execution is allowed.

An appeal against the order of enforcement of foreign award is not maintainable. But appeal against the order refusing enforcement of foreign award is maintainable.[113]

Letters Patent Appeal

The 1996 Act is self-contained and exhaustive code in itself. No Letters Patent Appeal will lie against an order which is not appealable under Section 50.[114]

Letters Patent Appeal under the Delhi High Court Act, 1966 is not maintainable against the order passed under Section 50, Arbitration and Conciliation Act, 1996 except for the orders provided to be appealable therein.[115]

Appeal under clause 15 of the Letters Patent is not barred as the right has not been specifically taken away by Section 50.[116]

An order not applicable under Section 50 is not open to further appeal under Letters Patent. Power and jurisdiction of the High Court under Letters Patent is ousted by 1996 Act. The 1996 Act is a self-contained code for the adjudication of all matters arising out of arbitration.[117]

Commercial Courts Act, 2015

In arbitration cases of enforcement of foreign awards, no appeal lies under Section 50. Hence appeal under Section 13, Commercial Courts Act is not maintainable.[118]

---

112. Ibid; *Noy Vallesina Engg. SpA* v. *Jindal Drugs Ltd.*, (2021) 1 SCC 382.
113. *Noy Vallesina Engg. SpA* v. *Jindal Drugs Ltd.*, (2021) 1 SCC 382.
114. *Fuerst Day Lawson Ltd.* v. *Jindal Exports Ltd.*, (2011) 8 SCC 333; *Jindal Exports Ltd.* v. *Fuerst Day Lawson FDL Head Office*, 2010 SCC OnLine Del 1643: (2010) 117 DRJ 515; *Shivnath Rai Harnarain India Co.* v. *Glencore Grain Rotterdam*, 2009 SCC OnLine Del 3564: (2009) 113 DRJ 509.
115. *Jindal Exports Ltd.* v. *Fuerst Day Lawson FDL Head Office*, 2010 SCC OnLine Del 1643: (2010) 117 DRJ 515.
116. *LMJ International Ltd.* v. *SEA Stream Navigation Ltd.*, 2007 SCC OnLine Cal 252: (2007) 4 CHN 798.
117. *Fuerst Day Lawson Ltd.* v. *Jindal Exports Ltd.*, (2011) 8 SCC 333.
118. *Kandla Export Corpn.* v. *OCI Corpn.*, (2018) 14 SCC 715.

SAVING [S. 51]

51. *Saving.*—Nothing in this Chapter shall prejudice any rights which any person would have had of enforcing in India of any award or of availing himself in India of any award if this Chapter had not been enacted.

COMMENTS

Corresponding old law

Section 51 corresponds to Section 9(*a*), Foreign Awards (Recognition and Enforcement) Act, 1961. The said Section 9 provided as under:

> **9.** *Saving.*—Nothing in this Act shall—
>
> (*a*) prejudice any rights which any person would have had of enforcing in India of any award or of availing himself in India of any award if this Act had not been passed; or
>
> (*b*) apply to any award made on an arbitration agreement governed by the law of India.

CHAPTER II NOT TO APPLY [S. 52]

52. *Chapter II not to apply.*—Chapter II of this Part shall not apply in relation to foreign awards to which this Chapter applies.

COMMENTS

Corresponding old law

This section gives effect to Article VII(2) of the Convention on the Recognition and Enforcement of Foreign Arbitral Awards at New York, 1958 which read as follows:

> "The Geneva Protocol on Arbitration Clauses of 1923 and the Geneva Convention on the Execution of Foreign Arbitral Awards of 1927 shall cease to have effect between Contracting States on their becoming bound and to the extent that they become bound by this Convention."

Chapter II
Geneva Convention Awards

INTERPRETATION [S. 53]

53. *Interpretation.*—In this Chapter "foreign award" means an arbitral award on differences relating to matters considered as commercial under the law in force in India made after the 28th day of July, 1924,—

(*a*) in pursuance of an agreement for arbitration to which the Protocol set forth in the Second Schedule applies, and

(*b*) between persons of whom one is subject to the jurisdiction of some one of such powers as the Central Government, being satisfied that reciprocal provisions have been made, may, by notification in the Official Gazette, declare to be parties to the Convention set forth in the Third Schedule, and of whom the other is subject to the jurisdiction of some other of the powers aforesaid, and

(*c*) in one of such territories as the Central Government, being satisfied that reciprocal provisions have been made, may, by like notification, declare to be territories to which the said Convention applies,

and for the purposes of this Chapter an award shall not be deemed to be final if any proceedings for the purpose of contesting the validity of the award are pending in the country in which it was made.

COMMENTS

Corresponding old law

Section 53 is verbatim reproduction of Section 2, Arbitration (Protocol and Convention) Act, 1937 except for certain marginal changes. Section 2 of the said Act read as under:

2. *Interpretation.*—In this Act [1][* * *] "foreign award" means an award on differences relating to matters considered as commercial under the law in force in [2][India], made after the 28th day of July, 1924,—

1. Definition of "States" *ins.* by the A.O. 1950 was *omitted* by Act 3 of 1951, S. 3 and Sch.
2. *Subs.*, ibid., for "the States".

(*a*) in pursuance of an agreement for arbitration to which the Protocol set forth in the First Schedule applies;

(*b*) between persons of whom one is subject to the jurisdiction of some one of such powers as the Central Government, being satisfied that reciprocal provisions have been made, may, by notification [3]in the Official Gazette, declare to be parties to the Convention set forth in the Second Schedule, and of whom the other is subject to the jurisdiction of some other of the powers aforesaid; and

(*c*) in one of such territories as the Central Government being satisfied that reciprocal provisions have been may by like notification, declare to be territories to which the said convention applies,

and for the purposes of this Act an award shall not be deemed to be final if any proceedings for the purposes of contesting the validity of the award are pending in the country in which it was made.

POWER OF JUDICIAL AUTHORITY TO REFER PARTIES TO ARBITRATION [S. 54]

54. *Power of judicial authority to refer parties to arbitration.*—Notwithstanding anything contained in Part I or in the Code of Civil Procedure, 1908 (5 of 1908), a judicial authority, on being seized of a dispute regarding a contract made between persons to whom Section 53 applies and including an arbitration agreement, whether referring to present or future differences, which is valid under that section and capable of being carried into effect, shall refer the parties on the application of either of them or any person claiming through or under him to the decision of the arbitrators and such reference shall not prejudice the competence of the judicial authority in case the agreement or the arbitration cannot proceed or becomes inoperative.

COMMENTS

Corresponding old law

Section 54 partly reproduces Section 3, Arbitration (Protocol and Convention) Act, 1937. Section 3 of the said Act provided as under:

3. *Stay of proceedings in respect of matters to be referred to arbitration.*—Notwithstanding anything contained in the [4][Arbitration Act, 1940], or in the Code of Civil Procedure, 1908, if any party to a submission made in pursuance of an agreement to which the Protocol set forth in the First Schedule as modified by the reservation subject to which it was signed by India applies,

3. For such notification, *see* Gazette of India, 1938, Pt. I, p. 24.
4. *Subs.* by the Act 32 of 1940, S. 3 and Sch. II, for "Indian Arbitration Act, 1899".

or any person claiming through or under him, commences any legal proceeding in any court against any other party to the submission or any person claiming through or under him in respect of any matter agreed to be referred, any party to such legal proceedings may, at any time after appearance and before filing a written statement or taking any other steps in the proceedings, apply to the Court to stay the proceedings and the Court, unless satisfied that the agreement or arbitration has become inoperative or cannot proceed, or that there is not in fact any dispute between the parties with regard to the matter agreed to be referred, shall make an order staying the proceedings.

FOREIGN AWARDS WHEN BINDING [S. 55]

55. *Foreign awards when binding.*—Any foreign award which would be enforceable under this Chapter shall be treated as binding for all purposes on the persons as between whom it was made, and may accordingly be relied on by any of those persons by way of defence, set-off or otherwise in any legal proceedings in India and any references in this Chapter to enforcing a foreign award shall be construed as including references to relying on an award.

COMMENTS

Corresponding old law

Section 55 is verbatim reproduction of Section 4(2), Arbitration (Protocol and Convention) Act, 1937 except for marginal changes. The said Section 4 read as under:

(2) Any foreign award which would be enforceable under this Act shall be treated as binding for all purposes on the persons as between whom it was made and may accordingly be relied on by any of those persons by way of defence, set off or otherwise in any legal proceedings in [5][India] and any references in this Act to enforcing a foreign award shall be construed as including references to relying on an award.

EVIDENCE [S. 56]

56. *Evidence.*—(1) The party applying for the enforcement of a foreign award shall, at the time of application produce before the Court—

(*a*) the original award or a copy thereof duly authenticated in the manner required by the law of the country in which it was made;

(*b*) evidence proving that the award has become final; and

5. *Subs.* by Act 3 of 1951, S. 3 and Sch., for "the States".

(*c*) such evidence as may be necessary to prove that the conditions mentioned in clauses (*a*) and (*c*) of sub-section (1) of Section 57 are satisfied.

(2) Where any document requiring to be produced under sub-section (1) is in a foreign language, the party seeking to enforce the award shall produce a translation into English certified as correct by a diplomatic or consular agent of the country to which that party belongs or certified as correct in such other manner as may be sufficient according to the law in force in India.

[6][*Explanation.*—In this section and in the sections following in this Chapter, "court" means the High Court having original jurisdiction to decide the questions forming the subject-matter of the arbitral award if the same had been the subject-matter of a suit on its original civil jurisdiction and in other cases, in the High Court having jurisdiction to hear appeals from decrees of courts subordinate to such High Court.]

COMMENTS

Corresponding old law

Section 56 is verbatim reproduction of Section 8, Arbitration (Protocol and Convention) Act, 1937 except for marginal changes. Section 8 of the said Act reads as under:

8. *Evidence.*—(1) The party seeking to enforce a foreign award must produce—

(*a*) the original award or a copy thereof duly authenticated in manner required by the law of the country in which it was made;

(*b*) evidence providing that the award has become final; and

(*c*) such evidence as may be necessary to prove that the award is a foreign award and that the conditions mentioned in clauses (*a*), (*b*) and (*c*) of sub-section (1) of Section 7 are satisfied.

(2) Where any document requiring to be produced under sub-section (1) is in a foreign language, the party seeking to enforce the award shall produce a translation into English certified as correct by a diplomatic or consular agent of the country to which that party belongs or certified as correct in such other manner as may be sufficient according to the law in force in [7][India].

6. *Subs.* by Act 3 of 2016, S. 23 (w.r.e.f. 23-10-2015). Prior to substitution it read as:

"*Explanation.*—In this section and all the following sections of this Chapter, "court" means the Principal Civil Court of Original Jurisdiction in a district, and includes the High Court in exercise of its ordinary original civil jurisdiction, having jurisdiction over the subject-matter of the award if the same had been the subject-matter of a suit, but does not include any civil court of a grade inferior to such Principal Civil Court, or any Court of Small Causes."

7. *Subs.* by Act 3 of 1951, S. 3 and Sch., for "the States".

Legislative changes

Arbitration and Conciliation (Amendment) Act, 2015 (3 of 2016)

Present *Explanation* has been substituted for old *Explanation* by Amendment Act 3 of 2016 to provide that the court referred to in that section means the High Court.

NOTES ON CLAUSES

Clause 23 of the Bill seeks to substitute the *Explanation* in Section 56 of the principal Act to provide that the court referred to in that section to mean the High Court.

CONDITIONS FOR ENFORCEMENT OF FOREIGN AWARDS [S. 57]

57. *Conditions for enforcement of foreign awards.*—(1) In order that a foreign award may be enforceable under this Chapter, it shall be necessary that—

(*a*) the award has been made in pursuance of a submission to arbitration which is valid under the law applicable thereto;

(*b*) the subject-matter of the award is capable of settlement by arbitration under the law of India;

(*c*) the award has been made by the arbitral tribunal provided for in the submission to arbitration or constituted in the manner agreed upon by the parties and in conformity with the law governing the arbitration procedure;

(*d*) the award has become final in the country in which it has been made, in the sense that it will not be considered as such if it is open to opposition or appeal or if it is proved that any proceedings for the purpose of contesting the validity of the award are pending;

(*e*) the enforcement of the award is not contrary to the public policy or the law of India.

[8][*Explanation 1.*—For the avoidance of any doubt, it is clarified that an award is in conflict with the public policy of India, only if,—

(*i*) the making of the award was induced or affected by fraud or corruption or was in violation of Section 75 or Section 81; or

(*ii*) it is in contravention with the fundamental policy of Indian law; or

(*iii*) it is in conflict with the most basic notions of morality or justice.

---

8. *Subs.* by Act 3 of 2016, S. 24 (w.r.e.f. 23-10-2015). Prior to substitution it read as:

"*Explanation.*—Without prejudice to the generality of clause (*e*), it is hereby declared, for the avoidance of any doubt, that an award is in conflict with the public policy of India if the making of the award was induced or affected by fraud or corruption."

Explanation 2.—For the avoidance of doubt, the test as to whether there is a contravention with the fundamental policy of Indian law shall not entail a review on the merits of the dispute.]

(2) Even if the conditions laid down in sub-section (1) are fulfilled, enforcement of the award shall be refused if the Court is satisfied that—

(*a*) the award has been annulled in the country in which it was made;

(*b*) the party against whom it is sought to use the award was not given notice of the arbitration proceedings in sufficient time to enable him to present his case; or that, being under a legal incapacity, he was not properly represented;

(*c*) the award does not deal with the differences contemplated by or falling within the terms of the submission to arbitration or that it contains decisions on matters beyond the scope of the submission to arbitration:

Provided that if the award has not covered all the differences submitted to the arbitral tribunal, the Court may, if it thinks fit, postpone such enforcement or grant it subject to such guarantee as the Court may decide.

(3) If the party against whom the award has been made proves that under the law governing the arbitration procedure there is a ground, other than the grounds referred to in clauses (*a*) and (*c*) of sub-section (1) and clauses (*b*) and (*c*) of sub-section (2) entitling him to contest the validity of the award, the Court may, if it thinks fit, either refuse enforcement of the award or adjourn the consideration thereof, giving such party a reasonable time within which to have the award annulled by the competent tribunal.

COMMENTS

Corresponding old law

Section 57 corresponds to Section 7, Arbitration (Protocol and Convention) Act, 1937 except for certain verbal changes. Section 57 contains the provisions of Section 7 of the said Act. Section 7, Arbitration Act, 1937 read thus:

7. *Conditions for enforcement of foreign awards.*—(1) In order that a foreign award may be enforceable under this Act it must have—

(*a*) been made in pursuance of an agreement for arbitration which was valid under the law by which it was governed;

(*b*) been made by the tribunal provided for in the agreement or constituted in manner agreed upon by the parties;

(*c*) been made in conformity with the law governing the arbitration procedure;

(*d*) become final in the country in which it was made;

(*e*) been in respect of a matter which may lawfully be referred to arbitration under the law of [9][India],

and the enforcement thereof must not be contrary to the public policy or the law of [10][India].

(2) A foreign award shall not be enforceable under this Act if the court dealing with the case is satisfied that—

(*a*) the award has been annulled in the country in which it was made; or

(*b*) the party against whom it is sought to enforce the award was not given notice of the arbitration proceedings in sufficient time to enable him to present his case, or was under some legal incapacity and was not properly represented; or

(*c*) the award does not deal with all the questions referred or contains decisions on matters beyond the scope of the agreement for arbitration:

Provided that if that award does not deal with all questions referred the Court may, if it thinks fit, either postpone the enforcement of the award or order its enforcement subject to the giving of such security by the person seeking to enforce it as the Court may think fit.

(3) If a party seeking to resist the enforcement of a foreign award proves that there is any ground other than the non-existence of the conditions, specified in clauses (*a*), (*b*) and (*c*) of sub-section (1), or the existence of the conditions specified in clauses (*b*) and (*c*) of sub-section (2), entitling him to contest the validity of the award, the Court may, if it thinks fit, either refuse to enforce the award or adjourn the hearing until after the expiration of such period as appears to the Court to be reasonably sufficient to enable that party to take the necessary steps to have the award annulled by the competent tribunal.

Legislative changes

Arbitration and Conciliation (Amendment) Act, 2015 (3 of 2016)

In sub-section (1), two *Explanations* 1 and 2 have been substituted for the existing *Explanation*. The new *Explanation* 1 provides that an arbitral award is in conflict with the public policy of India only if the making of the award was induced or affected by fraud or corruption or was in violation of Section 75 or Section 81; or is in contravention with the fundamental policy of Indian law; or is in conflict with the most basic notions of morality or justice. *Explanation* 2 has been added to explain that the test as to whether there is a contravention with the fundamental policy of Indian law shall not entail a review on the merits of the dispute.

9. *Subs.* by Act 3 of 1951, S. 3 and Sch., for "the States".
10. *Ibid.*

ENFORCEMENT OF FOREIGN AWARDS [S. 58]

58. *Enforcement of foreign awards.*—Where the Court is satisfied that the foreign award is enforceable under this Chapter, the award shall be deemed to be a decree of the Court.

COMMENTS

Corresponding old law

Section 58 is new, no such provision existed in the Arbitration Act, 1940.

Scope and application

Against an order passed under the Foreign Awards (Recognition and Enforcement) Act, 1961 revision is maintainable.[11]

When a court is asked to enforce an award, it must recognise not only the legal effect of the award, but must also use legal sanctions to ensure that it is carried out.[12] An award cannot be executed against a party who does not own any assets in India.[13] If an award is for money, its subject-matter may be said to be money, just as the subject-matter of money-decree may be said to be money.[14] The appropriate court for initiating legal proceedings will be the court in whose jurisdiction the money is held.[15] Awards covered by Part II of the Arbitration and Conciliation Act, 1996 are deemed to be decree of the court.[16]

Registration

A foreign award does not require registration for its enforcement. The award in question did not have the effect of a transfer. It only directed the parties in terms of their settlement for division of business properties to execute necessary transfers and closing documents after the division had been effectuated. The award only created a right to obtain transfer and closing documents.[17]

---

11. *Fresenius A.G.* v. *Dalmia Industries Ltd.*, 1997 SCC OnLine All 374: 1997 All LJ 2290.
12. *Brace Transport Corpn. of Monrovia* v. *Orient Middle East Lines*, 1995 Supp (2) SCC 280.
13. *Ibid.*
14. *Ibid.*
15. *Ibid.*
16. *Bhatia International* v. *Bulk Trading S.A.*, (2002) 4 SCC 105.
17. *Harendra H. Mehta* v. *Mukesh H. Mehta*, (1999) 5 SCC 108.

Application of compulsory purchase provisions of Income Tax Act, 1961

It has been held that in the case of a foreign award, the provisions of the Income Tax Act in Chapter XX-C relating to pre-emptive purchase by the Central Government do not apply. Though the Chapter creates a wide net to cover all kinds of immovable property, that net is not wide enough to cover a foreign award relating to businesses and properties both in India and in a foreign country.[18]

Judgment on award on country of origin

Enforcement in India of a foreign award does not become barred by the fact that a judgment on the basis of the award has been obtained in the country of its origin.[19]

APPEALABLE ORDERS [S. 59]

59. *Appealable orders.*—(1) An appeal shall lie from the order refusing—

(*a*) to refer the parties to arbitration under Section 54; and

(*b*) to enforce a foreign award under Section 57,

to the court authorised by law to hear appeals from such order.

(2) No second appeal shall lie from an order passed in appeal under this section, but nothing in this section shall affect or take away any right to appeal to the Supreme Court.

COMMENTS

Corresponding old law

Section 59(1) is new and Section 59(2) is verbatim reproduction of Section 39(2), Arbitration Act, 1940.

Scope

No second appeal shall lie from an order passed under this section. But an appeal to the Supreme Court is not barred.

18. *Ibid.*
19. *Ibid.*

SAVING [S. 60]

60. *Saving.*—Nothing in this Chapter shall prejudice any rights which any person would have had of enforcing in India of any award or of availing himself in India of any award if this Chapter had not been enacted.

COMMENTS

Corresponding old law

Section 60 corresponds to Section 9(*a*), Arbitration (Protocol and Convention) Act, 1937. The said Section 9(*a*) provided as under:

9. *Saving.*—Nothing in this Act shall—

(*a*) prejudice any rights which any person would have had of enforcing in [20][India] any award or of availing himself in [21][India] of any award if this Act had not been passed; or

Scope and application

The arbitrator has jurisdiction to decide about the validity of the arbitration clause.

Contention was that no concluded contract came into existence. Direction was given to parties to appoint arbitrator in terms of the arbitration clause.[22]

---

20. *Subs.* by Act 3 of 1951, S. 3 and Sch., for "the States".
21. *Ibid.*
22. *International Pharmaceuticals* v. *Union of India*, 1998 SCC OnLine Del 345: (1998) 46 DRJ 99.

Part III

CONCILIATION

CHAPTER I
Conciliation

REFERENCE OF CONCILIATION IN ENACTMENTS [S. 61]

[1][**61.** *Reference of conciliation in enactments.*—(1) Any provision, in any other enactment for the time being in force, providing for resolution of disputes

1. Sections 61 and 62 *subs.* for Sections 61 to 81 by Act 32 of 2023, S. 61 and Sch. VI(*b*) (w.e.f. the date to be notified). Prior to substitution it read as:

"**61.** *Application and scope.*—(1) Save as otherwise provided by any law for the time being in force and unless the parties have otherwise agreed, this Part shall apply to conciliation of disputes arising out of legal relationship, whether contractual or not, and to all proceedings relating thereto.

62. *Commencement of conciliation proceedings.*—(1) The party initiating conciliation shall send to the other party a written invitation to conciliate under this Part, briefly identifying the subject of the dispute.

63. *Number of conciliators.*—(1) There shall be one conciliator unless the parties agree that there shall be two or three conciliators.

64. *Appointment of conciliators.*—(1) Subject to sub-section (2),—

(*a*) in conciliation proceedings with one conciliator, the parties may agree on the name of a sole conciliator;

(*b*) in conciliation proceedings with two conciliators, each party may appoint one conciliator;

(*c*) in conciliation proceedings with three conciliators, each party may appoint one conciliator and the parties may agree on the name of the third conciliator who shall act as the presiding conciliator.

65. *Submission of statements to conciliator.*—(1) The conciliator, upon his appointment, may request each party to submit to him a brief written statement describing the general nature of the dispute and the points at issue. Each party shall send a copy of such statement to the other party.

66. *Conciliator not bound by certain enactments.*—The conciliator is not bound by the Code of Civil Procedure, 1908 (5 of 1908), or the Indian Evidence Act, 1872 (1 of 1872).

67. *Role of conciliator.*—(1) The conciliator shall assist the parties in an independent and impartial manner in their attempt to reach an amicable settlement of their dispute.

68. *Administrative assistance.*—In order to facilitate the conduct of the conciliation proceedings, the parties, or the conciliator with the consent of the parties, may arrange for administrative assistance by a suitable institution or person.

69. *Communication between conciliator and parties.*—(1) The conciliator may invite the parties to meet him or may communicate with them orally or in writing. He may meet or communicate with the parties together or with each of them separately.

70. *Disclosure of information.*—When the conciliator receives factual information concerning the dispute from a party, he shall disclose the substance of that information to the other party in order that the other party may have the opportunity to present any explanation which he considers appropriate:

71. *Cooperation of parties with conciliator.*—The parties shall in good faith cooperate with the conciliator and, in particular, shall endeavour to comply with requests by the conciliator to submit written materials, provide evidence and attend meetings.

72. *Suggestions by parties for settlement of dispute.*—Each party may, on his own initiative or at the invitation of the conciliator, submit to the conciliator suggestions for the settlement of the dispute.

73. *Settlement agreement.*—(1) When it appears to the conciliator that there exist elements of a settlement which may be acceptable to the parties, he shall formulate the terms of a possible settlement and submit them to the parties for their observations. After receiving the observations of the parties, the conciliator may reformulate the terms of a possible settlement in the light of such observations.

74. *Status and effect of settlement agreement.*—The settlement agreement shall have the same status and effect as if it is an arbitral award on agreed terms on the substance of the dispute rendered by an arbitral tribunal under Section 30.

75. *Confidentiality.*—Notwithstanding anything contained in any other law for the time being in force, the conciliator and the parties shall keep confidential all matters relating to the conciliation proceedings. Confidentiality shall extend also to the settlement agreement, except where its disclosure is necessary for purposes of implementation and enforcement.

76. *Termination of conciliation proceedings.*—The conciliation proceedings shall be terminated—

(*a*) by the signing of the settlement agreement by the parties, on the date of the agreement; or

(*b*) by a written declaration of the conciliator, after consultation with the parties, to the effect that further efforts at conciliation are no longer justified, on the date of the declaration; or

(*c*) by a written declaration of the parties addressed to the conciliator to the effect that the conciliation proceedings are terminated, on the date of the declaration; or

(*d*) by a written declaration of a party to the other party and the conciliator, if appointed, to the effect that the conciliation proceedings are terminated, on the date of the declaration.

77. *Resort to arbitral or judicial proceedings.*—The parties shall not initiate, during the conciliation proceedings, any arbitral or judicial proceedings in respect of a dispute that is the subject-matter of the conciliation proceedings except that a party may initiate arbitral or judicial proceedings where, in his opinion, such proceedings are necessary for preserving his rights.

78. *Costs.*—(1) Upon termination of the conciliation proceedings, the conciliator shall fix the costs of the conciliation and give written notice thereof to the parties.

79. *Deposits.*—(1) The conciliator may direct each party to deposit an equal amount as an advance for the costs referred to in sub-section (2) of Section 78 which he expects will be incurred.

80. *Role of conciliator in other proceedings.*—Unless otherwise agreed by the parties,—

(*a*) the conciliator shall not act as an arbitrator or as a representative or counsel of a party in any arbitral or judicial proceeding in respect of a dispute that is the subject of the conciliation proceedings;

(*b*) the conciliator shall not be presented by the parties as a witness in any arbitral or judicial proceedings.

81. *Admissibility of evidence in other proceedings.*—The parties shall not rely on or introduce as evidence in arbitral or judicial proceedings, whether or not such proceedings relate to the dispute that is the subject of the conciliation proceedings,—

through conciliation in accordance with the provisions of this Act, shall be construed as reference to mediation as provided under the Mediation Act, 2023.

(2) Conciliation as provided under this Act and the Code of Civil Procedure, 1908 (5 of 1908), shall be construed as mediation referred to in clause (*h*) of Section 3 of the Mediation Act, 2023.

1. Legislative changes

This section has been substituted by the Mediation Act, 2023.

COMMENTS

This section provides that any provision in any other Act for the time in force which provides for resolution of disputes in accordance with the provisions of the Arbitration and Conciliation Act, 1996 shall be construed as reference to mediation as provided under the Mediation Act, 2023.

"Mediation" includes a process whether referred by the expression

1. mediation, [S. 4]
2. pre-litigation mediation, [S. 5]
3. online mediation, [S. 30]
4. community mediation, [Ss. 43–44]
5. conciliation or an expression of similar import,
6. whereby the parties try to reach an amicable settlement of their dispute with the assistance of a third person called as mediator who does not have the authority to impose a settlement upon the parties to the dispute.

SAVING [S. 62]

62. *Saving.*—Notwithstanding anything contained in Section 61, any conciliation proceeding initiated in pursuance of Sections 61 to 81 of this Act as in force before the commencement of the Mediation Act, 2023, shall be continued as such, as if the Mediation Act, 2023, had not been enacted.]

(*a*) views expressed or suggestions made by the other party in respect of a possible settlement of the dispute;
(*b*) admissions made by the other party in the course of the conciliation proceedings;
(*c*) proposals made by the conciliator;
(*d*) the fact that the other party had indicated his willingness to accept a proposal for settlement made by the conciliator."

COMMENTS

This section contains a saving clause. Any conciliation proceedings in pursuance of Sections 61 to 81, Arbitration and Conciliation Act, 1996 as in force before the commencement of the Mediation Act, 2023 shall continue as such as if the Mediation Act had not been enacted.

PART IV

SUPPLEMENTARY PROVISIONS

CHAPTER I
Supplementary Provisions

POWER OF HIGH COURT TO MAKE RULES [S. 82]

82. *Power of High Court to make rules.*—The High Court may make rules consistent with this Act as to all proceedings before the Court under this Act.

COMMENTS

Corresponding old law

Section 82 corresponds to Section 44, Arbitration Act, 1940. Section 44 of the 1940 Act was an exhaustive one, provided as under:

44. *Power to High Court to make rules.*—The High Court may make rules consistent with this Act as to—

(*a*) the filing of awards and all proceedings consequent thereon or incidental thereto;

(*b*) the filing and hearing of special cases and all proceedings consequent thereon or incidental thereto;

(*c*) the staying of any suit or proceeding in contravention of an arbitration agreement;

(*d*) the forms to be used for the purposes of this Act;

(*e*) generally, all proceedings in Court under this Act.

Scope and application

Section 82 of the 1996 Act gives the High Court power to make rules consistent with the provisions of the Act. The High Court should make rules under this section consistent with the Act regarding manner of filing and dealing with the application under Section 9 and documents to be attached with the application.[1]

1. *Sundaram Finance Ltd.* v. *NEPC India Ltd.*, (1999) 2 SCC 479.

REMOVAL OF DIFFICULTIES [S. 83]

83. *Removal of difficulties.*—(1) If any difficulty arises in giving effect to the provisions of this Act, the Central Government may, by order published in the Official Gazette, make such provisions, not inconsistent with the provisions of this Act as appear to it to be necessary or expedient for removing the difficulty:

Provided that no such order shall be made after the expiry of a period of two years from the date of commencement of this Act.

(2) Every order made under this section shall, as soon as may be after it is made, be laid before each House of Parliament.

COMMENTS

Corresponding old law

This section is new.

POWER TO MAKE RULES [S. 84]

84. *Power to make rules.*—(1) The Central Government may, by notification in the Official Gazette, make rules for carrying out the provisions of this Act.

(2) Every rule made by the Central Government under this Act shall be laid, as soon as may be, after it is made before each House of Parliament while it is in session, for a total period of thirty days which may be comprised in one session or in two or more successive sessions, and if, before the expiry of the session immediately following the session or the successive sessions aforesaid, both Houses agree in making any modification in the rule or both Houses agree that the rule should not be made, the rule shall thereafter have effect only in such modified form or be of no effect, as the case may be; so, however, that any such modification or annulment shall be without prejudice to the validity of anything previously done under that rule.

COMMENTS

Corresponding old law

This section is new.

REPEAL AND SAVINGS [S. 85]

85. *Repeal and savings.*—(1) The Arbitration (Protocol and Convention) Act, 1937 (6 of 1937), the Arbitration Act, 1940 (10 of 1940) and the Foreign Awards (Recognition and Enforcement) Act, 1961 (45 of 1961) are hereby repealed.

(2) Notwithstanding such repeal,—

(*a*) the provisions of the said enactments shall apply in relation to arbitral proceedings which commenced before this Act came into force unless otherwise agreed by the parties but this Act shall apply in relation to arbitral proceedings which commenced on or after this Act comes into force;

(*b*) all rules made and notifications published, under the said enactments shall, to the extent to which they are not repugnant to this Act, be deemed respectively to have been made or issued under this Act.

COMMENTS

Corresponding old law

Section 85(2) corresponds to Section 48, Arbitration Act, 1940. Section 48 of the 1940 Act provided as under:

48. *Saving for pending references.*—The provisions of this Act shall not apply to any reference pending at the commencement of this Act, to which the law in force immediately before the commencement of this Act shall notwithstanding any repeal effected by this Act continue to apply.

Scope and application

Section 85 is the repeal and savings section in the Act. By Section 85(1), the following Acts have been repealed:

1. Arbitration (Protocol and Convention Act, 1937 (6 of 1937);
2. Arbitration Act, 1940 (10 of 1940); and
3. Foreign Awards (Recognition and Enforcement Act), 1961 (45 of 1961).

The saving clause in Section 85(2)(*a*) provides that the provisions of the aforesaid three Acts shall continue to apply in relation to the arbitral proceedings which commenced before the Arbitration and Conciliation Act, 1996 came into force unless otherwise agreed by the parties. Notwithstanding the repeal, the provisions of the 1940 Act shall apply in relation to arbitral proceedings which commenced before the 1996 Act came into force unless otherwise agreed by the parties.[2]

The provisions of the Arbitration and Conciliation Act, 1996 shall apply in relation to arbitration proceedings which commenced on or after this Act, *viz.* Arbitration and Conciliation Act, 1996 came into force.

---

2. *Monoranjan Mondal* v. *Union of India*, 1998 SCC OnLine Cal 342: (1999) 1 CHN 400.

Where the applicant had agreed to the procedure under the 1996 Act, he cannot be permitted to raise a plea at the appellate stage that the provisions of the 1940 Act would apply for challenging or seeking modification of the award made under the 1996 Act.[3]

Whether 1940 Act or 1996 Act applicable

To ascertain whether 1940 Act or 1996 Act was applicable, the conduct of the proceedings can be looked into. Parties can agree that law prevailing at the relevant time would apply, Section 85(2) recognises such an agreement. Where such an agreement existed between the parties and though request for appointment of arbitrator was made while the old Act was in force but arbitrator was appointed after the commencement of the new Act and the manner in which the arbitration proceedings were conducted showed that the parties acted under the new Act, and the award also showed that the arbitrator had proceeded accordingly, held application for the enforcement of the award under the new Act was maintainable.[4]

The parties, at the time of entering into the partnership deed, wanted to incorporate the arbitration clause for getting their disputes resolved through the means of arbitration, and that was incorporated in the deed. At the same time, instead of incorporating the name of the statute, *i.e.* the Arbitration Act of 1996, the Act of 1940 was mentioned. At that time the Act of 1940 was repealed. It can only be viewed as a mere misquoting of the name of the statute. By merely naming the statute applicable as the Arbitration Act, 1940, it cannot be said that the arbitration clause itself is inoperative. The law that has to be applied is one under the 1996 Act.[5]

Arbitration proceedings commences from the date of the filing of the plaint and not from the date when notice for appointment of arbitrator is served. Plaint in the case was filed after the enforcement of the new Act 1996. The provisions of the new Act were held applicable.[6]

The arbitral proceedings cannot be said to have commenced when the arbitrator fails to express his willingness to act as an arbitrator.[7]

"Unless otherwise agreed by the parties" [Sub-s. (2)(*a*)]

In cases where the arbitral proceedings have commenced before the coming into force of the new Act and are pending before the arbitrator, it is open

3. *National Aluminium Co. Ltd.* v. *Pressteel & Fabrications (P) Ltd.*, (2004) 1 SCC 540.
4. *Delhi Transport Corpn. Ltd.* v. *Rose Advertising*, (2003) 6 SCC 36.
5. *G. TEC* v. *Koulath Kareem*, 2015 SCC OnLine Ker 20276: (2015) 3 KLJ 652.
6. *Wimco Ltd.* v. *Vikram Singh*, 2002 SCC OnLine All 52: 2002 All LJ 1980; *State of Orissa* v. *Sarbeswar Rout*, (1989) 4 SCC 578, followed.
7. *Monoranjan Mondal* v. *Union of India*, 1998 SCC OnLine Cal 342: (1999) 1 CHN 400.

to the parties to agree that the new Act be applicable to such arbitral proceedings and they could so agree even before the coming into force of the new Act. There is nothing in the language of Section 85(2)(*a*), which barred the parties from agreeing. There is, however, a bar that they cannot agree to the applicability of the old Act after the new Act has come into force, when arbitral proceedings under the old Act have not commenced though the arbitration agreement was under the old Act.[8] The new Act would be applicable in relation to arbitral proceedings which commenced on or after the new Act came into force.[9]

The phrase "unless otherwise agreed by the parties" used in various sections of the Arbitration and Conciliation Act gives option to the parties to opt for the procedure as per their agreement during the arbitral proceedings before the arbitrator. So if there is an agreement between the parties with regard to the procedure to be followed by the arbitrator, the arbitrator is required to follow the said procedure. However, this would not mean that, in appeal, parties can contend that the appellate procedure should be as per their agreement. The appellate procedure would be governed as per the statutory provisions and parties have no right to change the same.[10]

The Arbitration and Conciliation Act, 1996 is a re-enactment of the Arbitration Act, 1940 with modification.[11]

Commencement of arbitration proceedings [Sub-s. (2), Cl. (*a*)]

Arbitrator appointed in the case failed to give an award within the stipulated period. New arbitrator was appointed by the court on 22 August 1996 after the 1996 Act came into force. It was held, arbitral proceedings shall be deemed to have commenced when the earlier arbitrator was appointed, the appointment of new arbitrator was governed by the Arbitration Act, 1940.[12]

Section 85(2)(*a*)—Object and ingredients

Section 85(2)(*a*) is the saving clause. It exempts the old Act from the complete obliteration so far as the pending arbitration proceedings are concerned. That would include saving of the whole of the old Act till the time of the enforcement of the award. Thus, Section 85(2)(*a*) prevents the accrued right under the old Act from being affected. Saving provision preserves the existing right accrued under the old Act. Once the arbitration proceedings have commenced, it cannot be stated that the right to be governed by the old

8. *Thyssen Stahlunion Gmbh* v. *SAIL*, (1999) 9 SCC 334.
9. *Ibid.*
10. *N.S. Nayak & Sons* v. *State of Goa*, (2003) 6 SCC 56.
11. *Puneet Malhotra* v. *R.S. Gai*, 2008 SCC OnLine Bom 1043: (2008) 6 Mah LJ 867.
12. *State of W.B.* v. *Amritlal Chatterjee*, (2003) 10 SCC 572.

Act for enforcement of the award was an inchoate right. It is certainly a right accrued. It is not imperative that for the right to accrue to have the award enforced under the old Act some legal proceedings for its enforcement must be pending under that Act at the time the new Act came into force.[13]

Section 85(2)(*a*)—Scope and application

Section 85(2)(*a*) of the new Act is in two limbs:

(1) provisions of the old Act shall apply in relation to arbitration proceedings which commenced before the new Act came into force unless otherwise agreed by the parties, and

(2) the new Act shall apply in relation to arbitral proceedings which commenced on or after the new Act came into force.

The first limb can further be bifurcated into two:

(*a*) the provisions of the old Act shall apply in relation to arbitral proceedings commenced before the new Act came into force; and

(*b*) the old Act will not apply in such cases where the parties agree that it will not apply in relation to arbitral proceedings which commenced before the new Act came into force.[14]

Agreement between the parties contemplated reference of all disputes arising out of agreement to arbitration for resolution of such disputes and such clause specifically provided that arbitration shall be in accordance with the provisions of the Arbitration Act, 1940 or any statutory amendments thereof. The Arbitration and Conciliation Act, 1996 came into force on 25 January 1996, and the agreement between the parties was executed on 21 December 1998. Held, the arbitration shall be governed by the 1996 Act.[15]

The arbitration agreement made prior to the commencement of the new Act is enforceable. The proceedings can be commenced under the new Act as per the arbitration clause in the agreement made prior to the coming into force of the new Act. Parties to the suit were referred to arbitration as per Section 8 of the Act.[16]

Suit was filed by the plaintiff under Section 20 of the 1940 Act for appointment of arbitrator. The defendant though received the notice did not file a written statement. In the meanwhile suit was withdrawn and

13. *Thyssen Stahlunion Gmbh* v. *SAIL*, (1999) 9 SCC 334.

14. *Ibid.*

15. *Kirloskar Computer Services Ltd.* v. *Lakshmi General Finance Ltd.*, 2006 SCC OnLine Mad 496: (2006) 4 CTC 509.

16. *Subhash Projects and Mktg. Ltd.* v. *Jain Farms and Resorts Ltd.*, 2003 SCC OnLine Kar 455: ILR 2003 Kar 4343.

application under the new Act was filed for the appointment of the arbitrator. Held, application under the new Act was maintainable as no arbitration proceedings had commenced under the repealed Act of 1940.[17]

Arbitration proceedings had commenced before the new Act 1996 came into force. The record of the case did not show that the parties had agreed before the arbitrator for application of the procedure under the new Act. Both the parties had not agreed to and opted for the applicability of the new Act after the new Act came into force. Award passed by the arbitrator under the new Act was vitiated and accordingly set aside.[18]

The application of the new Act is not dependent either on the date of drawing/signing the contract or the date of completion of the work or the date of preparation of the final bill or on the date when cause of action has arisen. It depends upon the date of commencement of the arbitral proceedings related to the disputes in question. If the arbitral proceedings have commenced before coming into force of the new Act, then the provisions of the old Act will apply. If the arbitral proceedings have commenced after the new Act came into force, the new Act will apply. This is clear from Section 85(2)(*a*) of the new Act 1996.[19] As per Section 85(2)(*a*), the proceedings which have commenced under the old Act have not only been saved but it also indicates which of the Acts should apply, taking into consideration the arbitration clause agreed to between the parties and also the stage of the proceedings.[20]

Provisions of 1996 Act can be made applicable in pending arbitral proceedings under the Arbitration Act, 1940 if parties so agree.[21]

Under Section 85(2) unless otherwise the parties agree to adopt the new enactment, *viz.* the Arbitration and Conciliation Act, 1996 the proceedings initiated and the decisions arrived at under the respective enactments would be proceeded with only under the respective enactments.[22]

---

17. *Y. Parthasarathy* v. *Railway Electrification*, 1997 SCC OnLine AP 166: (1997) 1 AP LJ 409.
18. *State of Goa* v. *Chinna Nachimuthu Constructions, Engineers and Contractors*, 2008 SCC OnLine Bom 634: (2009) 1 Mah LJ 342.
19. *Venkateswara Construction Co.* v. *Union of India*, 2001 SCC OnLine AP 116: (2001) 1 AP LJ 141.
20. *P. Gopal Raju* v. *Union of India*, 2006 SCC OnLine Kar 491: ILR 2006 Kar 3523.
21. *Mohanlal* v. *Choudhary Builders (P) Ltd.*, 2010 SCC OnLine MP 219: (2010) 4 MP LJ 395.
22. *Moolchand Exports (P) Ltd.* v. *Man-Producten Rotterdam BV*, 2004 SCC OnLine Mad 536: (2004) 4 CTC 690.

Mere filing of application under Section 34, Arbitration Act, 1940 does not amount to commencement of arbitration proceedings within the meaning of sub-section (2) of Section 85 of 1996 Act.[23]

Arbitration proceedings commence when the arbitrator expresses his willingness to act as such. In case if proceedings were not started under the Arbitration Act, 1940, Arbitration and Conciliation Act, 1996 was held applicable.[24]

Section 85(2) provides that the proceedings initiated and decisions arrived at under the Foreign Awards (Recognition and Enforcement) Act, 1961; Arbitration (Protocol and Convention) Act, 1937; Arbitration Act, 1940 prior to coming into force of the Arbitration and Conciliation Act, would be governed by the respective enactments unless the parties had agreed that they would be covered by the Arbitration and Conciliation Act, 1996. Award was passed on 15 November 1995 and the parties had not agreed to abide by the new Act, which, then, would be governed by the earlier legislation.[25]

When the arbitral proceedings commence after the coming into force of 1996 Act, only the provisions of 1996 Act will apply.[26]

Despite repeal, the provisions of the old Act will apply in relation to arbitration proceedings which commenced before the new Act came into force unless otherwise agreed by the parties.[27]

The arbitration proceedings commenced before the commencement of the new Act, *execution proceedings* shall be governed by the 1940 Act.[28]

Once the arbitration proceedings had commenced before the Arbitration and Conciliation Act, 1996 then the Arbitration Act, 1940 would continue to apply in view of the strict provisions of sub-section (1) of the 1996 Act.[29] Arbitration clause of the contract in question stipulated that the arbitration shall be conducted in accordance with the provisions of the Arbitration Act, 1940, or any statutory modifications thereof; it excluded the applicability of new Arbitration Act, 1996.[30]

---

23. *Bombay Gas Co. Ltd.* v. *Parmeshwar Mittal*, 1997 SCC OnLine Bom 314: (1997) 3 Mah LJ 863.
24. *Monoranjan Mondal* v. *Union of India*, 1998 SCC OnLine Cal 342: (1999) 1 CHN 400.
25. *Moolchand Exports (P) Ltd.* v. *Man-Producten Rotterdam BV*, 2004 SCC OnLine Mad 536: (2004) 4 CTC 690.
26. *Maheswari Steel (P) Ltd.* v. *Aravali Leasing Ltd.*, 2001 SCC OnLine Cal 685: (2001) 3 ICC 568.
27. *Enkay Construction Co.* v. *DDA*, 2002 SCC OnLine Del 33: (2002) 96 DLT 417.
28. *Thysen Stahlunion GMBH* v. *SAIL*, 1998 SCC OnLine Del 617: (1999) 48 DRJ 210.
29. *Good Value Engineers* v. *M.M.S. Nanda*, 2001 SCC OnLine Del 1177: ILR (2001) 2 Del 563.
30. *Vijay Industries* v. *NTPC Ltd.*, 2003 SCC OnLine Del 75: (2003) 71 DRJ 457.

Dispute referred to arbitrator before the commencement of Arbitration and Conciliation Act, 1996 under the Arbitration Act, 1940. Award of the arbitrator after the commencement of the new Act of 1996 is to be governed by the law after the new Act.[31] The arbitration clause provided that the provisions of the 1940 Act or any other enactment shall apply. Held, the provisions of the new Act would apply to the arbitration proceedings.[32]

Where the arbitration proceedings had commenced before the commencement of the new Act held the proceedings shall be governed by the old Act and the provisions of the new Act would have no application.[33]

Where the arbitration proceedings had commenced before coming into force of the new Act, the old Act would apply to the proceedings at all stages including the objection to the award, even to appeal against the rejection of the objection.[34]

Applicability of the 1996 Act to arbitration agreement entered into before the commencement of the Act

Arbitral proceedings relating to agreement entered into under the Arbitration Act, 1940 which have commenced subsequent to the enforcement of the 1996 Act would be governed by the Arbitration and Conciliation Act, 1996.[35]

The phrase "in relation to arbitral proceedings" occurring in Section 85(2) cannot be given a narrow meaning to mean only pendency of the proceedings before the arbitrator. It would cover not only proceedings pending before the arbitrator but would also cover the proceedings before the court and any proceedings which are required to be taken under the old Act for the award becoming a decree under Section 17 thereof and also appeal arising thereunder. Once the arbitral proceedings have started under the old Act, the old Act would apply for the award becoming a decree and also for appeal arising thereunder.[36] Even though the proceedings had commenced under the 1940 Act, parties by virtue of arbitration agreement can make provisions of the 1996 Act applicable.[37]

31. *National Project Construction Corpn. Ltd.* v. *Royal Construction Co. (P) Ltd.*, 2003 SCC OnLine Del 298.
32. *Interstate Equipment (India) (P) Ltd.* v. *Bharat Aluminum Co. Ltd.*, 2004 SCC OnLine Del 147: (2004) 73 DRJ 506.
33. *Selected Marbles Home* v. *Arun Kumar Kamal Kumar*, 2004 SCC OnLine Del 992: (2004) 78 DRJ 710.
34. *DDA.* v. *Bhai Sardar Singh & Sons*, 2004 SCC OnLine Del 297: ILR (2004) 1 Del 341.
35. *National Aluminium Co. Ltd.* v. *Metalimpex Ltd.*, (2001) 6 SCC 372.
36. *N.S. Nayak & Sons* v. *State of Goa*, (2003) 6 SCC 56.
37. *Union of India* v. *R.K. Goel and Associates Engineers and Contractors*, 2000 SCC OnLine Bom 210: (2000) 3 Mah LJ 616.

New arbitrator—Appointment of

Where an arbitrator resigned and a new Act came into force meanwhile, a new arbitrator will have to be appointed as per the provisions of the new 1996 Act.[38]

"In relation to arbitral proceedings which commenced on or after this Act comes into force" [Sub-s. (2)(*a*)]

The expression "in relation to arbitral proceedings which commenced on or after this Act comes into force" in clause (*a*) of sub-section (2) of Section 85 comprehends not only proceedings for arbitration but also proceedings for the enforcement of the award rendered in the arbitration proceedings pending at the time of the commencement of the new Act. If a narrow meaning is given to the expression, it would create confusion and inconvenience. Section 48, Arbitration Act, 1940 is not relevant to interpret Section 85(2)(*a*) of the new Act. If a narrow meaning of the aforesaid expression is accepted, it is likely to create a good deal of confusion with regard to the matters where award is made under the old Act. Provisions for the conduct of arbitral proceedings are vastly different in both the old and the new Acts. Challenge of award can be with reference to the conduct of arbitral proceedings.[39]

Applicability of 1996 Act to appeals pending under 1940 Act

Section 85(2)(*a*) of the new Act specifically provides that: (1) the provisions of the old Act shall apply in relation to arbitral proceedings which commenced on or before the new Act came into force, unless otherwise agreed to by the parties; and (2) it also provides that the new Act shall apply in relation to arbitral proceedings which commenced on or after the new Act came into force. In all these matters arbitrators were appointed prior to 25 January 1996, arbitral proceedings commenced before that date and even the awards were passed before 25 January 1996. On the basis of Section 85(2)(*a*), the provisions of the old Act would apply to the arbitral proceedings which commenced on or before the new Act came into force.[40] Parties may agree to be bound by the new law. Such agreement may be expressed or implied.[41]

38. *Sukhwant Rai* v. *Justice D.V. Sehgal*, (1999) 9 SCC 56.
39. *Thyssen Stahlunion Gmbh* v. *SAIL*, (1999) 9 SCC 334.
40. *N.S. Nayak & Sons* v. *State of Goa*, (2003) 6 SCC 56.
41. *Bhilai Wires Ltd.* v. *BSNL*, 2010 SCC OnLine Cal 1788: (2010) 3 CHN 329.

Foreign award passed after 13 August 1996

Foreign awards rendered after the commencement of the 1996 Act, even if proceedings had commenced prior to the commencement of the Act will be governed by the provisions of the new Act.[42]

Applicability of Arbitration Act, 1940

It is not imperative that for the right to accrue to have the award enforced under the 1940 Act, some legal proceedings for its enforcement must be pending under the Act at the time the new Act came into force.[43]

In cases where the arbitral proceedings have commenced before coming into force of the new Act and are pending before the arbitrator, it is open to the parties to agree that the new Act be applicable to such proceedings and they could so agree even before the coming into force of the new Act. There is nothing in the language of Section 85(2)(*a*) which bars the parties from so agreeing. There is, however, a bar that they cannot agree to the applicability of the old Act after the new Act came into force where arbitral proceedings under the old Act have not commenced though the arbitral agreement was under the old Act.[44]

Once arbitral proceedings have commenced under the Arbitration Act, 1940 the right to enforcement of award would be a right accrued. For such a right to accrue, any legal proceedings for enforcement need not be pending under the 1940 Act at the time when the 1996 Act came into force.[45]

Partnership deed executed much after the enactment of the Arbitration and Conciliation Act, 1996 provided for reference of disputes to arbitration as per the provisions of the 1940 Act. Such reference to arbitration under the 1940 Act would be of no consequence after coming into force of the new Act of 1996. Reference would be governed by the provisions of 1996 Act.[46]

Where the arbitration proceedings commenced before coming into force of 1996 Act but award was rendered after the commencement thereof, held award would be enforced under the provisions of 1940 Act.[47]

The provisions of the old Arbitration Act, 1940 shall apply in relation to arbitration proceedings which have commenced before the new Act 1996 came into force. So the enforcement of the award has to be examined on the touchstone of the proceedings held under the old Act.[48]

---

42. *Fuerst Day Lawson Ltd.* v. *Jindal Exports Ltd.*, (2001) 6 SCC 356.
43. *Thyssen Stahlunion Gmbh* v. *SAIL*, (1999) 9 SCC 334.
44. *Ibid.*
45. *Ibid.*
46. *Ibid.*
47. *Ibid.*
48. *Ibid.*

The new Act 1996 would be applicable in relation to proceedings which commenced on or after the new Act came into force.[49]

Dispute was referred to an arbitrator prior to the 1996 Act but the award was made subsequent to the date of commencement of the 1996 Act. Parties did not proceed on the basis that the 1996 Act would govern the proceedings. It was held that in such circumstances, proceedings arising out of the award would be governed by the provisions of the 1940 Act and not by the provisions of the 1996 Act.[50]

Section 85(2)(*a*) and Foreign Awards (Recognition and Enforcement Act), 1961

A foreign award given after the commencement of the new 1996 Act can be enforced under the new Act. There is no vested right to have the foreign award enforced under the Foreign Awards (Recognition and Enforcement) Act, 1961.[51]

After the repeal of the Foreign Awards (Recognition and Enforcement) Act, 1961 a foreign award can now be enforced under the new Act on the basis of the provisions contained in Part II of the new Act depending whether it is a New York Convention Award or a Geneva Convention Award. It is irrespective of the fact when the arbitral proceedings commenced in a foreign jurisdiction. Since no right has accrued, Section 6, General Clauses Act, 1897 would not apply.[52]

It cannot be agreed that Section 85(2)(*a*) of the new Act would keep Foreign Awards Act, 1961 alive for the purpose of the enforcement of the foreign award given after the commencement of the new Act though arbitral proceedings in a foreign land had commenced prior to Foreign Awards Act. However, if provisions of Foreign Awards Act and the new Act relating to the enforcement of the foreign award are juxtaposed there would appear to be hardly any difference.[53]

Execution of foreign award and domestic arbitration

Where a foreign award is to be executed which is itself a decree, there Section 85(2)(*a*) will have no application whereas it will have in relation to a domestic arbitration proceedings.[54]

---

49. *Ibid.*
50. *Neeraj Munjal (3)* v. *Atul Grover*, (2005) 5 SCC 404.
51. *Thyssen Stahlunion Gmbh* v. *SAIL*, (1999) 9 SCC 334.
52. *Ibid.*
53. *Ibid.*
54. *Milkfood Ltd.* v. *GMC Ice Cream (P) Ltd.*, (2004) 7 SCC 288.

Right to file appeal—An accrued right

In cases where the arbitral proceedings commenced under the old Act, it is an accrued right to proceed in accordance with that law and it would be the old Act which would apply even for enforcing the award. The right to file an appeal is an accrued right that cannot be taken away unless there is specific provision to the contrary. There is no such provision in the new Act. In the present cases, the appeals were pending before the High Court under the provisions of the old Act and, therefore, appeals were required to be decided on the basis of the statutory provisions under the said Act.[55]

Rules and notifications published under the repealed Acts [S. 85(2)(*b*)]

All rules and notifications published under the Arbitration (Protocol and Convention) Act, 1937 (6 of 1937), Arbitration Act, 1940 (10 of 1940) and Foreign Awards (Recognition and Enforcement) Act, 1961 (45 of 1961) shall to the extent to which they are not repugnant to the Arbitration and Conciliation Act, 1996 be deemed to have been made or issued under the Arbitration and Conciliation Act, 1996.

REPEAL OF ORDINANCE 27 OF 1996 AND SAVING [S. 86]

86. *Repeal of Ordinance 27 of 1996 and saving.*—(1) The Arbitration and Conciliation (Third) Ordinance, 1996 (27 of 1996) is hereby repealed.

(2) Notwithstanding such repeal, any order, rule, notification or scheme made or anything done or any action taken in pursuance of any provision of the said Ordinance shall be deemed to have been made, done or taken under the corresponding provisions of this Act.

EFFECT OF ARBITRAL AND RELATED COURT PROCEEDINGS COMMENCED PRIOR TO 23rd OCTOBER, 2015 [S. 87]

[56][**87.** *Effect of arbitral and related court proceedings commenced prior to 23rd October, 2015.*—Unless the parties otherwise agree, the amendments made to this Act by the Arbitration and Conciliation (Amendment) Act, 2015 (3 of 2016) shall—

(*a*) not apply to—

(*i*) arbitral proceedings commenced before the commencement of the Arbitration and Conciliation (Amendment) Act, 2015 (3 of 2016);

---

55. *N.S. Nayak & Sons* v. *State of Goa*, (2003) 6 SCC 56.
56. *Ins.* by Act 33 of 2019, S. 13 (w.r.e.f. 23-10-2015).

(*ii*) court proceedings arising out of or in relation to such arbitral proceedings irrespective of whether such court proceedings are commenced prior to or after the commencement of the Arbitration and Conciliation (Amendment) Act, 2015 (3 of 2016);

(*b*) apply only to arbitral proceedings commenced on or after the commencement of the Arbitration and Conciliation (Amendment) Act, 2015 (3 of 2016) and to court proceedings arising out of or in relation to such arbitral proceedings.]

COMMENTS

Corresponding old law

This section is new.

Legislative changes

Arbitration and Conciliation (Amendment) Act, 2015 (3 of 2016)

Section 87 has been inserted by the Amendment Act 33 of 2019 with effect from 23 October 2015.

Arbitration and Conciliation (Amendment) Act, 2019 (33 of 2019)

Deletion of Section 26 of the 2015 Amendment Act, together with the insertion of Section 87 by the 2019 Amendment Act is arbitrary and violative of Article 14 of the Constitution, hence struck down.[57]

---

57. *Hindustan Construction Co. Ltd.* v. *Union of India*, (2020) 17 SCC 324.

THE FIRST SCHEDULE

(*See* Section 44)

CONVENTION ON THE RECOGNITION AND ENFORCEMENT OF FOREIGN ARBITRAL AWARDS

Article I

1. This Convention shall apply to the recognition and enforcement of arbitral awards made in the territory of a State other than the State where the recognition and enforcement of such awards are sought, and arising out of differences between persons, whether physical or legal. It shall also apply to arbitral awards not considered as domestic awards in the State where their recognition and enforcement are sought.

2. The term "arbitral awards" shall include not only awards made by arbitrators appointed for each case but also those made by permanent arbitral bodies to which the parties have submitted.

3. When signing, ratifying or acceding to this Convention, or notifying extension under Article X hereof, any State may on the basis of reciprocity declare that it will apply the Convention to the recognition and enforcement of awards made only in the territory of another Contracting State. It may also declare that it will apply the Convention only to differences arising out of legal relationships, whether contractual or not, which are considered as commercial under the national law of the State making such declaration.

Article II

1. Each Contracting State shall recognise an agreement in writing under which the parties undertake to submit to arbitration all or any differences which have arisen or which may arise between them in respect of defined legal relationship, whether contractual or not, concerning a subject-matter capable of settlement by arbitration.

2. The term "agreement in writing" shall include an arbitral clause in a contract or an arbitration agreement, signed by the parties or contained in an exchange of letters or telegrams.

3. The court of a Contracting State, when seized of an action in a matter in respect of which the parties have made an agreement within the meaning of this Article, shall, at the request of one of the parties, refer the parties to arbitration, unless it finds that the said agreement is null and void, inoperative or incapable of being performed.

Article III

Each Contracting State shall recognize arbitral awards as binding and enforce them in accordance with the rules of procedure of the territory where the award is relied upon, under the conditions laid down in the following Articles. There shall not be imposed substantially more onerous conditions or higher fees or charges on the recognition or enforcement of arbitral awards to which this Convention applies than are imposed on the recognition or enforcement of domestic arbitral awards.

Article IV

1. To obtain the recognition and enforcement mentioned in the preceding Article, the party applying for recognition and enforcement shall, at the time of the application, supply:—

(*a*) the duly authenticated original award or a duly certified copy thereof;

(*b*) the original agreement referred to in Article II or a duly certified copy thereof.

2. If the said award or agreement is not made in an official language of the country in which the award is relied upon, the party applying for recognition and enforcement of the award shall produce a translation of these documents into such language. The translation shall be certified by an official or sworn translator or by a diplomatic or consular agent.

Article V

1. Recognition and enforcement of the award may be refused, at the request of the party against whom it is invoked, only if that party furnishes to the competent authority where the recognition and enforcement is sought, proof that—

(*a*) the parties to the agreement referred to in Article II were, under the law applicable to them, under some incapacity, or the said agreement is not valid under the law to which the parties have subjected it or, failing any indication thereon, under the law of the country where the award was made; or

(*b*) the party against whom the award is invoked was not given proper notice of the appointment of the arbitrator or of the arbitration proceedings or was otherwise unable to present his case; or

(*c*) the award deals with a difference not contemplated by or not falling within the terms of the submission to arbitration, or it contains decisions on matters beyond the scope of the submission to arbitration:

Provided that, if the decisions on matters submitted to arbitration can be separated from those not so submitted, that part of the award which contains decisions on matters submitted to arbitration may be recognised and enforced; or

(*d*) the composition of the arbitral authority or the arbitral procedure was not in accordance with the agreement of the parties, or, failing such agreement, was not in accordance with the law of the country where the arbitration took place; or

(*e*) the award has not yet become binding on the parties, or has been set aside or suspended by a competent authority of the country in which, or under the law of which, that award was made.

2. Recognition and enforcement of an arbitral award may also be refused if the competent authority in the country where recognition and enforcement is sought finds that —

(*a*) the subject-matter of the difference is not capable of settlement by arbitration under the law of that country; or

(*b*) the recognition or enforcement of the award would be contrary to the public policy of that country.

Article VI

If an application for the setting aside or suspension of the award has been made to a competent authority referred to in Article V(1)(*e*), the authority before which the award is sought to be relied upon may, if it considers it proper, adjourn the decision on the enforcement of the award and may also, on the application of the party claiming enforcement of the award, order the other party to give suitable security.

Article VII

1. The provisions of the present Convention shall not affect the validity of multilateral or bilateral agreements concerning the recognition and enforcement of arbitral awards entered into by the Contracting States nor deprive any interested party of any right he may have to avail himself of an arbitral award in the manner and to the extent allowed by the law or the treaties of the country where such award is sought to be relied upon.

2. The Geneva Protocol on Arbitration Clauses of 1923 and the Geneva Convention on the Execution of Foreign Arbitral Awards of 1927 shall cease to have effect between Contracting States on their becoming bound and to the extent that they become bound by this Convention.

Article VIII

1. This Convention shall be open until 31st December, 1958 for signature on behalf of any Member of the United Nations and also on behalf of any other

State which is or hereafter becomes member of any specialised agency of the United Nations, or which is or hereafter becomes a party to the Statute of the International Court of Justice, or any other State to which an invitation has been addressed by the General Assembly of the United Nations.

2. This Convention shall be ratified and the instrument of ratification shall be deposited with the Secretary-General of the United Nations.

Article IX

1. This Convention shall be open for accession to all States referred to in Article VIII.

2. Accession shall be effected by the deposit of an instrument of accession with the Secretary-General of the United Nations.

Article X

1. Any State may, at the time of signature, ratification or accession, declare that this Convention shall extend to all or any of the territories for the international relations of which it is responsible. Such a declaration shall take effect when the Convention enters into force for the State concerned.

2. At any time thereafter any such extension shall be made by notification addressed to the Secretary-General of the United Nations and shall take effect as from the ninetieth day after the day of receipt by the Secretary-General of the United Nations of this notification, or as from the date of entry into force of the Convention for the State concerned, whichever is the later.

3. With respect to those territories to which this Convention is not extended at the time of signature, ratification or accession, each State concerned shall consider the possibility of taking the necessary steps in order to extend the application of this Convention to such territories, subject, where necessary for constitutional reasons, to the consent of the Governments of such territories.

Article XI

In the case of a federal or non-unitary State, the following provisions shall apply:—

(*a*) with respect of those Articles of this Convention that come within the legislative jurisdiction of the federal authority, the obligations of the federal Government shall to this extent be the same as those of Contracting States which are not federal States;

(*b*) with respect to those Articles of this Convention that come within the legislative jurisdiction of constituent States or provinces which are not, under the constitutional system of the federation, bound to take legislative action, the federal Government shall bring such Articles with a favourable recommendation to the notice of the appropriate authorities of constituent States or provinces at the earliest possible moment;

(*c*) a federal State Party to this Convention shall, at the request of any other Contracting State transmitted through the Secretary-General of the United Nations, supply a statement of the law and practice of the federation and its constituent units in regard to any particular provision of this Convention, showing the extent to which effect has been given to that provision by legislative or other action.

Article XII

1. This Convention shall come into force on the ninetieth day following the date of deposit of the third instrument of ratification or accession.

2. For each State ratifying or acceding to this Convention after the deposit of the third instrument of ratification or accession, this Convention shall enter into force on the ninetieth day after deposit by such State of its instrument of ratification or accession.

Article XIII

1. Any Contracting State may denounce this Convention by a written notification to the Secretary-General of the United Nations. Denunciation shall take effect one year after the date of receipt of the notification by the Secretary-General.

2. Any State which has made a declaration or notification under Article X may, at any time thereafter, by notification to the Secretary-General of the United Nations, declare that this Convention shall cease to extend to the territory concerned one year after the date of the receipt of the notification by the Secretary-General.

3. This Convention shall continue to be applicable to arbitral awards in respect of which recognition or enforcement proceedings have been instituted before the denunciation takes effect.

Article XIV

A Contracting State shall not be entitled to avail itself of the present Convention against other Contracting States except to the extent that it is itself bound to apply the Convention.

Article XV

The Secretary-General of the United Nations shall notify the States contemplated in Article VIII of the following:—

(*a*) signatures and ratifications in accordance with Article VIII;
(*b*) accessions in accordance with Article IX;
(*c*) declarations and notifications under Articles I, X and XI;
(*d*) the date upon which this Convention enters into force in accordance with Article XII;
(*e*) denunciations and notifications in accordance with Article XIII.

Article XVI

1. This Convention, of which the Chinese, English, French, Russian and Spanish texts shall be equally authentic, shall be deposited in the archives of the United Nations.

2. The Secretary-General of the United Nations shall transmit a certified copy of this Convention to the States contemplated in Article XIII.

THE SECOND SCHEDULE

(*See* Section 53)

PROTOCOL ON ARBITRATION CLAUSES

The undersigned, being duly authorised, declare that they accept, on behalf of the countries which they represent, the following provisions:—

1. Each of the Contracting States recognises the validity of an agreement, whether relating to existing or future differences between parties subject respectively to the jurisdiction of different Contracting States by which the parties to a contract agree to submit to arbitration all or any differences that may arise in connection with such contract relating to commercial matters or to any other matter capable of settlement by arbitration, whether or not the arbitration is to take place in a country to whose jurisdiction none of the parties is subject.

Each Contracting State reserves the right to limit the obligation mentioned above to contracts which are considered as commercial under its national law. Any Contracting State which avails itself of this right will notify the Secretary-General of the League of Nations in order that the other Contracting States may be so informed.

2. The arbitral procedure, including the constitution of the Arbitral Tribunal, shall be governed by the will of the parties and by the law of the country in whose territory the arbitration takes place.

The Contracting States agree to facilitate all steps in the procedure which require to be taken in their own territories, in accordance with the provisions of their law governing arbitral procedure applicable to existing differences.

3. Each Contracting State undertakes to ensure the execution by its authorities and in accordance with the provisions of its national laws of arbitral awards made in its own territory under the preceding Articles.

4. The Tribunals of the Contracting Parties, on being seized of a dispute regarding a contract made between persons to whom Article 1 applies and including an Arbitration Agreement whether referring to present or future differences which is valid in virtue of the said Article and capable of being carried into effect, shall refer the parties on the application of either of them to the decision of the Arbitrators.

Such reference shall not prejudice the competence of the judicial tribunals in case the agreement or the arbitration cannot proceed or becomes inoperative.

5. The present Protocol, which shall remain open for signature by all States, shall be ratified. The ratification shall be deposited as soon as possible with the Secretary-General of the League of Nations, who shall notify such deposit to all the Signatory States.

6. The present Protocol will come into force as soon as two ratifications have been deposited. Thereafter it will take effect, in the case of each Contracting State, one month after the notification by the Secretary-General of the deposit of its ratification.

7. The present Protocol may be denounced by any Contracting State on giving one year's notice. Denunciation shall be effected by a notification addressed to the Secretary-General of the League of Nations, who will immediately transmit copies of such notification to all the other Signatory States and inform them of the date on which it was received. The denunciation shall take effect one year after the date on which it was notified to the Secretary-General, and shall operate only in respect of the notifying State.

8. The Contracting States may declare that their acceptance of the present Protocol does not include any or all of the undermentioned territories : that is to say, their colonies, overseas possessions or territories, protectorates or the territories over which they exercise a mandate.

The said States may subsequently adhere separately on behalf of any territory thus excluded. The Secretary-General of the League of Nations shall be informed as soon as possible of such adhesions. He shall notify such adhesions to all Signatory States. They will take effect one month after the notification by the Secretary-General to all Signatory States.

The Contracting States may also denounce the Protocol separately on behalf of any of the territories referred to above. Article 7 applies to such denunciation.

THE THIRD SCHEDULE

(*See* Section 53)

CONVENTION ON THE EXECUTION OF FOREIGN ARBITRAL AWARDS

Article 1.—(1) In the territories of any High Contracting Party to which the present Convention applies, an arbitral award made in pursuance of an agreement whether relating to existing or future differences (hereinafter called "a submission to arbitration") covered by the Protocol on Arbitration Clauses opened at Geneva on September 24th, 1923, shall be recognised as binding and shall be enforced in accordance with the rules of the procedure of the territory where the award is relied upon, provided that the said award has been made in a territory of one of the High Contracting Parties to which the present Convention applies and between persons who are subject to the jurisdiction of one of the High Contracting Parties.

(2) To obtain such recognition or enforcement, it shall, further, be necessary:—

(*a*) that the award has been made in pursuance of a submission to arbitration which is valid under the law applicable thereto;

(*b*) that the subject-matter of the award is capable of settlement by arbitration under the law of the country in which the award is sought to be relied upon;

(*c*) that the award has been made by the Arbitral Tribunal provided for in the submission to arbitration or constituted in the manner agreed upon by the parties and in conformity with the law governing the arbitration procedure;

(*d*) that the award has become final in the country in which it has been made, in the sense that it will not be considered as such if it is open to opposition, appeal or pourvoi en cassation (in the countries where such forms of procedure exist) or if it is proved that any proceedings for the purpose of contesting the validity of the award are pending;

(*e*) that the recognition or enforcement of the award is not contrary to the public policy or to the principles of the law of the country in which it is sought to be relied upon.

Article 2.—Even if the conditions laid down in Article 1 hereof are fulfilled, recognition and enforcement of the award shall be refused if the Court is satisfied:—

(*a*) that the award has been annulled in the country in which it was made;

(*b*) that the party against whom it is sought to use the award was not given notice of the arbitration proceedings in sufficient time to enable him to present his case; or that, being under a legal incapacity, he was not properly represented;

(*c*) that the award does not deal with the differences contemplated by or falling within the terms of the submission to arbitration or that it contains decisions on matters beyond the scope of the submission to arbitration.

If the award has not covered all the questions submitted to the arbitral tribunal, the competent authority of the country where recognition or enforcement of the award is sought can, if it thinks fit, postpone such recognition or enforcement or grant it subject to such guarantee as that authority may decide.

Article 3.—If the party against whom the award has been made proves that, under the law governing the arbitration procedure, there is a ground, other than the grounds referred to in Article 1(*a*) and (*c*), and Article 2(*b*) and (*c*), entitling him to contest the validity of the award in a Court of Law, the Court may, if it thinks fit, either refuse recognition or enforcement of the award or adjourn the consideration thereof, giving such party a reasonable time within which to have the award annulled by the competent tribunal.

Article 4.—The party relying upon an award or claiming its enforcement must supply, in particular:—

(1) the original award or a copy thereof duly authenticated, according to the requirements of the law of the country in which it was made;

(2) documentary or other evidence to prove that the award has become final, in the sense defined in Article 1(*d*), in the country in which it was made;

(3) when necessary, documentary or other evidence to prove that the conditions laid down in Article 1, paragraph (1) and paragraph (2)(*a*) and (*c*), have been fulfilled.

A translation of the award and of the other documents mentioned in this Article into the official language of the country where the award is sought to be relied upon may be demanded. Such translations must be certified correct by a diplomatic or consular agent of the country to which the party who seeks to rely upon the award belongs or by a sworn translator of the country where the award is sought to be relied upon.

Article 5.—The provisions of the above Articles shall not deprive any interested party of the right of availing himself of an arbitral award in the manner and to the extent allowed by the law or the treaties of the country where such award is sought to be relied upon.

Article 6.—The present Convention applies only to arbitral awards made after the coming into force of the Protocol on Arbitration Clauses opened at Geneva on September 24th, 1923.

Article 7.—The present Convention, which will remain open to the signature of all the signatories of the Protocol of 1923 on Arbitration Clauses, shall be ratified.

It may be ratified only on behalf of those Members of the League of Nations and non-Member States on whose behalf the Protocol of 1923 shall have been ratified.

Ratification shall be deposited as soon as possible with the Secretary-General of the League of Nations, who will notify such deposit to all the signatories.

Article 8.—The present Convention shall come into force three months after it shall have been ratified on behalf of two High Contracting Parties. Thereafter, it shall take effect, in the case of each High Contracting Party, three months after the deposit of the ratification on its behalf with the Secretary-General of the League of Nations.

Article 9.—The present Convention may be denounced on behalf of any Member of the League or non-Member State. Denunciation shall be notified in writing to the Secretary-General of the League of Nations, who will immediately send a copy thereof, certified to be in conformity with the notifications, to all the other Contracting Parties, at the same time informing them of the date on which he received it.

The denunciation shall come into force only in respect of the High Contracting Party which shall have notified it and one year after such notification shall have reached the Secretary-General of the League of Nations.

The denunciation of the Protocol on Arbitration Clauses shall entail, ipso facto, the denunciation of the present Convention.

Article 10.—The present Convention does not apply to the colonies, protectorates or territories under suzerainty or mandate of any High Contracting Party unless they are specially mentioned.

The application of this Convention to one or more of such colonies, protectorates or territories to which the Protocol on Arbitration Clauses opened at Geneva on September 24th, 1923, applies, can be effected at any time by means of a declaration addressed to the Secretary-General of the League of Nations by one of the High Contracting Parties.

Such declaration shall take effect three months after the deposit thereof.

The High Contracting Parties can at any time denounce the Convention for all or any of the colonies, protectorates or territories referred to above. Article 9 hereof applied to such denunciation.

Article 11.—A certified copy of the present Convention shall be transmitted by the Secretary-General of the League of Nations to every Member of the League of Nations and to every non-Member State which signs the same.

[58][THE FOURTH SCHEDULE

[[59][*See* Section 11(3-A)]]

Sl. No.	**Sum in dispute**	**Model fee**
(1)	**(2)**	**(3)**
1.	Up to Rs 5,00,000	Rs 45,000
2.	Above Rs 5,00,000 and up to Rs 20,00,000	Rs 45,000 plus 3.5 per cent of the claim amount over and above Rs 5,00,000.
3.	Above Rs 20,00,000 and up to Rs 1,00,00,000	Rs 97,500 plus 3 per cent of the claim amount over and above Rs 20,00,000.
4.	Above Rs 1,00,00,000 and up to Rs 10,00,00,000	Rs 3,37,500 plus 1 per cent of the claim amount over and above Rs 1,00,00,000.
5.	Above Rs 10,00,00,000 and up to Rs 20,00,00,000	Rs 12,37,500 plus 0.75 per cent of the claim amount over and above Rs 10,00,00,000.
6.	Above Rs 20,00,00,000	Rs 19,87,500 plus 0.5 per cent of the claim amount over and above Rs 20,00,00,000 with a ceiling of Rs 30,00,000.

Note: In the event the arbitral tribunal is a sole arbitrator, he shall be entitled to an additional amount of twenty-five per cent on the fee payable as per the above.]

[60][THE FIFTH SCHEDULE

[*See* Section 12(1)(*b*)]

The following grounds give rise to justifiable doubts as to the independence or impartiality of arbitrators:

Arbitrator's relationship with the parties or counsel

1. The arbitrator is an employee, consultant, advisor or has any other past or present business relationship with a party.
2. The arbitrator currently represents or advises one of the parties or an affiliate of one of the parties.
3. The arbitrator currently represents the lawyer or law firm acting as counsel for one of the parties.
4. The arbitrator is a lawyer in the same law firm which is representing one of the parties.

58. *Subs.* by S.O. 5674(E), dt. 12-11-2018 (w.r.e.f. 23-10-2015).
59. *Subs.* for "[*See* Section 11(14)]" by Act 33 of 2019, S. 16 (w.e.f. the date to be notified).
60. *Ins.* by Act 3 of 2016, S. 25 (w.r.e.f. 23-10-2015).

5. The arbitrator is a manager, director or part of the management, or has a similar controlling influence, in an affiliate of one of the parties if the affiliate is directly involved in the matters in dispute in the arbitration.
6. The arbitrator's law firm had a previous but terminated involvement in the case without the arbitrator being involved himself or herself.
7. The arbitrator's law firm currently has a significant commercial relationship with one of the parties or an affiliate of one of the parties.
8. The arbitrator regularly advises the appointing party or an affiliate of the appointing party even though neither the arbitrator nor his or her firm derives a significant financial income therefrom.
9. The arbitrator has a close family relationship with one of the parties and in the case of companies with the persons in the management and controlling the company.
10. A close family member of the arbitrator has a significant financial interest in one of the parties or an affiliate of one of the parties.
11. The arbitrator is a legal representative of an entity that is a party in the arbitration.
12. The arbitrator is a manager, director or part of the management, or has a similar controlling influence in one of the parties.
13. The arbitrator has a significant financial interest in one of the parties or the outcome of the case.
14. The arbitrator regularly advises the appointing party or an affiliate of the appointing party, and the arbitrator or his or her firm derives a significant financial income therefrom.

Relationship of the arbitrator to the dispute

15. The arbitrator has given legal advice or provided an expert opinion on the dispute to a party or an affiliate of one of the parties.
16. The arbitrator has previous involvement in the case.

Arbitrator's direct or indirect interest in the dispute

17. The arbitrator holds shares, either directly or indirectly, in one of the parties or an affiliate of one of the parties that is privately held.
18. A close family member of the arbitrator has a significant financial interest in the outcome of the dispute.
19. The arbitrator or a close family member of the arbitrator has a close relationship with a third party who may be liable to recourse on the part of the unsuccessful party in the dispute.

Previous services for one of the parties or other involvement in the case

20. The arbitrator has within the past three years served as counsel for one of the parties or an affiliate of one of the parties or has previously advised or been consulted by the party or an affiliate of the party making the appointment in an unrelated matter, but the arbitrator and the party or the affiliate of the party have no ongoing relationship.
21. The arbitrator has within the past three years served as counsel against one of the parties or an affiliate of one of the parties in an unrelated matter.
22. The arbitrator has within the past three years been appointed as arbitrator on two or more occasions by one of the parties or an affiliate of one of the parties.
23. The arbitrator's law firm has within the past three years acted for one of the parties or an affiliate of one of the parties in an unrelated matter without the involvement of the arbitrator.
24. The arbitrator currently serves, or has served within the past three years, as arbitrator in another arbitration on a related issue involving one of the parties or an affiliate of one of the parties.

Relationship between an arbitrator and another arbitrator or counsel

25. The arbitrator and another arbitrator are lawyers in the same law firm.
26. The arbitrator was within the past three years a partner of, or otherwise affiliated with, another arbitrator or any of the counsel in the same arbitration.
27. A lawyer in the arbitrator's law firm is an arbitrator in another dispute involving the same party or parties or an affiliate of one of the parties.
28. A close family member of the arbitrator is a partner or employee of the law firm representing one of the parties, but is not assisting with the dispute.
29. The arbitrator has within the past three years received more than three appointments by the same counsel or the same law firm.

Relationship between arbitrator and party and others involved in the arbitration

30. The arbitrator's law firm is currently acting adverse to one of the parties or an affiliate of one of the parties.
31. The arbitrator had been associated within the past three years with a party or an affiliate of one of the parties in a professional capacity, such as a former employee or partner.

Other circumstances

32. The arbitrator holds shares, either directly or indirectly, which by reason of number or denomination constitute a material holding in one of the parties or an affiliate of one of the parties that is publicly listed.
33. The arbitrator holds a position in an arbitration institution with appointing authority over the dispute.
34. The arbitrator is a manager, director or part of the management, or has a similar controlling influence, in an affiliate of one of the parties, where the affiliate is not directly involved in the matters in dispute in the arbitration.

Explanation 1.—The term "close family member" refers to a spouse, sibling, child, parent or life partner.

Explanation 2.—The term "affiliate" encompasses all companies in one group of companies including the parent company.

Explanation 3.—For the removal of doubts, it is clarified that it may be the practice in certain specific kinds of arbitration, such as maritime or commodities arbitration, to draw arbitrators from a small, specialised pool. If in such fields it is the custom and practice for parties frequently to appoint the same arbitrator in different cases, this is a relevant fact to be taken into account while applying the rules set out above.]

[61][THE SIXTH SCHEDULE

[*See* Section 12(1)(*b*)]

Name:

Contact Details:

Prior Experience (Including Experience with Arbitrations):

Number of ongoing arbitrations:

Circumstances disclosing any past or present relationship with or interest in any of the parties or in relation to the subject-matter in dispute, whether financial, business, professional or other kind, which is likely to give rise to justifiable doubts as to your independence or impartiality (list out):

Circumstances which are likely to affect your ability to devote sufficient time to the arbitration and in particular your ability to finish the entire arbitration within twelve months (list out) :]

---

61. *Ins.* by Act 3 of 2016, S. 25 (w.r.e.f. 23-10-2015).

[62][THE SEVENTH SCHEDULE

[*See* Section 12(5)]

Arbitrator's relationship with the parties or counsel

1. The arbitrator is an employee, consultant, advisor or has any other past or present business relationship with a party.
2. The arbitrator currently represents or advises one of the parties or an affiliate of one of the parties.
3. The arbitrator currently represents the lawyer or law firm acting as counsel for one of the parties.
4. The arbitrator is a lawyer in the same law firm which is representing one of the parties.
5. The arbitrator is a manager, director or part of the management, or has a similar controlling influence, in an affiliate of one of the parties if the affiliate is directly involved in the matters in dispute in the arbitration.
6. The arbitrator's law firm had a previous but terminated involvement in the case without the arbitrator being involved himself or herself.
7. The arbitrator's law firm currently has a significant commercial relationship with one of the parties or an affiliate of one of the parties.
8. The arbitrator regularly advises the appointing party or an affiliate of the appointing party even though neither the arbitrator nor his or her firm derives a significant financial income therefrom.
9. The arbitrator has a close family relationship with one of the parties and in the case of companies with the persons in the management and controlling the company.
10. A close family member of the arbitrator has a significant financial interest in one of the parties or an affiliate of one of the parties.
11. The arbitrator is a legal representative of an entity that is a party in the arbitration.
12. The arbitrator is a manager, director or part of the management, or has a similar controlling influence in one of the parties.
13. The arbitrator has a significant financial interest in one of the parties or the outcome of the case.
14. The arbitrator regularly advises the appointing party or an affiliate of the appointing party, and the arbitrator or his or her firm derives a significant financial income therefrom.

---

62. *Ins.* by Act 3 of 2016, S. 25 (w.r.e.f. 23-10-2015).

Relationship of the arbitrator to the dispute

15. The arbitrator has given legal advice or provided an expert opinion on the dispute to a party or an affiliate of one of the parties.
16. The arbitrator has previous involvement in the case.

Arbitrator's direct or indirect interest in the dispute

17. The arbitrator holds shares, either directly or indirectly, in one of the parties or an affiliate of one of the parties that is privately held.
18. A close family member of the arbitrator has a significant financial interest in the outcome of the dispute.
19. The arbitrator or a close family member of the arbitrator has a close relationship with a third party who may be liable to recourse on the part of the unsuccessful party in the dispute.

Explanation 1.—The term "close family member" refers to a spouse, sibling, child, parent or life partner.

Explanation 2.—The term "affiliate" encompasses all companies in one group of companies including the parent company.

Explanation 3.—For the removal of doubts, it is clarified that it may be the practice in certain specific kinds of arbitration, such as maritime or commodities arbitration, to draw arbitrators from a small, specialised pool. If in such fields it is the custom and practice for parties frequently to appoint the same arbitrator in different cases, this is a relevant fact to be taken into account while applying the rules set out above.]

THE EIGHTH SCHEDULE

[63][* * *]

63. *Omitted* by Act 3 of 2021, S. 4 (w.r.e.f. 4-11-2020).

MEDIATION ACT, 2023

Mediation Act, 2023[1]

[Act 32 of 2023 as amended up to S.O. 4506(E), dated 13-10-2023]

[14th September, 2023]

An Act to promote and facilitate mediation, especially institutional mediation, for resolution of disputes, commercial or otherwise, enforce mediated settlement agreements, provide for a body for registration of mediators, to encourage community mediation and to make online mediation as acceptable and cost effective process and for matters connected therewith or incidental thereto

Be it enacted by Parliament in the Seventy-fourth Year of the Republic of India as follows—

Prefatory Note—Statement of Objects and Reasons.—An effective dispute resolution process has a significant impact on the economy and doing business in the country, thereby promoting ease of living for citizens, access to justice and rule of law. The rapidly changing society and progress in various areas not limited to economic, industrial or financial sectors, demand commensurate expeditious settlement of dispute between the parties, which at present is time consuming. Thus, there is a need to further promote Alternative Dispute Resolution (ADR), inter alia, by institutional mediation. The ADR mechanism of mediation though finds mention in various existing laws, but as on date, there is no comprehensive law governing the various aspects of mediation.

2. Mediation results in amicable resolution of disputes in civil, commercial, family and matrimonial matters and fosters collaborative approach, reduces the burden on the courts, and preserves relationships amongst disputants. Therefore, bringing a comprehensive mediation law and providing for online mediation may serve the interests of all the stakeholders as effective alternative mechanism for resolving disputes.

3. The Bill covering the various aspects of mediation seeks to promote mediation as a preferred mode of ADR, inter alia, providing for—

(*i*) subsuming conciliation under Part III of the Arbitration and Conciliation Act, 1996, in mediation as per international practice of using the terms "conciliation" and "mediation" interchangeably;

---

1. Received the assent of the President on September 14, 2023 and published in the Gazette of India, Extra., Pt. II, S. 1, dt. 15-9-2023, No. 35.

(*ii*) compulsory pre-litigation mediation in matters of civil or commercial dispute, before parties approach a court or a tribunal as provided;

(*iii*) conduct of online mediation;

(*iv*) an indicative list of matters which are not fit for mediation under the First Schedule;

(*v*) mediation that will take place within the territorial jurisdiction of the court or tribunal of competent jurisdiction, unless parties agree otherwise or undertake mediation in online mode;

(*vi*) a period of one hundred and eighty days, for completing the mediation process which is further extendable to a maximum period of one hundred and eighty days with the mutual consent of the parties;

(*vii*) the mediated settlement agreement resulting from mediation which will be final and binding and will be enforceable in accordance with the provisions of Code of Civil Procedure, 1908, in the same manner as if it were a judgment or decree of a Court;

(*viii*) establishment of Mediation Council of India, objects of which would be, inter alia, to promote mediation and to develop India as a robust centre for domestic and international mediation, make regulations for registration of mediators, grade mediation service providers, specify criteria for recognition of mediation institutes and mediation service providers, to hold training workshops and courses in the area of mediation, etc.; and

(*ix*) conduct of community mediation with consent of parties for disputes which are likely to affect peace, harmony and tranquility amongst the residents or families of any area or locality.

4. The Bill seeks to achieve the above objectives.

CHAPTER I

PRELIMINARY

1. *Short title, extent and commencement.*—(1) This Act may be called the **Mediation Act, 2023**.

(2) It shall extend to the whole of India.

(3) It shall come into force on such date as the Central Government may, by notification, appoint and different dates may be appointed for different provisions of this Act and any reference in any such provision to the commencement of this Act shall be construed as a reference to the coming into force of that provision.

Date of Enforcement: Section 1 enforced w.e.f. 9-10-2023, *vide* Noti. No. S.O. 4384(E), dt. 9-10-2023.

COMMENTS

1. SHORT TITLE, EXTENT AND COMMENCEMENT [S. 1]

This section provides for short title, extent and commencement of the Act.

The Mediation Bill was tabled in the Rajya Sabha in December 2021. Rajya Sabha referred the Bill to the Department-related Parliamentary Standing Committee on Personnel, Public Grievances, Law and Justice for examination. The Committee considered the viewpoints of the various stakeholders—Judges, experts, mediation centres all over India, and the Mediation and Conciliation Project Committee of the Supreme Court (MCPC)—and presented its report before the Rajya Sabha on 11 July 2023. Rajya Sabha passed the Bill on 1 August 2023 and Lok Sabha passed the Bill on 7 August 2023. The Bill received the assent of the President of India on 15 September 2023, and came to be known as the Mediation Act, 2023.

2. AIMS AND OBJECTS

Mediation results in amicable settlement of disputes in 1) civil, 2) commercial, 3) family, and 4) community matters.

Prior to the enactment of the Mediation Act, 2023, there was no comprehensive enactment dealing with all aspects of mediation. The Act has been enacted to facilitate mediation, especially institutional mediation, for resolution of disputes, commercial or otherwise, enforce mediated settlement agreement, for registration of mediators to encourage community mediation and to make online mediation as acceptable mode of mediation. The various types of mediation contemplated by the Act are: 1) pre-mediation, 2) online mediation, 3) community mediation, 4) court-annexed mediation, and 5) institutional mediation.

The other enactments which provide for resolution by mediation are:

1. Civil Procedure Code, 1908 Section 89
2. Legal Services Authorities Act, 1987
3. Commercial Courts Act, 2015
4. Family Courts Act, 1984
5. Consumers Protection Act, 2019
6. Micro, Small and Medium Enterprises Development Act, 2006
7. Companies Act, 2013

3. MEDIATION, ITS PROCEDURE

For mediation under the Mediation Act, 2023, the other essential requirement is that the court/tribunal undertaking mediation must have territorial jurisdiction to decide the subject-matter of dispute. [S. 13]

For initiation of any mediation, the other requirement is that there should be a valid mediation agreement between the parties. The agreement must be in writing, providing for all or certain disputes arising out of the conflict between the two parties to be referred to mediation. It is not required that there should be a separate mediation agreement; it is enough if there is a particular clause in the agreement for mediation. There may be a mediation agreement in an exchange of communications or letters as provided in the Information Technology Act, 2000 (21 of 2000), or in any pleadings in a suit or other proceedings in which existence of mediation agreement is alleged, by one party and not denied by the other party. [S. 4]

A mediator 1) registered with the Mediation Council of India, or 2) empanelled by a court-annexed mediation centre, or 3) empanelled by an Authority constituted under the Legal Services Authorities Act, 1987, or 4) empanelled by a mediation service provider recognised under the Mediation Act, 2023, shall conduct the pre-litigation mediation.

Notwithstanding the non-settlement of dispute in pre-litigation mediation under Section 5(1), the court/tribunal may at any stage of the proceedings in the case refer the parties to undertake mediation.

Where the parties have voluntarily decided or have been directed by the court to undertake mediation, the next step in the process is the appointment of a mediator. As stated by Section 3(*i*), a mediator means a person who is appointed as mediator—

1. by the parties, or
2. by the mediation service provider to undertake mediation, and
3. includes a person registered as mediator with the Mediation Council of India.

Where more than one person is appointed for mediation, reference to a mediator under this Act shall be a reference to all the mediators.

Unless otherwise agreed upon by the parties, a person of any nationality may be appointed as mediator. However, the mediator of any foreign nationality shall possess such qualification, experience and accreditation as may be specified. [S. 8(1)] The parties shall be free to agree upon the name of the mediator and the procedure for their appointment. [S. 8(2)] If the parties do not reach any agreement on the name and procedure for appointment of the mediator, the party initiating the mediation shall make an application to the mediation service provider for the appointment of a mediator, who shall appoint mediator within a period of seven days. The mediation service provider shall provide all facilities, secretarial assistance and infrastructure for the efficient conduct of mediation, promote professional and ethical conduct amongst the mediators and shall also facilitate registration with the provisions of Section 20 of the Act.

The mediator cannot in any capacity enforce or impose any solution on either party or give any assurance that the mediation shall definitely reap positive results. [S. 16(2)] The mediator is bound to complete the mediation within 180 days. [S. 18]

4. QUALIFICATIONS OF PERSONS TO BE EMPANELLED AS MEDIATOR

The following shall be treated as qualified and eligible for being enlisted in the panel of mediators under Rule 3, *namely*:

(*a*) (*i*) Retired Judges of the Supreme Court of India;

(*ii*) Retired Judges of the High Court;

(*iii*) Retired District and Sessions Judges or retired Judges of the City Civil Court or Courts of equivalent status.

(*b*) Legal practitioners with at least 15 years standing at the Bar at the level of the Supreme Court or the High Court; or the District Courts or Courts of equivalent status.

(*c*) Experts or other professionals with at least 15 years standing or retired senior bureaucrats or retired senior executives.

(*d*) Institutions which are themselves experts in mediation and have been recognised as such by the High Court, provided the names of its members are approved by the High Court initially or whenever there is change in membership. [Maharashtra Alternative Dispute Resolution Rules, 2006, Part II, R. 4]

5. VENUE FOR CONDUCTING MEDIATION

The mediator shall conduct the mediation at one or other of the following places:

(*i*) Venue of the Lok Adalat or permanent Lok Adalat.

(*ii*) Any place identified by the High Court.

(*iii*) Any place identified by the District Judge or Principal Judge, City Civil Court or Principal Judge, Family Court, within the Court precincts for the purpose of conducting mediation.

(*iv*) Any place identified by the Bar Association or State Bar Council for the purpose of mediation, within the premises of the Bar Association or State Bar Council, as the case may be.

(*v*) Any other place as may be agreed upon by the parties subject to the approval of the Court. [Maharashtra Alternative Dispute Resolution Rules Part I, R. 6]

6. PROCEDURE OF MEDIATION

(*a*) The parties may agree on the procedure to be followed by the mediator in the conduct of the mediation proceedings.

(*b*) Where the parties do not agree on any particular procedure to be followed by the mediator, the mediator shall follow the procedure hereinafter mentioned, namely:

(*i*) he shall fix, in consultation with the parties, a time schedule, the dates and the time of each mediation session, where all parties have to be present;

(*ii*) he shall hold the mediation conference in accordance with the provisions of Rule 6;

(*iii*) he may conduct joint or separate meetings with the parties;

(*iv*) each party shall, ten days before a sessions, provide to the mediator a brief memorandum setting forth the issues, which according to it, need to be resolved, and its position in respect to these issues and all information reasonably required for the mediator to understand the issue; such memoranda shall also be mutually exchanged between the parties;

(*v*) each party shall furnish to the mediator, copies of pleadings or documents or such other information as may be required by him in connection with the issues to be resolved;

Provided that where the mediator is of the opinion that he should look into any original document, the Court may permit him to look into the original document before such officer of the Court and on such date or time as the Court may fix.

(*vi*) each party shall furnish to the mediator such other information as may be required by him in connection with the issues to be resolved.

(*c*) Where there is more than one mediator, the mediator nominated by each party shall first confer with the party that nominated him and shall thereafter interact with the other mediators, with a view to resolving the disputes. [Maharashtra Alternative Dispute Resolution Rules Part II, R. 11]

7. MEDIATOR NOT BOUND BY EVIDENCE ACT, 1872/ BSA 2023 OR CODE OF CIVIL PROCEDURE

The mediator shall not be bound by the Code of Civil Procedure, 1908 or the Evidence Act, 1872 but shall be guided by principles of fairness and justice, having regard to the rights and obligations of the parties, usages of trade, if any, and the nature of the dispute. [Maharashtra Alternative Dispute Resolution Rules Part II, R. 12] Section 15(5) of the Mediation Act, 2023 is also to the same effect.

8. NON-ATTENDANCE OF PARTIES AT SESSIONS OR MEETINGS ON DUE DATES

(*a*) The parties shall be present personally or may be represented by their counsel or power of attorney holders at the meetings or sessions notified by the mediator.

(*b*) If a party fails to attend a sessions or a meeting notified by the mediator, other parties or the mediator can apply to the Court in which the suit is filed, to issue appropriate directions to that party to attend before the mediator and if the Court finds that a party is absenting himself before the mediator without sufficient reason, the Court may take action against the said party by imposition of costs. [Maharashtra Alternative Dispute Resolution Rules, Part II, R. 13]

9. ROLE OF MEDIATOR

16. *Role of mediator.*—(1) The mediator shall attempt to facilitate voluntary resolution of the dispute by the parties and communicate the view of each party to the other to the extent agreed to by them, assist them in identifying issues, advancing better understanding, clarifying priorities, exploring areas of settlement and generating options in an attempt to resolve the dispute expeditiously, emphasising that it is the responsibility of the parties to take decision regarding their claims.

(2) The parties shall be informed expressly by the mediator that he only facilitates in arriving at a decision to resolve a dispute and that he shall not impose any settlement nor give any assurance that the mediation may result in a settlement.

CHAPTER II

APPLICATION

2. *Application.*—This Act shall apply where mediation is conducted in India, and—

(*i*) all or both parties habitually reside in or are incorporated in or have their place of business in India; or

(*ii*) the mediation agreement provides that any dispute shall be resolved in accordance with the provisions of this Act; or

(*iii*) there is an international mediation; or

(*iv*) wherein one of the parties to the dispute is the Central Government or a State Government or agencies, public bodies, corporations and local bodies, including entities controlled or owned by such Government and where the matter pertains to a commercial dispute; or

(*v*) to any other kind of dispute if deemed appropriate and notified by the Central Government or a State Government from time to time, for resolution through mediation under this Act, wherein such Governments, or agencies, public bodies, corporations and local bodies including entities controlled or owned by them, is a party.

COMMENTS

1. APPLICATION

This section provides for applicability of the Act.

2. APPLICABILITY OF THE ACT

The Mediation Act, 2023 shall apply—

(*i*) where the mediation is conducted in India;

(*ii*) the mediation agreement provides that any dispute shall be resolved in accordance with the provisions of this Act; or

(*iii*) there is an international mediation; or

(*iv*) where State Government or agencies, public bodies, corporations and local bodies, including entities controlled or owned by such Government and where the matter pertains to a commercial dispute; or

(*v*) Any other kind of disputes if deemed appropriate and notified by the Central Government or a State Government from time to time, for resolution through mediation under this Act, wherein such Government, or agencies, public bodies, corporations and local bodies including entities controlled or owned by them, is a party.

3. ACT NOT TO APPLY TO PENDING PROCEEDINGS

This Act shall not apply to or in relation to any mediation or conciliation commenced before coming into force of this Act. [S. 56] Thus, in view of this section only those matters which are referred to mediation after the commencement of this Act shall be governed by this Act.

4. PROCEEDINGS BEFORE LOK ADALAT/PERMANENT LOK ADALAT [S. 26]

Section 26, Mediation Act clearly provides that the provisions of the Act shall not apply to the proceedings conducted by Lok Adalat and Permanent Lok Adalat under the Legal Services Authorities Act, 1987 (39 of 1987).

3. *Definitions.*—In this Act, unless the context otherwise requires,—

(*a*) "commercial dispute" means a dispute defined in clause (*c*) of sub-section (1) of Section 2 of the Commercial Courts Act, 2015 (4 of 2016);

(*b*) "community mediator" means a mediator for the purposes of conduct of community mediation under Chapter X;

(*c*) "Council" means the Mediation Council of India established under Section 31;

(*d*) "court" means the competent court in India having pecuniary and territorial jurisdiction and having jurisdiction to decide the disputes forming the subject matter of mediation, if the same had been the subject matter of a suit or proceeding;

(*e*) "court-annexed mediation" means mediation including pre-litigation mediation conducted at the mediation centres established by any court or tribunal;

(*f*) "institutional mediation" means mediation conducted under the aegis of a mediation service provider;

(*g*) "international mediation" means mediation undertaken under this Act and relates to a commercial dispute arising out of a legal relationship, contractual or otherwise, under any law for the time being in force in India, and where at least one of the parties, is—

(*i*) an individual who is a national of, or habitually resides in, any country other than India; or

(*ii*) a body corporate including a Limited Liability Partnership of any nature, with its place of business outside India; or

(*iii*) an association or body of individuals whose place of business is outside India; or

(*iv*) the Government of a foreign country;

(*h*) "mediation" includes a process, whether referred to by the expression mediation, pre-litigation mediation, online mediation, community mediation, conciliation or an expression of similar import, whereby parties attempt to reach an amicable settlement of their dispute with the assistance of a third person referred to as mediator, who does not have the authority to impose a settlement upon the parties to the dispute;

(*i*) "mediator" means a person who is appointed to be a mediator, by the parties or by a mediation service provider, to undertake mediation, and includes a person registered as mediator with the Council.

Explanation.—Where more than one mediator is appointed for a mediation, reference to a mediator under this Act shall be a reference to all the mediators;

(*j*) "mediation agreement" means a mediation agreement referred to in sub-section (1) of Section 4;

(*k*) "mediation communication" means communication made, whether in electronic form or otherwise, through—

(*i*) anything said or done;

(*ii*) any document; or

(*iii*) any information provided, for the purposes of, or in relation to, or in the course of mediation, and includes a mediation agreement or a mediated settlement agreement;

(*l*) "mediation institute" means a body or organisation that provides training, continuous education and certification of mediators and carries out such other functions under this Act;

(*m*) "mediation service provider" means a mediation service provider referred to in sub-section (1) of Section 40;

(*n*) "mediated settlement agreement" means mediated settlement agreement referred to in sub-section (1) of Section 19;

(*o*) "Member" means a Full-Time or Part-Time Member of the Council and includes the Chairperson;

(*p*) "notification" means notification published in the Official Gazette and the expression "notified" with its cognate meanings and grammatical variations shall be construed accordingly;

(*q*) "online mediation" means online mediation referred to in Section 30;

(*r*) "participants" means persons other than the parties who participate in the mediation and includes advisers, advocates, consultants and any technical experts and observers;

(*s*) "party" means a party to a mediation agreement or mediation proceeding whose agreement or consent is necessary to resolve the dispute and includes their successors;

(*t*) "place of business" includes—

(*a*) a place from where the business is ordinarily carried on, and includes a warehouse, a godown or any other place where a party stores it's goods, supplies or receives goods or services or both; or

(*b*) a place where a party maintains its books of account; or

(*c*) a place where a party is engaged in business through an agent, by whatever name called;

(*u*) "pre-litigation mediation" means a process of undertaking mediation, as provided under Section 5, for settlement of disputes prior to the filing of a suit or proceeding of civil or commercial nature in respect thereof, before a court or notified tribunal under sub-section (2) of Section 5;

(*v*) "prescribed" means prescribed by rules made by the Central Government under this Act;

(*w*) "Schedule" means the Schedule annexed to this Act;

(*x*) "secure electronic signature" with reference to online mediation means, electronic signatures referred to in Section 15 of the Information Technology Act, 2000 (21 of 2000); and

(*y*) "specified" means specified by regulations made by the Council under this Act.

Date of Enforcement: Section 3 enforced w.e.f. 9-10-2023, *vide* Noti. No. S.O. 4384(E), dt. 9-10-2023.

COMMENTS

1. SCOPE

This section provides definitions of various expressions used in the Act.

2. COMMERCIAL DISPUTE [S. 3(*a*)]

"Commercial dispute" means a dispute defined in clause (*c*) of sub-section (1) of Section 2, Commercial Courts Act, 2015 (4 of 2016). Section 2(1)(*c*), Commercial Courts Act defines "commercial dispute" as under:

(*i*) ordinary transactions of merchants, bankers, financiers and traders such as those relating to mercantile documents, including enforcement and interpretation of such documents;

(*ii*) export or import of merchandise or services;

(*iii*) issues relating to admiralty and maritime law;

(*iv*) transactions relating to aircraft, aircraft engines, aircraft equipment and helicopters, including sales, leasing and financing of the same;

(*v*) carriage of goods;

(*vi*) construction and infrastructure contracts, including tenders;

(*vii*) agreements relating to immovable property used exclusively in trade or commerce;

(*viii*) franchising agreements;

(*ix*) distribution and licensing agreements;

(*x*) management and consultancy agreements;

(*xi*) joint venture agreements;

(*xii*) shareholders agreements;

(*xiii*) subscription and investment agreements pertaining to the services industry including outsourcing services and financial services;

(*xiv*) mercantile agency and mercantile usage;

(*xv*) partnership agreements;

(*xvi*) technology development agreements;

(*xvii*) intellectual property rights relating to registered and unregistered trademarks, copyright, patent, design, domain names, geographical indications and semiconductor integrated circuits;

(*xviii*) agreements for sale of goods or provision of services;

(*xix*) exploitation of oil and gas reserves or other natural resources including electromagnetic spectrum;

(*xx*) insurance and re-insurance;

(*xxi*) contracts of agency relating to any of the above; and

(*xxii*) such other commercial disputes as may be notified by the Central Government.

Explanation.—A commercial dispute shall not cease to be a commercial dispute merely because—

(*a*) it also involves action for recovery of immovable property or for realisation of monies out of immovable property given as security or involves any other relief pertaining to immovable property;

(*b*) one of the contracting parties is the State or any of its agencies or instrumentalities, or a private body carrying out public functions;

3. "MEDIATION" [S. 3(*h*)]

"Mediation" is a process whereby the parties attempt to reach an amicable settlement of their dispute with the assistance of a third person called as mediator, who does not have any authority to impose a settlement upon the parties to the dispute. A mediator is a person who is appointed to be a mediator

1. by the parties, or
2. by a mediation service provider to undertake mediation, and
3. includes a person registered as mediator with the Mediation Council of India.

Mediation includes:

1. pre-litigation mediation [S. 5],
2. online mediation [S. 30],
3. community mediation [Ss. 43 & 44], and
4. conciliation.

The word "mediation" is different from the word "consensus". Grammatically, mediation means connection between the parties not directly but through some other person or thing, *i.e.* it is an intervention for the purpose of reconciling them or for the formation of a connecting link between them. Such power cannot be equated grammatically with the words "compromise", "settlement", or "consensus".[2]

Settlement by "mediation" means the process by which a mediator appointed by parties or by the court, as the case may be, mediates the disputes between the parties to the suit by the application of the provisions of the Mediation Rules, 2003 in Part II and in particular, by facilitating discussion between the parties directly or by communicating with each other through the mediator, by assisting parties in identifying issues, reducing misunderstandings, clarifying priorities, exploring areas of compromise, generating options in an attempt to resolve the dispute and emphasising that it is the parties' own responsibility to make decisions which affect them. [*Vide* Civil Procedure (Alternative Dispute Resolution) (Bihar) Rules, 2008, R. 4; Maharashtra Alternative Dispute Resolution Rules, 2004, R. 4].

4. MEDIATOR [S. 3(*i*)]

Section 3(*i*) simply states that a "mediator" means a person who is appointed to be a mediator, by the parties or by a mediation service provider, to undertake mediation, and includes a person registered with the Mediation Council of India. The section is silent about the qualification or disqualification of a mediator. The rules framed by various High Courts envisage qualifications/disqualifications of a mediator; the provisions in this regard in the rules framed by various High Courts are practically the same.

5. QUALIFICATION OF PERSONS TO BE EMPANELLED AS MEDIATOR

The following shall be treated as qualified and eligible for being enlisted in the panel of mediators under Rule 3, *namely*:

(*a*) (*i*) Retired Judges of the Supreme Court of India;

(*ii*) Retired Judges of the High Court;

(*iii*) Retired District and Sessions Judges or retired Judges of the City Civil Court or Courts of equivalent status.

(*b*) Legal practitioners with at least 15 years standing at the Bar at the level of the Supreme Court or the High Court; or the District Courts or Courts of equivalent status.

(*c*) Experts or other professionals with at least 15 years standing or retired senior bureaucrats or retired senior executives.

---

2. *Chanda Engineers (India) Ltd.* v. *UCO Bank*, 2004 SCC OnLine Cal 416.

(*d*) Institutions which are themselves experts in mediation and have been recognised as such by the High Court, provided the names of its members are approved by the High Court initially or whenever there is change in membership. [Maharashtra Alternative Resolution Rules, 2006, Part II, R. 4]

6. DISQUALIFICATION OF PERSONS

The following persons shall be deemed to be disqualified for being empanelled as mediators:

(*i*) any person who has been adjudged as insolvent or is declared of unsound mind; or

(*ii*) any person against whom criminal charges involving moral turpitude are framed by a criminal court and are pending; or

(*iii*) any person who has been convicted by a criminal court for any offence involving moral turpitude;

(*iv*) any person against whom disciplinary proceedings or charges relating to moral turpitude have been initiated by the appropriate disciplinary authority which are pending or have resulted in a punishment;

(*v*) any person who is interested or connected with the subject-matter of dispute or is related to any one of the parties or to those who represent them, unless such objection is waived by all the parties in writing;

(*vi*) any legal practitioner who has or is appearing for any of the parties in the suit or in any other suit or proceedings;

(*vii*) such other categories of persons as may be notified by the High Court.

Chapter III

MEDIATION

4. *Mediation agreement.*—(1) A mediation agreement shall be in writing, by or between parties and anyone claiming through them, to submit to mediation all or certain disputes which have arisen or which may arise between the parties.

(2) A mediation agreement may be in the form of a mediation clause in a contract or in the form of a separate agreement.

(3) A mediation agreement is in writing, if it is contained in or recorded as—

(*a*) any document signed by the parties;

(*b*) an exchange of communications or letters including through electronic form as provided under the Information Technology Act, 2000 (21 of 2000);

(*c*) any pleadings in a suit or any other proceedings in which existence of mediation agreement is alleged by one party and not denied by the other.

(4) A reference in any agreement containing a mediation clause shall constitute a mediation agreement if the agreement is in writing and the reference is such as to make the mediation clause as part of the agreement.

(5) The parties may agree to submit to mediation any dispute arising between them under an agreement, whether entered prior to arising of the dispute or subsequent thereto.

(6) A mediation agreement in case of international mediation shall refer to an agreement for resolution in matters of commercial disputes referred to in clause (*a*) of Section 3.

COMMENTS

1. SCOPE

This section provides that the "mediation agreement shall be in writing, by or between parties and anyone claiming through them, to submit to mediation all or certain disputes which have arisen or which may arise between the parties". It further provides that the mediation agreement may be in the form of a mediation clause in a contract or in the form of a separate agreement.

Section 4, Mediation Act has been drafted on the lines of Section 7, Arbitration and Conciliation Act, 1996.

A dispute regarding immovable property between father and daughter was referred to the Supreme Court. The mediation centre had to explore the possibility of settlement through mediation. In mediation it is always open to the parties to explore the possibility of an overall amicable settlement including disputes that are not the subject-matter of proceedings before the court. That is the benefit of mediation. The amicable settlement arrived at is reduced into writing and/or a settlement agreement and thereafter it becomes part of the court's order and the court disposes of the matter in terms of the settlement agreement. The order in terms of the settlement agreement is executable, irrespective of whether the settlement agreement is with respect to properties which was/were not the subject-matter of proceedings before the court. The submission on behalf of the applicants that as the properties in question were not the subject-matter of the suit before trial, the same could have been the subject-matter of settlement agreement and/or order cannot be accepted. The order passed by the Supreme Court in the case was required to be complied with and the same is executable. The executing court has to execute the order passed by the Supreme Court in its true spirit.[3]

It has now been felt throughout the world that alternative modes should be found out to nip the disputes before they are bud. Those modalities are not supplant but supplemental to the existence of specified fora contemplated under different statutes. Greater emphasis has now been laid to resolve disputes—domestic as well as international—by holding conciliation, mediation and other procedures. As a matter of fact, keeping in view the International Centre for Alternative Dispute Resolution, the Ministry of Law, Justice and Company Affairs, Government of India, has established the International Centre for Alternative Dispute Resolution, inter alia, to provide, promote and popularise the resolution of domestic and international commercial disputes by different modes of alternative dispute resolutions and to establish facilities and provide administrative and other support services for holding conciliation, mediation and arbitration proceedings.[4]

The two warring fractions can try to resolve their disputes amicably through the intervention of any common well-wisher or even by approaching any functionary under the State Legal Services Authority or the mediation centre.[5]

2. ESSENTIALS OF MEDIATION AGREEMENT

The essentials of mediation agreement are:

1. It shall be in writing by or between the parties and anyone claiming through them to submit to mediation all/certain disputes which have arisen or which may arise between them.
2. A mediation agreement may be in the form of (*a*) a mediation clause in the contract or (*b*) in the form of a separate agreement.
3. A mediation clause is in writing if it is contained or recorded as (*a*) any document signed by the parties; (*b*) an exchange of communications or letters including through electronic form as provided under the Information Technology Act, 2000 (21 of 2000); (*c*) any pleadings in a suit or any other proceedings in which existence of mediation agreement is alleged by one party and not denied by the other.
4. A reference in any agreement containing a mediation clause shall constitute a mediation agreement if the agreement is in writing and

3. *Kaushaliya* v. *Jodha Ram*, (2019) 20 SCC 277.
4. *Manorama Mohapatra* v. *Collector*, 2000 SCC OnLine Ori 46.
5. C.M.S. *Evangelical Suvi David Memorial Higher Secondary School Committee* v. *District Registrar, Cheranmahadevi*, 2008 SCC OnLine Mad 803: (2008) 4 LW 1080 (DB).

the reference is such as to make the mediation clause as part of the agreement.

5. The parties may agree to submit to mediation any dispute arising between them under an agreement, whether entered prior to arising of the dispute or subsequent thereto.

3. INTERNATIONAL MEDIATION—MEDIATION AGREEMENT

A mediation agreement in case of international mediation shall refer to an agreement for resolution in matters of commercial disputes referred to in clause (*a*) of Section 3. [S. 4(6)]

4. FAMILY MATTERS TO BE DECIDED THROUGH MEDIATION

The question raised in the case is whether the defendant during the pendency of the suit can be accommodated in the demarcated position of the house. This being essentially a family matter, the court can do more than advise the parties to bridge the gap between them by having mediation proceedings.[6]

5. PROCEEDINGS UNDER SECTION 498-A IPC/ SECTION 85, BNS 2023—MEDIATION SETTLEMENT

Though the offence punishable under Section 498-A IPC/Section 85, BNS 2023 is not compoundable, in appropriate cases, if the parties are willing and if it appears to the criminal court that there exist elements of settlement, it should direct the parties to explore the possibility of settlement through mediation. This is, obviously, not to dilute the rigour, efficacy and purport of Section 498-A IPC/Section 85, BNS 2023, but to locate cases where the matrimonial dispute can be nipped in the bud in an equitable manner. The judges, with their expertise, must ensure that the exercise does not lead to the erring spouse using the mediation process to get out of the clutches of the law. During mediation, the parties can either decide to part company on mutually agreed terms, or they may decide to patch up and stay together. In either case, for the settlement to come through, the complaint will have to be quashed. In that event, they can approach the High Court and get the complaint quashed. If, however, they choose not to settle, they can proceed with the complaints. In this exercise, there is no loss to anyone. If there is a settlement, the parties will be saved from the trials and tribulations of a criminal case, and that will reduce the burden on the courts, which will be in the larger public interest. Obviously, the High Court will quash the

6. *Gita Abhyankar* v. *Vikram Abhyankar*, 2010 SCC OnLine Del 1407: (2010) 169 DLT 13; *Shyam Singh* v. *State of U.P.*, 2011 SCC OnLine All 2485.

complaint only if, after considering all circumstances, it finds the settlement to be equitable and genuine.

The courts dealing with matrimonial cases are directed to:

> In terms of Section 9 of the Family Courts Act, the Family Courts shall make all efforts to settle the matrimonial disputes through mediation. Even if the counsellors submit a failure report, the Family Courts shall, with the consent of the parties, refer the matter to the mediation centre. In such a case, however, the Family Courts shall set a reasonable time-limit for mediation centres to complete the process of mediation because otherwise the resolution of the disputes by the Family Court may get delayed. In a given case, if there is good chance of settlement, the Family Court in its discretion, can always extend the time-limit. The criminal courts dealing with the complaint under Section 498-A/Section 85, BNS 2023 should, at any stage and particularly, before they take up the complaint for hearing, refer the parties to mediation centre if they feel that there exist elements of settlement and both the parties are willing. However, they should take care to see that in this exercise, rigour, purport and efficacy of Section 498-A/Section 85, BNS 2023 is not diluted. Needless to say that the discretion to grant or not to grant bail is not in any way curtailed by this direction. It will be for the court concerned to work out the modalities taking into consideration the facts of each case. All mediation centres shall set up pre-litigation desks/clinics, give them wide publicity and make efforts to settle matrimonial disputes at pre-litigation stage.[7]

Proceedings under Section 498-A IPC quashed.

An attempt must be made to bring about reconciliation between the disputing spouses at the preliminary stage. Direction is given to courts concerned to consider releasing the accused in minor cases involving no injuries or minor injuries with no repetition of cruelty. A bail plea to be considered when the Magistrate comes to the conclusion that mediation or conciliation between the parties has failed.[8]

A matrimonial dispute between the parties was mutually/amicably resolved through the mediation centre. Hence, continuation of the proceedings under Section 498-A IPC/Section 85, BNS 2023 would not serve any useful purpose. The FIR filed under Section 498-A IPC/Section 85, BNS 2023 was quashed.[9]

---

7. *K. Srinivas Rao* v. *D.A. Deepa*, (2013) 5 SCC 226; *V. Saravankumar* v. *Inspector of Police*, 2014 SCC OnLine Mad 932.
8. *Sanjeev Kumar* v. *State of U.P.*, 2011 SCC OnLine All 2471.
9. *Anwar Ahmad* v. *State (NCT of Delhi)*, 2009 SCC OnLine Del 4208.

6. MATTER SETTLED THROUGH THE MEDIATION OF ELDERS—PROCEEDINGS UNDER SECTIONS 294(B), 323 341, 326 AND 506(II) IPC QUASHED

Where the dispute between the parties was settled through the mediation of elders, allowing the proceedings before the court would be futile exercise; proceedings for offences under Sections 294(*b*), 323, 326 and 506(*ii*) IPC were quashed.[10]

7. DISPUTES BETWEEN THE PARTIES REGARDING SHARE IN ANCESTRAL PROPERTY

Parties arrived at settlement at the mediation centre in the High Court. Appeal before the Supreme Court was disposed of in terms of the settlement.[11]

8. MUSLIM LAW

Prior mediation is not a mandatory condition precedent for valid talaq.[12]

9. FAMILY MATTERS—MEDIATION

The principal thrust of the law in family matters is to make an attempt for reconciliation before processing the disputes in the legal framework. Reconciliation is not mediation. Neither is it conciliation. No doubt, there is conciliation in reconciliation. But the concepts are totally different. Similarly, there is mediation in conciliation but there is no conciliation in mediation. In mediation, the role of the mediator is only to evolve solutions whereas in reconciliation, the duty-holders have to take a proactive role to assist the parties to reach an amicable solution. In conciliation, the conciliator persuades the parties to arrive at a solution as suggested by him in the course of the discussions. In reconciliation, the duty-holders remind the parties of the essential family values, the need to maintain a cordial relationship, both in the interest of the husband and wife or the children, as the case may be, and also make a persuasive effort to make the parties reconcile to the reality and restore the relationship, if possible. The Family Courts Act expects the duty-holders like the court, counsellors, welfare experts and any other collaborators to make efforts for reconciliation. However, reconciliation is not always the restoration of status quo ante; it can as well be a

---

10. *M. Sankara Mahadavan* v. *State*, 2010 SCC OnLine Mad 1391; *P.S. Shenoy* v. *G. Krishnamurthy*, 2008 SCC OnLine Mad 733 (Proceedings under Ss. 405, 406 and 409 IPC were quashed on petition under S. 482 CPC in view of amicable settlement of the matter through mediation and cancellation).
11. *Surjeet Singh* v. *Sucha Singh*, (2016) 13 SCC 314.
12. *Banu* v. *Kutubuddin Sulemanji Vimanwala*, 1994 SCC OnLine Bom 481: (1995) 2 Mah LJ 506.

solution as acceptable to both parties. In all these matters, the approaches are different.[13]

10. FAMILY COURTS ACT

In appeal against the judgment of decree of divorce passed by the Family Courts Act, the matter was referred to the mediation centre and was settled there.[14]

11. DUTY OF FAMILY COURTS

Under Section 9, the Family Court has a duty to make endeavour to assist and persuade the parties to arrive at a settlement. Unlike many other legislations, the legislature cast a duty on the Family Court in this regard. Jurisdiction is not just to decide the dispute, but on the contrary, the Family Court also has to involve itself in the process of conciliation/mediation between parties to assist them not only to settle disputes but also to secure speedy settlement of disputes. Such timely intervention of the Family Court will not only resolve disputes and settle the parties peacefully but also prevent sporadic litigation between the parties.[15]

12. MATRIMONIAL DISPUTE BEFORE THE PARTIES SETTLED THROUGH MEDIATION

Parties were living separately and litigating for more than a decade. Since the father of the respondent and the mother and sister of the appellant were also parties to litigations, the mediator had sought their presence, and all parties have agreed on terms of the settlement, reduced in writing, taken on record to form part of the judgment. An application under Section 13-B, Hindu Marriage Act, 1955 was taken on record, waiving the waiting period having regard to prolonged litigation and terms of the settlement. The marriage between the appellant and respondent was dissolved by way of a decree of divorce by mutual consent.[16] In another case, a matrimonial dispute between the parties was settled through the Supreme Court Mediation Centre. The FIR filed by the wife was quashed and the marriage was dissolved.[17]

---

13. *Santhini* v. *Vijaya Venketesh*, (2018) 1 SCC 62.
14. *Ramen Chandra Deka* v. *Sujata Deka*, 2008 SCC OnLine Gau 285; *Vishal Aggarwal* v. *Aarti*, 2009 SCC OnLine P&H 7770; *Narinder Kumar* v. *Rekha*, 2010 SCC OnLine P&H 5566; *Har Pal Singh* v. *Taranpeet Kaur*, 2011 SCC OnLine P&H 4150.
15. *Anu Bhandari* v. *Pradip Bhandari*, (2018) 6 SCC 389.
16. *Sachin Dinanath Dhuri* v. *Sneha Sachin Dhuri*, (2018) 15 SCC 157.
17. *Sneha Parikh* v. *Manit Kumar*, (2018) 4 SCC 501.

13. MATRIMONIAL CASES—SUPREME COURT ASSISTED MEDIATION AND CONCILIATION

In a divorce case, when the initial attempt at mediation remained unsuccessful, the Supreme Court directed the parties to appeal before it. Finally, a settlement was arrived at on the terms suggested by the court. The marriage between the parties was dissolved by a decree of divorce.[18]

14. INSURANCE CLAIM

It was a case of death caused by heart attack. Effort for mediation was made by the Ombudsman. It has to be presumed that the question of any falsity does not arise. Otherwise, the Ombudsman could not have poised down to a position of making effort of mediation to render equitable justice. No case of fraud or misstatement was made out to repudiate the agreement, ignoring payment of the meagre amount of ₹1 lakh. Orders passed repudiating the claim set aside; the claimant was entitled to the amount along with interest at the rate of 12 per cent p.a. Directions were issued to release the same within a period of one month.[19]

15. IN RAM JANMABHOOMI–BABRI MASJID SUIT—SUPREME COURT MONITORED MEDIATION

In the *Ram Janmabhoomi–Babri Masjid case*, the Supreme Court monitored mediation.[20] Mediators were appointed and the following directions were issued:

1. Mediation should be conducted with utmost confidentiality.
2. The venue of mediation should be Faizabad (UP) to ensure success in mediation.
3. Mediation proceedings should be held in camera.
4. Mediators are given liberty to take such legal assistance as deemed necessary at any stage of mediation proceedings.
5. Mediators are requested to complete the process and report to the court within four weeks.

Hearing in the case was resumed when the mediation failed.[21]

---

18. *Benoy Idicula Babu* v. *Nisha Saira Benoy*, (2020) 18 SCC 668.
19. *Shanti Devi* v. *Office of Insurance Ombudsman Chintel's House 1st Floor*, 2007 SCC OnLine All 821: (2008) 70 ALR 453.
20. *M. Siddiq* v. *Suresh Das*, (2019) 4 SCC 641.
21. *Mohd. Siddiq* v. *Suresh Das*, (2019) 7 SCC 633.

16. MOTOR VEHICLES ACT, 1988—DISPOSAL OF CLAIM PETITIONS—MEDIATION AS A METHOD SUGGESTED

Establishment of Mediation Authorities in districts to work out a resolution before it becomes an adversarial litigation, suggested. Necessary amendments in the Motor Vehicles Act suggested. As an interim measure until amendments are carried out, NALSA to establish Motor Accident Mediation Cells.[22]

17. APPLICATION FOR ANTICIPATORY BAIL

Once mediation proceedings fail, the application for anticipatory bail has to be considered on merits.[23]

5. *Pre-litigation mediation.*—(1) Subject to other provisions of this Act, whether any mediation agreement exists or not, the parties before filing any suit or proceedings of civil or commercial nature in any court, may voluntarily and with mutual consent take steps to settle the disputes by pre-litigation mediation in accordance with the provisions of this Act:

Provided that pre-litigation mediation in matters of commercial disputes of Specified Value shall be undertaken in accordance with the provisions of Section 12-A of the Commercial Courts Act, 2015 (4 of 2016), and the rules made thereunder.

(2) The provisions of sub-section (1) shall be applicable to the tribunals notified by the Central Government or a State Government, as the case may be.

(3) For the purposes of sub-sections (1) and (2), unless otherwise agreed upon by the parties, a mediator,—

(*i*) registered with the Council; or

(*ii*) empanelled by a court-annexed mediation centre; or

(*iii*) empanelled by an Authority constituted under the Legal Services Authorities Act, 1987 (39 of 1987); or

(*iv*) empanelled by a mediation service provider recognised under this Act, shall conduct pre-litigation mediation.

(4) For conducting pre-litigation mediation under clauses (*ii*) and (*iii*) of sub-section (3), a party may request any person designated for this purpose by the High Courts, or an Authority constituted under the Legal Services Authorities Act, 1987 (39 of 1987), as the case may be.

(5) The court-annexed mediation centre and an Authority constituted under the Legal Services Authorities Act, 1987 (39 of 1987), shall maintain a panel of mediators for the purposes of pre-litigation mediation.

---

22. *M.R. Krishna Murthi* v. *New India Insurance Co. Ltd.*, (2020) 15 SCC 493.
23. *Aman Gupta* v. *State (NCT of Delhi)*, (2023) 6 HCC (Del) 89: (2024) 122 GSTR 447.

(6) Notwithstanding anything contained in sub-sections (1) and (2) and the Motor Vehicles Act, 1988 (59 of 1988), when an application for compensation arising out of an accident is made before the Claims Tribunal, if the settlement as provided for in Section 149 of that Act is not arrived at between the parties, the Claims Tribunal shall refer the parties for mediation to a mediator or mediation service provider under this Act.

(7) Where the parties arrive at a settlement agreement under sub-section (6), it shall be placed before the Claims Tribunal for its consideration.

(8) If the parties do not reach to settlement agreement under sub-section (6), a non-settlement report prepared by the mediator shall be forwarded to the Claims Tribunal, which has referred the matter for mediation, for adjudication.

COMMENTS

1. SCOPE

This section provides that whether any mediation agreement exists or not, any party before filing any suit or proceeding of civil or commercial nature in any court shall take steps to settle the disputes by pre-litigation mediation in accordance with the provisions of the new law. It further provides that pre-litigation mediation in matters of commercial disputes of specified value shall be undertaken in accordance with the provisions of Section 12-A, Commercial Courts Act, 2015, and the rules made thereunder.

2. PRE-LITIGATION MEDIATION

This section envisages provision for pre-mediation in all suits or proceedings of civil or commercial nature, whether any mediation agreement between the parties exists or not [Sub-s. (1)].

The provisions of the section are applicable to all the courts and tribunals notified by the Central Government or a State Government, as the case may be. [Sub-s. (2)]

3. COMMERCIAL COURTS ACT, 2015, SECTION 12-A

The pre-litigation mediation contemplated by the section in matters of commercial disputes shall be undertaken in accordance with Section 12-A, Commercial Courts Act, 2015. *See*, comments under Section 64 *infra*.

4. PROCEDURE [SUB-Ss. (3) AND (4)]

For conducting pre-litigation mediation under clauses (*ii*) and (*iii*), a party may request any person designated for this purpose by the High Court or an authority constituted under the Legal Services Authorities Act, 1987.

A mediator registered with the Mediation Council, empanelled by a court-annexed mediation centre, or empanelled by an authority constituted under the Legal Services Authorities Act, 1987 or empanelled by a mediation service provider recognised under this Act shall conduct a pre-litigation mediation. [Sub-s. (4)]

5. PREPARATION OF PANEL OF MEDIATORS [SUB-s. (5)]

The court-annexed mediation centre and an authority constituted under the Legal Services Authorities Act shall maintain a panel of mediators for the purposes of pre-litigation mediation.

6. CLAIM PETITIONS UNDER SECTION 149, MOTOR VEHICLES ACT, 1988 [SUB-Ss. (6), (7) AND (8)]

Where in an application for compensation arising out of an accident is made before the Motor Accident Claims Tribunal, if settlement provided under Section 149, Motor Vehicles Act is not arrived at between the parties, the Claims Tribunal shall refer the parties for mediation to a mediator or mediation service provider under this Act. Where the parties arrive at a settlement, it shall be placed before the Claims Tribunal for consideration; where no settlement is arrived at, a non-settlement report prepared by the mediator shall be forwarded to the Claims Tribunal which referred the matter for mediation.

7. MATRIMONIAL DISPUTES

In matrimonial disputes, endeavour for alternate redress by courts is not only obligatory on courts but their duty towards public also.[24]

In matrimonial dispute cases, it is obligatory on the part of the Family Court to refer the dispute to the mediation centre for reconciliation/settlement between the parties. Earnest efforts have to be made to resolve the disputes. Refusal by the Family Court to refer the dispute to the mediation centre for mediation was held not proper.[25]

24. *T. Vineed* v. *Manju S. Nair*, 2008 SCC OnLine Ker 28 (DB); *Bhavana Ramaprasad* v. *Yadunandan Parthasarathy*, 2014 SCC OnLine Kar 12020: (2014) 5 KCCR 1558.
25. *Bhavana Ramaprasad* v. *Yadunandan Parthasarathy*, 2014 SCC OnLine Kar 12020: (2014) 5 KCCR 1558.

Mediation prescribed in a case of disputes between family and business relations. The duty of lawyers in this regard stated. Dispute between brothers, therefore, referred to mediation centre and matter adjourned till receipt of report therefrom.[26]

Section 89 CPC enables the court to refer the subject-matter of a case to either of the five alternative dispute resolution processes shown therein. In the instant case, the Family Court rejected the wife's petition for referring the husband's petition under Section 12, Hindu Marriage Act for mediation; the order was found unsustainable, was set aside, and the matter was referred to mediation.[27]

Mediation proceedings: After mediation proceedings were declared successful, no further order was passed by the civil court. Since the order passed by the mediator is not executable, execution proceedings are not maintainable.[28]

8. HINDU MARRIAGE ACT, 1955, SECTION 23(2)

Section 23(2) provides that before proceeding to grant any relief under this Act, it shall be the duty of the court in the first instance, in every case where it is possible so to do consistently with the nature and circumstances of the case, to make every endeavour to bring about a reconciliation between the parties.

For the purpose of aiding the court in bringing about such reconciliation, the court may, if the parties so desire or if the court thinks it just and proper so to do, adjourn the proceedings for a reasonable period not exceeding 15 days and refer the matter to any person named by the parties in this behalf or to any person nominated by the court if the parties fail to name any person, with directions to report to the court as to whether reconciliation can be and has been effected, and the court shall in disposing of the proceedings have due regard to the report.

On considering the agreement entered by the parties before the mediation centre and on that basis only, a divorce petition on mutual consent was filed; the High Court dispensed with the six-month cooling period and directed the Family Court to dispose of the petition filed under Section 13-B, Hindu Marriage Act, 1955.[29]

---

26. *B.S. Krishna Murthy* v. *B.S. Nagaraj*, (2011) 15 SCC 464.
27. *Bhavana Ramaprasad* v. *Yadunandan Parthasarathy*, 2014 SCC OnLine Kar 12020: (2014) 5 KCCR 1558, paras 21–25.
28. *Mohar Singh* v. *Gajendra Singh*, 2019 SCC OnLine MP 6901: (2020) 3 MPLJ 411.
29. *R. Jegannathan, re*, 2014 SCC OnLine Mad 8814: (2014) 6 CTC 74.

9. SPECIAL MARRIAGE ACT, 1954, SECTION 34(2)

Before proceeding to grant any relief under this Act, it shall be the duty of the court in the first instance, in every case where it is possible so to do consistently with the nature and circumstances of the case, to make every endeavour to bring about a reconciliation between the parties.

10. FAMILY COURTS ACT, 1984

In every suit or proceedings, endeavour shall be made by the Family Court in the first instance, where it is possible to do so consistent with the nature and circumstances of the case, to assist and persuade the parties in arriving at a settlement in respect of the subject-matter of the suit or proceedings and for this purpose a Family Court may, subject to any rules made by the High Court, follow such procedure as it may deem fit.

If, in any suit or proceeding, at any stage, it appears to the Family Court that there is a reasonable possibility of a settlement between the parties, the Family Court may adjourn the proceedings for such period as it thinks fit to enable attempts to be made to effect such a settlement.

The power conferred by sub-section (2) shall be in addition to, and not in derogation of, any other power of the Family Court to adjourn the proceedings.

11. INDUSTRIAL DISPUTES—INDUSTRIAL RELATIONS CODE (ACT NO. 35 OF 2020)

"Industrial dispute" means a dispute or difference between employers and employers or between employers and workers or between workers and workers which is connected with the employment or non-employment or the terms of employment or with the conditions of labour, of any person and includes any dispute or difference between an individual worker and an employer connected with, or arising out of discharge, dismissal, retrenchment or termination of such worker. [Industrial Relations Code, 2020, S. 2(*g*)]

The industrial disputes can be categorised into four kinds, *namely*:

1. interest-based disputes,
2. grievances/rights disputes,
3. unfair labour practices disputes, and
4. recognition dispute.

An interest-based dispute refers to a dispute related to the economic interest of the parties, which includes making demand for inclusion of a new term of agreement in the contract of employment; for example, one may seek improvement in wages, job securing, allied benefits. Such disputes are often recommended to be settled through conciliation/mediation.

Rights/grievances-based dispute involves non-fulfilment/dissatisfaction which arises out of the terms of the agreement.

Unfair labour practice concerns issues which arise out of the discriminatory or unfair practice of the employer towards the employee/workman.

Recognition disputes are disputes which arise out of non-recognition/insufficient recognition of the trade union by the management/organisation. The Industrial Relations Code, 2020 envisages extensive machinery for settlement of all such disputes. The Industrial Disputes Act, 1947 provided for collective bargaining, investigation, arbitration, adjudication and conciliation before a conciliation officer/Board of Conciliation. In collective bargaining, all the workers come together and collectively negotiate the terms. It is a voluntary and peaceful procedure that offers an amicable settlement through mutual discussion between the two parties.

The second way is investigation; a court of enquiry is set up by the government to investigate the dispute.

The third mode is arbitration. [S. 42, Industrial Relations Code, 2020]

The fourth mode is adjudication; the parties have the option of having their dispute adjudicated by an Industrial Tribunal set up by the government. In matters of national importance, the government may constitute a National Industrial Tribunal. [S. 46, Industrial Relations Code, 2020]

The Industrial Relations Code provides for the appointment of conciliation officers [S. 43], and for referring the matter to the conciliation officer. The conciliation officer is responsible for holding the conciliation proceedings within two years from the date on which the dispute arose. [S. 53, Industrial Relations Code, 2020]

The conciliation proceedings shall be deemed to have commenced on the date on which the first meeting is held by the conciliation officer after the receipt of the notice. [S. 60, Industrial Relations Code, 2020]

The conciliation officer is responsible for investigating the dispute and shall also undertake necessary measures to arrive at an amicable settlement of the dispute. Having done so, he shall forward the report to the government along with the memorandum signed by the parties. Such a report shall be binding on the parties from the date the memorandum was signed, and for the period agreed upon. [Ss. 57–58, Industrial Relations Code, 2020] For executing its function, the conciliation officer is vested with all the powers of the civil court for enforcing the attendance of any person, compelling the production of the document and material objects, and issuing commission for examination of the witness.

The new Industrial Relations Code, 2020 also makes provision for bipartite forums to foster harmonious relations between the employer and the employee. It also provides for the formation of the Works Committee and Grievance Redressal Committee. A Works Committee is mandatory where the industrial establishment employees are 100 or more. The committee is responsible for addressing individual grievance. An individual may file an application before the Works Committee within a period of one year from the date when the cause of action arose. The committee shall complete its proceedings within a period of 30 days. If not satisfied, the aggrieved employee may file an application before the Industrial Tribunal within 60 days of the decision. [S. 4(8)]

6. *Disputes or matters not fit for mediation.*—(1) A mediation under this Act shall not be conducted for resolution of any dispute or matter contained in the indicative list under the First Schedule:

Provided that nothing contained herein shall prevent any court, if deemed appropriate, from referring any dispute relating to compoundable offences including the matrimonial offences which are compoundable and pending between the parties, to mediation:

Provided further that the outcome of such mediation shall not be deemed to be a judgment or decree of court referred to in sub-section (2) of Section 27, and shall be further considered by the court in accordance with the law for the time being in force.

(2) If the Central Government is satisfied that it is necessary or expedient so to do, it may, by notification, amend the First Schedule.

COMMENTS

1. SCOPE

This section provides an indicative list of disputes or matters which cannot be referred to mediation except some compoundable offences or matrimonial offences connected with or arising out of civil proceedings which can be referred to mediation by court, if deemed appropriate. A settlement arrived in these cases not to have the effect of judgment or decree of court.

2. DISPUTES/MATTERS NOT FIT FOR MEDIATION

The First Schedule to the Mediation Act mentions the matters/disputes in which mediation cannot be conducted for resolution of the disputes. In view of the indicative list in the said Schedule, the following disputes/matters are not fit for mediation:

1. Disputes relating to claims against minors, deities, persons with intellectual disabilities, etc.
2. Disputes involving prosecution for criminal offences.
3. Complaints or proceedings initiated before any statutory authority or body in relation to registration, discipline, or misconduct of any practitioner or other registered professional, such as legal practitioner, medical practitioner, dentist, architect, chartered accountant, or in relation to any other profession of whatever description, which is regulated under any law for the time being in force.
4. Disputes which have the effect on the rights of a third party who are not a party to the mediation proceedings except only in matrimonial disputes where the interest of a child is involved.
5. Any proceeding in relation to any subject-matter, falling within any enactment over which the tribunal constituted under the National Green Tribunal Act, 2010 (19 of 2010) has jurisdiction.
6. Any dispute relating to levy, collection, penalties or offences in relation to any direct or indirect tax or refunds enacted by any State Legislature or Parliament.
7. Any investigation, inquiry or proceeding under the Competition Act, 2002 (12 of 2003), including proceedings before the Director General under the Act, proceedings before the Telecom Regulatory Authority of India under the Telecom Regulatory Authority of India Act, 1997 (24 of 1997) or the Telecom Disputes Settlement and Appellate Tribunal established under Section 14 of that Act.
8. Proceedings before appropriate commissions, and the Appellate Tribunal for Electricity under the Electricity Act, 2003 (36 of 2003).
9. Proceedings before the Petroleum and Natural Gas Regulatory Board, and appeals therefrom before the Appellate Tribunal under the Petroleum and Natural Gas Regulatory Board Act, 2006 (19 of 2006).
10. Proceedings before the Securities and Exchange Board of India, and the Securities Appellate Tribunal under the Securities and Exchange Board of India Act, 1992 (15 of 1992).
11. Land acquisition and determination of compensation under land acquisition laws, or any provision of law providing for land acquisition.

3. SUPREME COURT DECISION

The Supreme Court in *Afcons Infrastructure* v. *Cherian Varkey Construction Company (P) Ltd.*[30] considered the categories of cases normally suitable for the ADR process including mediation. It was held:

> **28.** All other suits and cases of civil nature in particular the following categories of cases (whether pending in civil courts or other special tribunals/forums) are normally suitable for ADR process:
>
> (*i*) all cases relating to trade, commerce and contracts, including
> - disputes arising out of contracts (including all money claims);
> - disputes relating to specific performance;
> - disputes between suppliers and customers;
> - disputes between bankers and customers;
> - disputes between developers/builders and customers;
> - disputes between landlords and tenants/licensor and licensees;
> - disputes between insurer and insured;
>
> (*ii*) All cases arising from strained or soured relationships, including
> - disputes relating to matrimonial causes, maintenance, custody of children;
> - disputes relating to partition/division among family members/coparceners/co-owners; and
> - disputes relating to partnership among partners.
>
> (*iii*) All cases where there is a need for continuation of the pre-existing relationship in spite of the disputes, including
> - disputes between neighbours (relating to easementary rights, encroachment, nuisance, etc.);
> - disputes between employers and employees;
> - disputes among members of societies/associations/apartment owners' association;
>
> (*iv*) All cases relating to tortious liability, including claims for compensation in motor accidents/other accidents; and
>
> (*v*) All consumer disputes, including disputes where a trader/supplier/manufacturer/service provider is keen to maintain his business/professional reputation and credibility or product popularity.
>
> The above enumeration of 'suitable' and 'unsuitable' categorisation of cases is not intended to be exhaustive or rigid. They are illustrative, which can be subjected to just exceptions or additions by the Court/Tribunal exercising its jurisdiction/discretion in referring a dispute/case to an ADR process.

---

30. *Afcons Infrastructure Ltd.* v. *Cherian Varkey Construction Co. (P) Ltd.*, (2010) 8 SCC 24.

4. DISPUTES RELATING TO COMPOUNDABLE OFFENCES, INCLUDING MATRIMONIAL OFFENCES WHICH ARE COMPOUNDABLE [SUB-S. (1) (PROVISO 1)]

If any court deems it appropriate, it may refer any dispute relating to compoundable offences including matrimonial offences which are compoundable and pending between the parties to mediation.

5. OUTCOME OF MEDIATION IS NOT A JUDGMENT/ DECREE OF COURT [S. 6(I) PROVISO 2]

The outcome of mediation referred to in the section shall not be deemed to be a judgment or decree of the court in terms of Section 27(2), Mediation Act, and shall be considered by the court in accordance with the law for the time being in force.

6. AMENDMENT OF FIRST SCHEDULE BY THE CENTRAL GOVERNMENT [S. 6(2)]

When the Central Government is satisfied that it is necessary or expedient to amend the First Schedule, it may do so.

7. INDUSTRIAL DISPUTES ACT, 1947—COLLECTIVE BARGAINING

The Industrial Disputes Act provides for collective bargaining. The Industrial Disputes Act, 1947 envisages negotiation, mediation and conciliation. Many grievances of the employees working in the department can be sorted out by resorting to the aforementioned modes of dispute resolution.[31]

8. INDUSTRIAL DISPUTES ACT, 1947—DISPUTE REFERRED TO MEDIATION CENTRE OF HIGH COURT

Having regard to the facts of the case, parties were directed to appear before the Mediation Centre of the High Court to resolve the dispute.[32]

7. *Power of court or tribunal to refer parties to mediation.*—(1) Notwithstanding the non-settlement of dispute under sub-section (1) of Section 5, the court or tribunal may, at any stage of proceeding, refer the parties to undertake mediation.

(2) If the court or tribunal refers the parties to undertake mediation, it may pass suitable interim order to protect the interest of any party if deemed appropriate.

---

31. *A.P. Public Health and Medical Employees Union* v. *State of A.P.*, 1998 SCC OnLine AP 330.
32. *John D'Souza* v. *Karnataka SRTC*, (2019) 18 SCC 47.

(3) The parties shall not be under obligation to come to a settlement in the mediation pursuant to a reference under sub-section (1).

COMMENTS

1. SCOPE

This section provides that the court or tribunal may, at any stage of pending proceedings, refer the parties to undertake mediation if a request to this effect is made by them.

2. INTERIM ORDER [SUB-S. (2)]

Where the court or tribunal refers the parties to undertake mediation, it may pass suitable interim orders to protect the interest of any party where deemed appropriate.

3. PARTIES SHALL NOT BE UNDER OBLIGATION TO COME TO A SETTLEMENT IN THE MEDIATION PROCEEDINGS [SUB-S. (3)]

The parties shall not be under obligation to come to a settlement in pursuance of a reference under sub-section (1).

4. PROTECTION OF WOMEN FROM DOMESTIC VIOLENCE ACT, 2005 (DV ACT)

A Magistrate exercising jurisdiction under the Domestic Violence Act has the power to refer the matter before it to mediation, record compromise and pass orders in terms of the settlement.[33]

5. DV ACT—SETTLEMENT OF DISPUTE BETWEEN WIFE AND HUSBAND—WITHDRAWAL FROM THE MEDIATION SETTLEMENT AGREEMENT—PERMISSIBILITY

In the absence of pleadings challenging the settlement that it has vitiated on the grounds enumerated in Chapter II of the Contract Act, the parties to the settlement are bound to honour the settlement, and the court has a duty to enforce the same. Unilateral withdrawal from the settlement agreement is impermissible.[34] A Division Bench of the Kerala High Court in *Teena M. Ansari* v. *Rinoj Eappen*[35] has held that after entering into a settlement through the process of mediation and after the court as well as the parties

33. *Mathew Danial* v. *Leena Mathew*, 2022 SCC OnLine Ker 4090: (2022) 3 KLJ 929.
34. *Ibid.*
35. 2019 SCC OnLine Ker 2828: (2019) 4 KHC 593.

have acted upon the settlement, one of the parties cannot be permitted to unilaterally withdraw from the same. A settlement agreement entered between the parties through mediation has got a certain solemnity attached to it, and granting permission for withdrawing from such an agreement would destroy the sanctity of the whole process of mediation.

In the present case, there was a settlement agreement between the husband and the wife in a case arising from the Domestic Violence Act. Nearly after one year of the settlement, the husband challenged its validity. The plea taken was that the husband affixed his signatures on the memorandum without understanding its terms which was not substantiated. The agreement was held valid.[36]

Chapter IV
MEDIATORS

8. *Appointment of mediators.*—(1) Unless otherwise agreed upon by the parties, a person of any nationality may be appointed as a mediator:

Provided that mediator of any foreign nationality shall possess such qualification, experience and accreditation as may be specified.

(2) The parties shall be free to agree upon the name of mediator and the procedure for their appointment.

(3) If the parties do not reach any agreement on a matter referred to in sub-section (2), then the party seeking initiation of mediation shall make an application to a mediation service provider for the appointment of a mediator.

(4) Upon receiving an application under sub-section (3), the mediation service provider shall, within a period of seven days, appoint,—

(*i*) the mediator as agreed by the parties; or

(*ii*) in case the parties are unable to reach agreement as to the appointment of mediator or mediator agreed by them refuses to act as mediator, a mediator from the panel maintained by it, with his consent.

(5) The person appointed under clause (*i*) of sub-section (4) shall communicate his willingness or otherwise within a period of seven days from the date of receipt of communication of such appointment.

COMMENTS

This section provides for the appointment of mediators.

Unless otherwise agreed upon by the parties, a person of any nationality may be appointed as arbitrator.

---

36. *M. Munikrishna* v. *S. Shanthakumari*, 2022 SCC OnLine Kar 1872.

The parties shall be free to agree upon the name of the mediator and the procedure for their appointment.

If the parties do not reach any agreement on a matter referred to in sub-section (2), then the party seeking initiation of mediation shall make an application to a mediation service provider for the appointment of a mediator.

Upon receiving an application under sub-section (3), the mediation service provider shall, within a period of seven days, appoint,—

(*i*) the mediator as agreed by the parties; or

(*ii*) in case the parties are unable to reach agreement as to the appointment of mediator or mediator agreed by them refuses to act as mediator, a mediator from the panel maintained by it, with his consent.

A person appointed as mediator shall communicate his willingness/or otherwise within a period of seven days from the date of receipt of communication of his appointment as mediator.

9. *Preference of parties.*—The mediation service provider shall, while appointing any person from the panel of mediators maintained by it, consider his suitability and the preference of the parties for resolving the dispute.

COMMENTS

This section provides that a mediation service provider while appointing any person as arbitrator shall consider the following two things:

1. suitability, and
2. preference of the parties for resolving the dispute.

10. *Conflict of interest and disclosure.*—(1) The person appointed as a mediator shall, prior to the conduct of mediation, disclose in writing to the parties regarding any circumstance or potential circumstance, personal, professional, financial, or otherwise, that may constitute any conflict of interest or that is likely to give rise to justifiable doubts as to his independence or impartiality as a mediator.

(2) During the mediation, the mediator shall, without delay, disclose to the parties in writing any conflict of interest, referred to in sub-section (1), that has newly arisen or has come to his knowledge.

(3) Upon disclosure under sub-section (1) or sub-section (2), the parties shall have the option to waive any objection if all of them express in writing, which shall be construed as the consent of parties.

(4) Upon disclosure under sub-section (1) or sub-section (2), if either party desires to replace the mediator, then, in case of—

(*i*) institutional mediation, such party shall apply to the mediation service provider for termination of the mandate of mediator;

(*ii*) mediation other than institutional mediation, such party shall terminate the mandate of mediator.

COMMENTS

This section provides that when a person is appointed as a mediator, he shall disclose in writing to the parties about any circumstances or potential circumstances, personal, professional or financial, that may constitute conflict of interest or that is likely to give rise to justifiable doubts as to such mediator's independence or impartiality in the conduct of the mediation process.

This section is in line with Section 12, Arbitration and Conciliation Act, 1996. Section 12(1), Arbitration and Conciliation Act, 1996 inter alia provides that when a person is approached in connection with his possible appointment as an arbitrator, he shall disclose in writing any circumstance such as the existence of either direct or indirect of any past or present relationship with or interest in any of the parties or in relation to the subject-matter in dispute, whether financial, business, professional or other kind, which is likely to give use to justifiable doubts as to his independence or impartibility.

Non-compliance/violation of the provisions of this Act may result in termination of the mandate of the arbitrator [S. 11(*ii*)] and can also be a ground for challenging the mediated settlement agreement under Section 28, Mediation Act, 2023.

11. *Termination of mandate of mediator.*—A mediation service provider may terminate the mandate of a mediator upon—

(*i*) the receipt of application from a party under clause (*i*) of sub-section (4) of Section 10; or

(*ii*) the receipt of information about the mediator being involved in a matter of conflict of interest from participants or any other person; or

(*iii*) his withdrawal from mediation for any reason:

Provided that termination under clause (*ii*) shall be effected if, after giving a hearing to the mediator, mediation service provider finds that there is justifiable doubt as to the independence or impartiality of the mediator and that the same has been brought to the notice of parties and that either party desires to replace the mediator.

COMMENTS

1. SCOPE

This section provides for the termination of the mandate of a mediator. The mandate of a mediator shall be terminated by the mediation service provider upon

(*i*) the receipt of application from a party under clause (*i*) of sub-section (4) of Section 10; or

(*ii*) the receipt of information about the mediator being involved in a matter of conflict of interest from participants or any other person; or

(*iii*) his withdrawal from mediation for any reason.

2. HEARING TO THE MEDIATOR (PROVISO)

Where mandate of the mediator is sought to be terminated on the ground of involvement of the mediator in a matter of conflict of interest, the termination order shall be passed/effected if, after hearing the mediator, the mediation service provider finds that there is justifiable doubt as to the independence or impartiality of the arbitrator and that the same has been brought to the notice of the parties and that either party desires the replacement of the mediator.

12. *Replacement of mediator.*—Upon termination of the mandate of mediator—

(*i*) in case of mediation other than institutional mediation under clause (*ii*) of sub-section (4) of Section 10, the parties may appoint another mediator within a period of seven days from such termination; and

(*ii*) under Section 11, the mediation service provider shall appoint another mediator from the panel maintained by it within a period of seven days from such termination.

COMMENTS

This section provides for the replacement of the mediator.

Upon the termination of the mandate of the mediator under Section 10(4)(*ii*), the parties may appoint another mediator within a period of seven days from such termination. Under Section 11, the mediation service provider shall appoint another mediator from the panel maintained by it within a period of seven days from the date of termination.

CHAPTER V
MEDIATION PROCEEDINGS

13. *Territorial jurisdiction to undertake mediation.*—Every mediation under this Act shall be undertaken within the territorial jurisdiction of the court or tribunal of competent jurisdiction to decide the subject matter of dispute:

Provided that on the mutual consent of the parties, mediation may be conducted at any place outside the territorial jurisdiction of the court or tribunal, or by way of online mediation.

Explanation.—For the removal of doubts, it is clarified that where the parties agree to conduct the mediation at any place outside the territorial jurisdiction or online, for the purpose of enforcement, challenge and registration of the mediated settlement agreement, the same shall be deemed to have been undertaken within the territorial jurisdiction of the court or tribunal of competent jurisdiction.

COMMENTS

This section provides that mediation under this Act shall take place within the territorial jurisdiction of the court or tribunal of competent jurisdiction unless parties agree to conduct mediation outside the said territorial jurisdiction or by way of online mediation.

Mediation proceeding under this Act shall be undertaken within the territorial jurisdiction of the court/tribunal of competent jurisdiction to decide the subject-matter of the dispute. Proceedings may be undertaken at any place outside the territorial jurisdiction of the court/tribunal only in two contingencies, *namely*:

1. by mutual consent of the parties, or
2. by way of online mediation.

The Explanation to Section 13 clarifies that where the parties agree to conduct the mediation at any place outside the territorial jurisdiction or online, for the purpose of enforcement, challenge and registration of the mediated settlement agreement, the same shall be deemed to have been undertaken within the territorial jurisdiction of the court or tribunal of competent jurisdiction.

14. *Commencement of mediation.*—The mediation proceedings with respect to a particular dispute shall be deemed to have commenced—

(*a*) where there is an existing agreement between the parties to settle the dispute through mediation, the date on which a party or parties receives notice from the party initiating the mediation, to refer such dispute to mediation; or

(*b*) in other cases—

(*i*) where the parties have agreed to appoint a mediator of their choice for mediation and settlement of disputes between them on the date the mediator provides his consent to appointment; or

(*ii*) where one of the parties applies to a mediation service provider for settlement of disputes through mediation, the date of appointment of a mediator.

COMMENTS

This section provides that mediation proceedings with respect to a particular dispute shall be deemed to have commenced on the date on which a party issues notice to the other party in case of prior mediation agreement and on other cases on the day the parties have agreed to appoint a mediator of their choice or on the day when a party applies to a mediation service provider for mediation.

Mediation proceedings with respect to a particular dispute shall be deemed to have commenced

(*a*) where there is an existing agreement between the parties to settle the dispute through mediation, the date on which a party or parties receives notice from the party initiating the mediation, to refer such dispute to mediation; or

(*b*) in other cases—

(*i*) where the parties have agreed to appoint a mediator of their choice for mediation and settlement of disputes between them on the date the mediator provides his consent to appointment; or

(*ii*) where one of the parties applies to a mediation service provider for settlement of disputes through mediation, the date of appointment of a mediator.

15. *Conduct of mediation.*—(1) The mediation process shall be conducted in the manner as may be specified.

(2) The mediator shall assist the parties in an independent, neutral and impartial manner in their attempt to reach an amicable settlement of their dispute.

(3) The mediator shall at all times be guided by the principles of objectivity and fairness and protect the voluntariness, confidentiality and self-determination of the parties, and the standards for professional and ethical conduct as may be specified.

(4) The mediation process may include the mediator taking such measures as may be considered appropriate, taking into account the circumstances of the case, including meeting with parties or participants, jointly or separately, as frequently as deemed fit by the mediator, both in order to convene the mediation, and during the mediation for the orderly and timely conduct of the process and to maintain its integrity.

(5) The mediator shall not be bound by the Code of Civil Procedure, 1908 (5 of 1908), or the Indian Evidence Act, 1872 (1 of 1872).

(6) The mediator with the consent of the parties shall determine the language or languages to be used in the mediation process.

COMMENTS

1. SCOPE

This section provides that the mediator shall assist the parties in an independent, neutral and impartial manner in their attempt to reach an amicable settlement of their dispute. It further provides that the mediator shall not be bound by the Code of Civil Procedure, 1908 or the Evidence Act, 1872.

2. MEDIATION PROCESS

The mediation process shall be conducted in the manner as may be specified. Section 82(1)(*f*) of the Act provides that the Mediation Council of India may make regulations laying down the manner of conducting mediation proceedings under Section 15(1) of the Act.

The mediator shall assist the parties in an independent, neutral and impartial manner in their attempt to reach an amicable settlement of their dispute.

The mediator shall at all times be guided by the principles of objectivity and fairness and protect the voluntariness, confidentiality and self-determination of the parties, and the standards for professional and ethical conduct as may be specified.

The mediation process may include the mediator taking such measures as may be considered appropriate, taking into account the circumstances of the case, including meeting with parties or participants, jointly or separately, as frequently as deemed fit by the mediator, both in order to convene the mediation, and during the mediation for the orderly and timely conduct of the process and to maintain its integrity.

3. VENUE FOR CONDUCTING MEDIATION

The mediator shall conduct the mediation at one or other of the following places:

(*i*) Venue of the Lok Adalat or permanent Lok Adalat;

(*ii*) Any place identified by the High Court;

(*iii*) Any place identified by the District Judge or Principal Judge, City Civil Court or Principal Judge, Family Court, within the Court precincts for the purpose of conducting mediation;

(*iv*) Any place identified by the Bar Association or State Bar Council for the purpose of mediation, within the premises of the Bar Association or State Bar Council, as the case may be;

(*v*) Any other place as may be agreed upon by the parties subject to the approval of the Court. [Maharashtra Alternative Dispute Resolution Rules, Part II, R. 6]

4. MEDIATOR NOT BOUND BY CODE OF CIVIL PROCEDURE, EVIDENCE ACT/BSA 2023 [SUB-S. (5)]

The mediator shall not be bound by the Code of Civil Procedure, 1908 and the Evidence Act/BSA 2023.

5. LANGUAGE TO BE USED IN THE "MEDIATION" PROCESS [SUB-S. (4)]

The mediator with the consent of the parties shall determine the language or languages to be used in the mediation process.

16. *Role of mediator.*—(1) The mediator shall attempt to facilitate voluntary resolution of the dispute by the parties and communicate the view of each party to the other to the extent agreed to by them, assist them in identifying issues, advancing better understanding, clarifying priorities, exploring areas of settlement and generating options in an attempt to resolve the dispute expeditiously, emphasising that it is the responsibility of the parties to take decision regarding their claims.

(2) The parties shall be informed expressly by the mediator that he only facilitates in arriving at a decision to resolve a dispute and that he shall not impose any settlement nor give any assurance that the mediation may result in a settlement.

COMMENTS

Section 18 provides that a mediator shall not act as an arbitrator or as a representative or counsel of a party in any arbitral or judicial proceeding in respect of a dispute that is the subject of the mediation proceedings, and he shall not be presented by the parties as a witness in any arbitral or judicial proceeding.

Section 16 has been drafted on the lines of Rules 16 and 17 of the Maharashtra Alternative Dispute Resolution Rules, 2006, Part II; Rules 17 and 18 of the Uttar Pradesh Alternative Dispute Resolution Rules, 2009, Part II.

17. *Role of mediator in other proceedings.*—The mediator shall not—

(*a*) act as an arbitrator or as a representative or counsel of a party in any arbitral or judicial proceeding in respect of a dispute that is the subject matter of the mediation proceedings;

(*b*) be presented by the parties as a witness in any arbitral or judicial proceeding.

COMMENTS

This section provides that mediator shall not act as an arbitrator or as a representative or counsel of a party in any arbitral proceeding in respect of a dispute that is the subject of the mediation proceedings and he shall not be presented by the parties as a witness in any arbitral or judicial proceeding. (Notes on clauses)

18. *Time-limit for completion of mediation.*—(1) Notwithstanding anything contained in any other law for the time being in force, mediation under this Act shall be completed within a period of one hundred and twenty days from the date fixed for the first appearance before the mediator.

(2) The period for mediation mentioned under sub-section (1) may be extended for a further period as agreed by the parties, but not exceeding sixty days.

COMMENTS

Section 18 provides that mediation proceedings under this Act shall be completed within a period of 120 days, which may be extended for a further period not exceeding 60 days. Thus, the arbitration proceedings have to be completed within a total period of 180 days, when the period is extended.

19. *Mediated settlement agreement.*—(1) A mediated settlement agreement includes an agreement in writing between some or all of the parties resulting from mediation, settling some or all of the disputes between such parties, and authenticated by the mediator:

Provided that the terms of the mediated settlement agreement may extend beyond the disputes referred to mediation.

Explanation.—A mediated settlement agreement which is void under the Indian Contract Act, 1872 (9 of 1872), shall not be deemed to be lawful settlement agreement within the meaning of mediated settlement agreement.

(2) Where a mediated settlement agreement is reached between the parties with regard to all or some of the disputes, the same shall be reduced in to writing and signed by the parties.

(3) Subject to the provisions of Section 26, the mediated settlement agreement signed,—

(*i*) in case of institutional mediation, shall be submitted to the mediator, who shall, after authenticating the same, forward it with a covering letter signed by him, to the mediation service provider and also provide a copy to the parties;

(*ii*) in all other cases, shall be submitted to the mediator who shall, after authenticating the mediated settlement agreement, provide a copy to all the parties.

(4) The parties, may, at any time during the mediation process, make an agreement with respect to any of the disputes which is the subject matter of mediation.

(5) Any mediated settlement agreement under this section includes a settlement agreement resulting from online mediation.

COMMENTS

This section provides that a mediated settlement agreement means and includes an agreement in writing between some or all the parties resulting from mediation, including online mediation, settling some or all of the disputes between such parties, and authenticated by the mediator.

20. *Registration of mediated settlement agreement.*—(1) For the purposes of record, mediated settlement agreement arrived at between the parties, other than those arrived in a court or tribunal referred mediation or award of Lok Adalat or final award of the Permanent Lok Adalat under Section 21 or Section 22-E of the Legal Services Authorities Act, 1987 (39 of 1987), may, at the option of parties, be registered with an Authority constituted under the said Act, or any other body as may be notified by the Central Government, in such manner as may be specified and such Authority or body shall issue a unique registration number to such settlement agreements:

Provided that the mediated settlement agreement under this section may be registered with such Authority or the body situated within the territorial jurisdiction of the court or tribunal of competent jurisdiction to decide the subject matter of dispute.

Explanation.—For the removal of doubts, it is clarified that nothing contained in this sub-section shall affect the rights of parties to enforce the mediated settlement agreement under Section 27 or challenge the same under Section 28.

(2) The registration referred to in sub-section (1) may be made by the parties or mediation service provider within a period of one hundred and eighty days from the date of receipt of authenticated copy of mediated settlement agreement:

Provided that mediated settlement agreement may be allowed to be registered after the expiry of period of one hundred and eighty days on payment of such fee as may be specified in consultation with the Authority or any other body referred to in sub-section (1).

COMMENTS

This section provides that a mediated settlement agreement arrived at between the parties other than those arrived in court-annexed mediation centres or under Sections 21 and 22-E, Legal Services Authorities Act, 1987 shall be registered with the authority constituted under the Legal Services Authorities Act, 1987 within a period of 180 days. However, registration is not mandatory till the time regulations specifying the manner of registration are made by the Council.

21. *Non-settlement report.*—Subject to the provisions of Section 26, where no agreement is arrived at between the parties, within the time period as provided under Section 18, or where, the mediator is of the view that no settlement is possible, he shall,—

(*i*) in the case of institutional mediation, submit a non-settlement report to the mediation service provider in writing;

(*ii*) in all other cases, prepare a non-settlement report and provide a signed copy to all the parties:

Provided that the report referred to in this section shall not disclose the cause of non-settlement, or any other matter or thing referring to their conduct, during mediation.

COMMENTS

This section provides for a non-settlement report. It lays down that where no settlement is arrived at between the parties within the time as provided under Section 18 or where the mediator is of the view that no settlement is possible, he shall (*i*) in the case of institutional mediation, submit a non-settlement report to the mediation service provider in writing;

(*ii*) in all other cases, prepare a non-settlement report and provide a signed copy to all the parties.

The non-settlement report submitted under this section shall not disclose the cause of non-settlement or thing referring to the conduct of the parties, during mediation.

In case of failure of mediation, the report should only state that mediation was unsuccessful. Discussion and proposals should not be disclosed.[37] An unsuccessful mediation would not amount to a concluded contract.[38]

22. *Confidentiality.*—(1) Subject to the other provisions of this Act, the mediator, mediation service provider, the parties and participants in the mediation shall keep confidential all the following matters relating to the mediation proceedings, namely—

(*i*) acknowledgements, opinions, suggestions, promises, proposals, apologies and admissions made during the mediation;

(*ii*) acceptance of, or willingness to, accept proposals made or exchanged in the mediation;

(*iii*) documents prepared solely for the conduct of mediation or in relation thereto;

(*iv*) any other mediation communication.

(2) No audio or video recording of the mediation proceedings shall be made or maintained by the parties or the participants including the mediator and mediation service provider, whether conducted in person or online to ensure confidentiality of the conduct of mediation proceedings.

(3) No party to the mediation shall in any proceeding before a court or tribunal including arbitral tribunal, rely on or introduce as evidence any information or communication set forth in clauses (*i*) to (*iv*) of sub-section (1), including any information in electronic form, or verbal communication and the court or tribunal including arbitral tribunal shall not take cognizance of such information or evidence.

(4) The provisions of this section shall not prevent the mediator from compiling or disclosing general information concerning matters that have been subject of mediation, for research, reporting or training purposes, if the information does not expressly or indirectly identify a party or participants or the specific disputes in the mediation.

Explanation.—For the removal of doubts, it is hereby clarified that nothing contained in this section shall apply to the mediated settlement agreement

---

37. *Moti Ram* v. *Ashok Kumar*, (2011) 1 SCC 466.

38. *Ibid.*

where its disclosure is necessary for the purpose of registration, enforcement and challenge.

COMMENTS

1. SCOPE

This section provides that the mediator, mediation service provider, the parties and participants in the mediation shall keep the information and communication relating to the mediation proceedings confidential, and no party to the mediation shall in any proceedings before a court or tribunal, including Arbitral Tribunal, rely on or introduce as evidence any such information or communication. However, confidentiality shall not apply to the mediated settlement agreement where its disclosure is necessary for the purpose of registration, implementation, enforcement and challenge.

2. REPORT OF THE MEDIATION—PROPER REPORT

Mediation proceedings are totally confidential proceedings. This is unlike proceedings in court which are conducted openly in the public gaze. If the mediation succeeds, then the mediator should send the agreement signed by both the parties to the court without mentioning what transpired during the mediation proceedings. If the mediation is unsuccessful, then the mediator should only write one sentence in his report and send it to the court stating that the "mediation has been unsuccessful". Beyond that, the mediator should not write anything which was discussed, proposed or done during the mediation proceedings. This is because in mediation very often offers, counter-offers and proposals are made by the parties but until and unless the parties reach an agreement signed by them, it will not amount to any concluded contract. If the happenings in the mediation proceedings are disclosed, it will destroy the confidentiality of the mediation process.[39]

3. KARNATAKA CIVIL PROCEDURE MEDIATION RULES, 2005

The trial court while dismissing divorce petition took note of the conciliation proceedings between husband and wife before the mediator. Communication between the parties and mediator are confidential under Rule 23 of the Rules. Held, the trial court was not justified in considering mediation proceedings as they were confidential and the same could not have been revealed to the court until party had advised to. Dismissal of the divorce petition was held not proper.[40]

---

39. *Moti Ram* v. *Ashok Kumar*, (2011) 1 SCC 466, 467.
40. *Shashidhar* v. *Vijayalaxmi*, 2022 SCC OnLine Kar 980: (2022) 3 KCCR 1932.

4. MEDIATION PROCEEDINGS ARE CONFIDENTIAL PROCEEDINGS—DELHI FAMILY COURTS (PROCEDURE) RULES, 1992

Mediation proceedings are totally confidential proceedings. This is unlike proceedings in court which are conducted openly in the public gaze. If the mediation succeeds, then the mediator should send the agreement signed by both the parties to the court without mentioning what transpired during the mediation proceedings. If the mediation is unsuccessful, then the mediator should only write one sentence in his report and send it to the court stating that the "mediation has been unsuccessful". Beyond that, the mediator should not write anything which was discussed, proposed or done during the mediation proceedings. This is because in mediation, very often, offers, counter-offers and proposals are made by the parties but until and unless the parties reach an agreement signed by them, it will not amount to any concluded contract. If the happenings in the mediation proceedings are disclosed, it will destroy the confidentiality of the mediation process. Both the conciliator and the parties must keep as confidential all matters relating to conciliation proceedings.[41]

23. *Admissibility and privilege against disclosure.*—(1) No mediator or participant in the mediation, including experts and advisers engaged for the purpose of the mediation and persons involved in the administration of the mediation, shall at any time be permitted, or compelled to disclose to any court or tribunal, or in any adjudicatory proceedings, by whatever description, any communication in mediation, or to state the contents or conditions of any document or nature or conduct of parties during mediation including the content of negotiations or offers or counter offers with which they have become acquainted during the mediation:

Provided that nothing in this section and Section 22 shall protect from disclosure, information sought or provided to prove or dispute a claim or complaint of professional misconduct of mediator or malpractice based on conduct occurring during the mediation.

(2) There shall be no privilege or confidentiality that will attach to—

(*a*) a threat or statement of a plan to commit an offence punishable under any law for the time being in force;

(*b*) information relating to domestic violence or child abuse; and

(*c*) statements made during a mediation showing a significant imminent threat to public health or safety.

41. *Perry Kansagra* v. *Smriti Madan Kansagra*, (2019) 20 SCC 753.

COMMENTS

This section provides immunity to the participants including experts and advisers engaged for the purpose of the mediation and person involved in the administration of the mediation from disclosing by whatever description, any communication in mediation, or stating the contents or conditions of any document or nature or conduct of parties during mediation including the content of negotiations or offers or counter-offers with which they have become acquainted during the mediation.

24. *Termination of mediation.*—The mediation proceedings under this Act shall be deemed to terminate—

(*a*) on the date of signing and authentication of the mediated settlement agreement; or

(*b*) on the date of the written declaration of the mediator, after consultation with the parties or otherwise, to the effect that further efforts at mediation are no longer justified; or

(*c*) on the date of the communication by a party or parties in writing, addressed to the mediator and the other parties to the effect that the party wishes to opt out of mediation;

(*d*) on the expiry of time limit under Section 18.

COMMENTS

This section provides for termination of mediation proceedings in certain circumstances.

25. *Cost of mediation.*—(1) The cost of mediation, other than community mediation shall be such as may be specified.

(2) Unless otherwise agreed by the parties, all costs of mediation, including the fees of the mediator and the charges of the mediation service provider shall be borne equally by the parties.

COMMENTS

This section provides that all costs of mediation, including the fees of the mediator and the charges of the mediation service provider shall be borne equally by the parties unless otherwise agreed by the parties.

26. *Proceedings of Lok Adalat and Permanent Lok Adalat not to be affected.*—The provisions of this Act shall not apply to the proceedings conducted by Lok Adalat and Permanent Lok Adalat under the Legal Services Authorities Act, 1987 (39 of 1987).

Date of Enforcement: Section 26 enforced w.e.f. 9-10-2023, *vide* Noti. No. S.O. 4384(E), dt. 9-10-2023.

COMMENTS

This section provides that the provisions of the proposed Act shall not apply to the proceedings conducted by Lok Adalat and Permanent Lok Adalat under the Legal Services Authorities Act, 1987.

CHAPTER VI

ENFORCEMENT OF MEDIATED SETTLEMENT AGREEMENT

27. *Enforcement of mediated settlement agreement.*—(1) A mediated settlement agreement resulting from a mediation signed by the parties and authenticated by the mediator shall be final and binding on the parties and persons claiming under them respectively and enforceable as per the provisions of sub-section (2).

(2) Subject to the provisions of Section 28, the mediated settlement agreement shall be enforced in accordance with the provisions of the Code of Civil Procedure, 1908 (5 of 1908), in the same manner as if it were a judgment or decree passed by a court, and may, accordingly, be relied on by any of the parties or persons claiming through them, by way of defence, set off or otherwise in any legal proceeding.

COMMENTS

This section provides that a mediated settlement agreement resulting from mediation is final and binding and is enforceable in accordance with the provisions of the Code of Civil Procedure, 1908, in the same manner as if it were a judgment or decree passed by a court.

28. *Challenge to mediated settlement agreement.*—(1) Notwithstanding anything contained in any other law for the time being in force, in any case in which the mediated settlement agreement is arrived at between the parties and is sought to be challenged by either of the parties, such party may file an application before the court or tribunal of competent jurisdiction.

(2) A mediated settlement agreement may be challenged only on all or any of the following grounds, namely—

(*i*) fraud;

(*ii*) corruption;

(*iii*) impersonation;

(*iv*) where the mediation was conducted in disputes or matters not fit for mediation under Section 6.

(3) An application for challenging the mediated settlement agreement shall not be made after ninety days have elapsed from the date on which the party making that application has received the copy of mediated settlement agreement under sub-section (3) of Section 19:

Provided that if the court or tribunal, as the case may be, is satisfied that the applicant was prevented by sufficient cause from making the application within the said period of ninety days, it may entertain the application within a further period of ninety days.

COMMENTS

1. SCOPE

This section provides that a mediated settlement agreement can be challenged on the grounds of fraud, corruption, impersonation or where mediation is conducted in a dispute or matter not fit for mediation and that such challenge can be made within a period of 90 days from the date of receipt of the copy of the mediated settlement agreement by the parties.

2. GROUNDS OF CHALLENGE

A party aggrieved by the mediated settlement agreement can challenge the same by filing an application under this section before the court/tribunal of competent jurisdiction on all or any of the following grounds, *namely*:

(*a*) fraud,

(*b*) corruption,

(*c*) impersonation, or

(*d*) where the mediation was conducted in disputes/matters not fit for mediation enumerated in First Schedule.

Where any of the above grounds is made out, the mediated settlement agreement shall be set aside.

(*i*) Fraud

Section 17, Contract Act defines the term "fraud" as under:

"Fraud" means and includes any of the following acts committed by a party to a contract, or with his connivance, or by his agent, with intent to deceive another party thereto or his agent, or to induce him to enter into the contract—

(1) the suggestion, as a fact, of that which is not true, by one who does not believe it to be true;
(2) the active concealment of a fact by one having knowledge or belief of the fact;
(3) a promise made without any intention of performing it;
(4) any other act fitted to deceive;
(5) any such act or omission as the law specially declares to be fraudulent.

Fraud vitiates all solemn proceedings of a court/tribunal. Fraud committed by the mediator can also be a ground for annulling a mediated settlement agreement.

(*ii*) Corruption

A mediated settlement agreement shall also be set aside when any of the parties, or the mediator or any one involved in the process of mediation is found to have committed corruption. The word "corruption" connotes allowing decisions and actions of a person to be influenced not by right or wrong of a cause but by the prospects of monetary gains or other selfish considerations.[42]

(*iii*) Impersonation

A mediated settlement agreement shall also be set aside where any of the parties to it or any other person involved in the process, *viz.* the mediator is found to have impersonated. The act of impersonation is also an offence punishable under Section 319, BNS 2023.

(*iv*) Matter/dispute not fit for mediation

Section 6, Mediation Act provides that disputes/matters mentioned in Schedule I cannot be referred to mediation. If the dispute or matter decided by the mediator falls in Schedule I, the mediated settlement agreement shall be set aside.

3. LIMITATION [SUB-S. (3)]

An application for setting a mediated settlement agreement can be filed within 90 days from the date on which the party making the application has received a copy of the mediated settlement under Section 19(3). Where the court/tribunal is satisfied that the applicant was prevented by sufficient cause from making the application within the said period of 90 days, it may

42. *State of A.P.* v. *V. Vasudeva Rao*, (2004) 9 SCC 319, 323.

entertain the application within a further period of 90 days. Thus, within a total period of 180 days, a petition for setting aside the mediated settlement agreement can be filed.

29. *Limitation.*—Notwithstanding anything contained in the Limitation Act, 1963 (36 of 1963) or in any other law for the time being in force, in computing the period of limitation fixed for any proceeding relating to disputes in respect of which a mediation has been undertaken under this Act, the period from the date of commencement of mediation under Section 14, and up to—

(*i*) submission of report under Section 21; or

(*ii*) termination of mediation under Section 24, shall be excluded.

COMMENTS

This section provides that the period during which the parties were engaged in the mediation shall be excluded for computing the period of limitation specified for any proceedings.

CHAPTER VII
ONLINE MEDIATION

30. *Online mediation.*—(1) Online mediation including pre-litigation mediation may be conducted at any stage of mediation under this Act, with the written consent of the parties including by the use of electronic form or computer networks but not limited to an encrypted electronic mail service, secure chat rooms or conferencing by video or audio mode or both.

(2) The process of online mediation shall be in such manner as may be specified.

(3) The conduct of online mediation shall be in the circumstances, which ensure that the essential elements of integrity of proceedings and confidentiality are maintained at all times and the mediator may take such appropriate steps in this regard as he deems fit.

(4) Subject to the other provisions of this Act, the mediation communications in the case of online mediation shall, ensure confidentiality of mediation.

COMMENTS

This section provides that online mediation including pre-litigation mediation may be conducted at any stage of mediation with the written consent of the parties and that such online mediation shall be conducted in the manner specified by the Council.

It refers to conducting the mediation proceedings by use of electronic means or computer network. There is not much difference between online and offline mediation proceedings; the parties are free to decide the course of their proceedings on their own. The mediator is equally bound to ensure the confidentiality of the online mediation proceedings.

Chapter VIII
MEDIATION COUNCIL OF INDIA

31. *Establishment and incorporation of Mediation Council.*—(1) The Central Government shall, by notification, establish for the purposes of this Act, a Council to be known as the Mediation Council of India to perform the duties and discharge the functions under this Act.

(2) The Council shall be a body corporate by the name aforesaid, having perpetual succession and a common seal, with power, subject to the provisions of this Act, to acquire, hold and dispose of property, both movable and immovable, and to enter into contract, and shall, by the said name, sue or be sued.

(3) The head office of the Council shall be at Delhi or at such other place as may be notified by the Central Government.

(4) The Council may, in consultation with the Central Government, establish offices at other places in India and abroad.

Date of Enforcement: Section 31 enforced w.e.f. 9-10-2023, *vide* Noti. No. S.O. 4384(E), dt. 9-10-2023.

COMMENTS

This section provides for the establishment of the Mediation Council of India as a body corporate having perpetual succession and a common seal, with the power to acquire, hold and dispose of property, both moveable and immoveable, and to enter into a contract, and shall, by the said same, sue or be sued.

32. *Composition of Council.*—(1) The Council shall consist of the following members, namely—

(*a*) a person of ability, integrity and standing having adequate knowledge and professional experience or shown capacity in dealing with problems relating to law, alternative dispute resolution preferably mediation, public affairs or administration to be appointed by the Central Government—Chairperson;

(*b*) a person having knowledge and experience in law related to mediation or alternative dispute resolution mechanisms, to be appointed by the Central Government — Member;

(*c*) an eminent person having experience in research or teaching in the field of mediation and alternative dispute resolution laws, to be appointed by the Central Government — Member;

(*d*) Secretary to the Government of India in the Department of Legal Affairs, Ministry of Law and Justice or his representative not below the rank of Joint Secretary — Member, *ex officio*;

(*e*) Secretary to the Government of India in the Department of Expenditure, Ministry of Finance or his representative not below the rank of Joint Secretary — Member, *ex officio*;

(*f*) Chief Executive Officer — Member-Secretary, *ex officio*; and

(*g*) one representative of a recognised body of commerce and industry, chosen by the Central Government — Part-Time Member.

(2) The Members of the Council, other than *ex officio* members, shall hold office as such, for a term of four years from the date on which they enter upon their office and shall be eligible for re-appointment:

Provided that no Member other than *ex officio* Member shall hold office after he has attained the age of seventy years, in the case of Chairperson, and sixty-seven years, in the case of other Members:

Provided further that if the Chairperson is appointed on Part-Time basis, then, at least one of the Members appointed under clauses (*b*) or (*c*) shall be a Full-Time Member.

(3) The salaries, allowances and other terms and conditions of Members other than *ex officio* Members shall be such as may be prescribed.

(4) The [43][Part-Time Member] shall be entitled to such travelling and other allowances as may be prescribed.

Date of Enforcement: Section 32 enforced w.e.f. 9-10-2023, *vide* Noti. No. S.O. 4384(E), dt. 9-10-2023.

COMMENTS

This section provides for the composition of the Council and appointment and qualifications, term of office, salary and allowances, etc. of the chairperson, full-time member and part-time member.

33. *Vacancies, etc., not to invalidate proceedings of Council.* — No act or proceeding of the Council shall be invalid merely by reason of —

43. *Subs.* for "Member" by S.O. 4506(E), dt. 13-10-2023 (w.e.f. 13-10-2023). *See* p. 930, below.

(*a*) any vacancy or any defect, in the constitution of the Council;

(*b*) any defect in the appointment of a person as a Member of the Council; or

(*c*) any irregularity in the procedure of the Council not affecting the merits of the case.

Date of Enforcement: Section 33 enforced w.e.f. 9-10-2023, *vide* Noti. No. S.O. 4384(E), dt. 9-10-2023.

COMMENTS

This section provides that any vacancy, defect in the appointment or any irregularity in procedure shall not invalidate the proceedings of the Council.

34. *Resignation.*—The Member may, by notice in writing, under his hand addressed to the Central Government, resign his office:

Provided that the Member shall, unless he is permitted by the Central Government to relinquish his office sooner, continue to hold office until the expiry of three months from the date of receipt of such notice or until a person duly appointed as his successor enters upon his office or until the expiry of his term of office, whichever is earlier.

Date of Enforcement: Section 34 enforced w.e.f. 9-10-2023, *vide* Noti. No. S.O. 4384(E), dt. 9-10-2023.

COMMENTS

This section provides for the procedure for resignation of the chairperson or the full-time member and part-time member by notice in writing addressed to the Central Government.

35. *Removal.*—The Central Government may, remove any Member from his office, if he—

(*a*) is an undischarged insolvent; or

(*b*) has engaged at any time, during his term of office, in any paid employment without the permission of the Central Government; or

(*c*) has been convicted of an offence which, in the opinion of the Central Government, involves moral turpitude; or

(*d*) has acquired such financial or other interest as is likely to affect prejudicially his functions as a Member; or

(*e*) has so abused his position as to render his continuance in office prejudicial to the public interest; or

(*f*) has become physically or mentally incapable of acting as a Member:

Provided that where a Member is proposed to be removed on any ground, he shall be informed of charges against him and given an opportunity of being heard in respect of those charges.

Date of Enforcement: Section 35 enforced w.e.f. 9-10-2023, *vide* Noti. No. S.O. 4384(E), dt. 9-10-2023.

COMMENTS

This section specifies the circumstances in which the Central Government may remove the chairperson or a full-time member or a part-time member of the Council.

36. *Appointment of experts and constitution of Committees.*—The Council may, appoint such experts and constitute such committees of experts as it may consider necessary to discharge its functions on such terms and conditions as may be specified.

Date of Enforcement: Section 36 enforced w.e.f. 9-10-2023, *vide* Noti. No. S.O. 4384(E), dt. 9-10-2023.

COMMENTS

This section provides for the appointment of experts and constitution of committees of experts as the Council may consider necessary for the effective discharge of its functions.

37. *Secretariat and Chief Executive Officer of Council.*—(1) There shall be a Chief Executive Officer of the Council, who shall be responsible for the day to day administration and implementation of the decisions of the Council.

(2) The qualification, appointment and other terms and conditions of service of the Chief Executive Officer shall be such as may be specified.

(3) There shall be a Secretariat to the Council consisting of such number of officers and employees as may be specified.

(4) The qualification, appointment and other terms and conditions of the service of the employees and other officers of the Council shall be such as may be specified.

(5) The Central Government shall provide such number of officers and employees as may be necessary for the functioning of the Council till regulations are made under this section.

Date of Enforcement: Section 37 enforced w.e.f. 9-10-2023, *vide* Noti. No. S.O. 4384(E), dt. 9-10-2023.

COMMENTS

This section provides for the Chief Executive Officer of the Council as well as the Secretariat of the Council, which shall comprise of such number of officers and employees as may be specified by the Council.

38. *Duties and functions of Council.*—The Council shall—

(*a*) endeavour to promote domestic and international mediation in India through appropriate guidelines;

(*b*) endeavour to develop India to be a robust centre for domestic and international mediation;

(*c*) lay down the guidelines for the continuous education, certification and assessment of mediators by the recognised mediation institutes;

(*d*) provide for the manner of conduct of mediation proceedings, under sub-section (1) of Section 15;

(*e*) provide for manner of registration of mediators and renew, withdraw, suspend or cancel registration on the basis of conditions as may be specified;

(*f*) lay down standards for professional and ethical conduct of mediators under sub-section (3) of Section 15;

(*g*) hold trainings, workshops and courses in the area of mediation in collaboration with mediation service providers, law firms and universities and other stakeholders, both Indian and international, and any other mediation institutes;

(*h*) enter into memoranda of understanding or agreements with domestic and international bodies or organisations or institutions;

(*i*) recognise mediation institutes and mediation service providers and renew, withdraw, suspend or cancel such recognition;

(*j*) specify the criteria for recognition of mediation institutes and mediation service providers;

(*k*) call for any information or record of mediation institutes and mediation service providers;

(*l*) lay down standards for professional and ethical conduct of the mediation institutes and mediation service providers;

(*m*) publish such information, data, research studies and such other information as may be required;

(*n*) maintain an electronic depository of the mediated settlement agreements made in India and for such other records related thereto in such manner as may be specified; and

(*o*) perform any other function as may be assigned to it by the Central Government.

Date of Enforcement: Section 38 enforced w.e.f. 9-10-2023, *vide* Noti. No. S.O. 4384(E), dt. 9-10-2023.

COMMENTS

This section provides the duties and functions of the Council.

39. *Monitoring and reporting.*—(1) The Council shall, as soon as practicable after the end of each year or at such other intervals as directed by the Central Government, prepare a report on the implementation of the provisions of this Act during the year or such interval and forward a copy thereof to the Central Government.

(2) The Central Government may take such additional measures as it deems necessary to supplement the functioning of the Council and for the effective implementation of the provisions of the Act.

COMMENTS

This section provides for monitoring and reporting by the Mediation Council of India.

CHAPTER IX

MEDIATION SERVICE PROVIDERS AND MEDIATION INSTITUTES

40. *Mediation service provider.*—(1) "mediation service provider" includes—

(*a*) a body or an organisation that provides for the conduct of mediation under this Act and the rules and regulations made thereunder and is recognised by the Council; or

(*b*) an Authority constituted under the Legal Services Authorities Act, 1987 (39 of 1987); or

(*c*) a court-annexed mediation centre; or

(*d*) any other body as may be notified by the Central Government:

Provided that the bodies referred to in clauses (*b*), (*c*) and (*d*) shall be deemed to be mediation service providers recognised by the Council.

(2) The mediation service provider shall be recognised by the Council in the manner as may be specified.

COMMENTS

This section provides the functions to be performed by the mediation service provider.

41. *Functions of mediation service providers.*—The mediation service providers shall perform the following functions, namely—

(*a*) accredit mediators and maintain panel of mediators;

(*b*) provide the services of mediator for conduct of mediation;

(*c*) provide all facilities, secretarial assistance and infrastructure for the efficient conduct of mediation;

(*d*) promote professional and ethical conduct amongst mediators;

(*e*) facilitate registration of mediated settlement agreements in accordance with the provisions of Section 20; and

(*f*) such other functions as may be specified.

COMMENTS

This section provides the functions to be performed by the mediation service provider.

42. *Mediation institutes.*—The Council shall recognise mediation institutes to perform such duties and exercise such functions as may be specified.

COMMENTS

This section provides for the recognition of mediation institutes by the Council and the functions and duties to be performed by such mediation institutes as may be specified by the Council.

Chapter X

COMMUNITY MEDIATION

43. *Community mediation.*—(1) Any dispute likely to affect peace, harmony and tranquillity amongst the residents or families of any area or locality may be settled through community mediation with prior mutual consent of the parties to the dispute.

(2) For the purposes of sub-section (1), any of the parties shall make an application before the concerned Authority constituted under the Legal Services Authorities Act, 1987 (39 of 1987) or District Magistrate or Sub-Divisional Magistrate in areas where no such Authority has been constituted, for referring the dispute to mediation.

(3) In order to facilitate settlement of a dispute for which an application has been received under sub-section (2), the concerned Authority constituted under the Legal Services Authorities Act, 1987 (39 of 1987) or the District Magistrate or Sub-Divisional Magistrate, as the case may be, shall constitute panel of three community mediators.

(4) For the purposes of this section, the Authority or District Magistrate or the Sub-Divisional Magistrate, as the case may be, shall notify a permanent panel of community mediators, which may be revised from time to time.

(5) The following persons may be included in the panel referred to in sub-section (4)—

(*a*) person of standing and integrity who are respectable in the community;

(*b*) any local person whose contribution to the society has been recognised;

(*c*) representative of area or resident welfare associations;

(*d*) person having experience in the field of mediation; and

(*e*) any other person deemed appropriate.

(6) While making panel referred to in sub-section (4) the representation of women or any other class or category of persons may be considered.

44. *Procedure for community mediation.*—(1) Any community mediation shall be conducted by the panel of three community mediators referred to in sub-section (3) of Section 43 who shall devise suitable procedure for the purpose of resolving the dispute.

(2) The community mediators shall endeavour to resolve disputes through community mediation and provide assistance to parties for resolving disputes amicably.

(3) In every case where a settlement agreement is arrived at through community mediation under this Act, the same may be reduced into writing with the signature of the parties and authenticated by the community mediators, a copy of which be provided to the parties and in cases where no settlement agreement is arrived at, a non-settlement report may be submitted by the community mediators to the Authority or the District Magistrate or the Sub-Divisional Magistrate, as the case may be, and to the parties.

(4) Any settlement agreement arrived at under this Chapter shall be for the purpose of maintaining the peace, harmony and tranquillity amongst the residents or families of any area or locality but shall not be enforceable as a judgment or decree of a civil court.

(5) The provisions of Section 20 shall, *mutatis mutandis* apply, in relation to the registration of mediated settlement agreement under this section.

COMMENTS

1. SCOPE

Section 43 provides for community mediation and Section 44 lays down the procedure for community mediation.

2. COMMUNITY MEDIATION—WHAT IS?

Any dispute likely to affect

1. peace,
2. harmony, and
3. tranquillity,
4. amongst the residents or families of any area or locality may with the prior mutual consent of the parties be settled through the community mediation.

3. APPLICATION TO BE FILED BEFORE THE CONCERNED AUTHORITY [S. 43(2)]

Any of the parties shall file an application before

1. the concerned authority constituted under the Legal Services Authorities Act, 1987, or
2. the District Magistrate or Sub-Divisional Magistrate of the area where no such authority has been constituted for referring the dispute to mediation.

4. CONSTITUTION OF PANEL OF THREE COMMUNITY MEDIATORS [S. 43(3)]

On the receipt of the application under Section 43(2), the concerned authority under the Legal Services Authorities Act, 1987 or the District Magistrate/ Sub-Divisional Magistrate, as the case may be, shall constitute a panel of three community mediators out of the permanent panel of community mediators prepared under Section 43(4) of the Act to facilitate the settlement of the dispute.

5. PERMANENT PANEL OF COMMUNITY MEDIATORS [S. 43(3) AND 43(4)]

The concerned authority constituted under the Legal Services Authorities Act, 1987 or the District Magistrate/Sub-Divisional Magistrate shall notify a permanent panel of community mediators, which shall consist of persons mentioned in clauses (*a*) to (*e*) of sub-section (5). While preparing the panel, the representation of women or any other class or category of persons may be considered.

6. PROCEDURE FOR COMMUNITY MEDIATION

Every community mediation shall be conducted by a panel of three community mediators, who shall devise suitable procedure for the purpose of resolving the dispute. [S. 44(1)]

The community mediators shall endeavour to resolve the dispute through community mediation and provide assistance to parties for resolving the disputes amicably. [S. 44(2)]

A settlement agreement arrived through community mediation shall be reduced into writing, signed by the parties, and authenticated by the community mediators, a copy of which shall be provided to the parties.

Where no settlement agreement is arrived at, a non-settlement report may be submitted by the community mediation to the authority/District Magistrate/Sub-Divisional Magistrate and also to the parties. [S. 44(3)]

A settlement agreement so arrived shall be used for the purpose of maintaining the peace, harmony and tranquillity amongst the residents/families of any area but cannot be enforced as a judgment or decree of a civil court. [S. 44(4)]

7. REGISTRATION OF MEDIATED SETTLEMENT AGREEMENT

The provisions of Section 20 of the Act shall apply. [S. 44(5)]

Chapter XI
MISCELLANEOUS

45. *Mediation Fund.*—(1) There shall be a fund to be called "Mediation Fund" (hereinafter referred to as the "Fund") for the purposes of promotion, facilitation and encouragement of mediation under this Act, which shall be administered by the Council.

(2) There shall be credited to the Fund the following, namely—

(*a*) all monies provided by the Central Government;

(*b*) all fees and other charges received from mediation service provider, mediation institutes or bodies or persons;

(*c*) all monies received by the Council in the form of donations, grants, contributions and income from other sources;

(*d*) grants made by the Central Government or the State Government for the purposes of the Fund;

(*e*) amounts deposited by persons as contributions to the Fund;

(*f*) amounts received in the Fund from any other source; and (*g*) interest on the above or other income received out of the investment made from the Fund.

(3) The Fund shall be applied towards meeting the salaries and other allowances of Member, Chief Executive Officer, Officers and employees and the expenses of the Council including expenses incurred in the exercise of its powers and discharge of its duties under this Act.

Date of Enforcement: Section 45 enforced w.e.f. 9-10-2023, *vide* Noti. No. S.O. 4384(E), dt. 9-10-2023.

46. *Accounts and audit.*—(1) The Council shall maintain proper accounts and other relevant records and prepare an annual statement of accounts, including the balance sheet, in such form and manner as may be prescribed in consultation with the Comptroller and Auditor-General of India.

(2) The accounts of the Council shall be audited by the Comptroller and Auditor-General of India and any expenditure incurred by him in connection with such audit shall be payable by the Council to the Comptroller and Auditor-General of India.

(3) The Comptroller and Auditor-General of India and any person appointed by him in connection with the audit of the accounts of the Council shall have the same rights, privileges and authority in connection with such audit as the Comptroller and Auditor-General of India has in connection with the audit of the Government accounts, and, in particular, shall have the right to demand the production of books, accounts, connected vouchers and other documents and papers and to inspect the offices of the Council.

(4) The accounts of the Council as certified by the Comptroller and Auditor-General of India or any other person appointed by him in this behalf together with the audit report thereon shall be forwarded annually to the Central Government and that Government shall cause the same to be laid before each House of Parliament.

Date of Enforcement: Section 46 enforced w.e.f. 9-10-2023, *vide* Noti. No. S.O. 4384(E), dt. 9-10-2023.

COMMENTS

This section provides that the Council shall maintain proper accounts and other relevant records and prepare an annual statement of accounts, including the balance sheet, in such form and manner as may be made in consultation with the Comptroller and Auditor-General of India. It further provides that the accounts of the Council shall be audited by the Comptroller and Auditor-General of India.

47. *Power of Central Government to issue directions.*—(1) Without prejudice to the foregoing provisions of this Act, the Council shall, in exercise of its powers or the performance of its functions under this Act, be bound by such directions on questions of policy as the Central Government may give in writing to it from time to time:

Provided that the views of the Council shall be taken into consideration before any direction is given under this sub-section.

(2) The decision of the Central Government whether a question is one of policy or not shall be final.

Date of Enforcement: Section 47 enforced w.e.f. 9-10-2023, *vide* Noti. No. S.O. 4384(E), dt. 9-10-2023.

COMMENTS

This section empowers the Central Government to issue directions to the Council on questions of policy which shall be binding on the Council.

48. *Power to frame schemes or guidelines.*—Subject to the provisions of this Act, the Central Government or the State Government or any of its entity or agency, as the case may be, may frame any schemes or guidelines, for resolution of any dispute through mediation or conciliation in cases where the Central Government or the State Government or any of its entity or agency is one of the parties and in such cases mediation or conciliation may be conducted in accordance with such schemes or guidelines.

COMMENTS

This section provides that the Central Government or State Government can frame any scheme or guidelines for resolution of any dispute through mediation or conciliation in cases where the Central Government or State Government or any of its entities or agencies is one of the parties.

49. *Mediated settlement agreement where Government or its, agency, etc., is a party.*—Notwithstanding anything contained in this Act, no dispute including a commercial dispute, wherein the Central Government or State Government or any of its agencies, public bodies, corporations and local bodies including entities controlled or owned by them is a party, the settlement agreement arrived at shall be signed only after obtaining the prior written consent of the competent authority of such Government or any of its entity or agencies, public bodies, corporations and local bodies, as the case may be.

COMMENTS

This section provides that the settlement agreement arrived at in a dispute, including a commercial dispute, wherein the Central Government or State

Government or any of its agencies, public bodies, corporations and local bodies, including entities is a party shall be signed only after obtaining the prior written consent of the competent authority.

50. *Protection of action taken in good faith.*—No suit, prosecution or other legal proceeding shall lie against the Central Government or a State Government or any officer of such Government, or the Member or Officer or employee of the Council or a mediator, mediation institutes, mediation service providers, which is done or is intended to be done in good faith under this Act or the rules or regulations made thereunder.

Date of Enforcement: Section 50 enforced w.e.f. 9-10-2023, *vide* Noti. No. S.O. 4384(E), dt. 9-10-2023.

COMMENTS

This section provides that no suit, prosecution or other legal proceedings shall lie against the Central Government or a State Government or any officer of such government, or the chairperson, full-time member or part-time member or officer or employee of the Council or a mediator, mediation institutes, mediation service providers, which is done or is intended to be done in good faith.

51. *Power to make rules.*—(1) The Central Government may, by notification, make rules for carrying out the provisions of this Act.

(2) In particular, and without prejudice to the generality of the foregoing power, such rules may make provision for—

(*a*) the salaries and allowances and the terms and conditions of the Members under sub-section (3) of Section 32;

(*b*) the travelling and other allowances payable to the [44][Part-Time Member] under sub-section (4) of Section 32;

(*c*) the form and manner of annual statement of accounts, including the balance sheet under sub-section (1) of Section 46; and

(*d*) any other matter which is to be, or may be prescribed.

Date of Enforcement: Section 51 enforced w.e.f. 9-10-2023, *vide* Noti. No. S.O. 4384(E), dt. 9-10-2023.

COMMENTS

This section empowers the Central Government to make rules to carry out the provisions of this Act.

---

44. *Subs.* for "Member" by S.O. 4506(E), dt. 13-10-2023 (w.e.f. 13-10-2023). *See* p. 930, below.

52. *Power to make regulations.*—(1) The Council may, with the previous approval of the Central Government, by notification, make regulations consistent with this Act and the rules made thereunder to carry out the provisions of this Act.

(2) In particular, and without prejudice to the generality of the foregoing power, such regulations may make provision for—

(*a*) qualification, experience and accreditation for mediators of foreign nationality under the proviso to sub-section (1) of Section 8;

(*b*) manner of conducting mediation proceeding under sub-section (1) of Section 15;

(*c*) standards for professional and ethical conduct of mediators under sub-section (3) of Section 15;

(*d*) manner of registration of mediated settlement agreement under sub-section (1) of Section 20;

(*e*) fees for registration of mediated settlement agreement under the proviso to sub-section (2) of Section 20;

(*f*) cost of mediation under sub-section (1) of Section 25;

(*g*) manner of process of conducting online mediation under sub-section (2) of Section 30;

(*h*) the terms and conditions of experts and committees of experts under Section 36;

(*i*) qualifications, appointment and other terms and conditions of service of the Chief Executive Officer under sub-section (2) of Section 37;

(*j*) the number of officers and employees of the Secretariat of the Council under sub-section (3) of Section 37;

(*k*) the qualification, appointment and other terms and conditions of the employees and other officers of the Council under sub-section (4) of Section 37;

(*l*) conditions for registration of mediators and renewal, withdrawal, suspension or cancellations of such registrations under clause (*e*) of Section 38;

(*m*) criteria for recognition of mediation institutes and mediation service providers under clause (*j*) of Section 38;

(*n*) manner of maintenance of electronic depository of mediated settlement agreement under clause (*n*) of Section 38;

(*o*) manner for recognition of mediation service provider under sub-section (2) of Section 40;

(*p*) such other functions of mediation service provider under clause (*f*) of Section 41;

(*q*) duties and functions to be performed by mediation institutes under Section 42; and

(*r*) any other matter in respect of which provision is necessary for the performance of functions of the Council under this Act.

Date of Enforcement: Section 52 enforced w.e.f. 9-10-2023, *vide* Noti. No. S.O. 4384(E), dt. 9-10-2023.

COMMENTS

This section empowers the Council to make regulations, by notification, with the previous approval of the Central Government. It further provides that the regulations shall be consistent with the provisions of the Act and the rules made thereunder.

53. *Laying.*—Every notification issued under sub-section (2) of Section 6, sub-section (2) of Section 55, rule and regulation made under this Act shall be laid, as soon as may be after it is issued or made, before each House of Parliament, while it is in session, for a total period of thirty days which may be comprised in one session or in two or more successive sessions, and if, before the expiry of the session immediately following the session or the successive sessions aforesaid, both Houses agree in making any modification in the notification, rule or regulation or both Houses agree that the notification, rule or regulation should not be issued or made, the notification, rule or regulation shall thereafter have effect only in such modified form or be of no effect, as the case may be; so, however, that any such modification or annulment shall be without prejudice to the validity of anything previously done under that notification, rule or regulation.

Date of Enforcement: Section 53 enforced w.e.f. 9-10-2023, *vide* Noti. No. S.O. 4384(E), dt. 9-10-2023.

COMMENTS

This section provides for laying of every notification issued under sub-clause (2) of clause 7 and sub-clause (2) of clause 56 and every rule made by the Central Government and every regulation made by the Council, as soon as may be after it is made, before each House of Parliament.

54. *Power to remove difficulties.*—(1) If any difficulty arises in giving effect to the provisions of this Act, the Central Government may, by order published in the Official Gazette, make such provisions, not inconsistent with the provisions of this Act, as may appear to it to be necessary for removing the difficulty:

Provided that no such order shall be made under this section after the expiry of a period of five years from the date of commencement of this Act.

(2) Every order made under sub-section (1) shall be laid, as soon as may be after it is made, before each House of Parliament.

Date of Enforcement: Section 54 enforced w.e.f. 9-10-2023, *vide* Noti. No. S.O. 4384(E), dt. 9-10-2023.

COMMENTS

This section provides that if any difficulty arises in giving effect to the provisions of this Act, the Central Government may, by order published in the Official Gazette, make such provisions, not inconsistent with the provisions of this Act, as may appear to it to be necessary for removing the difficulty.

55. *Provisions of Act to have overriding effect on mediation or conciliation contained in other laws.*—(1) Subject to the enactments mentioned in the Second Schedule, the provisions of this Act shall have overriding effect for conduct of mediation or conciliation notwithstanding anything inconsistent therewith contained in any other law for the time being in force, and any instrument having force of law.

(2) If the Central Government is satisfied that it is necessary or expedient so to do, it may, by notification, amend the Second Schedule and thereupon it shall be deemed to have been amended accordingly.

COMMENTS

This section provides that the provisions of this Act shall have an overriding effect for conduct of mediation or conciliation contained in other laws except those mentioned in the Second Schedule. It further provides that the Central Government may amend the Schedule by notification in the Official Gazette.

This section clarifies that the provisions of the Mediation Act, 2023 shall have an overriding effect over the provisions relating to mediation contained in other enactments except for those Acts mentioned in the Second Schedule of the Mediation Act, 2023. The Acts mentioned in the Second Schedule of the Mediation Act are:

1. The Industrial Disputes Act, 1947 (14 of 1947)
2. The Brahmaputra Board Act, 1980 (46 of 1980)
3. The Cine-Workers and Cinema Theatre Workers (Regulation of Employment) Act, 1981 (50 of 1981)
4. The Family Courts Act, 1984 (66 of 1984)
5. The Legal Services Authorities Act, 1987 (39 of 1987)
6. The Maintenance and Welfare of Parents and Senior Citizens Act, 2007 (56 of 2007)

7. The Sexual Harassment of Women at Workplace (Prevention, Prohibition and Redressal) Act, 2013 (14 of 2013)
8. The Finance Act, 2016 (28 of 2016)
9. The Industrial Relations Code, 2020 (35 of 2020).

56. *Act not to apply to pending proceedings.*—This Act shall not apply to, or in relation to, any mediation or conciliation commenced before the coming into force of this Act.

Date of Enforcement: Section 56 enforced w.e.f. 9-10-2023, *vide* Noti. No. S.O. 4384(E), dt. 9-10-2023.

COMMENTS

This section seeks to provide that the Act shall not apply to, or in relation to, any mediation or conciliation commenced before the coming into force of this Act.

57. *Transitory provision.*—The rules in force governing the conduct of court-annexed mediation shall continue to apply until regulations are made under sub-section (1) of Section 15:

Provided that the rules shall continue to apply in all court-annexed mediation pending as on the date of coming into force of the regulations.

Date of Enforcement: Section 57 enforced w.e.f. 9-10-2023, *vide* Noti. No. S.O. 4384(E), dt. 9-10-2023.

COMMENTS

This section provides that the rules in force governing the conduct of the court-annexed mediation shall continue to apply until regulations are made under Section 15(1) of this Act.

58. *Amendment of Act 9 of 1872.*—The Indian Contract Act, 1872, shall be amended in the manner specified in the Third Schedule.

COMMENTS

This section amends Section 28, Contract Act, 1872. By the amendment, two Exceptions 1 and 2 appended to Section 28 have been substituted by new Exceptions 1 and 2. The two new Exceptions are as under:

[45][*Exception 1*: **Saving of contract to refer to arbitration or mediation dispute that may arise.**—This section shall not render illegal a contract, by

45. *Subs.* by Act 32 of 2023, S. 58 and Sch. III (w.e.f. the date to be notified).

which two or more persons agree that any dispute which may arise between them in respect of any subject or class of subjects shall be referred to resolution through arbitration or mediation.

Exception 2: **Saving of contract to refer questions that have already arisen.**—Nor shall this section render illegal any contract in writing, by which two or more persons agree to refer to arbitration or mediation any question between them which has already arisen, or affect any provision of any law in force for the time being as to references to arbitration or mediation.]

Section 28, Contract Act provides that agreements in restraint of legal proceedings are void. The two exceptions save the contract between the two parties to refer to arbitration or mediation any dispute that may arise or has already arisen.

59. *Amendment of Act 5 of 1908.*—The Code of Civil Procedure, 1908, shall be amended in the manner specified in the Fourth Schedule.

COMMENTS

1. PROVISION OF MEDIATION IN CIVIL PROCEDURE CODE

This section has amended Section 89, Civil Procedure Code, 1908. The new Section 89 CPC provides as under:

[46][**89.** *Settlement of disputes outside the Court.*—Where it appears to the Court that the dispute between the parties may be settled and there exists elements of settlement which may be acceptable to the parties, the Court may—

(*a*) refer the dispute to arbitration, and thereafter, the provisions of the Arbitration and Conciliation Act, 1996 (26 of 1996) shall apply as if the proceedings for arbitration were referred for settlement under the provisions of that Act; or

(*b*) refer the parties to mediation, to the court-annexed mediation centre or any other mediation service provider or any mediator, as per the option of the parties, and thereafter the provisions of the Mediation Act, 2023 shall apply as if the proceedings for mediation were referred for settlement under the provisions of that Act; or

(*c*) refer the dispute to Lok Adalat, in accordance with the provisions of sub-section (1) of Section 20 of the Legal Services Authorities Act, 1987 (39 of 1987) and thereafter, all other provisions of that Act shall apply in respect of the dispute;

(*d*) effect compromise between the parties and shall follow such procedure as deemed fit for judicial settlement.]

---

46. *Subs.* by Act 32 of 2023, S. 59 and Sch. IV(*ii*) (w.e.f. the date to be notified).

Section 89 CPC provides for settlement of disputes outside the court by 1) reference to arbitration, 2) mediation, 3) Lok Adalat, and 4) by compromise between the parties.

Section 89 has been amended by Section 59, Mediation Act, 2023. Clause (*b*) of the amended Section 89 provides that the court may refer the parties to mediation to the court-annexed mediation centre or any other mediation service provider or any mediator as per option of the parties and thereafter the provisions of the Mediation Act, 2023 shall apply as if the proceedings for mediation were referred for settlement under the provisions of the Act.

The purpose of Section 89 CPC, as inserted by Act 46 of 1999, is to try and see that all the cases which are filed in court need not necessarily be decided by the court itself. Keeping in mind the law's delays and the limited number of judges which are available, it has now become imperative that resort should be had to alternative dispute resolution mechanism with a view to bringing to an end litigation between the parties at an early date. The ADR mechanism as contemplated by Section 89 is arbitration or conciliation or judicial settlement, including settlement through Lok Adalat or mediation. If the parties agree to arbitration, then the provisions of the Arbitration and Conciliation Act, 1996 will apply and that case will go outside the stream of the court, but resorting to conciliation or judicial settlement or mediation with a view to settling the dispute would not *ipso facto* take the case outside the judicial system. All that this means is that effort has to be made to bring about an amicable settlement between the parties but if conciliation or mediation or judicial settlement is not possible, despite efforts being made, the case will ultimately go to trial.[47]

Section 89 CPC specifically provides that a court hearing a suit may formulate terms of settlement between the parties and may either settle the same or refer the same for settlement by conciliation, judicial settlement, mediation or arbitration.[48]

Cases were referred to mediation under Section 89 CPC to help the parties to arrive at an amicable settlement outside the court. A settlement was arrived at between the parties and appeals were decided accordingly.[49]

A civil court exercising power under Section 89 CPC cannot refer a suit to arbitration unless all the parties to the suit agree to such reference. If the reference is to arbitration or conciliation, the court has to record

47. *Salem Advocate Bar Assn. (1)* v. *Union of India*, (2003) 1 SCC 49.
48. *Shailesh Dhairyawan* v. *Mohan Balkrishna Lulla*, (2016) 3 SCC 619.
49. *Vallabh Das Gupta* v. *Geeta Bai*, 2004 SCC OnLine MP 145: (2004) 3 MP LJ 37.

that the reference is by mutual consent. If the reference is to any other non-adjudicatory ADR process, the court should briefly record the same.[50]

2. MEDIATION—DIFFERENCE BETWEEN SECTION 89 CPC AND SECTION 12-A, COMMERCIAL COURTS ACT

Section 89 CPC contemplates mediation ordered by the court. However, Section 12-A, Commercial Courts Act contemplates mediation without any involvement of the court as it is done prior to the institution of the suit.[51]

3. SETTLEMENT OF DISPUTE—REFUND OF COURT FEE

Where the suit was decreed in terms of the compromise between the parties, the plaintiff was held entitled to the refund of court fees.[52] Where the suit is settled in appeal under Section 89 CPC, the plaintiff is entitled to the refund of the court fees as Section 89 applies to appeals also.[53]

Where a suit is dismissed for want of jurisdiction due to availability of alternative remedy under Section 89 CPC, since the suit is not decided in terms of requirement of Section 89, the plaintiff is not entitled to the refund of the court fees under Section 16, Court Fees Act.[54]

True intendment of Section 89 is legally arrived at settlement of disputes outside court without intervention of courts, and not necessarily by only the modes prescribed in Section 89, nor necessarily upon direction of court. Where the dispute between the parties is settled even outside the court, the refund of the court fee is permissible.[55]

4. MEDIATION IN CASES OF DISPUTES BETWEEN FAMILY AND BUSINESS RELATIONS

An effort should be made to resolve the dispute between the parties, who are brothers, by mediation. Lawyers should advise their clients to try for mediation to resolve the disputes, especially where relationships, like family relationships and business relationships, are involved; otherwise, the litigation drags on for years and decades often ruining both parties. Hence, the lawyers as well as litigants should follow Mahatma Gandhi's advice in

---

50. *Afcons Infrastructure Ltd.* v. *Cherian Varkey Construction Co. (P) Ltd.*, (2010) 8 SCC 24.
51. *Patil Automation (P) Ltd.* v. *Rakheja Engineers (P) Ltd.*, (2022) 10 SCC 1.
52. *Banwari Lal* v. *Mool Chand*, 2022 SCC OnLine P&H 4313.
53. *Vallabh Das Gupta* v. *Geeta Bai*, 2004 SCC OnLine MP 145: (2004) 3 MP LJ 37; *A. Sreeramaiah* v. *South Indian Bank Ltd.*, 2006 SCC OnLine Kar 563, paras 5–7 (DB).
54. *Shriji Ware House* v. *M.P. State Civil Supplies Corpn. Ltd.*, 2016 SCC OnLine MP 2128, paras 8–9: (2016) 3 MP LJ 655.
55. *High Court of Madras* v. *M.C. Subramaniam*, (2021) 3 SCC 560.

the matter and try for arbitration/mediation. This is also the purpose of Section 89 CPC.[56]

5. ROLE OF COURT ON SUCCESS/FAILURE OF MEDIATION

The court is not involved in actual mediation/conciliation. Section 89(2)(*d*) only means that when mediation succeeds, the court may pass a decree in accordance with the terms of settlement accepted by the parties and may execute it, if the parties so wish. However, if the parties do not want the settlement recorded or the decree passed, they can inform the court accordingly. Further, if mediation fails, the referring court is not barred from hearing the matter thereafter.[57] If conciliation, mediation, etc. before the Lok Adalat fails, the matter will ultimately go to the trial.[58]

6. NATURE OF PROCEEDINGS UNDER SECTION 89(2)

Section 89(2)(*d*) only means that when mediation succeeds and parties agree to the terms of settlement, the mediator will report to the court and the court, after giving notice and hearing to the parties, "effect" the compromise and pass a decree in accordance with the terms of settlement accepted by the parties.[59]

7. MEDIATION AND CONCILIATION—DIFFERENCE BETWEEN

In conciliation there is a little more latitude and the conciliator can suggest some terms of settlement also.[60]

8. SETTLEMENT OF DISPUTES—DEFAULT OF PARTIES IN APPEARANCE

The husband and his counsel failed to appear while the memorandum of settlement was drawn before the mediation centre. The settlement was accepted by the court and costs were imposed on the husband.[61]

---

56. *B.S. Krishna Murthy* v. *B.S. Nagaraj*, (2011) 15 SCC 464.
57. *Salem Advocate Bar Assn. (2)* v. *Union of India*, (2005) 6 SCC 344.
58. *Salem Advocate Bar Assn. (1)* v. *Union of India*, (2003) 1 SCC 49, 55.
59. *Salem Advocate Bar Assn. (2)* v. *Union of India*, (2005) 6 SCC 344.
60. *Ibid.*
61. *M. Munikrishna* v. *S. Shanthakumari*, 2022 SCC OnLine Kar 1872.

9. REPORT OF DISTRICT MEDIATION CENTRE AND JOINT COMPROMISE MEMO FILED BY THE PARTIES INDICATING THAT THE PARTIES ARE WILLING TO LIVE TOGETHER WITH CHILDREN

Further continuance of proceedings on issues like place of suing and consideration of the Supreme Court orders during pendency of proceedings, held were not necessary.[62]

10. FAILURE OF PARTY TO APPEAR BEFORE THE MEDIATOR [KARNATAKA CIVIL PROCEDURE (MEDIATION) RULES, 2005]

If the court finds that a party is absenting himself before the mediator without sufficient reason, the court may take action against the said party by imposition of costs. Neither Section 89 CPC nor Order 10, Rule 1-A nor the Karnataka (Case Flow Management in Subordinate Courts) Rules, 2005 nor the Karnataka Civil Procedure (Mediation) Rules, 2005 provide for striking off the defence for non-appearance of the parties before the mediator.[63]

11. KARNATAKA CIVIL PROCEDURE (MEDIATION) RULES, 2005

After the appearance of the parties, the court shall frame issues and thereafter direct the parties to opt for any one of the modes of settlement and, accordingly, issue appropriate directions. While referring the matter to Lok Adalat or mediation, the court shall fix the date of trial beyond 60 days, making it clear that if the mediation or Lok Adalat fails, the trial will begin on the said date and that it will go on day-to-day. The court, while fixing the date for trial, does so in consultation with the counsel and the parties.[64]

12. PARTIES BOUND BY THE SETTLEMENT ARRIVED AT BEFORE THE MEDIATOR

The whole purpose and import of Section 89 of the Code would become frustrated if settlements arrived at by the will and consent of the parties are thereafter permitted to be withdrawn; moreover it was also not the contention of the petitioner before the court below that this settlement was not arrived at between the parties; he had only sought a clarification on which application, the impugned order had relegated the parties to a regular trial. The parties are clearly bound by their settlement arrived at between them.[65]

---

62. *R. Manjula* v. *V. Raja*, (2009) 2 SCC 511.
63. *Rudraaradya* v. *Nanjundappa*, 2010 SCC OnLine Kar 354: (2010) 4 Kant LJ 545.
64. *M. Mahalingam* v. *Shashikala*, 2008 SCC OnLine Kar 89: ILR 2008 Kar 4055.
65. *Naresh Chand Jain* v. *K.M. Tayal*, 2012 SCC OnLine Del 1117: ILR (2012) 3 Del 133.

13. ENFORCEMENT OF A DOCUMENT SETTING FORTH TERMS OF MEDIATION—SUIT NOT MAINTAINABLE

Where there were disputes between the parties in relation to a partnership concern of theirs and a settlement was effected by some mediators, the terms of which were set forth in a document and also carried out by entries in the kathas, a suit for recovery of sums due on the basis of the settlement will not be one to enforce an award as evidenced by the documents. The suit will not be unmaintainable because it sought to enforce the award in seeking to enforce the documents. What would matter essentially is the contents of the documents and not the complexion which either party at a witness seeks to give to those contents.[66]

14. COURT AND ALTERNATIVE DISPUTE RESOLUTION PROCESS

Proceedings in court are different than proceedings initiated and/or referred before dispute resolution mechanisms and/or forums like arbitration, mediation, conciliation and Lok Adalat. "Forum" is not "Court" as contemplated under the Civil Procedure Code. When an alleged forum is not competent to grant declarative/interim reliefs, parties are not debarred to initiate and/or to file a civil suit in the competent court for such reliefs. Court in such a situation is required to pass an order based upon material available and/or merits of the matter. Return of plaint for presentation before proper forum by invoking Order 7 Rule 10, Civil Procedure Code, was not proper.[67]

60. *Amendment of Act 39 of 1987.*—The Legal Services Authorities Act, 1987, shall be amended in the manner specified in the Fifth Schedule.

COMMENTS

AMENDMENT OF LEGAL SERVICES AUTHORITIES ACT, 1987

In Section 4, Legal Services Authorities Act, 1987, which mentions the provisions of the Central Authority, clause (*f*) has been substituted by the new clause:

(*f*) encourage the settlement of disputes, including online by way of negotiations, arbitration, mediation and conciliation.

The old clause (*f*) provided as under:

66. *Gomraj Punamchand* v. *Sogmal Dhanaji*, 1950 SCC OnLine Mad 231: (1951) 64 LW 203.

67. *Pravin Pandurang Patil* v. *Pradhan Mantri Gram Sadak Yojana*, 2013 SCC OnLine Bom 1453: (2014) 1 Mah LJ 373.

(*f*) encourage the settlement of disputes by negotiations, arbitration and conciliation.

In the new clause, the word "mediation" has been added. Now it shall be the function of the Central Authority to encourage settlement of disputes by *mediation* and online also.

COMMENTS

1. AWARD OF LOK ADALAT

A case was listed before the Lok Adalat for disposal of compromise between the parties. The order sheet of the case showed that orders were passed behind the back of the parties and their counsel. Benches of Lok Adalat should comprise of two members; however, only the Additional Civil Judge signed the award. No settlement or compromise was arrived at before the Lok Adalat. No award was drawn as prescribed, no order of refund of court fee was passed, nor were signatures of parties verified as prescribed and affixed after the members ensured that the parties fully understood the compromise. The award was passed in gross violation of the provisions of the Act of 1987 and Regulations of 2009 by a single member in the purported capacity of the Lok Adalat. The award was quashed.[68] Where the award is passed by the Lok Adalat in gross violation of the provisions of the Act of 1987 and Regulations of 2009 by a single member in the purported capacity of the Lok Adalat, a petition under Article 227 of the Constitution for setting aside the same lies.[69]

New clause (*f*) in Section 4, Legal Services Authorities Act specifically provides that the National Legal Services Authority shall encourage the settlement of the disputes by way of negotiation, arbitration, mediation and reconciliation.

Under the Legal Services Authorities Act, the National Legal Services Committee (S. 1), Supreme Court Legal Services Committee (S. 2), State Legal Services Authority (S. 6), and District Legal Services Authority (S. 9) have been established. New clause (*f*) has been added in Section 4 by the Mediation Act, 2023. The new clause specifically provides that the Central Authority shall encourage the settlement of disputes, including "online" by way of negotiation, arbitration, mediation and conciliation. Lok Adalats for settlement of disputes between parties by mediation are held at national level, State level and district level. Section 19, Legal Services Authorities

68. *Sumitra Devi* v. *S.G. Rockbuild (P) Ltd.*, 2022 SCC OnLine All 211: (2022) 152 ALR 286.
69. *Ibid.*

Act, 1987 mandates that every State Authority, District Authority or the Supreme Court Legal Services Committee or every High Court Legal Services Committee may organise Lok Adalats at such intervals and places as it thinks fit for settlement of dispute between the parties. In pursuance of the provision, Lok Adalats are held in every State from time to time and decide a large number of cases under Section 22-B of the Act; permanent Lok Adalats have also been established.

2. DATE FOR TRIAL BEFORE THE COURT

While referring the matter to Lok Adalat for mediation, the court shall fix the date of trial beyond 60 days, making it clear that if the mediation or Lok Adalat fails, the trial would begin on the said date and that it will go on day-to-day.[70]

61. *Amendment of Act 26 of 1996.*—The Arbitration and Conciliation Act, 1996, shall be amended in the manner specified in the Sixth Schedule.

COMMENTS

Amendments have been carried out in Section 43-D and Sections 61 to 81, Arbitration and Conciliation Act, 1996. In Section 43-D, in sub-section (l), the words "mediation, conciliation" have been omitted; in sub-section (2), in clauses (*e*), (*f*) and (*i*), the words "and conciliation" wherever appeared have been omitted.

Sections 61 to 81 were substituted by the present Sections 61 and 62. In new Section 61, it has been provided that any provision in any other enactment providing for resolution of dispute through conciliation shall be construed as reference to mediation as provided under the Mediation Act, 2023. Conciliation as provided under the Arbitration and Conciliation Act, 1996 and the Code of Civil Procedure, 1908 shall be construed as mediation referred to in clause (*h*) of Section 23, Mediation Act, 2023.

Notwithstanding anything contained in Section 61, any conciliation proceeding initiated in pursuance of Sections 61 to 81, Arbitration and Conciliation Act, 1996 shall be continued as such as if the Mediation Act, 2023 has not been enacted.

62. *Amendment of Act 27 of 2006.*—The Micro, Small and Medium Enterprises Development Act, 2006, shall be amended in the manner specified in the Seventh Schedule.

---

70. *M. Mahalingam* v. *Shashikala*, 2008 SCC OnLine Kar 89, para 17: ILR 2008 Kar 4055.

COMMENTS

AMENDMENT OF MICRO, SMALL AND MEDIUM ENTERPRISES DEVELOPMENT ACT, 2006

Section 18 of the Act has been substituted by new Section 18, which envisages provision for mediation. Section 18 of the Act provides as under:

[71][**18.** *Reference to Micro and Small Enterprises Facilitation Council.*—(1) Notwithstanding anything contained in any other law for the time being in force, any party to a dispute may, with regard to any amount due under section 17, make a reference to the Micro and Small Enterprises Facilitation Council.

(2) On receipt of a reference under sub-section (1), the Council shall either conduct mediation itself or refer the matter to any mediation service provider as provided under the Mediation Act, 2023.

(3) The conduct of mediation under this section shall be as per the provisions of the Mediation Act, 2023.

(4) Where the mediation initiated under sub-section (3) is not successful and stands terminated without any settlement between the parties, the Council shall either itself take up the dispute for arbitration or refer it to any institution or centre providing alternative dispute resolution services for such arbitration and the provisions of the Arbitration and Conciliation Act, 1996 (26 of 1996), shall, then apply to the dispute as if the arbitration was in pursuance of an arbitration agreement referred to in sub-section (1) of section 7 of that Act.

(5) Notwithstanding anything contained in any other law for the time being in force, the Micro and Small Enterprises Facilitation Council or the centre providing alternative dispute resolution services shall have jurisdiction to act as an Arbitrator or mediator under this section in a dispute between the supplier located within its jurisdiction and a buyer located anywhere in India.]

There was nothing on the record to show that on the receipt of claim under Section 18(1) of the Act, conciliation was conducted and upon failure thereof the dispute was sent to the arbitrator. Since the mandate of Section 18(2) of the Act was not complied with, the order of adjudication did not amount to decree, award or order. The award was non-est for not complying with the mandatory provisions of Section 18(2), MSME Act, and was quashed.[72]

63. *Amendment of Act 18 of 2013.*—The Companies Act, 2013, shall be amended in the manner specified in the Eighth Schedule.

---

71. *Subs.* by Act 32 of 2023, S. 62 and Sch. VII (w.e.f. the date to be notified).
72. *Narmada Transmissions (P) Ltd.* v. *Rajasthan Rajya Vidyut Prasaran Nigam Ltd.*, 2022 SCC OnLine Raj 3554; *Ajmer Vidyut Vitran Nigam Ltd.* v. *Anamika Conductors Ltd.*, 2022 SCC OnLine Raj 3555.

COMMENTS

AMENDMENT IN COMPANIES ACT, 2013

Amendment in Section 442, Companies Act has been carried. New Section 442, Companies Act contains a provision for mediation. New Section 442 provides as under:

[73][**442.** *Reference to mediation.*—(1) Any of the parties to a proceedings before the Central Government, Tribunal or the Appellate Tribunal may, at any time apply to the Central Government, Tribunal or the Appellate Tribunal, as the case may be, in such form alongwith such fees, if any, as may be prescribed, for referring the matter pertaining to such proceedings for mediation and the Central Government, Tribunal or the Appellate Tribunal, as the case may be, shall refer the matter to mediation to be conducted under the provisions of the Mediation Act, 2023.

(2) Nothing in this section shall prevent the Central Government, Tribunal or the Appellate Tribunal before which any proceeding is pending from referring any matter pertaining to such proceeding suo motu to mediation to be conducted under the provisions of the Mediation Act, 2023 as the Central Government, Tribunal or the Appellate Tribunal, deems fit.

(3) The mediator or mediation service provider shall file the mediated settlement agreement arrived at between the parties with the Central Government or the Tribunal or the Appellate Tribunal under the Act.

(4) The Central Government or the Tribunal or the Appellate Tribunal shall pass an order or judgment making the said mediated settlement agreement as part thereof.

(5) The fee of the mediator shall be such as may be prescribed.]

64. *Amendment of Act 4 of 2016.*—The Commercial Courts Act, 2015, shall be amended in the manner specified in the Ninth Schedule.

COMMENTS

AMENDMENT IN COMMERCIAL COURTS ACT, 2015

Chapter III-A in the Act has been substituted by a new chapter. The new Section 12-A provides for pre-litigation mediation and settlement. New Section 12-A provides as under:

73. *Subs.* by Act 32 of 2023, S. 63 and Sch. VIII (w.e.f. the date to be notified).

[74][CHAPTER III-A

PRE-LITIGATION MEDIATION AND SETTLEMENT

12-A. *Pre-litigation Mediation and Settlement.*—(1) A suit, which does not contemplate any urgent interim relief under this Act, shall not be instituted unless the plaintiff exhausts the remedy of pre-litigation mediation in accordance with such manner and procedure as may be prescribed by rules made by the Central Government.

(2) For the purposes of pre-litigation mediation, the Central Government may, by notification, authorise—

(*i*) the Authority, constituted under the Legal Services Authorities Act, 1987 (39 of 1987); or

(*ii*) a mediation service provider as defined under clause (*m*) of Section 3 of the Mediation Act, 2023.

(3) Notwithstanding anything contained in the Legal Services Authorities Act, 1987 (39 of 1987), the Authority or mediation service provider authorised by the Central Government under sub-section (2) shall complete the process of mediation within a period of one hundred and twenty days from the date of application made by the plaintiff under sub-section (1):

Provided that the period of mediation may be extended for a further period of sixty days with the consent of the parties:

Provided further that, the period during which the parties spent for pre-litigation mediation shall not be computed for the purposes of limitation under the Limitation Act, 1963 (36 of 1963).

(4) If the parties to the commercial dispute arrive at a settlement, the same shall be reduced into writing and shall be signed by the parties and the mediator.

(5) The mediated settlement agreement arrived at under this section shall be dealt with in accordance with the provisions of Sections 27 and 28 of the Mediation Act, 2023.]

COMMENTS

This section provides for the pre-institution and settlement provision. The Central Government may authorise the authorities (State Authorities and District Authorities) constituted under the Legal Services Authorities Act, 1987 for the purpose of pre-institution mediation, which shall complete the process of mediation within a period of 120 days from the date of application. The settlement between the parties shall be reduced into writing duly signed by the parties and mediator.

74. *Subs.* by Act 32 of 2023, S. 64 and Sch. IX(*a*) (w.e.f. the date to be notified). Earlier Chapter III-A was *inserted* by Act 28 of 2018, S. 11 (w.r.e.f. 3-5-2018).

1. PRE-LITIGATION MEDIATION AND SETTLEMENT [S. 12-A]

This section envisages provision for pre-litigation mediation and settlement. A suit which does not contain any urgent relief under this Act shall not be instituted unless the plaintiff exhausts the remedy of pre-litigation mediation in accordance with the manner and procedure as may be prescribed by the rules framed by the Central Government. As per Section 12-A, in cases where interim relief is prayed for, the plaintiff cannot be non-suited for want of pre-institution mediation process.[75] Where the suit contemplates urgent interim relief, Section 12, Commercial Courts Act is not applicable.[76]

The trial court did not satisfy itself that the plaintiff required urgent orders and did not permit the plaintiff to institute suit without compliance with the provisions of Section 12-A; it failed to comply with the mandatory provisions of Section 12-A, and the case was remanded.[77]

Section 12-A, Commercial Courts Act does not take away the right to institute proceedings or the right of access to justice but merely directs parties to resort to another remedy before approaching the court. Section 12-A does not come into play if the suit contemplates an urgent relief and if a commercial suit (of specified value) contemplates urgent relief, it can be instituted in the court straightaway.[78]

Pre-institution mediation achieves a larger purpose of speedy resolution of commercial disputes. Section 12-A is not a facility but a mandate by the legislature. The legislature has enacted Section 12-A as an intervention to boost speedy disposal of the commercial cases.[79]

Section 12-A(3) excludes the period taken for mediation from the limitation period for filing suit.[80]

The Act did not originally contain Section 12-A. It is by an amendment in the year 2018 that Section 12-A was contemplated as compulsory. The object of the Act and the Amending Act of 2018 unerringly point to at least partly foisting compulsory mediation on a plaintiff who does not contemplate urgent interim relief. The provision has been contemplated only with reference to plaintiffs who do not contemplate urgent interim relief. The legislature has taken care to expressly exclude the period undergone during mediation for

75. *Visakhapatnam Metropolitan Regional Development Authority* v. *Pydi Sarvanamma*, 2023 SCC OnLine AP 4491.
76. *Bank of Baroda* v. *Bavaguthu Raghuram Shetty*, 2021 SCC OnLine Kar 12121: (2021) 5 Kant LJ 525 (DB).
77. *Tata Consumer Products Ltd.* v. *ITC Ltd.*, 2023 SCC OnLine TS 4451.
78. *Deepak Raheja* v. *Ganga Taro Vazirani*, (2021) 1 HCC (Bom) 685.
79. *Ibid.*
80. *Ibid.*

reckoning limitation under the Limitation Act, 1963. The object is clear. It is an untenable reality that courts in India are reeling under an extraordinary docket explosion. Mediation, as an alternative dispute mechanism, has been identified as a workable solution in commercial matters; in other words, the cases under the Act lend themselves to be resolved through mediation. Nobody has an absolute right to file a civil suit. A civil suit can be barred absolutely or the bar may operate unless certain conditions are fulfilled. The language used in Section 12-A, which includes the word "shall", shows the provision is mandatory. The entire procedure for carrying out the mediation has been spelt out in the rules. The parties are free to engage Counsel during mediation. The expense as far as the fee payable to the mediator is concerned is limited to a one-time fee, which appears to be reasonable, particularly, having regard to the fact that it is to be shared equally. A trained mediator can work wonders. Mediation must be perceived as a new mechanism of access to justice.[81]

Time prescribed under Section 12-A for completing the process of compulsory pre-litigation mediation and settlement was extended from the time when Covid-19 lockdown was lifted, plus 45 days thereafter.[82]

2. PRE-INSTITUTION MEDIATION AND SETTLEMENT—OBJECT AND ADVANTAGE

The settlement arrived at in pre-litigation mediation under Section 12-A is to be treated as an award under Section 30(4), Arbitration and Conciliation Act.[83]

3. SECTION 12-A IS MANDATORY

The word "shall" has been used in Section 12-A. The provisions of Section 12-A are mandatory.[84]

The plaintiff's consent for the institution of the mediation proceedings is irrelevant if the defendant refuses to move forward with it. All that is required on the part of the plaintiff is to initiate pre-institution mediation prior to filing of a commercial suit. Once this is satisfied, if it is the plaintiff who refuses to move forward with the mediation, then the suit that is instituted thereafter would be barred by law. However, if both the defendant and the plaintiff do not wish to pursue the mediation and a non-starter report is

81. *Patil Automation (P) Ltd.* v. *Rakheja Engineers (P) Ltd.*, (2022) 10 SCC 1.
82. *Cognizance For Extension of Limitation, re*, (2020) 9 SCC 468.
83. *Patil Automation (P) Ltd.* v. *Rakheja Engineers (P) Ltd.*, (2022) 10 SCC 1.
84. *Ibid.*

generated subsequent to the same, then if the plaintiff files a suit, the same would not be barred by law.[85]

The plaintiff does not have the absolute choice and right to bypass mandatory provision under Section 12-A, Commercial Courts Act by making a prayer for urgent interim relief. Camouflage and guise to bypass the statutory mandate of pre-litigation mediation should be checked when deception and falsity is apparent or established. The proposition that the commercial courts do have a role, *albeit* a limited one, should be accepted, otherwise it would be up to the plaintiff alone to decide whether to resort to the procedure under Section 12-A, Commercial Courts Act. An "absolute and unfettered right" approach is not justified if the pre-institution mediation under Section 12-A, Commercial Courts Act is mandatory.[86]

4. NON-COMPLIANCE WITH SECTION 12-A, MEDIATION PLAINT SHALL BE REJECTED

Section 12-A is mandatory. Any suit instituted violating the mandate of Section 12-A would result in rejection of the plaint. Court can also exercise powers under Order 7, Rule 11, *suo motu*. Declaration that Section 12-A is mandatory would apply from 20 August 2022 so that concerned stakeholders become sufficiently informed.[87]

5. SETTLEMENT AWARD AT IN PRE-LITIGATION MEDIATION UNDER SECTION 12-A—AWARD UNDER SECTION 30(4) OF A&C ACT, 1996

Section 12-A elevates the settlement under the Act and the rules to an award within the meaning of Section 30(4), Arbitration and Conciliation Act, giving it meaningful enforceability. The period spent in mediation is excluded for the purpose of limitation. The Act confers power to order costs based on conduct of the parties.[88]

6. PRE-INSTITUTION MEDIATION ONLY IN SUITS

Section 12-A provides for pre-institution mediation only in suits, which do not contemplate any urgent interim relief. Therefore, pre-institution mediation has been mandated only in a class of suits.[89]

85. *Kapil Goel* v. *Ram Dulare Yadav*, (2022) 6 HCC (Del) 540.
86. *Yamini Manohar* v. *T.K.D. Keerthi*, (2024) 5 SCC 815.
87. *Patil Automation (P) Ltd.* v. *Rakheja Engineers (P) Ltd.*, (2022) 10 SCC 1.
88. *Ibid.*
89. *Ibid.*

65. *Amendment of Act 35 of 2019.*—The Consumer Protection Act, 2019, shall be amended in the manner specified in the Tenth Schedule.

COMMENTS

In the Consumer Protection Act, 2019, amendments have been made. New Sections 37, 37-A and 37-B contain provisions for mediation of disputes. The said Sections 37, 37-A and 37-B provide as under:

[90][**37.** *Reference to mediation.*—The District Commission or State Commission or the National Commission, as the case may be, [91][may] at any stage of proceedings refer the disputes for settlement by mediation under the Mediation Act, 2023.]

[92][**37-A.** *Settlement through mediation.*—(1) Pursuant to mediation, if an agreement is reached between the parties with respect to all of the issues involved in the consumer dispute or with respect to only some of the issues, the terms of such agreement shall be reduced to writing accordingly, and signed by the parties to such dispute or their authorised representatives.

(2) The mediator shall prepare a settlement report of the settlement and forward the signed agreement along with such report to the concerned Commission.

(3) Where no agreement is reached between the parties within the specified time or the mediator is of the opinion that settlement is not possible, he shall prepare his report accordingly and submit the same to the concerned Commission.]

[93][**37-B.** *Recording settlement and passing of order.*—(1) The District Commission or the State Commission or the National Commission, as the case may be, shall, within seven days of the receipt of the settlement report, pass suitable order recording such settlement of consumer dispute and dispose of the matter accordingly.

(2) Where the consumer dispute is settled only in part, the District Commission or the State Commission or the National Commission, as the case may be, shall record settlement of the issues which have been so settled and continue to hear other issues involved in such consumer dispute.

(3) Where the consumer dispute could not be settled by mediation, the District Commission or the State Commission or the National Commission, as the case may be, shall continue to hear all the issues involved in such consumer dispute.]

---

90. *Subs.* for Section 37 by Act 32 of 2023, S. 65 and Sch. X(*b*) (w.e.f. the date to be notified).
91. *Subs.* for "shall either on an application by the parties" by S.O. 4506(E), dt. 13-10-2023 (w.e.f. 13-10-2023).
92. *Ins.* by Act 32 of 2023, S. 65 and Sch. X(*b*) (w.e.f. the date to be notified).
93. *Ibid.*

THE FIRST SCHEDULE

(*See* Section 6)

Disputes or matters not fit for mediation

1. Disputes which by virtue of any law for the time being in force may not be submitted for mediation.

2. Disputes relating to claims against minors, deities; persons with intellectual disabilities under Paragraph 2 of the Schedule and person with disability having high support needs as defined in clause (*t*) of Section 2 of the Rights of Persons with Disabilities Act, 2016 (49 of 2016); persons with mental illness as defined in clause (*s*) of sub-section (1) of Section 2 of the Mental Healthcare Act, 2017 (10 of 2017); persons of unsound mind, in relation to whom proceedings are to be conducted under Order XXXII of the Code of Civil Procedure, 1908 (5 of 1908); and suits for declaration of title against Government; declaration having effect of right *in rem*.

3. Disputes involving prosecution for criminal offences.

4. Complaints or proceedings, initiated before any statutory authority or body in relation to registration, discipline, misconduct of any practitioner, or other registered professional, such as legal practitioner, medical practitioner, dentist, architect, chartered accountant, or in relation to any other profession of whatever description, which is regulated under any law for the time being in force.

5. Disputes which have the effect on rights of a third party who are not a party to the mediation proceedings except only in matrimonial disputes where the interest of a child is involved.

6. Any proceeding in relation to any subject matter, falling within any enactment, over which the Tribunal constituted under the National Green Tribunal Act, 2010 (19 of 2010), has jurisdiction.

7. Any dispute relating to levy, collection, penalties or offences, in relation to any direct or indirect tax or refunds, enacted by any State legislature or the Parliament.

8. Any investigation, inquiry or proceeding, under the Competition Act, 2002 (12 of 2003), including proceedings before the Director General, under the Act; proceedings before the Telecom Regulatory Authority of India, under the Telecom Regulatory Authority of India Act, 1997 (24 of 1997) or the Telecom Disputes Settlement and Appellate Tribunal established under Section 14 of that Act.

9. Proceedings before appropriate Commissions, and the Appellate Tribunal for Electricity, under the Electricity Act, 2003 (36 of 2003).

10. Proceedings before the Petroleum and Natural Gas Regulatory Board, and appeals therefrom before the Appellate Tribunal under the Petroleum and Natural Gas Regulatory Board Act, 2006 (19 of 2006).

11. Proceedings before the Securities and Exchange Board of India, and the Securities Appellate Tribunal, under the Securities and Exchange Board of India Act, 1992 (15 of 1992).

12. Land acquisition and determination of compensation under land acquisition laws, or any provision of law providing for land acquisition.

13. Any other subject matter of dispute which may be notified by the Central Government.

THE SECOND SCHEDULE

(*See* Section 55)

1. The Industrial Disputes Act, 1947 (14 of 1947).

2. The Brahmaputra Board Act, 1980 (46 of 1980).

3. The Cine-workers and Cinema Theatre Workers (Regulation of Employment) Act, 1981 (50 of 1981).

4. The Family Courts Act, 1984 (66 of 1984).

5. The Legal Services Authorities Act, 1987 (39 of 1987).

6. The Maintenance and Welfare of Parents and Senior Citizens Act, 2007 (56 of 2007).

7. The Sexual Harassment of Women at Workplace (Prevention, Prohibition and Redressal) Act, 2013 (14 of 2013).

8. The Finance Act, 2016 (28 of 2016).

9. The Industrial Relations Code, 2020 (35 of 2020).

THE THIRD SCHEDULE

(*See* Section 58)

In Section 28 of the Indian Contract Act, 1872 (9 of 1872), for *Exception* 1 and *Exception* 2, the following shall be substituted, *namely*—

"*Exception* 1.—**Saving of contract to refer to arbitration or mediation dispute that may arise.**—This section shall not render illegal a contract, by which two or more persons agree that any dispute which may arise between them in respect of any subject or class of subjects shall be referred to resolution through arbitration or mediation.

Exception 2.—**Saving of contract to refer questions that have already arisen.**—Nor shall this section render illegal any contract in writing, by which two or more persons agree to refer to arbitration or mediation any question between them which has already arisen, or affect any provision of any law in force for the time being as to references to arbitration or mediation.".

THE FOURTH SCHEDULE

(*See* Section 59)

In the Code of Civil Procedure, 1908 (5 of 1908),—

(*i*) under Part V, under the heading SPECIAL PROCEEDINGS, the sub-heading "ARBITRATION" shall be omitted;

(*ii*) for Section 89, the following section shall be substituted, *namely*—

"**89. Settlement of disputes outside the Court.**—Where it appears to the Court that the dispute between the parties may be settled and there exists elements of settlement which may be acceptable to the parties, the Court may—

(*a*) refer the dispute to arbitration, and thereafter, the provisions of the Arbitration and Conciliation Act, 1996 (26 of 1996) shall apply as if the proceedings for arbitration were referred for settlement under the provisions of that Act; or

(*b*) refer the parties to mediation, to the court-annexed mediation centre or any other mediation service provider or any mediator, as per the option of the parties, and thereafter the provisions of the Mediation Act, 2023 shall apply as if the proceedings for mediation were referred for settlement under the provisions of that Act; or

(*c*) refer the dispute to Lok Adalat, in accordance with the provisions of sub-section (1) of Section 20 of the Legal Services Authorities Act, 1987 (39 of 1987) and thereafter, all other provisions of that Act shall apply in respect of the dispute;

(*d*) effect compromise between the parties and shall follow such procedure as deemed fit for judicial settlement.".

THE FIFTH SCHEDULE

(*See* Section 60)

In the Legal Services Authorities Act, 1987 (39 of 1987), in Section 4, for clause (*f*), the following clause shall be substituted, *namely*—

"(*f*) encourage the settlement of disputes, including online by way of negotiations, arbitration, mediation and conciliation;".

THE SIXTH SCHEDULE

(*See* Section 61)

In the Arbitration and Conciliation Act, 1996 (26 of 1996),—

(*a*) in Section 43-D,—

(*i*) in sub-section (1), the words "mediation, conciliation" shall be omitted;

(*ii*) in sub-section (2), in clauses (*e*), (*f*) and (*i*), the words "and conciliation" wherever they occur shall be omitted;

(*b*) for Sections 61 to 81, the following sections shall be substituted, *namely*—

"61. Reference of conciliation in enactments.—(1) Any provision, in any other enactment for the time being in force, providing for resolution of disputes through conciliation in accordance with the provisions of this Act, shall be construed as reference to mediation as provided under the Mediation Act, 2023.

(2) Conciliation as provided under this Act and the Code of Civil Procedure, 1908 (5 of 1908), shall be construed as mediation referred to in clause (*h*) of Section 3 of the Mediation Act, 2023.

62. Saving.—Notwithstanding anything contained in Section 61, any conciliation proceeding initiated in pursuance of Sections 61 to 81 of this Act as in force before the commencement of the Mediation Act, 2023, shall be continued as such, as if the Mediation Act, 2023, had not been enacted.".

THE SEVENTH SCHEDULE

(*See* Section 62)

In the Micro, Small and Medium Enterprises Development Act, 2006 (27 of 2006), for Section 18, the following section shall be substituted, *namely*—

"18. Reference to Micro and Small Enterprises Facilitation Council.—(1) Notwithstanding anything contained in any other law for the time being in force, any party to a dispute may, with regard to any amount due under Section 17, make a reference to the Micro and Small Enterprises Facilitation Council.

(2) On receipt of a reference under sub-section (1), the Council shall either conduct mediation itself or refer the matter to any mediation service provider as provided under the Mediation Act, 2023.

(3) The conduct of mediation under this section shall be as per the provisions of the Mediation Act, 2023.

(4) Where the mediation initiated under sub-section (3) is not successful and stands terminated without any settlement between the parties, the Council shall either itself take up the dispute for arbitration or refer it to any institution or centre providing alternative dispute resolution services for such arbitration and the provisions of the Arbitration and Conciliation Act, 1996 (26 of 1996), shall, then apply to the dispute as if the arbitration was in pursuance of an arbitration agreement referred to in sub-section (1) of Section 7 of that Act.

(5) Notwithstanding anything contained in any other law for the time being in force, the Micro and Small Enterprises Facilitation Council or the centre providing alternative dispute resolution services shall have jurisdiction to act as an Arbitrator or mediator under this section in a dispute between the supplier located within its jurisdiction and a buyer located anywhere in India.".

THE EIGHTH SCHEDULE

(*See* Section 63)

In the Companies Act, 2013 (18 of 2013), for Section 442, the following section shall be substituted, namely—

"**442. Reference to mediation.**—(1) Any of the parties to a proceedings before the Central Government, Tribunal or the Appellate Tribunal may, at any time apply to the Central Government, Tribunal or the Appellate Tribunal, as the case may be, in such form along with such fees, if any, as may be prescribed, for referring the matter pertaining to such proceedings for mediation and the Central Government, Tribunal or the Appellate Tribunal, as the case may be, shall refer the matter to mediation to be conducted under the provisions of the Mediation Act, 2023.

(2) Nothing in this section shall prevent the Central Government, Tribunal or the Appellate Tribunal before which any proceeding is pending from referring any matter pertaining to such proceeding *suo motu* to mediation to be conducted under the provisions of the Mediation Act, 2023 as the Central Government, Tribunal or the Appellate Tribunal, deems fit.

(3) The mediator or mediation service provider shall file the mediated settlement agreement arrived at between the parties with the Central Government or the Tribunal or the Appellate Tribunal under the Act.

(4) The Central Government or the Tribunal or the Appellate Tribunal shall pass an order or judgment making the said mediated settlement agreement as part thereof.

(5) The fee of the mediator shall be such as may be prescribed.".

THE NINTH SCHEDULE

(*See* Section 64)

In the Commercial Courts Act, 2015 (4 of 2016),—

(*a*) for Chapter IIIA, the following Chapter shall be substituted, *namely*—

"CHAPTER III A

Pre-litigation Mediation and Settlement

12-A. Pre-litigation Mediation and Settlement.—(1) A suit, which does not contemplate any urgent interim relief under this Act, shall not be instituted unless the plaintiff exhausts the remedy of pre-litigation mediation in accordance with such manner and procedure as may be prescribed by rules made by the Central Government.

(2) For the purposes of pre-litigation mediation, the Central Government may, by notification, authorise—

(*i*) the Authority, constituted under the Legal Services Authorities Act, 1987 (39 of 1987); or

(*ii*) a mediation service provider as defined under clause (*m*) of Section 3 of the Mediation Act, 2023.

(3) Notwithstanding anything contained in the Legal Services Authorities Act, 1987 (39 of 1987), the Authority or mediation service provider authorised by the Central Government under sub-section (2) shall complete the process of mediation within a period of one hundred and twenty days from the date of application made by the plaintiff under sub-section (1):

Provided that the period of mediation may be extended for a further period of sixty days with the consent of the parties:

Provided further that, the period during which the parties spent for pre-litigation mediation shall not be computed for the purposes of limitation under the Limitation Act, 1963 (36 of 1963).

(4) If the parties to the commercial dispute arrive at a settlement, the same shall be reduced into writing and shall be signed by the parties and the mediator.

(5) The mediated settlement agreement arrived at under this section shall be dealt with in accordance with the provisions of Sections 27 and 28 of the Mediation Act, 2023.";

(*b*) in Section 21-A, in sub-section (2), for clause (*a*), the following clause shall be substituted, *namely*—

"(*a*) the manner and procedure of pre-litigation mediation under sub-section (1) of Section 12-A;".

THE TENTH SCHEDULE

(*See* Section 65)

In the Consumer Protection Act, 2019 (35 of 2019),—

(*a*) in Section 2, clauses (25) and (26) shall be omitted;

(*b*) for Section 37, the following sections shall be substituted, *namely*—

"**37. Reference to mediation.**—The District Commission or State Commission or the National Commission, as the case may be, [94][may] at any stage of proceedings refer the disputes for settlement by mediation under the Mediation Act, 2023.

37-A. Settlement through mediation.—(1) Pursuant to mediation, if an agreement is reached between the parties with respect to all of the issues involved in the consumer dispute or with respect to only some of the issues, the terms of such agreement shall be reduced to writing accordingly, and signed by the parties to such dispute or their authorised representatives.

(2) The mediator shall prepare a settlement report of the settlement and forward the signed agreement along with such report to the concerned Commission.

(3) Where no agreement is reached between the parties within the specified time or the mediator is of the opinion that settlement is not possible, he shall prepare his report accordingly and submit the same to the concerned Commission.

37-B. Recording settlement and passing of order.—(1) The District Commission or the State Commission or the National Commission, as the case may be, shall, within seven days of the receipt of the settlement report, pass suitable order recording such settlement of consumer dispute and dispose of the matter accordingly.

(2) Where the consumer dispute is settled only in part, the District Commission or the State Commission or the National Commission, as the case may be, shall record settlement of the issues which have been so settled and continue to hear other issues involved in such consumer dispute.

(3) Where the consumer dispute could not be settled by mediation, the District Commission or the State Commission or the National Commission, as the case may be, shall continue to hear all the issues involved in such consumer dispute.";

(*c*) in Section 38, in sub-section (1), the words "or in respect of cases referred for mediation on failure of settlement by mediation," shall be omitted;

(*d*) in Section 41, the third proviso shall be omitted;

---

94. *Subs.* for "shall either on an application by the parties" by S.O. 4506(E), dated 13-10-2023 (w.e.f. 13-10-2023). *See* p. 930, below.

(*e*) Chapter V shall be omitted;

(*f*) in Section 101, in sub-section (2),—

(*i*) clause (*r*) shall be omitted;

(*ii*) clause (*zf*) shall be omitted;

(*g*) in Section 102, in sub-section (2), clause (*p*) shall be omitted;

(*h*) in Section 103, in sub-section (2), clauses (*c*) to (*h*) shall be omitted.

———

APPENDICES

Appendix 1

Mediation (Removal of Difficulties) Order, 2023[1]

[13th October, 2023]

Whereas, the Mediation Act, 2023 (32 of 2023) (hereinafter referred to as the said Act) received the assent of the President on the 14th September, 2023;

And, whereas, Section 32 of the said Act provides for the composition of the Mediation Council of India;

And, whereas, clause (*o*) of Section 3 of the said Act defines the term "Member" which means a Full-Time or Part-Time Member of the Council and includes the Chairperson;

And, whereas, sub-section (3) of Section 32 of the said Act provides for prescribing rules in respect of salaries, allowances and other terms and conditions of Members;

And, whereas, sub-section (4) of Section 32 and clause (b) of sub-section (2) of Section 51 of the said Act provides for prescribing rules in respect of travelling and other allowances payable to the Member;

And, whereas, rules being made under sub-section (4) of Section 32 of the said Act shall be applicable only to the Part-Time Members and allowances in respect of the Full-Time Members shall be covered under the rules being made under sub-section (3) of Section 32 of the said Act;

And, whereas, it may cause confusion and difficulty, in notifying the rules for the travelling and other allowances payable to Part-Time Member of the Mediation Council of India under sub-section (4) of Section 32 of the said Act unless the word "Member" is substituted with the words "Part-Time Member";

And, whereas, the Tenth Schedule to the said Act provides for amendments to the Consumer Protection Act, 2019 (35 of 2019);

And, whereas, Section 37 of the Consumer Protection Act, 2019 (35 of 2019) provides that District Commission or the State Commission or the National Commission, as the case may be, shall either on an application by the parties may refer the dispute for settlement by mediation under the Mediation Act, 2023 (32 of 2023);

And, whereas, Section 7 of the Mediation Act, 2023 (32 of 2023) provides for power of the court or tribunal to refer the parties to mediation and Section 37

---

1. *Vide* Noti. No. S.O. 4506(E), Extra., Pt. II, S. 3(*i*), dt. 13-10-2023, published in the Gazette of India, No. 4335, dt. 13-10-2023.

of the Consumer Protection Act, 2019 (35 of 2019), as amended through the Tenth Schedule of the Mediation Act, 2023 (32 of 2023) is not in consonance with Section 7 of the said Act and the words "shall either on an application by the parties" needs to be replaced with the word "may" to remove the difficulty in implementing the said provision.

Now, therefore, in exercise of the powers conferred by sub-section (1) of Section 54 of the Mediation Act, 2023, the Central Government hereby makes the following Order to remove the above said difficulties, namely:—

1. Short title and commencement.—(1) This order may be called the **Mediation (Removal of Difficulties) Order, 2023.**

(2) It shall come into force with effect from the 13th day of October, 2023.

2. In the Mediation Act, 2023,—

(*a*) in Section 32, in sub-section (4), for the word "Member", the words "Part-Time Member" shall be substituted;

(*b*) in Section 51, in sub-section (2), in clause (b), for the word "Member", the words "Part-Time Member" shall be substituted;

(*c*) in the Tenth Schedule, relating to amendments to the Consumer Protection Act, 2019, in Section 37, for the words "shall either on an application by the parties", the word "may" shall be substituted.

———

Appendix 2

Arbitration and Conciliation (Amendment) Act, 2015[1]

[Act 3 of 2016 as amended up to Act 33 of 2019]

[31st December, 2015]

An Act to amend the Arbitration and Conciliation Act, 1996.

Be it enacted by Parliament in the Sixty-sixth Year of the Republic of India as follows—

Statement of Objects and Reasons.—The general law relating to arbitration is contained in the Arbitration and Conciliation Act, 1996 (hereinafter referred to as the Act). The Act, which is based on the UNCITRAL Model Law on International Commercial Arbitration, as adopted in 1985 by the United Nations Commission on International Trade Law (UNCITRAL), applies to both international as well to domestic arbitration.

2. The Act was enacted to provide for speedy disposal of cases relating to arbitration with least court intervention. With the passage of time, some difficulties in the applicability of the Act have been noticed. Interpretation of the provisions of the Act by courts in some cases have resulted in delay of disposal of arbitration proceedings and increase in interference of courts in arbitration matters, which tend to defeat the object of the Act. With a view to overcome the difficulties, the matter was referred to the Law Commission of India, which examined the issue in detail and submitted its 176th Report. On the basis of the said report, the Arbitration and Conciliation (Amendment) Bill, 2003 was introduced in the Rajya Sabha on 22nd December, 2003. The said Bill was referred to the Department-related Parliamentary Standing Committee on Personnel, Public Grievances, Law and Justice for examination and Report. The said Committee, submitted its Report to the Parliament on 4th August, 2005, wherein the Committee recommended that since many provisions of the said Bill were contentious, the Bill may be withdrawn and a fresh legislation may be brought after considering its recommendations. Accordingly, the said Bill was withdrawn from the Rajya Sabha.

3. On a reference made again in pursuance of the above, the Law Commission examined and submitted its 246th Report on "Amendments to the Arbitration and Conciliation Act, 1996" in August, 2014 and recommended various amendments in the Act. The proposed amendments to the Act would facilitate and encourage Alternative Dispute Mechanism, especially arbitration, for settlement of disputes in a more user-friendly, cost effective and expeditious disposal of cases since India is committed to improve its legal framework to obviate in disposal of cases.

4. As India has been ranked at 178 out of 189 nations in the world in contract enforcement, it is high time that urgent steps are taken to facilitate quick enforcement of contracts, easy recovery of monetary claims and award of just compensation for damages suffered and reduce the pendency of cases in courts and hasten the process of dispute resolution through arbitration, so as to encourage investment and economic activity.

---

1. Received the assent of the President on December 31, 2015 and published in the Gazette of India, Extra., Pt. II, S. 1, dt. 1-1-2016, pp. 1-15, No. 3.

5. As Parliament was not in session and immediate steps were required to be taken to make necessary amendments to the Arbitration and Conciliation Act, 1996 to attract foreign investment by projecting India as an investor friendly country having a sound legal framework, the President was pleased to promulgate the Arbitration and Conciliation (Amendment) Ordinance, 2015.

6. It is proposed to introduce the Arbitration and Conciliation (Amendment) Bill, 2015, to replace the Arbitration and Conciliation (Amendment) Ordinance, 2015, which inter alia, provides for the following, namely—

(*i*) to amend the definition of "Court" to provide that in the case of international commercial arbitrations, the Court should be the High Court;

(*ii*) to ensure that an Indian Court can exercise jurisdiction to grant interim measures, etc., even where the seat of the arbitration is outside India;

(*iii*) an application for appointment of an arbitrator shall be disposed of by the High Court or Supreme Court, as the case may be, as expeditiously as possible and an endeavour should be made to dispose of the matter within a period of sixty days;

(*iv*) to provide that while considering any application for appointment of arbitrator, the High Court or the Supreme Court shall examine the existence of a prima facie arbitration agreement and not other issues;

(*v*) to provide that the arbitral tribunal shall make its award within a period of twelve months from the date it enters upon the reference and that the parties may, however, extend such period up to six months, beyond which period any extension can only be granted by the Court, on sufficient cause;

(*vi*) to provide that a model fee Schedule on the basis of which High Courts may frame rules for the purpose of determination of fees of arbitral tribunal, where a High Court appoints arbitrator in terms of Section 11 of the Act;

(*vii*) to provide that the parties to dispute may at any stage agree in writing that their dispute be resolved through fast track procedure and the award in such cases shall be made within a period of six months;

(*viii*) to provide for neutrality of arbitrators, when a person is approached in connection with possible appointment as an arbitrator;

(*ix*) to provide that application to challenge the award is to be disposed of by the Court within one year.

7. The amendments proposed in the Bill will ensure that arbitration process becomes more user-friendly, cost effective and lead to expeditious disposal of cases.

8. The Bill seeks to replace the aforesaid Ordinance.

1. Short title and commencement.—(1) This Act may be called the **Arbitration and Conciliation (Amendment) Act, 2015.**

(2) It shall be deemed to have come into force on the 23rd October, 2015.

2. Amendment of Section 2.—In the Arbitration and Conciliation Act, 1996 (26 of 1996)(hereinafter referred to as the principal Act), in Section 2,—

(I) in sub-section (1),—

(A) for clause (*e*), the following clause shall be *substituted*, namely—

'(*e*) "Court" means—

(*i*) in the case of an arbitration other than international commercial arbitration, the principal Civil Court of original jurisdiction in a district, and includes the High Court in exercise of its ordinary original civil jurisdiction, having jurisdiction to decide the questions forming the subject-matter of the arbitration if the same had been the subject-matter of a suit, but does not include any Civil Court of a grade inferior to such principal Civil Court, or any Court of Small Causes;

(*ii*) in the case of international commercial arbitration, the High Court in exercise of its ordinary original civil jurisdiction, having jurisdiction to decide the questions forming the subject-matter of the arbitration if the same had been the subject-matter of a suit, and in other cases, a High Court having jurisdiction to hear appeals from decrees of courts subordinate to that High Court;';

(B) in clause (*f*), in sub-clause (*iii*), the words "a company or" shall be *omitted*;

(II) in sub-section (2), the following proviso shall be *inserted*, namely—

"Provided that subject to an agreement to the contrary, the provisions of Sections 9, 27 and clause (*a*) of sub-section (1) and sub-section (3) of Section 37 shall also apply to international commercial arbitration, even if the place of arbitration is outside India, and an arbitral award made or to be made in such place is enforceable and recognised under the provisions of Part II of this Act.".

3. **Amendment of Section 7.**—In Section 7 of the principal Act, in sub-section (4), in clause (*b*), after the words "or other means of telecommunication", the words "including communication through electronic means" shall be *inserted*.

4. **Amendment of Section 8.**—In Section 8 of the principal Act,—

(*i*) for sub-section (1), the following sub-section shall be *substituted*, namely—

"(1) A judicial authority, before which an action is brought in a matter which is the subject of an arbitration agreement shall, if a party to the arbitration agreement or any person claiming through or under him, so applies not later than the date of submitting his first statement on the substance of the dispute, then, notwithstanding any judgment, decree or order of the Supreme Court or any court, refer the parties to arbitration unless it finds that prima facie no valid arbitration agreement exists.";

(*ii*) in sub-section (2), the following proviso shall be *inserted*, namely—

"Provided that where the original arbitration agreement or a certified copy thereof is not available with the party applying for reference to arbitration under sub-section (1), and the said agreement or certified copy is retained by the other party to that agreement, then, the party so applying shall file such application along with a copy of the arbitration agreement and a petition praying the Court to call upon the other party to produce the original arbitration agreement or its duly certified copy before that Court.".

5. **Amendment of Section 9.**—Section 9 of the principal Act shall be renumbered as sub-section (1) thereof, and after sub-section (1) as so renumbered, the following sub-sections shall be *inserted*, namely—

"(2) Where, before the commencement of the arbitral proceedings, a court passes an order for any interim measure of protection under sub-section (1), the arbitral proceedings shall be commenced within a period of ninety days from the date of such order or within such further time as the court may determine.

(3) Once the arbitral tribunal has been constituted, the court shall not entertain an application under sub-section (1), unless the court finds that

circumstances exist which may not render the remedy provided under Section 17 efficacious.".

6. Amendment of Section 11.—In Section 11 of the principal Act,—

(*i*) in sub-sections (4), (5) and (6), for the words "the Chief Justice or any person or institution designated by him" wherever they occur, the words "the Supreme Court or, as the case may be, the High Court or any person or institution designated by such court" shall be *substituted*;

(*ii*) after sub-section (6), the following sub-sections shall be *inserted*, namely—

"(6-A) The Supreme Court or, as the case may be, the High Court, while considering any application under sub-section (4) or sub-section (5) or sub-section (6), shall, notwithstanding any judgment, decree or order of any court, confine to the examination of the existence of an arbitration agreement.

(6-B) The designation of any person or institution by the Supreme Court or, as the case may be, the High Court, for the purposes of this section shall not be regarded as a delegation of judicial power by the Supreme Court or the High court.";

(*iii*) in sub-section (7), for the words "the Chief Justice or the person or institution designated by him is final", the words "the Supreme Court or, as the case may be, the High Court or the person or institution designated by such Court is final and no appeal including Letters Patent Appeal shall lie against such decision" shall be *substituted*;

(*iv*) for sub-section (8), the following sub-section shall be *substituted*, namely—

"(8) The Supreme Court or, as the case may be, the High Court or the person or institution designated by such Court, before appointing an arbitrator, shall seek a disclosure in writing from the prospective arbitrator in terms of sub-section (1) of Section 12, and have due regard to—

(*a*) any qualifications required for the arbitrator by the agreement of the parties; and

(*b*) the contents of the disclosure and other considerations as are likely to secure the appointment of an independent and impartial arbitrator.";

(*v*) in sub-section (9), for the words "the Chief Justice of India or the person or institution designated by him", the words "the Supreme Court or the person or institution designated by that court" shall be *substituted*;

(*vi*) for sub-section (10), the following sub-section shall be *substituted*, namely—

"(10) The Supreme Court or, as the case may be, the High Court, may make such scheme as the said court may deem appropriate for dealing with matters entrusted by sub-section (4) or sub-section (5) or sub-section (6), to it.";

(*vii*) in sub-section (11), for the words "the Chief Justices of different High Courts or their designates, the Chief Justice or his designate to whom the request has been first made", the words "different High Courts or their designates, the High Court or its designate to whom the request has been first made" shall be *substituted*;

(*viii*) for sub-section (12), the following sub-section shall be *substituted*, namely—

'(12)(*a*) Where the matters referred to in sub-sections (4), (5), (6), (7), (8) and sub-section (10) arise in an international commercial arbitration, the reference to the "Supreme Court or, as the case may be, the High Court" in those sub-sections shall be construed as a reference to the "Supreme Court"; and

(*b*) where the matters referred to in sub-sections (4), (5), (6), (7), (8) and sub-section (10) arise in any other arbitration, the reference to "the Supreme Court or, as the case may be, the High Court" in those sub-sections shall be construed as a reference to the "High Court" within whose local limits the principal civil court referred to in clause (*e*) of sub-section (1) of Section 2 is situate, and where the High Court itself is the court referred to in that clause, to that High Court.';

(*ix*) after sub-section (12), the following sub-sections shall be *inserted*, namely—

"(13) An application made under this section for appointment of an arbitrator or arbitrators shall be disposed of by the Supreme Court or the High Court or the person or institution designated by such court, as the case may be, as expeditiously as possible and an endeavour shall be made to dispose of the matter within a period of sixty days from the date of service of notice on the opposite party.

(14) For the purpose of determination of the fees of the arbitral tribunal and the manner of its payment to the arbitral tribunal, the High Court may frame such rules as may be necessary, after taking into consideration the rates specified in the Fourth Schedule.

Explanation.—For the removal of doubts, it is hereby clarified that this sub-section shall not apply to international commercial arbitration and in arbitrations (other than international commercial arbitration) in case where parties have agreed for determination of fees as per the rules of an arbitral institution.".

7. Insertion of new Section 11-A.—After Section 11 of the principal Act, the following new section shall be *inserted*, namely—

"11-A. *Power of Central Government to amend Fourth Schedule.*—(1) If the Central Government is satisfied that it is necessary or expedient so to do, it may, by notification in the Official Gazette, amend the Fourth Schedule and thereupon the Fourth Schedule shall be deemed to have been amended accordingly.

(2) A copy of every notification proposed to be issued under sub-section (1), shall be laid in draft before each House of Parliament, while it is in session, for a total period of thirty days which may be comprised in one session or in two or more successive sessions, and if, before the expiry of the session immediately following the session or the successive sessions aforesaid, both Houses agree in disapproving the issue of the notification or both Houses agree in making any modification in the notification, the notification shall

not be issued or, as the case may be, shall be issued only in such modified form as may be agreed upon by the both Houses of Parliament.".

8. Amendment of Section 12.—In Section 12 of the principal Act,—

(*i*) for sub-section (1), the following sub-section shall be *substituted*, namely—

"(1) When a person is approached in connection with his possible appointment as an arbitrator, he shall disclose in writing any circumstances,—

(*a*) such as the existence either direct or indirect, of any past or present relationship with or interest in any of the parties or in relation to the subject-matter in dispute, whether financial, business, professional or other kind, which is likely to give rise to justifiable doubts as to his independence or impartiality; and

(*b*) which are likely to affect his ability to devote sufficient time to the arbitration and in particular his ability to complete the entire arbitration within a period of twelve months.

Explanation 1.—The grounds stated in the Fifth Schedule shall guide in determining whether circumstances exist which give rise to justifiable doubts as to the independence or impartiality of an arbitrator.

Explanation 2.—The disclosure shall be made by such person in the form specified in the Sixth Schedule.";

(*ii*) after sub-section (4), the following sub-section shall be *inserted*, namely—

"(5) Notwithstanding any prior agreement to the contrary, any person whose relationship, with the parties or counsel or the subject-matter of the dispute, falls under any of the categories specified in the Seventh Schedule shall be ineligible to be appointed as an arbitrator:

Provided that parties may, subsequent to disputes having arisen between them, waive the applicability of this sub-section by an express agreement in writing."

9. Amendment of Section 14.—In Section 14 of the principal Act, in sub-section (1), in the opening portion, for the words "The mandate of an arbitrator shall terminate if", the words "The mandate of an arbitrator shall terminate and he shall be substituted by another arbitrator, if" shall be *substituted*.

10. Substitution of new section for Section 17.—For Section 17 of the principal Act, the following section shall be *substituted*, namely—

"17. *Interim measures ordered by arbitral tribunal.*—(1) A party may, during the arbitral proceedings or at any time after the making of the arbitral award but before it is enforced in accordance with Section 36, apply to the arbitral tribunal—

(*i*) for the appointment of a guardian for a minor or person of unsound mind for the purposes of arbitral proceedings; or

(*ii*) for an interim measure of protection in respect of any of the following matters, namely—

(*a*) the preservation, interim custody or sale of any goods which are the subject-matter of the arbitration agreement;

(*b*) securing the amount in dispute in the arbitration;

(*c*) the detention, preservation or inspection of any property or thing which is the subject-matter of the dispute in arbitration, or as to which any question may arise therein and authorising for any of the aforesaid purposes any person to enter upon any land or building in the possession of any party, or authorising any samples to be taken, or any observation to be made, or experiment to be tried, which may be necessary or expedient for the purpose of obtaining full information or evidence;

(*d*) interim injunction or the appointment of a receiver;

(*e*) such other interim measure of protection as may appear to the arbitral tribunal to be just and convenient,

and the arbitral tribunal shall have the same power for making orders, as the court has for the purpose of, and in relation to, any proceedings before it.

(2) Subject to any orders passed in an appeal under Section 37, any order issued by the arbitral tribunal under this section shall be deemed to be an order of the court for all purposes and shall be enforceable under the Code of Civil Procedure, 1908 (5 of 1908), in the same manner as if it were an order of the Court.".

11. Amendment of Section 23.—In Section 23 of the principal Act, after sub-section (2), the following sub-section shall be *inserted*, namely—

"(2-A) The respondent, in support of his case, may also submit a counter-claim or plead a set-off, which shall be adjudicated upon by the arbitral tribunal, if such counter-claim or set-off falls within the scope of the arbitration agreement.".

12. Amendment of Section 24.—In Section 24 of the principal Act, after the proviso to sub-section (1), the following proviso shall be *inserted*, namely—

"Provided further that the arbitral tribunal shall, as far as possible, hold oral hearings for the presentation of evidence or for oral argument on day-to-day basis, and not grant any adjournments unless sufficient cause is made out, and may impose costs including exemplary costs on the party seeking adjournment without any sufficient cause.".

13. Amendment of Section 25.—In Section 25 of the principal Act, in clause (*b*), at the end, after the words "allegations by the claimant", the words "and shall have the discretion to treat the right of the respondent to file such statement of defence as having been forfeited" shall be *inserted*.

14. Amendment of Section 28.—In Section 28 of the principal Act, for sub-section (3), the following sub-section shall be *substituted*, namely—

"(3) While deciding and making an award, the arbitral tribunal shall, in all cases, take into account the terms of the contract and trade usages applicable to the transaction.".

15. Insertion of new Sections 29-A and 29-B.—After Section 29 of the principal Act, the following new sections shall be *inserted*, namely—

"29-A. *Time limit for arbitral award.*—(1) The award shall be made within a period of twelve months from the date the arbitral tribunal enters upon the reference.

Explanation.—For the purpose of this sub-section, an arbitral tribunal shall be deemed to have entered upon the reference on the date on which the arbitrator or all the arbitrators, as the case may be, have received notice, in writing, of their appointment.

(2) If the award is made within a period of six months from the date the arbitral tribunal enters upon the reference, the arbitral tribunal shall be entitled to receive such amount of additional fees as the parties may agree.

(3) The parties may, by consent, extend the period specified in sub-section (1) for making award for a further period not exceeding six months.

(4) If the award is not made within the period specified in sub-section (1) or the extended period specified under sub-section (3), the mandate of the arbitrator(s) shall terminate unless the Court has, either prior to or after the expiry of the period so specified, extended the period:

Provided that while extending the period under this sub-section, if the court finds that the proceedings have been delayed for the reasons attributable to the arbitral tribunal, then, it may order reduction of fees of arbitrator(s) by not exceeding five per cent for each month of such delay.

(5) The extension of period referred to in sub-section (4) may be on the application of any of the parties and may be granted only for sufficient cause and on such terms and conditions as may be imposed by the court.

(6) While extending the period referred to in sub-section (4), it shall be open to the court to substitute one or all of the arbitrators and if one or all of the arbitrators are substituted, the arbitral proceedings shall continue from the stage already reached and on the basis of the evidence and material already on record, and the arbitrator(s) appointed under this section shall be deemed to have received the said evidence and material.

(7) In the event of arbitrator(s) being appointed under this section, the arbitral tribunal thus reconstituted shall be deemed to be in continuation of the previously appointed arbitral tribunal.

(8) It shall be open to the Court to impose actual or exemplary costs upon any of the parties under this section.

(9) An application filed under sub-section (5) shall be disposed of by the court as expeditiously as possible and endeavour shall be made to dispose of the matter within a period of sixty days from the date of service of notice on the opposite party.

29-B. *Fast track procedure.*—(1) Notwithstanding anything contained in this Act, the parties to an arbitration agreement, may, at any stage either before or at the time of appointment of the arbitral tribunal, agree in writing to have their dispute resolved by fast track procedure specified in sub-section (3).

(2) The parties to the arbitration agreement, while agreeing for resolution of dispute by fast track procedure, may agree that the arbitral tribunal shall consist of a sole arbitrator who shall be chosen by the parties.

(3) The arbitral tribunal shall follow the following procedure while conducting arbitration proceedings under sub-section (1):

(*a*) The arbitral tribunal shall decide the dispute on the basis of written pleadings, documents and submissions filed by the parties without any oral hearing;

(*b*) The arbitral tribunal shall have power to call for any further information or clarification from the parties in addition to the pleadings and documents filed by them;

(*c*) An oral hearing may be held only, if, all the parties make a request or if the arbitral tribunal considers it necessary to have oral hearing for clarifying certain issues;

(*d*) The arbitral tribunal may dispense with any technical formalities, if an oral hearing is held, and adopt such procedure as deemed appropriate for expeditious disposal of the case.

(4) The award under this section shall be made within a period of six months from the date the arbitral tribunal enters upon the reference.

(5) If the award is not made within the period specified in sub-section (4), the provisions of sub-sections (3) to (9) of Section 29-A shall apply to the proceedings.

(6) The fees payable to the arbitrator and the manner of payment of the fees shall be such as may be agreed between the arbitrator and the parties.".

16. Amendment of Section 31.—In Section 31 of the principal Act,—

(*i*) in sub-section (7), for clause (*b*), the following clause shall be *substituted*, namely—

'(*b*) A sum directed to be paid by an arbitral award shall, unless the award otherwise directs, carry interest at the rate of two per cent higher than the current rate of interest prevalent on the date of award, from the date of award to the date of payment.

Explanation.—The expression "current rate of interest" shall have the same meaning as assigned to it under clause (*b*) of Section 2 of the Interest Act, 1978 (14 of 1978).';

(*ii*) for sub-section (8), the following sub-section shall be *substituted*, namely—

"(8) The costs of an arbitration shall be fixed by the arbitral tribunal in accordance with Section 31-A.".

17. Insertion of new Section 31-A.—After Section 31 of the principal Act, the following new section shall be *inserted*, namely—

'31-A. *Regime for costs.*—(1) In relation to any arbitration proceeding or a proceeding under any of the provisions of this Act pertaining to the arbitration, the court or arbitral tribunal, notwithstanding anything contained in the Code of Civil Procedure, 1908 (5 of 1908), shall have the discretion to determine—

(*a*) whether costs are payable by one party to another;

(*b*) the amount of such costs; and

(*c*) when such costs are to be paid.

Explanation.—For the purpose of this sub-section, "costs" means reasonable costs relating to—

(*i*) the fees and expenses of the arbitrators, Courts and witnesses;

(*ii*) legal fees and expenses;

(*iii*) any administration fees of the institution supervising the arbitration; and

(*iv*) any other expenses incurred in connection with the arbitral or court proceedings and the arbitral award.

(2) If the Court or arbitral tribunal decides to make an order as to payment of costs,—

(*a*) the general rule is that the unsuccessful party shall be ordered to pay the costs of the successful party; or

(*b*) the Court or arbitral tribunal may make a different order for reasons to be recorded in writing.

(3) In determining the costs, the Court or arbitral tribunal shall have regard to all the circumstances, including—

(*a*) the conduct of all the parties;

(*b*) whether a party has succeeded partly in the case;

(*c*) whether the party had made a frivolous counter claim leading to delay in the disposal of the arbitral proceedings; and

(*d*) whether any reasonable offer to settle the dispute is made by a party and refused by the other party.

(4) The Court or arbitral tribunal may make any order under this section including the order that a party shall pay—

(*a*) a proportion of another party's costs;

(*b*) a stated amount in respect of another party's costs;

(*c*) costs from or until a certain date only;

(*d*) costs incurred before proceedings have begun;

(*e*) costs relating to particular steps taken in the proceedings;

(*f*) costs relating only to a distinct part of the proceedings; and

(*g*) interest on costs from or until a certain date.

(5) An agreement which has the effect that a party is to pay the whole or part of the costs of the arbitration in any event shall be only valid if such agreement is made after the dispute in question has arisen.'.

18. Amendment of Section 34.—In Section 34 of the principal Act,—

(I) in sub-section (2), in clause (*b*), for the Explanation, the following Explanations shall be *substituted*, namely—

"*Explanation 1.*—For the avoidance of any doubt, it is clarified that an award is in conflict with the public policy of India, only if,—

(*i*) the making of the award was induced or affected by fraud or corruption or was in violation of Section 75 or Section 81; or

(*ii*) it is in contravention with the fundamental policy of Indian law; or

(*iii*) it is in conflict with the most basic notions of morality or justice.

Explanation 2.—For the avoidance of doubt, the test as to whether there is a contravention with the fundamental policy of Indian law shall not entail a review on the merits of the dispute.";

(II) after sub-section (2), the following sub-section shall be *inserted*, namely—

"(2-A) An arbitral award arising out of arbitrations other than international commercial arbitrations, may also be set aside by the Court, if the Court finds that the award is vitiated by patent illegality appearing on the face of the award:

Provided that an award shall not be set aside merely on the ground of an erroneous application of the law or by reappreciation of evidence.";

(III) after sub-section (4), the following sub-sections shall be *inserted*, namely—

"(5) An application under this section shall be filed by a party only after issuing a prior notice to the other party and such application shall be accompanied by an affidavit by the applicant endorsing compliance with the said requirement.

(6) An application under this section shall be disposed of expeditiously, and in any event, within a period of one year from the date on which the notice referred to in sub-section (5) is served upon the other party.".

19. Substitution of new section for Section 36.—For Section 36 of the principal Act, the following section shall be *substituted*, namely—

"36. *Enforcement.*—(1) Where the time for making an application to set aside the arbitral award under Section 34 has expired, then, subject to the provisions of sub-section (2), such award shall be enforced in accordance with the provisions of the Code of Civil Procedure, 1908 (5 of 1908), in the same manner as if it were a decree of the court.

(2) Where an application to set aside the arbitral award has been filed in the Court under Section 34, the filing of such an application shall not by itself render that award unenforceable, unless the Court grants an order of stay of the operation of the said arbitral award in accordance with the provisions of sub-section (3), on a separate application made for that purpose.

(3) Upon filing of an application under sub-section (2) for stay of the operation of the arbitral award, the Court may, subject to such conditions as it may deem fit, grant stay of the operation of such award for reasons to be recorded in writing:

Provided that the Court shall, while considering the application for grant of stay in the case of an arbitral award for payment of money, have due regard to the provisions for grant of stay of a money decree under the provisions of the Code of Civil Procedure, 1908 (5 of 1908).".

20. Amendment of Section 37.—In Section 37 of the principal Act, in sub-section (1), for clauses (*a*) and (*b*), the following clauses shall be *substituted*, namely—

"(*a*) refusing to refer the parties to arbitration under Section 8;

(*b*) granting or refusing to grant any measure under Section 9;

(*c*) setting aside or refusing to set aside an arbitral award under Section 34.".

21. Amendment of Section 47.—In Section 47 of the principal Act, for the Explanation, the following Explanation shall be *substituted*, namely—

'*Explanation*.—In this section and in the sections following in this Chapter, "Court" means the High Court having original jurisdiction to decide the questions forming the subject-matter of the arbitral award if the same had been the subject-matter of a suit on its original civil jurisdiction and in other cases, in the High Court having jurisdiction to hear appeals from decrees of courts subordinate to such High Court.'.

22. Amendment of Section 48.—In Section 48 of the principal Act, for the Explanation to sub-section (2), the following Explanations shall be *substituted*, namely—

"*Explanation 1*.—For the avoidance of any doubt, it is clarified that an award is in conflict with the public policy of India, only if,—

(*i*) the making of the award was induced or affected by fraud or corruption or was in violation of Section 75 or Section 81; or

(*ii*) it is in contravention with the fundamental policy of Indian law; or

(*iii*) it is in conflict with the most basic notions of morality or justice.

Explanation 2.—For the avoidance of doubt, the test as to whether there is a contravention with the fundamental policy of Indian law shall not entail a review on the merits of the dispute.".

23. Amendment of Section 56.—In Section 56 of the principal Act, for the Explanation, the following Explanation shall be *substituted*, namely—

'*Explanation*.—In this section and in the sections following in this Chapter, "Court" means the High Court having original jurisdiction to decide the questions forming the subject-matter of the arbitral award if the same had been the subject-matter of a suit on its original civil jurisdiction and in other cases, in the High Court having jurisdiction to hear appeals from decrees of courts subordinate to such High Court.'.

24. Amendment of Section 57.—In Section 57 of the principal Act, in sub-section (1), for the Explanation, the following Explanations shall be *substituted*, namely—

"*Explanation 1*.—For the avoidance of any doubt, it is clarified that an award is in conflict with the public policy of India, only if,—

(*i*) the making of the award was induced or affected by fraud or corruption or was in violation of Section 75 or Section 81; or

(*ii*) it is in contravention with the fundamental policy of Indian law; or

(*iii*) it is in conflict with the most basic notions of morality or justice.

Explanation 2.—For the avoidance of doubt, the test as to whether there is a contravention with the fundamental policy of Indian law shall not entail a review on the merits of the dispute.".

25. Insertion of new Fourth Schedule, Fifth Schedule, Sixth Schedule and Seventh Schedule.—After the Third Schedule to the principal Act, the following new Schedules shall be *inserted*, namely—

'THE FOURTH SCHEDULE

[*See* Section 11(14)]

Sum in dispute	Model fee
Up to Rs 5,00,000	Rs 45,000
Above Rs 5,00,000 and up to Rs 20,00,000	Rs 45,000 plus 3.5 per cent of the claim amount over and above Rs 5,00,000
Above Rs 20,00,000 and up to Rs 1,00,00,000	Rs 97,500 plus 3 per cent of the claim amount over and above Rs 20,00,000
Above Rs 1,00,00,000 and up to Rs 10,00,00,000	Rs 3,37,500 plus 1 per cent of the claim amount over and above Rs 1,00,00,000
Above Rs 10,00,00,000 and up to Rs 20,00,00,000	Rs 12,37,500 plus 0.75 per cent of the claim amount over and above Rs 1,00,00,000
Above Rs 20,00,00,000	Rs 19,87,500 plus 0.5 per cent of the claim amount over and above Rs 20,00,00,000 with a ceiling of Rs 30,00,000

Note.—In the event, the arbitral tribunal is a sole arbitrator, he shall be entitled to an additional amount of twenty-five per cent. on the fee payable as per the table set out above.

THE FIFTH SCHEDULE

[*See* Section 12(1)(*b*)]

The following grounds give rise to justifiable doubts as to the independence or impartiality of arbitrators:

Arbitrator's relationship with the parties or counsel

1. The arbitrator is an employee, consultant, advisor or has any other past or present business relationship with a party.
2. The arbitrator currently represents or advises one of the parties or an affiliate of one of the parties.
3. The arbitrator currently represents the lawyer or law firm acting as counsel for one of the parties.
4. The arbitrator is a lawyer in the same law firm which is representing one of the parties.
5. The arbitrator is a manager, director or part of the management, or has a similar controlling influence, in an affiliate of one of the parties if the affiliate is directly involved in the matters in dispute in the arbitration.
6. The arbitrator's law firm had a previous but terminated involvement in the case without the arbitrator being involved himself or herself.
7. The arbitrator's law firm currently has a significant commercial relationship with one of the parties or an affiliate of one of the parties.

8. The arbitrator regularly advises the appointing party or an affiliate of the appointing party even though neither the arbitrator nor his or her firm derives a significant financial income therefrom.
9. The arbitrator has a close family relationship with one of the parties and in the case of companies with the persons in the management and controlling the company.
10. A close family member of the arbitrator has a significant financial interest in one of the parties or an affiliate of one of the parties.
11. The arbitrator is a legal representative of an entity that is a party in the arbitration.
12. The arbitrator is a manager, director or part of the management, or has a similar controlling influence in one of the parties.
13. The arbitrator has a significant financial interest in one of the parties or the outcome of the case.
14. The arbitrator regularly advises the appointing party or an affiliate of the appointing party, and the arbitrator or his or her firm derives a significant financial income therefrom.

Relationship of the arbitrator to the dispute

15. The arbitrator has given legal advice or provided an expert opinion on the dispute to a party or an affiliate of one of the parties.
16. The arbitrator has previous involvement in the case.

Arbitrator's direct or indirect interest in the dispute

17. The arbitrator holds shares, either directly or indirectly, in one of the parties or an affiliate of one of the parties that is privately held.
18. A close family member of the arbitrator has a significant financial interest in the outcome of the dispute.
19. The arbitrator or a close family member of the arbitrator has a close relationship with a third party who may be liable to recourse on the part of the unsuccessful party in the dispute.

Previous services for one of the parties or other involvement in the case

20. The arbitrator has within the past three years served as counsel for one of the parties or an affiliate of one of the parties or has previously advised or been consulted by the party or an affiliate of the party making the appointment in an unrelated matter, but the arbitrator and the party or the affiliate of the party have no ongoing relationship.
21. The arbitrator has within the past three years served as counsel against one of the parties or an affiliate of one of the parties in an unrelated matter.
22. The arbitrator has within the past three years been appointed as arbitrator on two or more occasions by one of the parties or an affiliate of one of the parties.
23. The arbitrator's law firm has within the past three years acted for one of the parties or an affiliate of one of the parties in an unrelated matter without the involvement of the arbitrator.

24. The arbitrator currently serves, or has served within the past three years, as arbitrator in another arbitration on a related issue involving one of the parties or an affiliate of one of the parties.

Relationship between an arbitrator and another arbitrator or counsel

25. The arbitrator and another arbitrator are lawyers in the same law firm.
26. The arbitrator was within the past three years a partner of, or otherwise affiliated with, another arbitrator or any of the counsel in the same arbitration.
27. A lawyer in the arbitrator's law firm is an arbitrator in another dispute involving the same party or parties or an affiliate of one of the parties.
28. A close family member of the arbitrator is a partner or employee of the law firm representing one of the parties, but is not assisting with the dispute.
29. The arbitrator has within the past three years received more than three appointments by the same counsel or the same law firm.

Relationship between arbitrator and party and others involved in the arbitration

30. The arbitrator's law firm is currently acting adverse to one of the parties or an affiliate of one of the parties.
31. The arbitrator had been associated within the past three years with a party or an affiliate of one of the parties in a professional capacity, such as a former employee or partner.

Other circumstances

32. The arbitrator holds shares, either directly or indirectly, which by reason of number or de-nomination constitute a material holding in one of the parties or an affiliate of one of the parties that is publicly listed.
33. The arbitrator holds a position in an arbitration institution with appointing authority over the dispute.
34. The arbitrator is a manager, director or part of the management, or has a similar controlling influence, in an affiliate of one of the parties, where the affiliate is not directly involved in the matters in dispute in the arbitration.

Explanation 1.—The term "close family member" refers to a spouse, sibling, child, parent or life partner.

Explanation 2.—The term "affiliate" encompasses all companies in one group of companies including the parent company.

Explanation 3.—For the removal of doubts, it is clarified that it may be the practice in certain specific kinds of arbitration, such as maritime or commodities arbitration, to draw arbitrators from a small, specialised pool. If in such fields it is the custom and practice for parties frequently to appoint the same arbitrator in different cases, this is a relevant fact to be taken into account while applying the rules set out above.

THE SIXTH SCHEDULE

[*See* Section 12(1)(*b*)]

Name:
Contact Details:
Prior Experience (Including Experience with Arbitrations):
Number of ongoing arbitrations:

Circumstances disclosing any past or present relationship with or interest in any of the parties or in relation to the subject matter in dispute, whether financial, business, professional or other kind, which is likely to give rise to justifiable doubts as to your independence or impartiality (list out):

Circumstances which are likely to affect your ability to devote sufficient time to the arbitration and in particular your ability to finish the entire arbitration within twelve months (list out):

THE SEVENTH SCHEDULE

[*See* Section 12(5)]

Arbitrator's relationship with the parties or counsel

1. The arbitrator is an employee, consultant, advisor or has any other past or present business relationship with a party.
2. The arbitrator currently represents or advises one of the parties or an affiliate of one of the parties.
3. The arbitrator currently represents the lawyer or law firm acting as counsel for one of the parties.
4. The arbitrator is a lawyer in the same law firm which is representing one of the parties.
5. The arbitrator is a manager, director or part of the management, or has a similar controlling influence, in an affiliate of one of the parties if the affiliate is directly involved in the matters in dispute in the arbitration.
6. The arbitrator's law firm had a previous but terminated involvement in the case without the arbitrator being involved himself or herself.
7. The arbitrator's law firm currently has a significant commercial relationship with one of the parties or an affiliate of one of the parties.
8. The arbitrator regularly advises the appointing party or an affiliate of the appointing party even though neither the arbitrator nor his or her firm derives a significant financial income therefrom.
9. The arbitrator has a close family relationship with one of the parties and in the case of companies with the persons in the management and controlling the company.
10. A close family member of the arbitrator has a significant financial interest in one of the parties or an affiliate of one of the parties.
11. The arbitrator is a legal representative of an entity that is a party in the arbitration.
12. The arbitrator is a manager, director or part of the management, or has a similar controlling influence in one of the parties.

13. The arbitrator has a significant financial interest in one of the parties or the outcome of the case.
14. The arbitrator regularly advises the appointing party or an affiliate of the appointing party, and the arbitrator or his or her firm derives a significant financial income therefrom.

Relationship of the arbitrator to the dispute

15. The arbitrator has given legal advice or provided an expert opinion on the dispute to a party or an affiliate of one of the parties.
16. The arbitrator has previous involvement in the case.

Arbitrator's direct or indirect interest in the dispute

17. The arbitrator holds shares, either directly or indirectly, in one of the parties or an affiliate of one of the parties that is privately held.
18. A close family member of the arbitrator has a significant financial interest in the outcome of the dispute.
19. The arbitrator or a close family member of the arbitrator has a close relationship with a third party who may be liable to recourse on the part of the unsuccessful party in the dispute.

Explanation 1.—The term "close family member" refers to a spouse, sibling, child, parent or life partner.

Explanation 2.—The term "affiliate" encompasses all companies in one group of companies including the parent company.

Explanation 3.—For the removal of doubts, it is clarified that it may be the practice in certain specific kinds of arbitration, such as maritime or commodities arbitration, to draw arbitrators from a small, specialised pool. If in such fields it is the custom and practice for parties frequently, to appoint the same arbitrator in different cases, this is a relevant fact to be taken into account while applying the rules set out above.

26. Act not to apply to pending arbitral proceedings.—[2][* * *]

27. Repeal and savings.—(1) The Arbitration and Conciliation (Amendment) Ordinance, 2015 (Ord. 9 of 2015), is hereby repealed.

(2) Notwithstanding such repeal, anything done or any action taken under the principal Act, as amended by the said Ordinance, shall be deemed to have been done or taken under the corresponding provisions of the principal Act, as amended by this Act.

———

2. *Omitted* by Act 33 of 2019, S. 15 (w.r.e.f. 23-10-2015). Prior to omission it read as:

"**26.** *Act not to apply to pending arbitral proceedings.*—Nothing contained in this Act shall apply to the arbitral proceedings commenced, in accordance with the provisions of section 21 of the principal Act, before the commencement of this Act unless the parties otherwise agree but this Act shall apply in relation to arbitral proceedings commenced on or after the date of commencement of this Act."

APPENDIX 3

Arbitration and Conciliation (Amendment) Act, 2019[1]

[Act 33 of 2019]

[9th August, 2019]

An Act further to amend the Arbitration and Conciliation Act, 1996.

Be it enacted by Parliament in the Seventieth Year of the Republic of India as follows:—

1. Short title and commencement.—(1) This Act may be called the **Arbitration and Conciliation (Amendment) Act, 2019.**

(2) Save as otherwise provided in this Act, it shall come into force on such date as the Central Government may, by notification in the Official Gazette, appoint and different dates may be appointed for different provisions of this Act and any reference in any such provision to the commencement of this Act shall be construed as a reference to the coming into force of that provision.

[Enforced w.e.f. 30-9-2019 *vide* Noti. no. S.O. 3154(E) dt. 30-9-2019.]

2. Amendment of Section 2.—In the Arbitration and Conciliation Act, 1996 (26 of 1996) (hereinafter referred to as the principal Act), in Section 2,—

(*i*) in sub-section (1),—

(A) after clause (*c*), the following clause shall be inserted, namely:—

'(*ca*) "arbitral institution" means an arbitral institution designated by the Supreme Court or a High Court under this Act;';

(B) after clause (*h*), the following clauses shall be inserted, namely:—

'(*i*) "prescribed" means prescribed by rules made under this Act;

(*j*) "regulations" means the regulations made by the Council under this Act.';

(*ii*) in sub-section (2), in the proviso, for the word, brackets and letter "clause (*a*)", the word, brackets and letter "clause (*b*)" shall be substituted.

3. Amendment of Section 11.—In Section 11 of the principal Act,—

(*i*) after sub-section (3), the following sub-section shall be inserted, namely:—

---

1. Received the assent of the President on 9-8-2019.

"(3-A) The Supreme Court and the High Court shall have the power to designate, arbitral institutions, from time to time, which have been graded by the Council under Section 43-I, for the purposes of this Act:

Provided that in respect of those High Court jurisdictions, where no graded arbitral institution are available, then, the Chief Justice of the concerned High Court may maintain a panel of arbitrators for discharging the functions and duties of arbitral institution and any reference to the arbitrator shall be deemed to be an arbitral institution for the purposes of this section and the arbitrator appointed by a party shall be entitled to such fee at the rate as specified in the Fourth Schedule:

Provided further that the Chief Justice of the concerned High Court may, from time to time, review the panel of arbitrators.";

(*ii*) in sub-section (4), in the long line, for the portion beginning with "the appointment shall be made" and ending with "designated by such Court", the following shall be substituted, namely:—

"the appointment shall be made, on an application of the party, by the arbitral institution designated by the Supreme Court, in case of international commercial arbitration, or by the High Court, in case of arbitrations other than international commercial arbitration, as the case may be";

(*iii*) in sub-section (5), for the portion beginning with "the appointment shall be made" and ending with "designated by such Court", the following shall be substituted, namely:—

"the appointment shall be made on an application of the party in accordance with the provisions contained in sub-section (4)";

(*iv*) in sub-section (6), in the long line, for the portion beginning with "party may request" and ending with "designated by such Court", the following shall be substituted, namely:—

"the appointment shall be made, on an application of the party, by the arbitral institution designated by the Supreme Court, in case of international commercial arbitration, or by the High Court, in case of arbitrations other than international commercial arbitration, as the case may be";

(*v*) sub-sections (6-A) and (7) shall be omitted;

(*vi*) in sub-section (8), for the words "The Supreme Court or, as the case may be, the High Court or the person or institution designated by such Court", the words, brackets and figures "The arbitral institution referred to in sub-sections (4), (5) and (6)" shall be substituted;

(*vii*) in sub-section (9), for the words "the Supreme Court or the person or institution designated by that Court", the words "the arbitral institution designated by the Supreme Court" shall be substituted;

(*viii*) sub-section (10) shall be omitted;

(*ix*) for sub-sections (11) to (14), the following sub-sections shall be substituted, namely:—

"(11) Where more than one request has been made under sub-section (4) or sub-section (5) or sub-section (6) to different arbitral institutions, the arbitral institution to which the request has been first made under the relevant sub-section shall be competent to appoint.

(12) Where the matter referred to in sub-sections (4), (5), (6) and (8) arise in an international commercial arbitration or any other arbitration, the reference to the arbitral institution in those sub-sections shall be construed as a reference to the arbitral institution designated under sub-section (3-A).

(13) An application made under this section for appointment of an arbitrator or arbitrators shall be disposed of by the arbitral institution within a period of thirty days from the date of service of notice on the opposite party.

(14) The arbitral institution shall determine the fees of the arbitral tribunal and the manner of its payment to the arbitral tribunal subject to the rates specified in the Fourth Schedule.

Explanation.—For the removal of doubts, it is hereby clarified that this sub-section shall not apply to international commercial arbitration and in arbitrations (other than international commercial arbitration) where parties have agreed for determination of fees as per the rules of an arbitral institution.".

4. **Amendment of Section 17.**—In Section 17 of the principal Act, in sub-section (1), the words and figures "or at any time after the making of the arbitral award but before it is enforced in accordance with Section 36" shall be omitted.

5. **Amendment of Section 23.**—In Section 23 of the principal Act, after sub-section (3), the following sub-section shall be inserted, namely:—

"(4) The statement of claim and defence under this section shall be completed within a period of six months from the date the arbitrator or all the arbitrators, as the case may be, received notice, in writing, of their appointment.".

6. **Amendment of Section 29-A.**—In Section 29-A of the principal Act,—

(*a*) for sub-section (1), the following sub-section shall be substituted, namely:—

"(1) The award in matters other than international commercial arbitration shall be made by the arbitral tribunal within a period of twelve months from the date of completion of pleadings under sub-section (4) of Section 23:

Provided that the award in the matter of international commercial arbitration may be made as expeditiously as possible and endeavour may be made to dispose of the matter within a period of twelve months from the date of completion of pleadings under sub-section (4) of Section 23.";

(*b*) in sub-section (4), after the proviso, the following provisos shall be inserted, namely:

"Provided further that where an application under sub-section (5) is pending, the mandate of the arbitrator shall continue till the disposal of the said application:

Provided also that the arbitrator shall be given an opportunity of being heard before the fees is reduced.".

7. **Amendment of Section 34.**—In Section 34 of the principal Act, in sub-section (2), in clause (*a*), for the words "furnishes proof that", the words "establishes on the basis of the record of the arbitral tribunal that" shall be substituted.

8. **Amendment of Section 37.**—In Section 37 of the principal Act, in sub-section (1), for the words "An appeal", the words "Notwithstanding anything contained in any other law for the time being in force, an appeal" shall be substituted.

9. **Insertion of new Sections 42-A and 42-B.**—After Section 42 of the principal Act, the following sections shall be inserted, namely:—

"**42-A. Confidentiality of information.**—Notwithstanding anything contained in any other law for the time being in force, the arbitrator, the arbitral institution and the parties to the arbitration agreement shall maintain confidentiality of all arbitral proceedings except award where its disclosure is necessary for the purpose of implementation and enforcement of award.

42-B. Protection of action taken in good faith.—No suit or other legal proceedings shall lie against the arbitrator for anything which is in good faith done or intended to be done under this Act or the rules or regulations made thereunder.".

10. **Insertion of new Part.**—After Part I of the principal Act, the following Part shall be inserted, namely:—

'PART I-A

ARBITRATION COUNCIL OF INDIA

43-A. Definitions.—In this Part, unless the context otherwise requires,—

(*a*) "Chairperson" means the Chairperson of the Arbitration Council of India appointed under clause (*a*) of sub-section (1) of Section 43-C;

(*b*) "Council" means the Arbitration Council of India established under Section 43-B;

(*c*) "Member" means a Member of the Council and includes the Chairperson.

43-B. Establishment and incorporation of Arbitration Council of India.—(1) The Central Government shall, by notification in the Official Gazette, establish, for the purposes of this Act, a Council to be known as the Arbitration Council of India to perform the duties and discharge the functions under this Act.

(2) The Council shall be a body corporate by the name aforesaid, having perpetual succession and a common seal, with power, subject to the provisions of this Act, to acquire, hold and dispose of property, both movable and immovable, and to enter into contract, and shall, by the said name, sue or be sued.

(3) The head office of the Council shall be at Delhi.

(4) The Council may, with the prior approval of the Central Government, establish offices at other places in India.

43-C. Composition of Council.—(1) The Council shall consist of the following Members, namely:—

(*a*) a person, who has been, a Judge of the Supreme Court or, Chief Justice of a High Court or, a Judge of a High Court or an eminent person, having special knowledge and experience in the conduct or administration of arbitration, to be appointed by the Central Government in consultation with the Chief Justice of India-Chairperson;

(*b*) an eminent arbitration practitioner having substantial knowledge and experience in institutional arbitration, both domestic and international, to be nominated by the Central Government-Member;

(*c*) an eminent academician having experience in research and teaching in the field of arbitration and alternative dispute resolution laws, to be appointed by the Central Government in consultation with the Chairperson-Member;

(*d*) Secretary to the Government of India in the Department of Legal Affairs, Ministry of Law and Justice or his representative not below the rank of Joint Secretary-Member, ex officio;

(*e*) Secretary to the Government of India in the Department of Expenditure, Ministry of Finance or his representative not below the rank of Joint Secretary-Member, ex officio;

(*f*) one representative of a recognised body of commerce and industry, chosen on rotational basis by the Central Government-Part-time Member; and

(*g*) Chief Executive Officer-Member-Secretary, ex officio.

(2) The Chairperson and Members of the Council, other than ex officio Members, shall hold office as such, for a term of three years from the date on which they enter upon their office:

Provided that no Chairperson or Member, other than ex officio Member, shall hold office as such after he has attained the age of seventy years in the case of Chairperson and sixty-seven years in the case of Member.

(3) The salaries, allowances and other terms and conditions of the Chairperson and Members referred to in clauses (*b*) and (*c*) of sub-section (1) shall be such as may be prescribed by the Central Government.

(4) The Part-time Member shall be entitled to such travelling and other allowances as may be prescribed by the Central Government.

43-D. Duties and functions of Council.—(1) It shall be the duty of the Council to take all such measures as may be necessary to promote and encourage arbitration, mediation, conciliation or other alternative dispute resolution mechanism and for that purpose to frame policy and guidelines for the establishment, operation and maintenance of uniform professional standards in respect of all matters relating to arbitration.

(2) For the purposes of performing the duties and discharging the functions under this Act, the Council may—

(*a*) frame policies governing the grading of arbitral institutions;

(*b*) recognise professional institutes providing accreditation of arbitrators;

(*c*) review the grading of arbitral institutions and arbitrators;

(*d*) hold training, workshops and courses in the area of arbitration in collaboration of law firms, law universities and arbitral institutes;

(*e*) frame, review and update norms to ensure satisfactory level of arbitration and conciliation;

(*f*) act as a forum for exchange of views and techniques to be adopted for creating a platform to make India a robust centre for domestic and international arbitration and conciliation;

(*g*) make recommendations to the Central Government on various measures to be adopted to make provision for easy resolution of commercial disputes;

(*h*) promote institutional arbitration by strengthening arbitral institutions;

(*i*) conduct examination and training on various subjects relating to arbitration and conciliation and award certificates thereof;

(*j*) establish and maintain depository of arbitral awards made in India;

(*k*) make recommendations regarding personnel, training and infra-structure of arbitral institutions; and

(*l*) such other functions as may be decided by the Central Government.

43-E. Vacancies, etc., not to invalidate proceedings of Council.—No act or proceeding of the Council shall be invalid merely by reason of—

(*a*) any vacancy or any defect, in the constitution of the Council;

(*b*) any defect in the appointment of a person acting as a Member of the Council; or

(*c*) any irregularity in the procedure of the Council not affecting the merits of the case.

43-F. Resignation of Members.—The Chairperson or the Full-time or Part-time Member may, by notice in writing, under his hand addressed to the Central Government, resign his office:

Provided that the Chairperson or the Full-time Member shall, unless he is permitted by the Central Government to relinquish his office sooner, continue to hold office until the expiry of three months from the date of receipt of such notice or until a person duly appointed as his successor enters upon his office or until the expiry of his term of office, whichever is earlier.

43-G. Removal of Member.—(1) The Central Government may, remove a Member from his office if he—

(*a*) is an undischarged insolvent; or

(*b*) has engaged at any time (except Part-time Member), during his term of office, in any paid employment; or

(*c*) has been convicted of an offence which, in the opinion of the Central Government, involves moral turpitude; or

(*d*) has acquired such financial or other interest as is likely to affect prejudicially his functions as a Member; or

(*e*) has so abused his position as to render his continuance in office prejudicial to the public interest; or

(*f*) has become physically or mentally incapable of acting as a Member.

(2) Notwithstanding anything contained in sub-section (1), no Member shall be removed from his office on the grounds specified in clauses (*d*) and (*e*) of that sub-section unless the Supreme Court, on a reference being made to it in this behalf by the Central Government, has, on an inquiry, held by it in accordance with such procedure as may be prescribed in this behalf by the Supreme Court, reported that the Member, ought on such ground or grounds to be removed.

43-H. Appointment of experts and constitution of Committees thereof.—The Council may, appoint such experts and constitute such Committees of experts as it may consider necessary to discharge its functions on such terms and conditions as may be specified by the regulations.

43-I. General norms for grading of arbitral institutions.—The Council shall make grading of arbitral institutions on the basis of criteria relating to infrastructure, quality and calibre of arbitrators, performance and compliance of time limits for disposal of domestic or international commercial arbitrations, in such manner as may be specified by the regulations.

43-J. Norms for accreditation.—The qualifications, experience and norms for accreditation of arbitrators shall be such as specified in the Eighth Schedule:

Provided that the Central Government may, after consultation with the Council, by notification in the Official Gazette, amend the Eighth Schedule and thereupon, the Eighth Schedule shall be deemed to have been amended accordingly.

43-K. Depository of awards.—The Council shall maintain an electronic depository of arbitral awards made in India and such other records related thereto in such manner as may be specified by the regulations.

43-L. Power to make regulations by Council.—The Council may, in consultation with the Central Government, make regulations, consistent with the provisions of this Act and the rules made thereunder, for the discharge of its functions and perform its duties under this Act.

43-M. Chief Executive Officer.—(1) There shall be a Chief Executive Officer of the Council, who shall be responsible for day-to-day administration of the Council.

(2) The qualifications, appointment and other terms and conditions of the service of the Chief Executive Officer shall be such as may be prescribed by the Central Government.

(3) The Chief Executive Officer shall discharge such functions and perform such duties as may be specified by the regulations.

(4) There shall be a Secretariat to the Council consisting of such number of officers and employees as may be prescribed by the Central Government.

(5) The qualifications, appointment and other terms and conditions of the service of the employees and other officers of the Council shall be such as may be prescribed by the Central Government.'.

11. Amendment of Section 45.—In Section 45 of the principal Act, for the words "unless it finds", the words "unless it prima facie finds", shall be substituted.

12. Amendment of Section 50.—In Section 50 of the principal Act, in sub-section (1), for the words "An appeal", the words "Notwithstanding anything contained in any other law for the time being in force, an appeal" shall be substituted.

13. Insertion of new Section 87.—After Section 86 of the principal Act, the following section shall be inserted and shall be deemed to have been inserted with effect from the 23rd October, 2015, namely:—

"**87. Effect of arbitral and related court proceedings commenced prior to 23rd October, 2015.**—Unless the parties otherwise agree, the amendments made to this Act by the Arbitration and Conciliation (Amendment) Act, 2015 (3 of 2016) shall—

(*a*) not apply to—

(*i*) arbitral proceedings commenced before the commencement of the Arbitration and Conciliation (Amendment) Act, 2015 (3 of 2016);

(*ii*) court proceedings arising out of or in relation to such arbitral proceedings irrespective of whether such court proceedings are commenced prior to or after the commencement of the Arbitration and Conciliation (Amendment) Act, 2015 (3 of 2016);

(*b*) apply only to arbitral proceedings commenced on or after the commencement of the Arbitration and Conciliation (Amendment) Act, 2015 (3 of 2016) and to court proceedings arising out of or in relation to such arbitral proceedings.".

14. Insertion of new Schedule.—After the Seventh Schedule to the principal Act, the following Schedule shall be inserted, namely:—

"THE EIGHTH SCHEDULE

(*See* Section 43-J)

Qualifications and Experience of Arbitrator

A person shall not be qualified to be an arbitrator unless he —

(*i*) is an advocate within the meaning of the Advocates Act, 1961 (25 of 1961) having ten years of practice experience as an advocate; or

(*ii*) is a chartered accountant within the meaning of the Chartered Accountants Act, 1949 (38 of 1949) having ten years of practice experience as a chartered accountant; or

(*iii*) is a cost accountant within the meaning of the Cost and Works Accountants Act, 1959 (23 of 1959) having ten years of practice experience as a cost accountant; or

(*iv*) is a company secretary within the meaning of the Company Secretaries Act, 1980 (56 of 1980) having ten years of practice experience as a company secretary; or

(*v*) has been an officer of the Indian Legal Service; or

(*vi*) has been an officer with law degree having ten years of experience in the legal matters in the Government, Autonomous Body, Public Sector Undertaking or at a senior level managerial position in private sector; or

(*vii*) has been an officer with engineering degree having ten years of experience as an engineer in the Government, Autonomous Body, Public

Sector Undertaking or at a senior level managerial position in private sector or self-employed; or

(*viii*) has been an officer having senior level experience of administration in the Central Government or State Government or having experience of senior level management of a Public Sector Undertaking or a Government company or a private company of repute;

(*ix*) is a person, in any other case, having educational qualification at degree level with ten years of experience in scientific or technical stream in the fields of telecom, information technology, Intellectual Property Rights or other specialised areas in the Government, Autonomous Body, Public Sector Undertaking or a senior level managerial position in a private sector, as the case may be.

General norms applicable to Arbitrator

(*i*) The arbitrator shall be a person of general reputation of fairness, integrity and capable to apply objectivity in arriving at settlement of disputes;

(*ii*) the arbitrator must be impartial and neutral and avoid entering into any financial business or other relationship that is likely to affect impartiality or might reasonably create an appearance of partiality or bias amongst the parties;

(*iii*) the arbitrator should not involve in any legal proceeding and avoid any potential conflict connected with any dispute to be arbitrated by him;

(*iv*) the arbitrator should not have been convicted of an offence involving moral turpitude or economic offence;

(*v*) the arbitrator shall be conversant with the Constitution of India, principles of natural justice, equity, common and customary laws, commercial laws, labour laws, law of torts, making and enforcing the arbitral awards;

(*vi*) the arbitrator should possess robust understanding of the domestic and international legal system on arbitration and international best practices in regard thereto;

(*vii*) the arbitrator should be able to understand key elements of contractual obligations in civil and commercial disputes and be able to apply legal principles to a situation under dispute and also to apply judicial decisions on a given matter relating to arbitration; and

(*viii*) the arbitrator should be capable of suggesting, recommending or writing a reasoned and enforceable arbitral award in any dispute which comes before him for adjudication.".

15. Amendment to Act 3 of 2016.—Section 26 of the Arbitration and Conciliation (Amendment) Act, 2015 shall be omitted and shall be deemed to have been omitted with effect from the 23rd October, 2015.

16. Amendment to Fourth Schedule.—In the Fourth Schedule to the principal Act, for the brackets, words and figures "[See Section 11(14)]", the brackets, words, figures and letter "[See Section 11(3-A)]" shall be substituted.

———

Appendix 4

Arbitration and Conciliation (Amendment) Act, 2021[1]

[Act 3 of 2021]

[11th March, 2021]

An Act further to amend the Arbitration and Conciliation Act, 1996.

Be it enacted by Parliament in the Seventy-second Year of the Republic of India as follows:—

1. **Short title and commencement.**—(1) This Act may be called the **Arbitration and Conciliation (Amendment) Act, 2021.**

(2) Save as otherwise provided in this Act, it shall be deemed to have come into force on the 4th day of November, 2020.

2. **Amendment of Section 36.**—In the Arbitration and Conciliation Act, 1996 (26 of 1996) (hereinafter referred to as the principal Act), in Section 36, in sub-section (3), after the proviso, the following shall be inserted and shall be deemed to have been inserted with effect from the 23rd day of October, 2015, namely:

"Provided further that where the Court is satisfied that a *prima facie* case is made out that,—

(*a*) the arbitration agreement or contract which is the basis of the award; or

(*b*) the making of the award,

was induced or effected by fraud or corruption, it shall stay the award unconditionally pending disposal of the challenge under Section 34 to the award.

Explanation.—For the removal of doubts, it is hereby clarified that the above proviso shall apply to all court cases arising out of or in relation to arbitral proceedings, irrespective of whether the arbitral or court proceedings were commenced prior to or after the commencement of the Arbitration and Conciliation (Amendment) Act, 2015 (3 of 2016).".

3. **Substitution of new section for Section 43-J.**—For Section 43-J of the principal Act, the following section shall be substituted, namely:—

---

1. Received the assent of the Governor on the 11th March, 2021. Published on 11-3-2021 in the Gazette of India, Pt. II(1), dt. 11-3-2021.

"**43-J. Norms for accreditation of arbitrators.**—The qualifications, experience and norms for accreditation of arbitrators shall be such as may be specified by the regulations.".

4. Omission of Eighth Schedule.—The Eighth Schedule to the principal Act shall be omitted.

5. Repeal and savings.—(1) The Arbitration and Conciliation (Amendment) Ordinance, 2020 (Ord. 14 of 2020) is hereby repealed.

(2) Notwithstanding such repeal, anything done or any action taken under the said Ordinance shall be deemed to have been done or taken under this Act.

———

Appendix 5

[1][India International Arbitration Centre] Act, 2019[2]

[Act 17 of 2019 as amended by Act 23 of 2022]
[Updated as on 5-1-2023]

[26th July, 2019]

An Act to provide for the establishment and incorporation of the [3][India International Arbitration Centre] for the purpose of creating an independent and autonomous regime for institutionalised arbitration and for acquisition and transfer of the undertakings of the International Centre for Alternative Dispute Resolution and to vest such undertakings in the [4][India International Arbitration Centre] for the better management of arbitration so as to make it a hub for institutional arbitration and to declare the [5][India International Arbitration Centre] to be an institution of national importance and for matters connected therewith or incidental thereto

Whereas dispute resolution process has a huge impact on the Indian economy and global perception on doing business in our country and it has become necessary to inspire confidence and credibility among the litigants of commercial disputes;

And whereas rapidly changing economic activity demands expeditious settlement of dispute and creation and establishment of institutional arbitration;

1. *Subs.* for "New Delhi International Arbitration Centre" by Act 23 of 2022, S. 2 (w.e.f. 27-1-2023).
2. Received the assent of the President on 26-7-2019 and published in the Gazette of India, Extra., Pt. II, S. 1, dt. 26-7-2019, pp. 1–11, No. 36.
3. *Subs.* for "New Delhi International Arbitration Centre" by Act 23 of 2022, S. 2 (w.e.f. 27-1-2023).
4. *Ibid.*
5. *Ibid.*

And whereas the International Centre for Alternative Dispute Resolution was set up in the Year 1995, under the aegis of the Central Government and registered under the Societies Registration Act, 1860 (21 of 1860), with the objective of promoting alternative dispute resolution mechanism and providing facilities for the same;

And whereas the International Centre for Alternative Dispute Resolution has received land and substantial funding by way of grants and other benefits from the Central Government for constructing infrastructure and making other facilities;

And whereas the International Centre for Alternative Dispute Resolution has not been able to actively engage and embrace developments in the arbitration ecosystem and to create a reputation par excellence keeping pace with the dynamic nature of arbitration over more than two decades;

And whereas studies conducted by the High Level Committee appointed by the Central Government indicate that the International Centre for Alternative Dispute Resolution has failed to address the growing needs for the institutional arbitration and also to bear optimum caseload and to become better choice to the parties for arbitration;

And whereas it has become expedient to take over the undertakings of the International Centre for Alternative Dispute Resolution including its regional offices without interfering with its activities and without adversely affecting its character as a Society but to utilise its existing infrastructure and other facilities which have been set up by using the public funds provided by the Government and to incorporate a robust institution for domestic and international arbitration to be known as the [6][India International Arbitration Centre];

And whereas it is considered necessary to declare the [7][India International Arbitration Centre] as an institution of national importance for its overall development as a major arbitration hub by promoting quick and efficient dispute resolution mechanism.

Be it enacted by Parliament in the Seventieth Year of the Republic of India as follows—

Statement of Objects and Reasons.—The dispute resolution process has a huge impact on the economy and doing business in our country. The rapidly changing economic activity demands expeditious settlement of disputes, creation and establishment of mechanism such as intitutional arbitration. This is necessary to inspire confidence and creadibility among the litigants of commercial disputes. The huge pendency of cases in courts further underlines the need for strengthening the Alternative Dispute Resolution Mechanism.

---

6. *Subs.* for "New Delhi International Arbitration Centre" by Act 23 of 2022, S. 3 (w.e.f. 27-1-2023).
7. *Ibid.*

2. With a view to promote institutional arbitration and to make India a hub of international arbitration, a High Level Committee headed by Mr. Justice B.N. Srikrishna former Judge, Supreme Court of India was constituted, inter alia, to identify the roadblocks in the development of institutional arbitration, examine specific issues affecting the Indian arbitration landscape and prepare a roadmap for making India a robust centre for international and domestic arbitration.

3. The Committee, inter alia, recommended that the International Centre for Alternative Dispute Resolution, which was set up in the year, 1995, with the Government funds to promote alternative dispute resolution mechanism has however not been able to achieve the objectives for which it had been set up. The Committee further recommended that International Centre for Alternative Dispute Resolution should be taken over with complete revamp of its governance structure to include only experts of repute who can lend credibility and respectability to the institution and be re-branded as a centre of national importance to highlight its character as a flagship arbitral institution.

4. In view of the above, it has been decided to establish a new institution to be called the New Delhi International Arbitration Centre for better management of arbitration in the country and to declare it as an institution of national importance. Further, the undertakings of the International Centre for Alternative Dispute Resolution needs to be taken over without interferring with its activities and without adversely affecting the character of it as a Society, so that the existing infrastructure and other facilities which have been set up by the public funds provided by the Government may be appropriately utilised by the NDIAC (New Delhi International Arbitration Centre) for the overall development of institutional arbitration.

5. In view of the above, a Bill, namely, the New Delhi International Arbitration Centre Bill, 2018 introduced in Lok Sabha on the 5th January, 2018 was passed by that House on the 4th January, 2019 and was pending in Rajya Sabha.

6. The Bill envisaged appointment of persons of repute and having knowledge and expertise in institutional arbitration as Chairperson and Members of the New Delhi International Arbitration Centre. The objects of the New Delhi International Arbitration Centre was to bring targeted reforms to develop it as a flagship institution for domestic and international arbitration and to conduct arbitration in a professional manner in the cost effective way. The Bill also proposed to set up an Arbitration Chamber, which would empanel reputed arbitrators at national and international level. An Arbitration Academy was also proposed to be set up by New Delhi International Arbitration Centre to train arbitrators in India, so as to empower them to compete on par with reputed arbitral institutions.

7. As the Bill was pending for consideration in Rajya Sabha, in the interest of promotion of institutional arbiration, it had become expedient to take over the undertakings of the Internation Centre for Alternative Dispute Resolution including its regional offices and vest the same in the Central Government before it is finally vested in the New Delhi International Arbitration Centre and also to declare the New Delhi International Arbitration Centre as an institution of national importance for its overall development as an arbitration hub for promoting quick and efficient dispute resolution.

8. In view of the above and since both Houses of Parliament were not in session and circumstances existed which render it necessary for the President to take immediate action in the matter, the New Delhi International Arbitration Centre Ordinance, 2019, was promulgated on the 2nd March, 2019, inter alia, for taking over the undertakings of the International Centre for Alternative Disputes Resolution. Thereafter, the Sixteenth Lok Sabha was dissolved on the 25th May, 2019 and the New Delhi International Arbitration Centre Bill, 2019 pending in Rajya Sabha lapsed.

9. The New Delhi International Arbitration Centre Bill, 2019 seeks to replace the said Ordinance.

CHAPTER I

PRELIMINARY

1. Short title and commencement.—(1) This Act may be called the [8][India International Arbitration Centre] Act, 2019.

(2) It shall be deemed to have come into force on the 2nd March, 2019.

---

8. *Subs.* for "New Delhi International Arbitration Centre" by Act 23 of 2022, S. 4 (w.e.f. 27-1-2023).

2. Definitions.—(1) In this Act, unless the context otherwise requires,—

(*a*) "Centre" means the [9][India International Arbitration Centre] established and incorporated under Section 3;

(*b*) "Chairperson" means the Chairperson of the Centre referred to in clause (*a*) of Section 5;

(*c*) "Chief Executive Officer" means the Chief Executive Officer appointed under Section 21;

(*d*) "Committee" means the relevant Committee of the Centre referred to in Section 19;

(*e*) "Custodian" means the person who is appointed as Custodian under sub-section (2) of Section 11 in respect of the undertakings;

(*f*) "Fund" means the Fund of the Centre to be maintained under Section 25;

(*g*) "Member" means full time or part time Member of the Centre and includes the Chairperson;

(*h*) "notification" means a notification published in the Official Gazette;

(*i*) "prescribed" means prescribed by rules made by the Central Government under this Act;

(*j*) "regulations" means regulations made by the Centre under this Act;

(*k*) "Society" means the International Centre for Alternative Dispute Resolution, registered as such under the Societies Registration Act, 1860 (21 of 1860) and having its registered office at New Delhi;

(*l*) "specified date" means the date as may be specified by the Central Government by notification;

(*m*) "undertakings" means the undertakings of the Society which vests with the Central Government under Section 7.

(2) All other words and expressions used herein but not defined and defined in the Arbitration and Conciliation Act, 1996 (26 of 1996), shall have the same meanings as assigned to them in that Act.

CHAPTER II

ESTABLISHMENT AND INCORPORATION OF [10][INDIA INTERNATIONAL ARBITRATION CENTRE]

3. Establishment and incorporation of [11][India International Arbitration Centre].—(1) The Central Government shall, by notification, establish a body to be called the [12][India International Arbitration Centre] for the purposes of exercising the powers and discharging the functions under this Act.

(2) The Centre shall be a body corporate by the name aforesaid, having perpetual succession and a common seal with power, subject to the provisions of

9. *Subs.* for "New Delhi International Arbitration Centre" by Act 23 of 2022, S. 5 (w.e.f. 27-1-2023).
10. *Subs.* for "New Delhi International Arbitration Centre" by Act 23 of 2022, S. 6 (w.e.f. 27-1-2023).
11. *Subs.* for "New Delhi International Arbitration Centre" by Act 23 of 2022, S. 7(*i*) (w.e.f. 27-1-2023).
12. *Subs.* for "New Delhi International Arbitration Centre" by Act 23 of 2022, S. 7(*ii*) (w.e.f. 27-1-2023).

this Act, to acquire, hold and dispose of property, both movable and immovable, and to enter into contract, and shall, by the said name, sue or be sued.

4. Declaration of [13][India International Arbitration Centre] as an institution of national importance.—(1) Whereas, the objects of the [14][India International Arbitration Centre] are such as to make it as an institution of national importance, it is hereby declared that the [15][India International Arbitration Centre] is an institution of national importance.

(2) The head office of the Centre shall be at New Delhi and it may with the previous approval of the Central Government, establish branches at other places in India and abroad.

5. Composition of Centre.—The Centre shall consist of the following Members, namely—

(*a*) a person, who has been a Judge of the Supreme Court or a Judge of a High Court or an eminent person, having special knowledge and experience in the conduct or administration of arbitration, law or management, appointed by the Central Government in consultation with the Chief Justice of India—Chairperson;

(*b*) two eminent persons having substantial knowledge and experience in institutional arbitration, both domestic and international, appointed by the Central Government—Full-time Members or Part-time Members;

(*c*) one representative of a recognised body of commerce and industry, chosen on rotational basis by the Central Government—Part-time Member;

(*d*) Secretary, Department of Legal Affairs, Ministry of Law and Justice or his representative, not below the rank of the Joint Secretary—Member, ex officio;

(*e*) one Financial Adviser nominated by the Department of Expenditure, Ministry of Finance—Member, ex officio; and

(*f*) Chief Executive Officer—Member, ex officio.

6. Terms and conditions, etc., of Chairperson and Members.—(1) The Chairperson and Members shall hold office for a term of three years from the date on which they enter upon their office and shall be eligible for re-appointment:

Provided that no Chairperson or Member shall hold office as such after he has attained the age of seventy years in the case of Chairperson and sixty seven years in the case of a Member.

(2) The terms and conditions, salaries and allowances payable to the Chairperson and Full-time Member shall be such as may be prescribed.

(3) The term of office of a Member appointed to fill a casual vacancy shall be for the remainder of the term of the Member in whose place he has been appointed.

---

13. *Subs.* for "New Delhi International Arbitration Centre" by Act 23 of 2022, S. 8(*i*) (w.e.f. 27-1-2023).
14. *Subs.* for "New Delhi International Arbitration Centre" by Act 23 of 2022, S. 8(*ii*) (w.e.f. 27-1-2023).
15. *Ibid.*

(4) The Part-time Member shall be entitled to such travelling and other allowances as may be prescribed.

CHAPTER III
ACQUISITION AND TRANSFER OF UNDERTAKINGS OF SOCIETY

7. **Transfer and vesting.**—On and from the specified date, so much of the undertakings of the Society as form part of, or are relatable to the Society, and the right, title and interest of the Society in relation to such undertakings, shall, by virtue of this Act, stand transferred to, and vest in, the Central Government.

8. **General effect of vesting.**—(1) The undertakings vested under Section 7 shall be deemed to include all assets, rights, leaseholds, powers, authorities and privileges, and all property (movable and immovable), including lands, buildings, works, projects, instruments, automobiles and other vehicles, cash balances, funds, including reserve funds, investments and book debts of the Society as form part of, or are relatable to, the Society and all other rights and interest arising out of such properties as were immediately before the commencement of the New Delhi International Arbitration Centre Ordinance, 2019 in the ownership, possession, power or control of the Society, and all books of account, registers and all other documents of whatever nature relating thereto.

(2) All properties and assets as aforesaid which have vested in the Central Government under Section 7 shall, by force of such vesting, be freed and discharged from any trust, obligation, mortgage, charge, lien and all other encumbrances affecting them or of any attachment, injunction, decree or order of any court or other authority restricting the use of such properties or assets in any manner or appointing any receiver in respect of the whole or any part of such properties or assets shall be deemed to have been withdrawn.

(3) Any licence or other instrument granted to the Society in relation to any undertaking which has vested in the Central Government under Section 7 at any time before the specified date and in force immediately before the specified date, shall continue to be in force on and after such day in accordance with its tenor in relation to and for the purpose of such undertaking or where the undertaking is directed under Section 10, to vest in the Centre, the Centre shall be deemed to be substituted in such licence or other instrument as if such licence or other instrument had been granted to the Centre and the Centre shall hold it for the remainder of the period which the Society would have held it under the terms thereof.

(4) If, on the specified date, any suit, appeal or other proceeding, of whatever nature, in relation to any property or asset which has vested in the Central Government under Section 7, instituted or preferred by or against the Society is pending, the same shall not abate, be discontinued or be, in any way, prejudicially affected by reason of the transfer of the undertaking of the Society of anything contained in this Act, but the suit, appeal or other proceeding may be continued, prosecuted or enforced by or against the Central Government or where the undertakings of the Society are directed under Section 10, to vest in the Centre, by or against the Centre.

9. Liability prior to specified date.—Every liability in relation to any undertaking in respect of any period prior to the specified date, shall be enforceable against the Society and not against the Central Government.

10. Power of Central Government to direct vesting of undertaking in Centre.—(1) Notwithstanding anything contained in Sections 7 and 8, the Central Government shall, as soon as may be after the specified date, direct by notification, that the undertakings and the right, title and interest of the Society in relation to such undertakings which had vested in the Central Government under Section 7, shall, vest in the Centre either on the date of publication of the notification or on such earlier or later date as may be specified in the notification.

(2) Where the right, title and interest of the Society in relation to the undertakings vest, under sub-section (1), in the Centre, the Centre shall, on and from the date of such vesting, be deemed to have become the owner in relation to such undertakings and the rights and liabilities of the Central Government in relation to such undertakings shall, on and from the date of such vesting, be deemed to have become, the rights and liabilities, respectively, of the Centre.

11. Management, etc., of undertakings.—(1) The general superintendence, direction, control and management of affairs of the undertakings, the right, the interest in relation to which have vested in the Central Government under Section 7, shall—

(*a*) where a direction has been made by the Central Government under sub-section (1) of Section 10, vest in the Centre; or

(*b*) where no such direction has been made by the Central Government, vest in the Custodian appointed by the Central Government under sub-section (2),

and, thereupon, the Centre or the Custodian so appointed, as the case may be, shall be entitled to exercise all such powers and do all such things as the Society, is authorised to exercise and do in relation to its undertakings.

(2) The Central Government may appoint any person as the Custodian of the undertakings in relation to which no direction has been made by it under sub-section (1) of Section 10.

(3) The Custodian so appointed shall receive such remuneration as the Central Government may fix and shall hold office during the pleasure of the Central Government.

12. Duties of persons in charge of management of undertakings to deliver all assets.—(1) On the vesting of the management of the undertakings in the Centre or on the appointment of a Custodian under sub-section (2) of Section 11, all persons in charge of management of the undertakings immediately before such vesting or appointment shall be bound to deliver to the Centre or Custodian, as the case may be, all assets, books of account, registers and other documents in their custody relating to the undertakings.

(2) The Central Government may issue such directions as it may deem desirable in the circumstances of the case to the Custodian as to the powers and duties of the Custodian and such Custodian may also, if it is considered necessary so to do, apply to the Central Government at any time for instructions as to the

manner in which the management of the undertaking shall be conducted or in relation to any other matter arising in the course of such management.

(3) Any person who on the specified date, has in his possession or under his control, any books, documents or other papers relating to the undertakings shall be liable to account for the said books, documents or other papers to the Central Government or the Custodian or the Centre, as the case may be, and shall deliver them to the Central Government or the Custodian or the Centre or to such person or body of persons as the Central Government or the Centre may specify in this behalf.

(4) The Central Government or the Centre may take or cause to be taken, all necessary steps for securing possession of all undertakings which have vested in the Central Government or the Centre under this Act.

(5) The Society shall, within such period as the Central Government may allow in this behalf, furnish to that Government a complete inventory of all its properties and assets, as on the commencement of the New Delhi International Arbitration Centre Ordinance, 2019 (Ord. 10 of 2019) pertaining to the undertaking and for this purpose, the Central Government or Custodian or the Centre shall afford to the Society, or body all reasonable facilities.

13. Certain powers of Central Government or Centre.—The Central Government or the Custodian or the Centre shall be entitled to receive up to the specified date, to the exclusion of all other persons, any money due to the Society in relation to its undertakings which have vested in the Central Government or Custodian or the Centre, as the case may be, and realised after the commencement of the New Delhi International Arbitration Centre Ordinance, 2019 (Ord. 10 of 2019), notwithstanding that the realisation pertains to a period prior to the commencement of the New Delhi International Arbitration Centre Ordinance, 2019.

14. Objects of Centre.—The objects of the Centre shall be,—

(*a*) to bring targeted reforms to develop itself as a flagship institution for conducting international and domestic arbitration;

(*b*) to promote research and study, providing teaching and training, and organising conferences and seminars in arbitration, conciliation, mediation and other alternative dispute resolution matters;

(*c*) to provide facilities and administrative assistance for conciliation, mediation and arbitral proceedings;

(*d*) to maintain panels of accredited arbitrators, conciliators and mediators both at national and international level or specialists such as surveyors and investigators;

(*e*) to collaborate with other national and international institutions and organisations for ensuring credibility of the Centre as a specialised institution in arbitration and conciliation;

(*f*) to set up facilities in India and abroad to promote the activities of the Centre;

(*g*) to lay down parameters for different modes of alternative dispute resolution mechanisms being adopted by the Centre; and

(*h*) such other objectives as it may deem fit with the approval of the Central Government.

15. Functions of Centre.—Without prejudice to the provisions contained in Section 14, the Centre shall strive,—

[16][(*a*) to facilitate the conduct of arbitration and other forms of alternative dispute resolution mechanism, both international and domestic, in the manner as may be specified by the regulations;]

(*b*) to provide cost effective and timely services for the conduct of arbitration and conciliation at national and international level;

(*c*) to promote studies in the field of alternative dispute resolution and related matters, and to promote reforms in the system of settlement of disputes;

(*d*) to undertake teaching and to provide for diffusion of knowledge of law and procedures on alternative dispute resolution and related matters and to award certificates and other academic or professional distinction;

(*e*) to impart training in alternative dispute resolution and related matters to those who are handling arbitration, conciliation and mediation;

(*f*) to co-operate with other societies, institutions and organisations, national or international for promoting alternative dispute resolution; and

(*g*) to perform such other functions as may be entrusted to it by the Central Government for promoting alternative dispute resolution.

16. Vacancies, etc., not to invalidate proceedings of Centre.—No act or proceedings of the Centre shall be invalid merely by reason of,—

(*a*) any vacancy or any defect in the constitution of the Centre; or

(*b*) any defect in the appointment of a person acting as a Member of the Centre; or

(*c*) any irregularity in the procedure of the Centre not affecting the merits of the case.

17. Resignation of Members.—The Chairperson or the Full-time Member or Part-time Member may, by notice in writing, under his hand addressed to the Central Government, resign his office:

Provided that the Chairperson or the Full-time Member shall, unless he is permitted by the Central Government to relinquish his office sooner, continue to hold office until the expiry of three months from the date of receipt of such notice or until a person duly appointed as his successor enters upon his office or until the expiry of his term of office, whichever is the earlier.

18. Removal of Members.—(1) The Central Government may, remove a Member from his office if he,—

(*a*) is an undischarged insolvent; or

(*b*) has engaged at any time (except Part-time Member), during his term of office, in any paid employment; or

(*c*) has been convicted of an offence which, in the opinion of the Central Government, involves moral turpitude; or

(*d*) has acquired such financial or other interest as is likely to affect prejudicially his functions as a Member; or

---

16. *Subs.* by Act 23 of 2022, S. 9 (w.e.f. 27-1-2023). Prior to substitution it read as:
"(*a*) to facilitate for conducting international and domestic arbitration and conciliation in the most professional manner;"

(*e*) has so abused his position as to render his continuance in office prejudicial to the public interest; or

(*f*) has become physically or mentally incapable of acting as a Member.

(2) Notwithstanding anything contained in sub-section (1), no Member shall be removed from his office on the grounds specified in clauses (*d*) and (*e*) of that sub-section unless the Supreme Court, on a reference being made to it in this behalf by the Central Government, has, on an inquiry, held by it in accordance with such procedure as may be prescribed in this behalf by the Supreme Court, reported that the Member, ought on such ground or grounds to be removed.

19. Committees of Centre.—(1) The Centre may constitute such Committees as may be considered necessary to administer various aspects of its functions.

(2) The composition and functions of the Committees referred to in sub-section (1) shall be such as may be prescribed.

(3) The Committee shall meet at such time and at such places and shall observe such rules of procedure in regard to the transaction of business at its meetings including the quorum as may be specified by the regulations.

20. Meetings of Centre.—(1) The Chairperson shall ordinarily preside at the meetings of the Centre:

Provided that, in his absence, the Member chosen by the other Members present amongst themselves shall preside at the meetings.

(2) It shall be the duty of the Chairperson to ensure that the decisions taken by the Centre are implemented.

(3) The Chairperson shall exercise such other powers and perform such other duties as are assigned to him under this Act.

(4) The Centre shall meet at least four times a year and follow such procedure in its meetings including quorum at such meetings in such manner as may be specified by the regulations.

(5) All questions which come up before any meeting of the Centre shall be—

(*a*) decided by a majority of votes by the Members present and voting, and in the event of an equality of votes, the Chairperson or in his absence, the person presiding, shall have a casting vote;

(*b*) dealt with as expeditiously as possible and the Centre shall dispose of the same within a period of sixty days from the date of receipt of the application:

Provided that where any such [17][question] could not be disposed of within the said period of sixty days, the Centre shall record its reasons in writing for not disposing of the [18][question] within that period.

(6) The Chairperson may invite any expert, not being a Member, to attend the meetings of the Centre, but such invitee shall not be entitled to vote at the meeting.

21. Chief Executive Officer.—(1) There shall be a Chief Executive Officer of the Centre who shall be responsible for day-to-day administration of the Centre and for this purpose, he shall maintain liaison with the Centre and the Secretariat.

---

17. *Subs.* for "application" by Act 23 of 2022, S. 10 (w.e.f. 27-1-2023).
18. *Ibid.*

(2) The appointment, qualifications and the terms and conditions of services of the Chief Executive Officer shall be such as may be specified by the regulations.

(3) The Chief Executive Officer shall exercise such powers and discharge such functions as may be specified by the regulations or as may be delegated to him by the Centre.

22. Delegation of powers.—The Centre may, for the purpose of discharging of its powers, functions and duties, by general or special order in writing, specify the powers and duties conferred or imposed upon the Centre by or under this Act (except the power to make regulation) which may also be exercised or performed by the Chief Executive Officer or any officer or officers of the Centre and the conditions and restrictions, if any, subject to which the powers and duties may be exercised and performed.

23. Secretariat.—(1) There shall be a Secretariat to the Centre consisting of—

(*a*) Registrar, who shall supervise the activities of the [19][Secretariat];

(*b*) Counsel, dealing with the matters relating to domestic and international arbitration; and

(*c*) such number of other officers and employees as may be prescribed.

(2) The qualifications, experience, method of selection and the functions of the Registrar, Counsel and other officers and employees shall be such as may be prescribed.

CHAPTER IV

FINANCE, ACCOUNTS AND AUDIT

24. Grants by Central Government.—The Central Government may, after due appropriation made by Parliament by law in this behalf, pay to the Centre in each financial year such sums of money and in such manner as it may think fit for being utilised for the purposes of this Act.

25. Fund of Centre.—(1) The Centre shall maintain a Fund to which shall be credited,—

(*a*) all monies provided by the Central Government;

(*b*) all fees and other charges received during or in connection with the arbitration, conciliation, mediation or other proceedings;

(*c*) all monies received by the Centre for the facilities provided by it to the parties;

(*d*) all monies received by the Centre in the form of donations, grants, contributions and income from other sources; and

(*e*) the amount received from the investment income.

(2) All monies credited to the Fund shall be deposited in such banks or invested in such manner as may be decided by the Centre.

(3) The Fund shall be applied towards meeting the salaries and other allowances of Members [20][, Registrar, Counsel and other officers and employees of the Centre] and the expenses of the Centre including expenses incurred in the exercise of its powers and discharge of its duties under this Act.

---

19. *Subs.* for "Centre" by Act 23 of 2022, S. 11 (w.e.f. 27-1-2023).
20. *Ins.* by Act 23 of 2022, S. 12 (w.e.f. 27-1-2023).

26. Accounts and audit.—(1) The Centre shall maintain proper accounts and other relevant records and prepare an annual statement of accounts, including the balance sheet, in such form and manner as may be prescribed in consultation with the Comptroller and Auditor-General of India.

(2) The accounts of the Centre shall be audited by the Comptroller and Auditor-General of India and any expenditure incurred by him in connection with such audit shall be payable by the Centre to the Comptroller and Auditor-General of India.

(3) The Comptroller and Auditor-General of India and any person appointed by him in connection with the audit of the accounts of the Centre shall have the same rights, privileges and authority in connection with such audit as the Comptroller and Auditor-General of India has in connection with the audit of the Government accounts, and, in particular, shall have the right to demand the production of books, accounts, connected vouchers and other documents and papers and to inspect the offices of the Centre.

(4) The accounts of the Centre as certified by the Comptroller and Auditor-General of India or any other person appointed by him in this behalf together with the audit report thereon shall be forwarded annually to the Central Government and the Central Government shall cause the same to be laid before each House of Parliament.

27. Assessment of assets and liabilities of undertaking.—The assets and liabilities in relation to any undertaking under this Act shall be caused to be assessed by any agency authorised by the Comptroller and Auditor-General of India in such manner as may be specified by him and any payment on a claim to be made in relation thereto shall be settled by him between the Society and the Central Government and shall be paid by the Society or the Central Government, as the case may be, in the manner as may be specified by the Comptroller and Auditor-General of India.

CHAPTER V

CHAMBER OF ARBITRATION AND ARBITRATION ACADEMY

28. Chamber of Arbitration.—(1) The Centre shall, establish a Chamber of Arbitration [21][to] empanel the Arbitrators and also scrutinise the applications for admission in the panel of reputed arbitrators to maintain a permanent panel of arbitrators.

(2) The Chamber of Arbitration shall consist of experienced arbitration practitioners of repute, at national and international level and persons having wide experience in the area of alternative dispute resolution and conciliation.

(3) The Centre shall by regulations lay down the criteria for admission to the panel of the cadre so as to maintain a pool of reputed arbitrators having expertise in international commercial arbitration and arbitration other than international commercial arbitration.

(4) The Registrar to the Secretariat of the Centre shall act as the Member-Secretary to the Chamber of Arbitration.

---

21. *Subs.* for "which shall" by Act 23 of 2022, S. 13 (w.e.f. 27-1-2023).

29. Arbitration Academy.—(1) The Centre may establish an Arbitration Academy—

(*a*) to train the arbitrators, particularly in the area of international commercial arbitration to compete on par with the reputed international arbitral institutions;

(*b*) to conduct research in the area of alternative dispute resolution and allied areas; and

(*c*) to give suggestions for achieving the objectives of the Act.

(2) For the purposes of sub-section (1), there may be constituted a permanent three member committee in order to suggest and to submit a report to the Centre with respect to the amendments, if any, necessary to the rules and regulations made under this Act.

CHAPTER VI
MISCELLANEOUS

30. Power to make rules.—(1) The Central Government may, by notification, make rules to carry out the provisions of this Act.

(2) In particular, and without prejudice to the generality of the foregoing power, such rules may make provision for—

(*a*) the terms and conditions and the salaries and allowances payable to the Chairperson and Full-time Members under sub-section (2) of Section 6;

(*b*) the travelling and other allowances payable to the Part-time Members under sub-section (4) of Section 6;

(*c*) the composition and functions of the Committees referred to in sub-section (2) of Section 19;

(*d*) the number of officers and employees of the Secretariat of the Centre under clause (*c*) of sub-section (1) of Section 23;

(*e*) the qualifications, experience, method of selection and the functions of the Registrar, Counsel and other officers and employees of the Centre under sub-section (2) of Section 23;

(*f*) annual statement of accounts, including the balance sheet under sub-section (1) of Section 26; and

(*g*) any other matter in respect of which provision is to be made or may be made under this Act.

31. Power to make regulations.—(1) The Centre may, with the previous approval of the Central Government, by notification, make regulations consistent with this Act and the rules made thereunder to provide for all matters for which provision is necessary or expedient for the purposes of giving effect to the purposes of this Act.

(2) In particular, and without prejudice to the generality of the foregoing power, such regulations may make provision for—

[22][(*a*) the manner of the conduct of arbitration and other forms of alternative dispute resolution mechanism under clause (*a*) of Section 15;

---

22. *Subs.* by Act 23 of 2022, S. 14 (w.e.f. 27-1-2023). Prior to substitution it read as:

"(*a*) the time and place and the rules of procedure to be observed in regard to the transaction of business of the Committee at the meetings including the quorum under sub-section (3) of Section 19;"

(*aa*) the time and place and the rules of procedure to be observed in regard to the transaction of business of the Committee at the meetings including the quorum under sub-section (3) of Section 19;]

(*b*) the time and place and rules of procedure in regard to the transaction of business of the Centre or any Committee including the quorum at the meeting under sub-section (4) of Section 20;

(*c*) the appointment, qualifications and the terms and conditions of service of the Chief Executive Officer under sub-section (2) of Section 21;

(*d*) the powers and functions of the Chief Executive Officer under sub-section (3) of Section 21;

(*e*) the criteria for admission to the panel of reputed arbitrators under sub-section (3) of Section 28; and

(*f*) any other matter in respect of which provision, in the opinion of the Centre, is necessary for the performance of its functions under this Act.

32. Laying of rules and regulations.—Every rule and regulation made under this Act shall be laid, as soon as may be after it is made, before each House of Parliament, while it is in session, for a total period of thirty days which may be comprised in one session or in two or more successive sessions, and if, before the expiry of the session immediately following the session or the successive sessions aforesaid, both Houses agree in making any modification in the rule or regulation or both Houses agree that the rule or regulation should not be made, the rule or regulation shall thereafter have effect only in such modified form or be of no effect, as the case may be; so, however, that any such modification or annulment shall be without prejudice to the validity of anything previously done under that rule or regulation.

33. Protection of action taken in good faith.—No suit, prosecution or other legal proceedings shall lie against the Centre, the Chairperson or Members or its employees and arbitrators for anything which is in good faith done or intended to be done under this Act or the rules or regulations made thereunder.

34. Power to remove difficulty.—(1) If any difficulty arises in giving effect to the provisions of this Act, the Central Government may, by order published in the Official Gazette, make such provisions, not inconsistent with the provisions of this Act, as may appear to it to be necessary for removing the difficulty:

Provided that no such order shall be made under this section after the expiry of a period of [23][five years] from the date of commencement of this Act.

(2) Every order made under this section shall be laid, as soon as may be after it is made, before each House of Parliament.

35. Repeal and savings.—(1) The New Delhi International Arbitration Centre Ordinance, 2019 (Ord. 10 of 2019) is hereby repealed.

(2) Notwithstanding such repeal, anything done or any action taken under the New Delhi International Arbitration Centre Ordinance, 2019 (Ord. 10 of 2019), shall be deemed to have been done or taken under the provisions of this Act.

---

23. *Subs.* for "two years" by Act 23 of 2022, S. 15 (w.e.f. 27-1-2023).

Appendix 6

Civil Procedure Code, 1908

[Act 5 of 1908 as amended up to Act 32 of 2023 and updated as of 31st May 2024][1]

[21st March, 1908]

PART V

SPECIAL PROCEEDINGS

[2][* * *]

[3][89. **Settlement of disputes outside the Court.**—Where it appears to the Court that the dispute between the parties may be settled and there exists elements of settlement which may be acceptable to the parties, the Court may—

---

1. As amended upto Act 34 of 2019 (w.e.f. 31-10-2019).
2. Sub-heading "Arbitration" *omitted* by Act 32 of 2023, S. 59 and Sch. IV(*i*) (w.e.f. the date to be notified).
3. *Subs.* by Act 32 of 2023, S. 59 and Sch. IV(*ii*) (w.e.f. the date to be notified). Prior to substitution it read as:

"89. *Settlement of disputes outside the Court.*—(1) Where it appears to the court that there exist elements of a settlement which may be acceptable to the parties, the Court shall formulate the terms of settlement and give them to the parties for their observations and after receiving the observations of the parties, the court may reformulate the terms of a possible settlement and refer the same for—

(*a*) arbitration;

(*b*) conciliation;

(*c*) judicial settlement including settlement through Lok Adalat; or

(*d*) mediation.

(2) Where a dispute has been referred—

(*a*) for arbitration or conciliation, the provisions of the Arbitration and Conciliation Act, 1996 (26 of 1996) shall apply as if the proceedings for arbitration or conciliation were referred for settlement under the provisions of that Act;

(*b*) to Lok Adalat, the Court shall refer the same to the Lok Adalat in accordance with the provisions of sub-section (1) of Section 20 of the Legal Services Authority Act, 1987 (39 of 1987) and all other provisions of that Act shall apply in respect of the dispute so referred to the Lok Adalat;

(*c*) for judicial settlement, the Court shall refer the same to a suitable institution or person and such institution or person shall be deemed to be a Lok Adalat and all the provisions of the Legal Services Authority Act, 1987 (39 of 1987) (*a*) refer the dispute to arbitration, and thereafter, the provisions of the Arbitration and Conciliation Act, 1996 (26 of 1996) shall apply as if the proceedings for arbitration were referred for settlement under the provisions of that Act; or

(*b*) refer the parties to mediation, to the court-annexed mediation centre or any other mediation service provider or any mediator, as per the option of the parties, and thereafter the provisions of the Mediation Act, 2023 shall apply as if the proceedings for mediation were referred for settlement under the provisions of that Act; or

(*c*) refer the dispute to Lok Adalat, in accordance with the provisions of sub-section (1) of Section 20 of the Legal Services Authorities Act, 1987 (39 of 1987) and thereafter, all other provisions of that Act shall apply in respect of the dispute;

(*d*) effect compromise between the parties and shall follow such procedure as deemed fit for judicial settlement.]

---

shall apply as if the dispute were referred to a Lok Adalat under the provisions of that Act;

(*d*) for mediation, the Court shall effect a compromise between the parties and shall follow such procedure as may be prescribed."

Appendix 7

Alternate Disputes Resolution Rules framed by High Courts under S. 89, CPC 1908

1.	Alternative Dispute Resolution (Gauhati High Court) Rules, 2007	
2.	Alternative Dispute Resolution (High Court of Manipur) Rules, 2019	
3.	Bihar Civil Procedure (Mediation) Rules, 2008	
4.	Chhattisgarh Mediation Rules, 2015	
5.	Civil Procedure (Alternative Dispute Resolution) (Bihar) Rules, 2008	
6.	Civil Procedure (Alternative Dispute Resolution) (Karnataka) Rules, 2005	
7.	Civil Procedure Mediation (Gauhati High Court) Rules, 2007	

8.	Civil Procedure Mediation (High Court of Manipur) Rules, 2019	
9.	Civil Procedure Mediation (High Court of Meghalaya) Rules, 2013	
10.	Mediation Rules, 2003 (Haryana)	
11.	High Court of Himachal Pradesh Civil Procedure Alternative Dispute Resolution Rules, 2005	
12.	High Court of Sikkim, Civil Procedure Alternative Dispute Resolution Rules, 2006	
13.	High Court of Sikkim, Civil Procedure Mediation Rules, 2006	
14.	Civil Procedure Alternative Dispute Resolution Rules, 2009 (Jammu and Kashmir)	
15.	Jammu and Kashmir Civil Procedure Mediation Rules, 2009	
16.	Mediation and Conciliation Rules, 2019 (Jammu and Kashmir)	

17.	Civil Procedure Alternative Dispute Resolution Rules, 2006 (Jharkhand)	
18.	Mediation Rules, 2015 (Jharkhand)	
19.	Karnataka Civil Procedure (Mediation) Rules, 2005	
20.	Civil Procedure (Alternative Dispute Resolution) Rules, 2008 (Kerala)	
21.	Madhya Pradesh Mediation Rules, 2016	
22.	Civil Procedure Mediation Rules, 2006 (Maharashtra)	
23.	Civil Procedure-Alternative Dispute Resolution Rules, 2006 (Maharashtra)	
24.	Mediation (High Court of Tripura) Rules, 2016	
25.	Mediation and Conciliation Rules of Punjab and Haryana High Court	

26.	Mediation Rules of the International Arbitration and Mediation Centre, Hyderabad	
27.	Civil Procedure Mediation Rules, 2007 (Orissa)	
28.	Alternative Disputes Resolution Rules, 2004 (Rajasthan)	
29.	Tamil Nadu Mediation Rules, 2010	
30.	Alternative Dispute Resolution and Mediation Rules, 2017 (Telangana and Andhra Pradesh)	
31.	Uttar Pradesh Civil Procedure (District Courts) Mediation Rules, 2021	
32.	Uttar Pradesh Civil Procedure Alternative Dispute Resolution Rules, 2009	
33.	Civil Procedure Alternative Dispute Resolution Rules, 2007 (Uttarakhand)	
34.	Civil Procedure Alternative Dispute Resolution Rules, 2006 (Calcutta)	

Subject Index